Index of Selected Applications

Mathematical Applications

for the Management, Life, and Social Sciences
Siena College

Tenth Edition

Ronald J. Harshbarger | James J. Reynolds

CENGAGE
Learning·

Australia • Brazil • Japan • Korea • Mexico • Singapore • Spain • United Kingdom • United States

Mathematical Applications for the Management, Life, and Social Sciences, Siena College, Tenth Edition

Mathematical Applications for the Management, Life, and Social Sciences, Tenth Edition
Ronald J. Harshbarger | James J. Reynolds

© 2013, 2009 Brooks/Cole, Cengage Learning. All rights reserved.

WebAssign: Student Quick Start Guide

Executive Editors:
Maureen Staudt
Michael Stranz

Senior Project Development Manager:
Linda deStefano

Marketing Specialist:
Courtney Sheldon

Senior Production/Manufacturing Manager:
Donna M. Brown

Production Editorial Manager:
Kim Frv

Sr. Rights Acquisition Account Manager:
Todd Osborne

For product information and technology assistance, contact us at
Cengage Learning Customer & Sales Support, 1-800-354-9706

For permission to use material from this text or product,
submit all requests online at **cengage.com/permissions**
Further permissions questions can be emailed to
permissionrequest@cengage.com

This book contains select works from existing Cengage Learning resources and was produced by Cengage Learning Custom Solutions for collegiate use. As such, those adopting and/or contributing to this work are responsible for editorial content accuracy, continuity and completeness.

Compilation © 2012 Cengage Learning

ISBN-13: 978-1-285-12707-1

ISBN-10: 1-285-12707-2

Cengage Learning
5191 Natorp Boulevard
Mason, Ohio 45040
USA
Cengage Learning is a leading provider of customized learning solutions with office locations around the globe, including Singapore, the United Kingdom, Australia, Mexico, Brazil, and Japan. Locate your local office at:
international.cengage.com/region.

Cengage Learning products are represented in Canada by Nelson Education, Ltd.
For your lifelong learning solutions, visit **www.cengage.com/custom.**
Visit our corporate website at **www.cengage.com.**

Printed in the United States of America

Brief Contents

Insert: WebAssign: Student Quick Start Guide

WebAssign Student Quick Start Guide

You can use WebAssign to access your homework, quizzes, and tests — whatever your instructor chooses — at any time of day or night, from any computer with a connection to the Internet and a Web browser. Your instructor creates your assignments, schedules them, and decides how many submissions you get. Your instructor also determines if you can have an extension, if you can save your work without submitting it at the time, and how much feedback you get after you submit an assignment.

The WebAssign support staff cannot change your username or password, give extensions, change your score, give you extra submissions, or help you with the content of your assignments.

Logging In
You can log in to WebAssign using any Web browser connected to the Internet. There are two different ways to log in to WebAssign. Each requires information from your teacher. If you are unsure about how to log in, please check with your teacher or another student in your class.

Go to the login page at http://webassign.net/login.html or the web address provided by your teacher. The way you log in depends on how your instructor set up the class:

- If your teacher created a WebAssign account for you, they will provide you with a **Username**, an **Institution** code and a **Password**. Simply enter this information in the boxes provided and click the **Log In** button.

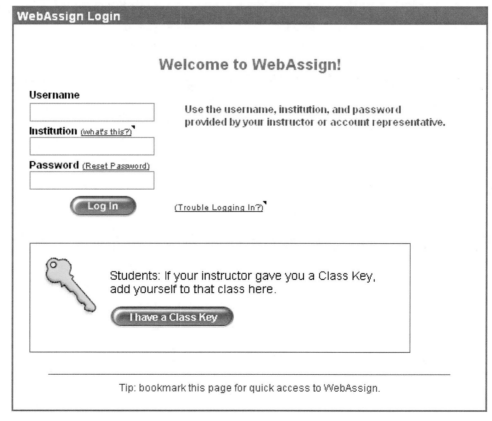

Web**Assign**.

- If your teacher wants you to **Self-Enroll** in the WebAssign course they will provide you with a **Class Key**. You will create your own username and password. It is important that you remember this information so you can log in for the remainder of the class. In this case, just click the **I have a Class Key** button. You don't need to enter any other information on this page.

  Then, enter the **Class Key** your instructor provided and click **Submit**. Verify you are enrolling in the correct class on the next page.

Class Key

Enter the Class Key that you received from your instructor. You will only need to complete this once. After you have created your account, you can log in on the main page.

Class Key

[_____] [_____] [_____]

Class Keys generally start with an institution code, followed by two sets of four digits.

[Submit]

- Enter your preferred Login and Student information.

- Click the **Create My Account** button to complete the enrollment process.

- A review screen will display, showing your username, institution code, and password. **Retain a copy of this information.** You will need it to log into WebAssign.

Log In Information

Required fields are marked with an asterisk (*).

Preferred Username	*	[_____] [Check Availability]
		Your username may contain letters, numbers, and the following characters: underscore (_), hyphen (-), period (.)
Institution Code		**webassign**
Password	*	[_____]
Re-Enter Password	*	[_____]
		Passwords are case-sensitive.

Student Information

Required fields are marked with an asterisk (*).

First Name	*	[_____]
Last Name	*	[_____]
Email Address	*	[_____]
Student ID Number		[_____]

[Create My Account]

Access Codes

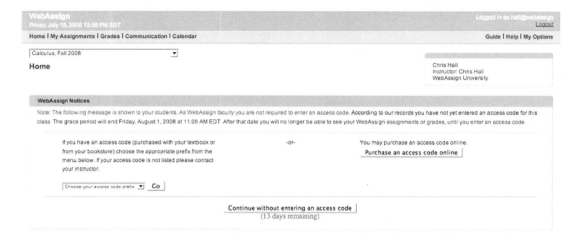

Once you log in, you may see a WebAssign Notice about entering an access code for your class. You can get an Access Code from any of the following places if you need to use one:

- A new textbook you purchased for the class.
- Your bookstore, which may sell Access Code cards.
- Online, where you can purchase an access code with a credit card.

You have a 14 day grace period to use WebAssign, starting with the WebAssign class start date. During this time you can work on and view your WebAssign assignments without registering a code.

After the grace period is over you will only see the code registration message until you submit or purchase a code.

There are two types of WebAssign access code cards. The small card requires you to scratch off the silver surface in order to reveal the complete access code.

WebAssign.

The larger security envelope card requires you to open the card to reveal the access code number.

If you would like to purchase an access code directly from WebAssign online, you may do so with a credit card. Your code will be automatically registered to your WebAssign account as soon as the transaction is complete. You will receive an email confirmation. Please keep a copy for your records.

Your WebAssign Home Page

Once you have successfully logged in you will see your WebAssign homepage. If you are taking more than one WebAssign class, you will need to select which class you wish to view first.

The upper right corner features links to a complete Student **Guide**, as well as a link to WebAssign Technical Support under **Help**. If you want to change your password or add or update your email address, simply click **My Options** in the upper right hand corner.

You will see your assignments and due dates listed, as well as any Communications, Grades, and Announcements posted by your teacher.

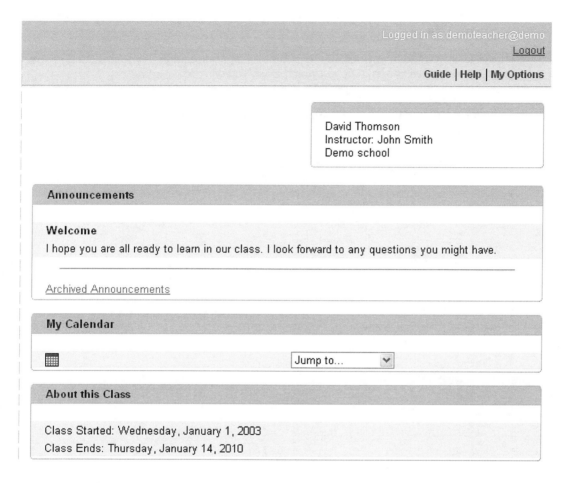

Answering Questions

WebAssign has a variety of different question types, ranging from multiple choice to fill-in-the-blank to symbolic questions. Here are some things to keep in mind as you work through your assignments:

- Some questions may include numbers or words that appear in red. This signifies that the number or word has been randomized, so that you receive a different version of the same basic question from your classmates.

- Some WebAssign questions check the number of significant figures in your answer. If you enter the correct value with the wrong number of significant figures, you will not receive credit, but you will receive a hint that your number does not have the correct number of significant figures.

- Some questions require entering symbolic notation. Answer symbolic questions by using calculator notation. You must use the exact variables specified in the questions. The order is not important as long as it is mathematically correct. Clicking on the eye button previews the expression you enter in proper mathematical notation. Clicking on the symbolic formatting help button provides tips for using the correct keystrokes.

- When you click on some WebAssign chemistry or math questions an input palette will open. These palettes, called chemPad and mathPad, will help you enter your answer in proper notation.

- Some questions may require the use of an Active Figure simulation. Active Figures require the free Macromedia Flash Player plug-in, downloadable from www.macromedia.com.

- If your instructor allows it, you can save your work without grading by selecting the Save Work button at the end of the question. After you save your work, it will be available to you the next time you click the assignment.

- Please note that WebAssign will **not** automatically submit your answers for scoring if you only **Save** your work. Your teacher will not be able to see your submissions. Please be sure to **Submit** prior to the due date and time.

- If your instructor allows it, you can submit answers by question part or for the entire assignment. To submit an individual question answer for grading, click the **Submit New Answers to Question __** button at the bottom of each question. To submit the entire assignment for grading, click the **Submit All New Answers** button at the end of the assignment.

Technical Support

If you are having difficulty logging in, please be sure to check with your teacher and verify whether an account has been created for you or whether you need to self-enroll. In either case your teacher needs to provide the appropriate information (username, institution code and password OR Class Key).

To email WebAssign Support go to http://www.webassign.net/info/support/report.html. This page also lists answers to **Common Problems**, and provides links to the **Student Guide**.

August 7, 2008

Mathematical Applications

for the Management, Life,
and Social Sciences

EDITION 10

O CHAPTER

Algebraic Concepts

Khoroshunova Olga/Shutterstock.com

This chapter provides a brief review of the algebraic concepts that will be used throughout the text. You may be familiar with these topics, but it may be helpful to spend some time reviewing them. In addition, each chapter after this one opens with a warm-up page that identifies prerequisite skills needed for that chapter. If algebraic skills are required, the warm-up cites their coverage in this chapter. Thus you will find that this chapter is a useful reference as you study later chapters.

The topics and applications studied in this chapter include the following.

SECTIONS		APPLICATIONS
0.1	**Sets** **Set operations** **Venn diagrams**	Dow Jones Average, jobs growth
0.2	**The Real Numbers** **Inequalities and intervals** **Absolute value**	Income taxes, health statistics
0.3	**Integral Exponents**	Personal income, endangered species
0.4	**Radicals and Rational Exponents** **Roots and fractional exponents** **Operations with radicals**	Richter scale, half-life
0.5	**Operations with Algebraic Expressions**	Revenue, profit
0.6	**Factoring** **Common factors** **Factoring trinomials**	Simple interest, revenue
0.7	**Algebraic Fractions** **Operations** **Complex fractions**	Average cost, advertising and sales

0.1

Sets

A **set** is a well-defined collection of objects. We may talk about a set of books, a set of dishes, a set of students, or a set of individuals with a certain blood type. There are two ways to tell what a given set contains. One way is by listing the **elements** (or **members**) of the set (usually between braces). We may say that a set A contains 1, 2, 3, and 4 by writing $A = \{1, 2, 3, 4\}$. To say that 4 is a member of set A, we write $4 \in A$. Similarly, we write $5 \notin A$ to denote that 5 is not a member of set A.

If all the members of the set can be listed, the set is said to be a **finite set.** $A = \{1, 2, 3, 4\}$ and $B = \{x, y, z\}$ are examples of finite sets. When we do not wish to list all the elements of a finite set, we can use three dots to indicate the unlisted members of the set. For example, the set of even integers from 8 to 8952, inclusive, could be written as

$$\{8, 10, 12, 14, \ldots, 8952\}$$

For an **infinite set,** we cannot list all the elements, so we use the three dots. For example, $N = \{1, 2, 3, 4, \ldots\}$ is an infinite set. This set N is called the set of **natural numbers.**

Another way to specify the elements of a given set is by description. For example, we may write $D = \{x: x \text{ is a Ford automobile}\}$ to describe the set of all Ford automobiles. Furthermore, $F = \{y: y \text{ is an odd natural number}\}$ is read "F is the set of all y such that y is an odd natural number."

EXAMPLE   1   Describing Sets

Write the following sets in two ways.
(a) The set A of natural numbers less than 6
(b) The set B of natural numbers greater than 10
(c) The set C containing only 3

Solution
(a) $A = \{1, 2, 3, 4, 5\}$ or $A = \{x: x \text{ is a natural number less than 6}\}$
(b) $B = \{11, 12, 13, 14, \ldots\}$ or $B = \{x: x \text{ is a natural number greater than 10}\}$
(c) $C = \{3\}$ or $C = \{x: x = 3\}$

Note that set C of Example 1 contains one member, 3; set A contains five members; and set B contains an infinite number of members. It is possible for a set to contain no members. Such a set is called the **empty set** or the **null set,** and it is denoted by $\varnothing$ or by $\{\ \}$. The set of living veterans of the War of 1812 is empty because there are no living veterans of that war. Thus

$$\{x: x \text{ is a living veteran of the War of 1812}\} = \varnothing$$

Special relations that may exist between two sets are defined as follows.

Relations between Sets

Definition	Example
1. Sets X and Y are **equal** if they contain the same elements.	1. If $X = \{1, 2, 3, 4\}$ and $Y = \{4, 3, 2, 1\}$, then $X = Y$.
2. A is called a **subset** of B, which is written $A \subseteq B$ if every element of A is an element of B. The empty set is a subset of every set. Each set A is a subset of itself.	2. If $A = \{1, 2, c, f\}$ and $B = \{1, 2, 3, a, b, c, f\}$, then $A \subseteq B$. Also, $\varnothing \subseteq A$, $\varnothing \subseteq B$, $A \subseteq A$, and $B \subseteq B$.
3. If C and D have no elements in common, they are called **disjoint.**	3. If $C = \{1, 2, a, b\}$ and $D = \{3, e, 5, c\}$, then C and D are disjoint.

In the discussion of particular sets, the assumption is always made that the sets under discussion are all subsets of some larger set, called the **universal set** *U*. The choice of the universal set depends on the problem under consideration. For example, in discussing the set of all students and the set of all female students, we may use the set of all humans as the universal set.

We may use **Venn diagrams** to illustrate the relationships among sets. We use a rectangle to represent the universal set, and we use closed figures inside the rectangle to represent the sets under consideration. Figures 0.1–0.3 show such Venn diagrams.

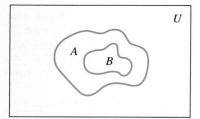

Figure 0.1
B is a subset of *A*; $B \subseteq A$.

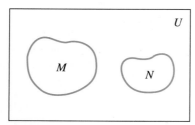

Figure 0.2
M and *N* are disjoint.

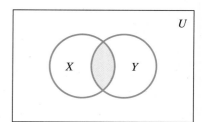

Figure 0.3
X and *Y* are not disjoint.

Set Operations   The shaded portion of Figure 0.3 indicates where the two sets overlap. The set containing the members that are common to two sets is said to be the **intersection** of the two sets.

Set Intersection

The intersection of *A* and *B*, written $A \cap B$, is defined by

$$A \cap B = \{x : x \in A \text{ and } x \in B\}$$

EXAMPLE 2   Set Intersection

(a) If $A = \{2, 3, 4, 5\}$ and $B = \{3, 5, 7, 9, 11\}$, find $A \cap B$.
(b) Which of *A*, *B*, and $A \cap B$ is a subset of *A*?

Solution

(a) $A \cap B = \{3, 5\}$ because 3 and 5 are the common elements of *A* and *B*. Figure 0.4 shows the sets and their intersection.
(b) $A \cap B$ and *A* are subsets of *A*.

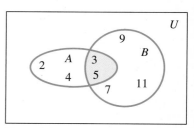

Figure 0.4

CHECKPOINT   Let $A = \{2, 3, 5, 7, 11\}$, $B = \{2, 4, 6, 8, 10\}$, and $C = \{6, 10, 14, 18, 22\}$. Use these sets to answer the following.

1. (a) Of which sets is 6 an element?
   (b) Of which sets is {6} an element?
2. Which of the following are true?
   (a) $2 \in A$
   (b) $2 \in B$
   (c) $2 \in C$
   (d) $5 \notin A$
   (e) $5 \notin B$
3. Which pair of *A*, *B*, and *C* is disjoint?

4. Which of $\varnothing$, A, B, and C are subsets of
   (a) the set P of all prime numbers?
   (b) the set M of all multiples of 2?
5. Which of A, B, and C is equal to $D = \{x: x = 4n + 2$ for natural numbers $1 \le n \le 5\}$?

The **union** of two sets is the set that contains all members of the two sets.

Set Union	The union of A and B, written $A \cup B$, is defined by

$$A \cup B = \{x: x \in A \text{ or } x \in B \text{ (or both)}\}^*$$

We can illustrate the intersection and union of two sets by the use of Venn diagrams. Figures 0.5 and 0.6 show Venn diagrams with universal set U represented by the rectangles and with sets A and B represented by the circles. The shaded region in Figure 0.5 represents $A \cap B$, the intersection of A and B, and the shaded region in Figure 0.6—which consists of all parts of both circles—represents $A \cup B$.

Figure 0.5

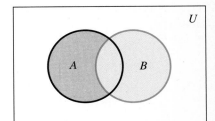

Figure 0.6

EXAMPLE 3 Set Union

If $X = \{a, b, c, f\}$ and $Y = \{e, f, a, b\}$, find $X \cup Y$.

Solution
$X \cup Y = \{a, b, c, e, f\}$

EXAMPLE 4 Set Intersection and Union

Let $A = \{x: x$ is a natural number less than 6$\}$ and $B = \{1, 3, 5, 7, 9, 11\}$.
(a) Find $A \cap B$.
(b) Find $A \cup B$.

Solution
(a) $A \cap B = \{1, 3, 5\}$
(b) $A \cup B = \{1, 2, 3, 4, 5, 7, 9, 11\}$

All elements of the universal set that are not contained in a set A form a set called the **complement** of A.

Set Complement	The complement of A, written A', is defined by

$$A' = \{x: x \in U \text{ and } x \notin A\}$$

We can use a Venn diagram to illustrate the complement of a set. The shaded region of Figure 0.7 represents A', and the *un*shaded region of Figure 0.5 represents $(A \cap B)'$.

*In mathematics, the word *or* means "one or the other or both."

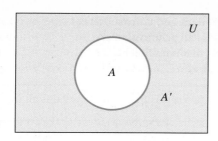

Figure 0.7

EXAMPLE 5   **Operations with Sets**

If $U = \{x \in N: x < 10\}$, $A = \{1, 3, 6\}$, and $B = \{1, 6, 8, 9\}$, find the following.
(a) A'
(b) B'
(c) $(A \cap B)'$
(d) $A' \cup B'$

Solution
(a) $U = \{1, 2, 3, 4, 5, 6, 7, 8, 9\}$ so $A' = \{2, 4, 5, 7, 8, 9\}$
(b) $B' = \{2, 3, 4, 5, 7\}$
(c) $A \cap B = \{1, 6\}$ so $(A \cap B)' = \{2, 3, 4, 5, 7, 8, 9\}$
(d) $A' \cup B' = \{2, 4, 5, 7, 8, 9\} \cup \{2, 3, 4, 5, 7\} = \{2, 3, 4, 5, 7, 8, 9\}$

CHECKPOINT   Given the sets $U = \{1, 2, 3, 4, 5, 6, 7, 8, 9, 10\}$, $A = \{1, 3, 5, 7, 9\}$, $B = \{2, 3, 5, 7\}$, and $C = \{4, 5, 6, 7, 8, 9, 10\}$, find the following.
6. $A \cup B$
7. $B \cap C$
8. A'

EXAMPLE 6   **Stocks**

Many local newspapers list "stocks of local interest." Suppose that on a certain day, a prospective investor categorized 23 stocks according to whether

- their closing price on the previous day was less than $50/share (set C)
- their price-to-earnings ratio was less than 20 (set P)
- their dividend per share was at least $1.50 (set D).

Of these 23 stocks,

16 belonged to set P	10 belonged to both C and P
12 belonged to set C	7 belonged to both D and P
8 belonged to set D	2 belonged to all three sets
3 belonged to both C and D	

Draw a Venn diagram that represents this information. Use the diagram to answer the following.
(a) How many stocks had closing prices of less than $50 per share or price-to-earnings ratios of less than 20?
(b) How many stocks had none of the characteristics of set C, P, or D?
(c) How many stocks had only dividends per share of at least $1.50?

Solution
The Venn diagram for three sets has eight separate regions (see Figure 0.8(a) on the next page). To assign numbers from our data, we must begin with some information that refers

to a single region, namely that two stocks belonged to all three sets (see Figure 0.8(b)). Because the region common to all three sets is also common to any pair, we can next use the information about stocks that belonged to two of the sets (see Figure 0.8(c)). Finally, we can complete the Venn diagram (see Figure 0.8(d)).

(a) We need to add the numbers in the separate regions that lie within $C \cup P$. That is, 18 stocks closed under $50 per share or had price-to-earnings ratios of less than 20.
(b) There are 5 stocks outside the three sets C, D, and P.
(c) Those stocks that had only dividends of at least $1.50 per share are inside D but outside both C and P. There are no such stocks.

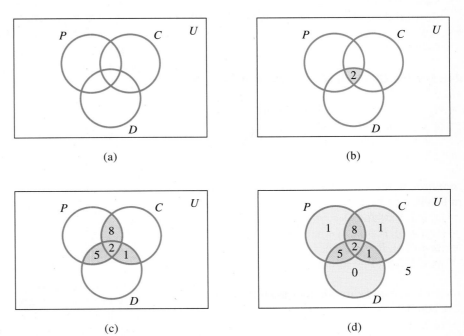

(a)　　　　　　　　　　　　　(b)

Figure 0.8　　(c)　　　　　　　　　　　　(d)

1. (a) Sets B and C have 6 as an element.
   (b) None of A, B, or C has {6} as an element; {6} is itself a set, and the elements of A, B, and C are not sets.
2. (a) True
   (b) True
   (c) False; $2 \notin C$
   (d) False; $5 \in A$
   (e) True
3. A and C are disjoint.
4. (a) $\varnothing \subseteq P$ and $A \subseteq P$
   (b) $\varnothing \subseteq M$, $B \subseteq M$, $C \subseteq M$
5. $C = D$
6. $A \cup B = \{1, 2, 3, 5, 7, 9\}$
7. $B \cap C = \{5, 7\}$
8. $A' = \{2, 4, 6, 8, 10\}$

| EXERCISES | 0.1

Use $\in$ or $\notin$ to indicate whether the given object is an element of the given set in the following problems.

1. 12 $\{1, 2, 3, 4, \dots\}$
2. 5 $\{x\colon x \text{ is a natural number greater than } 5\}$
3. 6 $\{x\colon x \text{ is a natural number less than } 6\}$
4. 3 $\varnothing$

In Problems 5–8, write the following sets a second way.

5. $\{x\colon x \text{ is a natural number less than } 8\}$
6. $\{x\colon x \text{ is a natural number greater than } 6, \text{ less than } 10\}$
7. $\{3, 4, 5, 6, 7\}$
8. $\{7, 8, 9, 10, \dots\}$

In Problems 9 and 10, which of $\varnothing$, A, and B are subsets of B?

9. $A = \{1, 2, 3, 4\}$ and $B = \{1, 2, 3, 4, 5, 6\}$
10. $A = \{a, b, c, d\}$ and $B = \{c, d, a, b\}$?
11. Is $A \subseteq B$ if $A = \{a, b, c, d\}$ and $B = \{a, b, d\}$?
12. Is $A \subseteq B$ if $A = \{6, 8, 10, 12\}$ and $B = \{6, 8, 10, 14, 18\}$?

Use $\subseteq$ notation to indicate which set is a subset of the other in Problems 13–16.

13. $C = \{a, b, 1, 2, 3\}$ and $D = \{a, b, 1\}$
14. $E = \{x, y, a, b\}$, $F = \{x, 1, a, y, b, 2\}$
15. $A = \{6, 8, 7, 4\}$, $B = \{8, 7, 6, 4\}$
16. $D = \{a, e, 1, 3, c\}$, $F = \{e, a, c, 1, 3\}$

In Problems 17–20, indicate whether the following pairs of sets are equal.

17. $A = \{a, b, \pi, \sqrt{3}\}$, $B = \{a, \pi, \sqrt{3}, b\}$
18. $A = \{x, g, a, b\}$, $D = \{x, a, b, y\}$
19. $D = \{x\colon x \text{ is a natural number less than } 4\}$,
    $E = \{1, 2, 3, 4\}$
20. $F = \{x\colon x \text{ is a natural number greater than } 6\}$,
    $G = \{7, 8, 9, \dots\}$
21. From the following list of sets, indicate which pairs of sets are disjoint.
    $A = \{1, 2, 3, 4\}$
    $B = \{x\colon x \text{ is a natural number greater than } 4\}$
    $C = \{4, 5, 6, \dots\}$
    $D = \{1, 2, 3\}$
22. If A and B are disjoint sets, what does $A \cap B$ equal?

In Problems 23–26, find $A \cap B$, the intersection of sets A and B.

23. $A = \{2, 3, 4, 5, 6\}$ and $B = \{4, 6, 8, 10, 12\}$
24. $A = \{a, b, c, d, e\}$ and $B = \{a, d, e, f, g, h\}$
25. $A = \varnothing$ and $B = \{x, y, a, b\}$
26. $A = \{x\colon x \text{ is a natural number less than } 4\}$
    and $B = \{3, 4, 5, 6\}$

In Problems 27–30, find $A \cup B$, the union of sets A and B.

27. $A = \{1, 2, 4, 5\}$ and $B = \{2, 3, 4, 5\}$
28. $A = \{a, e, i, o, u\}$ and $B = \{a, b, c, d\}$
29. $A = \varnothing$ and $B = \{1, 2, 3, 4\}$
30. $A = \{x\colon x \text{ is a natural number greater than } 5\}$
    and $B = \{x\colon x \text{ is a natural number less than } 5\}$

In Problems 31–42, assume that

$$A = \{1, 3, 5, 8, 7, 2\}$$
$$B = \{4, 3, 8, 10\}$$
$$C = \{2, 4, 6, 8, 10\}$$

and that U is the universal set of natural numbers less than 11. Find the following.

31. A'
32. B'
33. $A \cap B'$
34. $A' \cap B'$
35. $(A \cup B)'$
36. $(A \cap B)'$
37. $A' \cup B'$
38. $(A' \cup B)'$
39. $(A \cap B') \cup C'$
40. $A \cap (B' \cup C')$
41. $(A \cap B')' \cap C$
42. $A \cap (B \cup C)$

The difference of two sets, $A - B$, is defined as the set containing all elements of A except those in B. That is, $A - B = A \cap B'$. Find $A - B$ for each pair of sets in Problems 43–46 if $U = \{1, 2, 3, 4, 5, 6, 7, 8, 9\}$.

43. $A = \{1, 3, 7, 9\}$ and $B = \{3, 5, 8, 9\}$
44. $A = \{1, 2, 3, 6, 9\}$ and $B = \{1, 4, 5, 6, 7\}$
45. $A = \{2, 1, 5\}$ and $B = \{1, 2, 3, 4, 5, 6\}$
46. $A = \{1, 2, 3, 4, 5\}$ and $B = \{7, 8, 9\}$

APPLICATIONS

47. *Dow Jones Industrial Average* The following table shows information about yearly lows, highs, and percentage changes for the years 2000 to 2009. Let L be the set of years where the low was greater than 8000. Let H be the set of years where the high was greater than 11,000. Let C be the years when the percentage change (from low to high) exceeded 35%.
    (a) List the elements of L, H, and C.
    (b) Is any of L, H, or C a subset of one of the others (besides itself)?
    (c) Write a verbal description of C'.
    (d) Find $H' \cup C'$ and describe it in words.
    (e) Find $L' \cap C$ and describe it in words.

Dow Jones Industrial Average

Year	Low	High	% Change
2009	6547.05	10,092.19	54.1
2008	7552.29	13,056.72	72.9
2007	12,050.41	14,164.53	17.5
2006	10,667.39	12,510.57	17.3
2005	10,012.36	10,940.50	9.3
2004	9749.99	10,854.54	11.3
2003	7524.06	10,453.92	38.9
2002	7286.27	10,635.65	46.0
2001	8235.94	11,332.92	37.6
2000	9796.03	11,722.98	19.7

Source: Dow Jones & Company, 2010

48. *Job growth* The number of jobs in 2000, the number projected in 2025, and the projected annual growth rate for jobs in some cities are shown in the following table. Consider the following sets.

 A = set of cities with at least 2,000,000 jobs in 2000 or in 2025

 B = set of cities with at least 1,500,000 jobs in 2000

 C = set of cities with projected annual growth rate of at least 2.5%

  (a) List A, B, and C (using the letters to represent the cities).
  (b) Is any of A, B, or C a subset of the other?
  (c) Find $A \cap C$ and describe the set in words.
  (d) Give a verbal description of B'.

Cities	Jobs in 2000 (thousands)	Projected Jobs in 2025 (thousands)	Annual Rates of Increase (%)
O (Orlando)	1098	2207	2.83
M (Myrtle Beach)	133	256	2.64
L (Atlanta)	2715	4893	2.38
P (Phoenix)	1953	3675	2.56
B (Boulder)	233	420	2.38

Source: NPA Data Services, Inc.

National health care **Suppose that the following table summarizes the opinions of various groups on the issue of national health care. Use this table for Problems 49 and 50.**

Opinion	Whites Rep.	Whites Dem.	Nonwhites Rep.	Nonwhites Dem.	Total
Favor	100	250	30	200	580
Oppose	250	150	10	10	420
Total	350	400	40	210	1000

49. Identify the number of individuals in each of the following sets.
  (a) Republicans and those who favor national health care
  (b) Republicans or those who favor national health care
  (c) White Republicans or those who oppose national health care

50. Identify the number of individuals in each of the following sets.
  (a) Whites and those who oppose national health care
  (b) Whites or those who oppose national health care
  (c) Nonwhite Democrats and those who favor national health care

51. *Languages* A survey of 100 aides at the United Nations revealed that 65 could speak English, 60 could speak French, and 40 could speak both English and French.
  (a) Draw a Venn diagram representing the 100 aides. Use E to represent English-speaking aides and F to represent French-speaking aides.
  (b) How many aides are in $E \cap F$?
  (c) How many aides are in $E \cup F$?
  (d) How many aides are in $E \cap F'$?

52. *Advertising* Suppose that a survey of 100 advertisers in *U.S. News*, *These Times*, and *World* found the following.

   14 advertised in all three
   30 advertised in *These Times* and *U.S. News*
   26 advertised in *World* and *U.S. News*
   27 advertised in *World* and *These Times*
   60 advertised in *These Times*
   52 advertised in *U.S. News*
   50 advertised in *World*

 Draw a Venn diagram representing this information and use it to answer the following.
  (a) How many advertised in none of these publications?
  (b) How many advertised only in *These Times*?
  (c) How many advertised in *U.S. News* or *These Times*?

53. *College enrollments* Records at a small college show the following about the enrollments of 100 first-year students in mathematics, fine arts, and economics.

   38 take math
   42 take fine arts
   20 take economics
   4 take economics and fine arts
   15 take math and economics
   9 take math and fine arts
   12 take math and economics but not fine arts

 Draw a Venn diagram representing this information and label all the areas. Use this diagram to answer the following.
  (a) How many take none of these three courses?
  (b) How many take math or economics?
  (c) How many take exactly one of these three courses?

54. *Survey analysis* In a survey of the dining preferences of 110 dormitory students at the end of the spring semester, the following facts were discovered about Adam's Lunch (AL), Pizza Tower (PT), and the Dining Hall (DH).

   30 liked AL but not PT
   21 liked AL only
   63 liked AL
   58 liked PT
   27 liked DH
   25 liked PT and AL but not DH
   18 liked PT and DH

Draw a Venn diagram representing this survey and label all the areas. Use this diagram to answer the following.
   (a) How many liked PT or DH?
   (b) How many liked all three?
   (c) How many liked only DH?

55. *Blood types* Blood types are determined by the presence or absence of three antigens: A antigen, B antigen, and an antigen called the Rh factor. The resulting blood types are classified as follows:

   type A if the A antigen is present
   type B if the B antigen is present
   type AB if both the A and B antigens are present
   type O if neither the A nor the B antigen is present

These types are further classified as *Rh-positive* if the Rh-factor antigen is present and *Rh-negative* otherwise.
   (a) Draw a Venn diagram that illustrates this classification scheme.
   (b) Identify the blood type determined by each region of the Venn diagram (such as A$^+$ to indicate type A, Rh-positive).
   (c) Use a library or another source to find what percentage of the U.S. population has each blood type.

0.2

The Real Numbers

In this text we use the set of **real numbers** as the universal set. We can represent the real numbers along a line called the **real number line.** This number line is a picture, or graph, of the real numbers. Each point on the real number line corresponds to exactly one real number, and each real number can be located at exactly one point on the real number line. Thus, two real numbers are said to be equal whenever they are represented by the same point on the real number line. The equation $a = b$ (a equals b) means that the symbols a and b represent the same real number. Thus, $3 + 4 = 7$ means that $3 + 4$ and 7 represent the same number. Table 0.1 lists special subsets of the real numbers.

| TABLE 0.1 |

SUBSETS OF THE SET OF REAL NUMBERS

	Description	Example (some elements shown)
Natural numbers	$\{1, 2, 3, \ldots\}$ The counting numbers.	
Integers	$\{\ldots, -2, -1, 0, 1, 2, \ldots\}$ The natural numbers, 0, and the negatives of the natural numbers.	
Rational numbers	All numbers that can be written as the ratio of two integers, a/b, with $b \neq 0$. These numbers have decimal representations that either terminate or repeat.	
Irrational numbers	Those real numbers that *cannot* be written as the ratio of two integers. Irrational numbers have decimal representations that neither terminate nor repeat.	
Real numbers	The set containing all rational and irrational numbers (the entire number line).	

The following properties of the real numbers are fundamental to the study of algebra.

Properties of the Real Numbers

Let a, b, and c denote real numbers.

1. (Commutative Property) Addition and multiplication are commutative.
$$a + b = b + a \qquad ab = ba$$

2. (Associative Property) Addition and multiplication are associative.
$$(a + b) + c = a + (b + c) \qquad (ab)c = a(bc)$$

3. (Additive Identity) The additive identity is 0.
$$a + 0 = 0 + a = a$$

4. (Multiplicative Identity) The multiplicative identity is 1.
$$a \cdot 1 = 1 \cdot a = a$$

5. (Additive Inverse) Each element a has an additive inverse, denoted by $-a$.
$$a + (-a) = -a + a = 0$$
Note that there is a difference between a negative number and the negative of a number.

6. (Multiplicative Inverse) Each nonzero element a has a multiplicative inverse, denoted by a^{-1}.
$$a \cdot a^{-1} = a^{-1} \cdot a = 1$$
Note that $a^{-1} = 1/a$.

7. (Distributive Law) Multiplication is distributive over addition.
$$a(b + c) = ab + ac$$

Note that Property 5 provides the means to subtract by defining $a - b = a + (-b)$ and Property 6 provides a means to divide by defining $a \div b = a \cdot (1/b)$. The number 0 has no multiplicative inverse, so division by 0 is undefined.

Inequalities and Intervals

We say that a is less than b (written $a < b$) if the point representing a is to the left of the point representing b on the real number line. For example, $4 < 7$ because 4 is to the left of 7 on the real number line. We may also say that 7 is greater than 4 (written $7 > 4$). We may indicate that the number x is less than or equal to another number y by writing $x \leq y$. We may also indicate that p is greater than or equal to 4 by writing $p \geq 4$.

EXAMPLE 1   Inequalities

Use $<$ or $>$ notation to write the following.
(a) 6 is greater than 5.   (b) 10 is less than 15.
(c) 3 is to the left of 8 on the real number line.   (d) x is at most 12.

Solution
(a) $6 > 5$ (b) $10 < 15$ (c) $3 < 8$
(d) "x is at most 12" means it must be less than or equal to 12. Thus, $x \leq 12$.

The subset of the real numbers consisting of all real numbers x that lie between a and b, excluding a and b, can be denoted by the *double inequality* $a < x < b$ or by the **open interval** (a, b). It is called an open interval because neither of the endpoints is included in the interval. The **closed interval** $[a, b]$ represents the set of all real numbers x satisfying $a \leq x \leq b$. Intervals containing one endpoint, such as $(a, b]$ and $[a, b)$, are called **half-open intervals.**

We can use $[a, +\infty)$ to represent the inequality $x \geq a$ and $(-\infty, a)$ to represent $x < a$. In each of these cases, the symbols $+\infty$ and $-\infty$ are not real numbers but represent the fact that

x increases without bound $(+\infty)$ or decreases without bound $(-\infty)$. Table 0.2 summarizes three types of intervals.

| ■ | TABLE 0.2 | ■

INTERVALS

Type of Interval	Inequality Notation	Interval Notation	Graph
Open interval	$x > a$	(a, ∞)	
	$x < b$	$(-\infty, b)$	
	$a < x < b$	(a, b)	
Half-open interval	$x \geq a$	$[a, \infty)$	
	$x \leq b$	$(-\infty, b]$	
	$a \leq x < b$	$[a, b)$	
	$a < x \leq b$	$(a, b]$	
Closed interval	$a \leq x \leq b$	$[a, b]$	

CHECKPOINT

1. Evaluate the following, if possible. For any that are meaningless, so state.

   (a) $\dfrac{4}{0}$ (b) $\dfrac{0}{4}$

   (c) $\dfrac{4}{4}$ (d) $\dfrac{4 - 4}{4 - 4}$

2. For parts (a)–(d), write the inequality corresponding to the given interval and sketch its graph on a real number line.

   (a) $(1, 3)$ (b) $(0, 3]$

   (c) $[-1, \infty)$ (d) $(-\infty, 2)$

3. Express the following inequalities in interval notation and name the type of interval.

   (a) $3 \leq x \leq 6$ (b) $-6 \leq x < 4$

Absolute Value   Sometimes we are interested in the *distance* a number is from the origin (0) of the real number line, without regard to direction. The distance a number a is from 0 on the number line is the **absolute value** of a, denoted $|a|$. The absolute value of any nonzero number is positive, and the absolute value of 0 is 0.

EXAMPLE   2   **Absolute Value**

Evaluate the following.

(a) $|-4|$ (b) $|+2|$

(c) $|0|$ (d) $|-5 - |-3||$

Solution

(a) $|-4| = +4 = 4$ (b) $|+2| = +2 = 2$

(c) $|0| = 0$ (d) $|-5 - |-3|| = |-5 - 3| = |-8| = 8$

Note that if a is a nonnegative number, then $|a| = a$, but if a is negative, then $|a|$ is the *positive number* $(-a)$. Thus

Absolute Value

$$|a| = \begin{cases} a & \text{if } a \geq 0 \\ -a & \text{if } a < 0 \end{cases}$$

In performing computations with real numbers, it is important to remember the rules for computations.

Operations with Real (Signed) Numbers

Procedure	Example

1. (a) To add two real numbers with the same sign, add their absolute values and affix their common sign.

   (b) To add two real numbers with unlike signs, find the difference of their absolute values and affix the sign of the number with the larger absolute value.

2. To subtract one real number from another, change the sign of the number being subtracted and proceed as in addition.

3. (a) The product of two real numbers with like signs is positive.

   (b) The product of two real numbers with unlike signs is negative.

4. (a) The quotient of two real numbers with like signs is positive.

   (b) The quotient of two real numbers with unlike signs is negative.

1. (a) $(+5) + (+6) = +11$

$$\left(-\frac{1}{6}\right) + \left(-\frac{2}{6}\right) = -\frac{3}{6} = -\frac{1}{2}$$

   (b) $(-4) + (+3) = -1$
   $(+5) + (-3) = +2$
$$\left(-\frac{11}{7}\right) + (+1) = -\frac{4}{7}$$

2. $(-9) - (-8) = (-9) + (+8) = -1$
   $16 - (8) = 16 + (-8) = +8$

3. (a) $(-3)(-4) = +12$
$$\left(+\frac{3}{4}\right)(+4) = +3$$

   (b) $5(-3) = -15$
   $(-3)(+4) = -12$

4. (a) $(-14) \div (-2) = +7$
   $+36/4 = +9$

   (b) $(-28)/4 = -7$
   $45 \div (-5) = -9$

When two or more operations with real numbers are indicated in an evaluation, it is important that everyone agree on the order in which the operations are performed so that a unique result is guaranteed. The following **order of operations** is universally accepted.

Order of Operations

1. Perform operations within parentheses.
2. Find indicated powers ($2^3 = 2 \cdot 2 \cdot 2 = 8$).
3. Perform multiplications and divisions from left to right.
4. Perform additions and subtractions from left to right.

EXAMPLE 3   Order of Operations

Evaluate the following.
(a) $-4 + 3$
(b) $-4^2 + 3$
(c) $(-4 + 3)^2 + 3$
(d) $6 \div 2(2 + 1)$

Solution
(a) -1
(b) Note that with -4^2 the power 2 is applied only to 4, not to -4 (which would be written $(-4)^2$). Thus $-4^2 + 3 = -(4^2) + 3 = -16 + 3 = -13$
(c) $(-1)^2 + 3 = 1 + 3 = 4$
(d) $6 \div 2(3) = (6 \div 2)(3) = 3 \cdot 3 = 9$

CHECKPOINT

True or false:
4. $-(-5)^2 = 25$
5. $|4 - 6| = |4| - |6|$
6. $9 - 2(2)(-10) = 7(2)(-10) = -140$

We will assume that you have a scientific or graphing calculator. Discussions of some of the capabilities of graphing calculators and graphing utilities will be found throughout the text.

Most scientific and graphing calculators use standard algebraic order when evaluating arithmetic expressions. Working outward from inner parentheses, calculations are performed from left to right. Powers and roots are evaluated first, followed by multiplications and divisions, and then additions and subtractions.

CHECKPOINT SOLUTIONS

1. (a) Meaningless. A denominator of zero means division by zero, which is undefined.
   (b) $\frac{0}{4} = 0$. A numerator of zero (when the denominator is not zero) means the fraction has value 0.
   (c) $\frac{4}{4} = 1$
   (d) Meaningless. The denominator is zero.
2. (a) $1 < x < 3$
   (b) $0 < x \le 3$
   (c) $-1 \le x < \infty$ or $x \ge -1$
   (d) $-\infty < x < 2$ or $x < 2$

3. (a) $[3, 6]$; closed interval
   (b) $[-6, 4)$; half-open interval
4. False. $-(-5)^2 = (-1)(-5)^2 = (-1)(25) = -25$. Exponentiation has priority and applies only to -5.
5. False. $|4 - 6| = |-2| = 2$ and $|4| - |6| = 4 - 6 = -2$.
6. False. Without parentheses, multiplication has priority over subtraction.
   $9 - 2(2)(-10) = 9 - 4(-10) = 9 + 40 = 49$.

| EXERCISES | 0.2

In Problems 1–2, indicate whether the given expression is one or more of the following types of numbers: rational, irrational, integer, natural. If the expression is meaningless, so state.

1. (a) $\dfrac{-\pi}{10}$
   (b) -9
   (c) $\dfrac{9}{3}$
   (d) $\dfrac{4}{0}$

2. (a) $\dfrac{0}{6}$
   (b) -1.2916
   (c) 1.414
   (d) $\dfrac{9}{6}$

Which property of real numbers is illustrated in each part of Problems 3–6?

3. (a) $8 + 6 = 6 + 8$
   (b) $5(3 + 7) = 5(3) + 5(7)$

4. (a) $6(4 \cdot 5) = (6 \cdot 4)(5)$
   (b) $-15 + 0 = -15$
5. (a) $-e \cdot 1 = -e$
   (b) $4 + (-4) = 0$
6. (a) $\left(\dfrac{3}{2}\right)\left(\dfrac{2}{3}\right) = 1$
   (b) $(12)\left(\dfrac{3}{4}\right) = \left(\dfrac{3}{4}\right)(12)$

Insert the proper sign $<$, $=$, or $>$ to replace $\square$ in Problems 7–14.

7. $-6 \,\square\, 0$
8. $2 \,\square\, -20$
9. $-14 \,\square\, -3$
10. $\pi \,\square\, 3.14$
11. $0.333 \,\square\, \dfrac{1}{3}$
12. $\dfrac{1}{3} + \dfrac{1}{2} \,\square\, \dfrac{5}{6}$
13. $|-3| + |5| \,\square\, |-3 + 5|$
14. $|-9 - 3| \,\square\, |-9| + |3|$

In Problems 15–26, evaluate each expression.

15. $-3^2 + 10 \cdot 2$

16. $(-3)^2 + 10 \cdot 2$

17. $\dfrac{4 + 2^2}{2}$

18. $\dfrac{(4 + 2)^2}{2}$

19. $\dfrac{16 - (-4)}{8 - (-2)}$

20. $\dfrac{(-5)(-3) - (-2)(3)}{-9 + 2}$

21. $\dfrac{|5 - 2| - |-7|}{|5 - 2|}$

22. $\dfrac{|3 - |4 - 11||}{-|5^2 - 3^2|}$

23. $\dfrac{(-3)^2 - 2 \cdot 3 + 6}{4 - 2^2 + 3}$

24. $\dfrac{6^2 - 4(-3)(-2)}{6 - 6^2 \div 4}$

25. $\dfrac{-4^2 + 5 - 2 \cdot 3}{5 - 4^2}$

26. $\dfrac{3 - 2(5 - 2)}{(-2)^2 - 2^2 + 3}$

27. What part of the real number line corresponds to the interval $(-\infty, \infty)$?

28. Write the interval corresponding to $x \geq 0$.

In Problems 29–32, express each inequality or graph using interval notation, and name the type of interval.

29. $1 < x \leq 3$

30. $-4 \leq x \leq 3$

31.

32.

In Problems 33–36, write an inequality that describes each interval or graph.

33. $[-3, 5)$

34. $(-2, \infty)$

35.

36.

In Problems 37–44, graph the subset of the real numbers that is represented by each of the following and write your answer in interval notation.

37. $(-\infty, 4) \cap (-3, \infty)$

38. $[-4, 17] \cap [-20, 10]$

39. $x > 4$ and $x \geq 0$

40. $x < 10$ and $x < -1$

41. $[0, \infty) \cup [-1, 5]$

42. $(-\infty, 4) \cup (0, 2)$

43. $x > 7$ or $x < 0$

44. $x > 4$ and $x < 0$

In Problems 45–50, use your calculator to evaluate each of the following. List all the digits on your display in the answer.

45. $\dfrac{-1}{25916.8}$

46. $\dfrac{51.412}{127.01}$

47. $(3.679)^7$

48. $(1.28)^{10}$

49. $\dfrac{2500}{(1.1)^6 - 1}$

50. $100\left[\dfrac{(1.05)^{12} - 1}{0.05}\right]$

APPLICATIONS

51. *Take-home pay* A sales representative's take-home pay is found by subtracting all taxes and retirement contributions from gross pay (which consists of salary plus commission). Given the following information, complete parts (a)–(c).

    Salary = \$300.00   Commission = \$788.91

    Retirement = 5% of gross pay

    Taxes: State = 5% of gross pay
        Local = 1% of gross pay
        Federal withholding =
            25% of (gross pay less retirement)
        Federal social security and Medicare =
            7.65% of gross pay

    (a) Find the gross pay.
    (b) Find the amount of federal withholding.
    (c) Find the take-home pay.

52. *Public health expenditures* The expenditures E for government public health activities (in billions of dollars) can be approximated by
$$E = 5.03t^2 + 100t + 1380$$
    where t is the number of years past 2000 (*Source:* Centers for Medicare and Medicaid Services).

    (a) What t-value represents the year 2010?
    (b) Actual expenditures for 2010 were \$2879 billion. What does the formula give as the 2010 approximation?
    (c) Predict the expenditures for 2015.

53. *Health insurance coverage* The percentage P of the U.S. population with no health insurance can be approximated quite accurately either by
    (1) $P = 0.3179t + 13.85$ or by
    (2) $P = 0.0194t^3 - 0.1952t^2 + 0.8282t + 13.63$
    where t is the number of years past 2000 (*Source:* U.S. Census Bureau).

    (a) Both (1) and (2) closely approximate the data, but which is more accurate for 2006, when 15.8% of the population had no health insurance?
    (b) Use both formulas to estimate the percentage of the U.S. population not covered in 2012.

54. *Health statistics* From data adapted from the National Center for Health Statistics, the height H in inches and age A in years for boys between 4 and 16 years of age are related according to

$$H = 2.31A + 31.26$$

To account for normal variability among boys, normal height for a given age is $\pm 5\%$ of the height obtained from the equation.

(a) Find the normal height range for a boy who is 10.5 years old, and write it as an inequality.

(b) Find the normal height range for a boy who is 5.75 years old, and write it as an inequality.

55. *Income taxes* The federal tax brackets for a single person claiming one personal exemption are given in the following table.

Taxable Income *I*	Tax Due *T*
$0–$8375	10% I
$8376–$34,000	$837.50 + 15%($I$ − 8375)
$34,001–$82,400	$4681.25 + 25%($I$ − 34,000)
$82,401–$171,850	$16,781.25 + 28%($I$ − 82,400)
$171,851–$373,650	$41,827.25 + 33%($I$ − 171,850)
Over $373,650	$108,421.25 + 35%($I$ − 373,650)

Source: Internal Revenue Service

(a) Write the last three taxable income ranges as inequalities.

(b) If an individual has a taxable income of $34,000, calculate the tax due. Repeat this calculation for a taxable income of $82,400.

(c) Write an interval that represents the amount of tax due for a taxable income between $34,000 and $82,400.

0.3

Integral Exponents

If $1000 is placed in a 5-year savings certificate that pays an interest rate of 10% per year, compounded annually, then the amount returned after 5 years is given by

$$1000(1.1)^5$$

The 5 in this expression is an *exponent.* Exponents provide an easier way to denote certain multiplications. For example,

$$(1.1)^5 = (1.1)(1.1)(1.1)(1.1)(1.1)$$

An understanding of the properties of exponents is fundamental to the algebra needed to study functions and solve equations. Furthermore, the definition of exponential and logarithmic functions and many of the techniques in calculus also require an understanding of the properties of exponents.

For any real number a,

$$a^2 = a \cdot a, \quad a^3 = a \cdot a \cdot a, \quad \text{and} \quad a^n = a \cdot a \cdot a \cdot \ldots \cdot a \quad (n \text{ factors})$$

for any positive integer n. The positive integer n is called the **exponent,** the number a is called the **base,** and a^n is read "a to the nth power."

Note that $4a^n$ means $4(a^n)$, which is different from $(4a)^n$. The 4 is the coefficient of a^n in $4a^n$. Note also that $-x^n$ is not equivalent to $(-x)^n$ when n is even. For example, $-3^4 = -81$, but $(-3)^4 = 81$.

Some of the rules of exponents follow.

Positive Integer Exponents	For any real numbers a and b and positive integers m and n,

1. $a^m \cdot a^n = a^{m+n}$

2. For $a \neq 0$, $\quad \dfrac{a^m}{a^n} = \begin{cases} a^{m-n} & \text{if } m > n \\ 1 & \text{if } m = n \\ 1/a^{n-m} & \text{if } m < n \end{cases}$

3. $(ab)^m = a^m b^m$

4. $\left(\dfrac{a}{b}\right)^m = \dfrac{a^m}{b^m} \quad (b \neq 0)$

5. $(a^m)^n = a^{mn}$

EXAMPLE **1** **Positive Integer Exponents**

Use rules of positive integer exponents to rewrite the following. Assume all denominators are nonzero.

(a) $\dfrac{5^6}{5^4}$

(b) $\dfrac{x^2}{x^5}$

(c) $\left(\dfrac{x}{y}\right)^4$

(d) $(3x^2y^3)^4$

(e) $3^3 \cdot 3^2$

Solution

(a) $\dfrac{5^6}{5^4} = 5^{6-4} = 5^2$

(b) $\dfrac{x^2}{x^5} = \dfrac{1}{x^{5-2}} = \dfrac{1}{x^3}$

(c) $\left(\dfrac{x}{y}\right)^4 = \dfrac{x^4}{y^4}$

(d) $(3x^2y^3)^4 = 3^4(x^2)^4(y^3)^4 = 81x^8y^{12}$

(e) $3^3 \cdot 3^2 = 3^{3+2} = 3^5$

For certain calculus operations, use of negative exponents is necessary in order to write problems in the proper form. We can extend the rules for positive integer exponents to all integers by defining a^0 and a^{-n}. Clearly $a^m \cdot a^0$ should equal $a^{m+0} = a^m$, and it will if $a^0 = 1$.

Zero Exponent

For any nonzero real number a, we define $a^0 = 1$. We leave 0^0 undefined.

In Section 0.2, we defined a^{-1} as $1/a$ for $a \neq 0$, so we define a^{-n} as $(a^{-1})^n$.

Negative Exponents

$$a^{-n} = (a^{-1})^n = \left(\dfrac{1}{a}\right)^n = \dfrac{1}{a^n} \qquad (a \neq 0)$$

$$\left(\dfrac{a}{b}\right)^{-n} = \left[\left(\dfrac{a}{b}\right)^{-1}\right]^n = \left(\dfrac{b}{a}\right)^n \qquad (a \neq 0, \quad b \neq 0)$$

EXAMPLE **2** **Negative and Zero Exponents**

Write the following without exponents.

(a) $6 \cdot 3^0$

(b) 6^{-2}

(c) $\left(\dfrac{1}{3}\right)^{-1}$

(d) $-\left(\dfrac{2}{3}\right)^{-4}$

(e) $(-4)^{-2}$

Solution

(a) $6 \cdot 3^0 = 6 \cdot 1 = 6$

(b) $6^{-2} = \dfrac{1}{6^2} = \dfrac{1}{36}$

(c) $\left(\dfrac{1}{3}\right)^{-1} = \dfrac{3}{1} = 3$

(d) $-\left(\dfrac{2}{3}\right)^{-4} = -\left(\dfrac{3}{2}\right)^4 = \dfrac{-81}{16}$

(e) $(-4)^{-2} = \dfrac{1}{(-4)^2} = \dfrac{1}{16}$

As we'll see in the chapter on the mathematics of finance (Chapter 6), negative exponents arise in financial calculations when we have a future goal for an investment and want to know how much to invest now. For example, if money can be invested at 9%, compounded annually, then the amount we must invest now (which is called the present value) in order to have \$10,000 in the account after 7 years is given by $\$10,000(1.09)^{-7}$. Calculations such as this are often done directly with a calculator.

Using the definitions of zero and negative exponents enables us to extend the rules of exponents to all integers and to express them more simply.

Rules of Exponents	For real numbers a and b and *integers* m and n,

1. $a^m \cdot a^n = a^{m+n}$ 2. $a^m/a^n = a^{m-n} \ (a \neq 0)$
3. $(ab)^m = a^m b^m$ 4. $(a^m)^n = a^{mn}$
5. $(a/b)^m = a^m/b^m \ (b \neq 0)$ 6. $a^0 = 1 \ (a \neq 0)$
7. $a^{-n} = 1/a^n \ (a \neq 0)$ 8. $(a/b)^{-n} = (b/a)^n \ (a, b \neq 0)$

Throughout the remainder of the text, we will assume all expressions are defined.

EXAMPLE 3   Operations with Exponents

Use the rules of exponents and the definitions of a^0 and a^{-n} to simplify the following with positive exponents.

(a) $2(x^2)^{-2}$ (b) $x^{-2} \cdot x^{-5}$

(c) $\dfrac{x^{-8}}{x^{-4}}$ (d) $\left(\dfrac{2x^3}{3x^{-5}}\right)^{-2}$

Solution

(a) $2(x^2)^{-2} = 2x^{-4} = 2\left(\dfrac{1}{x^4}\right) = \dfrac{2}{x^4}$

(b) $x^{-2} \cdot x^{-5} = x^{-2-5} = x^{-7} = \dfrac{1}{x^7}$

(c) $\dfrac{x^{-8}}{x^{-4}} = x^{-8-(-4)} = x^{-4} = \dfrac{1}{x^4}$

(d) $\left(\dfrac{2x^3}{3x^{-5}}\right)^{-2} = \left(\dfrac{2x^8}{3}\right)^{-2} = \left(\dfrac{3}{2x^8}\right)^2 = \dfrac{9}{4x^{16}}$

CHECKPOINT	

1. Complete the following.
    (a) $x^3 \cdot x^8 = x^?$ (b) $x \cdot x^4 \cdot x^{-3} = x^?$

    (c) $\dfrac{1}{x^4} = x^?$ (d) $x^{24} \div x^{-3} = x^?$

    (e) $(x^4)^2 = x^?$ (f) $(2x^4y)^3 = ?$

2. True or false:

    (a) $3x^{-2} = \dfrac{1}{9x^2}$ (b) $-x^{-4} = \dfrac{-1}{x^4}$ (c) $x^{-3} = -x^3$

3. Evaluate the following, if possible. For any that are meaningless, so state. Assume $x > 0$.
(a) 0^4 (b) 0^0 (c) x^0 (d) 0^x (e) 0^{-4} (f) -5^{-2}

EXAMPLE 4 Rewriting a Quotient

Write $(x^2y)/(9wz^3)$ with all factors in the numerator.

Solution

$$\frac{x^2y}{9wz^3} = x^2y\left(\frac{1}{9wz^3}\right) = x^2y\left(\frac{1}{9}\right)\left(\frac{1}{w}\right)\left(\frac{1}{z^3}\right) = x^2y \cdot 9^{-1}w^{-1}z^{-3}$$
$$= 9^{-1}x^2yw^{-1}z^{-3}$$

EXAMPLE 5 Rewriting with Positive Exponents

Simplify the following so all exponents are positive.
(a) $(2^3x^{-4}y^5)^{-2}$
(b) $\dfrac{2x^4(x^2y)^0}{(4x^{-2}y)^2}$

Solution

(a) $(2^3x^{-4}y^5)^{-2} = 2^{-6}x^8y^{-10} = \dfrac{1}{2^6} \cdot x^8 \cdot \dfrac{1}{y^{10}} = \dfrac{x^8}{64y^{10}}$

(b) $\dfrac{2x^4(x^2y)^0}{(4x^{-2}y)^2} = \dfrac{2x^4 \cdot 1}{4^2x^{-4}y^2} = \dfrac{2}{4^2} \cdot \dfrac{x^4}{x^{-4}} \cdot \dfrac{1}{y^2} = \dfrac{2}{16} \cdot \dfrac{x^8}{1} \cdot \dfrac{1}{y^2} = \dfrac{x^8}{8y^2}$

CHECKPOINT SOLUTIONS

1. (a) $x^3 \cdot x^8 = x^{3+8} = x^{11}$ (b) $x \cdot x^4 \cdot x^{-3} = x^{1+4+(-3)} = x^2$

   (c) $\dfrac{1}{x^4} = x^{-4}$ (d) $x^{24} \div x^{-3} = x^{24-(-3)} = x^{27}$

   (e) $(x^4)^2 = x^{(4)(2)} = x^8$ (f) $(2x^4y)^3 = 2^3(x^4)^3y^3 = 8x^{12}y^3$

2. (a) False. $3x^{-2} = 3\left(\dfrac{1}{x^2}\right) = \dfrac{3}{x^2}$

   (b) True. $-x^{-4} = (-1)\left(\dfrac{1}{x^4}\right) = \dfrac{-1}{x^4}$

   (c) False. $x^{-3} = \dfrac{1}{x^3}$

3. (a) $0^4 = 0$ (b) Meaningless. 0^0 is undefined.
   (c) $x^0 = 1$ since $x \neq 0$ (d) $0^x = 0$ because $x > 0$

   (e) Meaningless. 0^{-4} would be $\dfrac{1}{0^4}$, which is undefined.

   (f) $-5^{-2} = (-1)\left(\dfrac{1}{5^2}\right) = \dfrac{-1}{25}$

| EXERCISES | 0.3

Evaluate in Problems 1–8. Write all answers without using exponents.

1. $(-4)^4$
2. -5^3
3. -2^6
4. $(-2)^5$
5. 3^{-2}
6. 6^{-1}
7. $-\left(\dfrac{3}{2}\right)^2$
8. $\left(\dfrac{2}{3}\right)^3$

In Problems 9–18, use rules of exponents to simplify the expressions. Express answers with positive exponents.

9. $6^5 \cdot 6^3$

10. $8^4 \cdot 8^2 \cdot 8$

11. $\dfrac{10^8}{10^9}$

12. $\dfrac{7^8}{7^3}$

13. $\dfrac{9^4 \cdot 9^{-7}}{9^{-3}}$

14. $\dfrac{5^4}{(5^{-2} \cdot 5^3)}$

15. $(3^3)^3$

16. $(2^{-3})^{-2}$

17. $\left(\dfrac{2}{3}\right)^{-2}$

18. $\left(\dfrac{-2}{5}\right)^{-4}$

In Problems 19–22, simplify by expressing answers with positive exponents ($x, y, z \neq 0$).

19. $(x^2)^{-3}$

20. x^{-4}

21. $xy^{-2}z^0$

22. $(xy^{-2})^0$

In Problems 23–36, use the rules of exponents to simplify so that only positive exponents remain.

23. $x^3 \cdot x^4$

24. $a^5 \cdot a$

25. $x^{-5} \cdot x^3$

26. $y^{-5} \cdot y^{-2}$

27. $\dfrac{x^8}{x^4}$

28. $\dfrac{a^5}{a^{-1}}$

29. $\dfrac{y^5}{y^{-7}}$

30. $\dfrac{y^{-3}}{y^{-4}}$

31. $(x^4)^3$

32. $(y^3)^{-2}$

33. $(xy)^2$

34. $(2m)^3$

35. $\left(\dfrac{2}{x^5}\right)^4$

36. $\left(\dfrac{8}{a^3}\right)^3$

In Problems 37–48, compute and simplify so that only positive exponents remain.

37. $(2x^{-2}y)^{-4}$

38. $(-32x^5)^{-3}$

39. $(-8a^{-3}b^2)(2a^5b^{-4})$

40. $(-3m^2y^{-1})(2m^{-3}y^{-1})$

41. $(2x^{-2}) \div (x^{-1}y^2)$

42. $(-8a^{-3}b^2c) \div (2a^5b^4)$

43. $\left(\dfrac{x^3}{y^{-2}}\right)^{-3}$

44. $\left(\dfrac{x^{-2}}{y}\right)^{-3}$

45. $\left(\dfrac{a^{-2}b^{-1}c^{-4}}{a^4b^{-3}c^0}\right)^{-3}$

46. $\left(\dfrac{4x^{-1}y^{-40}}{2^{-2}x^4y^{-10}}\right)^{-2}$

47. (a) $\dfrac{2x^{-2}}{(2x)^2}$ (b) $\dfrac{(2x)^{-2}}{(2x)^2}$

   (c) $\dfrac{2x^{-2}}{2x^2}$ (d) $\dfrac{2x^{-2}}{(2x)^{-2}}$

48. (a) $\dfrac{2^{-1}x^{-2}}{(2x)^2}$ (b) $\dfrac{2^{-1}x^{-2}}{2x^2}$

   (c) $\dfrac{(2x^{-2})^{-1}}{(2x)^{-2}}$ (d) $\dfrac{(2x^{-2})^{-1}}{2x^2}$

In many applications it is often necessary to write expressions in the form cx^n where c is a constant and n is an integer. In Problems 49–56, write the expressions in this form.

49. $\dfrac{1}{x}$

50. $\dfrac{1}{x^2}$

51. $(2x)^3$

52. $(3x)^2$

53. $\dfrac{1}{4x^2}$

54. $\dfrac{3}{2x^4}$

55. $\left(\dfrac{-x}{2}\right)^3$

56. $\left(\dfrac{-x}{3}\right)^2$

In Problems 57–60, use a calculator to evaluate the indicated powers.

57. 1.2^4

58. $(-3.7)^3$

59. $(1.5)^{-5}$

60. $(-0.8)^{-9}$

APPLICATIONS

Compound interest **If $\$P$ is invested for n years at rate i (as a decimal), compounded annually, the future value that accrues is given by $S = P(1 + i)^n$, and the interest earned is $I = S - P$. In Problems 61–64, find S and I for the given P, n, and i.**

61. $\$1200$ for 5 years at 12%

62. $\$1800$ for 7 years at 10%

63. $\$5000$ for 6 years at 11.5%

64. $\$800$ for 20 years at 10.5%

Present value **If an investment has a goal (future value) of $\$S$ after n years, invested at interest rate i (as a decimal), compounded annually, then the present value P that must be invested is given by $P = S(1 + i)^{-n}$. In Problems 65 and 66, find P for the given S, n, and i.**

65. $\$15,000$ after 6 years at 11.5%

66. $\$80,000$ after 20 years at 10.5%

67. *Personal income* For selected years from 1980 to 2006, total U.S. personal income I (in billions of dollars) can be approximated by the formula

$$I = 2568.9(1.059)^t$$

where t is the number of years past 1980.

(a) What t-values correspond to the years 1985, 1995, and 2002?

(b) The actual total personal incomes (in billions of dollars) for the years in part (a) were as follows.

1985	1995	2002
3526.7	6152.3	8881.9

What does the formula estimate for these years?

(c) What does the formula estimate for the total personal income in 2012?

(d) Does this formula seem to indicate that total personal income doubles almost every 12 years?

68. *Stock shares traded* On the New York Stock Exchange (NYSE) for 1970–2006, the average daily shares traded S (in millions of shares) can be approximated by the formula

$$S = 0.50274(1.1626)^t$$

where t is the number of years past 1950 (*Source:* New York Stock Exchange).

(a) What t-values correspond to the years 1990, 2000, and 2006?

(b) For the years in (a), the actual average millions of shares traded on the NYSE were as follows.

1990	2000	2006
156.777	1041.58	2343.16

What does the formula predict for these years?

(c) Suppose in 2015 that a stock market average (such as the Dow Jones Industrial Average) dramatically soared or tumbled; do you think this formula's predictions would be accurate, too low, or too high? Explain.

69. *Endangered species* The total number of endangered species y can be approximated by the formula

$$y = \frac{1883}{1 + 7.892(1.097)^{-t}}$$

where t is the number of years past 1980 (*Source:* U.S. Fish and Wildlife Service).

(a) The actual numbers of endangered species for selected years were as follows.

1990	2003	2007
442	987	1137

For each of these years, find the number of endangered species predicted by the formula. Round your answer to the nearest integer.

(b) How many more species does the formula estimate will be added to the endangered list for 2020 than the actual number given for 2007?

(c) Why do you think the answer to (b) is smaller than the number of species added from 1990 to 2003?

(d) Why is it reasonable for a formula such as this to have an upper limit that cannot be exceeded? Use large t-values in the formula to discover this formula's upper limit.

70. *Internet users* The percent p of U.S. households with Internet service can be approximated by the equation

$$p = \frac{73.92}{1 + 5.441(1.515)^{-t}}$$

where t is the number of years past 1995 (*Source:* U.S. Department of Commerce).

(a) The percents of U.S. households with Internet service for selected years were as follows.

2001	2004	2007
50.0%	68.8%	70.2%

For each of these years, use the equation to find the predicted percent of households with Internet service.

(b) From 2001 to 2004, the percent of households with Internet service increased by 18.8 percentage points. What increase does the equation predict from 2008 to 2011? Why do you think the 2008–2011 change is so different from the 2001–2004 change?

(c) Why is it reasonable for a formula such as this to have an upper limit that cannot be exceeded? Use large t-values in the formula to discover this formula's upper limit.

71. *Health care expenditures* The national health care expenditure H (in billions of dollars) can be modeled (that is, accurately approximated) by the formula

$$H = 738.1(1.065)^t$$

where t is the number of years past 1990 (*Source:* U.S. Department of Health and Human Services).

(a) What t-value corresponds to 2000?

(b) Approximate the national health care expenditure in 2000.

(c) Approximate the national health care expenditure in 2010.

(d) Estimate the national health care expenditure in 2018.

0.4

Radicals and Rational Exponents

Roots   A process closely linked to that of raising numbers to powers is that of extracting roots. From geometry we know that if an edge of a cube has a length of x units, its volume is x^3 cubic units. Reversing this process, we determine that if the volume of a cube is V cubic units, the length of an edge is the cube root of V, which is denoted

$$\sqrt[3]{V} \text{ units}$$

When we seek the **cube root** of a number such as 8 (written $\sqrt[3]{8}$), we are looking for a real number whose cube equals 8. Because $2^3 = 8$, we know that $\sqrt[3]{8} = 2$. Similarly, $\sqrt[3]{-27} = -3$ because $(-3)^3 = -27$. The expression $\sqrt[n]{a}$ is called a **radical,** where $\sqrt{}$ is the **radical sign,** n the **index,** and a the **radicand.** When no index is indicated, the index is assumed to be 2 and the expression is called a **square root;** thus $\sqrt{4}$ is the square root of 4 and represents the positive number whose square is 4.

Only one real number satisfies $\sqrt[n]{a}$ for a real number a and an odd number n; we call that number the **principal nth root** or, more simply, the **nth root.**

For an even index n, there are two possible cases:

1. If a is negative, there is no real number equal to $\sqrt[n]{a}$. For example, there are no real numbers that equal $\sqrt{-4}$ or $\sqrt[4]{-16}$ because there is no real number b such that $b^2 = -4$ or $b^4 = -16$. In this case, we say $\sqrt[n]{a}$ is not a real number.
2. If a is positive, there are two real numbers whose nth power equals a. For example, $3^2 = 9$ and $(-3)^2 = 9$. In order to have a unique nth root, we define the (principal) nth root, $\sqrt[n]{a}$, as the *positive* number b that satisfies $b^n = a$.

We summarize this discussion as follows.

nth Root of a	The **(principal) nth root** of a real number is defined as

$$\sqrt[n]{a} = b \quad \text{only if} \quad a = b^n$$

subject to the following conditions:

	$a = 0$	$a > 0$	$a < 0$
n even	$\sqrt[n]{a} = 0$	$\sqrt[n]{a} > 0$	$\sqrt[n]{a}$ not real
n odd	$\sqrt[n]{a} = 0$	$\sqrt[n]{a} > 0$	$\sqrt[n]{a} < 0$

When we are asked for the root of a number, we give the principal root.

EXAMPLE 1   Roots

Find the roots, if they are real numbers.

(a) $\sqrt[6]{64}$ (b) $-\sqrt{16}$ (c) $\sqrt[3]{-8}$ (d) $\sqrt{-16}$

Solution

(a) $\sqrt[6]{64} = 2$ because $2^6 = 64$ (b) $-\sqrt{16} = -(\sqrt{16}) = -4$ (c) $\sqrt[3]{-8} = -2$

(d) $\sqrt{-16}$ is not a real number because an even root of a negative number is not real. ▪

Fractional Exponents   In order to perform evaluations on a calculator or to perform calculus operations, it is sometimes necessary to rewrite radicals in exponential form with fractional exponents.

We have stated that for $a \geq 0$ and $b \geq 0$,

$$\sqrt{a} = b \quad \text{only if} \quad a = b^2$$

This means that $(\sqrt{a})^2 = b^2 = a$, or $(\sqrt{a})^2 = a$. In order to extend the properties of exponents to rational exponents, it is necessary to define

$$a^{1/2} = \sqrt{a} \quad \text{so that} \quad (a^{1/2})^2 = a$$

Exponent $1/n$	For a positive integer n, we define

$$a^{1/n} = \sqrt[n]{a} \quad \text{if} \quad \sqrt[n]{a} \text{ exists}$$

Thus $(a^{1/n})^n = a^{(1/n)\cdot n} = a$.

Because we wish the properties established for integer exponents to extend to rational exponents, we make the following definitions.

Rational Exponents

For positive integer n and any integer m (with $a \neq 0$ when $m \leq 0$ and with m/n in lowest terms):

1. $a^{m/n} = (a^{1/n})^m = (\sqrt[n]{a})^m$
2. $a^{m/n} = (a^m)^{1/n} = \sqrt[n]{a^m}$ if a is nonnegative when n is even.

Throughout the remaining discussion, we assume all expressions are real.

EXAMPLE 2   Radical Form

Write the following in radical form and simplify.
(a) $16^{3/4}$ (b) $y^{-3/2}$ (c) $(6m)^{2/3}$

Solution

(a) $16^{3/4} = \sqrt[4]{16^3} = (\sqrt[4]{16})^3 = (2)^3 = 8$

(b) $y^{-3/2} = \dfrac{1}{y^{3/2}} = \dfrac{1}{\sqrt{y^3}}$

(c) $(6m)^{2/3} = \sqrt[3]{(6m)^2} = \sqrt[3]{36m^2}$

EXAMPLE 3   Fractional Exponents

Write the following without radical signs.
(a) $\sqrt{x^3}$ (b) $\dfrac{1}{\sqrt[3]{b^2}}$ (c) $\sqrt[3]{(ab)^3}$

Solution

(a) $\sqrt{x^3} = x^{3/2}$ (b) $\dfrac{1}{\sqrt[3]{b^2}} = \dfrac{1}{b^{2/3}} = b^{-2/3}$ (c) $\sqrt[3]{(ab)^3} = (ab)^{3/3} = ab$

Our definition of $a^{m/n}$ guarantees that the rules for exponents will apply to fractional exponents. Thus we can perform operations with fractional exponents as we did with integer exponents.

EXAMPLE 4   Operations with Fractional Exponents

Simplify the following expressions.
(a) $a^{1/2} \cdot a^{1/6}$ (b) $a^{3/4}/a^{1/3}$ (c) $(a^3b)^{2/3}$ (d) $(a^{3/2})^{1/2}$ (e) $a^{-1/2} \cdot a^{-3/2}$

Solution

(a) $a^{1/2} \cdot a^{1/6} = a^{1/2 + 1/6} = a^{3/6 + 1/6} = a^{4/6} = a^{2/3}$

(b) $a^{3/4}/a^{1/3} = a^{3/4 - 1/3} = a^{9/12 - 4/12} = a^{5/12}$

(c) $(a^3b)^{2/3} = (a^3)^{2/3}b^{2/3} = a^2b^{2/3}$

(d) $(a^{3/2})^{1/2} = a^{(3/2)(1/2)} = a^{3/4}$

(e) $a^{-1/2} \cdot a^{-3/2} = a^{-1/2 - 3/2} = a^{-2} = 1/a^2$

CHECKPOINT

1. Which of the following are *not* real numbers?
    (a) $\sqrt[3]{-64}$ (b) $\sqrt{-64}$ (c) $\sqrt{0}$ (d) $\sqrt[4]{1}$ (e) $\sqrt[5]{-1}$ (f) $\sqrt[8]{-1}$

2. (a) Write as radicals: $x^{1/3}, x^{2/5}, x^{-3/2}$

    (b) Write with fractional exponents: $\sqrt[4]{x^3} = x^?, \dfrac{1}{\sqrt{x}} = \dfrac{1}{x^?} = x^?$

3. Evaluate the following.

    (a) $8^{2/3}$ (b) $(-8)^{2/3}$ (c) $8^{-2/3}$ (d) $-8^{-2/3}$ (e) $\sqrt[15]{71}$

4. Complete the following.

    (a) $x \cdot x^{1/3} \cdot x^3 = x^?$ (b) $x^2 \div x^{1/2} = x^?$ (c) $(x^{-2/3})^{-3} = x^?$

    (d) $x^{-3/2} \cdot x^{1/2} = x^?$ (e) $x^{-3/2} \cdot x = x^?$ (f) $\left(\dfrac{x^4}{y^2}\right)^{3/2} = \,?$

5. True or false:

    (a) $\dfrac{8x^{2/3}}{x^{-1/3}} = 4x$ (b) $(16x^8 y)^{3/4} = 12x^6 y^{3/4}$

    (c) $\left(\dfrac{x^2}{y^3}\right)^{-1/3} = \left(\dfrac{y^3}{x^2}\right)^{1/3} = \dfrac{y}{x^{2/3}}$

Operations with Radicals

We can perform operations with radicals by first rewriting in exponential form, performing the operations with exponents, and then converting the answer back to radical form. Another option is to apply directly the following rules for operations with radicals.

Rules for Radicals	**Example**
Given that $\sqrt[n]{a}$ and $\sqrt[n]{b}$ are real,*	
1. $\sqrt[n]{a^n} = (\sqrt[n]{a})^n = a$	1. $\sqrt[5]{6^5} = (\sqrt[5]{6})^5 = 6$
2. $\sqrt[n]{a} \cdot \sqrt[n]{b} = \sqrt[n]{ab}$	2. $\sqrt[3]{2}\sqrt[3]{4} = \sqrt[3]{8} = \sqrt[3]{2^3} = 2$
3. $\dfrac{\sqrt[n]{a}}{\sqrt[n]{b}} = \sqrt[n]{\dfrac{a}{b}}$ $\quad(b \neq 0)$	3. $\dfrac{\sqrt{18}}{\sqrt{2}} = \sqrt{\dfrac{18}{2}} = \sqrt{9} = 3$

*Note that this means $a \geq 0$ and $b \geq 0$ if n is even.

Let us consider Rule 1 for radicals more carefully. Note that if n is even and $a < 0$, then $\sqrt[n]{a}$ is not real, and Rule 1 does not apply. For example, $\sqrt{-2}$ is not a real number, and

$$\sqrt{(-2)^2} \neq -2 \quad \text{because} \quad \sqrt{(-2)^2} = \sqrt{4} = 2 = -(-2)$$

We can generalize this observation as follows: If $a < 0$, then $\sqrt{a^2} = -a > 0$, so

$$\sqrt{a^2} = \begin{cases} a & \text{if } a \geq 0 \\ -a & \text{if } a < 0 \end{cases}$$

This means

$$\sqrt{a^2} = |a|$$

EXAMPLE 5 Rules for Radicals

Simplify:

    (a) $\sqrt[3]{8^3}$ (b) $\sqrt[5]{x^5}$ (c) $\sqrt{x^2}$ (d) $\left[\sqrt{(3x^2 + 4)^3}\right]^7$

Solution

    (a) $\sqrt[3]{8^3} = 8$ by Rule 1 for radicals

    (b) $\sqrt[5]{x^5} = x$ (c) $\sqrt{x^2} = |x|$ (d) $\left[\sqrt{(3x^2 + 4)^3}\right]^7 = (3x^2 + 4)^3$

Up to now, to *simplify* a radical has meant to find the indicated root. More generally, a radical expression $\sqrt[n]{x}$ is considered simplified if x has no nth powers as factors. Rule 2 for radicals ($\sqrt[n]{a} \cdot \sqrt[n]{b} = \sqrt[n]{ab}$) provides a procedure for simplifying radicals.

EXAMPLE 6 ## Simplifying Radicals

Simplify the following radicals; assume the expressions are real numbers.

(a) $\sqrt{48x^5y^6}$ $(y \geq 0)$ (b) $\sqrt[3]{72a^3b^4}$

Solution

(a) To simplify $\sqrt{48x^5y^6}$, we first factor $48x^5y^6$ into perfect-square factors and other factors. Then we apply Rule 2.

$$\sqrt{48x^5y^6} = \sqrt{16 \cdot 3 \cdot x^4xy^6} = \sqrt{16}\sqrt{x^4}\sqrt{y^6}\sqrt{3x} = 4x^2y^3\sqrt{3x}$$

(b) In this case, we factor $72a^3b^4$ into factors that are perfect cubes and other factors.

$$\sqrt[3]{72a^3b^4} = \sqrt[3]{8 \cdot 9a^3b^3b} = \sqrt[3]{8} \cdot \sqrt[3]{a^3} \cdot \sqrt[3]{b^3} \cdot \sqrt[3]{9b} = 2ab\sqrt[3]{9b}$$

Rule 2 for radicals also provides a procedure for multiplying two roots with the same index.

EXAMPLE 7 ## Multiplying Radicals

Multiply the following and simplify the answers, assuming nonnegative variables.

(a) $\sqrt[3]{2xy} \cdot \sqrt[3]{4x^2y}$ (b) $\sqrt{8xy^3z}\sqrt{4x^2y^3z^2}$

Solution

(a) $\sqrt[3]{2xy} \cdot \sqrt[3]{4x^2y} = \sqrt[3]{2xy \cdot 4x^2y} = \sqrt[3]{8x^3y^2} = \sqrt[3]{8} \cdot \sqrt[3]{x^3} \cdot \sqrt[3]{y^2} = 2x\sqrt[3]{y^2}$

(b) $\sqrt{8xy^3z}\sqrt{4x^2y^3z^2} = \sqrt{32x^3y^6z^3} = \sqrt{16x^2y^6z^2}\sqrt{2xz} = 4xy^3z\sqrt{2xz}$

Rule 3 for radicals $(\sqrt[n]{a}/\sqrt[n]{b} = \sqrt[n]{a/b})$ indicates how to find the quotient of two roots with the same index.

EXAMPLE 8 ## Dividing Radicals

Find the quotients and simplify the answers, assuming nonnegative variables.

(a) $\dfrac{\sqrt[3]{32}}{\sqrt[3]{4}}$ (b) $\dfrac{\sqrt{16a^3x}}{\sqrt{2ax}}$

Solution

(a) $\dfrac{\sqrt[3]{32}}{\sqrt[3]{4}} = \sqrt[3]{\dfrac{32}{4}} = \sqrt[3]{8} = 2$

(b) $\dfrac{\sqrt{16a^3x}}{\sqrt{2ax}} = \sqrt{\dfrac{16a^3x}{2ax}} = \sqrt{8a^2} = 2a\sqrt{2}$

Rationalizing Occasionally, we wish to express a fraction containing radicals in an equivalent form that contains no radicals in the denominator. This is accomplished by multiplying the numerator *and* the denominator by the expression that will remove the radical from the denominator. This process is called **rationalizing the denominator.**

EXAMPLE 9 ## Rationalizing Denominators

Express the following with no radicals in the denominator. (Rationalize each denominator.)

(a) $\dfrac{15}{\sqrt{x}}$ (b) $\dfrac{2x}{\sqrt{18xy}}$ $(x, y > 0)$ (c) $\dfrac{3x}{\sqrt[3]{2x^2}}$ $(x \neq 0)$

Solution

(a) We wish to create a perfect square under the radical in the denominator.

$$\frac{15}{\sqrt{x}} \cdot \frac{\sqrt{x}}{\sqrt{x}} = \frac{15\sqrt{x}}{x}$$

(b) $\dfrac{2x}{\sqrt{18xy}} \cdot \dfrac{\sqrt{2xy}}{\sqrt{2xy}} = \dfrac{2x\sqrt{2xy}}{\sqrt{36x^2y^2}} = \dfrac{2x\sqrt{2xy}}{6xy} = \dfrac{\sqrt{2xy}}{3y}$

(c) We wish to create a perfect cube under the radical in the denominator.

$$\frac{3x}{\sqrt[3]{2x^2}} \cdot \frac{\sqrt[3]{4x}}{\sqrt[3]{4x}} = \frac{3x\sqrt[3]{4x}}{\sqrt[3]{8x^3}} = \frac{3x\sqrt[3]{4x}}{2x} = \frac{3\sqrt[3]{4x}}{2}$$

CHECKPOINT

6. Simplify:
   (a) $\sqrt[7]{x^7}$
   (b) $\left[\sqrt[5]{(x^2+1)^2}\right]^5$
   (c) $\sqrt{12xy^2} \cdot \sqrt{3x^2y}$

7. Rationalize the denominator of $\dfrac{x}{\sqrt{5x}}$ if $x \neq 0$.

It is also sometimes useful, especially in calculus, to *rationalize the numerator* of a fraction. For example, we can rationalize the numerator of

$$\frac{\sqrt[3]{4x^2}}{3x}$$

by multiplying the numerator and denominator by $\sqrt[3]{2x}$, which creates a perfect cube under the radical:

$$\frac{\sqrt[3]{4x^2}}{3x} \cdot \frac{\sqrt[3]{2x}}{\sqrt[3]{2x}} = \frac{\sqrt[3]{8x^3}}{3x\sqrt[3]{2x}} = \frac{2x}{3x\sqrt[3]{2x}} = \frac{2}{3\sqrt[3]{2x}}$$

CHECKPOINT SOLUTIONS

1. Only *even* roots of negatives are not real numbers. Thus part (b) $\sqrt{-64}$ and part (f) $\sqrt[8]{-1}$ are not real numbers.

2. (a) $x^{1/3} = \sqrt[3]{x}$, $\quad x^{2/5} = \sqrt[5]{x^2}$, $\quad x^{-3/2} = \dfrac{1}{x^{3/2}} = \dfrac{1}{\sqrt{x^3}}$

   (b) $\sqrt[4]{x^3} = x^{3/4}$, $\quad \dfrac{1}{\sqrt{x}} = \dfrac{1}{x^{1/2}} = x^{-1/2}$

3. (a) $8^{2/3} = (\sqrt[3]{8})^2 = 2^2 = 4$ (b) $(-8)^{2/3} = (\sqrt[3]{-8})^2 = (-2)^2 = 4$

   (c) $8^{-2/3} = \dfrac{1}{8^{2/3}} = \dfrac{1}{4}$ (d) $-8^{-2/3} = -\left(\dfrac{1}{8^{2/3}}\right) = -\dfrac{1}{4}$

   (e) $\sqrt[15]{71} = (71)^{1/15} \approx 1.32867$

4. (a) $x \cdot x^{1/3} \cdot x^3 = x^{1 + 1/3 + 3} = x^{13/3}$ (b) $x^2 \div x^{1/2} = x^{2 - 1/2} = x^{3/2}$
   (c) $(x^{-2/3})^{-3} = x^{(-2/3)(-3)} = x^2$ (d) $x^{-3/2} \cdot x^{1/2} = x^{-3/2 + 1/2} = x^{-1}$

   (e) $x^{-3/2} \cdot x = x^{-3/2 + 1} = x^{-1/2}$ (f) $\left(\dfrac{x^4}{y^2}\right)^{3/2} = \dfrac{(x^4)^{3/2}}{(y^2)^{3/2}} = \dfrac{x^6}{y^3}$

5. (a) False. $\dfrac{8x^{2/3}}{x^{-1/3}} = 8x^{2/3} \cdot x^{1/3} = 8x^{2/3 + 1/3} = 8x$

   (b) False. $(16x^8y)^{3/4} = 16^{3/4}(x^8)^{3/4}y^{3/4} = (\sqrt[4]{16})^3 x^6 y^{3/4} = 8x^6 y^{3/4}$
   (c) True.

6. (a) $\sqrt[7]{x^7} = x$
   (b) $\left[\sqrt[5]{(x^2+1)^2}\right]^5 = (x^2+1)^2$
   (c) $\sqrt{12xy^2} \cdot \sqrt{3x^2y} = \sqrt{36x^3y^3} = \sqrt{36x^2y^2 \cdot xy} = \sqrt{36x^2y^2}\sqrt{xy} = 6xy\sqrt{xy}$

7. $\dfrac{x}{\sqrt{5x}} = \dfrac{x}{\sqrt{5x}} \cdot \dfrac{\sqrt{5x}}{\sqrt{5x}} = \dfrac{x\sqrt{5x}}{5x} = \dfrac{\sqrt{5x}}{5}$

| EXERCISES | 0.4

Unless stated otherwise, assume all variables are nonnegative and all denominators are nonzero.

In Problems 1–8, find the powers and roots, if they are real numbers.

1. (a) $\sqrt{256/9}$ (b) $\sqrt{1.44}$
2. (a) $\sqrt[5]{-32^3}$ (b) $\sqrt[4]{-16^5}$
3. (a) $16^{3/4}$ (b) $(-16)^{-3/2}$
4. (a) $-27^{-1/3}$ (b) $32^{3/5}$
5. $\left(\dfrac{8}{27}\right)^{-2/3}$ 6. $\left(\dfrac{4}{9}\right)^{3/2}$
7. (a) $8^{2/3}$ (b) $(-8)^{-2/3}$
8. (a) $8^{-2/3}$ (b) $-8^{2/3}$

In Problems 9 and 10, rewrite each radical with a fractional exponent, and then approximate the value with a calculator.

9. $\sqrt[9]{(6.12)^4}$ 10. $\sqrt[12]{4.96}$

In Problems 11–14, replace each radical with a fractional exponent. Do not simplify.

11. $\sqrt{m^3}$ 12. $\sqrt[3]{x^5}$ 13. $\sqrt[4]{m^2 n^5}$ 14. $\sqrt[5]{x^3}$

In Problems 15–20, write in radical form. Do not simplify.

15. $2x^{1/2}$ 16. $12x^{1/4}$
17. $x^{7/6}$ 18. $y^{11/5}$
19. $-(1/4)x^{-5/4}$ 20. $-x^{-5/3}$

In Problems 21–34, use the properties of exponents to simplify each expression so that only positive exponents remain.

21. $y^{1/4} \cdot y^{1/2}$ 22. $x^{2/3} \cdot x^{1/5}$ 23. $z^{3/4} \cdot z^4$
24. $x^{-2/3} \cdot x^2$ 25. $y^{-3/2} \cdot y^{-1}$ 26. $z^{-2} \cdot z^{5/3}$
27. $\dfrac{x^{1/3}}{x^{-2/3}}$ 28. $\dfrac{x^{-1/2}}{x^{-3/2}}$ 29. $\dfrac{y^{-5/2}}{y^{-2/5}}$
30. $\dfrac{x^{4/9}}{x^{1/12}}$ 31. $(x^{2/3})^{3/4}$ 32. $(x^{4/5})^3$
33. $(x^{-1/2})^2$ 34. $(x^{-2/3})^{-2/5}$

In Problems 35–40, simplify each expression by using the properties of radicals. Assume nonnegative variables.

35. $\sqrt{64x^4}$ 36. $\sqrt[3]{-64x^6 y^3}$
37. $\sqrt{128x^4 y^5}$ 38. $\sqrt[3]{54x^5 x^8}$
39. $\sqrt[3]{40x^8 x^5}$ 40. $\sqrt{32x^5 y}$

In Problems 41–48, perform the indicated operations and simplify.

41. $\sqrt{12x^3 y} \cdot \sqrt{3x^2 y}$ 42. $\sqrt[3]{16x^2 y} \cdot \sqrt[3]{3x^2 y}$
43. $\sqrt{63x^5 y^3} \cdot \sqrt{28x^2 y}$ 44. $\sqrt{10xz^{10}} \cdot \sqrt{30x^{17} z}$

45. $\dfrac{\sqrt{12x^3 y^{12}}}{\sqrt{27xy^2}}$ 46. $\dfrac{\sqrt{250xy^7 z^4}}{\sqrt{18x^{17} y^2}}$

47. $\dfrac{\sqrt[4]{32a^9 b^5}}{\sqrt[4]{162a^{17}}}$ 48. $\dfrac{\sqrt[3]{-16x^3 y^4}}{\sqrt[3]{128y^2}}$

In Problems 49–52, use properties of exponents and radicals to determine a value for x that makes each statement true.

49. $(A^9)^x = A$ 50. $(B^{20})^x = B$
51. $(\sqrt[7]{R})^x = R$ 52. $(\sqrt{T^3})^x = T$

In Problems 53–58, rationalize each denominator and then simplify.

53. $\sqrt{2/3}$ 54. $\sqrt{5/8}$ 55. $\dfrac{\sqrt{m^2 x}}{\sqrt{mx^2}}$

56. $\dfrac{5x^3 w}{\sqrt{4xw^2}}$ 57. $\dfrac{\sqrt[3]{m^2 x}}{\sqrt[3]{mx^5}}$ 58. $\dfrac{\sqrt[4]{mx^3}}{\sqrt[4]{y^2 z^5}}$

In calculus it is frequently important to write an expression in the form cx^n, where c is a constant and n is a rational number. In Problems 59–62, write each expression in this form.

59. $\dfrac{-2}{3\sqrt[3]{x^2}}$ 60. $\dfrac{-2}{3\sqrt[4]{x^3}}$ 61. $3x\sqrt{x}$ 62. $\sqrt{x} \cdot \sqrt[3]{x}$

In calculus problems, the answers are frequently expected to be in a form with a radical instead of a fractional exponent. In Problems 63–66, write each expression with radicals.

63. $\dfrac{3}{2}x^{1/2}$ 64. $\dfrac{4}{3}x^{1/3}$

65. $\dfrac{1}{2}x^{-1/2}$ 66. $\dfrac{-1}{2}x^{-3/2}$

APPLICATIONS

67. *Richter scale* The Richter scale reading for an earthquake measures its intensity (as a multiple of some minimum intensity used for comparison). The intensity I corresponding to a Richter scale reading R is given by

$$I = 10^R$$

   (a) A quake measuring 8.5 on the Richter scale would be severe. Express the intensity of such a quake in exponential form and in radical form.
   (b) Find the intensity of a quake measuring 9.0.
   (c) The San Francisco quake that occurred during the 1989 World Series measured 6.9, and the March 2011 quake that devastated Sendai, Japan, measured 9.0. Calculate the ratio of these intensities (larger to smaller).

68. *Sound intensity* The intensity of sound I (as a multiple of the average minimum threshold of hearing intensity) is related to the decibel level D (or loudness of sound) according to

$$I = 10^{D/10}$$

(a) Express $10^{D/10}$ using radical notation.
(b) The background noise level of a relatively quiet room has a decibel reading of 32. Find the intensity I_1 of this noise level.
(c) A decibel reading of 140 is at the threshold of pain. If I_2 is the intensity of this threshold and I_1 is the intensity found in (b), express the ratio I_2/I_1 as a power of 10. Then approximate this ratio.

69. *Investment* If $1000 is invested at r% compounded annually, the future value S of the account after two and a half years is given by

$$S = 1000\left(1 + \frac{r}{100}\right)^{2.5} = 1000\left(1 + \frac{r}{100}\right)^{5/2}$$

(a) Express this equation with radical notation.
(b) Find the value of this account if the interest rate is 6.6% compounded annually.

70. *Life span* Life expectancy in the United States can be approximated with the equation

$$L = 29x^{0.21}$$

where x is the number of years that the birth year is past 1900 (*Source:* National Center for Health Statistics).
(a) Express this equation with radical notation.
(b) Use the equation to estimate the life expectancy for a person born in 2015.

71. *Population* The population P of India (in billions) for 2000–2050 can be approximated by the equation

$$P = 0.924t^{0.13}$$

where $t > 0$ is the number of years past 2000 (*Source:* United Nations).
(a) Express this equation with radical notation.
(b) Does this equation predict a greater increase from 2005 to 2010 or from 2045 to 2050? What might explain this difference?

72. *Transportation* The percent p of paved roads and streets in the United States can be approximated with the equation

$$p = 6.75t^{0.55}$$

where t is the number of years past 1940 (*Source:* U.S. Department of Transportation).

(a) Express this equation with radical notation.
(b) Does this equation estimate a greater percent change during the decade of the 1970s or during the decade from 2000 to 2010? What might explain this?
(c) When can you be certain this equation is no longer valid?

Half-life **In Problems 73 and 74, use the fact that the quantity of a radioactive substance after t years is given by $q = q_0(2^{-t/k})$, where q_0 is the original amount of radioactive material and k is its half-life (the number of years it takes for half the radioactive substance to decay).**

73. The half-life of strontium-90 is 25 years. Find the amount of strontium-90 remaining after 10 years if $q_0 = 98$ kg.
74. The half-life of carbon-14 is 5600 years. Find the amount of carbon-14 remaining after 10,000 years if $q_0 = 40.0$ g.
75. *Population growth* Suppose the formula for the growth of the population of a city for the next 10 years is given by

$$P = P_0(2.5)^{ht}$$

where P_0 is the population of the city at the present time and P is the population t years from now. If $h = 0.03$ and $P_0 = 30{,}000$, find P when $t = 10$.
76. *Advertising and sales* Suppose it has been determined that the sales at Ewing Gallery decline after the end of an advertising campaign, with daily sales given by

$$S = 2000(2^{-0.1x})$$

where S is in dollars and x is the number of days after the campaign ends. What are the daily sales 10 days after the end of the campaign?
77. *Company growth* The growth of a company can be described by the equation

$$N = 500(0.02)^{0.7^t}$$

where t is the number of years the company has been in existence and N is the number of employees.
(a) What is the number of employees when $t = 0$? (This is the number of employees the company has when it starts.)
(b) What is the number of employees when $t = 5$?

0.5

Operations with Algebraic Expressions

In algebra we are usually dealing with combinations of real numbers (such as 3, 6/7, and $-\sqrt{2}$) and letters (such as x, a, and m). Unless otherwise specified, the letters are symbols used to represent real numbers and are sometimes called **variables.** An expression obtained by performing additions, subtractions, multiplications, divisions, or extractions of roots with one or more real numbers or variables is called an **algebraic expression.** Unless otherwise specified, the variables represent all real numbers for which the algebraic expression is a real number. Examples of algebraic expressions include

$$3x + 2y, \quad \frac{x^3y + y}{x - 1}, \quad \text{and} \quad \sqrt{x} - 3$$

Note that the variable x cannot be negative in $\sqrt{x} - 3$ and that $(x^3y + y)/(x - 1)$ is not a real number when $x = 1$, because division by 0 is undefined.

Any product of a real number (called the **coefficient**) and one or more variables to powers is called a **term.** The sum of a finite number of terms with nonnegative integer powers on the variables is called a **polynomial.** If a polynomial contains only one variable x, then it is called a polynomial in x.

Polynomial in x	The general form of a **polynomial in x** is $$a_nx^n + a_{n-1}x^{n-1} + \cdots + a_1x + a_0$$ where each coefficient a_i is a real number for $i = 0, 1, 2, \ldots, n$. If $a_n \neq 0$, the **degree** of the polynomial is n, and a_n is called the **leading coefficient.** The term a_0 is called the **constant term.**

Thus $4x^3 - 2x - 3$ is a third-degree polynomial in x with leading coefficient 4 and constant term -3. If two or more variables are in a term, the degree of the term is the sum of the exponents of the variables. The degree of a nonzero constant term is zero. Thus the degree of $4x^2y$ is $2 + 1 = 3$, the degree of $6xy$ is $1 + 1 = 2$, and the degree of 3 is 0. The **degree of a polynomial** containing one or more variables is the degree of the term in the polynomial having the highest degree. Therefore, $2xy - 4x + 6$ is a second-degree polynomial.

A polynomial containing two terms is called a **binomial,** and a polynomial containing three terms is called a **trinomial.** A single-term polynomial is a **monomial.**

Operations with Algebraic Expressions

Because monomials and polynomials represent real numbers, the properties of real numbers can be used to add, subtract, multiply, divide, and simplify polynomials. For example, we can use the Distributive Law to add $3x$ and $2x$.

$$3x + 2x = (3 + 2)x = 5x$$

Similarly, $9xy - 3xy = (9 - 3)xy = 6xy$.

Terms with exactly the same variable factors are called **like terms.** We can add or subtract like terms by adding or subtracting the coefficients of the variables. Subtraction of polynomials uses the Distributive Law to remove the parentheses.

EXAMPLE **1** **Combining Polynomials**

Compute (a) $(4xy + 3x) + (5xy - 2x)$ and (b) $(3x^2 + 4xy + 5y^2 + 1) - (6x^2 - 2xy + 4)$.

Solution

(a) $(4xy + 3x) + (5xy - 2x) = 4xy + 3x + 5xy - 2x = 9xy + x$

(b) Removing the parentheses yields

$$3x^2 + 4xy + 5y^2 + 1 - 6x^2 + 2xy - 4 = -3x^2 + 6xy + 5y^2 - 3$$

Using the rules of exponents and the Commutative and Associative Laws for multiplication, we can multiply and divide monomials, as the following example shows.

EXAMPLE **2** **Products and Quotients**

Perform the indicated operations.

(a) $(8xy^3)(2x^3y)(-3xy^2)$ (b) $-15x^2y^3 \div (3xy^5)$

Solution

(a) $8 \cdot 2 \cdot (-3) \cdot x \cdot x^3 \cdot x \cdot y^3 \cdot y \cdot y^2 = -48x^5y^6$

(b) $\dfrac{-15x^2y^3}{3xy^5} = -\dfrac{15}{3} \cdot \dfrac{x^2}{x} \cdot \dfrac{y^3}{y^5} = -5 \cdot x \cdot \dfrac{1}{y^2} = -\dfrac{5x}{y^2}$

Symbols of grouping are used in algebra in the same way as they are used in the arithmetic of real numbers. We have removed parentheses in the process of adding and subtracting polynomials. Other symbols of grouping, such as brackets, [ ], are treated the same as parentheses.

When there are two or more symbols of grouping involved, we begin with the innermost and work outward.

EXAMPLE **3** **Symbols of Grouping**

Simplify $3x^2 - [2x - (3x^2 - 2x)]$.

Solution

$$3x^2 - [2x - (3x^2 - 2x)] = 3x^2 - [2x - 3x^2 + 2x]$$
$$= 3x^2 - [4x - 3x^2]$$
$$= 3x^2 - 4x + 3x^2 = 6x^2 - 4x$$

By the use of the Distributive Law, we can multiply a binomial by a monomial. For example,

$$x(2x + 3) = x \cdot 2x + x \cdot 3 = 2x^2 + 3x$$

We can extend the Distributive Law to multiply polynomials with more than two terms. For example,

$$5(x + y + 2) = 5x + 5y + 10$$

EXAMPLE **4** **Distributive Law**

Find the following products.

(a) $-4ab(3a^2b + 4ab^2 - 1)$ (b) $(4a + 5b + c)ac$

Solution

(a) $-4ab(3a^2b + 4ab^2 - 1) = -12a^3b^2 - 16a^2b^3 + 4ab$

(b) $(4a + 5b + c)ac = 4a \cdot ac + 5b \cdot ac + c \cdot ac = 4a^2c + 5abc + ac^2$

The Distributive Law can be used to show us how to multiply two polynomials. Consider the indicated multiplication $(a + b)(c + d)$. If we first treat the sum $(a + b)$ as a single quantity, then two successive applications of the Distributive Law gives

$$(a + b)(c + d) = (a + b) \cdot c + (a + b) \cdot d = ac + bc + ad + bd$$

Thus we see that the product can be found by multiplying $(a + b)$ by c, multiplying $(a + b)$ by d, and then adding the products. This is frequently set up as follows.

SECTION 0.5 Operations with Algebraic Expressions **31**

Product of Two Polynomials

Procedure	Example
To multiply two polynomials:	Multiply $(3x + 4xy + 3y)$ by $(x - 2y)$.
1. Write one of the polynomials above the other.	1. $3x + 4xy + 3y$ $\underline{x - 2y}$
2. Multiply each term of the top polynomial by each term of the bottom one, and write the similar terms of the product under one another.	2. $3x^2 + 4x^2y + 3xy$ $\underline{\qquad - 6xy - 8xy^2 - 6y^2}$
3. Add like terms to simplify the product.	3. $3x^2 + 4x^2y - 3xy - 8xy^2 - 6y^2$

EXAMPLE 5 ## The Product of Two Polynomials

Multiply $(4x^2 + 3xy + 4x)$ by $(2x - 3y)$.

Solution

$$4x^2 + 3xy + 4x$$
$$\underline{2x - 3y}$$
$$8x^3 + 6x^2y + 8x^2$$
$$\underline{\qquad -12x^2y \qquad\quad - 9xy^2 - 12xy}$$
$$8x^3 - 6x^2y + 8x^2 - 9xy^2 - 12xy$$

Because the multiplications we must perform often involve binomials, the following special products are worth remembering.

Special Products

A. $(x + a)(x + b) = x^2 + (a + b)x + ab$
B. $(ax + b)(cx + d) = acx^2 + (ad + bc)x + bd$

It is easier to remember these two special products if we note their structure. We can obtain these products by finding the products of the First terms, Outside terms, Inside terms, and Last terms, and then adding the results. This is called the FOIL method of multiplying two binomials.

EXAMPLE 6 ## Products of Binomials

Multiply the following.
(a) $(x - 4)(x + 3)$
(b) $(3x + 2)(2x + 5)$

Solution

$\qquad\qquad\quad$ First $\quad$ Outside $\quad$ Inside $\quad$ Last
(a) $(x - 4)(x + 3) = (x^2) + (3x) + (-4x) + (-12) = x^2 - x - 12$
(b) $(3x + 2)(2x + 5) = (6x^2) + (15x) + (4x) + (10) = 6x^2 + 19x + 10$

Additional special products are as follows:

Additional Special Products

C.	$(x + a)^2 = x^2 + 2ax + a^2$	binomial squared
D.	$(x - a)^2 = x^2 - 2ax + a^2$	binomial squared
E.	$(x + a)(x - a) = x^2 - a^2$	difference of two squares
F.	$(x + a)^3 = x^3 + 3ax^2 + 3a^2x + a^3$	binomial cubed
G.	$(x - a)^3 = x^3 - 3ax^2 + 3a^2x - a^3$	binomial cubed

EXAMPLE 7 | **Special Products**

Multiply the following.
(a) $(x + 5)^2$ (b) $(3x - 4y)^2$
(c) $(x - 2)(x + 2)$ (d) $(x^2 - y^3)^2$
(e) $(x + 4)^3$

Solution
(a) $(x + 5)^2 = x^2 + 2(5)x + 25 = x^2 + 10x + 25$
(b) $(3x - 4y)^2 = (3x)^2 - 2(3x)(4y) + (4y)^2 = 9x^2 - 24xy + 16y^2$
(c) $(x - 2)(x + 2) = x^2 - 4$
(d) $(x^2 - y^3)^2 = (x^2)^2 - 2(x^2)(y^3) + (y^3)^2 = x^4 - 2x^2y^3 + y^6$
(e) $(x + 4)^3 = x^3 + 3(4)(x^2) + 3(4^2)(x) + 4^3 = x^3 + 12x^2 + 48x + 64$

CHECKPOINT

1. Remove parentheses and combine like terms: $9x - 5x(x + 2) + 4x^2$
2. Find the following products.
    (a) $(2x + 1)(4x^2 - 2x + 1)$ (b) $(x + 3)^2$
    (c) $(3x + 2)(x - 5)$ (d) $(1 - 4x)(1 + 4x)$

All algebraic expressions can represent real numbers, so the techniques used to perform operations on polynomials and to simplify polynomials also apply to other algebraic expressions.

EXAMPLE 8 | **Operations with Algebraic Expressions**

Perform the indicated operations.
(a) $3\sqrt{3} + 4x\sqrt{y} - 5\sqrt{3} - 11x\sqrt{y} - (\sqrt{3} - x\sqrt{y})$
(b) $x^{3/2}(x^{1/2} - x^{-1/2})$
(c) $(x^{1/2} - x^{1/3})^2$
(d) $(\sqrt{x} + 2)(\sqrt{x} - 2)$

Solution
(a) We remove parentheses and then combine the terms containing $\sqrt{3}$ and the terms containing $x\sqrt{y}$.

$$(3 - 5 - 1)\sqrt{3} + (4 - 11 + 1)x\sqrt{y} = -3\sqrt{3} - 6x\sqrt{y}$$

(b) $x^{3/2}(x^{1/2} - x^{-1/2}) = x^{3/2} \cdot x^{1/2} - x^{3/2} \cdot x^{-1/2} = x^2 - x$
(c) $(x^{1/2} - x^{1/3})^2 = (x^{1/2})^2 - 2x^{1/2}x^{1/3} + (x^{1/3})^2 = x - 2x^{5/6} + x^{2/3}$
(d) $(\sqrt{x} + 2)(\sqrt{x} - 2) = (\sqrt{x})^2 - (2)^2 = x - 4$

In later chapters we will need to write problems in a simplified form so that we can perform certain operations on them. We can often use division of one polynomial by another to obtain the simplification, as shown in the following procedure.

Division of Polynomials

Procedure

Example

To divide one polynomial by another:

Divide $4x^3 + 4x^2 + 5$ by $2x^2 + 1$.

1. Write both polynomials in descending powers of a variable. Include missing terms with coefficient 0 in the dividend.

1. $2x^2 + 1 \overline{) 4x^3 + 4x^2 + 0x + 5}$

Division of Polynomials *(continued)*

Procedure	Example

2. (a) Divide the highest-power term of the divisor into the highest-power term of the dividend, and write this partial quotient above the dividend. Multiply the partial quotient times the divisor, write the product under the dividend, and subtract, getting a new dividend.

(b) Repeat until the degree of the new dividend is less than the degree of the divisor. Any remainder is written over the divisor and added to the quotient.

$$\begin{array}{r} 2x \\ 2x^2+1\overline{)4x^3+4x^2+0x+5} \\ \underline{4x^3\qquad\ +2x} \\ 4x^2-2x+5 \end{array}$$

2. (a)

$$\begin{array}{r} 2x+2 \\ 2x^2+1\overline{)4x^3+4x^2+0x+5} \\ \underline{4x^3\qquad\ +2x} \\ 4x^2-2x+5 \\ \underline{4x^2\qquad\ +2} \\ -2x+3 \end{array}$$

(b)

Degree $(-2x+3) <$ degree $(2x^2+1)$

Quotient: $2x+2+\dfrac{-2x+3}{2x^2+1}$

EXAMPLE 9   Division of Polynomials

Divide $(4x^3-13x-22)$ by $(x-3)$, $x\neq 3$.

Solution

$$\begin{array}{r} 4x^2+12x+23 \\ x-3\overline{)4x^3+0x^2-13x-22} \\ \underline{4x^3-12x^2} \\ 12x^2-13x-22 \\ \underline{12x^2-36x} \\ 23x-22 \\ \underline{23x-69} \\ 47 \end{array}$$ $0x^2$ is inserted so that each power of x is present.

The quotient is $4x^2+12x+23$, with remainder 47, or

$$4x^2+12x+23+\frac{47}{x-3}$$

CHECKPOINT   3.   Use long division to find $(x^3+2x+7)\div(x-4)$.

CHECKPOINT SOLUTIONS

1. $9x-5x(x+2)+4x^2 = 9x-5x^2-10x+4x^2$
   $\qquad\qquad\qquad\qquad\qquad = -x^2-x$

   Note: without parentheses around $9x-5x$, multiplication has priority over subtraction.

2. (a) $4x^2-2x+1$
$$\begin{array}{r} 2x+1 \\ \overline{8x^3-4x^2+2x} \\ \underline{4x^2-2x+1} \\ 8x^3\qquad\qquad +1 \end{array}$$

   (b) $(x+3)^2 = x^2+2(3x)+3^2 = x^2+6x+9$

   (c) $(3x+2)(x-5) = 3x^2-15x+2x-10 = 3x^2-13x-10$

   (d) $(1-4x)(1+4x) = 1-16x^2$ Note that this is different from $16x^2-1$.

3. $$\begin{array}{r} x^2+4x+18 \\ x-4\overline{)x^3+0x^2+2x+7} \\ \underline{x^3-4x^2} \\ 4x^2+2x+7 \\ \underline{4x^2-16x} \\ 18x+7 \\ \underline{18x-72} \\ 79 \end{array}$$ The answer is $x^2+4x+18+\dfrac{79}{x-4}$.

| EXERCISES | 0.5

For each polynomial in Problems 1–4, (a) give the degree of the polynomial, (b) give the coefficient (numerical) of the highest-degree term, (c) give the constant term, and (d) decide whether it is a polynomial of one or several variables.

1. $10 - 3x - x^2$
2. $5x^4 - 2x^9 + 7$
3. $7x^2y - 14xy^3z$
4. $2x^5 + 7x^2y^3 - 5y^6$

The expressions in Problems 5 and 6 are polynomials with the form $a_nx^n + a_{n-1}x^{n-1} + \cdots + a_1x + a_0$, where n is a positive integer. Complete the following.

5. For $2x^5 - 3x^2 - 5$,
   (a) $2 = a_?$
   (b) $a_3 = ?$
   (c) $-3 = a_?$
   (d) $a_0 = ?$
6. For $5x^3 - 4x - 17$,
   (a) $a_3 = ?$
   (b) $a_1 = ?$
   (c) $a_2 = ?$
   (d) $-17 = a_?$

In Problems 7–12, evaluate each algebraic expression at the indicated values of the variables.

7. $4x - x^2$ at $x = -2$
8. $10 - 6(4 - x)^2$ at $x = -1$
9. $10xy - 4(x - y)^2$ at $x = 5$ and $y = -2$
10. $3x^2 - 4y^2 - 2xy$ at $x = 3$ and $y = -4$
11. $\dfrac{2x - y}{x^2 - 2y}$ at $x = -5$ and $y = -3$
12. $\dfrac{16y}{1 - y}$ at $y = -3$
13. Evaluate $1.98T - 1.09(1 - H)(T - 58) - 56.8$ when $T = 74.7$ and $H = 0.80$.
14. Evaluate $R\left[\dfrac{0.083i}{1 - (1 + 0.083i)^{-n}}\right]$ when $R = 100,000$, $i = 0.07, n = 360$.

In Problems 15–22, simplify by combining like terms.

15. $(16pq - 7p^2) + (5pq + 5p^2)$
16. $(3x^3 + 4x^2y^2) + (3x^2y^2 - 7x^3)$
17. $(4m^2 - 3n^2 + 5) - (3m^2 + 4n^2 + 8)$
18. $(4rs - 2r^2s - 11rs^2) - (11rs^2 - 2rs + 4r^2s)$
19. $-[8 - 4(q + 5) + q]$
20. $x^3 + [3x - (x^3 - 3x)]$
21. $x^2 - [x - (x^2 - 1) + 1 - (1 - x^2)] + x$
22. $y^3 - [y^2 - (y^3 + y^2)] - [y^3 + (1 - y^2)]$

In Problems 23–60, perform the indicated operations and simplify.

23. $(5x^3)(7x^2)$
24. $(-3x^2y)(2xy^3)(4x^2y^2)$
25. $(39r^3s^2) \div (13r^2s)$
26. $(-15m^3n) \div (5mn^4)$
27. $ax^2(2x^2 + ax + ab)$
28. $-3(3 - x^2)$
29. $(3y + 4)(2y - 3)$
30. $(4x - 1)(x - 3)$
31. $6(1 - 2x^2)(2 - x^2)$
32. $2(x^3 + 3)(2x^3 - 5)$
33. $(4x + 3)^2$
34. $(2y + 5)^2$
35. $(0.1 - 4x)(0.1 + 4x)$
36. $(x^3y^3 - 0.3)^2$
37. $9(2x + 1)(2x - 1)$
38. $3(5y + 2)(5y - 2)$
39. $\left(x^2 - \dfrac{1}{2}\right)^2$
40. $\left(\dfrac{2}{3} + x\right)\left(\dfrac{2}{3} - x\right)$
41. $(0.1x - 2)(x + 0.05)$
42. $(6.2x + 4.1)(6.2x - 4.1)$
43. $(x - 2)(x^2 + 2x + 4)$
44. $(a + b)(a^2 - ab + b^2)$
45. $(x^3 + 5x)(x^5 - 2x^3 + 5)$
46. $(x^3 - 1)(x^7 - 2x^4 - 5x^2 + 5)$
47. (a) $(3x - 2)^2 - 3x - 2(3x - 2) + 5$
    (b) $(3x - 2)^2 - (3x - 2)(3x - 2) + 5$
48. (a) $(2x - 3)(3x + 2) - (5x - 2)(x - 3)$
    (b) $2x - 3(3x + 2) - 5x - 2(x - 3)$
49. $(18m^2n + 6m^3n + 12m^4n^2) \div (6m^2n)$
50. $(16x^2 + 4xy^2 + 8x) \div (4xy)$
51. $(24x^8y^4 + 15x^5y - 6x^7y) \div (9x^5y^2)$
52. $(27x^2y^2 - 18xy + 9xy^2) \div (6xy)$
53. $(x + 1)^3$
54. $(x - 3)^3$
55. $(2x - 3)^3$
56. $(3x + 4)^3$
57. $(x^3 + x - 1) \div (x + 2)$
58. $(x^5 + 5x - 7) \div (x + 1)$
59. $(x^4 + 3x^3 - x + 1) \div (x^2 + 1)$
60. $(x^3 + 5x^2 - 6) \div (x^2 - 2)$

In Problems 61–68, perform the indicated operations with expressions involving fractional exponents and radicals, and then simplify.

61. $x^{1/2}(x^{1/2} + 2x^{3/2})$
62. $x^{-2/3}(x^{5/3} - x^{-1/3})$
63. $(x^{1/2} + 1)(x^{1/2} - 2)$
64. $(x^{1/3} - x^{1/2})(4x^{2/3} - 3x^{3/2})$
65. $(\sqrt{x} + 3)(\sqrt{x} - 3)$
66. $(x^{1/5} + x^{1/2})(x^{1/5} - x^{1/2})$
67. $(2x + 1)^{1/2}[(2x + 1)^{3/2} - (2x + 1)^{-1/2}]$
68. $(4x - 3)^{-5/3}[(4x - 3)^{8/3} + 3(4x - 3)^{5/3}]$

APPLICATIONS

69. *Revenue* A company sells its product for \$55 per unit. Write an expression for the amount of money received (revenue) from the sale of x units of the product.
70. *Profit* Suppose a company's revenue R (in dollars) from the sale of x units of its product is given by

$$R = 215x$$

Suppose further that the total costs C (in dollars) of producing those x units is given by

$$C = 65x + 15,000$$

   (a) If profit is revenue minus cost, find an expression for the profit from the production and sale of x units.
   (b) Find the profit received if 1000 units are sold.
71. *Rental* A rental truck costs \$49.95 for a day plus 49¢ per mile.
   (a) If x is the number of miles driven, write an expression for the total cost of renting the truck for a day.
   (b) Find the total cost of the rental if it was driven 132 miles.
72. *Cell phones* Cell Pro makes cell phones and has weekly costs of \$1500 for rent, utilities, and equipment plus labor and material costs of \$18.50 for each phone it makes.
   (a) If x represents the number of phones produced and sold, write an expression for Cell Pro's weekly total cost.

(b) If Cell Pro sells the phones to dealers for $45.50 each, write an expression for the weekly total revenue for the phones.

(c) Cell Pro's weekly profit is the total revenue minus the total cost. Write an expression for Cell Pro's weekly profit.

73. *Investments* Suppose that you have $4000 to invest, and you invest x dollars at 10% and the remainder at 8%. Write expressions in x that represent
(a) the amount invested at 8%,
(b) the interest earned on the x dollars at 10%,
(c) the interest earned on the money invested at 8%,
(d) the total interest earned.

74. *Medications* Suppose that a nurse needs 10 cc (cubic centimeters) of a 15.5% solution (that is, a solution that is 15.5% ingredient) of a certain medication, which must be obtained by mixing x cc of a 20% solution and y cc of a 5% solution. Write expressions involving x for
(a) y, the amount of 5% solution,

(b) the amount of ingredient in the x cc of 20% solution,

(c) the amount of ingredient in the 5% solution,

(d) the total amount of ingredient in the mixture.

75. *Package design* The volume of a rectangular box is given by $V = $ (length)(width)(height). If a rectangular piece of cardboard that is 10 in. by 15 in. has a square with sides of length x cut from each corner (see Figure 0.9), and if the sides are folded up along the dotted lines to form a box, what expression of x would represent the volume?

Figure 0.9

0.6

Factoring

Common Factors   We can factor monomial factors out of a polynomial by using the Distributive Law in reverse; $ab + ac = a(b + c)$ is an example showing that a is a monomial factor of the polynomial $ab + ac$. But it is also a statement of the Distributive Law (with the sides of the equation interchanged). The monomial factor of a polynomial must be a factor of each term of the polynomial, so it is frequently called a **common monomial factor.**

EXAMPLE   **1**   **Monomial Factor**

Factor $-3x^2t - 3x + 9xt^2$.

Solution
1. We can factor out $3x$ and obtain
$$-3x^2t - 3x + 9xt^2 = 3x(-xt - 1 + 3t^2)$$

2. Or we can factor out $-3x$ (factoring out the negative will make the first term of the polynomial positive) and obtain
$$-3x^2t - 3x + 9xt^2 = -3x(xt + 1 - 3t^2)$$

If a factor is common to each term of a polynomial, we can use this procedure to factor it out, even if it is not a monomial. For example, we can factor $(a + b)$ out of the polynomial $2x(a + b) - 3y(a + b)$ and get $(a + b)(2x - 3y)$. The following example demonstrates the **factoring by grouping** technique.

EXAMPLE   **2**   **Factoring by Grouping**

Factor $5x - 5y + bx - by$.

Solution
We can factor this polynomial by the use of grouping. The grouping is done so that common factors (frequently binomial factors) can be removed. We see that we can factor 5 from the first two terms and b from the last two, which gives
$$5(x - y) + b(x - y)$$

This gives us two terms with the common factor $x - y$, so we get

$$(x - y)(5 + b)$$

Factoring Trinomials   We can use the formula for multiplying two binomials to factor certain trinomials. The formula

$$(x + a)(x + b) = x^2 + (a + b)x + ab$$

can be used to factor trinomials such as $x^2 - 7x + 6$.

EXAMPLE   3   Factoring a Trinomial

Factor $x^2 - 7x + 6$.

Solution

If this trinomial can be factored into an expression of the form

$$(x + a)(x + b)$$

then we need to find a and b such that

$$x^2 - 7x + 6 = x^2 + (a + b)x + ab$$

That is, we need to find a and b such that $a + b = -7$ and $ab = 6$. The two numbers whose sum is -7 and whose product is 6 are -1 and -6. Thus

$$x^2 - 7x + 6 = (x - 1)(x - 6)$$

A similar method can be used to factor trinomials such as $9x^2 - 31x + 12$. Finding the proper factors for this type of trinomial may involve a fair amount of trial and error, because we must find factors a, b, c, and d such that

$$(ax + b)(cx + d) = acx^2 + (ad + bc)x + bd$$

Another technique of factoring is used to factor trinomials such as those we have been discussing. It is useful in factoring more complicated trinomials, such as $9x^2 - 31x + 12$. This procedure for factoring second-degree trinomials follows.

Factoring a Trinomial

Procedure	Example
To factor a trinomial into the product of its binomial factors:	Factor $9x^2 - 31x + 12$.
1. Form the product of the second-degree term and the constant term.	1. $9x^2 \cdot 12 = 108x^2$
2. Determine whether there are any factors of the product of Step 1 that will sum to the middle term of the trinomial. (If the answer is no, the trinomial will not factor into two binomials.)	2. The factors $-27x$ and $-4x$ give a sum of $-31x$.
3. Use the sum of these two factors to replace the middle term of the trinomial.	3. $9x^2 - 31x + 12 = 9x^2 - 27x - 4x + 12$
4. Factor this four-term expression by grouping.	4. $9x^2 - 31x + 12 = (9x^2 - 27x) + (-4x + 12)$ $ = 9x(x - 3) - 4(x - 3)$ $ = (x - 3)(9x - 4)$

In the example just completed, note that writing the middle term ($-31x$) as $-4x - 27x$ rather than as $-27x - 4x$ (as we did) will also result in the correct factorization. (Try it.)

EXAMPLE 4   **Factoring a Trinomial**

Factor $9x^2 - 9x - 10$.

Solution

The product of the second-degree term and the constant is $-90x^2$. Factors of $-90x^2$ that sum to $-9x$ are $-15x$ and $6x$. Thus

$$9x^2 - 9x - 10 = 9x^2 - 15x + 6x - 10$$
$$= (9x^2 - 15x) + (6x - 10)$$
$$= 3x(3x - 5) + 2(3x - 5) = (3x - 5)(3x + 2)$$

We can check this factorization by multiplying.

$$(3x - 5)(3x + 2) = 9x^2 + 6x - 15x - 10$$
$$= 9x^2 - 9x - 10$$

Some special products that make factoring easier are as follows.

Special Factorizations

The perfect-square trinomials:

$$x^2 + 2ax + a^2 = (x + a)^2$$
$$x^2 - 2ax + a^2 = (x - a)^2$$

The difference of two squares:

$$x^2 - a^2 = (x + a)(x - a)$$

EXAMPLE 5   **Special Factorizations**

(a) Factor $25x^2 - 36y^2$.
(b) Factor $4x^2 + 12x + 9$.

Solution

(a) The binomial $25x^2 - 36y^2$ is the difference of two squares, so we get

$$25x^2 - 36y^2 = (5x - 6y)(5x + 6y)$$

These two factors are called binomial **conjugates** because they differ in only one sign.

(b) Although we can use the technique we have learned to factor trinomials, the factors come quickly if we recognize that this trinomial is a perfect square. It has two square terms, and the remaining term ($12x$) is twice the product of the square roots of the squares ($12x = 2 \cdot 2x \cdot 3$). Thus

$$4x^2 + 12x + 9 = (2x + 3)^2$$

Most of the polynomials we have factored have been second-degree polynomials, or **quadratic polynomials.** Some polynomials that are not quadratic are in a form that can be factored in the same manner as quadratics. For example, the polynomial $x^4 + 4x^2 + 4$ can be written as $a^2 + 4a + 4$, where $a = x^2$.

EXAMPLE 6   **Polynomials in Quadratic Form**

Factor (a) $x^4 + 4x^2 + 4$ and (b) $x^4 - 16$.

Solution

(a) The trinomial is in the form of a perfect square, so letting $a = x^2$ will give us

$$x^4 + 4x^2 + 4 = a^2 + 4a + 4 = (a + 2)^2$$

Thus

$$x^4 + 4x^2 + 4 = (x^2 + 2)^2$$

(b) The binomial $x^4 - 16$ can be treated as the difference of two squares, $(x^2)^2 - 4^2$, so

$$x^4 - 16 = (x^2 - 4)(x^2 + 4)$$

But $x^2 - 4$ can be factored into $(x - 2)(x + 2)$, so

$$x^4 - 16 = (x - 2)(x + 2)(x^2 + 4)$$

CHECKPOINT

1. Factor the following.
   (a) $8x^3 - 12x$ (b) $3x(x^2 + 5) - 5(x^2 + 5)$ (c) $x^2 - 10x - 24$
   (d) $x^2 - 5x + 6$ (e) $4x^2 - 20x + 25$ (f) $100 - 49x^2$
2. Consider $10x^2 - 17x - 20$ and observe that $(10x^2)(-20) = -200x^2$.
   (a) Find two expressions whose product is $-200x^2$ and whose sum is $-17x$.
   (b) Replace $-17x$ in $10x^2 - 17x - 20$ with the two expressions in (a).
   (c) Factor (b) by grouping.
3. True or false:
   (a) $4x^2 + 9 = (2x + 3)^2$ (b) $x^2 + x - 12 = (x - 4)(x + 3)$
   (c) $5x^5 - 20x^3 = 5x^3(x^2 - 4) = 5x^3(x + 2)(x - 2)$

A polynomial is said to be factored completely if all possible factorizations have been completed. For example, $(2x - 4)(x + 3)$ is not factored completely because a 2 can still be factored out of $2x - 4$. The following guidelines are used to factor polynomials completely.

Guidelines for Factoring Completely

Look for: Monomials first.
Then for: Difference of two squares.
Then for: Trinomial squares.
Then for: Other methods of factoring trinomials.

EXAMPLE 7 **Factoring Completely**

Factor completely (a) $12x^2 - 36x + 27$ and (b) $16x^2 - 64y^2$.

Solution
(a) $12x - 36x + 27 = 3(4x^2 - 12x + 9)$ Monomial
$$= 3(2x - 3)^2$$ Perfect Square
(b) $16x^2 - 64y^2 = 16(x^2 - 4y^2)$
$$= 16(x + 2y)(x - 2y)$$

Factoring the difference of two squares immediately would give $(4x + 8y)(4x - 8y)$, which is not factored completely (because we could still factor 4 from $4x + 8y$ and 4 from $4x - 8y$).

CHECKPOINT SOLUTIONS

1. (a) $8x^3 - 12x = 4x(2x^2 - 3)$
   (b) $3x(x^2 + 5) - 5(x^2 + 5) = (x^2 + 5)(3x - 5)$
   (c) $x^2 - 10x - 24 = (x - 12)(x + 2)$
   (d) $x^2 - 5x + 6 = (x - 3)(x - 2)$
   (e) $4x^2 - 20x + 25 = (2x - 5)^2$
   (f) $100 - 49x^2 = (10 + 7x)(10 - 7x)$
2. (a) $(-25x)(+8x) = -200x^2$ and $-25x + 8x = -17x$
   (b) $10x^2 - 17x - 20 = 10x^2 - 25x + 8x - 20$
   (c) $\qquad\qquad = (10x^2 - 25x) + (8x - 20)$
   $$= 5x(2x - 5) + 4(2x - 5)$$
   $$= (2x - 5)(5x + 4)$$
3. (a) False. $4x^2 + 9$ cannot be factored. In fact, sums of squares cannot be factored.
   (b) False. $x^2 + x - 12 = (x + 4)(x - 3)$
   (c) True.

| EXERCISES | 0.6

In Problems 1–4, factor by finding the common monomial factor.

1. $9ab - 12a^2b + 18b^2$
2. $8a^2b - 160x + 4bx^2$
3. $4x^2 + 8xy^2 + 2xy^3$
4. $12y^3z + 4yz^2 - 8y^2z^3$

In Problems 5–8, factor by grouping.

5. $7x^3 - 14x^2 + 2x - 4$
6. $5y - 20 - x^2y + 4x^2$
7. $6x - 6m + xy - my$
8. $x^3 - x^2 - 5x + 5$

Factor each expression in Problems 9–20 as a product of binomials.

9. $x^2 + 8x + 12$
10. $x^2 - 2x - 8$
11. $x^2 - 15x - 16$
12. $x^2 - 21x + 20$
13. $7x^2 - 10x - 8$
14. $12x^2 + 11x + 2$
15. $x^2 - 10x + 25$
16. $4y^2 + 12y + 9$
17. $49a^2 - 144b^2$
18. $16x^2 - 25y^2$
19. (a) $9x^2 + 21x - 8$ (b) $9x^2 + 22x + 8$
20. (a) $10x^2 - 99x - 63$ (b) $10x^2 - 27x - 63$
    (c) $10x^2 + 61x - 63$ (d) $10x^2 + 9x - 63$

In Problems 21–46, factor completely.

21. $4x^2 - x$
22. $2x^5 + 18x^3$
23. $x^3 + 4x^2 - 5x - 20$
24. $x^3 - 2x^2 - 3x + 6$
25. $x^2 - x - 6$
26. $x^2 + 6x + 8$
27. $2x^2 - 8x - 42$
28. $3x^2 - 21x + 36$
29. $2x^3 - 8x^2 + 8x$
30. $x^3 + 16x^2 + 64x$
31. $2x^2 + x - 6$
32. $2x^2 + 13x + 6$
33. $3x^2 + 3x - 36$
34. $4x^2 - 8x - 60$
35. $2x^3 - 8x$
36. $16z^2 - 81w^2$
37. $10x^2 + 19x + 6$
38. $6x^2 + 67x - 35$
39. $9 - 47x + 10x^2$
40. $10x^2 + 21x - 10$
41. $y^4 - 16x^4$
42. $x^8 - 81$
43. $x^4 - 8x^2 + 16$
44. $81 - 18x^2 + x^4$
45. $4x^4 - 5x^2 + 1$
46. $x^4 - 3x^2 - 4$

In Problems 47–50, determine the missing factor.

47. $x^{3/2} + x^{1/2} = x^{1/2}(?)$
48. $2x^{1/4} + 4x^{3/4} = 2x^{1/4}(?)$
49. $x^{-3} + x^{-2} = x^{-3}(?)$
50. $x^{-1} - x = x^{-1}(?)$

Use the following factorization formulas involving cubes to factor each expression in Problems 51–58.

Factorizations with Cubes

Perfect cube
$$a^3 + 3a^2b + 3ab^2 + b^3 = (a + b)^3$$
Perfect cube
$$a^3 - 3a^2b + 3ab^2 - b^3 = (a - b)^3$$
Difference of two cubes
$$a^3 - b^3 = (a - b)(a^2 + ab + b^2)$$
Sum of two cubes
$$a^3 + b^3 = (a + b)(a^2 - ab + b^2)$$

---

51. $x^3 + 3x^2 + 3x + 1$
52. $x^3 + 6x^2 + 12x + 8$
53. $x^3 - 12x^2 + 48x - 64$
54. $y^3 - 9y^2 + 27y - 27$
55. $x^3 - 64$
56. $8x^3 - 1$
57. $27 + 8x^3$
58. $a^3 + 216$

APPLICATIONS

59. *Simple interest* The future value of a simple-interest investment of P dollars at an annual interest rate r for t years is given by the expression $P + Prt$. Factor this expression.

60. *Reaction to medication* When medicine is administered, the reaction (measured in change of blood pressure or temperature) can be modeled by (that is, described by)
$$R = \frac{cm^2}{2} - \frac{m^3}{3}$$
where c is a positive constant and m is the amount of medicine absorbed into the blood.* Factor the expression for the reaction.

61. *Sensitivity to medication* From the formula for reaction to medication given in Problem 60, an expression for sensitivity S can be obtained, where
$$S = cm - m^2$$
Factor this expression for sensitivity.

62. *Volume* Suppose that squares of side x are cut from four corners of an 8-by-8-inch piece of cardboard and an open-top box is formed (see Figure 0.10). The volume of the box is given by $64x - 32x^2 + 4x^3$. Factor this expression.

Figure 0.10

63. *Consumer expenditure* The consumer expenditure for a commodity is the product of its market price, p, and the number of units demanded. Suppose that for a certain commodity, the consumer expenditure is given by
$$10{,}000p - 100p^2$$
   (a) Factor this in order to find an expression for the number of units demanded.
   (b) Use (a) to find the number of units demanded when the market price is $38.

*Source: R. M. Thrall et al., *Some Mathematical Models in Biology*, U.S. Department of Commerce, 1967.

64. *Power in a circuit* Factor the following expression for the maximum power in a certain electrical circuit.

$$(R + r)^2 - 2r(R + r)$$

65. *Revenue* Revenue R from the sale of x units of a product is found by multiplying the price by the number of items sold.

(a) Factor the right side of $R = 300x - x^2$.
(b) What is the expression for the price of the item?

66. *Poiseuille's law* The expression for the speed of blood through an artery of radius r at a distance x from the artery wall is given by $r^2 - (r - x)^2$. Factor and simplify this expression.

0.7

Algebraic Fractions

Evaluating certain limits and graphing rational functions require an understanding of algebraic fractions. The fraction 6/8 can be reduced to 3/4 by dividing both the numerator and the denominator by 2. In the same manner, we can reduce the algebraic fraction

$$\frac{(x + 2)(x + 1)}{(x + 1)(x + 3)} \quad \text{to} \quad \frac{x + 2}{x + 3}$$

by dividing both the numerator and the denominator by $x + 1$, if $x \neq -1$.

| **Simplifying Fractions** | We *simplify* algebraic fractions by factoring the numerator and denominator and then dividing both the numerator and the denominator by any common factors.* |

EXAMPLE 1   Simplifying a Fraction

Simplify $\dfrac{3x^2 - 14x + 8}{x^2 - 16}$ if $x^2 \neq 16$.

Solution

$$\frac{3x^2 - 14x + 8}{x^2 - 16} = \frac{(3x - 2)(x - 4)}{(x - 4)(x + 4)}$$

$$= \frac{(3x - 2)\overset{1}{\cancel{(x - 4)}}}{\underset{1}{\cancel{(x - 4)}}(x + 4)} = \frac{3x - 2}{x + 4}$$

Products of Fractions We can multiply fractions by writing the product as the product of the numerators divided by the product of the denominators. For example,

$$\frac{4}{5} \cdot \frac{10}{12} \cdot \frac{2}{5} = \frac{80}{300}$$

which reduces to 4/15.

We can also find the product by reducing the fractions before we indicate the multiplication in the numerator and denominator. For example, in

$$\frac{4}{5} \cdot \frac{10}{12} \cdot \frac{2}{5}$$

we can divide the first numerator and the second denominator by 4 and divide the second numerator and the first denominator by 5, which yields

$$\frac{\overset{1}{\cancel{4}}}{\underset{1}{\cancel{5}}} \cdot \frac{\overset{2}{\cancel{10}}}{\underset{3}{\cancel{12}}} \cdot \frac{2}{5} = \frac{1}{1} \cdot \frac{2}{3} \cdot \frac{2}{5} = \frac{4}{15}$$

*We assume that all fractions are defined.

Product of Fractions	We *multiply* algebraic fractions by writing the product of the numerators divided by the product of the denominators, and then reduce to lowest terms. We may also reduce prior to finding the product.

EXAMPLE 2   **Multiplying Fractions**

Multiply:

(a) $\dfrac{4x^2}{5y} \cdot \dfrac{10x}{y^2} \cdot \dfrac{y}{8x^2}$ (b) $\dfrac{-4x + 8}{3x + 6} \cdot \dfrac{2x + 4}{4x + 12}$

Solution

(a) $\dfrac{4x^2}{5y} \cdot \dfrac{10x}{y} \cdot \dfrac{y}{8x^2} = \dfrac{\overset{1}{4x^2}}{\underset{1\cdot1}{5y}} \cdot \dfrac{\overset{2}{10x}}{y^2} \cdot \dfrac{\overset{1}{y}}{\underset{2}{8x^2}} = \dfrac{1}{1} \cdot \dfrac{2x}{y^2} \cdot \dfrac{\overset{1}{1}}{\underset{1}{2}} = \dfrac{x}{y^2}$

(b) $\dfrac{-4x + 8}{3x + 6} \cdot \dfrac{2x + 4}{4x + 12} = \dfrac{-4(x - 2)}{3(x + 2)} \cdot \dfrac{2(x + 2)}{4(x + 3)}$

$\qquad\qquad\qquad\qquad = \dfrac{\overset{-1}{-4}(x - 2)}{3(x + 2)} \cdot \dfrac{2(x + 2)}{\underset{1}{4}(x + 3)} = \dfrac{-2(x - 2)}{3(x + 3)}$

Quotients of Fractions	In arithmetic we learned to divide one fraction by another by inverting the divisor and multiplying. The same rule applies to division of algebraic fractions.

EXAMPLE 3   **Dividing Fractions**

(a) Divide $\dfrac{a^2b}{c}$ by $\dfrac{ab}{c^2}$.   (b) Find $\dfrac{6x^2 - 6}{x^2 + 3x + 2} \div \dfrac{x - 1}{x^2 + 4x + 4}$.

Solution

(a) $\dfrac{a^2b}{c} \div \dfrac{ab}{c^2} = \dfrac{a^2b}{c} \cdot \dfrac{c^2}{ab} = \dfrac{\overset{a\cdot1}{a^2b}}{\underset{1}{c}} \cdot \dfrac{\overset{c}{c^2}}{\underset{1\cdot1}{ab}} = \dfrac{ac}{1} = ac$

(b) $\dfrac{6x^2 - 6}{x^2 + 3x + 2} \div \dfrac{x - 1}{x^2 + 4x + 4} = \dfrac{6x^2 - 6}{x^2 + 3x + 2} \cdot \dfrac{x^2 + 4x + 4}{x - 1}$

$\qquad\qquad\qquad\qquad = \dfrac{6(x - 1)(x + 1)}{(x + 2)(x + 1)} \cdot \dfrac{(x + 2)(x + 2)}{x - 1}$

$\qquad\qquad\qquad\qquad = 6(x + 2)$

CHECKPOINT	1. Reduce: $\dfrac{2x^2 - 4x}{2x}$
	2. Multiply: $\dfrac{x^2}{x^2 - 9} \cdot \dfrac{x + 3}{3x}$
	3. Divide: $\dfrac{5x^2(x - 1)}{2(x + 1)} \div \dfrac{10x^2}{(x + 1)(x - 1)}$

Adding and Subtracting Fractions	If two fractions are to be added, it is convenient that both be expressed with the same denominator. If the denominators are not the same, we can write the equivalents of each of the fractions with a common denominator. We usually use the least common denominator (LCD) when we write the equivalent fractions. The **least common denominator** is the lowest-degree variable expression into which all denominators will divide. If the denominators are polynomials, then the LCD is the lowest-degree polynomial into which all denominators will divide. We can find the least common denominator as follows.

Finding the Least Common Denominator

Procedure	**Example**
To find the least common denominator of a set of fractions:	Find the LCD of $\dfrac{1}{x^2 - x}, \dfrac{1}{x^2 - 1}, \dfrac{1}{x^2}$.
1. Completely factor each denominator.	1. The factored denominators are $x(x - 1)$, $(x + 1)(x - 1)$, and $x \cdot x$.
2. Identify the different factors that appear.	2. The different factors are x, $x - 1$, and $x + 1$.
3. The LCD is the product of these different factors, with each factor used the maximum number of times it occurs in any one denominator.	3. x occurs a maximum of twice in one denominator, $x - 1$ occurs once, and $x + 1$ occurs once. Thus the LCD is $x \cdot x(x - 1)(x + 1) = x^2(x - 1)(x + 1)$.

The procedure for combining (adding or subtracting) two or more fractions follows.

Adding or Subtracting Fractions

Procedure	**Example**
To combine fractions:	Combine $\dfrac{y - 3}{y - 5} + \dfrac{y - 23}{y^2 - y - 20}$.
1. Find the LCD of the fractions.	1. $y^2 - y - 20 = (y - 5)(y + 4)$, so the LCD is $(y - 5)(y + 4)$.
2. Write the equivalent of each fraction with the LCD as its denominator.	2. The sum is $\dfrac{(y - 3)(y + 4)}{(y - 5)(y + 4)} + \dfrac{y - 23}{(y - 5)(y + y)}$.
3. Add or subtract, as indicated, by combining like terms in the numerator over the LCD.	3. $= \dfrac{y^2 + y - 12 + y - 23}{(y - 5)(y + 4)}$ $= \dfrac{y^2 + 2y - 35}{(y - 5)(y + 4)}$
4. Reduce the fraction, if possible.	4. $= \dfrac{(y + 7)(y - 5)}{(y - 5)(y + 4)} = \dfrac{y + 7}{y + 4},$ if $y \neq 5$.

EXAMPLE 4 Adding Fractions

Add $\dfrac{3x}{a^2} + \dfrac{4}{ax}$.

Solution

1. The LCD is a^2x.

2. $\dfrac{3x}{a^2} + \dfrac{4}{ax} = \dfrac{3x}{a^2} \cdot \dfrac{x}{x} + \dfrac{4}{ax} \cdot \dfrac{a}{a} = \dfrac{3x^2}{a^2x} + \dfrac{4a}{a^2x}$

3. $\dfrac{3x^2}{a^2x} + \dfrac{4a}{a^2x} = \dfrac{3x^2 + 4a}{a^2x}$

4. The sum is in lowest terms.

EXAMPLE 5 Combining Fractions

Combine $\dfrac{y - 3}{(y - 5)^2} - \dfrac{y - 2}{y^2 - 4y - 5}$.

Solution

$y^2 - 4y - 5 = (y - 5)(y + 1)$, so the LCD is $(y - 5)^2(y + 1)$. Writing the equivalent fractions and then combining them, we get

$$\frac{y - 3}{(y - 5)^2} - \frac{y - 2}{(y - 5)(y + 1)} = \frac{(y - 3)(y + 1)}{(y - 5)^2(y + 1)} - \frac{(y - 2)(y - 5)}{(y - 5)(y + 1)(y - 5)}$$

$$= \frac{(y^2 - 2y - 3) - (y^2 - 7y + 10)}{(y - 5)^2(y + 1)}$$

$$= \frac{y^2 - 2y - 3 - y^2 + 7y - 10}{(y - 5)^2(y + 1)}$$

$$= \frac{5y - 13}{(y - 5)^2(y + 1)}$$

Complex Fractions

A fractional expression that contains one or more fractions in its numerator or denominator is called a **complex fraction**. An example of a complex fraction is

$$\frac{\dfrac{1}{3} + \dfrac{4}{x}}{3 - \dfrac{1}{xy}}$$

We can simplify fractions of this type using the property $\dfrac{a}{b} = \dfrac{ac}{bc}$, with c equal to the LCD

of *all* the fractions contained in the numerator and denominator of the complex fraction.

For example, all fractions contained in the preceding complex fraction have LCD $3xy$. We simplify this complex fraction by multiplying the numerator and denominator as follows:

$$\frac{\dfrac{1}{3} + \dfrac{4}{x}}{3 - \dfrac{1}{xy}} = \frac{3xy\left(\dfrac{1}{3} + \dfrac{4}{x}\right)}{3xy\left(3 - \dfrac{1}{xy}\right)} = \frac{3xy\left(\dfrac{1}{3}\right) + 3xy\left(\dfrac{4}{x}\right)}{3xy(3) - 3xy\left(\dfrac{1}{xy}\right)} = \frac{xy + 12y}{9xy - 3}$$

EXAMPLE 6   Complex Fractions

Simplify $\dfrac{x^{-3} + x^2 y^{-3}}{(xy)^{-2}}$ so that only positive exponents remain.

Solution

$$\frac{x^{-3} + x^2 y^{-3}}{(xy)^{-2}} = \frac{\dfrac{1}{x^3} + \dfrac{x^2}{y^3}}{\dfrac{1}{(xy)^2}}, \quad \text{LCD} = x^3 y^3$$

$$= \frac{x^3 y^3\left(\dfrac{1}{x^3} + \dfrac{x^2}{y^3}\right)}{x^3 y^3\left(\dfrac{1}{x^2 y^2}\right)} = \frac{y^3 + x^5}{xy}$$

CHECKPOINT

4. Add or subtract:

   (a) $\dfrac{5x - 1}{2x - 5} - \dfrac{x + 9}{2x - 5}$ (b) $\dfrac{x + 1}{x} + \dfrac{x}{x - 1}$

5. Simplify $\dfrac{\dfrac{y}{x} - 1}{\dfrac{y}{x} - \dfrac{x}{y}}$.

Rationalizing Denominators

We can simplify algebraic fractions whose denominators contain sums and differences that involve square roots by rationalizing the denominators. Using the fact that $(x + y)(x - y) = x^2 - y^2$, we multiply the numerator and denominator of an algebraic fraction of this type by the conjugate of the denominator to simplify the fraction.

EXAMPLE 7 **Rationalizing Denominators**

Rationalize the denominators.

(a) $\dfrac{1}{\sqrt{x} - 2}$ (b) $\dfrac{3 + \sqrt{x}}{\sqrt{x} + \sqrt{5}}$

Solution

Multiplying $\sqrt{x} - 2$ by $\sqrt{x} + 2$, its conjugate, gives the difference of two squares and removes the radical from the denominator in (a). We also use the conjugate in (b).

(a) $\dfrac{1}{\sqrt{x} - 2} \cdot \dfrac{\sqrt{x} + 2}{\sqrt{x} + 2} = \dfrac{\sqrt{x} + 2}{(\sqrt{x})^2 - (2)^2} = \dfrac{\sqrt{x} + 2}{x - 4}$

(b) $\dfrac{3 + \sqrt{x}}{\sqrt{x} + \sqrt{5}} \cdot \dfrac{\sqrt{x} - \sqrt{5}}{\sqrt{x} - \sqrt{5}} = \dfrac{3\sqrt{x} - 3\sqrt{5} + x - \sqrt{5x}}{x - 5}$

CHECKPOINT

6. Rationalize the denominator: $\dfrac{\sqrt{x}}{\sqrt{x} - 3}$.

CHECKPOINT SOLUTIONS

1. $\dfrac{2x^2 - 4x}{2x} = \dfrac{2x(x - 2)}{2x} = x - 2$

2. $\dfrac{x^2}{x^2 - 9} \cdot \dfrac{x + 3}{3x} = \dfrac{x^2 \cdot (x + 3)}{(x + 3)(x - 3) \cdot 3x} = \dfrac{x}{3(x - 3)} = \dfrac{x}{3x - 9}$

3. $\dfrac{5x^2(x - 1)}{2(x + 1)} \div \dfrac{10x^2}{(x + 1)(x - 1)} = \dfrac{5x^2(x - 1)}{2(x + 1)} \cdot \dfrac{(x + 1)(x - 1)}{10x^2}$
   $= \dfrac{(x - 1)^2}{4}$

4. (a) $\dfrac{5x - 1}{2x - 5} - \dfrac{x + 9}{2x - 5} = \dfrac{(5x - 1) - (x + 9)}{2x - 5} = \dfrac{5x - 1 - x - 9}{2x - 5}$
   $= \dfrac{4x - 10}{2x - 5} = \dfrac{2(2x - 5)}{2x - 5} = 2$

   (b) $\dfrac{x + 1}{x} + \dfrac{x}{x - 1}$ has LCD $= x(x - 1)$. Thus
   $$\dfrac{x + 1}{x} + \dfrac{x}{x - 1} = \dfrac{x + 1}{x} \cdot \dfrac{(x - 1)}{(x - 1)} + \dfrac{x}{x - 1} \cdot \dfrac{x}{x}$$
   $$= \dfrac{x^2 - 1}{x(x - 1)} + \dfrac{x^2}{x(x - 1)} = \dfrac{x^2 - 1 + x^2}{x(x - 1)} = \dfrac{2x^2 - 1}{x(x - 1)}$$

5. $\dfrac{\dfrac{y}{x} - 1}{\dfrac{y}{x} - \dfrac{x}{y}} = \dfrac{\left(\dfrac{y}{x} - 1\right)}{\left(\dfrac{y}{x} - \dfrac{x}{y}\right)} \cdot \dfrac{xy}{xy} = \dfrac{\dfrac{y}{x} \cdot xy - 1 \cdot xy}{\dfrac{y}{x} \cdot xy - \dfrac{x}{y} \cdot xy}$
   $= \dfrac{y^2 - xy}{y^2 - x^2} = \dfrac{y(y - x)}{(y + x)(y - x)} = \dfrac{y}{y + x}$

6. $\dfrac{\sqrt{x}}{\sqrt{x} - 3} = \dfrac{\sqrt{x}}{\sqrt{x} - 3} \cdot \dfrac{\sqrt{x} + 3}{\sqrt{x} + 3} = \dfrac{x + 3\sqrt{x}}{x - 9}$

| EXERCISES | 0.7

Simplify the following fractions.

1. $\dfrac{18x^3y^3}{9x^3z}$

2. $\dfrac{15a^4b^5}{30a^3b}$

3. $\dfrac{x - 3y}{3x - 9y}$

4. $\dfrac{x^2 - 6x + 8}{x^2 - 16}$

5. $\dfrac{x^2 - 2x + 1}{x^2 - 4x + 3}$

6. $\dfrac{x^2 - 5x + 6}{9 - x^2}$

In Problems 7–34, perform the indicated operations and simplify.

7. $\dfrac{6x^3}{8y^3} \cdot \dfrac{16x}{9y^2} \cdot \dfrac{15y^4}{x^3}$

8. $\dfrac{25ac^2}{15a^2c} \cdot \dfrac{4ad^4}{15abc^3}$

9. $\dfrac{8x - 16}{x - 3} \cdot \dfrac{4x - 12}{3x - 6}$

10. $(x^2 - 4) \cdot \dfrac{2x - 3}{x + 2}$

11. $\dfrac{x^2 + 7x + 12}{3x^2 + 13x + 4} \cdot (9x + 3)$

12. $\dfrac{4x + 4}{x - 4} \cdot \dfrac{x^2 - 6x + 8}{8x^2 + 8x}$

13. $\dfrac{x^2 - x - 2}{2x^2 - 8} \cdot \dfrac{18 - 2x^2}{x^2 - 5x + 4} \cdot \dfrac{x^2 - 2x - 8}{x^2 - 6x + 9}$

14. $\dfrac{x^2 - 5x - 6}{x^2 - 5x + 4} \cdot \dfrac{x^2 - x - 12}{x^3 - 6x^2} \cdot \dfrac{x - x^3}{x^2 - 2x + 1}$

15. $\dfrac{15ac^2}{7bd} \div \dfrac{4a}{14b^2d}$

16. $\dfrac{16}{x - 2} \div \dfrac{4}{3x - 6}$

17. $\dfrac{y^2 - 2y + 1}{7y^2 - 7y} \div \dfrac{y^2 - 4y + 3}{35y^2}$

18. $\dfrac{6x^2}{4x^2y - 12xy} \div \dfrac{3x^2 + 12x}{x^2 + x - 12}$

19. $(x^2 - x - 6) \div \dfrac{9 - x^2}{x^2 - 3x}$

20. $\dfrac{2x^2 + 7x + 3}{4x^2 - 1} \div (x + 3)$

21. $\dfrac{2x}{x^2 - x - 2} - \dfrac{x + 2}{x^2 - x - 2}$

22. $\dfrac{4}{9 - x^2} - \dfrac{x + 1}{9 - x^2}$

23. $\dfrac{a}{a - 2} - \dfrac{a - 2}{a}$

24. $x - \dfrac{2}{x - 1}$

25. $\dfrac{x}{x + 1} - x + 1$

26. $\dfrac{x - 1}{x + 1} - \dfrac{2}{x^2 + x}$

27. $\dfrac{4a}{3x + 6} + \dfrac{5a^2}{4x + 8}$

28. $\dfrac{b - 1}{b^2 + 2b} + \dfrac{b}{3b + 6}$

29. $\dfrac{3x - 1}{2x - 4} + \dfrac{4x}{3x - 6} - \dfrac{x - 4}{5x - 10}$

30. $\dfrac{2x + 1}{4x - 2} + \dfrac{5}{2x} - \dfrac{x + 4}{2x^2 - x}$

31. $\dfrac{x}{x^2 - 4} + \dfrac{4}{x^2 - x - 2} - \dfrac{x - 2}{x^2 + 3x + 2}$

32. $\dfrac{3x^2}{x^2 - 4} + \dfrac{2}{x^2 - 4x + 4} - 3$

33. $\dfrac{-x^3 + x}{\sqrt{3 - x^2}} + 2x\sqrt{3 - x^2}$

34. $\dfrac{3x^2(x + 1)}{\sqrt{x^3 + 1}} + \sqrt{x^3 + 1}$

In Problems 35–44, simplify each complex fraction.

35. $\dfrac{3 - \dfrac{2}{3}}{14}$

36. $\dfrac{4}{\dfrac{1}{4} + \dfrac{1}{4}}$

37. $\dfrac{x + y}{\dfrac{1}{x} + \dfrac{1}{y}}$

38. $\dfrac{\dfrac{5}{2y} + \dfrac{3}{y}}{\dfrac{1}{4} + \dfrac{1}{3y}}$

39. $\dfrac{2 - \dfrac{1}{x}}{2x - \dfrac{3x}{x + 1}}$

40. $\dfrac{1 - \dfrac{2}{x - 2}}{x - 6 + \dfrac{10}{x + 1}}$

41. $\dfrac{\sqrt{a} - \dfrac{b}{\sqrt{a}}}{a - b}$

42. $\dfrac{\sqrt{x - 1} + \dfrac{1}{\sqrt{x - 1}}}{x}$

43. $\dfrac{\sqrt{x^2 + 9} - \dfrac{13}{\sqrt{x^2 + 9}}}{x^2 - x - 6}$

44. $\dfrac{\sqrt{x^2 + 3} - \dfrac{x + 5}{\sqrt{x^2 + 3}}}{x^2 + 5x + 4}$

In Problems 45–48, rewrite each of the following so that only positive exponents remain, and simplify.

45. (a) $(2^{-2} - 3^{-1})^{-1}$ (b) $(2^{-1} + 3^{-1})^2$

46. (a) $(3^2 + 4^2)^{-1/2}$ (b) $(2^2 + 3^2)^{-1}$

47. $\dfrac{2a^{-1} - b^{-2}}{(ab^2)^{-1}}$

48. $\dfrac{x^{-2} + xy^{-2}}{(x^2y)^{-2}}$

In Problems 49 and 50, rationalize the denominator of each fraction and simplify.

49. $\dfrac{1 - \sqrt{x}}{1 + \sqrt{x}}$

50. $\dfrac{x - 3}{x - \sqrt{3}}$

In Problems 51 and 52, rationalize the numerator of each fraction and simplify.

51. $\dfrac{\sqrt{x + h} - \sqrt{x}}{h}$

52. $\dfrac{\sqrt{9 + 2h} - 3}{h}$

APPLICATIONS

53. *Time study* Workers A, B, and C can complete a job in a, b, and c hours, respectively. Working together, they can complete

$$\frac{1}{a} + \frac{1}{b} + \frac{1}{c}$$

of the job in 1 hour. Add these fractions over a common denominator to obtain an expression for what they can do in 1 hour, working together.

54. *Focal length* Two thin lenses with focal lengths p and q and separated by a distance d have their combined focal length given by the reciprocal of

$$\frac{1}{p} + \frac{1}{q} - \frac{d}{pq}$$

   (a) Combine these fractions.
   (b) Use the reciprocal of your answer in (a) to find the combined focal length.

Average cost **A company's average cost per unit when x units are produced is defined to be**

$$\text{Average cost} = \frac{\text{Total cost}}{x}$$

Use this equation in Problems 55 and 56.

55. Suppose a company's average costs are given by

$$\text{Average cost} = \frac{4000}{x} + 55 + 0.1x$$

(a) Express the average-cost formula as a single fraction.
(b) Write the expression that gives the company's total costs.

56. Suppose a company's average costs are given by

$$\text{Average cost} = \frac{40{,}500}{x} + 190 + 0.2x$$

(a) Express the average-cost formula as a single fraction.
(b) Write the expression that gives the company's total costs.

57. *Advertising and sales* Suppose that a company's daily sales volume attributed to an advertising campaign is given by

$$\text{Sales volume} = 1 + \frac{3}{t + 3} - \frac{18}{(t + 3)^2}$$

where t is the number of days since the campaign started. Express the sales volume as a single fraction.

58. *Annuity* The formula for the future value of an annuity due involves the expression

$$\frac{(1 + i)^{n+1} - 1}{i} - 1$$

Write this expression over a common denominator and factor the numerator to simplify.

KEY TERMS AND FORMULAS

Section	Key Terms	Formulas
0.1	Sets and set membership	
	Natural numbers	$N = \{1, 2, 3, 4 \ldots\}$
	Empty set	$\varnothing$
	Set equality	
	Subset	$A \subseteq B$
	Universal set	U
	Venn diagrams	
	Set intersection	$A \cap B$
	Disjoint sets	$A \cap B = \varnothing$
	Set union	$A \cup B$
	Set complement	A'
0.2	Real numbers	
	Subsets and properties	
	Real number line	
	Inequalities	
	Intervals and interval notation	
	Closed interval	$a \leq x \leq b$ or $[a, b]$
	Open interval	$a < x < b$ or (a, b)
	Absolute value	
	Order of operations	

Section	Key Terms	Formulas
0.3	Exponent and base	a^n has base a, exponent n
	Zero exponent	$a^0 = 1, a \neq 0$
	Negative exponent	$a^{-n} = \dfrac{1}{a^n}$
	Rules of exponents	
0.4	Radical	$\sqrt[n]{a}$
	Radicand, index	radicand $= a$; index $= n$
	Principal nth root	$\sqrt[n]{a} = b$ only if $b^n = a$ and $a \geq 0$ and $b \geq 0$ when n is even
	Fractional exponents	$a^{1/n} = \sqrt[n]{a}$
		$a^{m/n} = \sqrt[n]{a^m} = (\sqrt[n]{a})^m$
	Properties of radicals	
	Rationalizing the denominator	
0.5	Algebraic expression	
	Variable	
	Constant term	
	Coefficient; leading coefficient	
	Term	
	Polynomial	$a_n x^n + \cdots + a_1 x + a_0$
	Degree	
	Monomial	
	Binomial	
	Trinomial	
	Like terms	
	Distributive Law	$a(b + c) = ab + ac$
	Binomial products	
	Division of polynomials	
0.6	Factor	
	Common factor	
	Factoring by grouping	
	Special factorizations	
	Difference of squares	$a^2 - b^2 = (a + b)(a - b)$
	Perfect squares	$a^2 + 2ab + b^2 = (a + b)^2$
		$a^2 - 2ab + b^2 = (a - b)^2$
	Conjugates	$a + b; a - b$
	Quadratic polynomials	$ax^2 + bx + c$
	Factoring completely	
0.7	Algebraic fractions	
	Numerator	
	Denominator	
	Reduce	
	Product of fractions	
	Quotient of fractions	
	Common denominator	
	Least common denominator (LCD)	
	Addition and subtraction of fractions	
	Complex fraction	
	Rationalize the denominator	

REVIEW EXERCISES

1. Is $A \subseteq B$ if $A = \{1, 2, 5, 7\}$ and
    $B = \{x: x \text{ is a positive integer}, x \leq 8\}$?
2. Is it true that $3 \in \{x: x > 3\}$?
3. Are $A = \{1, 2, 3, 4\}$ and $B = \{x: x \leq 1\}$ disjoint?

**In Problems 4–7, use sets $U = \{1, 2, 3, 4, 5, 6, 7, 8, 9, 10\}$,
$A = \{1, 2, 3, 9\}$, and $B = \{1, 3, 5, 6, 7, 8, 10\}$ to find the
elements of the sets described.**

4. $A \cup B'$
5. $A' \cap B$
6. $(A' \cap B)'$
7. Does $(A' \cup B')' = A \cap B$?
8. State the property of the real numbers that is illustrated in each case.

    (a) $6 + \dfrac{1}{3} = \dfrac{1}{3} + 6$ (b) $2(3 \cdot 4) = (2 \cdot 3)4$

    (c) $\dfrac{1}{3}(6 + 9) = 2 + 3$

9. Indicate whether each given expression is one or more of the following: rational, irrational, integer, natural, or meaningless.

    (a) π (b) $0/6$ (c) $6/0$
10. Insert the proper sign ($<$, $=$, or $>$) to replace each $\square$.

    (a) $\pi \, \square \, 3.14$ (b) $-100 \, \square \, 0.1$ (c) $-3 \, \square \, -12$

**For Problems 11–18, evaluate each expression. Use a
calculator when necessary.**

11. $|5 - 11|$
12. $44 \div 2 \cdot 11 - 10^2$
13. $(-3)^2 - (-1)^3$
14. $\dfrac{(3)(2)(15) - (5)(8)}{(4)(10)}$
15. $2 - [3 - (2 - |-3|)] + 11$
16. $-4^2 - (-4)^2 + 3$
17. $\dfrac{4 + 3^2}{4}$
18. $\dfrac{(-2.91)^5}{\sqrt{3.29^5}}$
19. Write each inequality in interval notation, name the type of interval, and graph it on a real number line.

    (a) $0 \leq x \leq 5$
    (b) $x \geq -3$ and $x < 7$
    (c) $(-4, \infty) \cap (-\infty, 0)$
20. Write an inequality that represents each of the following.

    (a) $(-1, 16)$
    (b) $[-12, 8]$
    (c)
21. Evaluate the following without a calculator.

    (a) $\left(\dfrac{3}{8}\right)^0$ (b) $2^3 \cdot 2^{-5}$

    (c) $\dfrac{4^9}{4^3}$ (d) $\left(\dfrac{1}{7}\right)^3 \left(\dfrac{1}{7}\right)^{-4}$

22. Use the rules of exponents to simplify each of the following with positive exponents. Assume all variables are nonzero.

    (a) $x^5 \cdot x^{-7}$ (b) x^8/x^{-2} (c) $(x^3)^3$
    (d) $(y^4)^{-2}$ (e) $(-y^{-3})^{-2}$

**For Problems 23–28, rewrite each expression so that
only positive exponents remain. Assume all variables are
nonzero.**

23. $\dfrac{-(2xy^2)^{-2}}{(3x^{-2}y^{-3})^2}$ 24. $\left(\dfrac{2}{3}x^2y^{-4}\right)^{-2}$

25. $\left(\dfrac{x^{-2}}{2y^{-1}}\right)^2$ 26. $\dfrac{(-x^4y^{-2}z^2)^0}{-(x^4y^{-2}z^2)^{-2}}$

27. $\left(\dfrac{x^{-3}y^4z^{-2}}{3x^{-2}y^{-3}z^{-3}}\right)^{-1}$ 28. $\left(\dfrac{x}{2y}\right)\left(\dfrac{y}{x^2}\right)^{-2}$

29. Find the following roots.

    (a) $-\sqrt[3]{-64}$ (b) $\sqrt{4/49}$ (c) $\sqrt[7]{1.9487171}$
30. Write each of the following with an exponent and with the variable in the numerator.

    (a) $\sqrt{x}$ (b) $\sqrt[3]{x^2}$ (c) $1/\sqrt[4]{x}$
31. Write each of the following in radical form.

    (a) $x^{2/3}$ (b) $x^{-1/2}$ (c) $-x^{3/2}$
32. Rationalize each of the following denominators and simplify.

    (a) $\dfrac{5xy}{\sqrt{2x}}$ (b) $\dfrac{y}{x\sqrt[3]{xy^2}}$

**In Problems 33–38, use the properties of exponents to
simplify so that only positive exponents remain. Assume
all variables are positive.**

33. $x^{1/2} \cdot x^{1/3}$ 34. $y^{-3/4}/y^{-7/4}$ 35. $x^4 \cdot x^{1/4}$
36. $1/(x^{-4/3} \cdot x^{-7/3})$ 37. $(x^{4/5})^{1/2}$ 38. $(x^{1/2}y^2)^4$

**In Problems 39–44, simplify each expression. Assume all
variables are positive.**

39. $\sqrt{12x^3y^5}$ 40. $\sqrt{1250x^6y^9}$
41. $\sqrt[3]{24x^4y^4} \cdot \sqrt[3]{45x^4y^{10}}$ 42. $\sqrt{16a^2b^3} \cdot \sqrt{8a^3b^5}$
43. $\dfrac{\sqrt{52x^3y^6}}{\sqrt{13xy^4}}$ 44. $\dfrac{\sqrt{32x^4y^3}}{\sqrt{6xy^{10}}}$

**In Problems 45–62, perform the indicated operations and
simplify.**

45. $(3x + 5) - (4x + 7)$
46. $x(1 - x) + x[x - (2 + x)]$
47. $(3x^3 - 4xy - 3) + (5xy + x^3 + 4y - 1)$
48. $(4xy^3)(6x^4y^2)$ 49. $(3x - 4)(x - 1)$
50. $(3x - 1)(x + 2)$ 51. $(4x + 1)(x - 2)$
52. $(3x - 7)(2x + 1)$ 53. $(2x - 3)^2$
54. $(4x + 3)(4x - 3)$ 55. $(2x^2 + 1)(x^2 + x - 3)$
56. $(2x - 1)^3$ 57. $(x - y)(x^2 + xy + y^2)$

58. $\dfrac{4x^2y - 3x^3y^3 - 6x^4y^2}{2x^2y^2}$

59. $(3x^4 + 2x^3 - x + 4) \div (x^2 + 1)$

60. $(x^4 - 4x^3 + 5x^2 + x) \div (x - 3)$

61. $x^{4/3}(x^{2/3} - x^{-1/3})$

62. $(\sqrt{x} + \sqrt{a - x})(\sqrt{x} - \sqrt{a - x})$

In Problems 63–73, factor each expression completely.

63. $2x^4 - x^3$ 64. $4(x^2 + 1)^2 - 2(x^2 + 1)^3$

65. $4x^2 - 4x + 1$ 66. $16 - 9x^2$

67. $2x^4 - 8x^2$ 68. $x^2 - 4x - 21$

69. $3x^2 - x - 2$ 70. $x^2 - 5x + 6$

71. $x^2 - 10x - 24$ 72. $12x^2 - 23x - 24$

73. $16x^4 - 72x^2 + 81$

74. Factor as indicated: $x^{-2/3} + x^{-4/3} = x^{-4/3}(?)$

75. Reduce each of the following to lowest terms.

(a) $\dfrac{2x}{2x + 4}$ (b) $\dfrac{4x^2y^3 - 6x^3y^4}{2x^2y^2 - 3xy^3}$

In Problems 76–82, perform the indicated operations and simplify.

76. $\dfrac{x^2 - 4x}{x^2 + 4} \cdot \dfrac{x^4 - 16}{x^4 - 16x^2}$

77. $\dfrac{x^2 + 6x + 9}{x^2 - 7x + 12} \div \dfrac{x^2 + 4x + 3}{x^2 - 3x - 4}$

78. $\dfrac{x^4 - 2x^3}{3x^2 - x - 2} \div \dfrac{x^3 - 4x}{9x^2 - 4}$ 79. $1 + \dfrac{3}{2x} - \dfrac{1}{6x^2}$

80. $\dfrac{1}{x - 2} - \dfrac{x - 2}{4}$ 81. $\dfrac{x + 2}{x^2 - x} - \dfrac{x^2 + 4}{x^2 - 2x + 1} + 1$

82. $\dfrac{x - 1}{x^2 - x - 2} - \dfrac{x}{x^2 - 2x - 3} + \dfrac{1}{x - 2}$

In Problems 83 and 84, simplify each complex fraction.

83. $\dfrac{x - 1 - \dfrac{x - 1}{x}}{\dfrac{1}{x - 1} + 1}$ 84. $\dfrac{x^{-2} - x^{-1}}{x^{-2} + x^{-1}}$

85. Rationalize the denominator of $\dfrac{3x - 3}{\sqrt{x} - 1}$ and simplify.

86. Rationalize the numerator of $\dfrac{\sqrt{x} - \sqrt{x - 4}}{2}$ and simplify.

APPLICATIONS

87. *Job effectiveness factors* In an attempt to determine some off-the-job factors that might be indicators of on-the-job effectiveness, a company made a study of 200 of its employees. It was interested in whether the employees had been recognized for superior work by their supervisors within the past year, whether they were involved in community activities, and whether

they followed a regular exercise plan. The company found the following.

    30 answered "yes" to all three

    50 were recognized and they exercised

    52 were recognized and were involved in the community

    77 were recognized

    37 were involved in the community but did not exercise

    95 were recognized or were involved in the community

    95 answered "no" to all three

(a) Draw a Venn diagram that represents this information.

(b) How many exercised only?

(c) How many exercised or were involved in the community?

88. *Health insurance coverage* The percent of the U.S. population covered by an employment-based health insurance plan can be approximated by the expression

$$-0.75x + 63.8$$

where x is the number of years past 2000 (*Source:* U.S. Census Bureau). Use this expression to estimate the percent covered by such a plan in the year 2015.

89. *Poiseuille's law* The expression for the speed of blood through an artery of radius r at a distance x from the artery wall is given by $r^2 - (r - x)^2$. Evaluate this expression when $r = 5$ and $x = 2$.

90. *Future value* If an individual makes monthly deposits of $100 in an account that earns 9% compounded monthly, then the future value S of the account after n months is given by the formula

$$S = \$100 \left[\dfrac{(1.0075)^n - 1}{0.0075} \right]$$

(a) Find the future value after 36 months (3 years).

(b) Find the future value after 20 years.

91. *Health care* According to the American Hospital Association, the trends since 1975 indicate that the number of hospital beds B (in thousands) is related to the number of hospitals H by the formula

$$B = 176.896(1.00029)^H$$

(a) In 2004 the number of hospitals had fallen to 5759. How many beds does the equation estimate were available?

(b) If the number of hospitals reaches 5000, what does the equation predict for the number of beds?

92. *Severe weather ice makers* Thunderstorms severe enough to produce hail develop when an upper-level low (a pool of cold air high in the atmosphere) moves through a region where there is warm, moist air at the

surface. These storms create an updraft that draws the moist air into subfreezing air above 10,000 feet. The strength of the updraft, as measured by its speed s (in mph), affects the diameter of the hail h (in inches) according to

$$h = 0.000595s^{1.922} \quad \text{or equivalently} \quad s = 47.7h^{0.519}$$

(*Source*: National Weather Service).
(a) What size hail is produced by an updraft of 50 mph?
(b) When a storm produces softball-sized hail (about 4.5 inches in diameter), how fast is the updraft?

93. *Loan payment* Suppose you borrow $10,000 for n months to buy a car at an interest rate of 7.8% compounded monthly. The size of each month's payment R is given by the formula

$$R = \$10,000\left[\frac{0.0065}{1 - (1.0065)^{-n}}\right]$$

(a) Rewrite the expression on the right-hand side of this formula as a fraction with only positive exponents.
(b) Find the monthly payment for a 48-month loan. Use both the original formula and your result from (a). (Both formulas should give the same payment.)

94. *Environment* Suppose that in a study of water birds, the relationship between the number of acres of wetlands A and the number of species of birds S found in the wetlands area was given by

$$S = kA^{1/3}$$

where k is a constant.
(a) Express this formula using radical notation.
(b) If the area is expanded by a factor of 2.25 from 20,000 acres to 45,000 acres, find the expected increase in the number of species (as a multiple of the number of species on the 20,000 acres).

95. *Profit* Suppose that the total cost of producing and selling x units of a product is $300 + 4x$ and the total revenue from the sale of x units is $30x - 0.001x^2$. Find the difference of these expressions (total revenue minus total cost) to find the profit from the production and sale of x units of the product.

96. *Business loss* Suppose that a commercial building costs $1,450,000. After it is placed into service, it loses 0.25% of its original value in each of the x months it is in service. Write an expression for the value of the building after x months.

97. *Revenue* The revenue for a boat tour is $600 - 13x - 0.5x^2$, where x is the number of passengers above the minimum of 50. This expression will factor into two binomials, with one representing the total number of passengers. Factor this expression.

98. *Pollution: cost-benefit* Suppose that the cost C (in dollars) of removing p% of the pollution from the waste water of a manufacturing process is given by

$$C = \frac{1,200,000}{100 - p} - 12,000$$

(a) Express the right-hand side of this formula as a single fraction.
(b) Find the cost if $p = 0$. Write a sentence that explains the meaning of what you found.
(c) Find the cost of removing 98% of the pollution.
(d) What happens to this formula when $p = 100$? Explain why you think this happens.

99. *Average cost* The average cost of producing a product is given by the expression

$$1200 + 56x + \frac{8000}{x}$$

Write this expression with all terms over a common denominator.

---

0   CHAPTER TEST

1. Let $U = \{1, 2, 3, 4, 5, 6, 7, 8, 9\}$, $A = \{x: x \text{ is even and } x \geq 5\}$, and $B = \{1, 2, 5, 7, 8, 9\}$. Complete the following.
   (a) Find $A \cup B'$.
   (b) Find a two-element set that is disjoint from B.
   (c) Find a nonempty subset of A that is not equal to A.
2. Evaluate $(4 - 2^3)^2 - 3^4 \cdot 0^{15} + 12 \div 3 + 1$.
3. Use definitions and properties of exponents to complete the following.
   (a) $x^4 \cdot x^4 = x^?$
   (b) $x^0 = ?$, if $x \neq 0$
   (c) $\sqrt{x} = x^?$
   (d) $(x^{-5})^2 = x^?$
   (e) $a^{27} \div a^{-3} = a^?$
   (f) $x^{1/2} \cdot x^{1/3} = x^?$
   (g) $\dfrac{1}{\sqrt[3]{x^2}} = \dfrac{1}{x^?}$
   (h) $\dfrac{1}{x^3} = x^?$

4. Write each of the following as radicals.
   (a) $x^{1/5}$
   (b) $x^{-3/4}$
5. Simplify each of the following so that only positive exponents remain.
   (a) x^{-5}
   (b) $\left(\dfrac{x^{-8}y^2}{x^{-1}}\right)^{-3}$
6. Simplify the following radical expressions, and rationalize any denominators.
   (a) $\dfrac{x}{\sqrt{5x}}$
   (b) $\sqrt{24a^2b}\sqrt{a^3b^4}$
   (c) $\dfrac{1 - \sqrt{x}}{1 + \sqrt{x}}$

7. Given the expression $2x^3 - 7x^5 - 5x - 8$, complete the following.
   (a) Find the degree.
   (b) Find the constant term.
   (c) Find the coefficient of x.

8. Express $(-2, \infty) \cap (-\infty, 3]$ using interval notation, and graph it.

9. Completely factor each of the following.
   (a) $8x^3 - 2x^2$ (b) $x^2 - 10x + 24$
   (c) $6x^2 - 13x + 6$ (d) $2x^3 - 32x^5$

10. Identify the quadratic polynomial from among (a)–(c), and evaluate it using $x = -3$.
    (a) $2x^2 - 3x^3 + 7$ (b) $x^2 + 3/x + 11$
    (c) $4 - x - x^2$

11. Use long division to find $(2x^3 + x^2 - 7) \div (x^2 - 1)$.

12. Perform the indicated operations and simplify.
    (a) $4y - 5(9 - 3y)$ (b) $-3t^2(2t^4 - 3t^7)$
    (c) $(4x - 1)(x^2 - 5x + 2)$
    (d) $(6x - 1)(2 - 3x)$
    (e) $(2m - 7)^2$ (f) $\dfrac{x^6}{x^2 - 9} \cdot \dfrac{x - 3}{3x^2}$
    (g) $\dfrac{x^4}{3^2} \div \dfrac{9x^3}{x^6}$ (h) $\dfrac{4}{x - 8} - \dfrac{x - 2}{x - 8}$
    (i) $\dfrac{x - 1}{x^2 - 2x - 3} - \dfrac{3}{x^2 - 3x}$

13. Simplify $\dfrac{\dfrac{1}{x} - \dfrac{1}{y}}{\dfrac{1}{x} + y}$.

14. In a nutrition survey of 320 students, the following information was obtained.

   145 ate breakfast
   270 ate lunch
   280 ate dinner
   125 ate breakfast and lunch
   110 ate breakfast and dinner
   230 ate lunch and dinner
   90 ate all three meals

   (a) Make a Venn diagram that represents this information.
   (b) How many students in the survey ate only breakfast?
   (c) How many students skipped breakfast?

15. If \$1000 is invested for x years at 8% compounded quarterly, the future value of the investment is given by

$$S = 1000\left(1 + \frac{0.08}{4}\right)^{4x}$$

   What will be the future value of this investment in 20 years?

Campaign Management

A politician is trying to win election to the city council, and as his campaign manager, you need to decide how to promote the candidate. There are three ways you can do so: You can send glossy, full-color pamphlets to registered voters of the city; you can run a commercial during the television news on a local cable network; and/or you can buy a full-page ad in the newspaper.

Two hundred fifty thousand voters live in the city, and 36% of them read the newspaper. Fifty thousand voters watch the local cable network news, and 30% of them also read the newspaper.

You also know that the television commercial would cost $40,000, the newspaper ad $27,000, and the pamphlets mailed to voters 90 cents each, including printing and bulk-rate postage.

Suppose that the success of the candidate depends on your campaign reaching at least 125,000 voters and that, because your budget is limited, you must achieve this goal at a minimum cost. What would be your plan and the cost of that plan?

If you need help devising a method of solution for this problem, try answering the following questions first.

1. How many voters in the city read the newspaper but do not watch the local cable television news?
2. How many voters read the newspaper or watch the local cable television news, or both?
3. Complete the following chart by indicating the number of voters reached by each promotional option, the total cost, and the cost per voter reached.

	Number of Voters Reached	Total Cost	Cost per Voter Reached
Pamphlet			
Television			
Newspaper			

4. Now explain your plan and the cost of that plan.

1

Linear Equations and Functions

Joy Brown/Shutterstock.com

A wide variety of problems from business, the social sciences, and the life sciences may be solved using equations. Managers and economists use equations and their graphs to study costs, sales, national consumption, or supply and demand. Social scientists may plot demographic data or try to develop equations that predict population growth, voting behavior, or learning and retention rates. Life scientists use equations to model the flow of blood or the conduction of nerve impulses and to test theories or develop new models by using experimental data.

Numerous applications of mathematics are given throughout the text, but most chapters contain special sections emphasizing business and economics applications. In particular, this chapter introduces two important applications that will be expanded and used throughout the text as increased mathematical skills permit: supply and demand as functions of price (market analysis); and total cost, total revenue, and profit as functions of the quantity produced and sold (theory of the firm).

The topics and applications discussed in this chapter include the following.

SECTIONS

1.1 Solutions of Linear Equations and Inequalities in One Variable

1.2 Functions
Function notation
Operations with functions

1.3 Linear Functions
Graphs
Slopes
Equations

1.4 Graphs and Graphing Utilities
Graphical solutions of linear equations

1.5 Solutions of Systems of Linear Equations
Systems of linear equations in three variables

1.6 Applications of Functions in Business and Economics

APPLICATIONS

Future value of an investment, voting, normal height for a given age, profit

Income taxes, stock market, mortgage payments

Depreciation, U.S. banks, pricing

Water purity, women in the work force

Investment mix, medicine concentrations, college enrollment

Total cost, total revenue, profit, break-even analysis, demand and supply, market equilibrium

Prerequisite Problem Type	For Section	Answer	Section for Review
Evaluate: (a) $2(-1)^3 - 3(-1)^2 + 1$ (b) $3(-3) - 1$ (c) $14(10) - 0.02(10^2)$ (d) $\dfrac{3-1}{4-(-2)}$ (e) $\dfrac{-1-3}{2-(-2)}$ (f) $\dfrac{3(-8)}{4}$ (g) $2\left(\dfrac{23}{9}\right) - 5\left(\dfrac{2}{9}\right)$	**1.1** **1.2** **1.3** **1.5** **1.6**	(a) -4 (b) -10 (c) 138 (d) $\dfrac{1}{3}$ (e) -1 (f) -6 (g) 4	0.2 Signed numbers
Graph $x \le 3$.	**1.1**		0.2 Inequalities
(a) $\dfrac{1}{x}$ is *undefined* for which real number(s)? (b) $\sqrt{x-4}$ is a real number for which values of x?	**1.1, 1.2**	(a) Undefined for $x = 0$ (b) $x \ge 4$	0.2 Real numbers 0.4 Radicals
Identify the coefficient of x and the constant term for: (a) $-9x + 2$ (b) $\dfrac{x}{2}$ (c) $x - 300$	**1.1, 1.3** **1.5, 1.6**	*Coeff.* *Const.* (a) -9 2 (b) $\dfrac{1}{2}$ 0 (c) 1 -300	0.5 Algebraic expressions
Simplify: (a) $4(-c)^2 - 3(-c) + 1$ (b) $[3(x+h) - 1] - [3x - 1]$ (c) $12\left(\dfrac{3x}{4} + 3\right)$ (d) $9x - (300 + 2x)$ (e) $-\dfrac{1}{5}[x - (-1)]$ (f) $2(2y + 3) + 3y$	**1.1, 1.2** **1.3, 1.5** **1.6**	(a) $4c^2 + 3c + 1$ (b) $3h$ (c) $9x + 36$ (d) $7x - 300$ (e) $-\dfrac{1}{5}x - \dfrac{1}{5}$ (f) $7y + 6$	0.5 Algebraic expressions
Find the LCD of $\dfrac{3x}{2x+10}$ and $\dfrac{1}{x+5}$.	**1.1**	$2x + 10$	0.7 Algebraic fractions

OBJECTIVES

1.1

- To solve linear equations in one variable
- To solve applied problems by using linear equations
- To solve linear inequalities in one variable

Solutions of Linear Equations and Inequalities in One Variable

▌| APPLICATION PREVIEW |▌

Using data from 1980 and projected to 2050, the number of Hispanics in the U.S. civilian noninstitutional population is given by

$$y = 0.876x + 6.084$$

millions, where x is the number of years after 1980 (*Source:* U.S. Census Bureau). To find the year when this population will equal 36.74 million, we solve $36.74 = 0.876x + 6.084$. (See Example 2.) We will discuss solutions of linear equations and inequalities in this section.

Equations

An **equation** is a statement that two quantities or algebraic expressions are equal. An equation such as $3x - 2 = 7$ is known as an equation in one variable. The x in this case is called a **variable** because its value determines whether the equation is true. For example, $3x - 2 = 7$ is true only for $x = 3$. Finding the value(s) of the variable(s) that make the equation true—that is, finding the **solutions**—is called **solving the equation.** The set of solutions of an equation is called a **solution set** of the equation. The variable in an equation is sometimes called the **unknown.**

Equations that are true for all values of the variables are called **identities.** The equation $2(x - 1) = 2x - 2$ is an example of an identity. Equations that are true only for certain values of the variables are called **conditional equations** or simply **equations.**

Two equations are said to be **equivalent** if they have exactly the same solution set. We can often solve a complicated linear equation by finding an equivalent equation whose solution is easily found. We use the following properties of equality to reduce an equation to a simple equivalent equation.

Properties of Equality

Properties	Examples
Substitution Property	
The equation formed by substituting one expression for an equal expression is equivalent to the original equation.	$3(x - 3) - \frac{1}{2}(4x - 18) = 4$ is equivalent to $3x - 9 - 2x + 9 = 4$ and to $x = 4$. We say the solution set is $\{4\}$, or the solution is 4.
Addition Property	
The equation formed by adding the same quantity to both sides of an equation is equivalent to the original equation.	$x - 4 = 6$ is equivalent to $x - 4 + 4 = 6 + 4$, or to $x = 10$. $x + 5 = 12$ is equivalent to $x + 5 + (-5) = 12 + (-5)$, or to $x = 7$.
Multiplication Property	
The equation formed by multiplying both sides of an equation by the same nonzero quantity is equivalent to the original equation.	$\frac{1}{3}x = 6$ is equivalent to $3(\frac{1}{3}x) = 3(6)$, or to $x = 18$. $5x = 20$ is equivalent to $(5x)/5 = 20/5$, or to $x = 4$. (Dividing both sides by 5 is equivalent to multiplying both sides by $\frac{1}{5}$.)

Solving Linear Equations

If an equation contains one variable and if the variable occurs to the first degree, the equation is called a **linear equation in one variable.** The following procedure is based on three properties of equality and with it we can solve any linear equation in one variable.

Solving a Linear Equation

Procedure	Example
To solve a linear equation in one variable:	Solve $\dfrac{3x}{4} + 3 = \dfrac{x-1}{3}$.
1. If the equation contains fractions, multiply both sides by the least common denominator (LCD) of the fractions.	1. LCD is 12. $$12\left(\dfrac{3x}{4} + 3\right) = 12\left(\dfrac{x-1}{3}\right)$$
2. Remove any parentheses in the equation.	2. $9x + 36 = 4x - 4$
3. Perform any additions or subtractions to get all terms containing the variable on one side and all other terms on the other side.	3. $9x + 36 - 4x = 4x - 4 - 4x$ $$5x + 36 = -4$$ $$5x + 36 - 36 = -4 - 36$$ $$5x = -40$$
4. Divide both sides of the equation by the coefficient of the variable.	4. $\dfrac{5x}{5} = \dfrac{-40}{5}$ gives $x = -8$
5. Check the solution by substitution in the original equation.	5. $\dfrac{3(-8)}{4} + 3 \overset{?}{=} \dfrac{-8-1}{3}$ gives $-3 = -3$ ✔

EXAMPLE 1 Solving Linear Equations

(a) Solve for z: $\dfrac{2z}{3} = -6$ (b) Solve for x: $\dfrac{3x+1}{2} = \dfrac{x}{3} - 3$

Solution

(a) Multiply both sides by 3.

$$3\left(\frac{2z}{3}\right) = 3(-6) \quad \text{gives} \quad 2z = -18$$

Divide both sides by 2.

$$\frac{2z}{2} = \frac{-18}{2} \quad \text{gives} \quad z = -9$$

Check: $\dfrac{2(-9)}{3} \overset{?}{=} -6$ gives $-6 = -6$ ✔

(b) $\dfrac{3x+1}{2} = \dfrac{x}{3} - 3$

$6\left(\dfrac{3x+1}{2}\right) = 6\left(\dfrac{x}{3} - 3\right)$ Multiply both sides by the LCD, 6.

$3(3x + 1) = 6\left(\dfrac{x}{3} - 3\right)$ Simplify the fraction on the left side.

$9x + 3 = 2x - 18$ Distribute to remove parentheses.

$7x = -21$ Add $(-2x) + (-3)$ to both sides.

$x = -3$ Divide both sides by 7.

Check: $\dfrac{3(-3) + 1}{2} \overset{?}{=} \dfrac{-3}{3} - 3$ gives $-4 = -4$ ✔

When using an equation to describe (model) a set of data, it is sometimes useful to let a variable represent the number of years past a given year. This is called **aligning the data.** Consider the following example.

EXAMPLE   2   **U.S. Hispanic Population | APPLICATION PREVIEW |**

Using data from 1980 and projected to 2050, the number of Hispanics in the U.S. civilian noninstitutional population is given by $y = 0.876x + 6.084$ millions, where x is the number of years after 1980 (*Source:* U.S. Census Bureau). According to this equaton, in what year will the Hispanic population equal 36.74 million?

Solution
To answer this question, we solve

$$36.74 = 0.876x + 6.084$$
$$30.656 = 0.876x$$
$$34.995 \approx x$$

Checking reveals that $36.74 \approx 0.876(34.995) + 6.084$. ✔
Thus the number of Hispanics in the United States is estimated to be approximately 36.74 million in 2015.

Fractional Equations   A **fractional equation** is an equation that contains a variable in a denominator. It is solved by first multiplying both sides of the equation by the least common denominator (LCD) of the fractions in the equation. Some fractional equations lead to linear equations. Note that the solution to any fractional equation *must* be checked in the original equation, because multiplying both sides of a fractional equation by a variable expression may result in an equation that is not equivalent to the original equation. If a solution to the fraction-free linear equation makes a denominator of the original equation equal to zero, that value cannot be a solution to the original equation. Some fractional equations have no solutions.

EXAMPLE   3   **Solving Fractional Equations**

Solve for x: (a) $\dfrac{3x}{2x + 10} = 1 + \dfrac{1}{x + 5}$ (b) $\dfrac{2x - 1}{x - 3} = 4 + \dfrac{5}{x - 3}$

Solution
(a) First multiply each term on both sides by the LCD, $2x + 10$. Then simplify and solve.

$$(2x + 10)\left(\frac{3x}{2x + 10}\right) = (2x + 10)(1) + (2x + 10)\left(\frac{1}{x + 5}\right)$$
$$3x = (2x + 10) + 2 \ \text{ gives } \ x = 12$$

Check: $\dfrac{3(12)}{2(12) + 10} \overset{?}{=} 1 + \dfrac{1}{12 + 5}$ gives $\dfrac{36}{34} = \dfrac{18}{17}$ ✔

(b) First multiply each term on both sides by the LCD, $x - 3$. Then simplify.

$$(x - 3)\left(\frac{2x - 1}{x - 3}\right) = (x - 3)(4) + (x - 3)\left(\frac{5}{x - 3}\right)$$
$$2x - 1 = (4x - 12) + 5 \ \text{ or } \ 2x - 1 = 4x - 7$$

Add $(-4x) + 1$ to both sides.
$$-2x = -6 \ \text{ gives } \ x = 3$$

The value $x = 3$ gives undefined expressions because the denominators equal 0 when $x = 3$. Hence the equation has no solution.

CHECKPOINT

1. Solve the following for x, and check.

(a) $4(x - 3) = 10x - 12$ (b) $\dfrac{5(x - 3)}{6} - x = 1 - \dfrac{x}{9}$

(c) $\dfrac{x}{3x - 6} = 2 - \dfrac{2x}{x - 2}$

Linear Equations with Two Variables

The steps used to solve linear equations in one variable can also be used to solve linear equations in more than one variable for one of the variables in terms of the other. Solving an equation such as the one in the following example is important when using a graphing utility.

EXAMPLE 4

Solving an Equation for One of Two Variables

Solve $4x + 3y = 12$ for y.

Solution

No fractions or parentheses are present, so we subtract $4x$ from both sides to get only the term that contains y on one side.

$$3y = -4x + 12$$

Dividing both sides by 3 gives the solution.

$$y = -\frac{4}{3}x + 4$$

Check: $4x + 3\left(\dfrac{-4}{3}x + 4\right) \overset{?}{=} 12$

$\qquad 4x + (-4x + 12) = 12$ ✔

CHECKPOINT

2. Solve for y: $y - 4 = -4(x + 2)$

EXAMPLE 5

Profit

Suppose that the relationship between a firm's profit P and the number x of items sold can be described by the equation

$$5x - 4P = 1200$$

(a) How many units must be produced and sold for the firm to make a profit of \$150?
(b) Solve this equation for P in terms of x.
(c) Find the profit when 240 units are sold.

Solution

(a) $5x - 4(150) = 1200$
$\qquad 5x - 600 = 1200$
$\qquad\qquad 5x = 1800$
$\qquad\qquad\ x = 360$ units

$\qquad$ Check: $5(360) - 4(150) = 1800 - 600 = 1200$ ✔

(b) $\qquad\quad 5x - 4P = 1200$
$\qquad\quad 5x - 1200 = 4P$
$\qquad P = \dfrac{5x}{4} - \dfrac{1200}{4} = \dfrac{5}{4}x - 300$

(c) $P = \dfrac{5}{4}x - 300$

$\qquad P = \dfrac{5}{4}(240) - 300 = 0$

Because $P = 0$ when $x = 240$, we know that profit is $0 when 240 units are sold, and we say that the firm **breaks even** when 240 units are sold.

Stated Problems   With an applied problem, it is frequently necessary to convert the problem from its stated form into one or more equations from which the problem's solution can be found. The following guidelines may be useful in solving stated problems.

Guidelines for Solving Stated Problems

1. Begin by reading the problem carefully to determine what you are to find. Use variables to represent the quantities to be found.
2. Reread the problem and use your variables to translate given information into algebraic expressions. Often, drawing a figure is helpful.
3. Use the algebraic expressions and the problem statement to formulate an equation (or equations).
4. Solve the equation(s).
5. Check the solution in the problem, not just in your equation or equations. The answer should satisfy the conditions.

EXAMPLE 6   ## Investment Mix

Jill Ball has $90,000 to invest. She has chosen one relatively safe investment fund that has an annual yield of 10% and another, riskier one that has a 15% annual yield. How much should she invest in each fund if she would like to earn $10,000 in one year from her investments?

Solution

We want to find the amount of each investment, so we begin as follows:

Let $x =$ the amount invested at 10%, then
$90,000 - x =$ the amount invested at 15% (becuse the two investments total $90,000)

If P is the amount of an investment and r is the annual rate of yield (expressed as a decimal), then the annual earnings $I = Pr$. Using this relationship, we can summarize the information about these two investments in a table.

	P	**r**	**I**
10% investment	x	0.10	0.10x
15% investment	90,000 − x	0.15	0.15(90,000 − x)
Total investment	90,000		10,000

The column under I shows that the sum of the earnings is

$$0.10x + 0.15(90,000 - x) = 10,000$$

We solve this as follows.

$$0.10x + 13,500 - 0.15x = 10,000$$
$$-0.05x = -3500 \quad \text{or} \quad x = 70,000$$

Thus the amount invested at 10% is $70,000, and the amount invested at 15% is $90,000 - 70,000 = 20,000$. To check, we return to the problem and note that 10% of $70,000 plus 15% of $20,000 gives a yield of $7000 + $3000 = $10,000. ✔

Linear Inequalities   An **inequality** is a statement that one quantity is greater than (or less than) another quantity. The inequality $3x - 2 > 2x + 1$ is a first-degree (linear) inequality that states that the left member is greater than the right member. Certain values of the variable will satisfy the inequality. These values form the solution set of the inequality. For example, $x = 4$ is in the solution set of $3x - 2 > 2x + 1$ because $3 \cdot 4 - 2 > 2 \cdot 4 + 1$. On the other hand, $x = 2$ is not in the solution set because $3 \cdot 2 - 2 \not> 2 \cdot 2 + 1$. *Solving* an inequality means finding its solution set, and two inequalities are *equivalent* if they have the same solution set. As with equations, we find the solutions to inequalities by finding equivalent inequalities from which the solutions can be easily seen. We use the following properties to reduce an inequality to a simple equivalent inequality.

Properties of Inequalities

Properties	Examples
Substitution Property	
The inequality formed by substituting one expression for an equal expression is equivalent to the original inequality.	$5x - 4x < 6$ $\qquad x < 6$ The solution set is $\{x: x < 6\}$.
Addition Property	
The inequality formed by adding the same quantity to both sides of an inequality is equivalent to original inequality.	$2x - 4 > x + 6$ $2x - 4 + 4 > x + 6 + 4$ $2x > x + 10$ $2x + (-x) > x + 10 + (-x)$ $x > 10$
Multiplication Property I	
The inequality formed by multiplying both sides of an inequality by the same *positive* quantity is equivalent to the original inequality.	$\dfrac{1}{2}x > 8$ $\qquad\qquad 3x < 6$ $\dfrac{1}{2}x(2) > 8(2)$ $\qquad 3x\left(\dfrac{1}{3}\right) < 6\left(\dfrac{1}{3}\right)$ $x > 16$ $\qquad\qquad x < 2$
Multiplication Property II	
The inequality formed by multiplying both sides of an inequality by the same *negative* number and reversing the direction of the inequality symbol is equivalent to the original inequality.	$-x < 6$ $\qquad\qquad -3x > -27$ $-x(-1) > 6(-1)$ $\quad -3x\left(-\dfrac{1}{3}\right) < -27\left(-\dfrac{1}{3}\right)$ $x > -6$ $\qquad\qquad x < 9$

For some inequalities, several operations are required to find their solution sets. In this case, the order in which the operations are performed is the same as that used in solving linear equations.

EXAMPLE 7   Solving an Inequality

Solve the inequality $2(x - 4) < \dfrac{x - 3}{3}$.

Solution

$$2(x - 4) < \frac{x - 3}{3}$$

$$6(x - 4) < x - 3 \qquad \text{Clear fractions.}$$

$$6x - 24 < x - 3 \qquad \text{Remove parentheses.}$$

$$5x < 21 \qquad\qquad \text{Perform additions and subtractions.}$$

$$x < \frac{21}{5} \qquad\qquad \text{Multiply by } \frac{1}{5}.$$

Check: If we want to check that this solution is a reasonable one, we can substitute the integer values around 21/5 into the original inequality. Note that $x = 4$ satisfies the inequality because

$$2[(4) - 4] < \frac{(4) - 3}{3}$$

but that $x = 5$ does not because

$$2[(5) - 4] \not< \frac{(5) - 3}{3}$$

Thus $x < 21/5$ is a reasonable solution. ✔

We may also solve inequalities of the form $a \leq b$. This means "a is less than b or a equals b."

EXAMPLE 8 ### Solving an Inequality

Solve the inequality $3x - 2 \leq 7$ and graph the solution.

Solution
This inequality states that $3x - 2 = 7$ or $3x - 2 < 7$. By solving in the usual manner, we get $3x \leq 9$, or $x \leq 3$. Then $x = 3$ is the solution to $3x - 2 = 7$ and $x < 3$ is the solution to $3x - 2 < 7$, so the solution set for $3x - 2 \leq 7$ is $\{x: x \leq 3\}$.
    The graph of the solution set includes the point $x = 3$ and all points $x < 3$ (see Figure 1.1).

Figure 1.1

CHECKPOINT   Solve the following inequalities for y.

3. $3y - 7 \leq 5 - y$ 4. $2y + 6 > 4y + 5$ 5. $4 - 3y \geq 4y + 5$

EXAMPLE 9 ### Normal Height for a Given Age

For boys between 4 and 16 years of age, height and age are linearly related. That relation can be expressed as

$$H = 2.31A + 31.26$$

where H is height in inches and A is age in years. To account for natural variation among individuals, normal is considered to be any measure falling within ±5% of the height obtained from the equation.* Write as an inequality the range of normal height for a boy who is 9 years old.

Solution
For a 9-year-old boy, the height from the formula is $H = 2.31(9) + 31.26 = 52.05$ inches. To be considered of normal height, H would have to be within ±5% of 52.05 inches. That is, the boy's height H is considered normal if $H \geq 52.05 - (0.05)(52.05)$ and $H \leq 52.05 + (0.05)(52.05)$. We can express this range of normal heights by the compound inequality

$$52.05 - (0.05)(52.05) \leq H \leq 52.05 + (0.05)(52.05)$$

or

$$49.45 \leq H \leq 54.65$$

*Adapted from data from the National Center for Health Statistics

©istockphoto.com/Martin McElligott

CHECKPOINT SOLUTIONS

1. (a) $4(x - 3) = 10x - 12$
$4x - 12 = 10x - 12$
$-6x = 0$
$x = 0$
Check: $4(0 - 3) \stackrel{?}{=} 10 \cdot 0 - 12$
$-12 = -12$ ✔

(b) $\dfrac{5(x - 3)}{6} - x = 1 - \dfrac{x}{9}$

LCD of 6 and 9 is 18.

$18\left(\dfrac{5x - 15}{6}\right) - 18(x) = 18(1) - 18\left(\dfrac{x}{9}\right)$
$3(5x - 15) - 18x = 18 - 2x$
$15x - 45 - 18x = 18 - 2x$
$-45 - 3x = 18 - 2x$
$-63 = x$

Check: $\dfrac{5(-63 - 3)}{6} - (-63) \stackrel{?}{=} 1 - \dfrac{(-63)}{9}$
$5(-11) + 63 \stackrel{?}{=} 1 + 7$
$8 = 8$ ✔

(c) $\dfrac{x}{3x - 6} = 2 - \dfrac{2x}{x - 2}$
LCD is $3x - 6$, or $3(x - 2)$.
$(3x - 6)\left(\dfrac{x}{3x - 6}\right) = (3x - 6)(2) - (3x - 6)\left(\dfrac{2x}{x - 2}\right)$
$x = 6x - 12 - 3(2x)$ or $x = 6x - 12 - 6x$
$x = -12$
Check: $\dfrac{-12}{3(-12) - 6} \stackrel{?}{=} 2 - \dfrac{2(-12)}{-12 - 2}$

$\dfrac{-12}{-42} \stackrel{?}{=} 2 - \dfrac{12}{7}$

$\dfrac{2}{7} = \dfrac{2}{7}$ ✔

2. $y - 4 = -4(x + 2)$
$y - 4 = -4x - 8$
$y = -4x - 4$

3. $3y - 7 \le 5 - y$
$4y - 7 \le 5$
$4y \le 12$

$y \le 3$

4. $2y + 6 > 4y + 5$
$6 > 2y + 5$
$1 > 2y$
$y < \dfrac{1}{2}$

5. $4 - 3y \ge 4y + 5$
$4 \ge 7y + 5$
$-1 \ge 7y$
$y \le -\dfrac{1}{7}$

| EXERCISES | 1.1

In Problems 1–14, solve each equation.

1. $4x - 7 = 8x + 2$

2. $3x + 22 = 7x + 2$

3. $x + 8 = 8(x + 1)$

4. $x + x + x = x$

5. $-\dfrac{3}{4}x = 24$

6. $-\dfrac{1}{6}x = 12$

7. $2(x - 7) = 5(x + 3) - x$

8. $3(x - 4) = 4 - 2(x + 2)$

9. $8 - 2(3x + 9) - 6x = 50$

10. $10x + 6 - 2(1 - 5x) = 9$

11. $\dfrac{5x}{2} - 4 = \dfrac{2x - 7}{6}$

12. $\dfrac{2x}{3} - 1 = \dfrac{x - 2}{2}$

13. $x + \dfrac{1}{3} = 2\left(x - \dfrac{2}{3}\right) - 6x$

14. $\dfrac{3x}{4} - \dfrac{1}{3} = 1 - \dfrac{2}{3}\left(x - \dfrac{1}{6}\right)$

The equations in Problems 15–20 lead to linear equations. Because not all solutions to the linear equations are solutions to the original equations, be sure to check the solutions in the original equations.

15. $\dfrac{33 - x}{5x} = 2$

16. $\dfrac{3x + 3}{x - 3} = 7$

17. $\dfrac{2x}{2x + 5} = \dfrac{2}{3} - \dfrac{5}{4x + 10}$

18. $\dfrac{3}{x} + \dfrac{1}{4} = \dfrac{2}{3} + \dfrac{1}{x}$

19. $\dfrac{2x}{x - 1} + \dfrac{1}{3} = \dfrac{5}{6} + \dfrac{2}{x - 1}$

20. $\dfrac{2x}{x - 3} = 4 + \dfrac{6}{x - 3}$

In Problems 21–24, use a calculator to solve each equation. Round your answer to three decimal places.

21. $3.259x - 8.638 = -3.8(8.625x + 4.917)$
22. $3.319(14.1x - 5) = 9.95 - 4.6x$
23. $0.000316x + 9.18 = 2.1(3.1 - 0.0029x) - 4.68$
24. $3.814x = 2.916(4.2 - 0.06x) + 5.3$

In Problems 25–28, solve for y in terms of x.

25. $3x - 4y = 15$
26. $3x - 5y = 25$
27. $9x + \dfrac{3}{2}y = 11$
28. $\dfrac{3x}{2} + 5y = \dfrac{1}{3}$
29. Solve $S = P + Prt$ for t.
30. Solve $\dfrac{y - b}{x - a} = m$ for y.

In Problems 31–36, solve each inequality.

31. $3(x - 1) < 2x - 1$
32. $2(x + 1) > x - 1$
33. $1 - 2x > 9$
34. $17 - x < -4$
35. $\dfrac{3(x - 1)}{2} \le x - 2$
36. $\dfrac{x - 1}{2} + 1 > x + 1$

In Problems 37–42, solve each inequality and graph the solution.

37. $2(x - 1) - 3 > 4x + 1$
38. $7x + 4 \le 2(x - 1)$
39. $\dfrac{-3x}{2} > 3 - x$
40. $\dfrac{-2x}{5} \le -10 - x$
41. $\dfrac{3x}{4} - \dfrac{1}{6} < x - \dfrac{2(x - 1)}{3}$
42. $\dfrac{4x}{3} - 3 > \dfrac{1}{2} + \dfrac{5x}{12}$

APPLICATIONS

43. **Depreciation** A \$648,000 property is depreciated for tax purposes by its owner with the straight-line depreciation method. The value of the building, y, after x months of use is given by $y = 648,000 - 1800x$ dollars. After how many months will the value of the building be \$387,000?

44. **Depreciation** When an \$810,000 building is depreciated for tax purposes (by the straight-line method), its value, y, after x months of use is given by $y = 810,000 - 2250x$. How many months will it be before the building is fully depreciated (that is, its value is \$0)? How many years is this?

45. **Credit card debt** High interest rates make it difficult for people to pay off credit card debt in a reasonable period of time. The interest I (in dollars) paid on a \$10,000 debt over 3 years when the interest rate is r% can be approximated by the equation

$$\dfrac{I}{175.393} + 0.663 = r$$

(*Source*: Consumer Federation of America). If the credit card interest rate is 19.8%, find the amount of interest paid during the 3 years.

46. **Seawater pressure** In seawater, the pressure p is related to the depth d according to

$$33p - 18d = 495$$

where d is in feet and p is in pounds per square inch.
(a) Solve this equation for p in terms of d.
(b) The *Titanic* was discovered at a depth of 12,460 ft. Find the pressure at this depth.

47. **Break-even** Burnem, Inc. manufactures blank CDs and sells them to a distributor in packs of 500 CDs. Burnem's total cost and total revenue (in dollars) for x packs of 500 CDs are given by

$$\text{Total cost} = 2x + 7920 \quad \text{and} \quad \text{Total revenue} = 20x$$

How many packs of 500 CDs must Burnem sell to break even?

48. **Break-even** Dish Systems manufactures satellite systems and has its monthly profit P in dollars related to the number of satellite systems, x, by

$$4P = 81x - 29,970$$

Find the number of systems that Dish Systems needs to produce and sell in order to break even.

49. **Profit** In its second year of operation, a local Internet provider's profits were \$170,500. If this amount was 576% of the company's first-year profits, find the first-year profits (to the nearest hundred dollars).

50. **Sales tax** The total price of a new car (including 6% sales tax) is \$21,041. How much of this is tax?

51. **Internet access** The percent P of the U.S. population with Internet access at home is given by

$$4P - 11t = 200.7$$

where t is the number of years past 2000 (*Source*: 2009 Digital Future Report, USC Annenberg).
(a) What percent of the U.S. population had Internet access in 2010?
(b) In what year will 90% have Internet access?

52. **Median household income** The U.S. median household income for blacks can be described by the equation

$$B = 1.931W - 40,908$$

where W is the U.S. median household income for whites (*Source*: U.S. Bureau of the Census). When black households have a median income of \$60,000, what is the predicted median household income for whites?

53. **Course grades** To earn an A in a course, a student must get at least a 90 average on four tests and a final exam, with the final exam weighted twice that of any one test. If the four test scores are 93, 69, 89, and 97, what is the lowest score the student can earn on the final exam and still get an A in the course?

54. **Course grades** Suppose a professor counts the final exam as being equal to each of the other tests in her course, and she will also change the lowest test score

to match the final exam score if the final exam score is higher. If a student's four test scores are 83, 67, 52, and 90, what is the lowest score the student can earn on the final exam and still obtain at least an 80 average for the course?

55. *Investment mix* A retired woman has $120,000 to invest. She has chosen one relatively safe investment fund that has an annual yield of 9% and another, riskier fund that has a 13% annual yield. How much should she invest in each fund if she would like to earn $12,000 per year from her investments?

56. *Investment yields* One safe investment pays 10% per year, and a riskier investment pays 18% per year. A woman who has $145,600 to invest would like to have an income of $20,000 per year from her investments. How much should she invest at each rate?

57. *Salary increases* A woman making $2000 per month has her salary reduced by 10% because of sluggish sales. One year later, after a dramatic improvement in sales, she is given a 20% raise over her reduced salary. Find her salary after the raise. What percent change is this from the $2000 per month?

58. *Wildlife management* In wildlife management, the capture-mark-recapture technique is used to estimate the populations of fish or birds in an area or to measure the infestation of insects such as Japanese beetles. Suppose 100 individuals of the species being studied are caught, marked, and released, and one week later 100 more are caught. To estimate the total number of individuals, the following relationship is used:

$$\frac{\text{Total marked found in 2nd capture}}{\text{Total in 2nd capture}} = \frac{\text{Total number marked}}{\text{Total population}}$$

(a) If in the second capture of 100, it is found that 3 are marked, what is the total population?

(b) Suppose that 1000 beetles are captured, marked, and released. Suppose further that in the second capture of 1000, it is found that 63 are marked. What is the population estimate?

59. *Profit* For a certain product, the revenue is given by $R = 40x$ and the cost is given by $C = 20x + 1600$. To obtain a profit, the revenue must be greater than the cost. For what values of x will there be a profit? Graph the solution.

60. *Car rental* Thrift rents a compact car for $33 per day, and General rents a similar car for $20 per day plus an initial fee of $78. For how many days would it be cheaper to rent from General? Graph the solution.

61. *Purchasing* Sean can spend at most $900 for a camera and some memory sticks. He plans to buy the camera for $695 and sticks for $5.75 each. Write an inequality that could be used to find the number of sticks (x) that he could buy. How many sticks could he buy?

62. *Taxes* In Sweetwater, Arizona, water bills are taxed on the basis of the amount of the monthly bill in order to encourage conservation. If the bill is more than $0 but less than $60, the tax is 2% of the bill; if the bill is $60 or more but less than $80, the tax is 4% of the bill; and if the bill is $80 or more, the tax is 6% of the bill. Write the inequalities that represent the amounts of tax owed in these three cases.

63. *Wireless service spending* The total amount spent in the United States for wireless communication services, S (in billions of dollars), can be modeled (that is, approximated with some accuracy) by

$$S = 6.205 + 11.23t$$

where t is the number of years past 1995 (*Source:* Cellular Telecommunications and Internet Association).

(a) What value of t represents the year 2012?

(b) What values of t give $S > 250$?

(c) In what year does this equation project that spending for wireless communication services will exceed $250 billion?

64. *Cigarette use* With data from 1965 to 2009, the percent p of adults who smoke cigarettes can be modeled by the equation

$$p = 43.3 - 0.504t$$

where t is the number of years past 1960 (*Source:* Centers for Disease Control and Prevention).

(a) What value of t represents 2015?

(b) What percent does this equation predict for 2015?

(c) This equation ceases to be effective when p becomes negative and perhaps before that. Find the years when $p < 0$.

65. *Heat index* During a recent summer, Dallas, Texas, endured 29 consecutive days on which the temperature was at least 110°F. On many of those days, the combination of heat and humidity made it feel even hotter than it was. When the temperature is 100°F, the apparent temperature A (or heat index) depends on the humidity h (expressed as a decimal) according to

$$A = 90.2 + 41.3h^{\star}$$

(a) For what humidity levels is the apparent temperature at least 110°F? (Note that this answer will be a closed interval. Why?)

(b) For what humidity levels is the apparent temperature less than 100°F?

---

*Source: Bosch, W., and C. G. Cobb, "Temperature-Humidity Indices," UMAP Unit 691, *The UMAP Journal*, 10(3), Fall 1989, 237–256.

66. *Wind chill* The combination of cold temperatures and wind speed determine what is called wind chill. The wind chill is a temperature that is the still-air equivalent of the combination of cold and wind. When the wind speed is 25 mph, the wind chill *WC* depends on the temperature *t* (in degrees Fahrenheit) according to

$$WC = 1.337t - 24.094$$

For what temperatures does it feel at least 30°F colder than the air temperature? That is, find *t* such that $WC \leq t - 30$.

"I swear it wasn't this cold before they invented the wind chill factor."

OBJECTIVES   **1.2**

- To determine whether a relation is a function
- To state the domains and ranges of certain functions
- To use function notation
- To perform operations with functions
- To find the composite of two functions

Functions

▌| APPLICATION PREVIEW |▐

The number of individual income tax returns filed electronically has increased in recent years. The relationship between the number of returns filed electronically and the number of years after 1995 can be described by the equation

$$y = 5.091x + 11.545$$

where *y* is in millions and *x* is the number of years past 1995 (*Source*: Internal Revenue Service). In this equation, *y* depends uniquely on *x*, so we say that *y* is a function of *x*. Understanding the mathematical meaning of the phrase *function of* and learning to interpret and apply such relationships are the goals of this section. (The function here will be discussed in Example 4.)

Relations and Functions   A **relation** is defined by a set of **ordered pairs** of real numbers. These ordered pairs may be determined from a table, a graph, an equation, or an inequality. For example, the solutions to the equation $y = 4x - 3$ are pairs of numbers (one for *x* and one for *y*), so $y = 4x - 3$ expresses a relation between *x* and *y*. We write the ordered pairs in this relation in the form (x, y) so that the first number is the *x*-value and the second is the *y*-value. Because we cannot list all of the ordered pairs that define this relation, we use the equation to give its definition. Similarly, the inequality $R \leq 5x$ expresses a relation between the two variables *x* and *R*.

Relation   A **relation** is defined by a set of ordered pairs or by a rule that determines how the ordered pairs are found. The relation may also be defined by a table, a graph, an equation, or an inequality.

For example, the set of ordered pairs

$$\{(1, 3), (1, 6), (2, 6), (3, 9), (3, 12), (4, 12)\}$$

expresses a relation between the set of first components, $\{1, 2, 3, 4\}$, and the set of second components, $\{3, 6, 9, 12\}$. The set of first components is called the **domain** of the relation, and the set of second components is called the **range** of the relation. Figure 1.2(a) uses arrows to indicate how the inputs from the domain (the first components) are associated with the outputs in the range (the second components). Figure 1.2(b) shows another example of a relation. Because relations can also be defined by tables and graphs, Table 1.1 and Figure 1.3 are examples of relations.

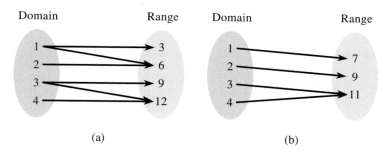

Figure 1.2   (a)   (b)

An equation frequently expresses how the second component (the output) is obtained from the first component (the input). For example, the equation

$$y = 4x - 3$$

expresses how the output y results from the input x. This equation expresses a special relation between x and y, because each value of x that is substituted into the equation results in exactly one value of y. If each value of x put into an equation results in one value of y, we say that the equation expresses y as a **function** of x.

Definition of a Function

A **function** is a relation between two sets such that to each element of the domain (input) there corresponds exactly one element of the range (output). A function may be defined by a set of ordered pairs, a table, a graph, or an equation.

When a function is defined, the variable that represents the numbers in the domain (input) is called the **independent variable** of the function, and the variable that represents the numbers in the range (output) is called the **dependent variable** (because its values depend on the values of the independent variable). The equation $y = 4x - 3$ defines y as a function of x, because only one value of y will result from each value of x that is substituted into the equation. Thus the equation defines a function in which x is the independent variable and y is the dependent variable.

■| TABLE 1.1 |■

Federal Income Tax

Income	Rate
$0–$8375	10%
$8376–$34,000	15%
$34,001–$82,400	25%
$82,401–$171,850	28%
$171,851–$373,650	33%
Over $373,650	35%

Source: Internal Revenue Service

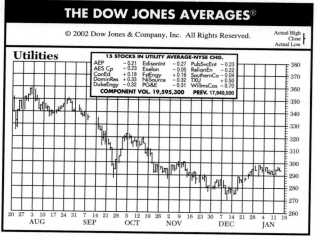

Figure 1.3

Source: Reprinted with permission of *The Wall Street Journal*, Copyright © 2002 Dow Jones & Company, Inc. All Rights Reserved Worldwide.

We can also apply this idea to a relation defined by a table or a graph. In Figure 1.2(b), because each input in the domain corresponds to exactly one output in the range, the relation is a function. Similarly, the data given in Table 1.1 (the tax brackets for U.S. income tax for single wage earners) represents the tax rate as a function of the income. Note in Table 1.1 that even though many different amounts of taxable income have the same tax rate, each amount of taxable income (input) corresponds to exactly one tax rate (output). On the other hand, the relation defined in Figure 1.3 is not a function because the graph representing the Dow Jones Utilities Average shows that for each day there are at least three different values—the actual high, the actual low, and the close. This particular figure also has historical interest because it shows a break in the graph when the New York Stock Exchange closed following the terrorist attacks of 9/11/2001.

EXAMPLE **1**   **Functions**

Does $y^2 = 2x$ express y as a function of x?

Solution

No, because some values of x are associated with more than one value of y. In fact, there are two y-values for each $x > 0$. For example, if $x = 8$, then $y = 4$ or $y = -4$, two different y-values for the same x-value. The equation $y^2 = 2x$ expresses a relation between x and y, but y is not a function of x.

Graphs of Functions   It is possible to picture geometrically the relations and functions that we have been discussing by sketching their graphs on a rectangular coordinate system. We construct a rectangular coordinate system by drawing two real number lines (called **coordinate axes**) that are perpendicular to each other and intersect at their origins (called the **origin** of the system).

The ordered pair (a, b) represents the point P that is located a units along the x-axis and b units along the y-axis (see Figure 1.4). Similarly, any point has a unique ordered pair that describes it.

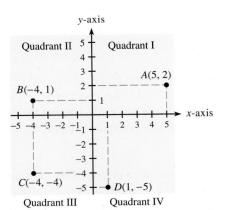

Figure 1.4

The values a and b in the ordered pair associated with the point P are called the **rectangular** (or **Cartesian**) **coordinates** of the point, where a is the **x-coordinate** (or **abscissa**), and b is the **y-coordinate** (or **ordinate**). The ordered pairs (a, b) and (c, d) are equal if and only if $a = c$ and $b = d$.

The **graph** of an equation that defines a function (or relation) is the picture that results when we plot the points whose coordinates (x, y) satisfy the equation. To sketch the graph, we plot enough points to suggest the shape of the graph and draw a smooth curve through the points. This is called the **point-plotting method** of sketching a graph.

EXAMPLE 2 Graphing a Function

Graph the function $y = 4x^2$.

Solution

We choose some sample values of x and find the corresponding values of y. Placing these in a table, we have sample points to plot. When we have enough to determine the shape of the graph, we connect the points to complete the graph. The table and graph are shown in Figure 1.5(a).

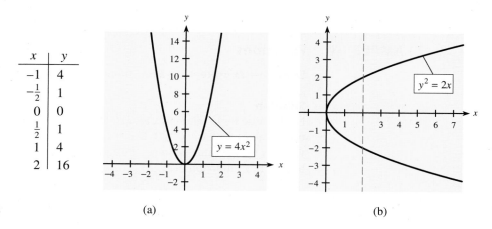

x	y
-1	4
$-\frac{1}{2}$	1
0	0
$\frac{1}{2}$	1
1	4
2	16

Figure 1.5   (a)   (b)

We can determine whether a relation is a function by inspecting its graph. If the relation is a function, then no one input (x-value) has two different outputs (y-values). This means that no two points on the graph will have the same first coordinate (component). Thus no two points of the graph will lie on the same vertical line.

Vertical-Line Test If no vertical line exists that intersects the graph at more than one point, then the graph is that of a function.

Performing this test on the graph of $y = 4x^2$ (Figure 1.5(a)), we easily see that this equation describes a function. The graph of $y^2 = 2x$ is shown in Figure 1.5(b), and we can see that the vertical-line test indicates that this is not a function (as we already saw in Example 1). For example, a vertical line at $x = 2$ intersects the curve at $(2, 2)$ and $(2, -2)$.

Function Notation We can use function notation to indicate that y is a function of x. The function is denoted by f, and we write $y = f(x)$. This is read "y is a function of x" or "y equals f of x." For specific values of x, $f(x)$ represents the values of the function (that is, outputs, or y-values) at those x-values. Thus if

$$f(x) = 3x^2 + 2x + 1$$

then

$$f(2) = 3(2)^2 + 2(2) + 1 = 17$$

and

$$f(-3) = 3(-3)^2 + 2(-3) + 1 = 22$$

Figure 1.6 shows the function notation $f(x)$ as (a) an operator on x and (b) a y-coordinate for a given x-value.

Figure 1.6

(a) (b)

Letters other than f may also be used to denote functions. For example, $y = g(x)$ or $y = h(x)$ may be used.

EXAMPLE 3 Evaluating Functions

If $y = f(x) = 2x^3 - 3x^2 + 1$, find the following.
(a) $f(3)$ (b) $f(-1)$ (c) $f(-a)$

Solution
(a) $f(3) = 2(3)^3 - 3(3)^2 + 1 = 2(27) - 3(9) + 1 = 28$
   Thus $y = 28$ when $x = 3$.
(b) $f(-1) = 2(-1)^3 - 3(-1)^2 + 1 = 2(-1) - 3(1) + 1 = -4$
   Thus $y = -4$ when $x = -1$.
(c) $f(-a) = 2(-a)^3 - 3(-a)^2 + 1 = -2a^3 - 3a^2 + 1$

When a function fits a set of data exactly or approximately, we say that the function **models** the data. The model includes descriptions of all involved variables.

EXAMPLE 4 Electronic Income Tax Returns | APPLICATION PREVIEW |

The relationship between the number y of individual income tax returns filed electronically and the number of years after 1995 can be modeled by the function

$$y = f(x) = 5.091x + 11.545$$

where y is in millions and x is the number of years after 1995 (*Source:* Internal Revenue Service).

(a) Find $f(8)$.
(b) Write a sentence that explains the meaning of the result in part (a).

Solution
(a) $f(8) = 5.091(8) + 11.545 = 52.273$
(b) The statement $f(8) = 52.273$ means that in $1995 + 8 = 2003$, 52.273 million income tax returns were filed electronically.

EXAMPLE 5 Mortgage Payment

■ | TABLE 1.2 | ■

r(%)	f(r)
2.6	12
5.2	15
6.3	17
7.4	20
9	30

Table 1.2 shows the number of years that it will take a couple to pay off a $100,000 mortgage at several different interest rates if they pay $800 per month. If r denotes the rate and $f(r)$ denotes the number of years:

(a) What is $f(6.3)$ and what does it mean?
(b) If $f(r) = 30$, what is r?
(c) Does $2 \cdot f(2.6) = f(2 \cdot 2.6)$?

Solution

(a) $f(6.3) = 17$. This means that with a 6.3% interest rate, a couple can pay off the $100,000 mortgage in 17 years by paying $800 per month.

(b) The table indicates that $f(9) = 30$, so $r = 9$.

(c) $2 \cdot f(2.6) = 2 \cdot 12 = 24$ and $f(2 \cdot 2.6) = f(5.2) = 15$, so $2 \cdot f(2.6) \neq f(2 \cdot 2.6)$.   ◼

EXAMPLE 6   **Function Notation**

Given $f(x) = x^2 - 3x + 8$, find $\dfrac{f(x + h) - f(x)}{h}$ and simplify (if $h \neq 0$).

Solution

We find $f(x + h)$ by replacing each x in $f(x)$ with the expression $x + h$.

$$\frac{f(x + h) - f(x)}{h} = \frac{[(x + h)^2 - 3(x + h) + 8] - [x^2 - 3x + 8]}{h}$$

$$= \frac{[(x^2 + 2xh + h^2) - 3x - 3h + 8] - x^2 + 3x - 8}{h}$$

$$= \frac{x^2 + 2xh + h^2 - 3x - 3h + 8 - x^2 + 3x - 8}{h}$$

$$= \frac{2xh + h^2 - 3h}{h} = \frac{h(2x + h - 3)}{h} = 2x + h - 3$$ ◼

Domains and Ranges   We will limit our discussion in this text to **real functions,** which are functions whose domains and ranges contain only real numbers. If the domain and range of a function are not specified, it is assumed that the domain consists of all real inputs (x-values) that result in real outputs (y-values), making the range a subset of the real numbers.

For the types of functions we are now studying, if the domain is unspecified, it will include all real numbers except

1. values that result in a denominator of 0, and
2. values that result in an even root of a negative number.

EXAMPLE 7   **Domain and Range**

Find the domain of each of the following functions; find the range for the functions in parts (a) and (b).

(a) $y = 4x^2$ (b) $y = \sqrt{4 - x}$ (c) $y = 1 + \dfrac{1}{x - 2}$

Solution

(a) There are no restrictions on the numbers substituted for x, so the domain consists of all real numbers. Because the square of any real number is nonnegative, $4x^2$ must be nonnegative. Thus the range is $y \geq 0$. The graph shown in Figure 1.7(a) illustrates our conclusions about the domain and range.

(b) We note the restriction that $4 - x$ cannot be negative. Thus the domain consists of only numbers less than or equal to 4. That is, the domain is the set of real numbers satisfying $x \leq 4$. Because $\sqrt{4 - x}$ is always nonnegative, the range is all $y \geq 0$. Figure 1.7(b) shows the graph of $y = \sqrt{4 - x}$. Note that the graph is located only where $x \leq 4$ and on or above the x-axis (where $y \geq 0$).

(c) $y = 1 + \dfrac{1}{x - 2}$ is undefined at $x = 2$ because $\dfrac{1}{0}$ is undefined. Hence, the domain consists of all real numbers except 2. Figure 1.7(c) shows the graph of $y = 1 + \dfrac{1}{x - 2}$.

The break where $x = 2$ indicates that $x = 2$ is not part of the domain.   ◼

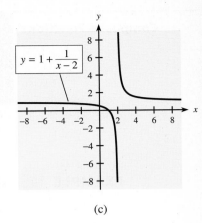

(a)   (b)   (c)

Figure 1.7

CHECKPOINT

1. If $y = f(x)$, the independent variable is _____ and the dependent variable is _____.
2. If $(1, 3)$ is on the graph of $y = f(x)$, then $f(1) = ?$
3. If $f(x) = 1 - x^3$, find $f(-2)$.
4. If $f(x) = 2x^2$, find $f(x + h)$.
5. If $f(x) = \dfrac{1}{x + 1}$, what is the domain of $f(x)$?

Operations with Functions

We can form new functions by performing algebraic operations with two or more functions. We define new functions that are the sum, difference, product, and quotient of two functions as follows.

Operations with Functions

Let f and g be functions of x, and define the following.

Sum $(f + g)(x) = f(x) + g(x)$
Difference $(f - g)(x) = f(x) - g(x)$
Product $(f \cdot g)(x) = f(x) \cdot g(x)$

Quotient $\left(\dfrac{f}{g}\right)(x) = \dfrac{f(x)}{g(x)}$ if $g(x) \neq 0$

EXAMPLE   8   Operations with Functions

If $f(x) = 3x + 2$ and $g(x) = x^2 - 3$, find the following functions.

(a) $(f + g)(x)$ (b) $(f - g)(x)$ (c) $(f \cdot g)(x)$ (d) $\left(\dfrac{f}{g}\right)(x)$

Solution

(a) $(f + g)(x) = f(x) + g(x) = (3x + 2) + (x^2 - 3) = x^2 + 3x - 1$
(b) $(f - g)(x) = f(x) - g(x) = (3x + 2) - (x^2 - 3) = -x^2 + 3x + 5$
(c) $(f \cdot g)(x) = f(x) \cdot g(x) = (3x + 2)(x^2 - 3) = 3x^3 + 2x^2 - 9x - 6$
(d) $\left(\dfrac{f}{g}\right)(x) = \dfrac{f(x)}{g(x)} = \dfrac{3x + 2}{x^2 - 3}$, if $x^2 - 3 \neq 0$

We now consider a new way to combine two functions. Just as we can substitute a number for the independent variable in a function, we can substitute a second function for the variable. This creates a new function called a **composite function.**

Composite Functions	Let f and g be functions. Then the **composite functions** g of f (denoted $g \circ f$) and f of g (denoted $f \circ g$) are defined as follows: $$(g \circ f)(x) = g(f(x))$$ $$(f \circ g)(x) = f(g(x))$$

Note that the domain of $g \circ f$ is the subset of the domain of f for which $g \circ f$ is defined. Similarly, the domain of $f \circ g$ is the subset of the domain of g for which $f \circ g$ is defined.

EXAMPLE 9   Composite Functions

If $f(x) = 2x^3 + 1$ and $g(x) = x^2$, find the following.
(a) $(g \circ f)(x)$ (b) $(f \circ g)(x)$

Solution

(a) $(g \circ f)(x) = g(f(x))$
$= g(2x^3 + 1)$
$= (2x^3 + 1)^2 = 4x^6 + 4x^3 + 1$

(b) $(f \circ g)(x) = f(g(x))$
$= f(x^2)$
$= 2(x^2)^3 + 1$
$= 2x^6 + 1$

Figure 1.8 illustrates both composite functions found in Example 9.

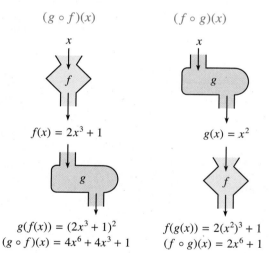

$(g \circ f)(x)$

x

f

$f(x) = 2x^3 + 1$

g

$g(f(x)) = (2x^3 + 1)^2$
$(g \circ f)(x) = 4x^6 + 4x^3 + 1$

$(f \circ g)(x)$

x

g

$g(x) = x^2$

f

$f(g(x)) = 2(x^2)^3 + 1$
$(f \circ g)(x) = 2x^6 + 1$

Figure 1.8

CHECKPOINT

6. If $f(x) = 1 - 2x$ and $g(x) = 3x^2$, find the following.
   (a) $(g - f)(x)$ (b) $(f \cdot g)(x)$ (c) $(f \circ g)(x)$ (d) $(g \circ f)(x)$
   (e) $(f \circ f)(x) = f(f(x))$

CHECKPOINT SOLUTIONS

1. Independent variable is x; dependent variable is y.
2. $f(1) = 3$
3. $f(-2) = 1 - (-2)^3 = 1 - (-8) = 9$
4. $f(x + h) = 2(x + h)^2$
   $= 2(x^2 + 2xh + h^2)$
5. The domain is all real numbers except $x = -1$, because $f(x)$ is undefined when $x = -1$.
6. (a) $(g - f)(x) = g(x) - f(x) = 3x^2 - (1 - 2x) = 3x^2 + 2x - 1$
   (b) $(f \cdot g)(x) = f(x) \cdot g(x) = (1 - 2x)(3x^2) = 3x^2 - 6x^3$
   (c) $(f \circ g)(x) = f(g(x)) = f(3x^2) = 1 - 2(3x^2) = 1 - 6x^2$
   (d) $(g \circ f)(x) = g(f(x)) = g(1 - 2x) = 3(1 - 2x)^2$
   (e) $(f \circ f)(x) = f(f(x)) = f(1 - 2x) = 1 - 2(1 - 2x) = 4x - 1$

| EXERCISES | 1.2

In Problems 1 and 2, use the values in the following table.

x	-7	-1	0	3	4.2	9	11	14	18	22
y	0	0	1	5	9	11	35	22	22	60

1. (a) Explain why the table defines y as a function of x.
   (b) State the domain and range of this function.
   (c) If the table expresses $y = f(x)$, find $f(0)$ and $f(11)$.
2. (a) If the function defined by the table is denoted by f, so that $y = f(x)$, is $f(9)$ an input or an output of f?
   (b) Does the table describe x as a function of y? Explain.

In Problems 3 and 4, are the relations defined by the tables functions? Explain why or why not and give the domain and range.

3.

x	1	2	3	8	9
y	-4	-4	5	16	5

4.

x	-1	0	1	3	1
y	0	2	4	6	9

5. Do either of the graphs in Figure 1.9 represent y as a function of x? Explain your choices.

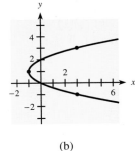

(a)   (b)

Figure 1.9

6. Do either of the graphs in Figure 1.10 represent y as a function of x? Explain your choices.

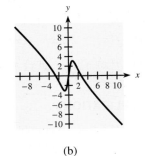

(a)   (b)

Figure 1.10

7. If $y = 3x^3$, is y a function of x?
8. If $y = 6x^2$, is y a function of x?
9. If $y^2 = 3x$, is y a function of x?
10. If $y^2 = 10x^2$, is y a function of x?
11. If $R(x) = 8x - 10$, find the following.
    (a) $R(0)$ (b) $R(2)$ (c) $R(-3)$ (d) $R(1.6)$
12. If $f(x) = 17 - 6x$, find the following.
    (a) $f(-3)$ (b) $f(1)$ (c) $f(10)$ (d) $f(\frac{2}{3})$
13. If $C(x) = 4x^2 - 3$, find the following.
    (a) $C(0)$ (b) $C(-1)$ (c) $C(-2)$ (d) $C(-\frac{3}{2})$
14. If $h(x) = 3x^2 - 2x$, find the following.
    (a) $h(3)$ (b) $h(-3)$ (c) $h(2)$ (d) $h(\frac{1}{6})$
15. If $h(x) = x - 2(4 - x)^3$, find the following.
    (a) $h(-1)$ (b) $h(0)$ (c) $h(6)$ (d) $h(2.5)$
16. If $R(x) = 100x - x^3$, find the following.
    (a) $R(1)$ (b) $R(10)$ (c) $R(2)$ (d) $R(-10)$
17. If $f(x) = x^3 - 4/x$, find the following.
    (a) $f(-\frac{1}{2})$ (b) $f(2)$ (c) $f(-2)$
18. If $C(x) = (x^2 - 1)/x$, find the following.
    (a) $C(1)$ (b) $C(\frac{1}{2})$ (c) $C(-2)$
19. Let $f(x) = 1 + x + x^2$ and $h \neq 0$.
    (a) Is $f(2 + 1) = f(2) + f(1)$?
    (b) Find $f(x + h)$.
    (c) Does $f(x + h) = f(x) + f(h)$?
    (d) Does $f(x + h) = f(x) + h$?
    (e) Find $\dfrac{f(x + h) - f(x)}{h}$ and simplify.
20. Let $f(x) = 3x^2 - 6x$ and $h \neq 0$.
    (a) Is $f(3 + 2) = f(3) + 2$?
    (b) Find $f(x + h)$.
    (c) Does $f(x + h) = f(x) + h$?
    (d) Does $f(x + h) = f(x) + f(h)$?
    (e) Find $\dfrac{f(x + h) - f(x)}{h}$ and simplify.
21. If $f(x) = x - 2x^2$ and $h \neq 0$, find the following and simplify.
    (a) $f(x + h)$ (b) $\dfrac{f(x + h) - f(x)}{h}$
22. If $f(x) = 2x^2 - x + 3$ and $h \neq 0$, find the following and simplify.
    (a) $f(x + h)$ (b) $\dfrac{f(x + h) - f(x)}{h}$
23. If $y = f(x)$ in Figure 1.9(a), find the following.
    (a) $f(9)$ (b) $f(5)$
24. Suppose $y = g(x)$ in Figure 1.10(b).
    (a) Find $g(0)$.
    (b) How many x-values in the domain of this function satisfy $g(x) = 0$?

25. The graph of $y = x^2 - 4x$ is shown in Figure 1.11.

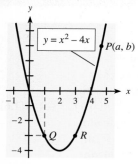

Figure 1.11

(a) What are the coordinates of the point Q? Do they satisfy the equation?
(b) What are the coordinates of R? Do they satisfy the equation?
(c) If the coordinates of the point P on the graph are (a, b), how are a and b related?
(d) What are the x-values of the points on the graph whose y-coordinates are 0? Are these x-values solutions to the equation $x^2 - 4x = 0$?

26. The graph of $y = 2x^2$ is shown in Figure 1.12.

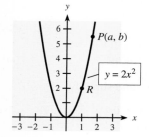

Figure 1.12

(a) Does the point $(1, 1)$ lie on the graph? Do the coordinates satisfy the equation?
(b) What are the coordinates of point R? Do they satisfy the equation?
(c) If the point P, with coordinates (a, b), is on the graph, how are a and b related?
(d) What is the x-value of the point whose y-coordinate is 0? Does this value of x satisfy the equation $0 = 2x^2$?

State the domain and range of each of the functions in Problems 27–30.
27. $y = x^2 + 4$
28. $y = x^2 - 1$
29. $y = \sqrt{x + 4}$
30. $y = \sqrt{x^2 + 1}$

In Problems 31–34, a function and its graph are given. In each problem, find the domain.

31. $f(x) = \dfrac{\sqrt{x - 1}}{x - 2}$

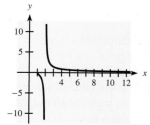

32. $f(x) = \dfrac{x + 1}{\sqrt{x + 3}}$

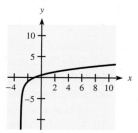

33. $f(x) = 4 + \sqrt{49 - x^2}$

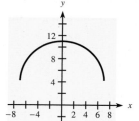

34. $f(x) = -2 - \sqrt{9 - x^2}$

For $f(x)$ and $g(x)$ given in Problems 35–38, find
    (a) $(f + g)(x)$
    (b) $(f - g)(x)$
    (c) $(f \cdot g)(x)$
    (d) $(f/g)(x)$
35. $f(x) = 3x \quad g(x) = x^3$
36. $f(x) = \sqrt{x} \quad g(x) = 1/x$
37. $f(x) = \sqrt{2x} \quad g(x) = x^2$
38. $f(x) = (x - 1)^2 \quad g(x) = 1 - 2x$

For $f(x)$ and $g(x)$ given in Problems 39–42, find
    (a) $(f \circ g)(x)$
    (b) $(g \circ f)(x)$
    (c) $f(f(x))$
    (d) $f^2(x) = (f \cdot f)(x)$
39. $f(x) = (x - 1)^3 \quad g(x) = 1 - 2x$
40. $f(x) = 3x \quad g(x) = x^3 - 1$
41. $f(x) = 2\sqrt{x} \quad g(x) = x^4 + 5$
42. $f(x) = \dfrac{1}{x^3} \quad g(x) = 4x + 1$

APPLICATIONS

43. *Mortgage* A couple seeking to buy a home decides that a monthly payment of $800 fits their budget. Their bank's interest rate is 7.5%. The amount they can borrow, A, is a function of the time t, in years, it will take to repay the

debt. If we denote this function by $A = f(t)$, then the following table defines the function.

t	A	t	A
5	40,000	20	103,000
10	69,000	25	113,000
15	89,000	30	120,000

Source: Comprehensive Mortgage Payment Tables,
Publication No. 492, Financial Publishing Co., Boston

(a) Find $f(20)$ and write a sentence that explains its meaning.
(b) Does $f(5 + 5) = f(5) + f(5)$? Explain.
(c) If the couple is looking at a house that requires them to finance $89,000, how long must they make payments? Write this correspondence in the form $A = f(t)$.

44. ***Debt refinancing*** When a debt is refinanced, sometimes the term of the loan (that is, the time it takes to repay the debt) is shortened. Suppose the current interest rate is 7%, and a couple's current debt is $100,000. The monthly payment R of the refinanced debt is a function of the term of the loan, t, in years. If we represent this function by $R = f(t)$, then the following table defines the function.

t	R	t	R
5	1980.12	15	898.83
10	1161.09	20	775.30
12	1028.39	25	706.78

Source: Comprehensive Mortgage Payment Tables,
Publication No. 492, Financial Publishing Co., Boston

(a) If they refinance for 20 years, what is the monthly payment? Write this correspondence in the form $R = f(t)$.
(b) Find $f(10)$ and write a sentence that explains its meaning.
(c) Is $f(5 + 5) = f(5) + f(5)$? Explain.

45. ***Social Security benefits funding*** Social Security benefits paid to eligible beneficiaries are funded by individuals who are currently employed. The following graph, based on known data until 2005, with projections into the future, defines a function that gives the number of workers, n, supporting each retiree as a function of time t (given by calendar year). Let us denote this function by $n = f(t)$.

(a) Find $f(1950)$ and explain its meaning.
(b) Find $f(1990)$.
(c) If, after the year 2050, actual data through 2050 regarding workers per Social Security beneficiary were graphed, what parts of the new graph *must* be the same as this graph and what parts *might* be the same? Explain.

(d) Find the domain and range of $n = f(t)$ if the function is defined by the graph.

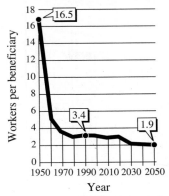

Source: Social Security Administration

46. ***Dow Jones Industrial Average*** The graph shows the Dow Jones Industrial Average on a particularly tumultuous day soon after the U.S. credit rating was downgraded from AAA to AA+ in August of 2011. If t represents the number of hours after 9:30 A.M., then the graph defines the Dow Jones Industrial Average D as a function of time t. If we represent this function by $D = f(t)$, use the graph to complete the following.

(a) Find $f(0)$ and $f(6.5)$.
(b) Find the domain and range for $D = f(t)$ as defined by the graph.
(c) About how many t-values satisfy $f(t) = 11,000$? Estimate one such t-value.

Dow Jones Industrial Average

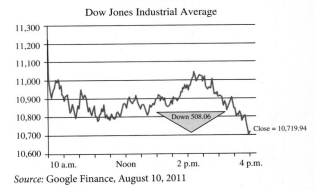

Source: Google Finance, August 10, 2011

47. ***Imprisonment and parole*** The figure on the next page shows the number of persons in state prisons at year's end and the number of parolees at year's end, both as functions of the years past 1900. If $y = f(t)$ gives the number of prisoners and $y = g(t)$ gives the number of parolees, use the figure to complete the following.

(a) Estimate $f(105)$ and $g(105)$.
(b) Find $f(107)$ and explain its meaning.
(c) Find $g(92)$ and explain its meaning.
(d) Find $(f - g)(107)$ and explain its meaning.
(e) Which of $(f - g)(95)$ and $(f - g)(105)$ is greater? Explain.

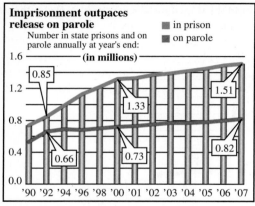

Imprisonment outpaces release on parole

Number in state prisons and on parole annually at year's end:

■ in prison
■ on parole

(in millions)

Source: U.S. Department of Justice

48. **Women in the work force** The number (in millions) of women in the work force, given as a function *f* of the year for selected years from 1920 and projected to 2016, is shown in the figure.
  (a) How many women were in the labor force in 1970?
  (b) Estimate $f(1930)$ and write a sentence that explains its meaning.
  (c) Estimate $f(2005) - f(1990)$ and explain its meaning.

Source: U.S. Bureau of Labor Statistics

49. **Wind chill** Dr. Paul Siple conducted studies testing the effect of wind on the formation of ice at various temperatures and developed the concept of the wind chill, which we hear reported during winter weather reports. Using Siple's original work, if the air temperature is $-5°F$, then the wind chill, *WC*, is a function of the wind speed, *s* (in mph), and is given by

$$WC = f(s) = 45.694 + 1.75s - 29.26\sqrt{s}$$

  (a) Based on the formula for $f(s)$ and the physical context of the problem, what is the domain of $f(s)$?
  (b) Find $f(10)$ and write a sentence that explains its meaning.
  (c) The working domain of this wind chill function is actually $s \geq 4$. How can you tell that $s = 0$ is not in the working domain, even though it is in the mathematical domain?

50. **Temperature measurement** The equation

$$C = \frac{5}{9}F - \frac{160}{9}$$

gives the relation between temperature readings in Celsius and Fahrenheit.
  (a) Is *C* a function of *F*?
  (b) What is the domain?
  (c) If we consider this equation as relating temperatures of water in its liquid state, what are the domain and range?
  (d) What is *C* when $F = 40°$?

51. **Cost** The total cost of producing a product is given by

$$C(x) = 300x + 0.1x^2 + 1200$$

where *x* represents the number of units produced. Give
  (a) the total cost of producing 10 units
  (b) the value of $C(100)$
  (c) the meaning of $C(100)$.

52. **Profit** The profit from the production and sale of a product is $P(x) = 47x - 0.01x^2 - 8000$, where *x* represents the number of units produced and sold. Give
  (a) the profit from the production and sale of 2000 units
  (b) the value of $P(5000)$
  (c) the meaning of $P(5000)$.

53. **Pollution** Suppose that the cost *C* (in dollars) of removing *p* percent of the particulate pollution from the smokestacks of an industrial plant is given by

$$C(p) = \frac{7300p}{100 - p}$$

  (a) Find the domain of this function. Recall that *p* represents the percent pollution that is removed.
  In parts (b)–(e), find the functional values and explain what each means.
  (b) $C(45)$ (c) $C(90)$
  (d) $C(99)$ (e) $C(99.6)$

54. **Test reliability** If a test that has reliability *r* is lengthened by a factor *n* ($n \geq 1$), the reliability *R* of the new test is given by

$$R(n) = \frac{nr}{1 + (n-1)r} \qquad 0 < r \leq 1$$

If the reliability is $r = 0.6$, the equation becomes

$$R(n) = \frac{0.6n}{0.4 + 0.6n}$$

  (a) Find $R(1)$.
  (b) Find $R(2)$; that is, find *R* when the test length is doubled.
  (c) What percent improvement is there in the reliability when the test length is doubled?

55. **Area** If 100 feet of fence is to be used to enclose a rectangular yard, then the resulting area of the fenced yard is given by

$$A = x(50 - x)$$

where x is the width of the rectangle.
(a) Is A a function of x?
(b) If $A = A(x)$, find $A(2)$ and $A(30)$.
(c) What restrictions must be placed on x (the domain) so that the problem makes physical sense?

56. **Postal restrictions** If a box with a square cross section is to be sent by a delivery service, there are restrictions on its size such that its volume is given by $V = x^2(108 - 4x)$, where x is the length of each side of the cross section (in inches).
(a) Is V a function of x?
(b) If $V = V(x)$, find $V(10)$ and $V(20)$.
(c) What restrictions must be placed on x (the domain) so that the problem makes physical sense?

57. **Profit** Suppose that the profit from the production and sale of x units of a product is given by

$$P(x) = 180x - \frac{x^2}{100} - 200$$

In addition, suppose that for a certain month the number of units produced on day t of the month is

$$x = q(t) = 1000 + 10t$$

(a) Find $(P \circ q)(t)$ to express the profit as a function of the day of the month.
(b) Find the number of units produced, and the profit, on the fifteenth day of the month.

58. **Fish species growth** For many species of fish, the weight W is a function of the length L that can be expressed by

$$W = W(L) = kL^3 \quad k = \text{constant}$$

Suppose that for a particular species $k = 0.02$, that for this species the length (in centimeters) is a function of the number of years t the fish has been alive, and that this function is given by

$$L = L(t) = 50 - \frac{(t - 20)^2}{10} \quad 0 \le t \le 20$$

Find $(W \circ L)(t)$ in order to express W as a function of the age t of the fish.

59. **Revenue and advertising** Suppose that a company's revenue $R = f(C)$ is a function f of the number of customers C. Suppose also that the amount spent on advertising A affects the number of customers so that $C = g(A)$ is a function g of A.
(a) Is $f \circ g$ defined? Explain.
(b) Is $g \circ f$ defined? Explain.
(c) For the functions in parts (a) and (b) that are defined, identify the input (independent variable) and the output (dependent variable) and explain what the function means.

60. **Manufacturing** Two of the processes (functions) used by a manufacturer of factory-built homes are sanding (denote this as function s) and painting (denote this as function p). Write a sentence of explanation for each of the following functional expressions involving s and p applied to a door.
(a) $s(\text{door})$ (b) $p(\text{door})$ (c) $(p \circ s)(\text{door})$
(d) $(s \circ p)(\text{door})$ (e) $(p \circ p)(\text{door})$

61. **Fencing a lot** A farmer wishes to fence the perimeter of a rectangular lot with an area of 1600 square feet. If the lot is x feet long, express the amount L of fence needed as a function of x.

62. **Cost** A shipping crate has a square base with sides of length x feet, and it is half as tall as it is wide. If the material for the bottom and sides of the box costs $2.00 per square foot and the material for the top costs $1.50 per square foot, express the total cost of material for the box as a function of x.

63. **Revenue** An agency charges $100 per person for a trip to a concert if 30 people travel in a group. But for each person above the 30, the amount charged each traveler will be reduced by $2.00. If x represents the number of people above the 30, write the agency's revenue R as a function of x.

64. **Revenue** A company handles an apartment building with 50 units. Experience has shown that if the rent for each of the units is $720 per month, all of the units will be filled, but one unit will become vacant for each $20 increase in the monthly rate. If x represents the number of $20 increases, write the revenue R from the building as a function of x.

Linear Functions

▮ | APPLICATION PREVIEW | ▮

The number of banks in the United States for selected years from 1980 to 2009 is given by

$$y = -380.961x + 18{,}483.167$$

where x is the number of years after 1980 (*Source:* Federal Deposit Insurance Corporation). What does this function tell about how the number of banks has changed per year during this period? (See Example 7.) In this section, we will find the slopes and intercepts of graphs of linear functions and apply them.

The function in the Application Preview is an example of a special function, called the **linear function,** defined as follows.

Linear Function

A **linear function** is a function of the form

$$y = f(x) = ax + b$$

where a and b are constants.

Intercepts

Because the graph of a linear function is a line, only two points are necessary to determine its graph. It is frequently possible to use **intercepts** to graph a linear function. The point(s) where a graph intersects the x-axis are called the x-intercept points, and the x-coordinates of these points are the **x-intercepts.** Similarly, the points where a graph intersects the y-axis are the y-intercept points, and the y-coordinates of these points are the **y-intercepts.** Because any point on the x-axis has y-coordinate 0 and any point on the y-axis has x-coordinate 0, we find intercepts as follows.

Intercepts

(a) To find the **y-intercept(s)** of the graph of an equation, set $x = 0$ in the equation and solve for y. *Note:* A function of x has at most one y-intercept.
(b) To find the **x-intercept(s),** set $y = 0$ and solve for x.

EXAMPLE **1** **Intercepts**

Find the intercepts and graph the following.
(a) $3x + y = 9$ (b) $x = 4y$

Solution
(a) To find the y-intercept, we set $x = 0$ and solve for y: $3(0) + y = 9$ gives $y = 9$, so the y-intercept is 9.

To find the x-intercept, we set $y = 0$ and solve for x: $3x + 0 = 9$ gives $x = 3$, so the x-intercept is 3. Using the intercepts gives the graph, shown in Figure 1.13.
(b) Letting $x = 0$ gives $y = 0$, and letting $y = 0$ gives $x = 0$, so the only intercept of the graph of $x = 4y$ is at the point $(0, 0)$. A second point is needed to graph the line. Hence, if we let $y = 1$ in $x = 4y$, we get $x = 4$ and have a second point $(4, 1)$ on the graph. It is wise to plot a third point as a check. The graph is shown in Figure 1.14. ▪

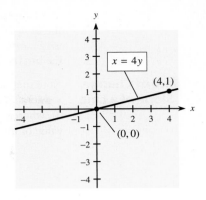

Figures 1.13 & 1.14

Note that the equation graphed in Figure 1.13 can be rewritten as

$$y = 9 - 3x \quad \text{or} \quad f(x) = 9 - 3x$$

We see in Figure 1.13 that the x-intercept $(3, 0)$ is the point where the function value is zero. The x-coordinate of such a point is called a **zero of the function.** Thus we see that the *x-intercepts of a function are the same as its zeros.*

EXAMPLE 2   Depreciation

A business property is purchased for \$122,880 and depreciated over a period of 10 years. Its value y is related to the number of months of service x by the equation

$$4096x + 4y = 491{,}520$$

Find the x-intercept and the y-intercept and use them to sketch the graph of the equation.

Solution

$$x\text{-intercept: } y = 0 \quad \text{gives} \quad 4096x = 491{,}520$$
$$x = 120$$

Thus 120 is the x-intercept.

$$y\text{-intercept: } x = 0 \quad \text{gives} \quad 4y = 491{,}520$$
$$y = 122{,}880$$

Thus 122,880 is the y-intercept. The graph is shown in Figure 1.15. Note that the units on the x- and y-axes are different and that the y-intercept corresponds to the value of the property 0 months after purchase. That is, the y-intercept gives the purchase price. The x-intercept corresponds to the number of months that have passed before the value is 0; that is, the property is fully depreciated after 120 months, or 10 years. Note that only positive values for x and y make sense in this application, so only the Quadrant I portion of the graph is shown.

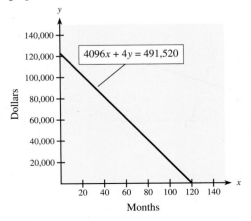

Figure 1.15

Despite the ease of using intercepts to graph linear equations, this method is not always the best. For example, vertical lines, horizontal lines, or lines that pass through the origin may have a single intercept, and if a line has both intercepts very close to the origin, using the intercepts may lead to an inaccurate graph.

Rate of Change; Slope of a Line

Note that in Figure 1.15, as the graph moves from the y-intercept point $(0, 122{,}880)$ to the x-intercept point $(120, 0)$, the y-value on the line changes $-122{,}880$ units (from 122,880 to 0), whereas the x-value changes 120 units (from 0 to 120). Thus the **rate of change** of the value of the business property is

$$\frac{-122{,}880}{120} = -1024 \text{ dollars per month}$$

This means that each month the value of the property changes by -1024 dollars, or the value decreases by \$1024 per month. This **rate of change** of a linear function is called the **slope** of the line that is its graph (see Figure 1.15). For the graph of a linear function, the ratio of the change in y to the corresponding change in x measures the slope of the line. For any nonvertical line, the slope can be found by using any two points on the line, as follows.

Slope of a Line

If a nonvertical line passes through the points $P_1(x_1, y_1)$ and $P_2(x_2, y_2)$, its **slope,** denoted by m, is found by using

$$m = \frac{y_2 - y_1}{x_2 - x_1} = \frac{\Delta y}{\Delta x}$$

where Δy, read "delta y," means "change in y" and Δx means "change in x."
The slope of a vertical line is undefined.

Note that for a given line, the slope is the same regardless of which two points are used in the calculation; this is because corresponding sides of similar triangles are in proportion.

EXAMPLE 3   Slopes

Find the slope of
(a) line ℓ_1, passing through $(-2, 1)$ and $(4, 3)$
(b) line ℓ_2, passing through $(3, 0)$ and $(4, -3)$

Solution

(a) $m = \dfrac{3 - 1}{4 - (-2)} = \dfrac{2}{6} = \dfrac{1}{3}$ or, equivalently, $m = \dfrac{1 - 3}{-2 - 4} = \dfrac{-2}{-6} = \dfrac{1}{3}$

This means that a point 3 units to the right and 1 unit up from any point on the line is also on the line. Line ℓ_1 is shown in Figure 1.16.

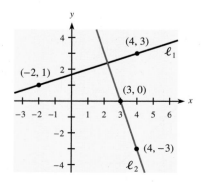

Figure 1.16

(b) $m = \dfrac{0 - (-3)}{3 - 4} = \dfrac{3}{-1} = -3$

This means that a point 1 unit to the right and 3 units down from any point on the line is also on the line. Line ℓ_2 is also shown in Figure 1.16.

From the previous discussion, we see that the slope describes the direction of a line as follows.

Orientation of a Line and Its Slope

1. The slope is *positive* if the line slopes upward toward the right. The function is increasing.

$$m = \dfrac{\Delta y}{\Delta x} > 0$$

3. The slope of a *horizontal line* is 0, because $\Delta y = 0$. The function is constant.

$$m = \dfrac{\Delta y}{\Delta x} = 0$$

2. The slope is *negative* if the line slopes downward toward the right. The function is decreasing.

$$m = \dfrac{\Delta y}{\Delta x} < 0$$

4. The slope of a *vertical line* is *undefined*, because $\Delta x = 0$.

$$m = \dfrac{\Delta y}{\Delta x} \text{ is undefined.}$$

Two distinct nonvertical lines that have the same slope are parallel, and conversely, two nonvertical parallel lines have the same slope.

Parallel Lines   Two distinct nonvertical lines are *parallel* if and only if their slopes are *equal*.

In general, two lines are perpendicular if they intersect at right angles. However, the appearance of this perpendicularity relationship can be obscured when we graph lines, unless the axes have the same scale. Note that the lines ℓ_1 and ℓ_2 in Figure 1.16 appear to be perpendicular. However, the same lines graphed with different scales on the axes will not look perpendicular. To avoid being misled by graphs with different scales, we use slopes to tell us when lines are perpendicular. Note that the slope of ℓ_1, $\frac{1}{3}$, is the negative reciprocal of the slope of ℓ_2, -3. In fact, as with lines ℓ_1 and ℓ_2, any two nonvertical lines that are perpendicular have slopes that are negative reciprocals of each other.

Slopes of Perpendicular Lines   A line ℓ_1 with slope m, where $m \neq 0$, is *perpendicular* to line ℓ_2 if and only if the slope of ℓ_2 is $-1/m$. (The slopes are *negative reciprocals*.)

Because the slope of a vertical line is undefined, we cannot use slope in discussing parallel and perpendicular relations that involve vertical lines. Two vertical lines are parallel, and any horizontal line is perpendicular to any vertical line.

CHECKPOINT

1. Find the slope of the line through $(4, 6)$ and $(28, -6)$.
2. If a line has slope $m = 0$, then the line is _____. If a line has an undefined slope, then the line is _____.

3. Suppose that line 1 has slope $m_1 = 5$ and line 2 has slope m_2.
   (a) If line 1 is perpendicular to line 2, find m_2.
   (b) If line 1 is parallel to line 2, find m_2.

Writing Equations of Lines

If the slope of a line is m, then the slope between a fixed point (x_1, y_1) and any other point (x, y) on the line is also m. That is,

$$m = \frac{y - y_1}{x - x_1}$$

Solving for $y - y_1$ gives the point-slope form of the equation of a line.

Point-Slope Form

The equation of the line passing through the point (x_1, y_1) and with slope m can be written in the **point-slope form**

$$y - y_1 = m(x - x_1)$$

EXAMPLE 4   Equations of Lines

Write the equation for each line that passes through $(1, -2)$ and has

(a) slope $\frac{2}{3}$ (b) undefined slope   (c) point $(2, 3)$ also on the line

Solution

(a) Here $m = \frac{2}{3}$, $x_1 = 1$, and $y_1 = -2$. An equation of the line is

$$y - (-2) = \frac{2}{3}(x - 1)$$

$$y + 2 = \frac{2}{3}x - \frac{2}{3}$$

$$y = \frac{2}{3}x - \frac{8}{3}$$

This equation also may be written in **general form** as $2x - 3y - 8 = 0$. Figure 1.17 shows the graph of this line; the point $(1, -2)$ and the slope are highlighted.

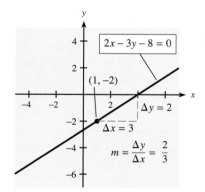

Figure 1.17

(b) Because m is undefined, we cannot use the point-slope form. This line is vertical, so every point on it has x-coordinate 1. Thus the equation is $x = 1$. Note that $x = 1$ is not a function.

(c) First use $(1, -2)$ and $(2, 3)$ to find the slope.

$$m = \frac{3 - (-2)}{2 - 1} = 5$$

Using $m = 5$ and the point $(1, -2)$ (the other point could also be used) gives

$$y - (-2) = 5(x - 1) \quad \text{or} \quad y = 5x - 7$$

The graph of $x = 1$ (from Example 4(b)) is a vertical line, as shown in Figure 1.18(a); the graph of $y = 1$ has slope 0, and its graph is a horizontal line, as shown in Figure 1.18(b).

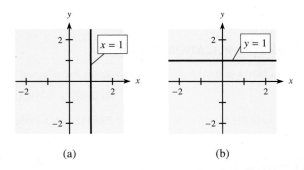

Figure 1.18   (a)   (b)

In general, **vertical lines** have undefined slope and the equation form $x = a$, where a is the x-coordinate of each point on the line. **Horizontal lines** have $m = 0$ and the equation form $y = b$, where b is the y-coordinate of each point on the line.

EXAMPLE 5   Pricing

U.S. Census Bureau data indicate that the average price p of digital television sets can be expressed as a linear function of the number of sets sold N (in thousands). In addition, as N increased by 1000, p dropped by \$10.40, and when 6485 (thousand) sets were sold, the average price per set was \$504.39. Write the equation of the line determined by this information.

Solution

We see that price p is a function of the number of sets N (in thousands), so the slope is given by

$$m = \frac{\text{change in } p}{\text{change in } N} = \frac{-10.40}{1000} = -0.0104$$

A point on the line is $(N_1, p_1) = (6485, 504.39)$. We use the point-slope form adapted to the variables N and p.

$$p - p_1 = m(N - N_1)$$
$$p - 504.39 = -0.0104(N - 6485)$$
$$p - 504.39 = -0.0104N + 67.444$$
$$p = -0.0104N + 571.834$$

The point-slope form, with the y-intercept point $(0, b)$, can be used to derive a special form for the equation of a line.

$$y - b = m(x - 0)$$
$$y = mx + b$$

Slope-Intercept Form

The **slope-intercept form** of the equation of a line with slope m and y-intercept b is

$$y = mx + b$$

Note that if a linear equation has the form $y = mx + b$, then the coefficient of x is the slope and the constant term is the y-intercept.

EXAMPLE 6   **Writing the Equation of a Line**

Write the equation of the line with slope $\frac{1}{2}$ and y-intercept -3.

Solution

Substituting $m = \frac{1}{2}$ and $b = -3$ in the equation $y = mx + b$ gives $y = \frac{1}{2}x + (-3)$ or $y = \frac{1}{2}x - 3$. ▪

EXAMPLE 7   **Banks | APPLICATION PREVIEW |**

The number of banks in the United States for selected years from 1980 to 2009 is given by

$$y = -380.961x + 18{,}483.167$$

where x is the number of years after 1980 (*Source:* Federal Deposit Insurance Corporation).

(a) Find the slope and the y-intercept of this function.
(b) What does the y-intercept tell us about the banks?
(c) Interpret the slope as a rate of change.
(d) Why is the number of banks decreasing?

Solution

(a) The slope is $m = -380.961$ and the y-intercept is $b = 18{,}483.167$.
(b) Because x is the number of years after 1980, $x = 0$ represents 1980 and the y-intercept tells us that there were approximately 18,483 banks in 1980.
(c) The slope is -380.961, which tells us that the number of banks was decreasing at a rate of approximately 381 banks per year during this period.
(d) The decrease in number is due to consolidation of banks, with larger banks acquiring smaller banks, and the 2008 financial crisis. ▪

When a linear equation does not appear in slope-intercept form (and does not have the form $x = a$), it can be put into slope-intercept form by solving the equation for y.

EXAMPLE 8   **Slope-Intercept Form**

(a) Find the slope and y-intercept of the line whose equation is $x + 2y = 8$.
(b) Use this information to graph the equation.

Solution

(a) To put the equation in slope-intercept form, we must solve it for y.

$$2y = -x + 8 \quad \text{or} \quad y = -\frac{1}{2}x + 4$$

Thus the slope is $-\frac{1}{2}$ and the y-intercept is 4.

(b) First we plot the y-intercept point $(0, 4)$. Because the slope is $-\frac{1}{2} = \frac{-1}{2}$, moving 2 units to the right and down 1 unit from $(0, 4)$ gives the point $(2, 3)$ on the line. A third point (for a check) is plotted at $(4, 2)$. The graph is shown in Figure 1.19. ▪

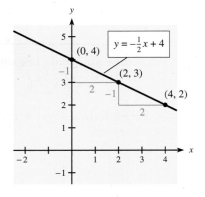

Figure 1.19

It is also possible to graph a straight line if we know its slope and any point on the line; we simply plot the point that is given and then use the slope to plot other points. The following summarizes the forms of equations of lines.

Forms of Linear Equations	General form: $ax + by + c = 0$
	Point-slope form: $y - y_1 = m(x - x_1)$
	Slope-intercept form: $y = mx + b$
	Vertical line: $x = a$
	Horizontal line: $y = b$

CHECKPOINT

4. Write the equation of the line that has slope $-\frac{3}{4}$ and passes through $(4, -6)$.
5. What are the slope and y-intercept of the graph of $x = -4y + 1$?

CHECKPOINT SOLUTIONS

1. $m = \dfrac{y_2 - y_1}{x_2 - x_1} = \dfrac{-6 - (6)}{28 - (4)} = \dfrac{-12}{24} = -\dfrac{1}{2}$

2. If $m = 0$, then the line is horizontal. If m is undefined, then the line is vertical.

3. (a) $m_2 = \dfrac{-1}{m_1} = -\dfrac{1}{5}$ (b) $m_2 = m_1 = 5$

4. Use $y - y_1 = m(x - x_1)$. Hence $y - (-6) = -\frac{3}{4}(x - 4)$, $y + 6 = -\frac{3}{4}x + 3$, or $y = -\frac{3}{4}x - 3$.

5. If $x = -4y + 1$, then the slope-intercept form is $y = mx + b$ or $y = -\frac{1}{4}x + \frac{1}{4}$. Hence $m = -\frac{1}{4}$ and the y-intercept is $\frac{1}{4}$.

| EXERCISES | 1.3

Find the intercepts and graph the following functions.

1. $3x + 4y = 12$
2. $6x - 5y = 90$
3. $5x - 8y = 60$
4. $2x - y + 17 = 0$

In Problems 5–10, find the slope of the line passing through the given pair of points.

5. $(22, 11)$ and $(15, -17)$
6. $(-6, -12)$ and $(-18, -24)$
7. $(3, -1)$ and $(-1, 1)$
8. $(-5, 6)$ and $(1, -3)$
9. $(3, 2)$ and $(-1, 2)$
10. $(-4, 2)$ and $(-4, -2)$
11. If a line is horizontal, then its slope is _____.
12. If a line is vertical, then its slope is _____.
13. What is the rate of change of the function whose graph is a line passing through $(3, 2)$ and $(-1, 2)$?
14. What is the rate of change of the function whose graph is a line passing through $(11, -5)$ and $(-9, -4)$?

In Problems 15 and 16, for each given graph, determine whether each line has a slope that is positive, negative, 0, or undefined.

15.

16.

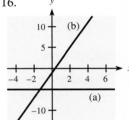

Find the slopes and y-intercepts of the lines whose equations are given in Problems 17–24. Then graph each equation.

17. $y = \dfrac{7}{3}x - \dfrac{1}{4}$
18. $y = \dfrac{4}{3}x + \dfrac{1}{2}$
19. $y = 3$
20. $y = -2$
21. $x = -8$
22. $x = -\dfrac{1}{2}$
23. $2x + 3y = 6$
24. $3x - 2y = 18$

In Problems 25–28, write the equation and sketch the graph of each line with the given slope and y-intercept.

25. Slope $\frac{1}{2}$ and y-intercept -3
26. Slope 4 and y-intercept 2

27. Slope -2 and y-intercept $\frac{1}{2}$
28. Slope $-\frac{2}{3}$ and y-intercept -1

In Problems 29–34, write the equation and graph the line that passes through the given point and has the slope indicated.

29. $(2, 0)$ with slope -5
30. $(1, 1)$ with slope $-\frac{1}{3}$
31. $(-1, 4)$ with slope $-\frac{3}{4}$
32. $(3, -1)$ with slope 1
33. $(-1, 1)$ with undefined slope
34. $(1, 1)$ with 0 slope

In Problems 35–38, write the equation of each line passing through the given pair of points.

35. $(3, 2)$ and $(-1, -6)$
36. $(-4, 2)$ and $(2, 4)$
37. $(7, 3)$ and $(-6, 2)$
38. $(10, 2)$ and $(8, 7)$

In Problems 39–42, determine whether the following pairs of equations represent parallel lines, perpendicular lines, or neither of these.

39. $3x + 2y = 6$; $2x - 3y = 6$
40. $5x - 2y = 8$; $10x - 4y = 8$
41. $6x - 4y = 12$; $3x - 2y = 6$
42. $5x + 4y = 7$; $y = \dfrac{4}{5}x + 7$

43. Write the equation of the line passing through $(-2, -7)$ that is parallel to $3x + 5y = 11$.
44. Write the equation of the line passing through $(6, -4)$ that is parallel to $4x - 5y = 6$.
45. Write the equation of the line passing through $(3, 1)$ that is perpendicular to $5x - 6y = 4$.
46. Write the equation of the line passing through $(-2, -8)$ that is perpendicular to $x = 4y + 3$.

APPLICATIONS

47. *Depreciation* A \$360,000 building is depreciated by its owner. The value y of the building after x months of use is $y = 360{,}000 - 1500x$.
    (a) Graph this function for $x \geq 0$.
    (b) How long is it until the building is completely depreciated (its value is zero)?
    (c) The point $(60, 270{,}000)$ lies on the graph. Explain what this means.
48. *U.S civilian population* Using data from the U.S. Census Bureau, the U.S. civilian population (in millions) can be described by

$$p(t) = 3.04t + 249.4$$

where t is the number of years past 1990.
    (a) Find $p(25)$ and write a sentence that explains its meaning.
    (b) Graph the equation for $p(t)$.
49. *Internet users* The percent of the U.S. population with Internet service can be described by

$$y = 4.97x - 6.49$$

where x is the number of years past 1995 (*Source:* Jupiter Media Metrix).
    (a) Find the slope and y-intercept of this equation.
    (b) What interpretation could be given to the slope?
    (c) Graph the function.
50. *Cigarette use* The percent p of high school students who occasionally smoke cigarettes can be described by

$$p = 38.56 - 1.53t$$

where t is the number of years past 1995 (*Source:* National Institute on Drug Abuse).
    (a) Find the slope and p-intercept of this equation.
    (b) Write a sentence that interprets the meaning of the slope as a rate of change.
    (c) Write a sentence that interprets the meaning of the p-intercept.
51. *World forest area* When x is the number of years past 1990, the world forest area (that is, natural forest or planted stands) as a percent of land area is given by

$$F(x) = -0.065x + 31.39$$

(*Source:* The World Bank, Food and Agriculture Organization)
    (a) Find the slope and F-intercept for this linear function.
    (b) Write a sentence that interprets the F-intercept.
    (c) Find the annual rate of change of world forest area as a percent of land area, and write a sentence that explains its meaning.
52. *Temperature–humidity models* Two models for measuring the effects of high temperature and humidity are the Summer Simmer Index and the Apparent Temperature.* For an outside temperature of 100°F, these indices relate the relative humidity, H (expressed as a decimal), to the perceived temperature as follows.

Summer Simmer: $S = 141.1 - 45.78(1 - H)$
Apparent Temperature: $A = 91.2 + 41.3H$

    (a) For each index, find the point that corresponds to a relative humidity of 40%.
    (b) For each point in part (a), write a sentence that explains its meaning.
    (c) Graph both equations for $0 \leq H \leq 1$.
53. *Earnings and gender* According to the U.S. Census Bureau, the relation between the average annual earnings of males and females with various levels of educational attainment can be modeled by the function

$$F = 0.78M - 1.316$$

where M and F represent the average annual earnings (in thousands of dollars) of males and females, respectively.

---

*Bosch, W., and C. G. Cobb, "Temperature-Humidity Indices," UMAP Unit 691, *The UMAP Journal*, 10(3), Fall 1989, 237–256.

(a) Viewing F as a function of M, what is the slope of the graph of this function?

(b) Interpret the slope as a rate of change.

(c) When the average annual earnings for males reach $60,000, what does the equation predict for the average annual earnings for females?

54. *Marijuana use* The percent of U.S. high school seniors from 1997 to 2006 who used marijuana can be modeled by

$$p(x) = 56.009 - 0.758x$$

where x is the number of years past 1990 (*Source:* monitoringthefuture.org).

(a) What is the slope of the graph of this function?

(b) Interpret the slope as a rate of change.

55. *Residential electric costs* An electric utility company determines the monthly bill for a residential customer by adding an energy charge of 8.38 cents per kilowatt-hour to its base charge of $16.37 per month. Write an equation for the monthly charge y in terms of x, the number of kilowatt-hours used.

56. *Residential heating costs* Residential customers who heat their homes with natural gas have their monthly bills calculated by adding a base service charge of $9.19 per month and an energy charge of 91.91 cents per hundred cubic feet. Write an equation for the monthly charge y in terms of x, the number of hundreds of cubic feet used.

57. *Earnings and race* Data from 2005 for various age groups show that for each $100 increase in the median weekly income for whites, the median weekly income of blacks increases by $105. Also, for workers of ages 25 to 54, the median weekly income for whites was $676 and for blacks was $527 (*Source:* U.S. Department of Labor).

(a) Let W represent the median weekly income for whites and B the median weekly income for blacks, and write the equation of the line that gives B as a linear function of W.

(b) When the median weekly income for whites is $850, what does the equation in (a) predict for the median weekly income for blacks?

58. *Retirement plans* The retirement plan for Pennsylvania state employees is based on the following formula: "2.5% of average final compensation multiplied by years of credited service" (*Source:* Pennsylvania State Employees Retirement System). Let p represent annual retirement pension, y years of service, and c average final compensation.

(a) For someone with average final compensation of $80,000, write the linear equation that gives p in terms of y.

(b) For someone intending to retire after 30 years, write the linear equation that gives p in terms of c.

59. *Consumer price index* The consumer price index for urban consumers (the CPI-U) for the years 1985 to 2005 can be accurately approximated by the linear model determined by the line connecting (1985, 113.2) and (2005, 324.9), where the x-coordinate is the year and the y-coordinate is the price consumers pay in year x for goods that cost $100 in 1982 (*Source:* U.S. Census Bureau).

(a) Write the equation of the line connecting these two points to find a linear model for these data.

(b) Interpret the slope of this line as a rate of change.

60. *Drinking and driving* The following table gives the number of drinks and the resulting blood alcohol percent for a 180-pound man legally considered driving under the influence (DUI).

(a) Is the average rate of change of the blood alcohol percent with respect to the number of drinks a constant?

(b) Use the rate of change and one point determined by a number of drinks and the resulting blood alcohol percent to write the equation of a linear model for these data.

(c) Verify that the values in the table fit the model.

Number of Drinks	5	6	7	8	9	10
Blood Alcohol Percent	0.11	0.13	0.15	0.17	0.19	0.21

Source: Pennsylvania Liquor Control Board

61. *Pollution effects* It has been estimated that a certain stream can support 85,000 fish if it is pollution-free. It has further been estimated that for each ton of pollutants in the stream, 1700 fewer fish can be supported. Assuming the relationship is linear, write the equation that gives the population of fish p in terms of the tons of pollutants x.

62. *Age–sleep relationship* Each day, a young person should sleep 8 hours plus $\frac{1}{4}$ hour for each year that the person is under 18 years of age. Assuming the relation is linear, write the equation relating hours of sleep y and age x.

63. *Insulation R-values* The R-value of insulation is a measure of its ability to resist heat transfer. For fiberglass insulation, $3\frac{1}{2}$ inches is rated at R-11 and 6 inches is rated at R-19. Assuming this relationship is linear, write the equation that gives the R-value of fiberglass insulation as a function of its thickness t (in inches).

64. *Depreciation* Suppose the cost of a business property is $960,000 and a company wants to use a straight-line depreciation schedule for a period of 240 months. If y is the value of this property after x months, then the company's depreciation schedule will be the equation of a line through (0, 960,000) and (240, 0). Write the equation of this depreciation schedule.

65. *Cholesterol and coronary heart disease risk* The Seven Countries Study, conducted by Ancel Keys, was a long-term study of the relationship of cholesterol to coronary heart disease (CHD) mortality in men. The

relationship was approximated by the line shown in the accompanying figure. The line passes through the points (200, 25) and (250, 49), which means there were 25 CHD deaths per 1000 among men with 200 mg/dl (milligrams per deciliter) of cholesterol and 49 CHD deaths per 1000 among men with 250 mg/dl of cholesterol. Using x to represent the cholesterol and y to represent CHD deaths, write the equation that represents this relationship.

OBJECTIVES

- To use a graphing utility to graph equations in the standard viewing window
- To use a graphing utility and a specified range to graph equations
- To use a graphing utility to evaluate functions, to find intercepts, and to find zeros of a function
- To solve linear equations with a graphing utility

1.4

Graphs and Graphing Utilities

| APPLICATION PREVIEW |

Suppose that for a certain city the cost C of obtaining drinking water with p percent impurities (by volume) is given by

$$C = \frac{120,000}{p} - 1200$$

where $0 < p \le 100$. A graph of this equation would illustrate how the purity of water is related to the cost of obtaining it. Because this equation is not linear, graphing it would require many more than two points. Such a graph could be efficiently obtained with a graphing utility. (See Example 1.)

In Section 1.3, "Linear Functions," we saw that a linear equation could easily be graphed by plotting points because only two points are required. When we want the graph of an equation that is not linear, we can still use point plotting, but we must have enough points to sketch an accurate graph.

Some computer software and all graphing calculators have **graphing utilities** (also called *graphics utilities*) that can be used to generate an accurate graph. All graphing utilities use the point-plotting method to plot scores of points quickly and thereby graph an equation.

The computer monitor or calculator screen consists of a fine grid that looks like a piece of graph paper. In this grid, each tiny area is called a pixel. Essentially, a pixel corresponds to a point on a piece of graph paper, and as a graphing utility plots points, the pixels corresponding to the points are lighted and then connected, revealing the graph. The graph is shown in a viewing window or viewing rectangle. The values that define the viewing window or calculator range can be set individually or by using ZOOM keys. The important values are

x-min:	the smallest value on the x-axis (the leftmost x-value in the window)
x-max:	the largest value on the x-axis (the rightmost x-value in the window)
y-min:	the smallest value on the y-axis (the lowest y-value in the window)
y-max:	the largest value on the y-axis (the highest y-value in the window)

Most graphing utilities have a *standard viewing window* that gives a window with x-values and y-values between −10 and 10.

x-min:	−10	y-min:	−10
x-max:	10	y-max:	10

The graph of $y = \frac{1}{3}x^3 - x^2 - 3x + 2$ with the standard viewing window is shown in Figure 1.20.

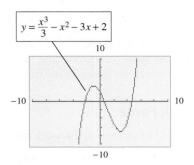

$$y = \frac{x^3}{3} - x^2 - 3x + 2$$

Figure 1.20

Calculator Note With a graphing calculator, as with a graph plotted by hand, the appearance of the graph is determined by the part of the graph we are viewing, and the standard window does not always give a **complete graph**. (A complete graph shows the important parts of the graph and suggests the unseen parts.) The steps for graphing a function with a graphing calculator are shown in Appendix C, Section 1.4. ■

EXAMPLE 1   **Water Purity** | APPLICATION PREVIEW |

For a certain city, the cost C of obtaining drinking water with p percent impurities (by volume) is given by

$$C = \frac{120{,}000}{p} - 1200$$

The equation for C requires that $p \neq 0$, and because p is the percent impurities, we know that $0 < p \leq 100$. Use the restriction on p and a graphing calculator to obtain an accurate graph of the equation.

Solution
To use a graphing calculator, we identify C with y and p with x. Thus we enter

$$y = \frac{120{,}000}{x} - 1200$$

Because $0 < p \leq 100$, we set the x-range to *include* these values, with the realization that only the portion of the graph above these values applies to our equation and that $p = 0$ (that is, $x = 0$) is excluded from the domain because it makes the denominator 0. With this x-range we can determine a y-, or C-, range from the equation or by tracing; see Figure 1.21(a). We see that when p is near 0 (the value excluded from the domain), the C-coordinates of the points are very large, indicating that water free of impurities is very costly. However, Figure 1.21(a) does not accurately show what happens for large p-values. Figure 1.21(b) shows another view of the equation with the C-range (that is, the y-range) from -500 to 3500. We see the p-intercept is $p = 100$, which indicates that water containing 100% impurities costs nothing ($C = 0$). Note that $p > 100$ has no meaning. Why? ■

Figure 1.21

Two views of $C = \dfrac{120{,}000}{p} - 1200$

CHECKPOINT

Use a graphing calculator and the standard viewing window to graph the following.

1. $x^2 + 4y = 0$ 2. $y = \dfrac{4(x + 1)^2}{x^2 + 1}$

We can evaluate a function $y = f(x)$ with a graphing calculator by using VALUE or TABLE to find the function values corresponding to values of the independent variable. We can also use TRACE to evaluate or approximate function values.

EXAMPLE 2 Women in the Work Force

The number y (in millions) of women in the work force is modeled by the function

$$y = -0.005x^2 + 1.38x + 0.07$$

where x is the number of years past 1940 (*Source:* Bureau of Labor Statistics).

(a) Graph this function from $x = 0$ to $x = 85$.
(b) Find the value of y when $x = 60$. Explain what this means.
(c) Use the model to predict the number of women in the work force in 2015.

Solution

(a) The graph is found by entering the equation with $x = 0$ to $x = 85$ in the window. Using TRACE for x-values between 0 and 85 helps determine that y-values between 0 and 85 give a complete graph. The graph, using this window, is shown in Figure 1.22(a).
(b) By using TRACE or TABLE, we can find $f(60) = 64.87$ (see Figure 1.22(b) and Figure 1.22(c)). This means that there were approximately 64.87 million, or 64,870,000, women in the work force in $1940 + 60 = 2000$.
(c) The year 2015 corresponds to $x = 75$ and $f(75) = 75.445$ (see Figure 1.22(c)). Thus in 2015, approximately 75,445,000 women are predicted to be in the work force.

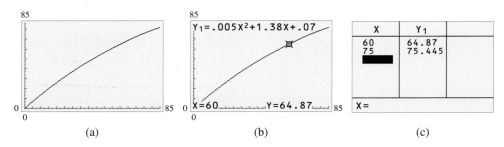

Figure 1.22

(a)   (b)   (c)

Spreadsheet Note

| TABLE 1.3 |

	A	B
1	x	f(x) = 6x −3
2	−5	−33
3	−2	−15
4	−1	−9
5	0	−3
6	1	3
7	3	15
8	5	27

The ability to represent quantities or their interrelationships algebraically is one of the keys to using spreadsheets. For details regarding spreadsheets, see Appendix D and the Online Excel Guide that accompanies this text.

Each cell in a spreadsheet has an address based on its row and column (see Table 1.3). These cell addresses can act like variables in an algebraic expression, and the "fill down" or "fill across" capabilities update this cell referencing while maintaining algebraic relationships.

We can use Excel to find the outputs of a function for given inputs. For details on entering data in a spreadsheet and evaluating functions with Excel, see Appendix D, Section 1.4. Table 1.3 shows a spreadsheet for the function $f(x) = 6x - 3$ for the input set $\{-5, -2, -1, 0, 1, 3, 5\}$, with these inputs listed as entries in the first column (column A). If -5 is in cell A2, then $f(-5)$ can be found in cell B2 by typing $= 6*A2 - 3$ in cell B2. By using the fill-down capability, we can obtain all the function values shown in column B. Excel can also graph this function (see Figure 1.23). (See Appendix D, Section 1.4, and the Online Excel Guide for details.)

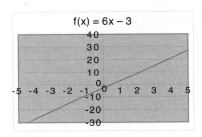

Figure 1.23

Graphical Solutions of Equations

We can use graphing utilities to find the x-intercepts of graphs of functions. Because an x-intercept is an x-value that makes the function equal to 0, the x-intercept is also a zero of the function. Thus if an equation is written in the form $0 = f(x)$, the x-intercept of $y = f(x)$ is a solution of the equation. This method of solving an equation is called the **x-intercept method.**

Calculator Note

Solving an Equation Using the x-Intercept Method with a Graphing Calculator

1. Rewrite the equation to be solved with 0 (and nothing else) on one side of the equation.
2. Enter the nonzero side of the equation found in the previous step in the equation editor of your graphing calculator, and graph the equation in an appropriate viewing window. Be certain that you can see the graph cross the horizontal axis.
3. Find or approximate the x-intercept by inspection with TRACE or by using the graphical solver that is often called ZERO or ROOT. The x-intercept is the value of x that makes the equation equal to zero, so it is the solution to the equation. The value of x found by this method is often displayed as a decimal approximation of the exact solution rather than as the exact solution.
4. Verify the solution in the original equation.

See Appendix C, Section 1.4, for more details for using the x-intercept method with a graphing calculator. ■

EXAMPLE 3   Solving an Equation with a Graphing Calculator

Graphically solve $5x + \dfrac{1}{2} = 7x - 8$ for x.

Solution
To solve this equation, we rewrite the equation with 0 on one side.

$$0 = 7x - 8 - \left(5x + \frac{1}{2}\right)$$

Graphing $y = 7x - 8 - (5x + \frac{1}{2})$ and finding the x-intercept gives x approximately equal to $4.25 = \frac{17}{4}$ (see Figure 1.24). Checking $x = \frac{17}{4}$ in the original equation, or solving the equation analytically, shows that $x = \frac{17}{4}$ is the exact solution. ■

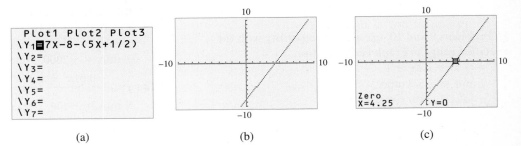

Figure 1.24   (a)   (b)   (c)

Spreadsheet Note 　We can use Excel to solve the equation $0 = 5x - 8$ by finding the value of x that makes $f(x) = 5x - 8$ equal to 0—that is, by finding the zero of $f(x) = 5x - 8$. To find the zero of $f(x)$ with Excel, we enter the formula for $f(x)$ in the worksheet and use Goal Seek.

	A	B
1	x	f(x) = 5x – 8
2	1	= 5*A2 – 8

Under the goal set menu, setting cell B2 to the value 0 and choosing A2 as the changing cell gives $x = 1.6$, which is the solution to the equation. (See Appendix D, Section 1.4, and the Online Excel Guide for details.)

	A	B
1	x	f(x) = 5x – 8
2	1.6	0

CHECKPOINT SOLUTIONS

1.　First solve $x^2 + 4y = 0$ for y.

$$4y = -x^2$$

$$y = \frac{-x^2}{4}$$

$$y = \frac{-x^2}{4}$$

2.　The equation $y = \dfrac{4(x + 1)^2}{x^2 + 1}$ can be entered directly, but some care with parentheses is needed. Enter

$$y_1 = (4(x + 1)^2)/(x^2 + 1)$$

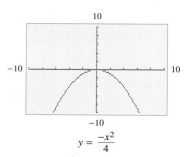

$$y = \frac{4(x + 1)^2}{x^2 + 1}$$

| EXERCISES |　1.4

 In Problems 1–8, use a graphing utility with the standard viewing window to graph each function.

1. $y = x^2 + 4x + 1$
2. $y = 4 - 3x - x^2$
3. $y = x^3 - 3x$
4. $y = x^3 - 6x^2$
5. $y = 0.1x^3 - 0.3x^2 - 2.4x + 3$
6. $y = \dfrac{1}{4}x^4 - \dfrac{1}{3}x^3 - 3x^2 + 8$
7. $y = \dfrac{12x}{x^2 + 1}$
8. $y = \dfrac{8}{x^2 + 1}$

In Problems 9 and 10, use a graphing utility with the specified range to graph each equation.

9. $y = x^3 - 12x - 1$
　x-min $= -5$, x-max $= 5$;
　y-min $= -20$, y-max $= 20$
10. $y = x^4 - 4x^3 + 6$
　x-min $= -4$, x-max $= 6$;
　y-min $= -40$, y-max $= 10$

In Problems 11 and 12, show the correct way to enter each function in a calculator.

11. $y = \dfrac{3x + 7}{x^2 + 4}$
12. $y = x^2 - \dfrac{4}{x - 1}$

In Problems 13–16, graph each equation with a graphing utility using
(a) the specified range
(b) the standard viewing window (for comparison).

13. $y = 0.01x^3 + 0.3x^2 - 72x + 150$
　x-min $= -100$, x-max $= 80$;
　y-min $= -2000$, y-max $= 4000$

14. $y = \dfrac{-0.01x^3 + 0.15x^2 + 60x + 700}{100}$
　x-min $= -100$, x-max $= 100$;
　y-min $= -50$, y-max $= 50$

15. $y = \dfrac{x + 15}{x^2 + 400}$

x-min $= -200$, x-max $= 200$;

y-min $= -0.02$, y-max $= 0.06$

16. $y = \dfrac{x - 80}{x^2 + 1700}$

x-min $= -200$, x-max $= 400$;

y-min $= -0.06$, y-max $= 0.01$

In Problems 17 and 18, do the following.

(a) **Algebraically find the x- and y-intercepts of the graph.**

(b) **Graph each equation with a graphing utility; use a window that includes the intercepts.**

17. $y = 0.001x - 0.03$ 18. $y = 50,000 - 100x$

In Problems 19–22, a standard viewing window graph of a function is shown. Experiment with the viewing window to obtain a complete graph, adjusting the ranges where necessary.

19. $y = -0.15(x - 10.2)^2 + 10$

20. $y = x^2 - x - 42$

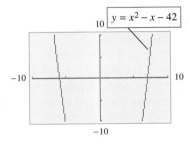

21. $y = \dfrac{x^3 + 19x^2 - 62x - 840}{20}$

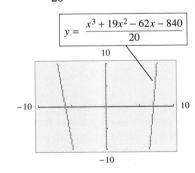

22. $y = \dfrac{-x^3 + 33x^2 + 120x}{20}$

In Problems 23–28, graph the equations with a standard window on a graphing utility. Identify any linear functions.

23. $4x - y = 8$ 24. $5x + y = 8$

25. $4x^2 + 2y = 5$ 26. $6x^2 + 3y = 8$

27. $x^2 - 2y - 6 = 0$ 28. $3x^2 - 4y = 8$

Complete Problems 29 and 30 by using VALUE or TABLE.

29. If $f(x) = x^3 - 3x^2 + 2$, find $f(-2)$ and $f(3/4)$.

30. If $f(x) = \dfrac{x^2 - 2x}{x - 1}$, find $f(3)$ and $f(-4)$.

In Problems 31–34, graph each function using a window that gives a complete graph.

31. $y = \dfrac{12x^2 - 12}{x^2 + 1}$ 32. $y = \dfrac{9x^3}{4x^4 + 9}$

33. $y = \dfrac{x^2 - x - 6}{x^2 + 5x + 6}$ 34. $y = \dfrac{x^2 - 4}{x^2 - 9}$

In Problems 35–38, use the x-intercept method to find one solution of each equation.

35. $0 = 6x - 21$ 36. $12x + 28 = 0$

37. $10 = x^2 - 3x$ 38. $6x^2 + 4x = 4$

In Problems 39 and 40, use a graphing utility to (a) approximate two x-intercepts of the graph of the function (to four decimal places) and (b) give the approximate zeros of the function.

39. $y = x^2 - 7x - 9$ 40. $y = 2x^2 - 4x - 11$

APPLICATIONS

41. *Earnings and gender* With U.S. Census Bureau data, the model that relates the average annual earnings (in thousands of dollars) of females, F, and males, M, with various levels of educational attainment was found to be

$$F = 0.78M - 1.316$$

(a) Use a graphing utility to graph this equation for the range M-min $= 0$, M-max $= 70$; F-min $= 0$, F-max $= 60$.

(b) The point $(50, 37.684)$ lies on the graph of this equation. Explain its meaning.

(c) Find the average annual female earnings that correspond to male earnings of $62,500.

42. **Earnings and minorities** With U.S. Census Bureau data, the model that relates the per capita annual income (in thousands of dollars) of blacks, B, and whites, W, was found to be

$$B = 1.05W - 18.691$$

(a) Use a graphing utility to graph this equation for the range W-min $= 0$, W-max $= 60$; B-min $= 0$, B-max $= 50$.

(b) The point $(50, 33.809)$ lies on the graph of this equation. Explain its meaning.

(c) Find the per capita annual income for blacks that corresponds to a white per capita annual income of $77,500.

43. **Consumer expenditure** Suppose that the consumer expenditure E (in dollars) depends on the market price p per unit (in dollars) according to

$$E = 10{,}000p - 100p^2$$

(a) Graph this equation with a graphing utility and the range p-min $= -50$, p-max $= 150$; E-min $= -50{,}000$, E-max $= 300{,}000$.

(b) Because E represents consumer expenditure, only values of $E \geq 0$ have meaning. For what p-values is $E \geq 0$?

44. **Rectilinear motion** The height above ground (in feet) of a ball thrown vertically into the air is given by

$$S = 112t - 16t^2$$

where t is the time in seconds since the ball was thrown.

(a) Graph this equation with a graphing utility and the range t-min $= -2$, t-max $= 10$; S-min $= -20$, S-max $= 250$.

(b) Estimate the time at which the ball is at its highest point, and estimate the height of the ball at that time.

45. **Advertising impact** An advertising agency has found that when it promotes a new product in a city of 350,000 people, the rate of change R of the number of people who are aware of the product is related to the number of people x who are aware of it and is given by

$$R = 28{,}000 - 0.08x$$

where $x \geq 0$ and $R \geq 0$.

(a) Use the intercepts to determine a window, and then use a graphing utility to graph the equation for $x \geq 0$.

(b) Is the rate of change increasing or decreasing? Explain why your answer makes sense in the context of the problem.

46. **Learning rate** In a study using 50 foreign-language vocabulary words, the learning rate L (in words per minute) was found to depend on the number of words

already learned, x, according to the equation

$$L = 20 - 0.4x$$

(a) Use the intercepts to determine a window, and then use a graphing utility to graph the equation for $x \geq 0$.

(b) Is the learning rate increasing or decreasing? Explain why your answer makes sense in the context of the problem.

47. **Elderly men in the work force** The percent P of men 65 years of age or older in the labor force can be modeled by

$$P = 78.92(0.987^x)$$

where x is the number of years past 1890 (*Source:* U.S. Census Bureau).

(a) What x-min and x-max should you use to view this graph for values representing 1890 to 2010?

(b) Use a table to determine y-min and y-max values that show a complete graph of the model.

(c) Graph this equation.

(d) If this model is valid until the year 2020, adjust the range to obtain a graph that extends to 2020, and with y-min equal to 0.

(e) Write a sentence that describes the percent of men 65 years of age or older in the work force.

48. **Cellular subscribers** The number of millions of U.S. cellular telephone subscribers can be described by

$$y = 0.73x^2 + 2.69x + 3.06$$

where x is the number of years past 1980 (*Source:* Cellular Telecommunications and Internet Association).

(a) Use a table to determine a viewing window that shows a complete graph of this model for the years from 1980 to 2010. State the window used.

(b) Graph this equation.

(c) For years beyond 2010, does this graph increase or decrease? (Look at this graph in a window that includes these years.) Explain why this means the model eventually will not accurately describe the relationship between the number of cellular subscribers and the year.

49. **Environment** The Millcreek watershed area was heavily strip mined for coal during the late 1960s. Because of the resulting pollution, the streams cannot support fish. Suppose the cost C of obtaining stream water that contains p percent of the current pollution levels is given by

$$C = \frac{285{,}000}{p} - 2850$$

where $0 < p \leq 100$.

(a) Use the restriction on p and determine a range for C so that a graphing utility can be used to obtain an accurate graph. Then graph the equation.

(b) Describe what happens to the cost as p takes on values near 0.

(c) The point (1, 282,150) lies on the graph of this equation. Explain its meaning.

(d) Explain the meaning of the p-intercept.

50. ***Pollution*** Suppose the cost C of removing p percent of the particulate pollution from the exhaust gases at an industrial site is given by

$$C = \frac{8100p}{100 - p}$$

where $0 \le p < 100$.

(a) Use the restriction on p and experiment with a C-range to obtain an accurate graph of the equation with a graphing utility.

(b) Describe what happens to C as p gets close to 100.

(c) The point (98, 396,900) lies on the graph of this equation. Explain the meaning of the coordinates.

(d) Explain the meaning of the p-intercept.

51. ***Tax burden*** The dollars per capita of federal tax burden T can be described by

$$T = 1.19x^2 + 34.61x + 104.7$$

where x is the number of years past 1960 (*Source:* Internal Revenue Service).

(a) Graph this function for values of x that correspond to the years 1960–2015.

(b) Is the graph increasing or decreasing over these years? What does this tell us about the per capita federal tax burden?

52. ***Carbon monoxide emissions*** The number of millions of short tons of carbon monoxide emissions, y, in the United States can be described by

$$y = 0.0043x^3 - 0.24x^2 + 0.583x + 199.8$$

where x is the number of years past 1970 (*Source:* Environmental Protection Agency).

(a) Graph this function for values of x that represent the years 1970–2010.

(b) According to this function, how many short tons of emissions occurred in 2010?

(c) For years beyond 2000, does the function increase or decrease? If the model is accurate for these future years, what does this tell planners?

OBJECTIVES   1.5

- To solve systems of linear equations in two variables by graphing
- To solve systems of linear equations by substitution
- To solve systems of linear equations by elimination
- To solve systems of three linear equations in three variables

Solutions of Systems of Linear Equations

| APPLICATION PREVIEW |

Suppose that a person has $200,000 invested, part at 9% and part at 8%, and that the yearly income from the two investments is $17,200. If x represents the amount invested at 9% and y represents the amount invested at 8%, then to find how much is invested at each rate we must find the values of x and y that satisfy both

$$x + y = 200{,}000 \quad \text{and} \quad 0.09x + 0.08y = 17{,}200$$

(See Example 3.)
Methods of solving systems of linear equations are discussed in this section.

Graphical Solution   In the previous sections, we graphed linear equations in two variables and observed that the graphs are straight lines. Each point on the graph represents an ordered pair of values (x, y) that satisfies the equation, so a point of intersection of two (or more) lines represents a solution to both (or all) the equations of those lines.

The equations are referred to as a **system of equations,** and the ordered pairs (x, y) that satisfy all the equations are the **solutions** (or **simultaneous solutions**) of the system. We can use graphing to find the solution of a system of equations.

EXAMPLE   1   Graphical Solution of a System

Use graphing to find the solution of the system

$$\begin{cases} 4x + 3y = 11 \\ 2x - 5y = -1 \end{cases}$$

Solution

The graphs of the two equations intersect (meet) at the point (2, 1). (See Figure 1.25.) The solution of the system is $x = 2$, $y = 1$. Note that these values satisfy both equations. ■

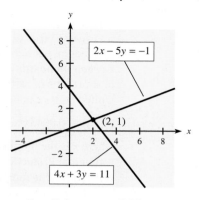

Figure 1.25

Two distinct nonparallel lines: one solution

If the graphs of two equations are parallel lines, they have no point in common, and thus the system has no solution. Such a system of equations is called **inconsistent.** For example,

$$\begin{cases} 4x + 3y = 4 \\ 8x + 6y = 18 \end{cases}$$

is an **inconsistent system** (see Figure 1.26(a)).

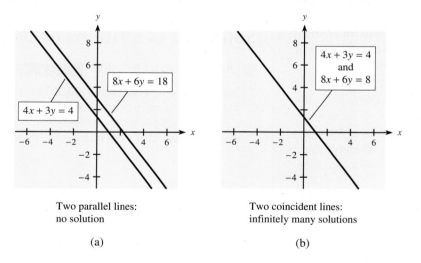

Figure 1.26

(a) Two parallel lines: no solution

(b) Two coincident lines: infinitely many solutions

It is also possible that two equations describe the same line. When this happens, the equations are equivalent, and values that satisfy either equation are solutions of the system. For example,

$$\begin{cases} 4x + 3y = 4 \\ 8x + 6y = 8 \end{cases}$$

is called a **dependent system** because all points that satisfy one equation also satisfy the other (see Figure 1.26(b)).

Figures 1.25, 1.26(a), and 1.26(b) represent the three possibilities that can occur when we are solving a system of two linear equations in two variables.

Solution by Substitution   Graphical solution methods may yield only approximate solutions to some systems. Exact solutions can be found using algebraic methods, which are based on the fact that equivalent systems result when any of the following operations is performed.

Equivalent Systems	**Equivalent systems** result when
	1. One expression is replaced by an equivalent expression.
	2. Two equations are interchanged.
	3. A multiple of one equation is added to another equation.
	4. An equation is multiplied by a nonzero constant.

The **substitution method** is based on operation (1).

Substitution Method for Solving Systems

Procedure	Example
To solve a system of two equations in two variables by substitution:	Solve the system $\begin{cases} 2x + 3y = 4 \\ x - 2y = 3 \end{cases}$
1. Solve one of the equations for one of the variables in terms of the other.	1. Solving $x - 2y = 3$ for x gives $x = 2y + 3$.
2. Substitute this expression into the other equation to give one equation in one unknown.	2. Replacing x by $2y + 3$ in $2x + 3y = 4$ gives $2(2y + 3) + 3y = 4$.
3. Solve this linear equation for the unknown.	3. $4y + 6 + 3y = 4$ $$7y = -2 \Rightarrow y = -\frac{2}{7}$$
4. Substitute this solution into the equation in Step 1 or into one of the original equations to solve for the other variable.	4. $x = 2\left(-\frac{2}{7}\right) + 3 \Rightarrow x = \frac{17}{7}$
5. Check the solution by substituting for x and y in both original equations.	5. $2\left(\frac{17}{7}\right) + 3\left(-\frac{2}{7}\right) = 4$ ✔ $$\frac{17}{7} - 2\left(-\frac{2}{7}\right) = 3 ✔$$

EXAMPLE 2 Solution by Substitution

Solve the system

$$\begin{cases} 4x + 5y = 18 & (1) \\ 3x - 9y = -12 & (2) \end{cases}$$

Solution

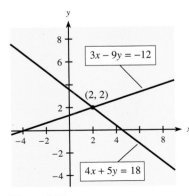

Figure 1.27

1. $x = \dfrac{9y - 12}{3} = 3y - 4$ Solve for x in equation (2).

2. $4(3y - 4) + 5y = 18$ Substitute for x in equation (1).

3. $12y - 16 + 5y = 18$ Solve for y.
$$17y = 34$$
$$y = 2$$

4. $x = 3(2) - 4$ Use $y = 2$ to find x.
$$x = 2$$

5. $4(2) + 5(2) = 18$ and $3(2) - 9(2) = -12$ ✔   Check.

Thus the solution is $x = 2$, $y = 2$. This means that when the two equations are graphed simultaneously, their point of intersection is $(2, 2)$. See Figure 1.27.

Solution by Elimination   We can also eliminate one of the variables in a system by the **elimination method,** which uses addition or subtraction of equations.

Elimination Method for Solving Systems

Procedure	Example
To solve a system of two equations in two variables by the elimination method:	Solve the system $\begin{cases} 2x - 5y = 4 & (1) \\ x + 2y = 3 & (2) \end{cases}$
1. If necessary, multiply one or both equations by a nonzero number that will make the coefficients of one of the variables identical, except perhaps for signs.	1. Multiply equation (2) by -2. $$\begin{aligned} 2x - 5y &= 4 \\ -2x - 4y &= -6 \end{aligned}$$
2. Add or subtract the equations to eliminate one of the variables.	2. Adding gives $0x - 9y = -2$
3. Solve for the variable in the resulting equation.	3. $y = \dfrac{2}{9}$
4. Substitute the solution into one of the original equations and solve for the other variable.	4. $2x - 5\left(\dfrac{2}{9}\right) = 4$ $$2x = 4 + \dfrac{10}{9} = \dfrac{36}{9} + \dfrac{10}{9}$$ $$2x = \dfrac{46}{9} \quad \text{so} \quad x = \dfrac{23}{9}$$
5. Check the solutions in both original equations.	5. $2\left(\dfrac{23}{9}\right) - 5\left(\dfrac{2}{9}\right) = 4$ ✔ $$\dfrac{23}{9} + 2\left(\dfrac{2}{9}\right) = 3 ✔$$

EXAMPLE 3   Investment Mix | APPLICATION PREVIEW |

A person has $200,000 invested, part at 9% and part at 8%. If the total yearly income from the two investments is $17,200, how much is invested at 9% and how much at 8%?

Solution

If x represents the amount invested at 9% and y represents the amount invested at 8%, then $x + y$ is the total investment.

$$x + y = 200,000 \qquad (1)$$

and $0.09x + 0.08y$ is the total income earned.

$$0.09x + 0.08y = 17,200 \qquad (2)$$

We solve these equations as follows:

$$\begin{aligned} -8x - 8y &= -1,600,000 \qquad (3) \\ 9x + 8y &= 1,720,000 \qquad (4) \\ \hline x &= 120,000 \end{aligned}$$

Multiply equation (1) by -8.
Multiply equation (2) by 100.
Add (3) and (4).

We find y by using $x = 120,000$ in equation (1).

$$120,000 + y = 200,000 \quad \text{gives} \quad y = 80,000$$

Thus \$120,000 is invested at 9%, and \$80,000 is invested at 8%.
As a check, we note that equation (1) is satisfied and

$$0.09(120,000) + 0.08(80,000) = 10,800 + 6400 = 17,200 \checkmark$$

EXAMPLE 4   Solution by Elimination

Solve the systems:

(a) $\begin{cases} 4x + 3y = 4 \\ 8x + 6y = 18 \end{cases}$ (b) $\begin{cases} 4x + 3y = 4 \\ 8x + 6y = 8 \end{cases}$

Solution

(a) $\begin{cases} 4x + 3y = 4 \\ 8x + 6y = 18 \end{cases}$

Multiply by –2 to get: $-8x - 6y = -8$

Leave as is, which gives: $8x + 6y = 18$

Add the equations to get: $0x + 0y = 10$

$$0 = 10$$

The system is solved when $0 = 10$. This is impossible, so there are no solutions of the system. The equations are inconsistent. Their graphs are parallel lines; see Figure 1.26(a) earlier in this section.

(b) $\begin{cases} 4x + 3y = 4 \\ 8x + 6y = 8 \end{cases}$

Multiply by –2 to get: $-8x - 6y = -8$

Leave as is, which gives: $8x + 6y = 8$

Add the equations to get: $0x + 0y = 0$

$$0 = 0$$

This is an identity, so the two equations share infinitely many solutions. The equations are dependent. Their graphs coincide, and each point on this graph represents a solution of the system; see Figure 1.26(b) earlier in this section.

EXAMPLE 5   Medicine Concentrations

A nurse has two solutions that contain different concentrations of a certain medication. One is a 12.5% concentration and the other is a 5% concentration. How many cubic centimeters of each should she mix to obtain 20 cubic centimeters of an 8% concentration?

Solution

Let x equal the number of cubic centimeters of the 12.5% solution, and let y equal the number of cubic centimeters of the 5% solution. The total amount of substance is

$$x + y = 20$$

and the total amount of medication is

$$0.125x + 0.05y = (0.08)(20) = 1.6$$

Solving this pair of equations simultaneously gives

$$\begin{aligned} 50x + 50y &= 1000 \\ -125x - 50y &= -1600 \\ \hline -75x &= -600 \\ x &= 8 \end{aligned}$$

$$8 + y = 20, \text{ so } y = 12$$

Thus 8 cubic centimeters of a 12.5% concentration and 12 cubic centimeters of a 5% concentration yield 20 cubic centimeters of an 8% concentration.

Checking, we see that $8 + 12 = 20$ and

$$0.125(8) + 0.05(12) = 1 + 0.6 = 1.6 \checkmark$$

CHECKPOINT

1. Solve by substitution: $\begin{cases} 3x - 4y = -24 \\ x + y = -1 \end{cases}$

2. Solve by elimination: $\begin{cases} 2x + 3y = 5 \\ 3x + 5y = -25 \end{cases}$

3. In Problems 1 and 2, the solution method is given.
   (a) In each case, explain why you think that method is appropriate.
   (b) In each case, would the other method work as well? Explain.

Calculator Note Solutions of systems of equations, if they exist, can be found by using INTERSECT. INTERSECT will give the point of intersection exactly or approximately to a large number of significant digits. Details of solving systems of linear equations are shown in Appendix C, Section 1.5. Figure 1.28 shows that the solution to the following system is $x = 2$, $y = 3$.

$$\begin{cases} 3x + 2y = 12 \\ 4x - 3y = -1 \end{cases}$$

Figure 1.28

Spreadsheet Note The details of how to use Goal Seek with Excel to solve a system of equations are shown in Appendix D, Section 1.5. The following spreadsheets show the input formulas and solution ($x = 2$, $y = 3$) for the system solved in Figure 1.28.

	A	B	C	D
1	x	= 6 − 1.5x	= 1/3 + 4x/3	= y1 − y2
2	1	= 6 − 1.5*A2	= 1/3 + 4*A2/3	= B2 − C2

	A	B	C	D
1	x	= 6 − 1.5x	= 1/3 + 4x/3	= y1 − y2
2	2	3	3	0

EXAMPLE 6   College Enrollment

Suppose the percent of males who enrolled in college within 12 months of high school graduation is given by

$$y = -0.126x + 55.72$$

Figure 1.29

and the percent of females who enrolled in college within 12 months of high school graduation is given by

$$y = 0.73x + 39.7$$

where x is the number of years past 1960 (*Source: Statistical Abstract of the United States*). Graphically find the year these models indicate that the percent of females will equal the percent of males.

Solution

Entering the two functions in a graphing utility and setting the window with x-min $= 0$, x-max $= 100$, y-min $= 0$, and y-max $= 100$ gives the graph in Figure 1.29(a). Using INTERSECT (see Figure 1.29(b)) gives a point of intersection of these two graphs at approximately $x = 18.71$, $y = 53.36$. Thus the percent of females will reach the percent of males in 1979. The models indicate that in 1979, the male percent was 53.33% and the female percent was 53.57%.

Solving a system of equations by graphing, whether by hand or with a graphing utility, is limited by two factors. (1) It may be difficult to determine a viewing window that contains the point of intersection, and (2) the solution may be only approximate. With *some* systems of equations, the only practical method may be graphical approximation.

However, systems of *linear* equations can be consistently and accurately solved with algebraic methods. Computer algebra systems, some software packages (including spreadsheets), and some graphing calculators have the capability of solving systems of linear equations.

Three Equations in Three Variables

If a, b, c, and d represent constants, then

$$ax + by + cz = d$$

is a first-degree (linear) equation in three variables. When equations of this form are graphed in a three-dimensional coordinate system, their graphs are planes. Two different planes may intersect in a line (like two walls) or may not intersect at all (like a floor and ceiling). Three different planes may intersect in a single point (as when two walls meet the ceiling), may intersect in a line (as in a paddle wheel), or may not have a common intersection. (See Figures 1.30, 1.31, and 1.32.) Thus three linear equations in three variables may have a unique solution, infinitely many solutions, or no solution. For example, the solution of the system

$$\begin{cases} 3x + 2y + z = 6 \\ x - y - z = 0 \\ x + y - z = 4 \end{cases}$$

is $x = 1$, $y = 2$, $z = -1$, because these three values satisfy all three equations, and these are the only values that satisfy them. In this section, we will discuss only systems of three linear equations in three variables that have unique solutions. Additional systems will be discussed in Section 3.3, "Gauss-Jordan Elimination: Solving Systems of Equations."

We can solve three equations in three variables using a systematic procedure called the **left-to-right elimination method.**

Unique solution

Figure 1.30

Infinitely many solutions

Figure 1.31

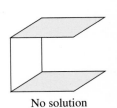

No solution

Figure 1.32

Left-to-Right Elimination Method

Procedure	Example

To solve a system of three equations in three variables by the left-to-right elimination method:

Solve: $\begin{cases} 2x + 4y + 5z = 4 \\ x - 2y - 3z = 5 \\ x + 3y + 4z = 1 \end{cases}$

1. If necessary, interchange two equations or use multiplication to make the coefficient of the first variable in equation (1) a factor of the other first variable coefficients.

1. Interchange the first two equations.

$$\begin{array}{ll} x - 2y - 3z = 5 & (1) \\ 2x + 4y + 5z = 4 & (2) \\ x + 3y + 4z = 1 & (3) \end{array}$$

2. Add multiples of the first equation to each of the following equations so that the coefficients of the first variable in the second and third equations become zero.

2. Add $(-2) \times$ equation (1) to equation (2) and add $(-1) \times$ equation (1) to equation (3).

$$\begin{array}{ll} x - 2y - 3z = 5 & (1) \\ 0x + 8y + 11z = -6 & (2) \\ 0x + 5y + 7z = -4 & (3) \end{array}$$

3. Add a multiple of the second equation to the third equation so that the coefficient of the second variable in the third equation becomes zero.

3. Add $\left(-\frac{5}{8}\right) \times$ equation (2) to equation (3).

$$\begin{array}{ll} x - 2y - 3z = 5 & (1) \\ 8y + 11z = -6 & (2) \\ 0y + \dfrac{1}{8}z = -\dfrac{2}{8} & (3) \end{array}$$

4. Solve the third equation and *back substitute* from the bottom to find the remaining variables.

4. $z = -2$ from equation   (3)

$y = \dfrac{1}{8}(-6 - 11z) = 2$ from equation   (2)

$x = 5 + 2y + 3z = 3$ from equation   (1)

so $x = 3, y = 2, z = -2$

EXAMPLE 7   Left-to-Right Elimination

Solve: $\begin{cases} x + 2y + 3z = 6 & (1) \\ 2x + 3y + 2z = 6 & (2) \\ -x + y + z = 4 & (3) \end{cases}$

Solution

Using equation (1) to eliminate x from the other equations gives the equivalent system

$$\begin{cases} x + 2y + 3z = 6 & (1) \\ -y - 4z = -6 & (2) \\ 3y + 4z = 10 & (3) \end{cases}$$
    $(-2) \times$ equation (1) added to equation (2)
    Equation (1) added to equation (3)

Using equation (2) to eliminate y from equation (3) gives

$$\begin{cases} x + 2y + 3z = 6 & (1) \\ -y - 4z = -6 & (2) \\ -8z = -8 & (3) \end{cases}$$
    $(3) \times$ equation (2) added to equation (3)

In a system of equations such as this, the first variable appearing in each equation is called the **lead variable.** Solving for each lead variable gives

$$x = 6 - 2y - 3z$$
$$y = 6 - 4z$$
$$z = 1$$

and using **back substitution** from the bottom gives

$$z = 1$$
$$y = 6 - 4 = 2$$
$$x = 6 - 4 - 3 = -1$$

Hence the solution is $x = -1$, $y = 2$, $z = 1$.

Although other methods for solving systems of equations in three variables may be useful, the left-to-right elimination method is important because it is systematic and can easily be extended to larger systems and to systems solved with matrices. (See Section 3.3, "Gauss-Jordan Elimination: Solving Systems of Equations.")

CHECKPOINT

4. Use left-to-right elimination to solve.

$$\begin{cases} x - y - z = 0 & (1) \\ y - 2z = -18 & (2) \\ x + y + z = 6 & (3) \end{cases}$$

CHECKPOINT SOLUTIONS

1. $x + y = -1$ means $x = -y - 1$, so $3x - 4y = -24$ becomes

$$3(-y - 1) - 4y = -24$$
$$-3y - 3 - 4y = -24$$
$$-7y = -21$$
$$y = 3$$

Hence $x = -3 - 1 = -4$, and the solution is $x = -4$, $y = 3$.

2. Multiply the first equation by (-3) and the second by (2). Add the resulting equations to eliminate the x-variable and solve for y.

$$-6x - 9y = -15$$
$$\underline{6x + 10y = -50}$$
$$y = -65$$

Hence $2x + 3(-65) = 5$ or $2x - 195 = 5$, so $2x = 200$. Thus $x = 100$ and $y = -65$.

3. (a) Substitution works well in Problem 1 because it is easy to solve for x (or for y). Substitution would not work well in Problem 2 because solving for x (or for y) would introduce fractions.

   (b) Elimination would work well in Problem 1 if we multiplied the first equation by 4. As stated in (a), substitution would not be as easy in Problem 2.

4.
$$\begin{cases} x - y - z = 0 & (1) \\ y - 2z = -18 & (2) \\ x + y + z = 6 & (3) \end{cases}$$

Add $(-1) \times$ equation (1) to equation (3).

$$\begin{cases} x - y - z = 0 & (1) \\ y - 2z = -18 & (2) \\ 2y + 2z = 6 & (3) \end{cases}$$

Add $(-2) \times$ equation (2) to equation (3).

$$\begin{cases} x - y - z = 0 \\ y - 2z = -18 \\ 6z = 42 \end{cases}$$

Solve the equations for x, y, and z.

$$x = y + z$$
$$y = 2z - 18$$
$$z = 7$$

Back substitution gives $y = 14 - 18 = -4$ and $x = -4 + 7 = 3$. Thus the solution is $x = 3$, $y = -4$, $z = 7$.

| EXERCISES | **1.5**

In Problems 1–4, the graphs of two equations are shown. Decide whether the system of equations in each problem has one solution, no solution, or an infinite number of solutions. If the system has one solution, estimate it.

1.

2.

3.

4.

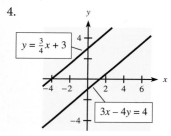

In Problems 5–8, solve the systems of equations by using graphical methods.

5. $\begin{cases} 4x - 2y = 4 \\ x - 2y = -2 \end{cases}$

6. $\begin{cases} x - y = -2 \\ 2x + y = -1 \end{cases}$

7. $\begin{cases} 3x - y = 10 \\ 6x - 2y = 5 \end{cases}$

8. $\begin{cases} 2x - y = 3 \\ 4x - 2y = 6 \end{cases}$

In Problems 9–12, solve the systems of equations by substitution.

9. $\begin{cases} 3x - 2y = 6 \\ 4y = 8 \end{cases}$

10. $\begin{cases} 3x = 6 \\ 4x - 3y = 5 \end{cases}$

11. $\begin{cases} 2x - y = 2 \\ 3x + 4y = 6 \end{cases}$

12. $\begin{cases} 4x - y = 3 \\ 2x + 3y = 19 \end{cases}$

In Problems 13–24, solve each system by elimination or by any convenient method.

13. $\begin{cases} 7x + 2y = 26 \\ 3x - 4y = 16 \end{cases}$

14. $\begin{cases} 2x + 5y = 24 \\ -6x + 2y = 30 \end{cases}$

15. $\begin{cases} 3x + 4y = 1 \\ 2x - 3y = 12 \end{cases}$

16. $\begin{cases} 5x - 2y = 4 \\ 2x - 3y = 5 \end{cases}$

17. $\begin{cases} -4x + 3y = -5 \\ 3x - 2y = 4 \end{cases}$

18. $\begin{cases} x + 2y = 3 \\ 3x + 6y = 6 \end{cases}$

19. $\begin{cases} 0.2x - 0.3y = 4 \\ 2.3x - y = 1.2 \end{cases}$

20. $\begin{cases} 0.5x + y = 3 \\ 0.3x + 0.2y = 6 \end{cases}$

21. $\begin{cases} \frac{5}{2}x - \frac{7}{2}y = -1 \\ 8x + 3y = 11 \end{cases}$

22. $\begin{cases} x - \frac{1}{2}y = 1 \\ \frac{2}{3}x - \frac{1}{3}y = 1 \end{cases}$

23. $\begin{cases} 4x + 6y = 4 \\ 2x + 3y = 2 \end{cases}$

24. $\begin{cases} 6x - 4y = 16 \\ 9x - 6y = 24 \end{cases}$

Use a graphing calculator or Excel to find the solution of each system of equations in Problems 25–28.

25. $\begin{cases} y = 8 - \dfrac{3x}{2} \\ y = \dfrac{3x}{4} - 1 \end{cases}$

26. $\begin{cases} y = 9 - \dfrac{2x}{3} \\ y = 5 + \dfrac{2x}{3} \end{cases}$

27. $\begin{cases} 5x + 3y = -2 \\ 3x + 7y = 4 \end{cases}$

28. $\begin{cases} 4x - 5y = -3 \\ 2x - 7y = -6 \end{cases}$

Use the left-to-right elimination method to solve the systems in Problems 29–34.

29. $\begin{cases} x + 2y + z = 2 \\ -y + 3z = 8 \\ 2z = 10 \end{cases}$

30. $\begin{cases} x - 2y + 2z = -10 \\ y + 4z = -10 \\ -3z = 9 \end{cases}$

31. $\begin{cases} x - y - 8z = 0 \\ y + 4z = 8 \\ 3y + 14z = 22 \end{cases}$

32. $\begin{cases} x + 3y - 8z = 20 \\ y - 3z = 11 \\ 2y + 7z = -4 \end{cases}$

33. $\begin{cases} x + 4y - 2z = 9 \\ x + 5y + 2z = -2 \\ x + 4y - 28z = 22 \end{cases}$

34. $\begin{cases} x - 3y - z = 0 \\ x - 2y + z = 8 \\ 2x - 6y + z = 6 \end{cases}$

APPLICATIONS

35. **Personal expenditures** Since 1995, the total personal expenditures (in billions of dollars) in the United States for food, $f(x)$, and for housing, $h(x)$, can be described by

$f(x) = 40.74x + 742.65$ and $h(x) = 47.93x + 725$

where x is the number of years past 1995 (*Source:* U.S. Department of Commerce). Find the year in which these expenditures were equal and the amount spent on each.

36. **Population distribution** Using U.S. Census Bureau data (and projections to 2050), the percent of the U.S.

population that is black $B(x)$ and Hispanic $H(x)$ can be described by

$$B(x) = 0.057x + 12.3 \quad \text{and} \quad H(x) = 0.224x + 9.01$$

where x is the number of years past 1990.

(a) In what year were the percents of these groups equal? What was the percent of each?

(b) Do these models indicate there are more blacks or more Hispanics in 2012?

37. *Pricing* A concert promoter needs to make $42,000 from the sale of 1800 tickets. The promoter charges $20 for some tickets and $30 for the others.

(a) If there are x of the $20 tickets sold and y of the $30 tickets sold, write an equation that states that the sum of the tickets sold is 1800.

(b) How much money is received from the sale of x tickets for 20 dollars each?

(c) How much money is received from the sale of y tickets for 30 dollars each?

(d) Write an equation that states that the total amount received from the sale is 42,000 dollars.

(e) Solve the equations simultaneously to find how many tickets of each type must be sold to yield the $42,000.

38. *Rental income* A woman has $500,000 invested in two rental properties. One yields an annual return of 10% on her investment, and the other returns 12% per year on her investment. Her total annual return from the two investments is $53,000. Let x represent the amount of the 10% investment and y represent the amount of the 12% investment.

(a) Write an equation that states that the sum of the investments is 500,000 dollars.

(b) What is the annual return on the 10% investment?

(c) What is the annual return on the 12% investment?

(d) Write an equation that states that the sum of the annual returns is 53,000 dollars.

(e) Solve these two equations simultaneously to find how much is invested in each property.

39. *Investment yields* One safe investment pays 10% per year, and a riskier investment pays 18% per year. A woman who has $145,600 to invest would like to have an income of $20,000 per year from her investments. How much should she invest at each rate?

40. *Loans* A bank lent $237,000 to a company for the development of two products. If the loan for product A was for $69,000 more than that for product B, how much was lent for each product?

41. *Rental income* A woman has $470,000 invested in two rental properties. One yields 10% on the investment, and the other yields 12%. Her total income from them is $51,000. How much is her income from each property?

42. *Loans* Mr. Jackson borrowed money from his bank and on his life insurance to start a business. His interest rate on the bank loan was 10%, and his rate on the

insurance loan was 12%. If the total amount borrowed was $100,000 and his total yearly interest payment was $10,900, how much did he borrow from the bank?

43. *Nutrition* Each ounce of substance A supplies 5% of the nutrition a patient needs. Substance B supplies 12% of the required nutrition per ounce. If digestive restrictions require that the ratio of substance A to substance B be 3/5, how many ounces of each should be in the diet to provide 100% of the required nutrition?

44. *Nutrition* A glass of skim milk supplies 0.1 mg of iron and 8.5 g of protein. A quarter pound of lean red meat provides 3.4 mg of iron and 22 g of protein. If a person on a special diet is to have 7.15 mg of iron and 73.75 g of protein, how many glasses of skim milk and how many quarter-pound servings of meat would provide this?

45. *Bacterial growth* Bacteria of species A and species B are kept in a single test tube, where they are fed two nutrients. Each day the test tube is supplied with 10,600 units of the first nutrient and 19,650 units of the second nutrient. Each bacterium of species A requires 2 units of the first nutrient and 3 units of the second, and each bacterium of species B requires 1 unit of the first nutrient and 4 units of the second. What populations of each species can coexist in the test tube so that all the nutrients are consumed each day?

46. *Botany* A biologist has a 40% solution and a 10% solution of the same plant nutrient. How many cubic centimeters of each solution should be mixed to obtain 25 cc of a 28% solution?

47. *Medications* A nurse has two solutions that contain different concentrations of a certain medication. One is a 20% concentration and the other is a 5% concentration. How many cubic centimeters of each should he mix to obtain 10 cc of a 15.5% solution?

48. *Medications* Medication A is given every 4 hours and medication B is given twice each day. The total intake of the two medications is restricted to 50.6 mg per day, for a certain patient. If the ratio of the dosage of A to the dosage of B is 5 to 8, find the dosage for each administration of each medication.

49. *Pricing* A concert promoter needs to take in $760,000 on the sale of 16,000 tickets. If the promoter charges $40 for some tickets and $60 for others, how many of each type must be sold to yield the $760,000?

50. *Pricing* A nut wholesaler sells a mix of peanuts and cashews. He charges $2.80 per pound for peanuts and $5.30 per pound for cashews. If the mix is to sell for $3.30 per pound, how many pounds each of peanuts and cashews should be used to make 100 pounds of the mix?

51. *Nutrient solutions* How many cubic centimeters of a 20% solution of a nutrient must be added to 100 cc of a 2% solution of the same nutrient to make a 10% solution of the nutrient?

52. *Mixtures* How many gallons of washer fluid that is 13.5% antifreeze must a manufacturer add to 200 gallons of washer fluid that is 11% antifreeze to yield washer fluid that is 13% antifreeze?

Application Problems 53–56 require systems of equations in three variables.

53. *Nutrition* Each ounce of substance A supplies 5% of the nutrition a patient needs. Substance B supplies 15% of the required nutrition per ounce, and substance C supplies 12% of the required nutrition per ounce. If digestive restrictions require that substances A and C be given in equal amounts, and the amount of substance B be one-fifth of either of these other amounts, find the number of ounces of each substance that should be in the meal to provide 100% of the required nutrition.

54. *Dietary requirements* A glass of skim milk supplies 0.1 mg of iron, 8.5 g of protein, and 1 g of carbohydrates. A quarter pound of lean red meat provides 3.4 mg of iron, 22 g of protein, and 20 g of carbohydrates. Two slices of whole grain bread supply 2.2 mg of iron, 10 g of protein, and 12 g of carbohydrates. If a person

on a special diet must have 10.5 mg of iron, 94.5 g of protein, and 61 g of carbohydrates, how many glasses of skim milk, how many quarter-pound servings of meat, and how many two-slice servings of whole grain bread will supply this?

55. *Social services* A social agency is charged with providing services to three types of clients: A, B, and C. A total of 500 clients are to be served, with $150,000 available for counseling and $100,000 available for emergency food and shelter. Type A clients require an average of $200 for counseling and $300 for emergencies, type B clients require an average of $500 for counseling and $200 for emergencies, and type C clients require an average of $300 for counseling and $100 for emergencies. How many of each type of client can be served?

56. *Social services* If funding for counseling is cut to $135,000 and funding for emergency food and shelter is cut to $90,000, only 450 clients can be served. How many of each type can be served in this case? (See Problem 55.)

OBJECTIVES

1.6

- To formulate and evaluate total cost, total revenue, and profit functions
- To find marginal cost, revenue, and profit, given linear total cost, total revenue, and profit functions
- To write the equations of linear total cost, total revenue, and profit functions by using information given about the functions
- To find break-even points
- To evaluate and graph supply and demand functions
- To find market equilibrium

Applications of Functions in Business and Economics

■ **| APPLICATION PREVIEW |**

Suppose a firm manufactures MP3 players and sells them for $50 each, with costs incurred in the production and sale equal to $200,000 plus $10 for each unit produced and sold. Forming the total cost, total revenue, and profit as functions of the quantity *x* that is produced and sold (see Example 1) is called the theory of the firm. We will also discuss market analysis, in which supply and demand are found as functions of price, and market equilibrium is found.

Total Cost, Total Revenue, and Profit

The **profit** a firm makes on its product is the difference between the amount it receives from sales (its revenue) and its cost. If *x* units are produced and sold, we can write

$$P(x) = R(x) - C(x)$$

where

$$P(x) = \text{profit from sale of } x \text{ units}$$
$$R(x) = \text{total revenue from sale of } x \text{ units}$$
$$C(x) = \text{total cost of production and sale of } x \text{ units*}$$

In general, **revenue** is found by using the equation

$$\text{Revenue} = (\text{price per unit})(\text{number of units})$$

The **cost** is composed of two parts: fixed costs and variable costs. **Fixed costs** (*FC*), such as depreciation, rent, utilities, and so on, remain constant regardless of the number of units produced. **Variable costs** (*VC*) are those directly related to the number of units produced. Thus the cost is found by using the equation

$$\text{Cost} = \text{variable costs} + \text{fixed costs}$$

---

*The symbols generally used in economics for total cost, total revenue, and profit are *TC*, *TR*, and *π*, respectively. In order to avoid confusion, especially with the use of *π* as a variable, we do not use these symbols.

EXAMPLE 1   **Cost, Revenue, and Profit | APPLICATION PREVIEW |**

Suppose a firm manufactures MP3 players and sells them for $50 each. The costs incurred in the production and sale of the MP3 players are $200,000 plus $10 for each player produced and sold. Write the profit function for the production and sale of x players.

Solution

The total revenue for x MP3 players is $50x$, so the total revenue function is $R(x) = 50x$. The fixed costs are $200,000, so the total cost for x players is $10x + 200,000$. Hence, $C(x) = 10x + 200,000$. The profit function is given by $P(x) = R(x) - C(x)$. Thus,

$$P(x) = 50x - (10x + 200,000)$$
$$P(x) = 40x - 200,000$$

Figure 1.33 shows the graphs of $R(x)$, $C(x)$, and $P(x)$.

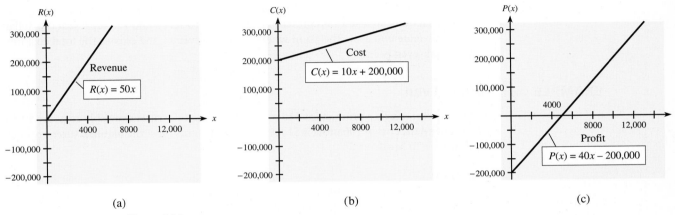

(a)   (b)   (c)

Figure 1.33

By observing the intercepts on the graphs in Figure 1.33, we note the following.

Revenue: 0 units produce 0 revenue; $R(0) = 0$.
Cost: 0 units' costs equal fixed costs = $200,000; $C(0) = FC = 200,000$.
Profit: 0 units yield a loss equal to fixed costs = $200,000;
            $P(0) = -FC = -200,000$.
            5000 units result in a profit of $0 (no loss or gain); $P(5000) = 0$.

Marginals   In Example 1, both the total revenue function and the total cost function are linear, so their difference, the profit function, is also linear. The slope of the profit function represents the rate of change in profit with respect to the number of units produced and sold. This is called the **marginal profit** $(\overline{MP})$ for the product. Thus the marginal profit for the MP3 players in Example 1 is $40. Similarly, the **marginal cost** $(\overline{MC})$ for this product is $10 (the slope of the cost function), and the **marginal revenue** $(\overline{MR})$ is $50 (the slope of the revenue function).

EXAMPLE 2   **Marginal Cost**

Suppose that the cost (in dollars) for a product is $C = 21.75x + 4890$. What is the marginal cost for this product, and what does it mean?

Solution

The equation has the form $C = mx + b$, so the slope is 21.75. Thus the marginal cost is $\overline{MC} = 21.75$ dollars per unit.

Because the marginal cost is the slope of the cost line, production of each additional unit will cost $21.75 more, at any level of production.

Note that when total cost functions are linear, the marginal cost is the same as the variable cost per unit. This is not the case if the functions are not linear, as we shall see later.

CHECKPOINT

1. Suppose that when a company produces its product, fixed costs are $12,500 and variable cost per item is $75.
   (a) Write the total cost function if x represents the number of units.
   (b) Are fixed costs equal to $C(0)$?
2. Suppose the company in Problem 1 sells its product for $175 per item.
   (a) Write the total revenue function.
   (b) Find $R(100)$ and give its meaning.
3. (a) Give the formula for profit in terms of revenue and cost.
   (b) Find the profit function for the company in Problems 1 and 2.

Break-Even Analysis

We can solve the equations for total revenue and total cost simultaneously to find the point where cost and revenue are equal. This point is called the **break-even point.** On the graph of these functions, we use x to represent the quantity produced and y to represent the dollar value of revenue *and* cost. The point where the total revenue line crosses the total cost line is the break-even point.

EXAMPLE 3   Break-Even

A manufacturer sells a product for $10 per unit. The manufacturer's variable costs are $2.50 per unit and the cost of 100 units is $1450. How many units must the manufacturer produce each month to break even?

Solution

The total revenue for x units of the product is $10x$, so the equation for total revenue is $R = R(x) = 10x$. The equation for total cost is

$$C - 1450 = 2.50(x - 100) \qquad \text{or} \qquad C = 2.50x + 1200$$

We find the break-even point by solving the two equations simultaneously ($R = C$ at the break-even point). By substitution,

$$10x = 2.50x + 1200$$
$$7.5x = 1200 \quad \text{so} \quad x = 160$$

Thus the manufacturer will break even if 160 units are produced per month. The manufacturer will make a profit if more than 160 units are produced. Figure 1.34 shows that for $x < 160$, $R(x) < C(x)$ (resulting in a loss) and that for $x > 160$, $R(x) > C(x)$ (resulting in a profit).

Figure 1.34

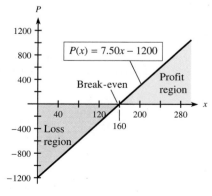

Figure 1.35

The profit function for Example 3 is given by

$$P(x) = R(x) - C(x) = 10x - (2.50x + 1200) \quad \text{or} \quad P(x) = 7.50x - 1200$$

We can find the point where the profit is zero (the break-even point) by setting $P(x) = 0$ and solving for x.

$$0 = 7.50x - 1200 \Rightarrow 1200 = 7.50x \Rightarrow x = 160$$

Note that this is the same break-even quantity that we found by solving the total revenue and total cost equations simultaneously (see Figure 1.35).

CHECKPOINT

4. Identify two ways in which break-even can be found.

Supply, Demand, and Market Equilibrium

Economists and managers also use points of intersection to determine market equilibrium. **Market equilibrium** occurs when the quantity of a commodity demanded is equal to the quantity supplied.

Demand by consumers for a commodity is related to the price of the commodity. The **law of demand** states that the quantity demanded will increase as price decreases and that the quantity demanded will decrease as price increases. The **law of supply** states that the quantity supplied for sale will increase as the price of a product increases. Note that although quantity demanded and quantity supplied are both functions of price p, economists traditionally graph these with price on the vertical axis. We will follow this tradition (see Figure 1.36).

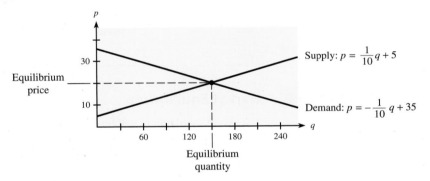

Figure 1.36

If the supply and demand curves for a commodity are graphed on the same coordinate system, with the same units, market equilibrium occurs at the point where the curves intersect. The price at that point is the **equilibrium price,** and the quantity at that point is the **equilibrium quantity.**

For the supply and demand functions shown in Figure 1.36, we see that the curves intersect at the point (150, 20). This means that when the price is $20, consumers are willing to purchase the same number of units (150) that producers are willing to supply.

In general, the equilibrium price and the equilibrium quantity must both be positive for the market equilibrium to have meaning.

We can find the market equilibrium by graphing the supply and demand functions on the same coordinate system and observing their point of intersection. As we have seen, finding the point(s) common to the graphs of two (or more) functions is called **solving a system of equations** or **solving simultaneously.**

EXAMPLE 4   Market Equilibrium

Find the market equilibrium point for the following supply and demand functions.

$$\text{Demand:} \quad p = -3q + 36$$
$$\text{Supply:} \quad p = 4q + 1$$

Solution

At market equilibrium, the demand price equals the supply price. Thus,

$$-3q + 36 = 4q + 1$$
$$35 = 7q$$
$$q = 5$$
$$p = 21$$

The equilibrium point is $(5, 21)$.

Checking, we see that

$$21 = -3(5) + 36 \checkmark \quad \text{and} \quad 21 = 4(5) + 1 \checkmark$$

Spreadsheet Note We can use Goal Seek with Excel to find the market equilibrium for given supply and demand functions, as we did to find solutions of systems in Section 1.5. The following spreadsheets show the Excel setup and solution for the market equilibrium problem of Example 4.

	A	B	C	D
1	q	p: demand	p: supply	demand − supply
2	1	= − 3*A2 + 36	=4*A2 + 1	=B2 − C2

	A	B	C	D
1	q	p: demand	p: supply	demand − supply
2	5	21	21	0

EXAMPLE 5   **Market Equilibrium**

A group of wholesalers will buy 50 dryers per month if the price is \$200 and 30 per month if the price is \$300. The manufacturer is willing to supply 20 if the price is \$210 and 30 if the price is \$230. Assuming that the resulting supply and demand functions are linear, find the equilibrium point for the market.

Solution

Representing price by p and quantity by q, we can write the equations for the supply and demand functions as follows.

Demand function:

$$m = \frac{300 - 200}{30 - 50} = -5$$
$$p - 200 = -5(q - 50)$$
$$p = -5q + 450$$

Supply function:

$$m = \frac{230 - 210}{30 - 20} = 2$$
$$p - 230 = 2(q - 30)$$
$$p = 2q + 170$$

Because the prices are equal at market equilibrium, we have

$$-5q + 450 = 2q + 170$$
$$280 = 7q$$
$$q = 40$$
$$p = 250$$

The equilibrium point is $(40, 250)$. See Figure 1.37 for the graphs of these functions.

Figure 1.37

Supply and Demand with Taxation

Suppose a supplier is taxed $K per unit sold, and the tax is passed on to the consumer by adding $K to the selling price of the product. If the original supply function $p = f(q)$ gives the supply price per unit, then passing the tax on gives a new supply function, $p = f(q) + K$. Because the value of the product is not changed by the tax, the demand function is unchanged. Figure 1.38 shows the effect that this has on market equilibrium.

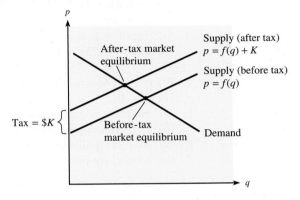

Figure 1.38

Note that the new market equilibrium point is the point of intersection of the original demand function and the new (after-tax) supply function.

EXAMPLE 6   Taxation

In Example 5 the supply and demand functions for dryers were given as follows.

$$\text{Supply:} \quad p = 2q + 170$$
$$\text{Demand:} \quad p = -5q + 450$$

The equilibrium point was $q = 40$, $p = \$250$. If the wholesaler is taxed \$14 per unit sold, what is the new equilibrium point?

Solution

The \$14 tax per unit is passed on by the wholesaler, so the new supply function is

$$p = 2q + 170 + 14$$

and the demand function is unchanged. Thus we solve the system

$$\begin{cases} p = 2q + 184 \\ p = -5q + 450 \end{cases}$$
$$2q + 184 = -5q + 450$$
$$7q = 266$$
$$q = 38$$
$$p = 2(38) + 184 = 260$$

The new equilibrium point is $q = 38$, $p = \$260$.
Checking, we see that

$$260 = 2(38) + 184 \checkmark \quad \text{and} \quad 260 = -5(38) + 450 \checkmark$$

CHECKPOINT

5. (a) Does a typical linear demand function have positive slope or negative slope? Why?
   (b) Does a typical linear supply function have positive slope or negative slope? Why?
6. (a) What do we call the point of intersection of a supply function and a demand function?
   (b) If supply is given by $p = 0.1q + 20$ and demand is given by $p = 130 - 0.1q$, find the market equilibrium point.

CHECKPOINT SOLUTIONS

1. (a) $C(x) = 75x + 12{,}500$
   (b) Yes. $C(0) = 12{,}500 = $ Fixed costs. In fact, fixed costs are defined to be $C(0)$.
2. (a) $R(x) = 175x$
   (b) $R(100) = 175(100) = \$17{,}500$, which means that revenue is $17,500 when 100 units are sold.
3. (a) Profit = Revenue − Cost or $P(x) = R(x) - C(x)$
   (b) $P(x) = 175x - (75x + 12{,}500)$
       $= 175x - 75x - 12{,}500 = 100x - 12{,}500$
4. Break-even occurs where revenue equals cost $[R(x) = C(x)]$, or where profit is zero $[P(x) = 0]$.
5. (a) Negative slope, because demand falls as price increases.
   (b) Positive slope, because supply increases as price increases.
6. (a) Market equilibrium
   (b) Market equilibrium occurs when $0.1q + 20 = 130 - 0.1q$
       $$0.2q = 110 \text{ or } q = 550$$
       $$\text{and } p = 0.1(550) + 20 = 75.$$

| EXERCISES | 1.6

TOTAL COST, TOTAL REVENUE, AND PROFIT

1. Suppose a calculator manufacturer has the total cost function $C(x) = 34x + 6800$ and the total revenue function $R(x) = 68x$.
   (a) What is the equation of the profit function for the calculator?
   (b) What is the profit on 3000 units?
2. Suppose a stereo receiver manufacturer has the total cost function $C(x) = 210x + 3300$ and the total revenue function $R(x) = 430x$.
   (a) What is the equation of the profit function for this commodity?
   (b) What is the profit on 500 items?
3. Suppose a ceiling fan manufacturer has the total cost function $C(x) = 43x + 1850$ and the total revenue function $R(x) = 80x$.
   (a) What is the equation of the profit function for this commodity?
   (b) What is the profit on 30 units? Interpret your result.
   (c) How many fans must be sold to avoid losing money?
4. Suppose a computer manufacturer has the total cost function $C(x) = 85x + 3300$ and the total revenue function $R(x) = 385x$.

   (a) What is the equation of the profit function for this commodity?
   (b) What is the profit on 351 items?
   (c) How many items must be sold to avoid losing money?
5. A linear cost function is $C(x) = 5x + 250$.
   (a) What are the slope and the C-intercept?
   (b) What is the marginal cost, and what does it mean?
   (c) How are your answers to parts (a) and (b) related?
   (d) What is the cost of producing *one more* item if 50 are currently being produced? What is it if 100 are currently being produced?
6. A linear cost function is $C(x) = 27.55x + 5180$.
   (a) What are the slope and the C-intercept?
   (b) What is the marginal cost, and what does it mean?
   (c) How are your answers to parts (a) and (b) related?
   (d) What is the cost of producing *one more* item if 50 are currently being produced? What is it if 100 are currently being produced?
7. A linear revenue function is $R = 27x$.
   (a) What is the slope?
   (b) What is the marginal revenue, and what does it mean?

(c) What is the revenue received from selling *one more* item if 50 are currently being sold? If 100 are being sold?

8. A linear revenue function is $R = 38.95x$.
   (a) What is the slope?
   (b) What is the marginal revenue, and what does it mean?
   (c) What is the revenue received from selling *one more* item if 50 are currently being sold? If 100 are being sold?

9. Let $C(x) = 5x + 250$ and $R(x) = 27x$.
   (a) Write the profit function $P(x)$.
   (b) What is the slope of the profit function?
   (c) What is the marginal profit?
   (d) Interpret the marginal profit.

10. Given $C(x) = 21.95x + 1400$ and $R(x) = 20x$, find the profit function.
    (a) What is the marginal profit, and what does it mean?
    (b) What should a firm with these cost, revenue, and profit functions do? (*Hint:* Graph the profit function and see where it goes.)

11. A company charting its profits notices that the relationship between the number of units sold, x, and the profit, P, is linear. If 200 units sold results in $3100 profit and 250 units sold results in $6000 profit, write the profit function for this company. Find the marginal profit.

12. Suppose that the total cost function for an MP3 player is linear, that the marginal cost is $54, and that the total cost for 50 players is $8700. Write the equation of this cost function and then graph it.

13. Extreme Protection, Inc. manufactures helmets for skiing and snow boarding. The fixed costs for one model of helmet are $6600 per month. Materials and labor for each helmet of this model are $35, and the company sells this helmet to dealers for $60 each.
    (a) For this helmet, write the function for monthly total costs.
    (b) Write the function for total revenue.
    (c) Write the function for profit.
    (d) Find $C(200)$, $R(200)$, and $P(200)$ and interpret each answer.
    (e) Find $C(300)$, $R(300)$, and $P(300)$ and interpret each answer.
    (f) Find the marginal profit and write a sentence that explains its meaning.

14. A manufacturer of DVD players has monthly fixed costs of $9800 and variable costs of $65 per unit for one particular model. The company sells this model to dealers for $100 each.
    (a) For this model DVD player, write the function for monthly total costs.
    (b) Write the function for total revenue.
    (c) Write the function for profit.
    (d) Find $C(250)$, $R(250)$, and $P(250)$ and interpret each answer.

(e) Find $C(400)$, $R(400)$, and $P(400)$ and interpret each answer.
(f) Find the marginal profit and write a sentence that explains its meaning.

BREAK-EVEN ANALYSIS

15. The figure shows graphs of the total cost function and the total revenue function for a commodity.

   (a) Label each function correctly.
   (b) Determine the fixed costs.
   (c) Locate the break-even point and determine the number of units sold to break even.
   (d) Estimate the marginal cost and marginal revenue.

16. A manufacturer of shower-surrounds has a revenue function of

$$R(x) = 81.50x$$

   and a cost function of

$$C(x) = 63x + 1850$$

   Find the number of units that must be sold to break even.

17. A jewelry maker incurs costs for a necklace according to

$$C(x) = 35x + 1650$$

   If the revenue function for the necklaces is

$$R(x) = 85x$$

   how many necklaces must be sold to break even?

18. A small business recaps and sells tires. If a set of four tires has the revenue function

$$R(x) = 89x$$

   and the cost function

$$C(x) = 1400 + 75x$$

   find the number of sets of recaps that must be sold to break even.

19. A manufacturer sells belts for $12 per unit. The fixed costs are $1600 per month, and the variable cost per unit is $8.
    (a) Write the equations of the revenue and cost functions.
    (b) Find the break-even point.

20. A manufacturer sells watches for $50 per unit. The fixed cost related to this product are $10,000 per month, and the variable cost per unit is $30.
    (a) Write the equations of the revenue and cost functions.
    (b) How many watches must be sold to break even?
21. (a) Write the profit function for Problem 19.
    (b) Set profit equal to zero and solve for x. Compare this x-value with the break-even point from Problem 19(b).
22. (a) Write the profit function for Problem 20.
    (b) Set profit equal to zero and solve for x. Compare this x-value with the break-even point from Problem 20(b).
23. Electronic equipment manufacturer Dynamo Electric, Inc. makes several types of surge protectors. Their base model surge protector has monthly fixed costs of $1045. This particular model wholesales for $10 each and costs $4.50 per unit to manufacture.
    (a) Write the function for Dynamo's monthly total costs.
    (b) Write the function for Dynamo's monthly total revenue.
    (c) Write the function for Dynamo's monthly profit.
    (d) Find the number of this type of surge protector that Dynamo must produce and sell each month to break even.
24. Financial Paper, Inc. is a printer of checks and forms for financial institutions. For individual accounts, boxes of 200 checks cost $0.80 per box to print and package and sell for $4.95 each. Financial Paper's monthly fixed costs for printing and packaging these checks for individuals are $1245.
    (a) Write the function for Financial Paper's monthly total costs.
    (b) Write the function for Financial Paper's monthly total revenue.
    (c) Write the function for Financial Paper's monthly profit.
    (d) Find the number of orders for boxes of checks for individual accounts that Financial Paper must receive and fill each month to break even.
25. A company manufactures and sells bookcases. The selling price is $54.90 per bookcase. The total cost function is linear, and costs amount to $50,000 for 2000 bookcases and $32,120 for 800 bookcases.
    (a) Write the equation for revenue.
    (b) Write the equation for total costs.
    (c) Find the break-even quantity.
26. A company distributes college logo sweatshirts and sells them for $50 each. The total cost function is linear, and the total cost for 100 sweatshirts is $4360, whereas the total cost for 250 sweatshirts is $7060.
    (a) Write the equation for the revenue function.
    (b) Write the equation for the total cost function.
    (c) Find the break-even quantity.

In Problems 27 and 28, *some* of the graphs of total revenue (R), total cost (C), variable cost (VC), fixed cost (FC), and profit (P) are shown as functions of the number of units, x.
    (a) **Correctly label the graphs shown.**
    (b) **Carefully sketch and label the graphs of the other functions. Explain your method.**

27.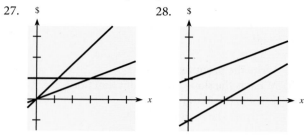

28.

SUPPLY, DEMAND, AND MARKET EQUILIBRIUM

29. As the price of a commodity increases, what happens to demand?
30. As the price of a commodity increases, what happens to supply?

Figure 1.39 is the graph of the demand function for a product, and Figure 1.40 is the graph of the supply function for the same product. Use these graphs to answer the questions in Problems 31 and 32.

Figure 1.39

Figure 1.40

31. (a) How many units q are *demanded* when the price p is $100?
    (b) How many units q are *supplied* when the price p is $100?
    (c) Will there be a market surplus (more supplied) or shortage (more demanded) when $p = \$100$?

32. (a) How many units q are *demanded* when the price p is $200?
    (b) How many units q are *supplied* when the price p is $200?
    (c) Will there be a market surplus or shortage when the price p is $200?

33. If the demand for a pair of shoes is given by $2p + 5q = 200$ and the supply function for it is $p - 2q = 10$, compare the quantity demanded and the quantity supplied when the price is $60. Will there be a surplus or shortfall at this price?

34. If the demand function and supply function for Z-brand phones are $p + 2q = 100$ and $35p - 20q = 350$, respectively, compare the quantity demanded and the quantity supplied when $p = 14$. Are there surplus phones or not enough to meet demand?

35. Suppose a certain outlet chain selling appliances has found that for one brand of stereo system, the monthly demand is 240 when the price is $900. However, when the price is $850, the monthly demand is 315. Assuming that the demand function for this system is linear, write the equation for the demand function. Use p for price and q for quantity.

36. Suppose a certain home improvements outlet knows that the monthly demand for framing studs is 2500 when the price is $1.00 each but that the demand is 3500 when the price is $0.90 each. Assuming that the demand function is linear, write its equation. Use p for price and q for quantity.

37. Suppose the manufacturer of a board game will supply 10,000 games if the wholesale price is $1.50 each but will supply only 5000 if the price is $1.00 each. Assuming that the supply function is linear, write its equation. Use p for price and q for quantity.

38. Suppose a mining company will supply 100,000 tons of ore per month if the price is $30 per ton but will supply only 80,000 tons per month if the price is $25 per ton. Assuming that the supply function is linear, write its equation.

Complete Problems 39–43 by using the accompanying figure, which shows a supply function and a demand function.

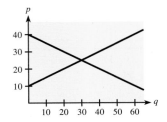

39. (a) Label each function as "demand" or "supply."
    (b) Label the equilibrium point and determine the price and quantity at which market equilibrium occurs.

40. (a) If the price is $30, what quantity is demanded?
    (b) If the price is $30, what quantity is supplied?
    (c) Is there a surplus or shortage when the price is $30? How many units is this surplus or shortage?

41. (a) If the price is $20, what quantity is supplied?
    (b) If the price is $20, what quantity is demanded?
    (c) Is there a surplus or a shortage when the price is $20? How many units is this surplus or shortage?

42. Will a price above the equilibrium price result in a market surplus or shortage?

43. Will a price below the equilibrium price result in a market surplus or shortage?

44. Find the market equilibrium point for the following demand and supply functions.

$$\text{Demand:} \quad p = -2q + 320$$
$$\text{Supply:} \quad p = 8q + 2$$

45. Find the market equilibrium point for the following demand and supply functions.

$$\text{Demand:} \quad 2p = -q + 56$$
$$\text{Supply:} \quad 3p - q = 34$$

46. Find the equilibrium point for the following supply and demand functions.

$$\text{Demand:} \quad p = 480 - 3q$$
$$\text{Supply:} \quad p = 17q + 80$$

47. Find the equilibrium point for the following supply and demand functions.

$$\text{Demand:} \quad p = -4q + 220$$
$$\text{Supply:} \quad p = 15q + 30$$

48. Retailers will buy 45 cordless phones from a wholesaler if the price is $10 each but only 20 if the price is $60. The wholesaler will supply 35 phones at $30 each and 70 at $50 each. Assuming the supply and demand functions are linear, find the market equilibrium point.

49. A group of retailers will buy 80 televisions from a wholesaler if the price is $350 and 120 if the price is $300. The wholesaler is willing to supply 60 if the price is $280 and 140 if the price is $370. Assuming the resulting supply and demand functions are linear, find the equilibrium point for the market.

50. A shoe store owner will buy 10 pairs of a certain shoe if the price is $75 per pair and 30 pairs if the price is $25. The supplier of the shoes is willing to provide 35 pairs if the price is $80 per pair but only 5 pairs if the price is $20. Assuming the supply and demand functions for the shoes are linear, find the market equilibrium point.

Problems 51–58 involve market equilibrium after taxation. Use the figure to answer Problems 51 and 52.

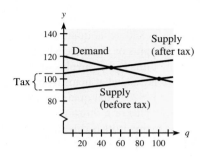

51. (a) What is the amount of the tax?
    (b) What are the original equilibrium price and quantity?
    (c) What are the new equilibrium price and quantity?
    (d) Does the supplier suffer from the tax even though it is passed on?
52. (a) If the tax is doubled, how many units will be sold?
    (b) Can a government lose money by increasing taxes?
53. If a \$38 tax is placed on each unit of the product of Problem 47, what are the new equilibrium price and quantity?
54. If a \$56 tax is placed on each unit of the product of Problem 46, what is the new equilibrium point?

55. Suppose that a certain product has the following demand and supply functions.

$$\text{Demand:} \quad p = -0.05q + 65$$
$$\text{Supply:} \quad p = 0.05q + 10$$

If a \$5 tax per item is levied on the supplier and this tax is passed on to the consumer, find the market equilibrium point after the tax.

56. Suppose that a certain product has the following demand and supply functions.

$$\text{Demand:} \quad p = -8q + 2800$$
$$\text{Supply:} \quad p = 3q + 35$$

If a \$15 tax per item is levied on the supplier, who passes it on to the consumer as a price increase, find the market equilibrium point after the tax.

57. Suppose that in a certain market the demand function for a product is given by $60p + q = 2100$ and the supply function is given by $120p - q = 540$. Then a tax of \$0.50 per item is levied on the supplier, who passes it on to the consumer as a price increase. Find the equilibrium price and quantity after the tax is levied.

58. Suppose that in a certain market the demand function for a product is given by $10p + q = 2300$ and the supply function is given by $45p - q = 360$. If the government levies a tax of \$2 per item on the supplier, who passes the tax on to the consumer as a price increase, find the equilibrium price and quantity after the tax is levied.

KEY TERMS AND FORMULAS

Section	Key Terms	Formulas
1.1	Equation, members; variable; solution	
	Identities; conditional equations	
	Properties of equality	
	Linear equation in one variable	
	Fractional equation	
	Linear equation in two variables	
	Aligning the data	
	Linear inequalities	
	Properties	
	Solutions	
1.2	Relation	
	Function	
	Vertical-line test	
	Domain, range	

Section	Key Terms	Formulas
	Coordinate system	
	Ordered pair, origin, x-axis, y-axis	
	Graph	
	Function notation	
	Operations with functions	
	Composite functions	$(f \circ g)(x) = f(g(x))$
1.3	Linear function	$y = ax + b$
	Intercepts	
	x-intercept (zero of a function)	where $y = 0$
	y-intercept	where $x = 0$
	Slope of a line	$m = \dfrac{y_2 - y_1}{x_2 - x_1}$
	Rate of change	
	Parallel lines	$m_1 = m_2$
	Perpendicular lines	$m_2 = -1/m_1$
	Point-slope form	$y - y_1 = m(x - x_1)$
	Slope-intercept form	$y = mx + b$
	Vertical line	$x = a$
	Horizontal line	$y = b$
1.4	Graphing utilities	
	Standard viewing window	
	Range	
	Evaluating functions	
	x-intercept	
	Zeros of functions	
	Solutions of equations	
	x-intercept method	
1.5	Systems of linear equations	
	Solutions	
	Graphical solutions	
	Equivalent systems	
	Substitution method	
	Elimination method	
	Left-to-right elimination method	
	Lead variable	
	Back substitution	
1.6	Cost and revenue functions	$C(x)$ and $R(x)$
	Profit functions	$P(x) = R(x) - C(x)$
	Marginal profit	Slope of linear profit function
	Marginal cost	Slope of linear cost function
	Marginal revenue	Slope of linear revenue function
	Break-even point	$C(x) = R(x)$ or $P(x) = 0$
	Supply and demand functions	
	Market equilibrium	

REVIEW EXERCISES

Solve the equations in Problems 1–6.

1. $3x - 8 = 23$

2. $2x - 8 = 3x + 5$

3. $\dfrac{6x + 3}{6} = \dfrac{5(x - 2)}{9}$

4. $2x + \dfrac{1}{2} = \dfrac{x}{2} + \dfrac{1}{3}$

5. $\dfrac{6}{3x - 5} = \dfrac{6}{2x + 3}$

6. $\dfrac{2x + 5}{x + 7} = \dfrac{1}{3} + \dfrac{x - 11}{2x + 14}$

7. Solve for y: $3(y - 2) = -2(x + 5)$

8. Solve $3x - 9 \le 4(3 - x)$ and graph the solution.

9. Solve $\frac{2}{5}x \le x + 4$ and graph the solution.

10. Solve $5x + 1 \ge \frac{2}{3}(x - 6)$ and graph the solution.

11. If $p = 3q^3$, is p a function of q?

12. If $y^2 = 9x$, is y a function of x?

13. If $R = \sqrt[3]{x + 4}$, is R a function of x?

14. What are the domain and range of the function $y = \sqrt{9 - x}$?

15. If $f(x) = x^2 + 4x + 5$, find the following.

    (a) $f(-3)$ (b) $f(4)$ (c) $f\left(\dfrac{1}{2}\right)$

16. If $g(x) = x^2 + 1/x$, find the following.

    (a) $g(-1)$ (b) $g\left(\dfrac{1}{2}\right)$ (c) $g(0.1)$

17. If $f(x) = 9x - x^2$, find $\dfrac{f(x + h) - f(x)}{h}$ and simplify.

18. Does the graph in Figure 1.41 represent y as a function of x?

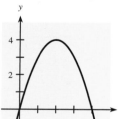

Figure 1.41

19. Does the graph in Figure 1.42 represent y as a function of x?

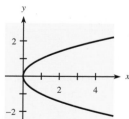

Figure 1.42

20. For the function f graphed in Figure 1.41, what is $f(2)$?

21. For the function f graphed in Figure 1.41, for what values of x does $f(x) = 0$?

22. The following table defines y as a function of x, denoted $y = f(x)$.

x	-2	-1	0	1	3	4
y	8	2	-3	4	2	7

Use the table to complete the following.

    (a) Identify the domain and range of $y = f(x)$.
    (b) Find $f(4)$.
    (c) Find all x-values for which $f(x) = 2$.
    (d) Graph $y = f(x)$.
    (e) Does the table define x as a function of y? Explain.

23. If $f(x) = 3x + 5$ and $g(x) = x^2$, find

    (a) $(f + g)(x)$ (b) $(f / g)(x)$
    (c) $f(g(x))$ (d) $(f \circ f)(x)$

In Problems 24–26, find the intercepts and graph.

24. $5x + 2y = 10$

25. $6x + 5y = 9$

26. $x = -2$

In Problems 27 and 28, find the slope of the line that passes through each pair of points.

27. $(2, -1)$ and $(-1, -4)$

28. $(-3.8, -7.16)$ and $(-3.8, 1.16)$

In Problems 29 and 30, find the slope and y-intercept of each line.

29. $2x + 5y = 10$

30. $x = -\dfrac{3}{4}y + \dfrac{3}{2}$

In Problems 31–37, write the equation of each line described.

31. Slope 4 and y-intercept 2

32. Slope $-\frac{1}{2}$ and y-intercept 3

33. Through $(-2, 1)$ with slope $\frac{2}{5}$

34. Through $(-2, 7)$ and $(6, -4)$

35. Through $(-1, 8)$ and $(-1, -1)$

36. Through $(1, 6)$ and parallel to $y = 4x - 6$

37. Through $(-1, 2)$ and perpendicular to $3x + 4y = 12$

In Problems 38 and 39, graph each equation with a graphing utility and the standard viewing window.

38. $x^2 + y - 2x - 3 = 0$

39. $y = \dfrac{x^3 - 27x + 54}{15}$

In Problems 40 and 41, use a graphing utility and
    (a) graph each equation in the viewing window given.
    (b) graph each equation in the standard viewing window.
    (c) explain how the two views differ and why.

40. $y = (x + 6)(x - 3)(x - 15)$ with x-min $= -15$, x-max $= 25$; y-min $= -700$, y-max $= 500$

41. $y = x^2 - x - 42$ with x-min $= -15$, x-max $= 15$; y-min $= -50$, y-max $= 50$

42. What is the domain of $y = \dfrac{\sqrt{x + 3}}{x}$? Check with a graphing utility.

43. Use a graphing utility and the x-intercept method to approximate the solution of $7x - 2 = 0$.

In Problems 44–50, solve each system of equations.

44. $\begin{cases} 4x - 2y = 6 \\ 3x + 3y = 9 \end{cases}$ 45. $\begin{cases} 2x + y = 19 \\ x - 2y = 12 \end{cases}$

46. $\begin{cases} 3x + 2y = 5 \\ 2x - 3y = 12 \end{cases}$ 47. $\begin{cases} 6x + 3y = 1 \\ y = -2x + 1 \end{cases}$

48. $\begin{cases} 4x - 3y = 253 \\ 13x + 2y = -12 \end{cases}$

49. $\begin{cases} x + 2y + 3z = 5 \\ y + 11z = 21 \\ 5y + 9z = 13 \end{cases}$ 50. $\begin{cases} x + y - z = 12 \\ 2y - 3z = -7 \\ 3x + 3y - 7z = 0 \end{cases}$

APPLICATIONS

51. *Endangered animals* The number of species of endangered animals, A, can be described by
$$A = 9.78x + 167.90$$
where x is the number of years past 1980 (*Source:* U.S. Fish and Wildlife Service).
    (a) To what year does $x = 17$ correspond?
    (b) What x-value corresponds to the year 2007?
    (c) If this equation remains valid, in what year will the number of species of endangered animals reach 461?

52. *Course grades* In a certain course, grades are based on three tests worth 100 points each, three quizzes worth 50 points each, and a final exam worth 200 points. A student has test grades of 91, 82, and 88, and quiz grades of 50, 42, and 42. What is the lowest percent the student can get on the final and still earn an A (90% or more of the total points) in the course?

53. *Cost analysis* The owner of a small construction business needs a new truck. He can buy a diesel truck for $38,000 and it will cost him $0.24 per mile to operate. He can buy a gas engine truck for $35,600 and it will cost him $0.30 per mile to operate. Find the number of miles he must drive before the costs are equal. If he normally keeps a truck for 5 years, which is the better buy?

54. *Heart disease risk* The Multiple Risk Factor Intervention Trial (MRFIT) used data from 356,222 men aged 35 to 57 to investigate the relationship between serum cholesterol and coronary heart disease (CHD) risk. Figure 1.43 shows the graph of the relationship of CHD risk and cholesterol, where a risk of 1 is assigned to 200 mg/dl of serum cholesterol and where the CHD risk is 4 times as high when serum cholesterol is 300 mg/dl.

Figure 1.43   Serum cholesterol (mg/dl)

    (a) Does this graph indicate that the CHD risk is a function of the serum cholesterol?
    (b) Is the relationship a linear function?
    (c) If CHD risk is a function f of serum cholesterol, what is $f(300)$?

55. *Mortgage loans* When a couple purchases a home, one of the first questions they face deals with the relationship between the amount borrowed and the monthly payment. In particular, if a bank offers 25-year loans at 7% interest, then the data in the following table would apply.

Amount Borrowed	Monthly Payment
$40,000	$282.72
50,000	353.39
60,000	424.07
70,000	494.75
80,000	565.44
90,000	636.11
100,000	706.78

Source: Comprehensive Mortgage Payment Tables,
Publication No. 492, Financial Publishing Co., Boston

Assume that the monthly payment P is a function of the amount borrowed A (in thousands) and is denoted by $P = f(A)$, and answer the following.
    (a) Find $f(80)$.
    (b) Write a sentence that explains the meaning of $f(70) = 494.75$.

56. *Profit* Suppose that the profit from the production and sale of x units of a product is given by
$$P(x) = 330x - 0.05x^2 - 5000$$

In addition, suppose that for a certain month, the number of units produced on day t of the month is

$$x = q(t) = 100 + 10t$$

(a) Find $(P \circ q)(t)$ to express the profit as a function of the day of the month.

(b) Find the number of units produced, and the profit, on the fifteenth day of the month.

57. **Fish species growth** For many species of fish, the weight W is a function of the length L that can be expressed by

$$W = W(L) = kL^3 \quad k = \text{constant}$$

Suppose that for a particular species $k = 0.03$ and that for this species, the length (in centimeters) is a function of the number of years t the fish has been alive and that this function is given by

$$L = L(t) = 65 - 0.1(t - 25)^2 \quad 0 \le t \le 25$$

Find $(W \circ L)(t)$ in order to express W as a function of the age t of the fish.

58. **Distance to a thunderstorm** The distance d (in miles) to a thunderstorm is given by

$$d = \frac{t}{4.8}$$

where t is the number of seconds that elapse between seeing the lightning and hearing the thunder.

(a) Graph this function for $0 \le t \le 20$.

(b) The point $(9.6, 2)$ satisfies the equation. Explain its meaning.

59. **Body-heat loss** Body-heat loss due to convection depends on a number of factors. If H_c is body-heat loss due to convection, A_c is the exposed surface area of the body, $T_s - T_a$ is skin temperature minus air temperature, and K_c is the convection coefficient (determined by air velocity and so on), then we have

$$H_c = K_c A_c (T_s - T_a)$$

When $K_c = 1$, $A_c = 1$, and $T_s = 90$, the equation is

$$H_c = 90 - T_a$$

Sketch the graph.

60. **Profit** A company charting its profits notices that the relationship between the number of units sold, x, and the profit, P, is linear.

(a) If 200 units sold results in $3100 profit and 250 units sold results in $6000 profit, write the profit function for this company.

(b) Interpret the slope from part (a) as a rate of change.

61. **Health care costs** The average annual cost per consumer for health care can be modeled by

$$A = 427x + 4541$$

where x is the number of years from 2000 and projected to 2018 (*Source*: U.S. Census Bureau and U.S. Centers for Medicare and Medicaid Services).

(a) Is A a linear function of x?

(b) Find the slope and A-intercept of this function.

(c) Write a sentence that interprets the A-intercept.

(d) Write a sentence that interprets the slope of this function as a rate of change.

62. **Temperature** Write the equation of the linear relationship between temperature in Celsius (C) and Fahrenheit (F) if water freezes at 0°C and 32°F and boils at 100°C and 212°F.

63. **Photosynthesis** The amount y of photosynthesis that takes place in a certain plant depends on the intensity x of the light present, according to

$$y = 120x^2 - 20x^3 \quad \text{for } x \ge 0$$

(a) Graph this function with a graphing utility. (Use $y\text{-min} = -100$ and $y\text{-max} = 700$.)

(b) The model is valid only when $f(x) \ge 0$ (that is, on or above the x-axis). For what x-values is this true?

64. **Flow rates of water** The speed at which water travels in a pipe can be measured by directing the flow through an elbow and measuring the height to which it spurts out the top. If the elbow height is 10 cm, the equation relating the height h (in centimeters) of the water above the elbow and its velocity v (in centimeters per second) is given by

$$v^2 = 1960(h + 10)$$

(a) Solve this equation for h and graph the result, using the velocity as the independent variable.

(b) If the velocity is 210 cm/sec, what is the height of the water above the elbow?

65. **Investment mix** A retired couple have $150,000 to invest and want to earn $15,000 per year in interest. The safer investment yields 9.5%, but they can supplement their earnings by investing some of their money at 11%. How much should they invest at each rate to earn $15,000 per year?

66. **Botany** A botanist has a 20% solution and a 70% solution of an insecticide. How much of each must be used to make 4.0 liters of a 35% solution?

67. **Supply and demand** A certain product has supply and demand functions $p = 4q + 5$ and $p = -2q + 81$, respectively.

(a) If the price is $53, how many units are supplied and how many are demanded?

(b) Does this give a shortfall or a surplus?

(c) Is the price likely to increase from $53 or decrease from it?

68. **Market analysis** Of the equations $p + 6q = 420$ and $p = 6q + 60$, one is the supply function for a product and one is the demand function for that product.

(a) Graph these equations on the same set of axes.

(b) Label the supply function and the demand function.

(c) Find the market equilibrium point.

69. *Cost, revenue, and profit* The total cost and total revenue for a certain product are given by

$$C(x) = 38.80x + 4500$$
$$R(x) = 61.30x$$

(a) Find the marginal cost.
(b) Find the marginal revenue.
(c) Find the marginal profit.
(d) Find the number of units required to break even.

70. *Cost, revenue, and profit* A certain commodity has the following costs for a period.

Fixed cost: $1500
Variable cost per unit: $22

The commodity is sold for $52 per unit.
(a) What is the total cost function?
(b) What is the total revenue function?
(c) What is the profit function?
(d) What is the marginal cost?
(e) What is the marginal revenue?
(f) What is the marginal profit?
(g) What is the break-even quantity?

71. *Market analysis* The supply function and the demand function for a product are linear and are determined by the tables that follow. Find the quantity and price that will give market equilibrium.

Supply Function		Demand Function	
Price	Quantity	Price	Quantity
100	200	200	200
200	400	100	400
300	600	0	600

72. *Market analysis* Suppose that for a certain product the supply and demand functions prior to any taxation are

Supply: $p = \dfrac{q}{10} + 8$

Demand: $10p + q = 1500$

If a tax of $2 per item is levied on the supplier and is passed on to the consumer as a price increase, find the market equilibrium after the tax is levied.

---

1   CHAPTER TEST

In Problems 1–4, solve the equations.

1. $10 - 2(2x - 9) - 4(6 + x) = 52$

2. $4x - 3 = \dfrac{x}{2} + 6$

3. $\dfrac{3}{x} + 4 = \dfrac{4x}{x + 1}$ 4. $\dfrac{3x - 1}{4x - 9} = \dfrac{5}{7}$

5. For $f(x) = 7 + 5x - 2x^2$, find and simplify
$$\dfrac{f(x + h) - f(x)}{h}.$$

6. Solve $1 + \dfrac{2}{3}t \leq 3t + 22$ and graph the solution.

In Problems 7 and 8, find the intercepts and graph the functions.

7. $5x - 6y = 30$ 8. $7x + 5y = 21$

9. Consider the function $f(x) = \sqrt{4x + 16}$.
(a) Find the domain and range.
(b) Find $f(3)$.
(c) Find the y-coordinate on the graph of $y = f(x)$ when $x = 5$.

10. Write the equation of the line passing through $(-1, 2)$ and $(3, -4)$. Write your answer in slope-intercept form.

11. Find the slope and the y-intercept of the graph of $5x + 4y = 15$.

12. Write the equation of the line through $(-3, -1)$ that
(a) has undefined slope
(b) is perpendicular to $x = 4y - 8$.

13. Which of the following relations [(a), (b), (c)] are functions? Explain.

(a)

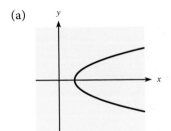

(b)

x	y
1	3
-1	3
4	2

(c) $y = \pm\sqrt{x^2 - 1}$

14. Graph $y = x^2 - 12x$
(a) in the standard window and
(b) in x-min $= -10$, x-max $= 30$; y-min $= -40$, y-max $= 40$.

15. Solve the system
$$\begin{cases} 3x + 2y = -2 \\ 4x + 5y = 2 \end{cases}$$

16. Given $f(x) = 5x^2 - 3x$ and $g(x) = x + 1$, find
(a) $(fg)(x)$
(b) $g(g(x))$
(c) $(f \circ g)(x)$

17. The total cost function for a product is $C(x) = 30x + 1200$, and the total revenue is $R(x) = 38x$, where x is the number of units produced and sold.
    (a) Find the marginal cost.
    (b) Find the profit function.
    (c) Find the number of units that gives the break-even point.
    (d) Find the marginal profit and explain what it means.

18. The selling price for each item of a product is $50, and the total cost is given by $C(x) = 10x + 18,000$, where x is the number of items.
    (a) Write the revenue function.
    (b) Find $C(100)$ and write a sentence that explains its meaning.
    (c) Find the number of units that gives the break-even point.

19. The supply function for a product is $p = 5q + 1500$ and the demand function is $p = -3q + 3100$. Find the quantity and price that give market equilibrium.

20. A building is depreciated by its owner, with the value y of the building after x months given by $y = 720,000 - 2000x$.
    (a) Find the y-intercept of the graph of this function, and explain what it means.
    (b) Find the slope of the graph and tell what it means.

21. An airline has 360 seats on a plane for one of its flights. If 90% of the people making reservations actually buy a ticket, how many reservations should the airline accept to be confident that it will sell 360 tickets?

22. Amanda plans to invest $20,000, part of it at a 9% interest rate and part of it in a safer fund that pays 6%. How much should be invested in each fund to yield an annual return of $1560?

I. Hospital Administration

Southwest Hospital has an operating room used only for eye surgery. The annual cost of rent, heat, and electricity for the operating room and its equipment is $360,000, and the annual salaries of the people who staff this room total $540,000.

Each surgery performed requires the use of $760 worth of medical supplies and drugs. To promote goodwill, every patient receives a bouquet of flowers the day after surgery. In addition, one-quarter of the patients require dark glasses, which the hospital provides free of charge. It costs the hospital $30 for each bouquet of flowers and $40 for each pair of glasses.

The hospital receives a payment of $2000 for each eye operation performed.

1. Identify the revenue per case and the annual fixed and variable costs for running the operating room.
2. How many eye operations must the hospital perform each year in order to break even?
3. Southwest Hospital currently averages 70 eye operations per month. One of the nurses has just learned about a machine that would reduce by $100 per patient the amount of medical supplies needed. It can be leased for $100,000 annually. Keeping in mind the financial cost and benefits, advise the hospital on whether it should lease this machine.
4. An advertising agency has proposed to the hospital's president that she spend $20,000 per month on television and radio advertising to persuade people that Southwest Hospital is the best place to have any eye surgery performed. Advertising account executives estimate that such publicity would increase business by 40 operations per month. If they are correct and if this increase is not big enough to affect fixed costs, what impact would this advertising have on the hospital's profits?
5. In case the advertising agency is being overly optimistic, how many extra operations per month are needed to cover the cost of the proposed ads?
6. If the ad campaign is approved and subsequently meets its projections, should the hospital review its decision about the machine discussed in Question 3?

II. Fundraising

At most colleges and universities, student organizations conduct fundraising activities, such as selling T-shirts or candy. If a club or organization decided to sell coupons for submarine sandwiches, it would want to find the best deal, based on the amount the club thought it could sell and how much profit it would make. In this project, you'll try to discover the best deal for this type of fundraiser conducted in your area.

1. Contact at least two different sub shops in your area from among local sub shops, a national chain, or a regional or national convenience store chain. From each contact, find the details of selling sub sandwich coupons as a fundraiser. In particular, determine the following for each sub shop, and present your findings in a chart.
   (a) The selling price for each coupon and its value to the coupon holder, including any expiration date
   (b) Your cost for each coupon sold and for each one returned
   (c) The total number of coupons provided
   (d) The duration of the sale
2. For each sub shop, determine a club's total revenue and total costs as linear functions of the number of coupons sold.
3. Form the profit function for each sub shop, and graph the profit functions together. For each function, determine the break-even point. Find the marginal profit for each function, and interpret its meaning.
4. The shop with the best deal will be the one whose coupons will provide the maximum profit for a club.
   (a) For each shop, determine a sales estimate that is based on location, local popularity, and customer value.
   (b) Use each estimate from part (a) with that shop's profit function to determine which shop gives the maximum profit.

Fully explain and support your claims; make and justify a recommendation.

Quadratic and Other Special Functions

© Martin Strmiska/Alamy

In Chapter 1 we discussed functions in general and linear functions in particular. In this chapter we will discuss quadratic functions and their applications, and we will also discuss other types of functions, including identity, constant, power, absolute value, piecewise defined, and reciprocal functions. Graphs of polynomial and rational functions will also be introduced; they will be studied in detail in Chapter 10. We will pay particular attention to quadratic equations and to quadratic functions, and we will see that cost, revenue, profit, supply, and demand are sometimes modeled by quadratic functions. We also include, in an optional section on modeling, the creation of functions that approximately fit real data points.

The topics and some of the applications discussed in this chapter follow.

Prerequisite Problem Type	For Section	Answer	Section for Review
Find $b^2 - 4ac$ if (a) $a = 1, b = 2, c = -2$ (b) $a = -2, b = 3, c = -1$ (c) $a = -3, b = -3, c = -2$	2.1 2.2 2.3	(a) 12 (b) 1 (c) -15	0.2 Signed numbers
(a) Factor $6x^2 - x - 2$. (b) Factor $6x^2 - 9x$.	2.1 2.2 2.3	(a) $(3x - 2)(2x + 1)$ (b) $3x(2x - 3)$	0.6 Factoring
Is $\dfrac{1 + \sqrt{-3}}{2}$ a real number?	2.1	No	0.4 Radicals
(a) Find the y-intercept of $y = x^2 - 6x + 8$. (b) Find the x-intercept of $y = 2x - 3$.	2.2 2.3	(a) 8 (b) $\frac{3}{2}$	1.3 x- and y-intercepts
If $f(x) = -x^2 + 4x$, find $f(2)$. Find the domain of $$f(x) = \frac{12x + 8}{3x - 9}$$	2.2 2.3 2.4	4 All $x \neq 3$	1.2 Functions
Assume revenue is $R(x) = 500x - 2x^2$ and cost is $C(x) = 3600 + 100x + 2x^2$. (a) Find the profit function $P(x)$. (b) Find $P(50)$.	2.3	(a) $P(x) = -3600 +$ $400x - 4x^2$ (b) $P(50) = 6400$	1.6 Cost, revenue, and profit

OBJECTIVES   **2.1**

- To solve quadratic equations with factoring methods
- To solve quadratic equations with the quadratic formula

Quadratic Equations

■ | APPLICATION PREVIEW |

With fewer workers, future income from payroll taxes used to fund Social Security benefits won't keep pace with scheduled benefits. The function

$$B = -1.057t^2 + 8.259t + 74.071$$

describes the Social Security trust fund balance B, in billions of dollars, where t is the number of years past the year 2000 (*Source:* Social Security Administration). For planning purposes, it is important to know when the trust fund balance will be 0. That is, for what t-value does

$$0 = -1.057t^2 + 8.259t + 74.071?$$

(See Example 7 for the solution.)

In this section, we learn how to solve equations of this type, using factoring methods and using the quadratic formula.

Factoring Methods   A **quadratic equation** in one variable is an equation that can be written in the *general form*

$$ax^2 + bx + c = 0 \qquad (a \neq 0)$$

where a, b, and c represent constants. For example, the equations

$$3x^2 + 4x + 1 = 0 \qquad \text{and} \qquad 2x^2 + 1 = x^2 - x$$

are quadratic equations; the first of these is in general form, and the second can easily be rewritten in general form.

When we solve quadratic equations, we will be interested only in real number solutions and will consider two methods of solution: factoring and the quadratic formula. We will discuss solving quadratic equations by factoring first. (For a review of factoring, see Section 0.6, "Factoring.")

Solution by factoring is based on the following property of the real numbers.

Zero Product Property   For real numbers a and b, $ab = 0$ if and only if $a = 0$ or $b = 0$ or both.

Hence, to solve by factoring, we must first write the equation with zero on one side.

EXAMPLE   **1**   **Solving Quadratic Equations**

Solve: (a) $6x^2 + 3x = 4x + 2$ (b) $6x^2 = 9x$

Solution

(a)
$$6x^2 + 3x = 4x + 2$$
$$6x^2 - x - 2 = 0 \qquad \text{Proper form for factoring}$$
$$(3x - 2)(2x + 1) = 0 \qquad \text{Factored}$$
$$3x - 2 = 0 \quad \text{or} \quad 2x + 1 = 0 \qquad \text{Factors equal to zero}$$
$$3x = 2 \qquad\qquad 2x = -1$$
$$x = \frac{2}{3} \qquad\qquad x = -\frac{1}{2} \qquad \text{Solutions}$$

We now check that these values are, in fact, solutions to our original equation.

$$6\left(\frac{2}{3}\right)^2 + 3\left(\frac{2}{3}\right) \overset{?}{=} 4\left(\frac{2}{3}\right) + 2 \qquad 6\left(-\frac{1}{2}\right)^2 + 3\left(-\frac{1}{2}\right) \overset{?}{=} 4\left(-\frac{1}{2}\right) + 2$$

$$\frac{14}{3} = \frac{14}{3} \; \checkmark \qquad\qquad\qquad 0 = 0 \; \checkmark$$

(b)
$$6x^2 = 9x$$
$$6x^2 - 9x = 0$$
$$3x(2x - 3) = 0$$

$$3x = 0 \quad \text{or} \quad 2x - 3 = 0$$
$$x = 0 \qquad\qquad 2x = 3$$
$$x = \frac{3}{2}$$

Check: $6(0)^2 = 9(0)$ ✔ $6\left(\frac{3}{2}\right)^2 = 9\left(\frac{3}{2}\right)$ ✔

Thus the solutions are $x = 0$ and $x = \frac{3}{2}$.

Note that in Example 1(b) it is tempting to divide both sides of the equation by x, but this is incorrect because it results in the loss of the solution $x = 0$. Never divide both sides of an equation by an expression containing the variable.

EXAMPLE 2   Solving by Factoring

Solve: (a) $(y - 3)(y + 2) = -4$ (b) $\dfrac{x + 1}{3x + 6} = \dfrac{3}{x} + \dfrac{2x + 6}{x(3x + 6)}$

Solution

(a) Note that the left side of the equation is factored, but the right member is not 0. Therefore, we must multiply the factors before we can rewrite the equation in general form.

$$(y - 3)(y + 2) = -4$$
$$y^2 - y - 6 = -4$$
$$y^2 - y - 2 = 0$$
$$(y - 2)(y + 1) = 0$$
$$y - 2 = 0 \quad \text{or} \quad y + 1 = 0$$
$$y = 2 \qquad\qquad y = -1$$

Check: $(2 - 3)(2 + 2) = -4$ ✔ $(-1 - 3)(-1 + 2) = -4$ ✔

(b) The LCD of all fractions is $x(3x + 6)$. Multiplying both sides of the equation by this LCD gives a quadratic equation that is equivalent to the original equation for $x \neq 0$ and $x \neq -2$. (The original equation is undefined for these values.)

$$\frac{x + 1}{3x + 6} = \frac{3}{x} + \frac{2x + 6}{x(3x + 6)}$$

$$x(3x + 6)\frac{x + 1}{3x + 6} = x(3x + 6)\left(\frac{3}{x} + \frac{2x + 6}{x(3x + 6)}\right) \quad \text{Multiply both sides by } x(3x + 6).$$

$$x(x + 1) = 3(3x + 6) + (2x + 6)$$
$$x^2 + x = 9x + 18 + 2x + 6$$
$$x^2 - 10x - 24 = 0$$
$$(x - 12)(x + 2) = 0$$
$$x - 12 = 0 \text{ or } x + 2 = 0$$
$$x = 12 \text{ or } x = -2$$

Checking $x = 12$ and $x = -2$ in the original equation, we see that $x = -2$ makes the denominator equal to zero. Hence the only solution is $x = 12$. ✔

CHECKPOINT

1. The factoring method for solving a quadratic equation is based on the _____ product property. Hence, in order for us to solve a quadratic equation by factoring, one side of the equation must equal _____.
2. Solve the following equations by factoring.
   (a) $x^2 - 19x = 20$ (b) $2x^2 = 6x$

EXAMPLE **3** ## Falling Object

A tennis ball is thrown into a swimming pool from the top of a tall hotel. The height of the ball from the pool is modeled by $D(t) = -16t^2 - 4t + 300$ feet, where t is the time, in seconds, after the ball was thrown. How long after the ball was thrown was it 144 feet above the pool?

Both: Shutterstock.com

Solution

To find the number of seconds until the ball is 144 feet above the pool, we solve the equation

$$144 = -16t^2 - 4t + 300$$

for t. The solution follows.

$$144 = -16t^2 - 4t + 300$$
$$0 = -16t^2 - 4t + 156$$
$$0 = 4t^2 + t - 39$$
$$0 = (t - 3)(4t + 13)$$
$$t - 3 = 0 \text{ or } 4t + 13 = 0$$
$$t = 3 \text{ or } t = -13/4$$

This indicates that the ball will be 144 feet above the pool 3 seconds after it is thrown. The negative value for t has no meaning in this application.

The Quadratic Formula   Factoring does not lend itself easily to solving quadratic equations such as

$$x^2 - 5 = 0$$

However, we can solve this equation by writing

$$x^2 = 5$$
$$x = \pm\sqrt{5}$$

In general, we can solve quadratic equations of the form $x^2 = C$ (no x-term) by taking the square root of both sides.

Square Root Property   The solution of $x^2 = C$ is

$$x = \pm\sqrt{C}$$

This property also can be used to solve equations such as those in the following example.

EXAMPLE 4 Square Root Method

Solve the following equations.
(a) $4x^2 = 5$ (b) $(3x - 4)^2 = 9$

Solution
We can use the square root property for both parts.
(a) $4x^2 = 5$ is equivalent to $x^2 = \frac{5}{4}$. Thus

$$x = \pm\sqrt{\frac{5}{4}} = \pm\frac{\sqrt{5}}{\sqrt{4}} = \pm\frac{\sqrt{5}}{2}$$

(b) $(3x - 4)^2 = 9$ is equivalent to $3x - 4 = \pm\sqrt{9}$. Thus

$3x - 4 = 3$	$3x - 4 = -3$
$3x = 7$	$3x = 1$
$x = \dfrac{7}{3}$	$x = \dfrac{1}{3}$

The solution of the general quadratic equation $ax^2 + bx + c = 0$, where $a \neq 0$, is called the **quadratic formula**. It can be derived by using the square root property, as follows:

$$ax^2 + bx + c = 0 \qquad \text{Standard form}$$
$$ax^2 + bx = -c \qquad \text{Subtract } c \text{ from both sides.}$$
$$x^2 + \frac{b}{a}x = -\frac{c}{a} \qquad \text{Divide both sides by } a.$$

We would like to make the left side of the last equation a perfect square of the form $(x + k)^2 = x^2 + 2kx + k^2$. If we let $2k = b/a$, then $k = b/(2a)$ and $k^2 = b^2/(4a^2)$. Hence we continue as follows:

$$x^2 + \frac{b}{a}x + \frac{b^2}{4a^2} = \frac{b^2}{4a^2} - \frac{c}{a} \qquad \text{Add } \frac{b^2}{4a^2} \text{ to both sides.}$$

$$\left(x + \frac{b}{2a}\right)^2 = \frac{b^2 - 4ac}{4a^2} \qquad \text{Simplify.}$$

$$x + \frac{b}{2a} = \pm\sqrt{\frac{b^2 - 4ac}{4a^2}} \qquad \text{Square root property}$$

$$x = \frac{-b}{2a} \pm \frac{\sqrt{b^2 - 4ac}}{2|a|} \qquad \text{Solve for } x.$$

Because $\pm 2|a|$ represents the same numbers as $\pm 2a$, we obtain the following.

Quadratic Formula

If $ax^2 + bx + c = 0$, where $a \neq 0$, then

$$x = \frac{-b \pm \sqrt{b^2 - 4ac}}{2a}$$

We may use the quadratic formula to solve all quadratic equations, but especially those in which factorization is difficult or impossible to see. The proper identification of values for a, b, and c to be substituted into the formula requires that the equation be in general form.

EXAMPLE 5   **Quadratic Formula**

Use the quadratic formula to solve $2x^2 - 3x - 6 = 0$ for x.

Solution

The equation is already in general form, with $a = 2$, $b = -3$, and $c = -6$. Hence

$$x = \frac{-b \pm \sqrt{b^2 - 4ac}}{2a} = \frac{-(-3) \pm \sqrt{(-3)^2 - 4(2)(-6)}}{2(2)}$$

$$= \frac{3 \pm \sqrt{9 + 48}}{4} = \frac{3 \pm \sqrt{57}}{4}$$

Thus the solutions are

$$x = \frac{3 + \sqrt{57}}{4} \quad \text{and} \quad x = \frac{3 - \sqrt{57}}{4}$$

EXAMPLE 6   **Nonreal Solution**

Using the quadratic formula, find the (real) solutions to $x^2 = x - 1$.

Solution

We must rewrite the equation in general form before we can determine the values of a, b, and c. We write $x^2 = x - 1$ as $x^2 - x + 1 = 0$. Note that $a = 1$, $b = -1$, and $c = 1$.

$$x = \frac{-(-1) \pm \sqrt{(-1)^2 - 4(1)(1)}}{2(1)} = \frac{1 \pm \sqrt{1 - 4}}{2} = \frac{1 \pm \sqrt{-3}}{2}$$

Because $\sqrt{-3}$ is not a real number, the values of x are not real. Hence there are no real solutions to the given equation.

In Example 6 there were no real solutions to the quadratic equation because the radicand of the quadratic formula was negative. In general, when solving a quadratic equation, we can use the sign of the radicand in the quadratic formula—that is, the sign of $b^2 - 4ac$—to determine how many real solutions there are. Thus we refer to $b^2 - 4ac$ as the **quadratic discriminant.**

Quadratic Discriminant

Given $ax^2 + bx + c = 0$ and $a \neq 0$,

If $b^2 - 4ac > 0$, the equation has two distinct real solutions.
If $b^2 - 4ac = 0$, the equation has exactly one real solution.
If $b^2 - 4ac < 0$, the equation has no real solutions.

The quadratic formula is especially useful when the coefficients of a quadratic equation are decimal values that make factorization impractical. This occurs in many applied problems.

EXAMPLE 7   **Social Security Trust Fund | APPLICATION PREVIEW |**

The function

$$B = -1.057t^2 + 8.259t + 74.071$$

describes the Social Security trust fund balance B, in billions of dollars, where t is the number of years past the year 2000 (*Source:* Social Security Administration). For planning purposes, it is important to know when the trust fund balance will be 0. To find when this occurs, solve

$$0 = -1.057t^2 + 8.259t + 74.071$$

Solution

We use the quadratic formula with

$$a = -1.057, \quad b = 8.259, \quad c = 74.071$$

Thus

$$
\begin{aligned}
t &= \frac{-b \pm \sqrt{b^2 - 4ac}}{2a} \\[2mm]
&= \frac{-8.259 \pm \sqrt{(8.259)^2 - 4(-1.057)(74.071)}}{2(-1.057)} \\[2mm]
&\approx \frac{-8.259 \pm \sqrt{381.383}}{-2.114} \\[2mm]
&\approx \frac{-8.259 \pm 19.529}{-2.114}
\end{aligned}
$$

We are interested only in the positive solution, so

$$t = \frac{-8.259 - 19.529}{-2.114} \approx 13.145$$

Therefore, the trust fund balance is projected to reach zero slightly more than 13 years after 2000, during the year 2014.

Calculator Note   We can use graphing calculators to determine (or approximate) the solutions of quadratic equations. The solutions can be found by using commands (such as ZERO or SOLVER) or programs. TRACE can be used to approximate where the graph of the function $y = f(x)$ intersects the x-axis. This **x-intercept** is also the value of x that makes the function zero, so it is called a **zero of the function**. Because this value of x makes $f(x) = 0$, it is also a **solution** (or **root**) of the equation $0 = f(x)$. The steps in solving an equation with a graphing utility are shown in Appendix C, Section 2.1.

For example, we can find the solutions of the equation $0 = -7x^2 + 16x - 4$ by graphing $y = -7x^2 + 16x - 4$, as in Figures 2.1(a) and 2.1(b). The graphs show $y = 0$ when $x = 2$ and when $x = 0.2857$ (approximately).

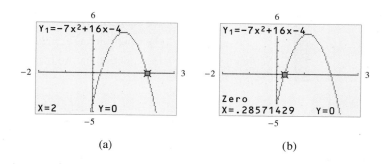

Figure 2.1   (a)   (b)

Solving $f(x) = 0$ algebraically gives solutions $x = 2$ and $x = \frac{2}{7} \approx 0.2857$. These values agree with those found graphically.

Spreadsheet Note   Excel can also be used to solve a quadratic equation. (See Appendix D, Section 2.1 for details.) For example, to solve the equation $0 = -7x^2 + 16x - 4$, we use its graph to approximate the x-intercepts (approximately 2 and 0).

The following screens show the input formula with values near 0 and 2, and the approximate solutions (in column A) after we enter 0 in column B and use Goal Seek. Goal Seek gives $-7x^2 + 16x - 4 = 0$ when $x = 2$ and when x is approximately 0.2857.

	A	B
1	x	$-7x^2 + 16x - 4$
2	2	= −7*A2^2 + 16*A2 − 4
3	0	= −7*A3^2 + 16*A3 − 4

	A	B
1	x	$-7x^2 + 16x - 4$
2	2	0
3	0.285688	−0.00032

CHECKPOINT

3. The statement of the quadratic formula says that if _____ and $a \neq 0$, then $x = $ _____.

4. Solve $2x^2 - 5x = 9$ using the quadratic formula.

CHECKPOINT SOLUTIONS

1. Zero; zero

2. (a)
$$x^2 - 19x - 20 = 0$$
$$(x - 20)(x + 1) = 0$$

$x - 20 = 0$	$x + 1 = 0$
$x = 20$	$x = -1$

   (b)
$$2x^2 - 6x = 0$$
$$2x(x - 3) = 0$$

$2x = 0$	$x - 3 = 0$
$x = 0$	$x = 3$

3. If $ax^2 + bx + c = 0$ with $a \neq 0$, then
$$x = \frac{-b \pm \sqrt{b^2 - 4ac}}{2a}$$

4. $2x^2 - 5x - 9 = 0$, so $a = 2, b = -5, c = -9$

$$x = \frac{-b \pm \sqrt{b^2 - 4ac}}{2a} = \frac{5 \pm \sqrt{25 - 4(2)(-9)}}{4}$$
$$= \frac{5 \pm \sqrt{25 + 72}}{4}$$
$$= \frac{5 \pm \sqrt{97}}{4}$$

$$x = \frac{5 + \sqrt{97}}{4} \approx 3.712 \quad \text{or} \quad x = \frac{5 - \sqrt{97}}{4} \approx -1.212$$

| EXERCISES | 2.1

In Problems 1–4, write the equations in general form.

1. $2x^2 + 3 = x^2 - 2x + 4$
2. $x^2 - 2x + 5 = 2 - 2x^2$
3. $(y + 1)(y + 2) = 4$
4. $(z - 1)(z - 3) = 1$

In Problems 5–12, solve each equation by factoring.

5. $x^2 - 4x = 12$
6. $x^2 = 11x - 10$
7. $9 - 4x^2 = 0$
8. $25x^2 - 16 = 0$
9. $x = x^2$
10. $t^2 - 4t = 3t^2$
11. $4t^2 - 4t + 1 = 0$
12. $49z^2 + 14z + 1 = 0$

In Problems 13–16, solve each equation by using the quadratic formula. Give real answers (a) exactly and (b) rounded to two decimal places.

13. $x^2 - 4x = 4$
14. $x^2 + 7 = 6x$
15. $2w^2 + w + 1 = 0$
16. $z^2 + 2z + 4 = 0$

In Problems 17–22, find the exact real solutions to each equation, if they exist.

17. $y^2 = 7$
18. $z^2 = 12$
19. $5x^2 = 80$
20. $3x^2 = 75$
21. $(x + 4)^2 = 25$
22. $(x + 1)^2 = 2$

In Problems 23–32, use any method to find the exact real solutions, if they exist.

23. $x^2 + 5x = 21 + x$
24. $x^2 + 17x = 8x - 14$
25. $\dfrac{w^2}{8} - \dfrac{w}{2} - 4 = 0$
26. $\dfrac{y^2}{2} - \dfrac{11}{6}y + 1 = 0$
27. $16z^2 + 16z - 21 = 0$
28. $10y^2 - y - 65 = 0$
29. $(x - 1)(x + 5) = 7$
30. $(x - 3)(1 - x) = 1$
31. $5x^2 = 2x + 6$
32. $3x^2 = -6x - 2$

In Problems 33–38, solve each equation by using a graphing utility.

33. $21x + 70 = 7x^2$
34. $3x^2 - 11x + 6 = 0$
35. $300 - 2x - 0.01x^2 = 0$
36. $-9.6 + 2x - 0.1x^2 = 0$
37. $25.6x^2 - 16.1x - 1.1 = 0$
38. $6.8z^2 - 4.9z - 2.6 = 0$

In Problems 39–42, multiply both sides of the equation by the LCD, and solve the resulting quadratic equation.

39. $x + \dfrac{8}{x} = 9$
40. $\dfrac{x}{x - 2} - 1 = \dfrac{3}{x + 1}$
41. $\dfrac{x}{x - 1} = 2x + \dfrac{1}{x - 1}$
42. $\dfrac{5}{z + 4} - \dfrac{3}{z - 2} = 4$

In Problems 43 and 44, solve using quadratic methods.

43. $(x + 8)^2 + 3(x + 8) + 2 = 0$
44. $(s - 2)^2 - 5(s - 2) - 24 = 0$

APPLICATIONS

45. **Profit** If the profit from the sale of x units of a product is $P = 90x - 200 - x^2$, what level(s) of production will yield a profit of $1200?

46. **Profit** If the profit from the sale of x units of a product is $P = 16x - 0.1x^2 - 100$, what level(s) of production will yield a profit of $180?

47. **Profit** Suppose the profit from the sale of x units of a product is $P = 6400x - 18x^2 - 400$.
    (a) What level(s) of production will yield a profit of $61,800?
    (b) Can a profit of more than $61,800 be made?

48. **Profit** Suppose the profit from the sale of x units of a product is $P = 50x - 300 - 0.01x^2$.
    (a) What level(s) of production will yield a profit of $250?
    (b) Can a profit of more than $250 be made?

49. **Flight of a ball** If a ball is thrown upward at 96 feet per second from the top of a building that is 100 feet high, the height of the ball can be modeled by

$$S = 100 + 96t - 16t^2 \text{ feet}$$

where t is the number of seconds after the ball is thrown. How long after it is thrown is the height 100 feet?

50. **Flight of a ball** A tennis ball is thrown into the air from the top of a hotel that is 350 feet above the ground. The height of the ball from the ground is modeled by

$$D(t) = -16t^2 + 10t + 350 \text{ feet}$$

where t is the time, in seconds, after the ball is thrown. How long after the ball is thrown does it hit the ground?

51. **Wind and pollution** The amount of airborne particulate pollution p from a power plant depends on the wind speed s, among other things, with the relationship between p and s approximated by

$$p = 25 - 0.01s^2$$

    (a) Find the value(s) of s that will make $p = 0$.
    (b) What value of s makes sense in the context of this application? What does $p = 0$ mean in this application?

52. **Drug sensitivity** The sensitivity S to a drug is related to the dosage size by

$$S = 100x - x^2$$

where x is the dosage size in milliliters.
    (a) What dosage(s) will yield 0 sensitivity?
    (b) Explain what your answer in part (a) might mean.

53. *Corvette acceleration* The time t, in seconds, that it takes a 2008 Corvette to accelerate to x mph can be described by

$$t = 0.001(0.732x^2 + 15.417x + 607.738)$$

(*Source: Motor Trend*). How fast is the Corvette going after 8.99 seconds? Give your answer to the nearest tenth.

54. *Social Security trust fund* Social Security benefits are paid from a trust fund. As mentioned in the Application Preview, the trust fund balance, B, in billions of dollars, t years past the year 2000 is described by

$$B = -1.057t^2 + 8.259t + 74.071$$

(*Source: Social Security Administration*). Find in what year the trust fund balance is projected to be $1000 billion in the red—that is, when $B = -1000$.

55. *Marijuana use* For the years from 1995 to 2006, the percent p of high school seniors who have tried marijuana can be considered as a function of time t according to

$$p = f(t) = -0.22t^2 + 4.49t + 26.3$$

where t is the number of years past 1990 (*Source: National Institute on Drug Abuse*). In what year after 1990 will the percent predicted by the function fall to 18.6% if this function remains valid?

56. *Projectile motion* Two projectiles are shot into the air over a lake. The paths of the projectiles are given by

(a) $y = -0.0013x^2 + x + 10$ and

(b) $y = -\dfrac{x^2}{81} + \dfrac{4}{3}x + 10$

where y is the height and x is the horizontal distance traveled. Determine which projectile travels farther by substituting $y = 0$ in each equation and finding x.

57. *Percent profit* The Ace Jewelry Store sold a necklace for $144. If the percent profit (based on cost) equals the cost of the necklace to the store, how much did the store pay for it? Use

$$P = \left(\frac{C}{100}\right) \cdot C$$

where P is profit and C is cost.

58. *Tourism spending* The global spending on travel and tourism (in billions of dollars) can be described by the equation

$$y = 0.787x^2 - 11.0x + 290$$

where x equals the number of years past 1990 (*Source: World Tourism Organization*). Find the year after 1990 in which spending is projected to reach $1000 billion.

59. *National health care* The total annual U.S. expenditures for national health care (in billions of dollars) can be described by

$$E = 3.51x^2 + 24.4x + 780$$

where x is the number of years past 1990 (*Source: U.S. Centers for Medicare and Medicaid Services*). If the pattern indicated by the model remains valid, when does this model predict these expenditures will reach $4 trillion (that is, $4000 billion)?

60. *Velocity of blood* Because of friction from the walls of an artery, the velocity of a blood corpuscle in an artery is greatest at the center of the artery and decreases as the distance r from the center increases. The velocity of the blood in the artery can be modeled by the function

$$v = k(R^2 - r^2)$$

where R is the radius of the artery and k is a constant that is determined by the pressure, the viscosity of the blood, and the length of the artery. In the case where $k = 2$ and $R = 0.1$ centimeters, the velocity is $v = 2(0.01 - r^2)$ centimeters per second.

(a) What distance r would give a velocity of 0.02 cm/sec?

(b) What distance r would give a velocity of 0.015 cm/sec?

(c) What distance r would give a velocity of 0 cm/sec? Where is the blood corpuscle?

61. *Body-heat loss* The model for body-heat loss depends on the coefficient of convection K, which depends on wind speed v according to the equation

$$K^2 = 16v + 4$$

where v is in miles per hour. Find the positive coefficient of convection when the wind speed is

(a) 20 mph

(b) 60 mph.

(c) What is the change in K for a change in speed from 20 mph to 60 mph?

62. *Depth of a fissure* A fissure in the earth appeared after an earthquake. To measure its vertical depth, a stone was dropped into it, and the sound of the stone's impact was heard 3.9 seconds later. The distance (in feet) the stone fell is given by $s = 16t_1^2$, and the distance (in feet) the sound traveled is given by $s = 1090t_2$. In these equations, the distances traveled by the sound and the stone are the same, but their times are not. Using the fact that the total time is 3.9 seconds, find the depth of the fissure.

- To find the vertex of the graph of a quadratic function
- To determine whether a vertex is a maximum point or a minimum point
- To find the zeros of a quadratic function
- To graph quadratic functions

Quadratic Functions: Parabolas

| APPLICATION PREVIEW |

Because additional equipment, raw materials, and labor may cause variable costs of some products to increase dramatically as more units are produced, total cost functions are not always linear functions. For example, suppose that the total cost of producing a product is given by the equation

$$C = C(x) = 300x + 0.1x^2 + 1200$$

where x represents the number of units produced. That is, the cost of this product is represented by a second-degree function, or a quadratic function. We can find the cost of producing 10 units by evaluating

$$C(10) = 300(10) + 0.1(10)^2 + 1200 = 4210$$

If the revenue function for this product is

$$R = R(x) = 600x$$

then the profit is also a quadratic function:

$$P = R - C = 600x - (300x + 0.1x^2 + 1200)$$
$$P = -0.1x^2 + 300x - 1200$$

We can use this function to find how many units give maximum profit and what that profit is. (See Example 2.) In this section we will describe ways to find the maximum point or minimum point for a quadratic function.

Parabolas   In Chapter 1, we studied functions of the form $y = ax + b$, called linear (or first-degree) functions. We now turn our attention to **quadratic** (or second-degree) **functions.** The general equation of a quadratic function has the form

$$y = f(x) = ax^2 + bx + c$$

where a, b, and c are real numbers and $a \neq 0$.

The graph of a quadratic function,

$$y = ax^2 + bx + c \quad (a \neq 0)$$

has a distinctive shape called a **parabola.**

The basic function $y = x^2$ and a variation of it, $y = -\frac{1}{2}x^2$ are parabolas whose graphs are shown in Figure 2.2.

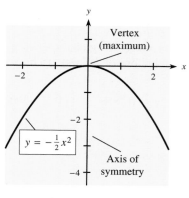

Figure 2.2   (a)   (b)

Vertex of a Parabola   As these examples illustrate, the graph of $y = ax^2$ is a parabola that opens upward if $a > 0$ and downward if $a < 0$. The **vertex,** where the parabola turns, is a **minimum point** if $a > 0$ and a **maximum point** if $a < 0$. The vertical line through the vertex of a parabola is called the **axis of symmetry** because one half of the graph is a reflection of the other half through this line.

The graph of $y = (x - 2)^2 - 1$ is the graph of $y = x^2$ shifted to a new location that is 2 units to the right and 1 unit down; its vertex is shifted from $(0, 0)$ to $(2, -1)$ and its axis of symmetry is shifted 2 units to the right. (See Figure 2.3(a).) The graph of $y = -\frac{1}{2}(x + 1)^2 + 2$ is the graph of $y = -\frac{1}{2}x^2$ shifted 1 unit to the left and 2 units up, with its vertex at $(-1, 2)$. (See Figure 2.3(b).)

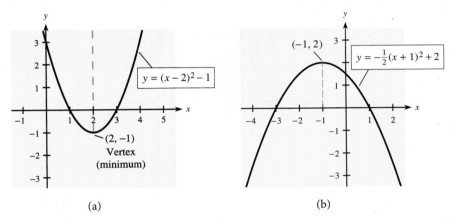

Figure 2.3   (a)   (b)

We can find the x-coordinate of the vertex of the graph of $y = ax^2 + bx + c$ by using the fact that the axis of symmetry of a parabola passes through the vertex. Regardless of the location of the vertex of $y = ax^2 + bx + c$ or the direction it opens, the y-intercept of the graph of $y = ax^2 + bx + c$ is $(0, c)$ and there is another point on the graph with y-coordinate c. See Figure 2.4.

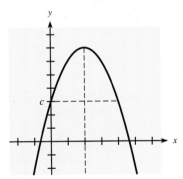

Figure 2.4

The x-coordinates of the points on this graph with y-coordinate c satisfy

$$c = ax^2 + bx + c$$

Solving this equation gives

$$0 = ax^2 + bx$$
$$0 = x(ax + b)$$
$$x = 0 \quad \text{or} \quad x = \frac{-b}{a}$$

The x-coordinate of the vertex is on the axis of symmetry, which is halfway from $x = 0$ to $x = \dfrac{-b}{a}$, at $x = \dfrac{-b}{2a}$. Thus we have the following.

Vertex of a Parabola

The quadratic function $y = f(x) = ax^2 + bx + c$ has its **vertex** at

$$\left(\frac{-b}{2a}, \; f\left(\frac{-b}{2a} \right) \right)$$

The optimum value (either maximum or minimum) of the function occurs at $x = \dfrac{-b}{2a}$ and is $f\left(\dfrac{-b}{2a} \right)$. See Figure 2.5.

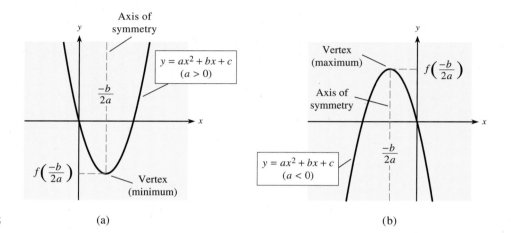

Figure 2.5

(a)   (b)

If we know the location of the vertex and the direction in which the parabola opens, we need very few other points to make a good sketch.

EXAMPLE   1   **Vertex and Graph of a Parabola**

Find the vertex and sketch the graph of

$$f(x) = 2x^2 - 4x + 4$$

Solution

Because $a = 2 > 0$, the graph of $f(x)$ opens upward and the vertex is the minimum point. We can calculate its coordinates as follows:

$$x = \frac{-b}{2a} = \frac{-(-4)}{2(2)} = 1$$

$$y = f(1) = 2$$

Thus the vertex is $(1, 2)$. Using x-values on either side of the vertex to plot additional points enables us to sketch the graph accurately. (See Figure 2.6.)

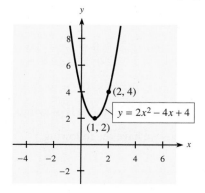

Figure 2.6

We can also use the coordinates of the vertex to find maximum or minimum values without a graph.

| EXAMPLE | **2** | **Profit Maximization | APPLICATION PREVIEW |** |

For the profit function

$$P(x) = -0.1x^2 + 300x - 1200$$

find the number of units that give maximum profit and find the maximum profit.

Solution
$P(x)$ is a quadratic function with $a < 0$. Thus the graph of $y = P(x)$ is a parabola that opens downward, so the vertex is a maximum point. The coordinates of the vertex are

$$x = \frac{-b}{2a} = \frac{-300}{2(-0.1)} = 1500$$
$$P = P(1500) = -0.1(1500)^2 + 300(1500) - 1200 = 223{,}800$$

Therefore, the maximum profit is $223,800 when 1500 units are sold.

Calculator Note   We can also use a graphing calculator to graph the quadratic function in Example 2. Even with a graphing calculator, recognizing that the graph is a parabola and locating the vertex help us to set the viewing window (to include the vertex) and to know when we have a complete graph. Details of graphing the function of Example 2 are shown in Appendix C, Section 2.2. Figure 2.7 shows the graph. Note that the graph of this function has two x-intercepts.

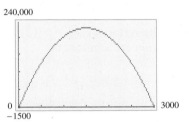

Figure 2.7

Zeros of Quadratic Functions   As we noted in Chapter 1, "Linear Equations and Functions," the x-intercepts of the graph of a function $y = f(x)$ are the values of x for which $f(x) = 0$, called the **zeros** of the function. As we saw in the previous section, the zeros of the quadratic function $y = f(x) = ax^2 + bx + c$ are the solutions of the quadratic equation $ax^2 + bx + c = 0$, which are given by the quadratic formula

$$x = \frac{-b \pm \sqrt{b^2 - 4ac}}{2a}$$

The information that is useful in graphing quadratic functions is summarized as follows.

Graphs of Quadratic Functions

Form: $y = f(x) = ax^2 + bx + c$
Graph: parabola

$a > 0$ parabola opens upward; vertex is a minimum point
$a < 0$ parabola opens downward; vertex is a maximum point

Coordinates of vertex: $x = \dfrac{-b}{2a}$, $y = f\left(\dfrac{-b}{2a}\right)$

Axis of symmetry equation: $x = \dfrac{-b}{2a}$

(continued)

x-intercepts or zeros (if real*):

$$x = \frac{-b + \sqrt{b^2 - 4ac}}{2a},$$

$$x = \frac{-b - \sqrt{b^2 - 4ac}}{2a}$$

y-intercept: Let $x = 0$; then $y = c$.

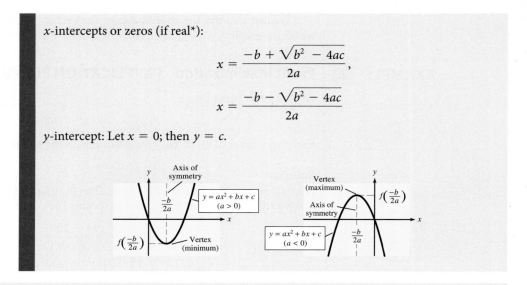

EXAMPLE 3   Graph of a Quadratic Function

For the function $y = 4x - x^2$, determine whether its vertex is a maximum point or a minimum point and find the coordinates of this point, find the zeros, if any exist, and sketch the graph.

Solution

The proper form is $y = -x^2 + 4x + 0$, so $a = -1$. Thus the parabola opens downward, and the vertex is the highest (maximum) point.

The vertex occurs at $x = \dfrac{-b}{2a} = \dfrac{-4}{2(-1)} = 2$.

The y-coordinate of the vertex is $f(2) = -(2)^2 + 4(2) = 4$.

The zeros of the function are solutions to

$$-x^2 + 4x = 0$$
$$x(-x + 4) = 0$$
$$\text{or } x = 0 \text{ and } x = 4$$

The graph of the function can be found by drawing a parabola with these three points (see Figure 2.8(a)), or by using a graphing calculator or a spreadsheet. Details of graphing quadratic (and other polynomial) functions with Excel are shown in Appendix D, Section 2.2 and the Online Excel Guide (see Figure 2.8(b)).

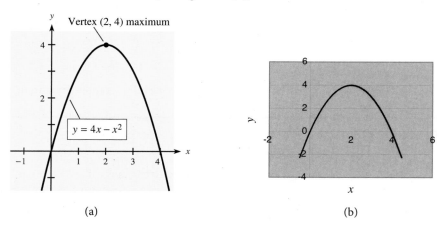

Figure 2.8   (a)   (b)

*If the zeros are not real, the graph does not cross the x-axis.

Example 3 shows how to use the solutions of $f(x) = 0$ to find the x-intercepts of a parabola if $y = f(x)$ is a quadratic function. Conversely, we can use the x-intercepts of $y = f(x)$, if they exist, to find or approximate the solutions of $f(x) = 0$. Exact integer solutions found in this way can also be used to determine factors of $f(x)$.

EXAMPLE 4   Graph Comparison

Figure 2.9 shows the graphs of two different quadratic functions. Use the figure to answer the following.

(a) Determine the vertex of each function.
(b) Determine the real solutions of $f_1(x) = 0$ and $f_2(x) = 0$.
(c) One of the graphs in Figure 2.9 is the graph of $y = 7 + 6x - x^2$, and one is the graph of $y = x^2 - 6x + 10$. Determine which is which, and why.

Solution
(a) For $y = f_1(x)$, the vertex is the maximum point, at $(3, 16)$.
     For $y = f_2(x)$, the vertex is the minimum point, at $(3, 1)$.
(b) For $y = f_1(x)$, the real solutions of $f_1(x) = 0$ are the zeros, or x-intercepts, at $x = -1$ and $x = 7$. For $y = f_2(x)$, the graph has no x-intercepts, so $f_2(x) = 0$ has no real solutions.
(c) Because the graph of $y = f_1(x)$ opens downward, the coefficient of x^2 must be negative. Hence Figure 2.9(a) shows the graph of $y = f_1(x) = 7 + 6x - x^2$. Similarly, the coefficient of x^2 in $y = f_2(x)$ must be positive, so Figure 2.9(b) shows the graph of $y = f_2(x) = x^2 - 6x + 10$.

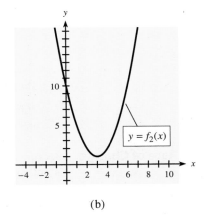

Figure 2.9   (a)   (b)

CHECKPOINT

1. Name the graph of a quadratic function.
2. (a) What is the x-coordinate of the vertex of $y = ax^2 + bx + c$?
    (b) For $y = 12x - \frac{1}{2}x^2$, what is the x-coordinate of the vertex? What is the y-coordinate of the vertex?
3. (a) How can you tell whether the vertex of $f(x) = ax^2 + bx + c$ is a maximum point or a minimum point?
    (b) In part 2(b), is the vertex a maximum point or a minimum point?
4. The zeros of a function correspond to what feature of its graph?

EXAMPLE 5   Maximizing Revenue

Ace Cruises offers a sunset cruise to a group of 50 people for a price of $30 per person, but it reduces the price per person by $0.50 for each additional person above the 50.

(a) Does reducing the price per person to get more people in the group give the cruise company more revenue?

(b) How many people will provide maximum revenue for the cruise company?

Solution

(a) The revenue to the company if 50 people are in the group and each pays $30 is $50(\$30) = \$1500$. The following table shows the revenue for the addition of people to the group. The table shows that as the group size begins to increase past 50 people, the revenue also increases. However, it also shows that increasing the group size too much (to 70 people) reduces revenue.

Increase in Group Size	Number of People	Decrease in Price	New Price ($)	Revenue ($)
0	50	0	30	$50(30) = 1500$
1	51	$0.50(1)$	29.50	$51(29.50) = 1504.50$
2	52	$0.50(2) = 1$	29	$52(29) = 1508$
3	53	$0.50(3) = 1.50$	28.50	$53(28.50) = 1510.50$
$\vdots$	$\vdots$	$\vdots$	$\vdots$	$\vdots$
20	70	$0.50(20) = 10$	20	$70(20) = 1400$
$\vdots$	$\vdots$	$\vdots$	$\vdots$	$\vdots$
x	$50 + x$	$0.50(x)$	$30 - 0.50x$	$(50 + x)(30 - 0.50x)$

(b) The last entry in the table shows the revenue for an increase of x people in the group.

$$R(x) = (50 + x)(30 - 0.50x)$$

Expanding this function gives a form from which we can find the vertex of its graph.

$$R(x) = 1500 + 5x - 0.50x^2$$

The vertex of the graph of this function is $x = \dfrac{-b}{2a} = \dfrac{-5}{2(-0.50)} = 5$, $R(5) = 1512.50$.

This means that the revenue will be maximized at $1512.50 when $50 + 5 = 55$ people are in the group, with each paying $30 - 0.50(5) = 27.50$ dollars.   ■

Average Rate of Change   Because the graph of a quadratic function is not a line, the rate of change of the function is not constant. We can, however, find the **average rate of change** of a function between two input values if we know how much the function output values change between the two input values.

Average Rate of Change

The **average rate of change** of $f(x)$ with respect to x over the interval from $x = a$ to $x = b$ (where $a < b$) is calculated as

$$\text{Average rate of change} = \frac{\text{change of } f(x)}{\text{corresponding change in } x\text{-values}} = \frac{f(b) - f(a)}{b - a}$$

The average rate of change is also the slope of the segment (or secant line) joining the points $(a, f(a))$ and $(b, f(b))$.

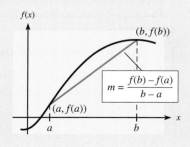

EXAMPLE 6 Average Rate of Change of Revenue

We found that the revenue for the cruise in Example 5 was defined by the quadratic function

$$R(x) = 1500 + 5x - 0.50x^2$$

where x is the increase in the group size beyond 50 people. What is the average rate of change of revenue if the group increases from 50 to 55 persons?

Solution

The average rate of change of revenue from 50 to 55 persons is the average rate of change of the function from $x = 0$ to $x = 5$.

$$\frac{R(5) - R(0)}{5 - 0} = \frac{1512.50 - 1500}{5} = 2.50 \text{ dollars per person}$$

This average rate of change is also the slope of the **secant line** connecting the points $(0, 1500)$ and $(5, 1512.50)$ on the graph of the function (see Figure 2.10).

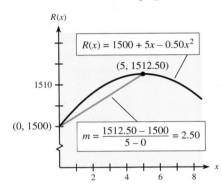

Figure 2.10

CHECKPOINT SOLUTIONS

1. Parabola
2. (a) $x = \dfrac{-b}{2a}$

    (b) $x = \dfrac{-12}{2(-1/2)} = \dfrac{-12}{(-1)} = 12$

    $y = 12(12) - \dfrac{1}{2}(12)^2 = 144 - 72 = 72$

3. (a) Maximum point if $a < 0$; minimum point if $a > 0$.
   (b) $(12, 72)$ is a maximum point because $a = -\frac{1}{2}$.
4. The x-intercepts

| EXERCISES | 2.2

In Problems 1–6, (a) find the vertex of the graph of the equation, (b) determine if the vertex is a maximum or minimum point, (c) determine what value of x gives the optimal value of the function, and (d) determine the optimal (maximum or minimum) value of the function.

1. $y = \dfrac{1}{2}x^2 + x$
2. $y = x^2 - 2x$
3. $y = 8 + 2x - x^2$
4. $y = 6 - 4x - 2x^2$
5. $f(x) = 6x - x^2$
6. $f(x) = x^2 + 2x - 3$

In Problems 7–12, determine whether each function's vertex is a maximum point or a minimum point and find the coordinates of this point. Find the zeros, if any exist, and sketch the graph of the function.

7. $y = x - \dfrac{1}{4}x^2$
8. $y = -2x^2 + 18x$
9. $y = x^2 + 4x + 4$
10. $y = x^2 - 6x + 9$
11. $\dfrac{1}{2}x^2 + x - y = 3$
12. $x^2 + x + 2y = 5$

For each function in Problems 13–16, (a) tell how the graph of $y = x^2$ is shifted, and (b) graph the function.

13. $y = (x - 3)^2 + 1$ 14. $y = (x - 10)^2 + 1$
15. $y = (x + 2)^2 - 2$ 16. $y = (x + 12)^2 - 8$

In Problems 17–20, graph each function with a graphing utility. Use the graph to find the vertex and zeros. Check your results algebraically.

17. $y = \dfrac{1}{2}x^2 - x - \dfrac{15}{2}$

18. $y = 0.1(x^2 + 4x - 32)$

19. $y = \dfrac{1}{4}x^2 + 3x + 12$

20. $y = x^2 - 2x + 5$

In Problems 21 and 22, find the average rate of change of the function between the given values of x.

21. $y = -5x - x^2$ between $x = -1$ and $x = 1$.
22. $y = 8 + 3x + 0.5x^2$ between $x = 2$ and $x = 4$.

In Problems 23–26, find the vertex and zeros and use them to determine a range for a graphing utility that includes these values; graph the function with that range.

23. $y = 63 + 0.2x - 0.01x^2$
24. $y = 0.2x^2 + 16x + 140$
25. $y = 0.0001x^2 - 0.01$
26. $y = 0.01x - 0.001x^2$

In Problems 27 and 28, (a) find the vertex of each function $f(x)$. Use the vertex to set the window in which to graph $y = f(x)$ and then (b) graphically approximate the solutions to $f(x) = 0$.

27. $f(x) = 8x^2 - 16x - 16$
28. $f(x) = 3x^2 - 18x + 16$

In Problems 29 and 30, complete the following.
(a) Use the graph of $y = f(x)$ to find an integer solution to $f(x) = 0$.
(b) Use the solution from (a) to find a factor of $f(x)$.
(c) Factor $f(x)$.
(d) Solve $f(x) = 0$.

29. $f(x) = 3x^2 - 8x + 4$ 30. $f(x) = 5x^2 - 2x - 7$

APPLICATIONS

31. *Profit* The daily profit from the sale of a product is given by $P = 16x - 0.1x^2 - 100$ dollars.
    (a) What level of production maximizes profit?
    (b) What is the maximum possible profit?

32. *Profit* The daily profit from the sale of x units of a product is $P = 80x - 0.4x^2 - 200$ dollars.
    (a) What level of production maximizes profit?
    (b) What is the maximum possible profit?

33. *Crop yield* The yield in bushels from a grove of orange trees is given by $Y = x(800 - x)$, where x is the number of orange trees per acre. How many trees will maximize the yield?

34. *Stimulus-response* One of the early results in psychology relating the magnitude of a stimulus x to the magnitude of a response y is expressed by the equation

$$y = kx^2$$

where k is an experimental constant. Sketch this graph for $k = 1$, $k = 2$, and $k = 4$.

35. *Drug sensitivity* The sensitivity S to a drug is related to the dosage x (in milligrams) by

$$S = 1000x - x^2$$

Sketch the graph of this function and determine what dosage gives maximum sensitivity. Use the graph to determine the maximum sensitivity.

36. *Maximizing an enclosed area* If 100 feet of fence is used to enclose a rectangular yard, then the resulting area is given by

$$A = x(50 - x)$$

where x feet is the width of the rectangle and $50 - x$ feet is the length. Graph this equation and determine the length and width that give maximum area.

37. *Photosynthesis* The rate of photosynthesis R for a certain plant depends on the intensity of light x, in lumens, according to

$$R = 270x - 90x^2$$

Sketch the graph of this function, and determine the intensity that gives the maximum rate.

38. *Projectiles* A ball thrown vertically into the air has its height above ground given by

$$s = 112t - 16t^2$$

where t is in seconds and s is in feet. Find the maximum height of the ball.

39. *Projectiles* Two projectiles are shot into the air from the same location. The paths of the projectiles are parabolas and are given by

(a) $y = -0.0013x^2 + x + 10$ and

(b) $y = \dfrac{-x^2}{81} + \dfrac{4}{3}x + 10$

where x is the horizontal distance and y is the vertical distance, both in feet. Determine which projectile goes higher by locating the vertex of each parabola.

40. *Flow rates of water* The speed at which water travels in a pipe can be measured by directing the flow through an elbow and measuring the height to which it spurts out the top. If the elbow height is 10 cm, the equation

relating the height h (in centimeters) of the water above the elbow and its velocity v (in centimeters per second) is given by

$$v^2 = 1960(h + 10)$$

Solve this equation for h and graph the result, using the velocity as the independent variable.

41. *Cost* The following figure shows the graph of a total cost function, with x equal to the number of units produced.
    (a) Is the average rate of change of cost greater from $x = a$ to $x = b$ or from $x = b$ to $x = c$? Explain.
    (b) Would the number of units d need to satisfy $d < b$ or $d > b$ for the average rate of change of cost from $x = a$ to $x = d$ to be greater than that from $x = a$ to $x = b$? Explain.

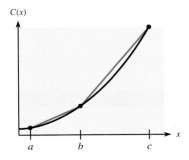

42. *Revenue* The following figure shows the graph of a total revenue function, with x equal to the number of units sold.
    (a) Is the average rate of change of revenue negative from $x = a$ to $x = b$ or from $x = b$ to $x = c$? Explain.
    (b) Would the number of units d need to satisfy $d < b$ or $d > b$ for the average rate of change of revenue from $x = a$ to $x = d$ to be greater than that from $x = a$ to $x = b$? Explain.

43. *Apartment rental* The owner of an apartment building can rent all 50 apartments if she charges $600 per month, but she rents one fewer apartment for each $20 increase in monthly rent.
    (a) Construct a table that gives the revenue generated if she charges $600, $620, and $640.
    (b) Does her revenue from the rental of the apartments increase or decrease as she increases the rent from $600 to $640?

(c) Write an equation that gives the revenue from rental of the apartments if she makes x increases of $20 in the rent.
(d) Find the rent she should charge to maximize her revenue.

44. *Revenue* The owner of a skating rink rents the rink for parties at $600 if 50 or fewer skaters attend, so that the cost per person is $12 if 50 attend. For each 5 skaters above 50, she reduces the price per skater by $0.50.
    (a) Construct a table that gives the revenue generated if 50, 60, and 70 skaters attend.
    (b) Does the owner's revenue from the rental of the rink increase or decrease as the number of skaters increases from 50 to 70?
    (c) Write the equation that describes the revenue for parties with x more than 50 skaters.
    (d) Find the number of skaters that will maximize the revenue.

45. *Pension resources* The Pension Benefit Guaranty Corporation is the agency that insures pensions. The figure shows one study's projection for the agency's total resources, initially rising (from taking over the assets of failing plans) but then falling (as more workers retire and payouts increase).
    (a) What kind of function might be used to model the agency's total resources?
    (b) If a function of the form $f(x) = ax^2 + bx + c$ were used to model these total resources, would $f(x)$ have $a > 0$ or $a < 0$? Explain.
    (c) If the model from part (b) used x as the number of years past 2004, explain why the model would have $b > 0$ and $c > 0$.

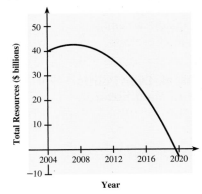

46. *Projectile motion* When a stone is thrown upward, it follows a parabolic path given by a form of the equation

$$y = ax^2 + bx + c$$

If $y = 0$ represents ground level, find the equation of a stone that is thrown from ground level at $x = 0$ and lands on the ground 40 units away if the stone reaches a maximum height of 40 units. (*Hint:* Find the coordinates of the vertex of the parabola and two other points.)

47. *Health care* Many politicians are discussing national health insurance because health care costs are increasing so rapidly. Health care costs in the United States (in billions of dollars) are given by

$$y = 5.033x^2 + 100.5x + 1378$$

where x is the number of years past 2000 (*Source:* U.S. Centers for Medicare and Medicaid Services). Does the model indicate that the cost projections from 2010 to 2015 increase more rapidly than the costs during the years 2005 to 2010?

48. *Women in the work force* The percent of the total work force that is female is given by

$$p(t) = -0.0034t^2 + 0.45t + 34$$

where t is the number of years past 1970.
(a) Graph the function $y = p(t)$.
(b) From the equation, identify the maximum point on the graph of $y = p(t)$.

(c) In what year is the percent of women workers at its maximum, according to this model?

Union participation The percent of U.S. workers who belonged to unions for selected years from 1930 to 2005 can be described by

$$u(x) = -0.013x^2 + 1.56x - 18.87$$

where x is the number of years past 1900 (*Source: World Almanac*). Use this function in Problems 49–51.
49. Graph the function $u(x)$.
50. For what year does the function $u(x)$ indicate a maximum percentage of workers belonged to unions?
51. (a) For what years does the function $u(x)$ predict that 0% of U.S. workers will belong to unions?
    (b) When can you guarantee that $u(x)$ can no longer be used to describe the percent of U.S. workers who belong to unions?

Business Applications Using Quadratics

- To find break-even points by using quadratic cost and revenue functions
- To maximize quadratic revenue and profit functions
- To graph quadratic supply and demand functions
- To find market equilibrium by using quadratic supply and demand functions

| APPLICATION PREVIEW |

Suppose that the supply function for a product is given by $2p - q - 38 = 0$ and the demand function is given by $p(q + 4) = 400$. Finding the market equilibrium involves solving a quadratic equation (see Example 3).

In this section, we graph quadratic supply and demand functions and find market equilibrium by solving supply and demand functions simultaneously using quadratic methods. We will also discuss quadratic revenue, cost, and profit functions, including break-even points and profit maximization.

Break-Even Points and Maximization

When we know the functions for total costs, $C(x)$, and total revenue, $R(x)$, we can find the break-even point by finding the quantity x that makes $C(x) = R(x)$.

For example, if $C(x) = 360 + 40x + 0.1x^2$ and $R(x) = 60x$, then setting $C(x) = R(x)$ we have

$$360 + 40x + 0.1x^2 = 60x$$
$$0.1x^2 - 20x + 360 = 0$$
$$x^2 - 200x + 3600 = 0$$
$$(x - 20)(x - 180) = 0$$
$$x = 20 \quad \text{or} \quad x = 180$$

Thus $C(x) = R(x)$ at $x = 20$ and at $x = 180$. If 20 items are produced and sold, $C(x)$ and $R(x)$ are both \$1200; if 180 items are sold, $C(x)$ and $R(x)$ are both \$10,800. Thus there are two break-even points. (See Figure 2.11.)

In a monopoly market, the revenue of a company is restricted by the demand for the product. In this case, the relationship between the price p of the product and the number of units sold x is described by the demand function $p = f(x)$, and the total revenue function for the product is given by

$$R = px = [f(x)]x$$

If, for example, the demand for a product is given by $p = 300 - x$, where x is the number of units sold and p is the price, then the revenue function for this product is the quadratic function

$$R = px = (300 - x)x = 300x - x^2$$

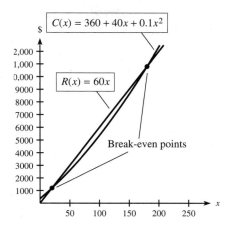

Figure 2.11

EXAMPLE 1 Break-Even Point

Suppose that in a monopoly market the total cost per week of producing a high-tech product is given by $C = 3600 + 100x + 2x^2$. Suppose further that the weekly demand function for this product is $p = 500 - 2x$. Find the number of units that will give the break-even point for the product.

Solution

The total cost function is $C(x) = 3600 + 100x + 2x^2$, and the total revenue function is $R(x) = px = (500 - 2x)x = 500x - 2x^2$.

Setting $C(x) = R(x)$ and solving for x gives

$$3600 + 100x + 2x^2 = 500x - 2x^2$$
$$4x^2 - 400x + 3600 = 0$$
$$x^2 - 100x + 900 = 0$$
$$(x - 90)(x - 10) = 0$$
$$x = 90 \quad \text{or} \quad x = 10$$

Does this mean the firm will break even at 10 units and at 90 units? Yes. Figure 2.12 shows the graphs of $C(x)$ and $R(x)$. From the graph we can observe that the firm makes a profit after $x = 10$ until $x = 90$, because $R(x) > C(x)$ in that interval. At $x = 90$, the profit is 0, and the firm loses money if it produces more than 90 units per week.

Figure 2.12

CHECKPOINT

1. The point of intersection of the revenue function and the cost function is called _____.
2. If $C(x) = 120x + 15,000$ and $R(x) = 370x - x^2$, finding the break-even points requires solution of what equation? Find the break-even points.

Note that for Example 1, the revenue function

$$R(x) = (500 - 2x)x = 500x - 2x^2$$

is a parabola that opens downward. Thus the vertex is the point at which revenue is maximum. We can locate this vertex by using the methods discussed in the previous section.

$$\text{Vertex: } x = \frac{-b}{2a} = \frac{-500}{2(-2)} = \frac{500}{4} = 125 \text{ (units)}$$

It is interesting to note that when $x = 125$, the firm achieves its maximum revenue of

$$R(125) = 500(125) - 2(125)^2 = 31,250 \text{ (dollars)}$$

but the costs when $x = 125$ are

$$C(125) = 3600 + 100(125) + 2(125)^2 = 47,350 \text{ (dollars)}$$

which results in a loss. This illustrates that maximizing revenue is not a good goal. We should seek to maximize profit. Figure 2.12 shows that maximum profit will occur where the distance between the revenue and cost curves (that is, $R(x) - C(x)$) is largest. This appears to be near $x = 50$, which is midway between the x-values of the break-even points. This is verified in the next example.

EXAMPLE 2 | Profit Maximization

For the total cost function $C(x) = 3600 + 100x + 2x^2$ and the total revenue function $R(x) = 500x - 2x^2$ (from Example 1), find the number of units that maximizes profit and find the maximum profit.

Solution

Using Profit = Revenue − Cost, we can determine the profit function:

$$P(x) = (500x - 2x^2) - (3600 + 100x + 2x^2) = -3600 + 400x - 4x^2$$

This profit function is a parabola that opens downward, so the vertex will be the maximum point.

$$\text{Vertex: } x = \frac{-b}{2a} = \frac{-400}{2(-4)} = \frac{-400}{-8} = 50$$

Furthermore, when $x = 50$, we have

$$P(50) = -3600 + 400(50) - 4(50)^2 = 6400 \text{ (dollars)}$$

Thus, when 50 items are produced and sold, a maximum profit of $6400 is made (see Figure 2.13).

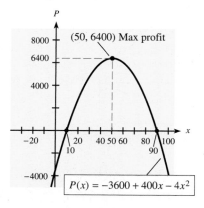

Figure 2.13

Figure 2.13 shows that the break-even points are at $x = 10$ and $x = 90$ and that the maximum profit occurs at the x-value midway between these x-values. This is reasonable because the graph of the profit function is a parabola, and the x-value of any parabola's vertex occurs midway between its x-intercepts.

It is important to note that the procedures for finding maximum revenue and profit in these examples depend on the fact that these functions are parabolas. For more general functions, procedures for finding maximum or minimum values are discussed in Chapter 10, "Applications of Derivatives."

Technology Note   Using methods discussed in Sections 2.1 and 2.2, we can use graphing utilities to locate maximum points, minimum points, and break-even points.

Supply, Demand, and Market Equilibrium   The first-quadrant parts of parabolas or other quadratic equations are frequently used to represent supply and demand functions. For example, the first-quadrant part of $p = q^2 + q + 2$ (Figure 2.14(a)) may represent a supply curve, whereas the first-quadrant part of $q^2 + 2q + 6p - 23 = 0$ (Figure 2.14(b)) may represent a demand curve.

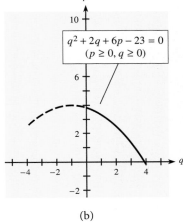

Figure 2.14   (a)   (b)

When quadratic equations are used to represent supply or demand curves, we can solve their equations simultaneously to find the market equilibrium as we did with linear supply and demand functions. As in Section 1.5, we can solve two equations in two variables by eliminating one variable and obtaining an equation in the other variable. When the functions are quadratic, the substitution method of solution is perhaps the best, and the resulting equation in one unknown will usually be quadratic.

EXAMPLE   3   Market Equilibrium | APPLICATION PREVIEW |

If the demand function for a commodity is given by $p(q + 4) = 400$ and the supply function is given by $2p - q - 38 = 0$, find the market equilibrium.

Solution
Solving the supply equation $2p - q - 38 = 0$ for p gives $p = \frac{1}{2}q + 19$. Substituting for p in $p(q + 4) = 400$ gives

$$\left(\frac{1}{2}q + 19\right)(q + 4) = 400$$

$$\frac{1}{2}q^2 + 21q + 76 = 400$$

$$\frac{1}{2}q^2 + 21q - 324 = 0$$

Multiplying both sides of the equation by 2 yields $q^2 + 42q - 648 = 0$. Factoring gives

$$(q - 12)(q + 54) = 0$$
$$q = 12 \quad \text{or} \quad q = -54$$

Thus the market equilibrium occurs when 12 items are sold, at a price of $p = \frac{1}{2}(12) + 19 = \$25$ each. The graphs of the demand and supply functions are shown in Figure 2.15.

Figure 2.15

Calculator Note   Graphing calculators also can be used to sketch these graphs. A command such as INTERSECT could be used to determine points of intersection that give market equilibrium.

Figure 2.16(a) shows the graph of the supply and demand functions for the commodity in Example 3. Using the INTERSECT command gives the same market equilibrium point determined in Example 3 (see Figure 2.16(b)).

Figure 2.16   (a)   (b)

CHECKPOINT

3. The point of intersection of the supply and demand functions is called _____.
4. If the demand and supply functions for a product are

$$p + \frac{1}{10} q^2 = 1000 \quad \text{and} \quad p = \frac{1}{10} q + 10$$

respectively, finding the market equilibrium point requires solution of what equation? Find the market equilibrium.

CHECKPOINT SOLUTIONS

1. The break-even point
2. Solution of $C(x) = R(x)$. That is, solution of $120x + 15{,}000 = 370x - x^2$, or $x^2 - 250x + 15{,}000 = 0$.

$$(x - 100)(x - 150) = 0$$
$$x = 100 \quad \text{or} \quad x = 150$$

Thus the break-even points are when 100 units and 150 units are produced.

3. The market equilibrium point or market equilibrium

4. Solve $-\dfrac{1}{10}q^2 + 1000 = \dfrac{1}{10}q + 10$:

$$-q^2 + 10{,}000 = q + 100$$
$$0 = q^2 + q - 9900$$
$$0 = (q + 100)(q - 99)$$
$$q = -100 \text{ or } q = 99$$

Thus market equilibrium occurs when $q = 99$ and $p = 9.9 + 10 = 19.90$.

| EXERCISES | 2.3

BREAK-EVEN POINTS AND MAXIMIZATION

1. The total costs for a company are given by

$$C(x) = 2000 + 40x + x^2$$

and the total revenues are given by

$$R(x) = 130x$$

Find the break-even points.

2. If a firm has the following cost and revenue functions, find the break-even points.

$$C(x) = 3600 + 25x + \frac{1}{2}x^2,$$

$$R(x) = \left(175 - \frac{1}{2}x\right)x$$

3. If a company has total costs $C(x) = 15{,}000 + 35x + 0.1x^2$ and total revenues given by $R(x) = 385x - 0.9x^2$, find the break-even points.

4. If total costs are $C(x) = 1600 + 1500x$ and total revenues are $R(x) = 1600x - x^2$, find the break-even points.

5. Given that $P(x) = 11.5x - 0.1x^2 - 150$ and that production is restricted to fewer than 75 units, find the break-even points.

6. If the profit function for a firm is given by $P(x) = -1100 + 120x - x^2$ and limitations on space require that production is less than 100 units, find the break-even points.

7. Find the maximum revenue for the revenue function $R(x) = 385x - 0.9x^2$.

8. Find the maximum revenue for the revenue function $R(x) = 1600x - x^2$.

9. If, in a monopoly market, the demand for a product is $p = 175 - 0.50x$ and the revenue function is $R = px$, where x is the number of units sold, what price will maximize revenue?

10. If, in a monopoly market, the demand for a product is $p = 1600 - x$ and the revenue is $R = px$, where x is the number of units sold, what price will maximize revenue?

11. The profit function for a certain commodity is $P(x) = 110x - x^2 - 1000$. Find the level of production that yields maximum profit, and find the maximum profit.

12. The profit function for a firm making widgets is $P(x) = 88x - x^2 - 1200$. Find the number of units at which maximum profit is achieved, and find the maximum profit.

13. (a) Graph the profit function $P(x) = 80x - 0.1x^2 - 7000$.
    (b) Find the vertex of the graph. Is it a maximum point or a minimum point?
    (c) Is the average rate of change of this function from $x = a < 400$ to $x = 400$ positive or negative?
    (d) Is the average rate of change of this function from $x = 400$ to $x = a > 400$ positive or negative?
    (e) Does the average rate of change of the profit get closer to or farther from 0 when a is closer to 400?

14. (a) Graph the profit function $P(x) = 50x - 0.2x^2 - 2000$.
    (b) Find the vertex of the graph. Is it a maximum point or a minimum point?
    (c) Is the average rate of change of this function from $x = a < 125$ to $x = 125$ positive or negative?
    (d) Is the average rate of change of this function from $x = 125$ to $x = a > 125$ positive or negative?
    (e) Does the average rate of change of the profit get closer to or farther from 0 when a is closer to 125?

15. (a) Form the profit function for the cost and revenue functions in Problem 3, and find the maximum profit.
    (b) Compare the level of production to maximize profit with the level to maximize revenue (see Problem 7). Do they agree?
    (c) How do the break-even points compare with the zeros of $P(x)$?

16. (a) Form the profit function for the cost and revenue functions in Problem 4, and find the maximum profit.
    (b) Compare the level of production to maximize profit with the level to maximize revenue (see Problem 8). Do they agree?

(c) How do the break-even points compare with the zeros of $P(x)$?

17. Suppose a company has fixed costs of $28,000 and variable cost per unit of $\frac{2}{5}x + 222$ dollars, where x is the total number of units produced. Suppose further that the selling price of its product is $1250 - \frac{3}{5}x$ dollars per unit.
    (a) Find the break-even points.
    (b) Find the maximum revenue.
    (c) Form the profit function from the cost and revenue functions and find maximum profit.
    (d) What price will maximize the profit?

18. Suppose a company has fixed costs of $300 and variable cost per unit of $\frac{3}{4}x + 1460$ dollars, where x is the total number of units produced. Suppose further that the selling price of its product is $1500 - \frac{1}{4}x$ dollars per unit.
    (a) Find the break-even points.
    (b) Find the maximum revenue.
    (c) Form the profit function from the cost and revenue functions and find maximum profit.
    (d) What price will maximize the profit?

19. The following table gives the total revenues of Cablenet Communications for selected years.

Year	Total Revenues (millions)
2005	$63.13
2006	62.91
2007	60.53
2008	60.27
2009	61.10
2010	62.19
2011	63.09
2012	64.90
2013	67.16

Suppose the data can be described by the equation

$$R(t) = 0.271t^2 - 2.76t + 67.83$$

where t is the number of years past 2003.
    (a) Use the function to find the year in which revenue was minimum and find the minimum predicted revenue.
    (b) Check the result from part (a) against the data in the table.
    (c) Graph $R(t)$ and the data points from the table.
    (d) Write a sentence to describe how well the function fits the data.

The data in the table give sales revenues and costs and expenses for Continental Divide Mining for various years. Use this table in Problems 20 and 21.

Year	Sales Revenue (millions)	Costs and Expenses (millions)
2003	$2.6155	$2.4105
2004	2.7474	2.4412
2005	2.934	2.6378
2006	3.3131	2.9447
2007	3.9769	3.5344
2008	4.5494	3.8171
2009	4.8949	4.2587
2010	5.1686	4.8769
2011	4.9593	4.9088
2012	5.0913	4.6771
2013	4.7489	4.9025

20. Assume that sales revenues for Continental Divide Mining can be described by

$$R(t) = -0.031t^2 + 0.776t + 0.179$$

where t is the number of years past 2000.
    (a) Use the function to determine the year in which maximum revenue occurs and the maximum revenue it predicts.
    (b) Check the result from (a) against the data in the table.
    (c) Graph $R(t)$ and the data points from the table.
    (d) Write a sentence to describe how well the function fits the data.

21. Assume that costs and expenses for Continental Divide Mining can be described by

$$C(t) = -0.012t^2 + 0.492t + 0.725$$

where t is the number of years past 2000.
    (a) Use $R(t)$ as given in Problem 20 and form the profit function (as a function of time).
    (b) Use the function from (a) to find the year in which maximum profit occurs.
    (c) Graph the profit function from (a) and the data points from the table.
    (d) Through the decade from 2008 to 2018, does the function project increasing or decreasing profits? Do the data support this trend (as far as it goes)?
    (e) How might management respond to this kind of projection?

SUPPLY, DEMAND, AND MARKET EQUILIBRIUM

In Problems 22–24, a supply function and a demand function are given. (a) Sketch the first-quadrant portions of those functions on the same set of axes. (b) Label the market equilibrium point. (c) Algebraically determine the market equilibrium point.

22. Supply: $p = q^2 + 8q + 16$
    Demand: $p = 216 - 2q$

23. Supply: $p = \frac{1}{4}q^2 + 10$
    Demand: $p = 86 - 6q - 3q^2$

24. Supply: $p = q^2 + 8q + 22$

Demand: $p = 198 - 4q - \frac{1}{4}q^2$

25. If the supply function for a commodity is $p = q^2 + 8q + 16$ and the demand function is $p = -3q^2 + 6q + 436$, find the equilibrium quantity and equilibrium price.

26. If the supply function for a commodity is $p = q^2 + 8q + 20$ and the demand function is $p = 100 - 4q - q^2$, find the equilibrium quantity and equilibrium price.

27. If the demand function for a commodity is given by the equation $p^2 + 4q = 1600$ and the supply function is given by the equation $300 - p^2 + 2q = 0$, find the equilibrium quantity and equilibrium price.

28. If the supply and demand functions for a commodity are given by $4p - q = 42$ and $(p + 2)q = 2100$, respectively, find the price that will result in market equilibrium.

29. If the supply and demand functions for a commodity are given by $p - q = 10$ and $q(2p - 10) = 2100$, what is the equilibrium price and what is the corresponding number of units supplied and demanded?

30. If the supply and demand functions for a certain product are given by the equations $2p - q + 6 = 0$ and $(p + q)(q + 10) = 3696$, respectively, find the price and quantity that give market equilibrium.

31. The supply function for a product is $2p - q - 10 = 0$, while the demand function for the same product is $(p + 10)(q + 30) = 7200$. Find the market equilibrium point.

32. The supply and demand for a product are given by $2p - q = 50$ and $pq = 100 + 20q$, respectively. Find the market equilibrium point.

33. For the product in Problem 31, if a \$22 tax is placed on production of the item, then the supplier passes this tax on by adding \$22 to his selling price. Find the new equilibrium point for this product when the tax is passed on. (The new supply function is given by $p = \frac{1}{2}q + 27$.)

34. For the product in Problem 32, if a \$12.50 tax is placed on production and passed through by the supplier, find the new equilibrium point.

OBJECTIVES

2.4

- To graph and apply basic functions, including constant and power functions
- To graph and apply polynomial and rational functions
- To graph and apply absolute value and piecewise defined functions

Special Functions and Their Graphs

| APPLICATION PREVIEW |

The average cost per item for a product is calculated by dividing the total cost by the number of items. Hence, if the total cost function for x units of a product is

$$C(x) = 900 + 3x + x^2$$

and if we denote the average cost function by $\overline{C}(x)$, then

$$\overline{C}(x) = \frac{C(x)}{x} = \frac{900 + 3x + x^2}{x}$$

This average cost function is a special kind of function, called a rational function. We can use this function to find the minimum average cost. (See Example 4.)

In this section, we discuss polynomial, rational, and other special functions.

Basic Functions   The special linear function

$$y = f(x) = x$$

is called the **identity function** (see Figure 2.17(a) on the next page), and a linear function defined by

$$y = f(x) = C \quad C \text{ a constant}$$

is called a **constant function.** Figure 2.17(b) shows the graph of the constant function $y = f(x) = 2$. (Note that the slope of the graph of any constant function is 0.)

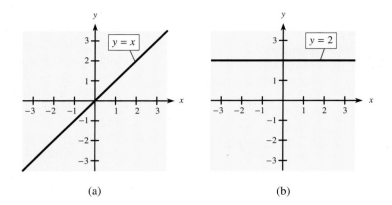

Figure 2.17   (a)   (b)

The functions of the form $y = ax^b$, where $b > 0$, are called **power functions.** Examples of power functions include $y = x^2$, $y = x^3$, $y = \sqrt{x} = x^{1/2}$, and $y = \sqrt[3]{x} = x^{1/3}$. (See Figure 2.18(a)–(d).) The functions $y = \sqrt{x}$ and $y = \sqrt[3]{x}$ are also called **root functions,** and $y = x^2$ and $y = x^3$ are basic **polynomial functions.**

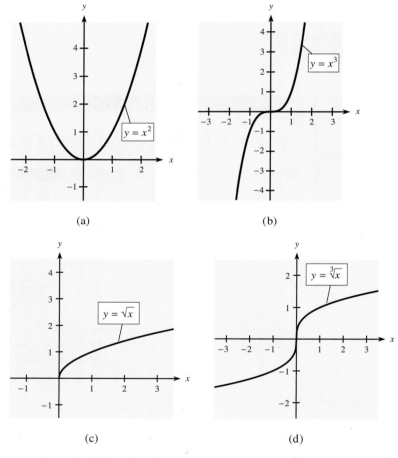

(a)   (b)

Figure 2.18   (c)   (d)

The general shape for the power function $y = ax^b$, where $b > 0$, depends on the value of b. Figure 2.19 shows the first-quadrant portions of typical graphs of $y = x^b$ for different values of b. Note how the direction in which the graph bends differs for $b > 1$ and for $0 < b < 1$. Getting accurate graphs of these functions requires plotting a number of points by hand or with a graphing utility. Our goal at this stage is to recognize the basic shapes of certain functions.

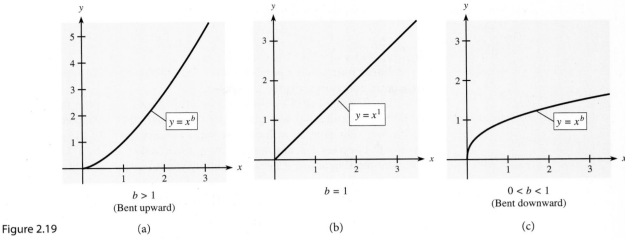

Figure 2.19   (a)   (b)   (c)

Shifts   In Section 2.2, "Quadratic Functions: Parabolas," we noted that the graph of $y = (x - h)^2 + k$ is a parabola that is shifted h units in the x-direction and k units in the y-direction. In general, we have the following.

Shifts of Graphs	The graph of $y = f(x - h) + k$ is the graph of $y = f(x)$ shifted h units in the x-direction and k units in the y-direction.

EXAMPLE **1**   **Shifted Graph**

The graph of $y = x^3$ is shown in Figure 2.18(b) on the preceding page.

(a) Describe the graph of $y = x^3 - 3$ and graph this function.
(b) Describe the graph of $y = (x - 2)^3$ and graph this function.
(c) Describe the graph of $y = (x - 2)^3 - 3$ and graph this function.

Solution

(a) The graph of $y = x^3 - 3$ is the graph of $y = x^3$ shifted -3 units in the y-direction (down 3 units). The graph is shown in Figure 2.20(a).
(b) The graph of $y = (x - 2)^3$ is the graph of $y = x^3$ shifted 2 units in the x-direction (to the right 2 units). The graph is shown in Figure 2.20(b).
(c) The graph of $y = (x - 2)^3 - 3$ is the graph of $y = x^3$ shifted to the right 2 units and down 3 units. The graph is shown in Figure 2.20(c).

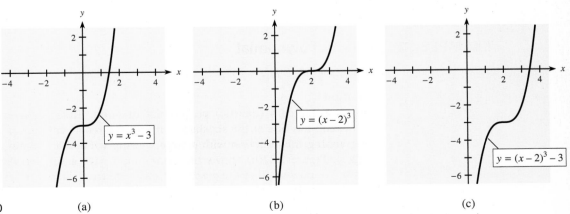

Figure 2.20   (a)   (b)   (c)

Polynomial Functions   A **polynomial function of degree** n has the form

$$y = a_n x^n + a_{n-1} x^{n-1} + \cdots + a_1 x + a_0$$

where $a_n \neq 0$, and n is an integer, $n \geq 0$.

A **linear function** is a polynomial function of degree 1, and a **quadratic function** is a polynomial function of degree 2.

Accurate graphing of a polynomial function of degree greater than 2 may require the methods of calculus; we will investigate these methods in Chapter 10, "Applications of Derivatives." For now, we will observe some characteristics of the graphs of polynomial functions of degrees 2, 3, and 4; these are summarized in Table 2.1. Using this information and point plotting or using a graphing utility yields the graphs of these functions.

■ | **TABLE 2.1** | ■

GRAPHS OF SOME POLYNOMIALS

	Degree 2	Degree 3	Degree 4
Turning points	1	0 or 2	1 or 3
x-intercepts	0, 1, or 2	1, 2, or 3	0, 1, 2, 3, or 4
Possible shapes	∪ or ∩ (a) (b)	(a) (b) (c) (d)	(a) (b) (c) (d) (e) (f)

Calculator Note   The function $y = x^3 - 16x$ is a third-degree (cubic) polynomial function, so it has one of the four shapes shown in the "Degree 3" column in Table 2.1. Details of graphing this function are shown in Appendix C, Section 2.4 (see Figure 2.21). ■

Figure 2.21   (a)   (b)
Two views of $y = x^3 - 16x$

EXAMPLE   2   Quartic Polynomial

Graph $y = x^4 - 2x^2$.

Solution

This is a degree 4 (quartic) polynomial function. Thus it has one or three turning points and has one of the six shapes in the "Degree 4" column of Table 2.1. We begin by graphing this function with a large viewing window to obtain the graph in Figure 2.22(a). Figure 2.22(b) shows the same graph with a smaller viewing window, near $x = 0$. We now see that the graph has shape (f) from Table 2.1, with turning points at $x = -1$, $x = 0$, and $x = 1$. ■

(a)

(b)

Figure 2.22   Two views of $y = x^4 - 2x^2$

Spreadsheet Note   It is also possible to graph polynomials with Excel. See Appendix D, Section 2.4 and the Online Excel Guide.

CHECKPOINT

1. All constant functions (such as $f(x) = 8$) have graphs that are _____.
2. Which of the following are polynomial functions?
   (a) $f(x) = x^3 - x + 4$
   (b) $f(x) = \dfrac{x + 1}{4x}$
   (c) $f(x) = 1 + \sqrt{x}$
   (d) $g(x) = \dfrac{1 + \sqrt{x}}{1 + x + \sqrt{x}}$
   (e) $h(x) = 5x$
3. A third-degree polynomial can have at most _____ turning points.

Rational Functions   The function $f(x) = \dfrac{1}{x}$ is a special function called a **reciprocal function.** A table of sample values and the graph of $y = \dfrac{1}{x}$ are shown in Figure 2.23. Because division by 0 is not possible, $x = 0$ is not in the domain of the function.

x	y
−3	−0.33
−2	−0.5
−1	−1
−0.1	−10
−0.04	−25
−0.001	−1000
3	0.33
2	0.5
1	1
0.1	10
0.04	25
0.001	1000

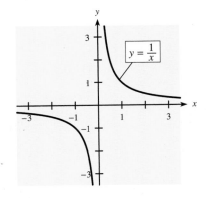

Figure 2.23

The reciprocal function $y = \dfrac{1}{x}$ is also a **rational function,** which is defined below.

Rational Function   A **rational function** is a function of the form

$$y = \frac{f(x)}{g(x)} \quad \text{with } g(x) \neq 0$$

where $f(x)$ and $g(x)$ are both polynomials. Its domain is the set of all real numbers for which $g(x) \neq 0$.

Asymptotes The table of values and the graph in Figure 2.23 show that $|y|$ gets very large as x approaches 0, and that y is undefined at $x = 0$. In this case, we call the line $x = 0$ (that is, the y-axis) a **vertical asymptote**. On the graphs of polynomial functions, the turning points are usually the features of greatest interest. However, on graphs of rational functions, vertical asymptotes frequently are the most interesting features.

Rational functions sometimes have **horizontal asymptotes** as well as vertical asymptotes. Whenever the values of y approach some finite number b as $|x|$ becomes very large, we say that there is a horizontal asymptote at $y = b$.

Note that the graph of $y = \frac{1}{x}$ appears to get close to the x-axis as $|x|$ becomes large. Testing values of x for which $|x|$ is large, we see that y is close to 0. Thus, we say that the line $y = 0$ (or the x-axis) is a horizontal asymptote for the graph of $y = \frac{1}{x}$. The graph in the following example has both a vertical and a horizontal asymptote.

EXAMPLE 3   Rational Function

(a) Use values of x from -5 to 5 to develop a table of function values for the graph of

$$y = \frac{12x + 8}{3x - 9}$$

(b) Sketch the graph.

Solution

(a) Because $3x - 9 = 0$ when $x = 3$, it follows that $x = 3$ is not in the domain of this function. The values in the table indicate that the graph is approaching a vertical asymptote at $x = 3$.

x	-5	-4	-3	-2	-1	0	1
y	2.17	1.90	1.56	1.07	0.33	-0.89	-3.33

2	2.5	2.9	3.1	3.5	4	5
-10.7	-25.33	-142.67	150.67	33.33	18.67	11.33

To see if the function has a horizontal asymptote, we calculate y as $|x|$ becomes larger.

x	$-10{,}000$	-1000	1000	10,000
y	3.999	3.99	4.01	4.001

This table indicates that the graph is approaching $y = 4$ as $|x|$ increases, so we have a horizontal asymptote at $y = 4$.

(b) Using the information about vertical and horizontal asymptotes and plotting these points give the graph in Figure 2.24(a).

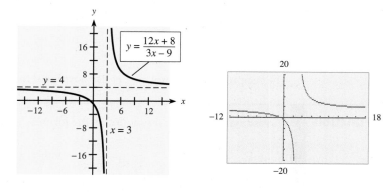

Figure 2.24   (a)   (b)

Calculator Note

When a graphing calculator is used to graph a discontinuous function, the discontinuity will be visible if the window is chosen carefully. For example, Figure 2.24(b) shows the graph of $y = \dfrac{12x + 8}{3x - 9}$ on a TI-84 calculator with the window $[-12, 18]$ by $[-20, 20]$.

Note that a window centered at the x-value of the vertical asymptote $(x = 3)$ shows the discontinuity. For details, see Appendix C, Section 2.4. ■

Spreadsheet Note

When graphing a function that is discontinuous at $x = a$ with Excel, we must leave the cell corresponding to $f(a)$ blank so that Excel will not connect the values. See Appendix D, Section 2.4 and the Online Excel Guide for details. ■

A general procedure for finding vertical and horizontal asymptotes of rational functions follows (see proof in Chapter 9) .

Asymptotes

Vertical Asymptote

The graph of the rational function $y = \dfrac{f(x)}{g(x)}$ has a vertical asymptote at $x = c$ if $g(c) = 0$ and $f(c) \neq 0$.

Horizontal Asymptote

Consider the rational function $y = \dfrac{f(x)}{g(x)} = \dfrac{a_n x^n + \cdots + a_1 x + a_0}{b_m x^m + \cdots + b_1 x + b_0}$.

1. If $n < m$ (that is, if the degree of the numerator is less than that of the denominator), a horizontal asymptote occurs at $y = 0$ (the x-axis).
2. If $n = m$ (that is, if the degree of the numerator equals that of the denominator), a horizontal asymptote occurs at $y = \dfrac{a_n}{b_m}$ (the ratio of the leading coefficients).
3. If $n > m$ (that is, if the degree of the numerator is greater than that of the denominator), there is no horizontal asymptote.

Recall that the graph of the function $y = \dfrac{12x + 8}{3x - 9}$ (shown in Figure 2.24) has a vertical asymptote at $x = 3$, and that $x = 3$ makes the denominator 0 but does not make the numerator 0. Observe also that this graph also has a horizontal asymptote at $y = 4$, and that the degree of the numerator is the same as that of the denominator with the ratio of the leading coefficients equal to $12/3 = 4$.

Determining the vertical and/or horizontal asymptotes of a rational function, if any exist, is very useful in determining a window for graphing. A rational function may or may not have turning points. The graph of the rational function in the following example has a vertical asymptote and a turning point.

EXAMPLE 4   **Total Costs and Average Costs | APPLICATION PREVIEW |**

Suppose the total cost function for x units of a product is given by

$$C(x) = 900 + 3x + x^2$$

Graph the average cost function for this product, and determine the minimum average cost.

Solution

The average cost per unit is

$$\overline{C}(x) = \frac{C(x)}{x} = \frac{900 + 3x + x^2}{x} \qquad \text{or} \qquad \overline{C}(x) = \frac{900}{x} + 3 + x$$

Because x represents the number of units produced, $x \geq 0$. Because $x = 0$ cannot be in the domain of the function, we choose a window with $x \geq 0$. Figure 2.25 shows the graph of $\overline{C}(x)$. The graph appears to have a minimum near $x = 30$. By plotting points or using MINIMUM on a graphing utility, we can verify that the minimum point occurs at $x = 30$ and $\overline{C} = 63$. Thus the minimum average cost is $63 per unit when 30 units are produced.

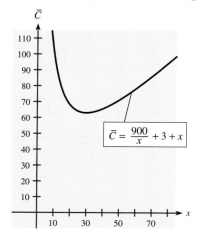

Figure 2.25

CHECKPOINT

4. Given $f(x) = \dfrac{3x}{x - 4}$, decide whether the following are true or false.

   (a) $f(x)$ has a vertical asymptote at $x = 4$.
   (b) $f(x)$ has a horizontal asymptote at $x = 3$.

Piecewise Defined Functions

Another special function comes from the definition of $|x|$. The **absolute value function** can be written as

$$f(x) = |x| \quad \text{or} \quad f(x) = \begin{cases} x & \text{if } x \geq 0 \\ -x & \text{if } x < 0 \end{cases}$$

Note that restrictions on the domain of the absolute value function specify different formulas for different parts of the domain. To graph $f(x) = |x|$, we graph the portion of the line $y = x$ for $x \geq 0$ (see Figure 2.26(a)) and the portion of the line $y = -x$ for $x < 0$ (see Figure 2.26(b)). When we put these pieces on the same graph (Figure 2.26(c)), they give us the graph of $f(x) = |x|$. Because the absolute value function is defined by two equations, we say it is a **piecewise defined function.**

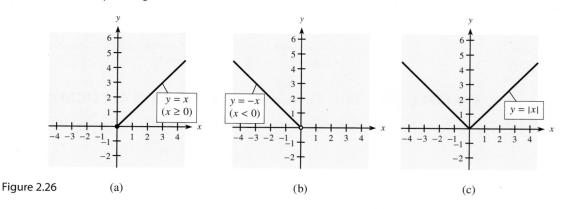

Figure 2.26   (a)   (b)   (c)

It is possible for the selling price S of a product to be defined as a piecewise function of the cost C of the product. For example, the selling price might be defined by two different equations on two different intervals, as follows:

$$S = f(C) = \begin{cases} 3C & \text{if } 0 \leq C \leq 20 \\ 1.5C + 30 & \text{if } C > 20 \end{cases}$$

When we write the equations in this way, the value of S depends on the value of C, so C is the independent variable and S is the dependent variable.

Note that the selling price of a product that costs \$15 would be $f(15) = 3(15) = 45$ (dollars) and that the selling price of a product that costs \$25 would be $f(25) = 1.5(25) + 30 = 67.50$ (dollars). Each of the two pieces of the graph of this function is a line and is easily graphed. It remains only to graph each in the proper interval. The graph is shown in Figure 2.27(a).

Figure 2.27

(a)   (b)   (c)

Calculator Note   Graphing calculators can be used to graph piecewise defined functions by entering each piece as a separate equation, along with the interval over which it is defined. The details of graphing piecewise defined functions with a graphing calculator are shown in Appendix C, Section 2.4. Figure 2.27(b) shows how the selling price function graphed in Figure 2.27(a) could be entered on a TI-84 calculator, using x to represent C and Figure 2.27(c) shows the graph.

EXAMPLE 5   **Residential Electrical Costs**

The 2012 monthly charge in dollars for x kilowatt hours (kWh) of electricity used by a residential customer of Excelsior Electric Membership Corporation during the months of November through June is given by the function

$$C(x) = \begin{cases} 10 + 0.094x & \text{if } 0 \le x \le 100 \\ 19.40 + 0.075(x - 100) & \text{if } 100 < x \le 500 \\ 49.40 + 0.05(x - 500) & \text{if } x > 500 \end{cases}$$

(a) What is the monthly charge if 1100 kWh of electricity are consumed in a month?
(b) What is the monthly charge if 450 kWh are consumed in a month?

Solution
(a) We need to find $C(1100)$. Because $1100 > 500$, we use it in the third formula line.

$$C(1100) = 49.40 + 0.05(1100 - 500) = \$79.40$$

(b) We evaluate $C(450)$ by using the second formula line for $C(x)$.

$$C(450) = 19.40 + 0.075(450 - 100) = \$45.65$$

CHECKPOINT

5. If $f(x) = \begin{cases} 5 & \text{if } x \le 0 \\ 2x & \text{if } 0 < x < 5, \\ x + 6 & \text{if } x \ge 5 \end{cases}$ find the following.

(a) $f(-5)$ (b) $f(4)$ (c) $f(20)$

CHECKPOINT SOLUTIONS

1. Horizontal lines
2. Polynomial functions are (a) and (e).
3. Two
4. (a) True.
    (b) False. The horizontal asymptote is $y = 3$.
5. (a) $f(-5) = 5$. In fact, for any negative value of x, $f(x) = 5$.
    (b) $f(4) = 2(4) = 8$
    (c) $f(20) = 20 + 6 = 26$

| EXERCISES | 2.4

In Problems 1–12, match each of the functions with one of the graphs labeled (a)–(l) shown following these functions. Recognizing special features of certain types of functions and plotting points for the functions will be helpful.

1. $f(x) = -3$
2. $y = \sqrt{x}$
3. $y = \sqrt[3]{x}$
4. $y = (\sqrt{x})^5$
5. $y = (x + 4)^3 + 1$
6. $y = \dfrac{1}{x}$
7. $y = |x|$
8. $y = |x - 2|$
9. $f(x) = \begin{cases} x^2 & \text{if } x \le 2 \\ 4 & \text{if } x > 2 \end{cases}$
10. $f(x) = \begin{cases} 2 & \text{if } x < 0 \\ x^3 & \text{if } x \ge 0 \end{cases}$
11. $y = \begin{cases} -x & \text{if } x < -1 \\ 1 & \text{if } -1 \le x \le 1 \\ x & \text{if } x > 1 \end{cases}$
12. $y = \sqrt{x - 2}$

(a)

(b)

(c)

(d)

(e)

(f)

(g)

(h)

(i)

(j)

(k)

(l)

In Problems 13 and 14, decide whether each function whose graph is shown is the graph of a cubic (third-degree) or quartic (fourth-degree) function.

13.

(a)

(b)

14.

(a)

(b)

By recognizing shapes and features of polynomial and rational functions, match each equation in Problems 15–22 with the correct graph among those labeled (a)–(h). Use a graphing utility to confirm your choice.

15. $y = x^3 - x$

16. $y = (x - 3)^2(x + 1)$

17. $y = 16x^2 - x^4$

18. $y = x^4 - 3x^2 - 4$

19. $y = x^2 + 7x$

20. $y = 7x - x^2$

21. $y = \dfrac{x - 3}{x + 1}$

22. $y = \dfrac{1 - 3x}{2x + 5}$

(a)

(b)

(c)

(d)

(e)

(f)

(g)

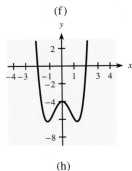

(h)

In Problems 23–28, graph the function.

23. $y = (x + 1)(x - 3)(x - 1)$

24. $y = x^3 - 8x^2 + 19x - 12$

25. $y = \dfrac{1 - 2x}{x}$

26. $y = \dfrac{x}{x - 1}$

27. $y = \begin{cases} x^3 + 2 & \text{if } x < 1 \\ \sqrt{x - 1} & \text{if } x \ge 1 \end{cases}$

28. $y = \begin{cases} x^2 & \text{if } x < 2 \\ 4 - x & \text{if } x \ge 2 \end{cases}$

29. If $F(x) = \dfrac{x^2 - 1}{x}$, find the following.

   (a) $F(-\frac{1}{3})$ (b) $F(10)$
   (c) $F(0.001)$ (d) Is $F(0)$ defined?

30. If $H(x) = |x - 1|$, find the following.

   (a) $H(-1)$ (b) $H(1)$
   (c) $H(0)$ (d) Does $H(-x) = H(x)$?

31. If $f(x) = x^{3/2}$, find the following.

   (a) $f(16)$ (b) $f(1)$ (c) $f(100)$ (d) $f(0.09)$

32. If $k(x) = \begin{cases} 4 - 2x & \text{if } x < 0 \\ |x - 4| & \text{if } 0 < x < 4, \end{cases}$

   find the following.

   (a) $k(-0.1)$ (b) $k(0.1)$ (c) $k(3.9)$ (d) $k(4.1)$

33. If $k(x) = \begin{cases} 2 & \text{if } x < 0 \\ x + 4 & \text{if } 0 \le x < 1, \\ 1 - x & \text{if } x \ge 1 \end{cases}$

   find the following.

   (a) $k(-5)$ (b) $k(0)$ (c) $k(1)$ (d) $k(-0.001)$

34. If $g(x) = \begin{cases} 0.5x + 4 & \text{if } x < 0 \\ 4 - x & \text{if } 0 \le x < 4, \\ 0 & \text{if } x > 4 \end{cases}$

   find the following.

   (a) $g(-4)$ (b) $g(1)$ (c) $g(7)$ (d) $g(3.9)$

 In Problems 35–40, (a) graph each function with a graphing utility; (b) classify each function as a polynomial function, a rational function, or a piecewise defined function; (c) identify any asymptotes; and (d) use the graphs to locate turning points.

35. $f(x) = 1.6x^2 - 0.1x^4$

36. $f(x) = \dfrac{x^4 - 4x^3}{3}$

37. $f(x) = \dfrac{2x + 4}{x + 1}$

38. $f(x) = \dfrac{x - 3}{x + 2}$

39. $f(x) = \begin{cases} -x & \text{if } x < 0 \\ 5x & \text{if } x \ge 0 \end{cases}$

40. $f(x) = \begin{cases} 2x - 1 & \text{if } x < 1 \\ -x & \text{if } x \ge 1 \end{cases}$

APPLICATIONS

41. *Postal restrictions* If a box with a square cross section is to be sent by the postal service, there are restrictions on its size such that its volume is given by $V = x^2(108 - 4x)$, where x is the length of each side of the cross section (in inches).

   (a) If $V = V(x)$, find $V(10)$ and $V(20)$.
   (b) What restrictions must be placed on x (the domain) so that the problem makes physical sense?

42. **Fixed costs** Fixed costs FC are business costs that remain constant regardless of the number of units produced. Some items that might contribute to fixed costs are rent and utilities.

$$FC = 2000$$

is an equation indicating that a business has fixed costs of $2000. Graph $FC = 2000$ by putting x (the number of units produced) on the horizontal axis. (Note that FC does not mean the product of F and C.)

43. **Tourism spending** Global spending on travel and tourism (in billions of dollars) can be modeled by

$$f(x) = 252.576x^{0.296}$$

where x is the number of years after 1990 (*Source: World Almanac*).
(a) Does the graph of this function bend upward or bend downward?
(b) Graph this function.
(c) Use numerical or graphical methods to find when the model predicts that global spending will reach $613,000,000,000.

44. **Allometric relationships** For fiddler crabs, data gathered by Thompson show that the relationship between the weight C of the claw and the weight W of the body is given by

$$C = 0.11W^{1.54}$$

where W and C are in grams (*Source:* d'Arcy Thompson, *On Growth and Form,* Cambridge University Press, 1961).
(a) Does the graph of this function bend upward or bend downward?
(b) Graph this function.
(c) Use this function to compute the weight of a claw if the weight of the crab's body is 10 grams.

45. **Pollution** Suppose that the cost C (in dollars) of removing p percent of the particulate pollution from the smokestacks of an industrial plant is given by

$$C(p) = \frac{7300p}{100 - p}$$

(a) Is $C(p)$ undefined at any p-value? If so, what value?
(b) What is the domain of $C(p)$ as given by the equation?
(c) What is the domain of $C(p)$ in the context of the application?
(d) What happens to the cost as the percent of pollution removed approaches 100%?

46. **Average cost** If the weekly total cost of producing 27″ Toshiba television sets is given by $C(x) = 50,000 + 105x$, where x is the number of sets produced per week, then the average cost per unit is given by

$$\overline{C}(x) = \frac{50,000 + 105x}{x}$$

(a) What is the average cost per set if 3000 sets are sold?
(b) Graph this function.
(c) Does the average cost per set continue to fall as the number of sets produced increases?

47. **Area** If 100 feet of fence is to be used to enclose a rectangular yard, then the resulting area of the fenced yard is given by

$$A = x(50 - x)$$

where x is the width of the rectangle.
(a) If $A = A(x)$, find $A(2)$ and $A(30)$.
(b) What restrictions must be placed on x (the domain) so that the problem makes physical sense?

48. **Water usage** The monthly charge for water in a small town is given by

$$f(x) = \begin{cases} 58 & \text{if } 0 \le x \le 20 \\ 58 + 0.4(x - 20) & \text{if } x > 20 \end{cases}$$

where x is water usage in hundreds of gallons and $f(x)$ is in dollars. Find the monthly charge for each of the following usages: (a) 30 gallons, (b) 3000 gallons, and (c) 4000 gallons. (d) Graph the function for $0 \le x \le 100$.

49. **Gross domestic product** By using data for selected years since 1950, the gross domestic product (GDP), in billions of dollars, of the United States is given by

$$y = \begin{cases} 90.742x + 210.291 & \text{for } 10 \le x \le 60 \\ 66.786x^2 - 7820.90x + 238,565.429 & \text{for } 60 < x \end{cases}$$

where x is the number of years past 1940 (*Source: Bureau of Economic Analysis*).
(a) Graph the function for $10 \le x \le 65$.
(b) What does the model estimate the GDP to be in 1980?
(c) What does the model predict the GDP to be in 2015?

50. **Commercial electrical usage** The monthly charge (in dollars) for x kilowatt hours (kWh) of electricity used by a commercial customer is given by the following function.

$$C(x) = \begin{cases} 7.52 + 0.1079x & \text{if } 0 \le x \le 5 \\ 19.22 + 0.1079x & \text{if } 5 < x \le 750 \\ 20.795 + 0.1058x & \text{if } 750 < x \le 1500 \\ 131.345 + 0.0321x & \text{if } x > 1500 \end{cases}$$

Find the monthly charges for the following usages.
(a) 5 kWh   (b) 6 kWh   (c) 3000 kWh

51. **First-class postage** The postage charged for first-class mail is a function of its weight. The U.S. Postal Service uses the following table to describe the rates.

Weight Increment	Rate ($)
First ounce or fraction of an ounce	0.44
Each additional ounce or fraction	0.20

Source: United States Postal Service, pe.usps.gov/text

(a) Convert this table to a piecewise defined function that represents postage for letters weighing between 0 and 4 ounces, using x as the weight in ounces and P as the postage in cents.

(b) Find $P(1.2)$ and explain what it means.

(c) Give the domain and range of P as it is defined above.

(d) Find the postage for a 2-ounce letter and for a 2.01-ounce letter.

52. *Income tax* In a given year the U.S. federal income tax owed by a married couple filing jointly can be found from the following table (*Source:* Internal Revenue Service, Form 1040 Instructions).

Filing Status: Married Filing Jointly

If taxable income is between	Tax due is			Of the amount over
$0−$16,750	$0.00	+	10.0%	$0
$16,750−$68,000	$1,675.00	+	15.0%	$16,750
$68,000−$137,300	$9,362.50	+	25.0%	$68,000
$137,300−$209,250	$26,687.50	+	28.0%	$137,300
$209,250−$373,650	$46,833.50	+	33.0%	$209,250
$373,650−Up	$101,085.50	+	35.0%	$373,650

(a) For incomes up to $137,300, write the piecewise defined function T with input x that models the federal tax dollars due as a function of x, the taxable income dollars earned.

(b) Use the function to find $T(70,000)$.

(c) Find the tax due on a taxable income of $50,000.

(d) A friend tells Jack Waddell not to earn any money over $68,000 because it would raise his tax rate to 25% on all of his taxable income. Test this statement by finding the tax due on $68,000 and $68,000 + $1. What do you conclude?

53. *Demand* The demand function for a product is given by

$$p = \frac{200}{2 + 0.1x}$$

where x is the number of units and p is the price in dollars.

(a) Graph this demand function for $0 \leq x \leq 250$, with x on the horizontal axis.

(b) Does the demand ever reach 0?

54. *Mob behavior* In studying lynchings between 1899 and 1946, psychologist Brian Mullin found that the size of a lynch mob relative to the number of victims predicted the level of brutality. He developed a formula for the other-total ratio (y) that predicts the level of self-attentiveness of people in a crowd of size x with 1 victim.

$$y = \frac{1}{x + 1}$$

The lower the value of y, the more likely an individual is to be influenced by "mob psychology." Graph this function; use positive integers as its domain.

55. *Production costs* A manufacturer estimates that the cost of a production run for a product is

$$C(x) = 30(x - 1) + \frac{3000}{x + 10}$$

where x is the number of machines used.

(a) Graph this total cost function for values of $x \geq 0$.

(b) Interpret any turning points.

(c) Interpret the y-intercept.

- To graph data points in a scatter plot
- To determine the function type that will best model data
- To use a graphing utility to create an equation that models the data
- To graph the data points and model on the same graph

Modeling; Fitting Curves to Data with Graphing Utilities (optional)

■ | APPLICATION PREVIEW | ■

When the plot of a set of data points looks like a line, we can use a technique called linear regression (or the least-squares method) to find the equation of the line that is the best fit for the data points. The resulting equation (model) describes the data and gives a formula to plan for the future. We can use technology to fit linear and other functions to sets of data.

For selected years from 1970 to 2010, the data in Table 2.2 show the amount of tax paid per capita (per person). In this section we develop a model for these data (see Example 3).

Linear Regression

| TABLE 2.2 |

Year	Federal Tax per Capita
1970	$955
1975	1376
1980	2276
1985	3099
1990	4208
1995	5144
2000	7404
2005	7625
2010	7211

Source: Internal Revenue Service

We saw in Section 1.3, "Linear Functions," that it is possible to write the equation of a straight line if we have two points on the line. Business firms frequently like to treat demand functions as though they were linear, even when they are not exactly linear. They do this because linear functions are much easier to handle than other functions. If a firm has more than two points describing the demand for its product, it is likely that the points will not all lie on the same straight line. However, by using a technique called **linear regression,** the firm can determine the "best line" that fits these points.

Suppose we have the points shown in Figure 2.28, and we seek the line that is the "best fit" for the points.

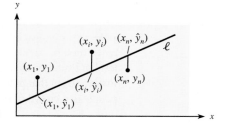

Figure 2.28

The formulas that give the best-fitting line for given data are developed in Chapter 14, "Functions of Two or More Variables," but graphing calculators, computer programs, and spreadsheets have built-in formulas or programs that give the equation of the best-fitting line for a set of data.

Modeling

Creating an equation, or **mathematical model,** for a set of data is a complex process that involves careful analysis of the data in accordance with a number of guidelines. Our approach to creating a model is much simplified and relies on a knowledge of the appearance of linear, quadratic, power, cubic, and quartic functions and the capabilities of computers and graphing calculators. We should note that the equations the computers and calculators provide are based on sophisticated formulas that are derived using calculus of several variables. These formulas provide the best fit for the data using the function type we choose, but we should keep the following limitations in mind.

1. The computer/calculator will give the best fit for whatever type of function we choose (even if the selected function is a bad fit for the points), so we must choose a function type carefully. To choose a function type, compare the plot of the data with the graphs of the functions discussed earlier in this chapter. The model will not fit the data if we choose a function type whose graph does not match the shape of the plotted data.
2. Some sets of data have no pattern, so they cannot be modeled by functions. Other data sets cannot be modeled by the functions we have studied.
3. Modeling provides a formula that relates the data. Even though a model may accurately fit a data set, it may not be a good predictor for values outside the data set.

To find a function that models a set of data, the first step is to plot the data and determine the shape of the curve that would best fit the data points. The plot of the data points is called a **scatter plot.** The scatter plot's shape determines the type of function that will be the best model for the data. Details of creating a scatter plot with a graphing calculator are shown in Appendix C, Section 2.5.

EXAMPLE 1 Curve Fitting

Graphs of three scatter plots are shown in Figure 2.29(a–c). Determine what type of function is your choice as the best-fitting curve for each scatter plot. If it is a polynomial function, state the degree.

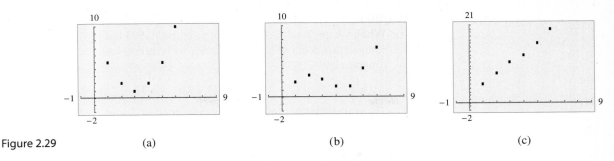

Figure 2.29   (a)   (b)   (c)

Solution

(a) It appears that a parabola will fit the data points in Figure 2.29(a), so the data points can be modeled by a second-degree (quadratic) function.

(b) The two "turns" in the scatter plot in Figure 2.29(b) suggest that it could be modeled by a cubic function.

(c) The data points in Figure 2.29(c) appear to lie (approximately) along a line, so the data can be modeled by a linear function.

After the type of function that gives the best fit for the data is chosen, a graphing utility or spreadsheet can be used to develop the best-fitting equation for the function chosen. The following steps are used to find an equation that models data.

Modeling Data

1. Enter the data and use a graphing utility or spreadsheet to plot the data points. (This gives a scatter plot.)
2. Visually determine what type of function (including degree, if it is a polynomial function) would have a graph that best fits the data.
3. Use a graphing utility or spreadsheet to determine the equation of the chosen type that gives the best fit for the data.
4. To see how well the equation models the data, graph the equation and the data points on the same set of axes. If the graph of the equation does not fit the data points well, another type of function may model the data better.
5. After the model for a data set has been found, it can be rounded for reporting purposes. However, use the unrounded model in graphing and in calculations, unless otherwise instructed. Numerical answers found using a model should be rounded in a way that agrees with the context of the problem and with no more accuracy than the original output data.

The graphing calculator steps used to create a function that approximately fits a scatter plot are shown in Appendix C, Section 2.5.

EXAMPLE 2   **U.S. Households with Internet Access**

The following table gives the percent of U.S. households with Internet access in various years.

Year	1996	1997	1998	1999	2000	2001	2003	2008
Percent	8.5	14.3	26.2	28.6	41.5	50.5	52.4	78.0

Source: U.S. Census Bureau

(a) Use a graphing utility to create a scatter plot of the data, with x equal to the number of years after 1995.
(b) Use the utility to create an equation that models the data.
(c) Graph the function and the data on the same graph to see how well the function models ("fits") the data.

Solution

(a) When we use x as the number of years past 1995 (so $x = 0$ in 1995) and use y to represent the percent of U.S. households with Internet access, the points representing this function are

$$(1, 8.5) \quad (2, 14.3) \quad (3, 26.2) \quad (4, 28.6) \quad (5, 41.5) \quad (6, 50.5) \quad (8, 52.4) \quad (13, 78.0)$$

The scatter plot of these points is developed in Appendix C, Section 2.5, and shown in Figure 2.30(a).

(b) It appears that a line could be found that would fit close to the points in Figure 2.30(a). The points do not fit exactly on a line, because the percent of U.S. households with Internet access did not increase by exactly the same amount each year. The steps used to create the linear function that models these points are shown in Appendix C, Section 2.5. The linear equation that is the best fit for the points is

$$y = 5.79x + 7.13$$

(c) Figure 2.30(b) shows the graph of the function and the data on the same graph. Note that not all points fit on the graph of the equation, even though this is the line that is the best fit for the data. ■

Figure 2.30   (a)   (b)

EXAMPLE **3**   **Federal Tax per Capita** | APPLICATION PREVIEW |

The following table gives the amount of federal tax paid per capita (per person) for selected years from 1970 to 2010.

(a) Create a scatter plot of these data, with $x = 0$ representing 1970.
(b) Find a cubic model that fits the data points.
(c) Use the model to estimate the per capita tax for 2010.

Year	Federal Tax per Capita	Year	Federal Tax per Capita
1970	$955	1995	$5144
1975	1376	2000	7404
1980	2276	2005	7625
1985	3099	2010	7211
1990	4208		

Source: Internal Revenue Service

Solution

(a) The scatter plot is shown in Figure 2.31(a). The "turns" in the graph indicate that a cubic function would be a good fit for the data.

(b) The cubic function that is the best fit for the data is

$$y = -0.278x^3 + 16.2x^2 - 46.9x + 1110$$

The graph of the function and the scatter plot are shown in Figure 2.31(b).

(c) The value of y for $x = 40$ (shown in Figure 2.31(c)) predicts about \$7362 as the tax per capita in 2010. However, the downward turn in the graph suggests a decrease in future tax per capita and this is highly unlikely with current government debt. Thus, the model cannot be applied beyond 2010.

Figure 2.31   (a)   (b)   (c)

If it is not obvious what model will best fit a given set of data, several models can be developed and compared graphically with the data.

EXAMPLE 4   Expected Life Span

The expected life span of people in the United States depends on their year of birth.

Year	Life Span (years)	Year	Life Span (years)	Year	Life Span (years)	Year	Life Span (years)
1920	54.1	1960	69.7	1985	74.7	2005	77.9
1930	59.7	1970	70.8	1990	75.4	2010	78.1
1940	62.9	1975	72.6	1995	75.8	2015	78.9
1950	68.2	1980	73.7	2000	77.0	2020	79.5

Source: National Center for Health Statistics

(a) Create linear and quadratic models that give life span as a function of birth year with $x = 0$ representing 1900 and, by visual inspection, decide which model gives the better fit.
(b) Use both models to estimate the life span of a person born in the year 2000.
(c) Which model's prediction for the life span in 2015 seems better?

Solution

(a) The scatter plot for the data is shown in Figure 2.32(a). It appears that a linear function could be used to model the data. The linear equation that is the best fit for the data is

$$y = 0.233x + 53.71$$

The graph in Figure 2.32(b) shows how well the line fits the data points. The quadratic function that is the best fit for the data is

$$y = -0.00186x^2 + 0.498x + 46.0$$

Its graph is shown in Figure 2.32(c).

Figure 2.32   (a)   (b)   (c)

| TABLE 2.3 |

X	Y₁	Y₂
90	74.68	75.754
100	77.01	77.2
110	79.34	78.274
115	80.505	78.672

X =

The quadratic model appears to fit the data points better than the linear model. A table can be used to compare the models (see Table 2.3 with y_1 giving values from the linear model and y_2 giving values from the quadratic model).

(b) We can estimate the life span of people born in the year 2000 with either model by evaluating the functions at $x = 100$. The x-values in Table 2.3 represent the years 1990, 2000, 2010, and 2015. From the linear model the expected life span in 2000 is 77.0, and from the quadratic model the expected life span is 77.2.

(c) Looking at Table 2.3, we see that the linear model may be giving optimistic values in 2015, when $x = 115$, so the quadratic model may be better in the years after 2010. ■

Spreadsheet Note   Excel can also be used to model data. See Appendix D, Section 2.5 and the Online Excel Guide for details. ■

EXAMPLE 5   ## Corvette Acceleration

The following table shows the times that it takes a Corvette to reach speeds from 0 mph to 100 mph, in increments of 10 mph after 30 mph.

Time (sec)	Speed (mph)	Time (sec)	Speed (mph)
1.7	30	5.5	70
2.4	40	7.0	80
3.5	50	8.5	90
4.3	60	10.2	100

(a) Use a power function to model the data, and graph the points and the function to see how well the function fits the points.
(b) What does the model indicate the speed is 5 seconds after the car starts to move?
(c) Use the model to determine the number of seconds until the Corvette reaches 110 mph.

Solution
(a) Using x as the time and y as the speed, the scatter plot (found with Excel) is shown in Figure 2.33(a). An equation found using the power function $y = ax^b$ (graphed in Figure 2.33(b)) is

$$y = 21.875x^{0.6663}$$

Figure 2.33

(b) Using $x = 5$ in this equation gives 64 mph as the speed of the Corvette.
(c) Using Excel Goal Seek with $y = 21.875x^{0.6663}$ set equal to 110 gives $x = 11.3$, so the time required to reach 110 mph is 11.3 seconds. ■

| EXERCISES | 2.5

In Problems 1–8, determine whether the scatter plot should be modeled by a linear, power, quadratic, cubic, or quartic function.

1.

2.

3.

4.

5.

6.

7.

8.

In Problems 9–16, find the equation of the function of the specified type that is the best fit for the given data. Plot the data and the equation.

9. linear

x	y
−2	−7
−1	−5
0	−3
1	−1
2	1
3	3
4	5

10. linear

x	y
−1	−5.5
0	−4
1	−2.5
2	−1
3	0.5
4	2
5	3.5

11. quadratic

x	y
−2	7
−1	−0.5
0	−4
1	−3.5
2	1
3	9.5
4	22

12. quadratic

x	y
−4	−8
−3	−4
−2	−2
−1	−2
0	−4
1	−8
2	−14

13. cubic

x	y
−4	−72
−3	−31
−2	−10
−1	−3
0	−4
1	−7
2	−6

14. cubic

x	y
−3	−22
−2	−6
−1	−2
0	−4
1	−6
2	−2
3	14

15. power

x	y
1	2
2	2.8284
3	3.4641
4	4
5	4.4721
6	4.899

16. power

x	y
1	3
2	8.4853
3	15.588
4	24
5	33.541
6	44.091

In Problems 17–24, (a) plot the given points, (b) determine what type of function best models the data, and (c) find the equation that is the best fit for the data.

17.

x	y
−1	−8
0	−3
1	2
2	7
3	12
4	17
5	22

18.

x	y
−1	−2
0	2
1	6
2	10
3	14
4	18
5	22

19.

x	y
-1	2
0	0
1	2
2	3.1748
3	4.1602
4	5.0397
5	5.848

20.

x	y
0.01	0.3
1	3
2	4.2426
3	5.1962
4	6
5	6.7082
6	7.3485

21.

x	y
-2	19
-1	8
0	1
1	-2
2	-1
3	4
4	13

22.

x	y
-4	37
-3	19
-2	7
-1	1
0	1
1	7
2	19

23.

x	y
-3	-11
-2	3
-1	5
0	1
1	-3
2	-1
3	13

24.

x	y
-3	-54
-2	-14
-1	0
0	0
1	-2
2	6
3	36

APPLICATIONS

25. *Earnings and gender* The table shows the 2007 average earnings of year-round full-time workers by gender and educational attainment.

(a) Let x represent earnings for males and y represent earnings for females, and create a scatter plot of these data.

(b) Find a linear model that expresses women's annual earnings as a function of men's.

(c) Find the slope of the linear model in part (b) and write a sentence that interprets it.

Educational Attainment	Average Annual Earnings (thousands)	
	Males	Females
Less than 9th grade	$21.659	$17.023
Some high school	26.277	19.162
High school graduate	35.725	26.029
Some college	41.875	30.816
Associate's degree	44.404	33.481
Bachelor's degree	57.220	41.681
Master's degree	71.530	51.316
Doctorate	82.401	68.875

Source: U.S. Census Bureau

26. *Earnings and race* The table gives the median household income for whites and blacks in various years.

(a) Let x represent the median household income for whites and y represent the corresponding median household income for blacks, and make a scatter plot of these data.

(b) Find a linear model that expresses the median household income for blacks as a function of the median household income for whites.

(c) Find the slope of the linear model in part (b) and write a sentence that interprets it.

Median Household Income

Year	Whites	Blacks
1981	$38,954	$21,859
1985	40,614	24,163
1990	42,622	25,488
1995	42,871	26,842
2000	46,910	31,690
2001	46,261	30,625
2002	46,119	29,691
2003	45,631	29,645
2005	48,554	30,858

Source: U.S. Census Bureau

27. *Executions* The numbers of executions carried out in the United States for selected years from 1984 through 2007 are given in the table.

(a) Find the cubic function that best fits the data, using x as the number of years past 1980.

(b) According to the model developed in part (a), for what year was the number of executions a maximum? Does this result agree with the data?

Year	U.S. Executions	Year	U.S. Executions
1984	21	2000	85
1986	18	2001	66
1988	11	2002	71
1990	23	2003	65
1992	31	2004	59
1994	31	2005	60
1996	45	2007	42
1998	68		

Source: www.cuadp.org

28. *Mobile Internet advertising* The table and figure show the dollar value of the U.S. mobile Internet advertising market from 2006 with projections to 2012.

(a) With x representing the number of years past 2006, find a quadratic function that models this data.

(b) Use the model to find the year in which the mobile Internet advertising market is projected to reach $2 billion.

Year	Mobile Internet Advertising (billions)
2006	$0.045
2007	0.114
2008	0.273
2009	0.409
2010	0.545
2011	0.791
2012	1.023

U.S. Mobile Internet Advertising Market

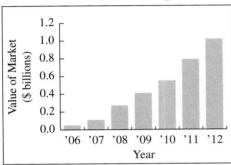

Sources: Pricewaterhouse Coopers; Wilkofsky Gruen Associates; *Wall Street Journal,* August 16, 2010

29. **Gross domestic product** The table gives the gross domestic product (GDP), in billions of dollars, of the United States for selected years from 1940 to 2005.
    (a) Create a scatter plot of the data, with *y* representing GDP in billions of dollars and *x* representing the number of years past 1940.
    (b) Find the linear function that best fits the data, with *x* equal to the number of years past 1940.
    (c) Find the cubic function that best fits the data, with *x* equal to the number of years past 1940.
    (d) Graph each of these functions on the same axes as the data points, and visually determine which model is the better fit for the data.

Year	Gross Domestic Product (billions)	Year	Gross Domestic Product (billions)
1940	$837	1985	$4207
1945	1559	1990	4853
1950	1328	1995	5439
1955	1700	2000	9817
1960	1934	2001	10,128
1965	2373	2002	10,470
1970	2847	2003	10,976
1975	3173	2004	11,713
1980	3746	2005	12,456

Source: U.S. Bureau of Economic Analysis

30. **Poverty** The table shows the number of millions of people in the United States who lived below the poverty level for selected years.
    (a) Find a cubic model that approximately fits the data, using *x* as the number of years after 1980.
    (b) Does this model look like it would be a good predictor for years past 2008? Explain.

Year	Persons Living below the Poverty Level (millions)
1986	32.4
1989	31.5
1990	33.6
1991	35.7
1992	38.0
1993	39.3
1994	38.1
1995	36.4
1996	36.5
1997	35.6
1998	34.5
1999	32.3
2000	31.1
2002	34.6
2003	35.9
2004	37.0
2005	37.0
2006	36.5
2007	37.2
2008	39.8

Sources: U.S. Census Bureau; U.S. Department of Commerce

31. **Wind chill** The table gives the wind chill temperature when the outside temperature is 20°F.

Wind (mph)	Wind Chill (°F)	Wind (mph)	Wind Chill (°F)
5	13	35	0
10	9	40	−1
15	6	45	−2
20	4	50	−3
25	3	55	−3
30	1	60	−4

Source: National Weather Service

(a) Use *x* as the wind speed and create a quadratic model for these data.
(b) At what wind speed does the model predict that the wind chill temperature will be lowest?
(c) Do you think the model found in part (a) is valid for *x* > 60? Explain.

32. *Income tax per capita* The U.S. personal income tax per capita is given in the table for selected years.
(a) Use x as the number of years past 1960 and write the equation of the function that is the best fit for the data.
(b) In what year does the model predict the personal income tax per capita will reach $7500?

Year	Tax per Capita	Year	Tax per Capita
1960	$252.31	1999	$3607.05
1965	280.06	2000	4047.59
1970	513.40	2001	4151.49
1975	731.56	2002	3622.61
1980	1274.47	2003	3416.05
1985	1679.20	2004	3395.55
1990	2178.49	2005	3762.28
1995	2550.81	2006	4159.93
1997	3039.94	2007	4552.09

Source: U.S. Census Bureau and IRS

33. *National health care* The table shows the national expenditures for health care in the United States for selected years, with projections to 2015.

Year	National Expenditures for Health Care (billions)
1960	$28
1970	75
1980	255
1990	717
1995	1020
2000	1359
2005	2016
2010	2879
2015	4032

Source: U.S. Centers for Medicare and Medicaid Services

(a) Use a scatter plot with x as the number of years past 1950 and y as the total expenditures for health care (in billions) to identify what type (or types) of function(s) would make a good model for these data.
(b) Find a power model and a quadratic model for the data.
(c) Which model from part (b) more accurately estimates the 2010 expenditures for national health care?
(d) Use the better model from part (c) to estimate the 2020 expenditures for national health care.

34. *U.S. population* The table gives the U.S. population, in millions, for selected years, with projections to 2050.
(a) Create a scatter plot for the data in the table, with x equal to the number of years past 1960.

(b) Use the scatter plot to determine the type of function that can be used to model the data, and create a function that best fits the data, with x equal to the number of years past 1960.

Year	U.S. Population (millions)
1960	180.671
1965	194.303
1970	205.052
1975	215.973
1980	227.726
1985	238.466
1990	249.948
1995	263.044
1998	270.561
2000	281.422
2003	294.043
2025	358.030
2050	408.695

Source: U.S. Census Bureau

35. *Cell phones* The table gives the number of thousands of U.S. cell phone subscriberships.
(a) Find the power function and cubic function models for these data, with x equal to the number of years after 1980.
(b) Use both models to estimate the number of subscriberships in 2015.
(c) Why do these estimates seem overly optimistic?

Year	Subscriberships (thousands)	Year	Subscriberships (thousands)
1985	340	1997	55,312
1986	682	1998	69,209
1987	1231	1999	86,047
1988	2069	2000	109,478
1989	3509	2001	128,375
1990	5283	2002	140,767
1991	7557	2003	158,722
1992	11,033	2004	182,140
1993	16,009	2005	207,896
1994	24,134	2006	233,041
1995	33,786	2007	255,396
1996	44,043	2008	270,334

Source: Semiannual CTIA Wireless Industry Survey

36. *Foreign-born population* The table gives the percent of the U.S. population that is foreign born.
   (a) With x equal to the number of years past 1900, use a scatter plot to determine whether a linear or quadratic function is the best fit for the data.
   (b) Find the best-fitting function for the data.
   (c) Use the function to estimate the percent in 2015.

Year	Percent Foreign Born	Year	Percent Foreign Born
1910	14.7	1970	4.7
1920	13.2	1980	6.2
1930	11.6	1990	8.0
1940	8.8	2000	10.4
1950	6.9	2005	11.7
1960	5.4	2007	12.6

Source: U.S. Census Bureau

KEY TERMS AND FORMULAS

Section	Key Terms	Formulas
2.1	Quadratic equation	$ax^2 + bx + c = 0 \quad (a \neq 0)$
	Square root property	$x^2 = C \Rightarrow x = \pm\sqrt{C}$
	Quadratic formula	$x = \dfrac{-b \pm \sqrt{b^2 - 4ac}}{2a}$
	Quadratic discriminant	$b^2 - 4ac$
2.2	Quadratic function; parabola	$y = f(x) = ax^2 + bx + c$
	Vertex of a parabola	$(-b/2a, f(-b/2a))$ Maximum point if $a < 0$ Minimum point if $a > 0$
	Axis of symmetry	$x = -b/2a$
	Zeros of a quadratic function	$x = \dfrac{-b \pm \sqrt{b^2 - 4ac}}{2a}$
2.3	Supply function Demand function Market equilibrium Cost, revenue, and profit functions Break-even points	 $P(x) = R(x) - C(x)$ $R(x) = C(x)$ or $P(x) = 0$
2.4	Basic functions	$f(x) = ax + b$ (linear) $f(x) = C, \ C = $ constant $f(x) = ax^b$ (power) $f(x) = x$ (identity) $f(x) = x^2, f(x) = x^3, f(x) = 1/x$
	Shifts of graphs	$f(x - h)$ shifts $f(x)$ h units horizontally $f(x) + k$ shifts $f(x)$ k units vertically
	Polynomial function of degree n	$f(x) = a_n x^n + a_{n-1} x^{n-1} + \cdots + a_1 x + a_0$ $a_n \neq 0, n \geq 0, n$ an integer
	Rational function	$f(x) = p(x)/q(x)$, where $p(x)$ and $q(x)$ are polynomials
	Vertical asymptote Horizontal asymptote	
	Absolute value function	$f(x) = |x| = \begin{cases} x & \text{if } x \geq 0 \\ -x & \text{if } x < 0 \end{cases}$
	Piecewise defined functions	
2.5	Scatter plots Function types Mathematical model Fitting curves to data points Predicting from models	

REVIEW EXERCISES

In Problems 1–10, find the real solutions to each quadratic equation.

1. $3x^2 + 10x = 5x$
2. $4x - 3x^2 = 0$
3. $x^2 + 5x + 6 = 0$
4. $11 - 10x - 2x^2 = 0$
5. $(x - 1)(x + 3) = -8$
6. $4x^2 = 3$
7. $20x^2 + 3x = 20 - 15x^2$
8. $8x^2 + 8x = 1 - 8x^2$
9. $7 = 2.07x - 0.02x^2$
10. $46.3x - 117 - 0.5x^2 = 0$

In Problems 11–14, solve each equation by using a graphing utility to find the zeros of the function. Solve the equation algebraically to check your results.

11. $4z^2 + 25 = 0$
12. $z(z + 6) = 27$
13. $3x^2 - 18x - 48 = 0$
14. $3x^2 - 6x - 9 = 0$
15. Solve $x^2 + ax + b = 0$ for x.
16. Solve $xr^2 - 4ar - x^2c = 0$ for r.

In Problems 17 and 18, approximate the real solutions to each quadratic equation to two decimal places.

17. $23.1 - 14.1x - 0.002x^2 = 0$
18. $1.03x^2 + 2.02x - 1.015 = 0$

For each function in Problems 19–24, find the vertex and determine if it is a maximum or minimum point, find the zeros if they exist, and sketch the graph.

19. $y = \frac{1}{2}x^2 + 2x$
20. $y = 4 + \frac{1}{4}x^2$
21. $y = 6 + x - x^2$
22. $y = x^2 - 4x + 5$
23. $y = x^2 + 6x + 9$
24. $y = 12x - 9 - 4x^2$

In Problems 25–30, use a graphing utility to graph each function. Use the vertex and zeros to determine an appropriate range. Be sure to label the maximum or minimum point.

25. $y = \frac{1}{3}x^2 - 3$
26. $y = \frac{1}{2}x^2 - 2$
27. $y = x^2 + 2x + 5$
28. $y = -10 + 7x - x^2$
29. $y = 20x - 0.1x^2$
30. $y = 50 - 1.5x + 0.01x^2$

31. Find the average rate of change of $f(x) = 100x - x^2$ from $x = 30$ to $x = 50$.

32. Find the average rate of change of
$$f(x) = x^2 - 30x + 22$$
over the interval $[10, 50]$.

In Problems 33–36, a graph is given. Use the graph to
(a) locate the vertex,
(b) determine the zeros, and
(c) match the graph with one of the equations A, B, C, or D.
  A. $y = 7x - \frac{1}{2}x^2$
  B. $y = \frac{1}{2}x^2 - x - 4$
  C. $y = 8 - 2x - x^2$
  D. $y = 49 - x^2$

33.

34.

35.

36.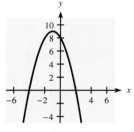

37. Sketch a graph of each of the following basic functions.
  (a) $f(x) = x^2$ (b) $f(x) = 1/x$ (c) $f(x) = x^{1/4}$

38. If $f(x) = \begin{cases} -x^2 & \text{if } x \le 0 \\ 1/x & \text{if } x > 0 \end{cases}$, find the following.
  (a) $f(0)$ (b) $f(0.0001)$
  (c) $f(-5)$ (d) $f(10)$

39. If $f(x) = \begin{cases} x & \text{if } x \le 1 \\ 3x - 2 & \text{if } x > 1 \end{cases}$, find the following.
  (a) $f(-2)$ (b) $f(0)$ (c) $f(1)$ (d) $f(2)$

In Problems 40 and 41, graph each function.

40. $f(x) = \begin{cases} x & \text{if } x \le 1 \\ 3x - 2 & \text{if } x > 1 \end{cases}$

41. (a) $f(x) = (x - 2)^2$ (b) $f(x) = (x + 1)^3$

In Problems 42 and 43, use a graphing utility to graph each function. Find any turning points.

42. $y = x^3 + 3x^2 - 9x$
43. $y = x^3 - 9x$

In Problems 44 and 45, graph each function. Find and identify any asymptotes.

44. $y = \dfrac{1}{x - 2}$ 45. $y = \dfrac{2x - 1}{x + 3}$

46. *Modeling* Consider the data given in the table.
  (a) Make a scatter plot.
  (b) Fit a linear function to the data and comment on the fit.
  (c) Try other function types and find one that fits better than a linear function.

x	0	4	8	12	16	20	24
y	153	151	147	140	128	115	102

47. *Modeling* Consider the data given in the table.
    (a) Make a scatter plot.
    (b) Fit a linear function to the data and comment on the fit.
    (c) Try other function types and find one that fits better than a linear function.

x	3	5	10	15	20	25	30
y	35	45	60	70	80	87	95

APPLICATIONS

48. *Physics* A ball is thrown into the air from a height of 96 ft above the ground, and its height is given by $S = 96 + 32t - 16t^2$, where t is the time in seconds.
    (a) Find the values of t that make $S = 0$.
    (b) Do both of the values of t have meaning for this application?
    (c) When will the ball strike the ground?

49. *Profit* The profit for a product is given by $P(x) = 82x - 0.10x^2 - 1600$, where x is the number of units produced and sold. Break-even points will occur at values of x where $P(x) = 0$. How many units will give a break-even point for the product?

50. *Drug use* Data indicate that the percent of high school seniors who have tried hallucinogens can be described by the function

    $$f(t) = -0.037t^2 + 1.006t + 1.75$$

    where t is the number of years since 1990 (*Source:* monitoringthefuture.org).
    (a) For what years does the function estimate that the percent will be 8.1%?
    (b) For what year does the function estimate the percent will be a maximum? Find that maximum estimated percent.

51. *Maximum area* A rectangular lot is to be fenced in and then divided down the middle to create two identical fenced lots (see the figure). If 1200 ft of fence is to be used, the area of each lot is given by

    $$A = x\left(\frac{1200 - 3x}{4}\right)$$

    (a) Find the x-value that maximizes this area.
    (b) Find the maximum area.

52. *Supply* Graph the first-quadrant portion of the supply function

    $$p = 2q^2 + 4q + 6$$

53. *Demand* Graph the first-quadrant portion of the demand function

    $$p = 18 - 3q - q^2$$

54. *Market equilibrium*
    (a) Suppose the supply function for a product is $p = 0.1q^2 + 1$ and the demand function is $p = 85 - 0.2q - 0.1q^2$. Sketch the first-quadrant portion of the graph of each function. Use the same set of axes for both and label the market equilibrium point.
    (b) Use algebraic methods to find the equilibrium price and quantity.

55. *Market equilibrium* The supply function for a product is given by $p = q^2 + 300$, and the demand is given by $p + q = 410$. Find the equilibrium quantity and price.

56. *Market equilibrium* If the demand function for a commodity is given by the equation $p^2 + 5q = 200$ and the supply function is given by $40 - p^2 + 3q = 0$, find the equilibrium quantity and price.

57. *Break-even points* If total costs for a product are given by $C(x) = 1760 + 8x + 0.6x^2$ and total revenues are given by $R(x) = 100x - 0.4x^2$, find the break-even quantities.

58. *Break-even points* If total costs for a commodity are given by $C(x) = 900 + 25x$ and total revenues are given by $R(x) = 100x - x^2$, find the break-even quantities.

59. *Maximizing revenue and profit* Find the maximum revenue and maximum profit for the functions described in Problem 58.

60. *Break-even and profit maximization* Given total profit $P(x) = 1.3x - 0.01x^2 - 30$, find maximum profit and the break-even quantities and sketch the graph.

61. *Maximum profit* Given $C(x) = 360 + 10x + 0.2x^2$ and $R(x) = 50x - 0.2x^2$, find the level of production that gives maximum profit and find the maximum profit.

62. *Break-even and profit maximization* A certain company has fixed costs of $15,000 for its product and variable costs given by $140 + 0.04x$ dollars per unit, where x is the total number of units. The selling price of the product is given by $300 - 0.06x$ dollars per unit.
    (a) Formulate the functions for total cost and total revenue.
    (b) Find the break-even quantities.
    (c) Find the level of sales that maximizes revenue.
    (d) Form the profit function and find the level of production and sales that maximizes profit.
    (e) Find the profit (or loss) at the production levels found in parts (c) and (d).

63. *Spread of AIDS* The function $H(t) = 8.81t^{0.476}$, where t is the number of years since 1990 and $H(t)$ is the number of world HIV infections (in millions), in year t, can be used as one means of predicting the spread of AIDS.
    (a) What type of function is this?
    (b) What does this function predict as the number of HIV cases in the year 2010?
    (c) Find $H(25)$ and write a sentence that explains its meaning.

64. *Photosynthesis* The amount y of photosynthesis that takes place in a certain plant depends on the intensity x of the light present, according to

$$y = 120x^2 - 20x^3 \text{ for } x \geq 0$$

(a) Graph this function with a graphing utility. (Use y-min $= -100$ and y-max $= 700$.)

(b) The model is valid only when $f(x) \geq 0$ (that is, on or above the x-axis). For what x-values is this true?

65. *Cost-benefit* Suppose the cost C, in dollars, of eliminating p percent of the pollution from the emissions of a factory is given by

$$C(p) = \frac{4800p}{100 - p}$$

(a) What type of function is this?

(b) Given that p represents the percent of pollution removed, what is the domain of $C(p)$?

(c) Find $C(0)$ and interpret its meaning.

(d) Find the cost of removing 99% of the pollution.

66. *Municipal water costs* The Borough Municipal Authority of Beaver, Pennsylvania, used the following function to determine charges for water.

$$C(x) = \begin{cases} 2.557x & \text{if } 0 \leq x \leq 100 \\ 255.70 + 2.04\,(x - 100) & \text{if } 100 < x \leq 1000 \\ 2091.07 + 1.689(x - 1000) & \text{if } x > 1000 \end{cases}$$

where $C(x)$ is the cost in dollars for x thousand gallons of water.

(a) Find the monthly charge for 12,000 gallons of water.

(b) Find the monthly charge for 825,000 gallons of water.

67. *Modeling (Subaru WRX)* The table shows the times that it takes a Subaru WRX to accelerate from 0 mph to speeds of 30 mph, 40 mph, etc., up to 90 mph, in increments of 10 mph.

Time (sec)	Speed (mph)	Time (sec)	Speed (mph)
1.6	30	7.8	70
2.7	40	10.2	80
4.0	50	12.9	90
5.6	60		

Source: Motor Trend

(a) Represent the times by x and the speeds by y, and model the function that is the best fit for the points.

(b) Graph the points and the function to see how well the function fits the points.

(c) What does the model indicate the speed is 5 seconds after the car starts to move?

(d) According to the model, in how many seconds will the car reach 79.3 mph?

68. *Modeling (public health care expenditures)* The total public expenditures (in billions of dollars) for national health care in the United States are given in the table for 2000 to 2007 with projections to 2018.

(a) Use x as the number of years past 2000 and find a quadratic model for these data.

(b) According to this model, when will public health care expenditures exceed $3 trillion (that is, $3000 billion)?

(c) How much confidence can we have in the projections beyond 2012? Explain.

Year	Health Care Expenditures (billions)	Year	Health Care Expenditures (billions)
2000	$597	2010	$1251
2001	662	2011	1332
2002	722	2012	1424
2003	779	2013	1527
2004	840	2014	1640
2005	899	2015	1768
2006	973	2016	1909
2007	1036	2017	2064
2008	1109	2018	2233
2009	1190		

Source: U.S Centers for Medicare & Medicaid Services

69. *Modeling (cohabiting households)* The table gives the number of cohabiting (without marriage) households (in thousands) for selected years.

(a) Find the power function that best fits the data, with x representing the number of years past 1950.

(b) Find a quadratic function that is the best fit for the data, with x equal to the number of years past 1950.

(c) Which model appears to fit the data better, or are they both good fits?

Year	Cohabiting Households (thousands)
1960	439
1970	523
1980	1589
1985	1983
1990	2856
1993	3510
1997	4130
2000	5457
2004	5841
2008	6214

Source: U.S. Census Bureau

2   CHAPTER TEST

1. Sketch a graph of each of the following functions.
   (a) $f(x) = x^4$
   (b) $g(x) = |x|$
   (c) $h(x) = -1$
   (d) $k(x) = \sqrt{x}$

2. The following figures show graphs of the power function $y = x^b$. Which is the graph for $b > 1$? Which is the graph for $0 < b < 1$?

(a)

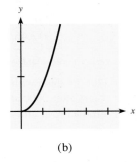

(b)

3. If $f(x) = ax^2 + bx + c$ and $a < 0$, sketch the shape of the graph of $y = f(x)$.

4. Graph:
   (a) $f(x) = (x + 1)^2 - 1$
   (b) $f(x) = (x - 2)^3 + 1$

5. Which of the following three graphs is the graph of $f(x) = x^3 - 4x^2$? Explain your choice.

(a)

(b)

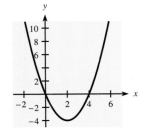

(c)

6. Let $f(x) = \begin{cases} 8x + 1/x & \text{if } x < 0 \\ 4 & \text{if } 0 \le x \le 2 \\ 6 - x & \text{if } x > 2 \end{cases}$

   Find (a) the y-coordinate of the point on the graph of $y = f(x)$ where $x = 16$; (b) $f(-2)$; (c) $f(13)$.

7. Sketch the graph of $g(x) = \begin{cases} x^2 & \text{if } x \le 1 \\ 4 - x & \text{if } x > 1 \end{cases}$

8. Find the vertex and zeros, if they exist, and sketch the graph of $f(x) = 21 - 4x - x^2$.

9. Solve $3x^2 + 2 = 7x$.

10. Solve $2x^2 + 6x = 9$.

11. Solve $\dfrac{1}{x} + 2x = \dfrac{1}{3} + \dfrac{x + 1}{x}$.

12. Which of the following three graphs is that of $g(x) = \dfrac{3x - 12}{x + 2}$? Explain your choice.

(a)

(b)

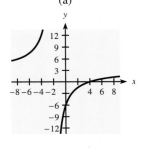

(c)

13. Find the horizontal and vertical asymptotes of the graph of
$$f(x) = \frac{8}{2x - 10}$$

14. Find the average rate of change of
$$P(x) = 92x - x^2 - 1760$$
over the interval from $x = 10$ to $x = 40$.

15. Choose the type of function that models each of the following graphs.

(a)

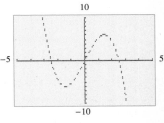

(b)

16. *Modeling*
    (a) Make a scatter plot, then develop a model, for the following data.
    (b) What does the model predict for $x = 40$?
    (c) When does the model predict $f(x) = 0$?

x	0	2	4	6	8	10	12	14	16	18	20
y	20.1	19.2	18.8	17.5	17.0	15.8	16	14.9	13.8	13.7	13.0

17. Suppose the supply and demand functions for a product are given by $6p - q = 180$ and $(p + 20)q = 30{,}000$, respectively. Find the equilibrium price and quantity.

18. Suppose a company's total cost for a product is given by $C(x) = 15{,}000 + 35x + 0.1x^2$ and the total revenue for the product is given by $R(x) = 285x - 0.9x^2$, where x is the number of units produced and sold.
    (a) Find the profit function.
    (b) Determine the number of units at which the profit for the product is maximized, and find the maximum possible profit.
    (c) Find the break-even point(s) for the product.

19. The wind chill expresses the combined effects of low temperatures and wind speeds as a single temperature reading. When the outside temperature is $0°F$, the wind chill, WC, is a function of the wind speed s (in mph) and is approximated by the following function.*

$$WC = f(s) = \begin{cases} 0 & \text{if } 0 \le s \le 1.13 \\ 36.23 - 35.50\sqrt[6]{s} & \text{if } 1.13 < s < 55 \\ -33 & \text{if } s \ge 55 \end{cases}$$

*Source: National Weather Service

(a) Find $f(15)$ and write a sentence that explains its meaning.
(b) Find the wind chill when the wind speed is 48 mph.

20. The table gives the per capita out-of-pocket expenses for health care in the United States for selected years from 2000 and projected to 2018.

Year	Expenses	Year	Expenses
2000	$683.91	2010	$938.10
2002	733.40	2012	992.73
2004	802.32	2014	1070.10
2006	854.56	2016	1165.20
2008	917.46	2018	1274.63

Source: U.S. Centers for Medicare & Medicaid Services

(a) Plot the data, with x representing the number of years after 2000 and y representing the expenses.
(b) Find a linear and a cubic function model for the data.
(c) Use both models to estimate the per capita expenses in 2020.
(d) Can we be sure that the actual expenses for 2018 agree with the model's output for 2018?

I. An Inconvenient Truth

There are many functions mentioned in the movie *An Inconvenient Truth*. Read the questions below, then watch the movie and describe the functions in it as follows.

1. (a) Find a function in the movie that is described by a graph and answer the following questions for it.
    (b) What does the input describe? What units does it have?
    (c) What does the output describe? What units does it have?
    (d) How does Al Gore use this function to support his arguments on climate change?
2. (a) Find a second function in the movie and answer the following questions for it.
    (b) Is the function described by a graph, a table, an equation, or words?
    (c) What does the input describe? What units does it have?
    (d) What does the output describe? What units does it have?
    (e) How does Al Gore use this function to support his arguments on climate change?
    (f) Does Al Gore use extrapolation with this function to support his position? If so, do you think this extrapolation supports his position?
3. (a) For a function described in the movie, find a set of data that also describes the same or a similar function and use your function to answer the following questions.
    (b) What does the input describe? What units does it have?
    (c) What does the output describe? What units does it have?
    (d) Does your function support Al Gore's arguments on climate change?

II. Body Mass Index

Obesity is a risk factor for the development of several medical problems, including high blood pressure, high cholesterol, heart disease, and diabetes. Of course, whether a person is considered obese depends not only on weight but also on height. One way of comparing weights that accounts for height is the *body mass index (BMI)*. The table below gives the BMI for a variety of heights and weights for people. Medical professionals generally agree that a BMI of 30 or greater increases the risk of developing medical problems associated with obesity.

Describe how to assist a group of people in using this information. Some things you would want to include in your description follow.

A. How a person uses the table to determine his or her BMI.
B. How a person determines the weight that will put him or her at medical risk.
C. How a person whose weight or height is not in the table can determine whether his or her BMI is 30 or higher. To address this particular issue, develop a formula to find the weight that would give a BMI of 30 for a person of a given height, including how you would:
    1. Pick the points from the table that correspond to a BMI of 30 and create a table of these heights and weights. Change the units of height measurement to simplify the data.
    2. Determine what type of model seems to be the best fit for the data.
    3. Create a model for the data.
    4. Test the model with existing data.
    5. Explain how to use the model to test for obesity. In particular, use the model to find the obesity threshold for someone who is 5 feet tall and someone who is 6 feet 2 inches tall (heights that are not in the table).
    6. Use the Internet to find the definition of BMI, and, if necessary, convert it to a formula that uses inches and pounds.
    7. Make a table for heights from 61 inches to 73 inches that compares the threshold weights for a BMI of 30 from your model, from the definition of BMI, and from the table.

Body Mass Index for Specified Height (ft/in.) and Weight (lb)														
Height/Weight	120	130	140	150	160	170	180	190	200	210	220	230	240	250
5'1"	23	25	27	28	30	32	34	36	38	40	42	44	45	47
5'2"	22	24	26	27	29	31	33	35	37	38	40	42	44	46
5'3"	21	23	25	27	28	30	32	34	36	37	39	41	43	44
5'4"	21	22	24	26	28	29	31	33	34	36	38	40	41	43
5'5"	20	22	23	25	27	28	30	32	33	35	37	38	40	42
5'6"	19	21	23	24	26	27	29	31	32	34	36	37	39	40
5'7"	19	20	23	24	25	27	28	30	31	33	35	36	38	39
5'8"	18	20	21	23	24	26	27	29	30	32	34	35	37	38
5'9"	18	19	21	22	24	25	27	28	30	31	33	34	36	37
5'10"	17	19	20	22	23	24	25	27	28	29	31	33	35	36
5'11"	17	18	20	21	22	24	25	27	28	29	31	32	34	35
6'0"	16	18	19	20	22	23	24	26	27	29	30	31	33	34
6'1"	16	17	19	20	21	22	24	25	26	28	29	30	32	33

Source: Roche Pharmaceuticals

III. Operating Leverage and Business Risk

Once you have determined the break-even point for your product, you can use it to examine the effects of increasing or decreasing the role of fixed costs in your operating structure. The extent to which a business uses fixed costs (compared to variable costs) in its operations is referred to as **operating leverage.** The greater the use of operating leverage (fixed costs, often associated with fixed assets), the larger the increase in profit as sales rise, and the larger the increase in loss as sales fall (*Source:* **www.toolkit.cch.com/text/P06_7540.asp**). The higher the break-even quantity for your product, the greater your **business risk.** To see how operating leverage is related to business risk, complete the following.

1. If x is the number of units of a product that is sold and the price is $\$p$ per unit, write the function that gives the revenue R for the product.
2. (a) If the fixed cost for production of this product is $\$10,000$ and the variable cost is $\$100$ per unit, find the function that gives the total cost C for the product.
   (b) What type of function is this?
3. Write an equation containing only the variables p and x that describes when the break-even point occurs.
4. (a) Solve the equation from Question 3 for x, so that x is written as a function of p.
   (b) What type of function is this?
   (c) What is the domain of this function?
   (d) What is the domain of this function in the context of this application?
5. (a) Graph the function from Question 4 for the domain of the problem.
   (b) Does the function increase or decrease as p increases?
6. Suppose that the company has a monopoly for this product so that it can set the price as it chooses. What are the benefit and the danger to the company of pricing its product at $\$1100$ per unit?
7. If the company has a monopoly for this product so that it can set the price, what are the benefit and the danger to the company of pricing its product at $\$101$ per unit?
8. Suppose the company currently is labor-intensive, so that the monthly fixed cost is $\$10,000$ and the variable cost is $\$100$ per unit, but installing modern equipment will reduce the variable cost to $\$50$ per unit while increasing the monthly fixed cost to $\$30,000$. Also suppose the selling price per unit is $P = \$200$.
   (a) Which of these operations will have the highest operating leverage? Explain.
   (b) Which of these operations will have the highest business risk? Explain.
   (c) What is the relation between high operating leverage and risk? Discuss the benefit and danger of the second operating plan to justify your answer.

3 Matrices

CHAPTER

A wide variety of application problems can be solved using matrices. A **matrix** (plural: matrices) is a rectangular array of numbers. In addition to storing data in a matrix and making comparisons of data, we can analyze data and make business decisions by defining the operations of addition, subtraction, scalar multiplication, and matrix multiplication. Matrices can be used to solve systems of linear equations, as we will see in this chapter. Matrices and matrix operations are the basis for computer spreadsheets such as Excel, which are used extensively in education, research, and business. Matrices are also useful in linear programming, which is discussed in Chapter 4.

The topics and applications discussed in this chapter include the following.

SECTIONS	APPLICATIONS
3.1 Matrices **Operations with matrices**	Balance of trade, supply charges, power to influence
3.2 Multiplication of Matrices	Material supply, encoding messages, venture capital
3.3 Gauss-Jordan Elimination: **Solving Systems of Equations** **Systems with unique solutions** **Systems with nonunique solutions**	Manufacturing, investment, traffic flow
3.4 Inverse of a Square Matrix; **Matrix Equations** **Matrix equations** **Determinants**	Decoding messages, venture capital, freight logistics
3.5 Applications of Matrices: **Leontief Input-Output** **Models**	Simple economy, outputs of an economy, production, open economy, closed economy, manufacturing

Prerequisite Problem Type	For Section	Answer	Section for Review
Evaluate: (a) $4-(-2)$ (b) $-4\left(\dfrac{2}{3}\right) + 3$ (c) $(-5)(4) + (8)(1) + (2)(5)$ (d) Multiply each of the numbers $0, -3, -2, 2$ by $-\dfrac{1}{3}$.	**3.1** **3.2** **3.3** **3.4** **3.5**	(a) 6 (b) $\dfrac{1}{3}$ (c) -2 (d) $0, 1, \dfrac{2}{3}, -\dfrac{2}{3}$	0.2 Signed numbers

Write the coefficients of x, y and z and the constant term in each equation:
(a) $2x + 5y + 4z = 4$
(b) $x - 3y - 2z = 5$
(c) $3x + y = 4$

3.3
3.4
3.5

Coefficients			Const. term
x	y	z	
2	5	4	4
1	-3	-2	5
3	1	0	4

0.5 Algebraic expressions

Solve:
(a) $x_1 - 2x_3 = 2$ for x_1
(b) $x_2 + x_3 = -3$ for x_2
(c) $450,000 - 3z \geq 0$ for z

3.3
3.4
3.5

(a) $x_1 = 2 + 2x_3$
(b) $x_2 = -3 - x_3$
(c) $z \leq 150,000$

1.1 Linear equations and inequalities

Solve the system:
$\begin{cases} x - 0.25y = 11,750 \\ -0.20x + y = 10,000 \end{cases}$

3.3
3.4
3.5

$x = 15,000$
$y = 13,000$

1.5 Systems of linear equations

OBJECTIVES

3.1

- To organize and interpret data stored in matrices
- To add and subtract matrices
- To find the transpose of a matrix
- To multiply a matrix by a scalar (real number)

Matrices

| APPLICATION PREVIEW |

Data in tabular form can be stored in matrices, which are useful for solving an assortment of problems, including the following. Table 3.1 summarizes the dollar value (in millions) of 2006 U.S. exports and imports of cars, trucks, and automotive parts for selected countries. If the data in Table 3.1 are formed into two matrices, one for exports and one for imports, then the balance of trade with the selected countries for cars, trucks, and parts will be the difference of those two matrices.

| TABLE 3.1 |

	Exports			Imports		
	Cars	Trucks	Parts	Cars	Trucks	Parts
Canada	13,165	11,992	31,952	36,600	12,250	20,132
Japan	477	59	1755	43,522	986	15,704
Mexico	3451	1007	12,606	14,201	9559	25,217

Source: U.S. Bureau of Economic Analysis

As we noted in the introduction to this chapter, matrices can be used to store data and to perform operations with the data. The information in Table 3.1 can be organized into an export matrix A and an import matrix B, as follows.

$$A = \begin{bmatrix} 13{,}165 & 11{,}992 & 31{,}952 \\ 477 & 59 & 1755 \\ 3451 & 1007 & 12{,}606 \end{bmatrix} \quad B = \begin{bmatrix} 36{,}600 & 12{,}250 & 20{,}132 \\ 43{,}522 & 986 & 15{,}704 \\ 14{,}201 & 9559 & 25{,}217 \end{bmatrix}$$

We will discuss how to find the difference of these two and other pairs of matrices, how to find the sum of two matrices, and how to multiply a matrix by a real number. (The difference of these two matrices is found in Example 5.)

In the export matrix A in the Application Preview, the *rows* correspond to the countries and the *columns* correspond to items exported. The rows of a matrix are numbered from the top to the bottom, and the columns are numbered from left to right, as the following example matrix illustrates.

$$\begin{array}{cccc} \text{Column 1} & \text{Column 2} & \text{Column 3} & \text{Column 4} \end{array}$$
$$M = \begin{bmatrix} 20 & 25 & 22 & 18 \\ 27 & 40 & 31 & 25 \\ 16 & 16 & 19 & 16 \end{bmatrix} \begin{array}{l} \text{Row 1} \\ \text{Row 2} \\ \text{Row 3} \end{array}$$

Matrices are classified in terms of the numbers of rows and columns they have. Matrix M has three rows and four columns, so we say this is a 3×4 (read "three by four") matrix.

The matrix

$$A = \begin{bmatrix} a_{11} & a_{12} & a_{13} & \cdots & a_{1n} \\ a_{21} & a_{22} & a_{23} & \cdots & a_{2n} \\ & \vdots & & & \vdots \\ a_{m1} & a_{m2} & a_{m3} & \cdots & a_{mn} \end{bmatrix}$$

has m rows and n columns, so it is an $m \times n$ matrix. When we designate A as an $m \times n$ matrix, we are indicating the size of the matrix. Two matrices are said to have the same **order** (be the same size) if they have the same number of rows and the same number of columns. For example, $C = \begin{bmatrix} 1 & 3 & 2 \\ 4 & 1 & 2 \end{bmatrix}$ and $D = \begin{bmatrix} 1 & 4 \\ 2 & 1 \\ 3 & 0 \end{bmatrix}$ do not have the same order. C is a 2×3 matrix and D is a 3×2 matrix.

The numbers in a matrix are called its **entries** or **elements.** Note that the subscripts on an entry in matrix A above correspond respectively to the row and column in which the entry is located. Thus a_{23} represents the entry in the second row and the third column, and we refer to it as the "two-three entry." In matrix B below, the entry denoted by b_{23} is 1.

Some matrices take special names because of their size. If the number of rows equals the number of columns, we say the matrix is a **square matrix.** Matrix B below is a 3×3 square matrix.

$$B = \begin{bmatrix} 4 & 3 & 0 \\ 0 & 0 & 1 \\ -4 & 0 & 0 \end{bmatrix}$$

EXAMPLE 1 Population and Labor Force

Figure 3.1 gives the U.S. population and labor force (in millions, actual and projected) for the years 2008, 2012, and 2016.

Population and labor force

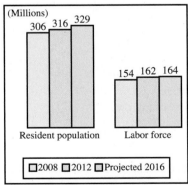

Figure 3.1

Source: U.S. Bureau of Labor Statistics and U.S. Census Bureau

A partial table of values from Figure 3.1 is shown. Complete the table that summarizes these data, and use it to create a 2×3 matrix describing the information.

	2008	**2012**	**2016**
Resident Population	306		
Labor Force		162	

Solution

Reading the data from Figure 3.1 and completing the table give

	2008	2012	2016
Resident Population	306	316	329
Labor Force	154	162	164

Writing these data in a matrix gives

$$\begin{bmatrix} 306 & 316 & 329 \\ 154 & 162 & 164 \end{bmatrix}$$

A matrix with one row, such as $[9 \quad 5]$ or $[3 \quad 2 \quad 1 \quad 6]$, is called a **row matrix,** and a matrix with one column, such as

$$\begin{bmatrix} 1 \\ 3 \\ 5 \end{bmatrix}$$

is called a **column matrix.** Row and column matrices are also called **vectors.**

Any matrix in which *every* entry is zero is called a **zero matrix;** examples include

$$\begin{bmatrix} 0 & 0 \\ 0 & 0 \end{bmatrix}, \quad \begin{bmatrix} 0 & 0 \\ 0 & 0 \\ 0 & 0 \end{bmatrix}, \quad \text{and} \quad \begin{bmatrix} 0 & 0 & 0 & 0 \\ 0 & 0 & 0 & 0 \\ 0 & 0 & 0 & 0 \end{bmatrix}$$

We define two matrices to be **equal** if they are of the same order and if each entry in one equals the corresponding entry in the other.

When the columns and rows of matrix A are interchanged to create a matrix B, and vice versa, we say that A and B are **transposes** of each other and write $A^T = B$ and $B^T = A$. We will see valuable uses for transposes of matrices in Chapter 4, "Inequalities and Linear Programming."

EXAMPLE 2   **Matrices**

(a) Which element of

$$A = \begin{bmatrix} 1 & 0 & 3 \\ 3 & 4 & 2 \\ 7 & 8 & 3 \end{bmatrix} \quad B = \begin{bmatrix} 1 & 0 & 3 \\ 3 & 4 & 2 \\ 7 & 8 & 4 \end{bmatrix}$$

is represented by a_{32}?
(b) Is A a square matrix?
(c) Find the transpose of matrix A.
(d) Does $A = B$?

Solution

(a) a_{32} represents the element in row 3 and column 2 of matrix A—that is, $a_{32} = 8$.
(b) Yes, it is a 3×3 (square) matrix.
(c)
$$A^T = \begin{bmatrix} 1 & 3 & 7 \\ 0 & 4 & 8 \\ 3 & 2 & 3 \end{bmatrix}$$
(d) No, $a_{33} \neq b_{33}$.

CHECKPOINT

1. (a) Do matrices A and B have the same order?

$$A = \begin{bmatrix} 1 & 2 & 3 \\ 4 & 5 & 6 \\ 7 & 8 & 9 \end{bmatrix} \quad \text{and} \quad B = \begin{bmatrix} 1 & 4 & 7 \\ 2 & 5 & 8 \\ 3 & 6 & 9 \end{bmatrix}$$

(b) Does matrix A equal matrix B?
(c) Does $B^T = A$?

Addition and Subtraction of Matrices

If two matrices have the same number of rows and columns, we can add the matrices by adding their corresponding entries.

Sum of Two Matrices

If matrix A and matrix B are of the same order and have elements a_{ij} and b_{ij}, respectively, then their **sum** $A + B$ is a matrix C whose elements are $c_{ij} = a_{ij} + b_{ij}$ for all i and j. That is,

$$A + B = \begin{bmatrix} a_{11} & a_{12} & \cdots & a_{1n} \\ a_{21} & a_{22} & \cdots & a_{2n} \\ \vdots & & & \vdots \\ a_{m1} & a_{m2} & \cdots & a_{mn} \end{bmatrix} + \begin{bmatrix} b_{11} & b_{12} & \cdots & b_{1n} \\ b_{21} & b_{22} & \cdots & b_{2n} \\ \vdots & & & \vdots \\ b_{m1} & b_{m2} & \cdots & b_{mn} \end{bmatrix}$$

$$= \begin{bmatrix} a_{11}+b_{11} & a_{12}+b_{12} & \cdots & a_{1n}+b_{1n} \\ a_{21}+b_{21} & a_{22}+b_{22} & \cdots & a_{2n}+b_{2n} \\ \vdots & & & \vdots \\ a_{m1}+b_{m1} & a_{m2}+b_{m2} & \cdots & a_{mn}+b_{mn} \end{bmatrix} = C$$

EXAMPLE 3 **Matrix Sums**

Find the sum of A and B if

$$A = \begin{bmatrix} 1 & 2 & 3 \\ 4 & -1 & -2 \end{bmatrix} \quad \text{and} \quad B = \begin{bmatrix} -1 & 2 & -3 \\ -2 & 0 & 1 \end{bmatrix}$$

Solution

$$A + B = \begin{bmatrix} 1+(-1) & 2+2 & 3+(-3) \\ 4+(-2) & -1+0 & -2+1 \end{bmatrix} = \begin{bmatrix} 0 & 4 & 0 \\ 2 & -1 & -1 \end{bmatrix}$$

Note that the sum of A and B in Example 3 could be found by adding the matrices in either order. That is, $A + B = B + A$. This is known as the **commutative law of addition** for matrices. We will see in the next section that multiplication of matrices is *not* commutative.

The matrix $-B$ is called the **negative** of the matrix B, and each element of $-B$ is the negative of the corresponding element of B. For example, if

$$B = \begin{bmatrix} -1 & 2 & -3 \\ -2 & 0 & 1 \end{bmatrix}, \quad \text{then} \quad -B = \begin{bmatrix} 1 & -2 & 3 \\ 2 & 0 & -1 \end{bmatrix}$$

Using the negative, we can define the difference $A - B$ (when A and B have the same order) by $A - B = A + (-B)$, or by subtracting corresponding elements.

EXAMPLE 4   Matrix Differences

For matrices A and B in Example 3, find $A - B$.

Solution

$A - B$ can be found by subtracting corresponding elements.

$$A - B = \begin{bmatrix} 1 - (-1) & 2 - 2 & 3 - (-3) \\ 4 - (-2) & -1 - 0 & -2 - 1 \end{bmatrix} = \begin{bmatrix} 2 & 0 & 6 \\ 6 & -1 & -3 \end{bmatrix}$$

CHECKPOINT

2. If $A = \begin{bmatrix} 1 & 2 & 0 \\ 3 & 1 & 2 \end{bmatrix}$, $B = \begin{bmatrix} 3 & 6 & 1 \\ 0 & 2 & 1 \end{bmatrix}$, and $C = \begin{bmatrix} 1 & 0 & 2 \\ 0 & 1 & 1 \end{bmatrix}$, find $A + B - C$.

3. (a) What matrix D must be added to matrix A so that their sum is matrix Z?

$$A = \begin{bmatrix} 1 & -2 & 3 \\ -5 & 1 & 2 \end{bmatrix} \text{ and } Z = \begin{bmatrix} 0 & 0 & 0 \\ 0 & 0 & 0 \end{bmatrix}$$

   (b) Does $D = -A$?

EXAMPLE 5   Balance of Trade | APPLICATION PREVIEW |

Table 3.2 summarizes the dollar value (in millions) of 2006 U.S. exports and imports of cars, trucks, and automotive parts for selected countries. Write the matrix that describes the balance of trade with the selected countries for cars, trucks, and parts.

| TABLE 3.2 |

	Exports			Imports		
	Cars	Trucks	Parts	Cars	Trucks	Parts
Canada	13,165	11,992	31,952	36,600	12,250	20,132
Japan	477	59	1755	43,522	986	15,704
Mexico	3451	1007	12,606	14,201	9559	25,217

Source: U.S. Bureau of Economic Analysis

Solution

From Table 3.2 we represent the exports as matrix A and the imports as matrix B.

$$A = \begin{bmatrix} 13,165 & 11,992 & 31,952 \\ 477 & 59 & 1755 \\ 3451 & 1007 & 12,606 \end{bmatrix} \quad B = \begin{bmatrix} 36,600 & 12,250 & 20,132 \\ 43,522 & 986 & 15,704 \\ 14,201 & 9559 & 25,217 \end{bmatrix}$$

The balance of trade we seek is given by the difference $A - B$, as follows.

$$A - B = \begin{bmatrix} 13,165 - 36,600 & 11,992 - 12,250 & 31,952 - 20,132 \\ 477 - 43,522 & 59 - 986 & 1755 - 15,704 \\ 3451 - 14,201 & 1007 - 9559 & 12,606 - 25,217 \end{bmatrix}$$

$$= \begin{bmatrix} -23,435 & -258 & 11,820 \\ -43,045 & -927 & -13,949 \\ -10,750 & -8552 & -12,611 \end{bmatrix}$$

Note that any negative entry indicates an unfavorable balance of trade for the item and with the country corresponding to that entry. Also note that the 1–3 entry is the only positive one and that it indicates a favorable trade balance, in automotive parts with Canada, worth $11,820,000,000.

Calculator Note   Graphing calculators have the capability to perform a number of operations on matrices. Steps for entering data in matrices and performing operations with matrices using a graphing calculator are shown in Appendix C, Section 3.1.

To compute $A + B$ and $A - B$ for

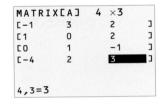

We enter matrices in a graphing calculator (see Figure 3.2) and find the sum and difference of the two matrices by using the regular ⊞ and ⊟ keys (see Figure 3.3).

```
MATRIX[A]   4 ×3
[-1      3       2    ]
[1       0       2    ]
[0       1      -1    ]
[-4      2       3    ]

4,3=3
```

```
MATRIX[B]   4 ×3
[-3      2       1    ]
[0      -2       2    ]
[-1      6       8    ]
[3       2       4    ]

4,3=4
```

Figure 3.2

```
[A] + [B]
    [[-4    5     3]
     [1    -2     4]
     [-1    7     7]
     [-1    4     7]]
```

```
[A] - [B]
    [[2     1     1]
     [1     2     0]
     [1    -5    -9]
     [-7    0    -1]]
```

Figure 3.3

Scalar Multiplication   Consider the matrix

$$A = \begin{bmatrix} 3 & 2 \\ 1 & 1 \\ 2 & 0 \end{bmatrix}$$

Because $2A$ is $A + A$, we see that

$$2A = \begin{bmatrix} 3 & 2 \\ 1 & 1 \\ 2 & 0 \end{bmatrix} + \begin{bmatrix} 3 & 2 \\ 1 & 1 \\ 2 & 0 \end{bmatrix} = \begin{bmatrix} 6 & 4 \\ 2 & 2 \\ 4 & 0 \end{bmatrix}$$

Note that $2A$ could have been found by multiplying each entry of A by 2. In the same manner, it can be shown that $3A = A + A + A$. (Try it.)

We can define **scalar multiplication** as follows.

Scalar Multiplication   Multiplying a matrix by a real number (called a *scalar*) results in a matrix in which each entry of the original matrix is multiplied by the real number. Thus, if

$$A = \begin{bmatrix} a_{11} & a_{12} \\ a_{21} & a_{22} \end{bmatrix}, \quad \text{then} \quad cA = \begin{bmatrix} ca_{11} & ca_{12} \\ ca_{21} & ca_{22} \end{bmatrix}$$

EXAMPLE 6   **Scalar Multiplication**

If

$$A = \begin{bmatrix} 4 & 1 & 4 & 0 \\ 2 & -7 & 3 & 6 \\ 0 & 0 & 2 & 5 \end{bmatrix}$$

find $5A$ and $-2A$.

Solution

$$5A = \begin{bmatrix} 5 \cdot 4 & 5 \cdot 1 & 5 \cdot 4 & 5 \cdot 0 \\ 5 \cdot 2 & 5(-7) & 5 \cdot 3 & 5 \cdot 6 \\ 5 \cdot 0 & 5 \cdot 0 & 5 \cdot 2 & 5 \cdot 5 \end{bmatrix} = \begin{bmatrix} 20 & 5 & 20 & 0 \\ 10 & -35 & 15 & 30 \\ 0 & 0 & 10 & 25 \end{bmatrix}$$

$$-2A = \begin{bmatrix} -2 \cdot 4 & -2 \cdot 1 & -2 \cdot 4 & -2 \cdot 0 \\ -2 \cdot 2 & -2(-7) & -2 \cdot 3 & -2 \cdot 6 \\ -2 \cdot 0 & -2 \cdot 0 & -2 \cdot 2 & -2 \cdot 5 \end{bmatrix} = \begin{bmatrix} -8 & -2 & -8 & 0 \\ -4 & 14 & -6 & -12 \\ 0 & 0 & -4 & -10 \end{bmatrix}$$

Figure 3.4 shows the matrix $-2A$ on a graphing calculator.

Figure 3.4

CHECKPOINT

4. (a) Find $3D - D$ if $D = \begin{bmatrix} 1 & 3 & 2 & 10 \\ 20 & 5 & 6 & 3 \end{bmatrix}$

    (b) Does $3D - D = 2D$?

EXAMPLE 7   **Supply Charges**

Suppose the purchase prices and delivery costs (per unit) for wood, siding, and roofing used in construction are given by Table 3.3. Then the table of unit costs may be represented by the matrix C.

■ | TABLE 3.3 | ■■■■■■■■■■

	Wood	Siding	Roofing
Purchase	6	4	2
Delivery	1	1	0.5

$$C = \begin{bmatrix} 6 & 4 & 2 \\ 1 & 1 & 0.5 \end{bmatrix}$$

If the supplier announces a 10% increase on both purchase and delivery of these items, find the new unit cost matrix.

Solution

A 10% increase means that the new unit costs are the former costs plus 0.10 times the former cost. That is, the new costs are 1.10 times the former, so the new unit cost matrix is given by

$$1.10C = 1.10 \begin{bmatrix} 6 & 4 & 2 \\ 1 & 1 & 0.5 \end{bmatrix} = \begin{bmatrix} 6.60 & 4.40 & 2.20 \\ 1.10 & 1.10 & 0.55 \end{bmatrix}$$

EXAMPLE 8   **Power to Influence**

Suppose that in a government agency, paperwork is constantly flowing among offices according to the diagram.

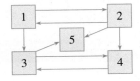

(a) Construct matrix A with elements

$$a_{ij} = \begin{cases} 1 & \text{if paperwork flows directly from } i \text{ to } j. \\ 0 & \text{if paperwork does not flow directly from } i \text{ to } j. \end{cases}$$

(b) Construct matrix B with elements

$$b_{ij} = \begin{cases} 1 & \text{if paperwork can flow from } i \text{ to } j \text{ through at most} \\ & \text{one intermediary, with } i \neq j. \\ 0 & \text{if this is not true.} \end{cases}$$

(c) The person in office i has the most power to influence others if the sum of the elements of row i in the matrix $A + B$ is the largest. What is the office number of this person?

Solution

$$\text{(a)} \quad A = \begin{bmatrix} 0 & 1 & 1 & 0 & 0 \\ 1 & 0 & 0 & 1 & 1 \\ 0 & 0 & 0 & 1 & 1 \\ 0 & 0 & 1 & 0 & 0 \\ 0 & 0 & 0 & 0 & 0 \end{bmatrix} \qquad \text{(b)} \quad B = \begin{bmatrix} 0 & 1 & 1 & 1 & 1 \\ 1 & 0 & 1 & 1 & 1 \\ 0 & 0 & 0 & 1 & 1 \\ 0 & 0 & 1 & 0 & 1 \\ 0 & 0 & 0 & 0 & 0 \end{bmatrix}$$

$$\text{(c)} \quad A + B = \begin{bmatrix} 0 & 2 & 2 & 1 & 1 \\ 2 & 0 & 1 & 2 & 2 \\ 0 & 0 & 0 & 2 & 2 \\ 0 & 0 & 2 & 0 & 1 \\ 0 & 0 & 0 & 0 & 0 \end{bmatrix}$$

Because the sum of the elements in row 2 is the largest (7), the person in office 2 has the most power to influence others. Because row 5 has the smallest sum (0), the person in office 5 has the least power.

Spreadsheet Note   Once data are entered in a spreadsheet, they can be stored in a matrix and then added to or subtracted from other matrices. See Appendix D, Section 3.1 and the Online Excel Guide for details.

CHECKPOINT SOLUTIONS

1. (a) Yes, A and B have the same order (size).
   (b) No. They have the same elements, but they are not equal because their corresponding elements are not equal.
   (c) Yes.

2. $\begin{bmatrix} 3 & 8 & -1 \\ 3 & 2 & 2 \end{bmatrix}$ 3. (a) $\begin{bmatrix} -1 & 2 & -3 \\ 5 & -1 & -2 \end{bmatrix}$ (b) Yes

4. (a) $3D - D = \begin{bmatrix} 3 & 9 & 6 & 30 \\ 60 & 15 & 18 & 9 \end{bmatrix} - \begin{bmatrix} 1 & 3 & 2 & 10 \\ 20 & 5 & 6 & 3 \end{bmatrix}$

   $= \begin{bmatrix} 2 & 6 & 4 & 20 \\ 40 & 10 & 12 & 6 \end{bmatrix}$

   (b) Yes

| EXERCISES | 3.1

Use the following matrices for Problems 1–28.

$$A = \begin{bmatrix} 1 & 0 & -2 \\ 3 & 2 & 1 \\ 4 & 0 & 3 \end{bmatrix} \quad B = \begin{bmatrix} 1 & 1 & 3 & 0 \\ 4 & 2 & 1 & 1 \\ 3 & 2 & 0 & 1 \end{bmatrix}$$

$$C = \begin{bmatrix} 5 & 3 \\ 1 & 2 \end{bmatrix} \quad D = \begin{bmatrix} 4 & 2 \\ 3 & 5 \end{bmatrix} \quad E = \begin{bmatrix} 1 & 0 & 4 \\ 5 & 1 & 0 \end{bmatrix}$$

$$F = \begin{bmatrix} 1 & 2 & 3 \\ -1 & 0 & 1 \\ 2 & -3 & -4 \end{bmatrix} \quad G = \begin{bmatrix} 2 & 1 & 1 \\ 1 & 0 & 4 \\ 5 & 1 & 0 \end{bmatrix}$$

$$Z = \begin{bmatrix} 0 & 0 & 0 \\ 0 & 0 & 0 \\ 0 & 0 & 0 \end{bmatrix}$$

1. How many rows does matrix B have?
2. What is the order of matrix E?
3. Which matrices have the same order as G?
4. Write the negative of D.
5. Write the negative of matrix F.
6. Write a zero matrix that is the same order as D.
7. Which of the matrices $A, B, C, D, E, F, G,$ and Z are square?
8. Write the matrix that is the negative of matrix B.
9. What is the element a_{23}?
10. What is element b_{24}?
11. Write the transpose of matrix A.
12. Write the transpose of matrix F.
13. What is the sum of matrix A and its negative?
14. If matrix A has element $a_{3j} = 0$, what is j?

In Problems 15–28, perform the operations, if possible.

15. $C + D$
16. $A + F$
17. $A - F$
18. $Z + G^T$
19. $A + A^T$
20. $A + F^T$
21. $D - G$
22. $B + F$
23. $3B$
24. $4D$
25. $4C + 2D$
26. $8C - 3D$
27. $2A - 3B$
28. $4F + 3G$

In Problems 29–32, find $x, y, z,$ and w.

29. $\begin{bmatrix} x & 1 & 0 \\ 0 & y & z \\ w & 2 & 1 \end{bmatrix} = \begin{bmatrix} 3 & 1 & 0 \\ 0 & 2 & 3 \\ 4 & 2 & 1 \end{bmatrix}$

30. $\begin{bmatrix} 0 & x & 1 \\ 3 & y & y \\ z & 0 & 2 \end{bmatrix} = \begin{bmatrix} 0 & 4 & 1 \\ 3 & 1 & y \\ 1 & 0 & w \end{bmatrix}$

31.

$\begin{bmatrix} x & 3 & (2x - 1) \\ y & 4 & 4y \end{bmatrix} = \begin{bmatrix} (2x - 4) & z & 7 \\ 1 & (w + 1) & (3y + 1) \end{bmatrix}$

32. $\begin{bmatrix} x & y & (x + 3) \\ z & 4 & 4y \end{bmatrix} = \begin{bmatrix} (2x - 1) & -1 & w \\ x & (5 + y) & -4 \end{bmatrix}$

33. Solve for $x, y,$ and z if

$$3\begin{bmatrix} x & y \\ y & z \end{bmatrix} + 2\begin{bmatrix} 2x & -y \\ 3y & -4z \end{bmatrix} = \begin{bmatrix} 14 & (4 - y) \\ 18 & 15 \end{bmatrix}$$

34. Find $x, y, z,$ and w if

$$3\begin{bmatrix} x & 4 \\ 4y & w \end{bmatrix} - 2\begin{bmatrix} 4x & 2z \\ -3 & -2w \end{bmatrix} = \begin{bmatrix} 20 & 20 \\ 6 & 14 \end{bmatrix}$$

APPLICATIONS

35. *Endangered species* The tables on the next page give the numbers of some species of threatened and endangered wildlife in the United States and in foreign countries in 2007.

United States

	Mammals	Birds	Reptiles	Amphibians	Fishes
Endangered	69	75	13	13	74
Threatened	12	14	24	10	65

Foreign

	Mammals	Birds	Reptiles	Amphibians	Fishes
Endangered	256	176	65	8	11
Threatened	20	6	16	1	1

Source: U.S. Fish and Wildlife Service

(a) Write a matrix A that contains the number of each of these species in the United States in 2007 and a matrix B that contains the number of each of these species outside the United States in 2007.

(b) Find a matrix with the total number of these species. Assume that U.S. and foreign species are different.

(c) Find the matrix $B - A$. What do the negative entries in matrix $B - A$ mean?

36. *Top ten dog breeds* The following tables give the rank and number of registered dogs for the top ten breeds for 1995 and their 2006 data.

(a) Form a matrix for the 1995 data and a matrix for the 2006 data.

(b) Use a matrix operation to find the change from 1995 to 2006 in rank for each breed and in registration numbers for each breed.

(c) Which breed had the greatest improvement in rank?

(d) Which breed had the largest increase in the number of registrations?

1995

Breed	Rank	Number Registered
Labrador retriever	1	132,051
Rottweiler	2	93,656
German shepherd	3	76,088
Golden retriever	4	64,107
Beagle	5	57,063
Poodle	6	54,784
Cocker spaniel	7	48,065
Dachshund	8	44,680
Pomeranian	9	37,894
Yorkshire terrier	10	36,881

2006

Breed	Rank	Number Registered
Labrador retriever	1	123,760
Rottweiler	17	14,709
German shepherd	3	43,575
Golden retriever	4	42,962
Beagle	5	39,484
Poodle	8	29,939
Cocker spaniel	16	14,790
Dachshund	6	36,033
Pomeranian	14	18,218
Yorkshire terrier	2	48,346

Source: American Kennel Club

37. *Pollution abatement* The following tables give the capital expenditures and gross operating costs of manufacturing establishments for pollution abatement, in millions of dollars.

(a) Use a calculator or spreadsheet to find the sum of the matrices containing these data. This will yield the total costs of manufacturing establishments for air, water, and solid contained waste pollution abatement for the years 2010–2013.

(b) Which type of pollution abatement was most expensive in 2013?

Pollution Abatement Capital Expenditures

	Air	Water	Solid Contained Waste
2010	6030.8	2562.0	817.5
2011	3706.3	2814.6	869.1
2012	4403.1	2509.8	953.9
2013	4122.0	2294.9	760.9

Pollution Abatement Gross Operating Costs

	Air	Water	Solid Contained Waste
2010	5010.9	6416.4	5643.5
2011	5033.5	6345.0	6008.2
2012	5395.0	6576.9	5494.5
2013	5574.6	6631.8	5348.6

38. *Death rates* The following tables give the death rates, per 100,000 population, by age for selected years for males and females.

(a) If matrix M gives the male data and matrix F gives the female data, use matrix operations to find the death rate per 100,000 for all people in the age categories given and for the given years.

(b) Find matrix $M - F$ and describe what it means.

Males

	Under 1	1–4	5–14	15–24	25–34	35–44	45–54
1970	2410	93	51	189	215	403	959
1980	1429	73	37	172	196	299	767
1990	1083	52	29	147	204	310	610
1994	899	52	26	151	207	337	585
2006	756	31	18	120	144	237	548

Females

	Under 1	1–4	5–14	15–24	25–34	35–44	45–54
1970	1864	75	32	68	102	231	517
1980	1142	55	24	58	76	159	413
1990	856	41	19	49	74	138	343
1994	719	37	19	47	76	144	326
2006	622	26	13	43	65	141	321

Source: U.S. Department of Health and Human Services, National Center for Health Statistics

39. **Sales** Let matrix A represent the sales (in thousands of dollars) for the Walbash Company in 2011 in various cities, and let matrix B represent the sales (in thousands of dollars) for the same company in 2012 in the same cities.

$$A = \begin{bmatrix} \text{Chicago} & \text{Atlanta} & \text{Memphis} \\ 450 & 280 & 850 \\ 400 & 350 & 150 \end{bmatrix} \begin{matrix} \text{Wholesale} \\ \text{Retail} \end{matrix}$$

$$B = \begin{bmatrix} \text{Chicago} & \text{Atlanta} & \text{Memphis} \\ 375 & 300 & 710 \\ 410 & 300 & 200 \end{bmatrix} \begin{matrix} \text{Wholesale} \\ \text{Retail} \end{matrix}$$

(a) Write the matrix that represents the total sales by type and city for both years.

(b) Write the matrix that represents the change in sales by type and city from 2011 to 2012.

40. **Opinion polls** A poll of 3320 people revealed that of the respondents that were registered Republicans, 843 approved of their representative's job performance, 426 did not, and 751 had no opinion. Of the registered Democrats, 257 approved of their representative's job performance, 451 did not, and 92 had no opinion. Of those registered as Independents, 135 approved, 127 did not approve, and 38 had no opinion. Of the remaining respondents, who were not registered, 92 approved, 64 did not approve, and 44 had no opinion. Represent these data in a 3×4 matrix.

41. **Life expectancy** The following table gives the years of life expected at birth for blacks and whites born in the United States in selected years from 1920 to 2006.

	Whites		Blacks	
	Males	Females	Males	Females
1920	54.4	55.6	45.5	45.2
1940	62.1	66.6	51.5	54.9
1960	67.4	74.1	61.1	67.4
1980	70.7	78.1	63.8	72.5
2000	74.9	80.1	68.3	75.2
2006	75.7	80.6	69.7	76.5

Source: National Center for Health Statistics

Make a matrix A containing the information for whites and a matrix B for blacks. Use these to find how many more years whites in each category are expected to live than blacks.

42. **Weekly earnings** The following table shows median weekly earnings for men and women of different ages in 2009.

(a) Use the data to make a 6×2 matrix with each row representing an age category and each column representing a sex.

(b) If union members' median weekly earnings are 20% more than the earnings given in the table, use a matrix operation to find a matrix giving the results by sex and age for union members.

Age	16–24	25–34	35–44	45–54	55–64	65+
Men	458	715	916	967	965	791
Women	424	634	709	712	727	602

Source: Bureau of Labor Statistics, U.S. Department of Labor

43. **International trade** The following tables show the value (in billions of dollars) of U.S. international trade in goods and services for the years 2007–2009.

Exports			Imports		
Year	Goods	Services	Year	Goods	Services
2007	1160.4	488.3	2007	1983.6	367.2
2008	1304.9	534.1	2008	2139.5	398.3
2009	1068.5	502.3	2009	1575.4	370.3

Source: U.S. Census Bureau

Let E be a 3×2 matrix representing the export data, and let M be a similar matrix for the import data. Find each of the following matrices and indicate what information each provides.

(a) $E - M$ (b) $E + M$ (c) $\dfrac{1}{12}E$

44. **Debt payment** Ace, Baker, and Champ are being purchased by ALCO, Inc., and their outstanding debts must be paid by the purchaser. The matrix

below gives the amounts of debt and the terms for the companies being purchased.

$$\begin{array}{c} \\ \text{Ace} \\ \text{Baker} \\ \text{Champ} \end{array}\begin{array}{cc} \text{Due in 30 days} & \text{Due in 60 days} \\ \begin{bmatrix} \$40{,}000 & \$60{,}000 \\ \$25{,}000 & \$15{,}000 \\ \$35{,}000 & \$58{,}000 \end{bmatrix} \end{array}$$

(a) If ALCO pays 35% of the amount owed on each debt, write the matrix giving the remaining debts.

(b) Suppose ALCO decides to pay 80% of all debts due in 30 days and to increase the debts due in 60 days by 20%. Write a matrix that gives the debts after these transactions are made.

45. *Expense accounts* A sales associate's expense account for the first week of a certain month has the daily expenses (in dollars) shown in matrix A.

$$A = \begin{array}{c} \\ \\ \\ \\ \\ \end{array}\begin{array}{cccc} \text{Meals} & \text{Lodging} & \text{Travel} & \text{Other} \\ \begin{bmatrix} 44 & 80 & 200 & 10 \\ 40 & 80 & 40 & 0 \\ 56 & 140 & 90 & 0 \\ 30 & 140 & 40 & 20 \\ 40 & 0 & 200 & 10 \end{bmatrix} & & & \end{array}\begin{array}{c} \text{Monday} \\ \text{Tuesday} \\ \text{Wednesday} \\ \text{Thursday} \\ \text{Friday} \end{array}$$

(a) The associate finds that expenses for the second week are 5% more (in each category) than for the first week. Find the expenses matrix for the second week (note that this is 1.05A).

(b) Find the associate's expenses matrix for the third week if expenses for that week are 10% more (in each category) than they were in the first week.

46. *Debt payment* When a firm buys another company, the company frequently has some outstanding debt that the purchaser must pay. Consider three companies, A, B, and C, that are purchased by Maxx Industries. The following table gives the amount of each company's debt, classified by the number of days remaining until the debt must be paid.

Company	30 Days	60 Days	More than 60 Days
A	$25,000	$26,000	$12,000
B	15,000	52,000	5,000
C	8,000	20,000	120,000

(a) Suppose Maxx Industries pays 20% of the amount owed on each loan. Write the matrix that would give the remaining debt in each category.

(b) What payment plan did Maxx Industries use if the outstanding debt is given by the following matrix?

$$\begin{bmatrix} 25{,}000 & 26{,}000 & 12{,}000 \\ 15{,}000 & 52{,}000 & 5{,}000 \\ 8{,}000 & 20{,}000 & 120{,}000 \end{bmatrix}$$
$$- 0.50\begin{bmatrix} 0 & 26{,}000 & 0 \\ 0 & 52{,}000 & 0 \\ 0 & 20{,}000 & 0 \end{bmatrix} - \begin{bmatrix} 25{,}000 & 0 & 0 \\ 15{,}000 & 0 & 0 \\ 8{,}000 & 0 & 0 \end{bmatrix}$$

47. *Management* Management is attempting to identify the most active person in labor's efforts to unionize. The following diagram shows how influence flows from one employee to another among the four most active employees.

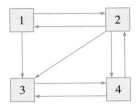

(a) Construct matrix A with elements

$$a_{ij} = \begin{cases} 1 & \text{if } i \text{ influences } j \text{ directly.} \\ 0 & \text{otherwise.} \end{cases}$$

(b) Construct matrix B with elements

$$b_{ij} = \begin{cases} 1 & \text{if } i \text{ influences } j \text{ through at most} \\ & \text{one person, with } i \neq j. \\ 0 & \text{otherwise.} \end{cases}$$

(c) The person i is most active in influencing others if the sum of the elements in row i of the matrix $A + B$ is the largest. Who is the most active person?

48. *Ranking* In order to rank the five members of a school's chess team for play against another school, the coach draws the following diagram. An arrow from 1 to 2 means player 1 has defeated player 2.

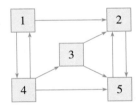

(a) Construct matrix A with elements

$$a_{ij} = \begin{cases} 1 & \text{if } i \text{ defeated } j. \\ 0 & \text{otherwise.} \end{cases}$$

(b) Construct matrix B with elements

$$b_{ij} = \begin{cases} 1 & \text{if } i \text{ defeated someone who} \\ & \text{defeated } j \text{ and } i \neq j. \\ 0 & \text{otherwise.} \end{cases}$$

(c) The player i is the top-ranked player if the sum of row i in the matrix $A + B$ is the largest. What is the number of this player?

49. *Production and inventories* Operating from two plants, the Book Equipment Company (BEC) produces bookcases and filing cabinets. Matrix A summarizes its production for a week, with row 1 representing the number of bookcases and row 2 representing the number of filing cabinets. Matrix B gives the production for the second week, and matrix C that of the third and fourth weeks combined.

$$A = \begin{bmatrix} 50 & 30 \\ 36 & 44 \end{bmatrix} \quad B = \begin{bmatrix} 30 & 45 \\ 22 & 62 \end{bmatrix} \quad C = \begin{bmatrix} 96 & 52 \\ 81 & 37 \end{bmatrix}$$

If column 1 in each matrix represents production from plant 1 and column 2 represents production from plant 2, answer the following.

(a) Write a matrix that describes production for the first 2 weeks.

(b) Find a matrix that describes production for the first 4 weeks.

(c) If matrix D

$$D = \begin{bmatrix} 40 & 26 \\ 29 & 42 \end{bmatrix}$$

describes the shipments made during the first week, write the matrix that describes the units added to the plants' inventories in the first week.

(d) If D also describes the shipments during the second week, describe the change in inventory at the end of two weeks. What happened at plant 1?

50. *Management* The following figure depicts the mean (average) flow time for a job when the critical-ratio rule is used to dispatch workers at several machines required to complete the job. In the figure, WHN 1, WHN 2, and WHN 3 represent three different rules for determining when a worker should be transferred to another machine, and Where represents six rules for determining the machine to which the worker is transferred. Construct a 3×6 matrix A to represent these data, with entries rounded to the nearest integer.

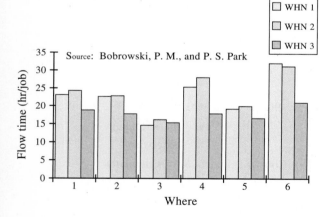

51. *Management* In an evaluation of labor assignment rules when workers are not perfectly interchangeable, Paul M. Bobrowski and Paul Sungchil Park created a dynamic job shop with 9 work centers and 9 workers, both numbered 1–9. The efficiency of each worker is specified in the following labor efficiency matrix, which represents the degree of worker cross-training (*Source:* Bobrowski, P. M., and P. S. Park, "An evaluation of labor assignment rules," *Journal of Operations Management*, Vol. 11, September 1993).

(a) For what work center(s) is worker 7 least efficient?

(b) For what work center is worker 1 most efficient?

Work Centers

$$\begin{bmatrix} 1.00 & 0.95 & 0.95 & 0.95 & 0.95 & 0.85 & 0.85 & 0.85 & 0.85 \\ 0.85 & 1.00 & 0.95 & 0.95 & 0.95 & 0.95 & 0.85 & 0.85 & 0.85 \\ 0.85 & 0.85 & 1.00 & 0.95 & 0.95 & 0.95 & 0.95 & 0.85 & 0.85 \\ 0.85 & 0.85 & 0.85 & 1.00 & 0.95 & 0.95 & 0.95 & 0.95 & 0.85 \\ 0.85 & 0.85 & 0.85 & 0.85 & 1.00 & 0.95 & 0.95 & 0.95 & 0.95 \\ 0.95 & 0.85 & 0.85 & 0.85 & 0.85 & 1.00 & 0.95 & 0.95 & 0.95 \\ 0.95 & 0.95 & 0.85 & 0.85 & 0.85 & 0.85 & 1.00 & 0.95 & 0.95 \\ 0.95 & 0.95 & 0.95 & 0.85 & 0.85 & 0.85 & 0.85 & 1.00 & 0.95 \\ 0.95 & 0.95 & 0.95 & 0.95 & 0.85 & 0.85 & 0.85 & 0.85 & 1.00 \end{bmatrix} \begin{matrix} \text{W} \\ \text{o} \\ \text{r} \\ \text{k} \\ \text{e} \\ \text{r} \\ \text{s} \end{matrix}$$

52. Suppose that for the workers and the work centers described in the matrix in Problem 51, changes in rules cause efficiency to decrease by 0.01 at work centers 2 and 5 and to decrease by 0.02 at work center 7. Write the matrix that describes the new efficiencies.

53. For the data in Problem 51, use a computer spreadsheet to find the average efficiency for each worker over the first four work centers. Which worker is the least efficient? Where does this worker perform best?

54. For the data in Problem 51, use a computer spreadsheet to find the average efficiency for each work center over the first five workers. Which work center is the most efficient? Which work center should be studied for improvement?

OBJECTIVE

3.2

• To multiply two matrices

Multiplication of Matrices

█ | APPLICATION PREVIEW | ███████████

Pentico Industries is a manufacturing company that has two divisions, located at Clarion and Brooks, each of which needs different amounts (units) of production materials as described by the following table.

	Steel	Wood	Plastic
Clarion	20	30	8
Brooks	22	25	15

These raw materials are supplied by Western Supply and Coastal Supply, with prices given in dollars per unit in the following table.

	Western	Coastal
Steel	300	290
Wood	100	90
Plastic	145	180

If one supplier must be chosen to provide all materials for either or both divisions of Pentico, company officials can decide which supplier to choose by constructing matrices from these tables and using matrix multiplication. (See Example 2.)

In this section we will discuss finding the product of two matrices.

Many computations that occur in business and manufacturing operations can be expressed and analyzed by using matrix multiplication. For example, suppose one store of an electronics retailer has 30 plasma TVs, 20 LCD TVs, and 10 home theater systems in its inventory. If the value of each plasma TV is $800, that of each LCD TV is $750, and that of each home theater system is $500, then the value of this inventory is

$$30 \cdot 800 + 20 \cdot 750 + 10 \cdot 500 = \$44,000$$

If we write the value of each of the items in the *row matrix, A*, and the number of each of the items in the *column matrix, B*, then the value of this inventory may be represented by

$$AB = \begin{bmatrix} 800 & 750 & 500 \end{bmatrix} \begin{bmatrix} 30 \\ 20 \\ 10 \end{bmatrix} = \begin{bmatrix} 800 \cdot 30 + 750 \cdot 20 + 500 \cdot 10 \end{bmatrix} = \begin{bmatrix} \$44,000 \end{bmatrix}$$

This useful way of operating with a row matrix and a column matrix is called the **product** AB.

In general, we can multiply a row matrix A times a column matrix B if A and B have the same number of elements. The product AB is then

$$AB = \begin{bmatrix} a_1 & a_2 & a_3 \cdots a_n \end{bmatrix} \begin{bmatrix} b_1 \\ b_2 \\ b_3 \\ \vdots \\ b_n \end{bmatrix} = \begin{bmatrix} a_1b_1 + a_2b_2 + a_3b_3 + \cdots + a_nb_n \end{bmatrix}$$

Suppose the retailer has a second store with 40 plasma TVs, 25 LCD TVs, and 5 home theater systems. We can use matrix C to represent the inventories of the two stores.

$$C = \begin{bmatrix} 30 & 40 \\ 20 & 25 \\ 10 & 5 \end{bmatrix} \begin{matrix} \text{Plasma TVs} \\ \text{LCD TVs} \\ \text{Home theater systems} \end{matrix}$$

Store I   Store II

If the values of the items are \$800, \$750, and \$500, respectively, we have already seen that the value of the inventory of store I is \$44,000. The value of the inventory of store II is

$$800 \cdot 40 + 750 \cdot 25 + 500 \cdot 5 = \$53,250$$

Because the value of the inventory of store I can be found by multiplying the row matrix A times the first column of matrix C, and the value of the inventory of store II can be found by multiplying matrix A times the second column of matrix C, we can write this result as

$$AC = \begin{bmatrix} 800 & 750 & 500 \end{bmatrix} \begin{bmatrix} 30 & 40 \\ 20 & 25 \\ 10 & 5 \end{bmatrix} = \begin{bmatrix} 44{,}000 & 53{,}250 \end{bmatrix}$$

The matrix we have represented as AC is called the **product** of the row matrix A and the 3×2 matrix C. We should note that matrix A is a 1×3 matrix, matrix C is a 3×2 matrix, and their product is a 1×2 matrix. In general, we can multiply an $m \times n$ matrix times an $n \times p$ matrix and the product will be an $m \times p$ matrix, as follows.

Product of Two Matrices

Given an $m \times n$ matrix A and an $n \times p$ matrix B, the **matrix product** AB is an $m \times p$ matrix C, with the ij entry of C given by the formula

$$c_{ij} = a_{i1}b_{1j} + a_{i2}b_{2j} + \cdots + a_{in}b_{nj}$$

which is illustrated in Figure 3.5.

Figure 3.5

EXAMPLE   1   Matrix Product

(a) Find AB if

$$A = \begin{bmatrix} 3 & 4 \\ 2 & 5 \\ 6 & 10 \end{bmatrix} \quad \text{and} \quad B = \begin{bmatrix} a & b & c & d \\ e & f & g & h \end{bmatrix}$$

(b) Find AB and BA if

$$A = \begin{bmatrix} 3 & 2 \\ 1 & 0 \end{bmatrix} \text{ and } B = \begin{bmatrix} 1 & 2 \\ 3 & 1 \end{bmatrix}$$

Solution

(a) A is a 3×2 matrix and B is a 2×4 matrix, so the number of columns of A equals the number of rows of B. Thus we can find the product AB, which is a 3×4 matrix, as follows:

$$AB = \begin{bmatrix} 3 & 4 \\ 2 & 5 \\ 6 & 10 \end{bmatrix} \begin{bmatrix} a & b & c & d \\ e & f & g & h \end{bmatrix}$$

$$= \begin{bmatrix} 3a + 4e & 3b + 4f & 3c + 4g & 3d + 4h \\ 2a + 5e & 2b + 5f & 2c + 5g & 2d + 5h \\ 6a + 10e & 6b + 10f & 6c + 10g & 6d + 10h \end{bmatrix}$$

This example shows that if $AB = C$, element c_{32} is found by multiplying each entry of A's *third* row by the corresponding entry of B's *second* column and then adding these products.

(b) Both A and B are 2×2 matrices, so both AB and BA are defined.

$$AB = \begin{bmatrix} 3 & 2 \\ 1 & 0 \end{bmatrix} \begin{bmatrix} 1 & 2 \\ 3 & 1 \end{bmatrix} = \begin{bmatrix} 3 \cdot 1 + 2 \cdot 3 & 3 \cdot 2 + 2 \cdot 1 \\ 1 \cdot 1 + 0 \cdot 3 & 1 \cdot 2 + 0 \cdot 1 \end{bmatrix} = \begin{bmatrix} 9 & 8 \\ 1 & 2 \end{bmatrix}$$

$$BA = \begin{bmatrix} 1 & 2 \\ 3 & 1 \end{bmatrix} \begin{bmatrix} 3 & 2 \\ 1 & 0 \end{bmatrix} = \begin{bmatrix} 1 \cdot 3 + 2 \cdot 1 & 1 \cdot 2 + 2 \cdot 0 \\ 3 \cdot 3 + 1 \cdot 1 & 3 \cdot 2 + 1 \cdot 0 \end{bmatrix} = \begin{bmatrix} 5 & 2 \\ 10 & 6 \end{bmatrix}$$

Note that for these matrices, the two products AB and BA are matrices of the same size, but they are not equal. That is, $BA \neq AB$. Thus we say that *matrix multiplication is not commutative.*

CHECKPOINT

1. What is element c_{23} if $C = AB$ with

$$A = \begin{bmatrix} 1 & 2 & 0 \\ 2 & 1 & 3 \end{bmatrix} \text{ and } B = \begin{bmatrix} 1 & 0 & 2 \\ 3 & 1 & 1 \\ -2 & 1 & 0 \end{bmatrix}?$$

2. Find the product AB.

EXAMPLE 2 **Material Supply | APPLICATION PREVIEW |**

Pentico Industries must choose a supplier for the raw materials that it uses in its two manufacturing divisions at Clarion and Brooks. Each division uses different unit amounts of steel, wood, and plastic as shown in the table below.

	Steel	Wood	Plastic
Clarion	20	30	8
Brooks	22	25	15

The two supply companies being considered, Western and Coastal, can each supply all of these materials, but at different prices per unit, as described in the following table.

	Western	Coastal
Steel	300	290
Wood	100	90
Plastic	145	180

Use matrix multiplication to decide which supplier should be chosen to supply (a) the Clarion division and (b) the Brooks division.

Solution

The different amounts of products needed can be placed in matrix A and the prices charged by the suppliers in matrix B.

$$A = \begin{array}{c} \\ \text{Clarion} \\ \text{Brooks} \end{array} \overset{\text{Steel Wood Plastic}}{\begin{bmatrix} 20 & 30 & 8 \\ 22 & 25 & 15 \end{bmatrix}} \qquad B = \begin{bmatrix} 300 & 290 \\ 100 & 90 \\ 145 & 180 \end{bmatrix} \begin{array}{c} \text{Steel} \\ \text{Wood} \\ \text{Plastic} \end{array}$$

The price from each supplier for each division is found from the product AB.

$$AB = \begin{bmatrix} 20 & 30 & 8 \\ 22 & 25 & 15 \end{bmatrix} \begin{bmatrix} 300 & 290 \\ 100 & 90 \\ 145 & 180 \end{bmatrix}$$

$$= \begin{bmatrix} 20 \cdot 300 + 30 \cdot 100 + 8 \cdot 145 & 20 \cdot 290 + 30 \cdot 90 + 8 \cdot 180 \\ 22 \cdot 300 + 25 \cdot 100 + 15 \cdot 145 & 22 \cdot 290 + 25 \cdot 90 + 15 \cdot 180 \end{bmatrix}$$

$$= \overset{\text{Western   Coastal}}{\begin{bmatrix} 10{,}160 & 9940 \\ 11{,}275 & 11{,}330 \end{bmatrix}} \begin{array}{c} \text{Clarion} \\ \text{Brooks} \end{array}$$

(a) The price for the Clarion division for supplies from Western is in the first row, first column and is \$10,160; the price for Clarion for supplies from Coastal is in the first row, second column and is \$9940. Thus the best price for Clarion is from Coastal.

(b) The price for the Brooks division for supplies from Western is in the second row, first column and is \$11,275; the price for Brooks for supplies from Coastal is in the second row, second column and is \$11,330. Thus the best price for Brooks is from Western.

An $n \times n$ (square) matrix (where n is any natural number) that has 1s down its diagonal and 0s everywhere else is called an **identity matrix.** The matrix

$$I = \begin{bmatrix} 1 & 0 & 0 \\ 0 & 1 & 0 \\ 0 & 0 & 1 \end{bmatrix}$$

is a 3×3 identity matrix. The matrix I is called an identity matrix because for any 3×3 matrix A, $AI = IA = A$. That is, if I is multiplied by a 3×3 matrix A, the product matrix is A. Note that when one of two square matrices being multiplied is an identity matrix, the product is *commutative*.

EXAMPLE 3   **Identity Matrix**

(a) Write the 2×2 identity matrix.

(b) Given $A = \begin{bmatrix} 4 & -7 \\ 13 & 2 \end{bmatrix}$, show that $AI = IA = A$.

Solution

(a) We denote the 2×2 identity matrix by

$$I = \begin{bmatrix} 1 & 0 \\ 0 & 1 \end{bmatrix}$$

(b) $AI = \begin{bmatrix} 4 & -7 \\ 13 & 2 \end{bmatrix}\begin{bmatrix} 1 & 0 \\ 0 & 1 \end{bmatrix} = \begin{bmatrix} 4+0 & 0-7 \\ 13+0 & 0+2 \end{bmatrix} = \begin{bmatrix} 4 & -7 \\ 13 & 2 \end{bmatrix}$

$IA = \begin{bmatrix} 1 & 0 \\ 0 & 1 \end{bmatrix}\begin{bmatrix} 4 & -7 \\ 13 & 2 \end{bmatrix} = \begin{bmatrix} 4 & -7 \\ 13 & 2 \end{bmatrix}$

Therefore, $AI = IA = A$.

EXAMPLE 4   Encoding Messages

Messages can be encoded through the use of a code and an encoding matrix. For example, given the code

a	b	c	d	e	f	g	h	i	j	k	l
1	2	3	4	5	6	7	8	9	10	11	12

m	n	o	p	q	r	s	t	u	v	w	x
13	14	15	16	17	18	19	20	21	22	23	24

y	z	blank
25	26	27

and the encoding matrix

$$A = \begin{bmatrix} 3 & 5 \\ 4 & 6 \end{bmatrix}$$

we can encode a message by separating it into number pairs (because A is a 2 × 2 matrix) and then multiplying each pair by A. Use this code and matrix to encode the message "good job."

Solution

The phrase "good job" is written

g	o	o	d	blank	j	o	b
7	15	15	4	27	10	15	2

and is encoded by writing each pair of numbers as a column matrix and multiplying each matrix by matrix A. Performing this multiplication gives the encoded message.

$$\begin{bmatrix} 3 & 5 \\ 4 & 6 \end{bmatrix}\begin{bmatrix} 7 \\ 15 \end{bmatrix} = \begin{bmatrix} 96 \\ 118 \end{bmatrix}$$

$$\begin{bmatrix} 3 & 5 \\ 4 & 6 \end{bmatrix}\begin{bmatrix} 15 \\ 4 \end{bmatrix} = \begin{bmatrix} 65 \\ 84 \end{bmatrix}$$

$$\begin{bmatrix} 3 & 5 \\ 4 & 6 \end{bmatrix}\begin{bmatrix} 27 \\ 10 \end{bmatrix} = \begin{bmatrix} 131 \\ 168 \end{bmatrix}$$

$$\begin{bmatrix} 3 & 5 \\ 4 & 6 \end{bmatrix}\begin{bmatrix} 15 \\ 2 \end{bmatrix} = \begin{bmatrix} 55 \\ 72 \end{bmatrix}$$

Thus the code sent is 96, 118, 65, 84, 131, 168, 55, 72. Notice that the letter "o" occurred three times in the original message but was encoded differently each time. We can also get the same code to send by putting the pairs of numbers as columns in one 2 × 4 matrix and multiplying by A.

$$\begin{bmatrix} 3 & 5 \\ 4 & 6 \end{bmatrix}\begin{bmatrix} 7 & 15 & 27 & 15 \\ 15 & 4 & 10 & 2 \end{bmatrix} = \begin{bmatrix} 96 & 65 & 131 & 55 \\ 118 & 84 & 168 & 72 \end{bmatrix}$$

In this case, the code is sent column by column.

Note in Example 4 that if we used a different encoding matrix, then the same message would be sent with a different sequence of code. We will discuss the methods of decoding messages in Section 3.4, "Inverse of a Square Matrix; Matrix Equations."

CHECKPOINT

3. (a) Compute AB if $A = \begin{bmatrix} 2 & 4 \\ 3 & 6 \end{bmatrix}$ and $B = \begin{bmatrix} 2 & -6 \\ -1 & 3 \end{bmatrix}$.

   (b) Can the product of two matrices be a zero matrix even if neither matrix is a zero matrix?

   (c) Does BA result in a zero matrix?

Calculator Note   Graphing calculators can be used to perform matrix multiplications. For example, if

$$A = \begin{bmatrix} 2 & 3 & 4 & 5 \\ 3 & 1 & 3 & 5 \\ 3 & -4 & 3 & 1 \end{bmatrix} \quad B = \begin{bmatrix} 2 & 2 & 5 \\ 3 & 5 & 7 \\ 1 & 1 & 2 \\ 5 & 4 & 3 \end{bmatrix} \quad C = \begin{bmatrix} 0.5 & 3.5 & 2.4 \\ 2 & 7 & 0.8 \\ 5.5 & 3.5 & 7 \\ 2.5 & 4 & 3 \end{bmatrix}$$

then Figure 3.6 shows the matrix products AB and BA and Figure 3.7 shows that the product BC is not defined. Details of finding matrix products with graphing calculators are shown in Appendix C, Section 3.2.

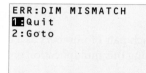

```
[A][B]
     [[42   43   54]
      [37   34   43]
      [2   -7   -4]]
```

```
[B][A]
     [[25  -12   29   25]
      [42  -14   48   47]
      [11   -4   13   12]
      [31    7   41   48]]
```

Figure 3.6   (a)   (b)

```
ERR:DIM MISMATCH
1:Quit
2:Goto
```

Figure 3.7

Spreadsheet Note   Like graphing calculators and software programs, Excel can be used to multiply two matrices.

EXAMPLE   5   Venture Capital

Suppose that a bank has three main sources of income—business loans, auto loans, and home mortgages—and that it draws funds from these sources for venture capital used to provide start-up funds for new businesses. Suppose the income from these sources for each of 3 years is given in Table 3.4, and the bank uses 45% of its income from business loans, 20% of its income from auto loans, and 30% of its income from home mortgages to get its venture capital funds. Write a matrix product that gives the venture capital for these years, and find the available venture capital in each of the 3 years.

■ | TABLE 3.4 | ■■■■■■■■■■■■■

INCOME FROM LOANS

Year	Business	Auto	Home
2010	63,300	20,024	51,820
2011	48,305	15,817	63,722
2012	55,110	18,621	64,105

Solution

The matrix that describes the sources of income for the 3 years is

$$\begin{bmatrix} 63,300 & 20,024 & 51,820 \\ 48,305 & 15,817 & 63,722 \\ 55,110 & 18,621 & 64,105 \end{bmatrix}$$

and the matrix that describes the percent of each that is used for venture capital is

$$\begin{bmatrix} 0.45 \\ 0.20 \\ 0.30 \end{bmatrix}$$

We can find the product of these matrices with Excel by using the MMULT command as shown in Table 3.5 (see Appendix D, Section 3.2 and the Online Excel Guide for details).

| TABLE 3.5 |

= MMULT(B3:C5,B11:B13)			
	A	**B**	**C**	**D**
1		Income from Loans		
2		Business	Auto	Home
3	Matrix A	63,300	20,024	51,820
4		48,305	15,817	63,722
5		55,110	18,621	64,105
6				
7	Matrix B	0.45		
8		0.20		
9		0.30		
10				
11	Product AxB	48,035.80		
12		44,017.25		
13		47,755.20		

Thus the available venture capital for each of the 3 years is as follows.

2010:	$48,035,80
2011:	$44,017.25
2012:	$47,755.20

CHECKPOINT SOLUTIONS

1. $2 \cdot 2 + 1 \cdot 1 + 3 \cdot 0 = 5$

2. $\begin{bmatrix} 7 & 2 & 4 \\ -1 & 4 & 5 \end{bmatrix}$

3. (a) $AB = \begin{bmatrix} 0 & 0 \\ 0 & 0 \end{bmatrix}$ (b) Yes. See (a).   (c) No. $BA = \begin{bmatrix} -14 & -28 \\ 7 & 14 \end{bmatrix}$

| EXERCISES | 3.2

In Problems 1 and 2, multiply the matrices.

1. (a) $\begin{bmatrix} 1 & 2 & 3 \end{bmatrix} \begin{bmatrix} 4 \\ 5 \\ 6 \end{bmatrix}$ (b) $\begin{bmatrix} 1 & 2 \end{bmatrix} \begin{bmatrix} 3 & 5 \\ 4 & 6 \end{bmatrix}$

2. (a) $\begin{bmatrix} 2 & 0 & 3 \end{bmatrix} \begin{bmatrix} 0 \\ 1 \\ -3 \end{bmatrix}$ (b) $\begin{bmatrix} 3 & 0 \end{bmatrix} \begin{bmatrix} 1 & 2 \\ 4 & 5 \end{bmatrix}$

In Problems 3–22, use matrices A through F. In Problems 3–18, perform the indicated operations, when possible.

$$A = \begin{bmatrix} 1 & 0 & 2 \\ 3 & 2 & 1 \\ 4 & 0 & 3 \end{bmatrix} \quad B = \begin{bmatrix} 1 & 1 & 3 & 0 \\ 4 & 2 & 1 & 1 \\ 3 & 2 & 0 & 1 \end{bmatrix}$$

$$C = \begin{bmatrix} 5 & 3 \\ 1 & 2 \end{bmatrix} \quad D = \begin{bmatrix} 4 & 2 \\ 3 & 5 \end{bmatrix}$$

$$E = \begin{bmatrix} 1 & 0 & 4 \\ 5 & 1 & 0 \end{bmatrix} \quad F = \begin{bmatrix} 1 & 0 & -1 & 3 \\ 2 & -1 & 3 & -4 \end{bmatrix}$$

3. CD 4. DC 5. DE
6. CF 7. AB 8. EC
9. BA 10. FB^T 11. EB
12. BE 13. EA^T 14. AE^T
15. A^2 16. A^3 17. C^3
18. F^2
19. Does $(AA^T)^T = A^T A$?
20. Are $(CD)E$ and $C(DE)$ equal?
21. Does $CD = DC$? (See Problems 3 and 4.)
22. Are $\left(\dfrac{1}{4}A\right)B$ and $\dfrac{1}{4}(AB)$ equal?

In Problems 23–32, use the matrices below. Perform the indicated operations.

$$A = \begin{bmatrix} 2 & 5 & 4 \\ 1 & 4 & 3 \\ 1 & -3 & -2 \end{bmatrix} \quad B = \begin{bmatrix} -1 & 2 & 1 \\ -5 & 8 & 2 \\ -7 & 11 & -3 \end{bmatrix}$$

$$I = \begin{bmatrix} 1 & 0 & 0 \\ 0 & 1 & 0 \\ 0 & 0 & 1 \end{bmatrix} \quad C = \begin{bmatrix} 3 & 0 & 4 \\ 1 & 7 & -1 \\ 3 & 0 & 4 \end{bmatrix}$$

$$D = \begin{bmatrix} 4 & 4 & -8 \\ -1 & -1 & 2 \\ -3 & -3 & 6 \end{bmatrix} \quad F = \begin{bmatrix} 0 & 1 & 2 \\ 0 & 0 & -4 \\ 0 & 0 & 0 \end{bmatrix}$$

$$Z = \begin{bmatrix} 0 & 0 & 0 \\ 0 & 0 & 0 \\ 0 & 0 & 0 \end{bmatrix}$$

23. AB 24. BA 25. CD 26. DC
27. F^3 28. AZ 29. AI 30. IA
31. ZCI 32. IFZ
33. Is it true for matrices (as it is for real numbers) that AB equals a zero matrix if and only if either A or B equals a zero matrix? (Refer to Problems 23–32.)
34. Is it true for matrices (as it is for real numbers) that multiplication by a zero matrix gives a result of a zero matrix?
35. (a) Find AB and BA if

$$A = \begin{bmatrix} a & b \\ c & d \end{bmatrix} \text{ and } B = \frac{1}{ad - bc}\begin{bmatrix} d & -b \\ -c & a \end{bmatrix}$$

   (b) For B to exist, what restriction must $ad - bc$ satisfy?

36. For $F = \begin{bmatrix} 1 & 0 & -1 & 3 \\ 2 & -1 & 3 & -4 \end{bmatrix}$:

   (a) Are FF^T and $F^T F$ defined?
   (b) What size is each product?
   (c) Can $FF^T = F^T F$? Explain.

In each of Problems 37–40, substitute the given values of x, y, and z into the matrix equation and use matrix multiplication to see whether the values are the solution of the equation.

37. $\begin{bmatrix} 1 & 2 & 1 \\ 3 & 4 & -2 \\ 2 & 0 & -1 \end{bmatrix}\begin{bmatrix} x \\ y \\ z \end{bmatrix} = \begin{bmatrix} 2 \\ -2 \\ 2 \end{bmatrix}$ $x = 2, y = -1, z = 2$

38. $\begin{bmatrix} 3 & 1 & 0 \\ 2 & -2 & 1 \\ 1 & 1 & 2 \end{bmatrix}\begin{bmatrix} x \\ y \\ z \end{bmatrix} = \begin{bmatrix} 4 \\ 9 \\ 2 \end{bmatrix}$ $x = 2, y = -2, z = 1$

39. $\begin{bmatrix} 1 & 1 & 2 \\ 4 & 0 & 1 \\ 2 & 1 & 1 \end{bmatrix}\begin{bmatrix} x \\ y \\ z \end{bmatrix} = \begin{bmatrix} 5 \\ 5 \\ 5 \end{bmatrix}$ $x = 1, y = 2, z = 1$

40. $\begin{bmatrix} 1 & 0 & 2 \\ 3 & 1 & 0 \\ 1 & 2 & 1 \end{bmatrix}\begin{bmatrix} x \\ y \\ z \end{bmatrix} = \begin{bmatrix} 0 \\ 7 \\ 3 \end{bmatrix}$ $x = 2, y = 1, z = 1$

In Problems 41 and 42, use technology to find the product AB of the following matrices.

41. $A = \begin{bmatrix} 0.1 & 0.0 & 0.1 & 0.1 & 0.2 \\ 0.1 & 0.2 & -0.1 & 0.1 & -0.1 \\ 0.1 & -0.1 & 0.1 & -0.2 & 0.1 \\ 0.1 & 0.2 & 0.1 & 0.1 & 0.1 \\ 0.1 & 0.0 & 0.0 & 0.0 & 0.0 \end{bmatrix}$

$$B = \begin{bmatrix} 0 & 0 & 0 & 0 & 10 \\ 0 & 5 & \frac{10}{3} & \frac{5}{3} & -10 \\ -10 & -15 & -\frac{20}{3} & \frac{35}{3} & 20 \\ 0 & -5 & -\frac{20}{3} & \frac{5}{3} & 10 \\ 10 & 10 & \frac{20}{3} & -\frac{20}{3} & -20 \end{bmatrix}$$

42. $A = \dfrac{1}{12} \begin{bmatrix} 3 & 15 & -9 & -15 & 6 \\ 3 & -9 & 3 & 9 & -6 \\ -1 & -17 & 3 & 23 & -4 \\ 0 & 12 & 0 & -12 & 0 \\ -1 & -5 & 3 & 5 & 2 \end{bmatrix}$

$$B = \begin{bmatrix} 2 & 3 & 0 & 1 & 3 \\ 1 & 0 & 2 & 3 & 1 \\ 0 & 1 & 0 & 2 & 3 \\ 1 & 0 & 2 & 2 & 1 \\ 1 & 0 & 0 & 0 & 3 \end{bmatrix}$$

APPLICATIONS

43. *Car pricing* A car dealer can buy midsize cars for 12% under the list price, and he can buy luxury cars for 15% under the list price. The following table gives the list prices for two midsize and two luxury cars.

Midsize	36,000	42,000
Luxury	50,000	56,000

Write these data in a matrix and multiply it on the left by the matrix

$$\begin{bmatrix} 0.88 & 0 \\ 0 & 0.85 \end{bmatrix}$$

What does each entry in this product matrix represent?

44. *Revenue* A clothing manufacturer has factories in Atlanta, Chicago, and New York. Sales (in thousands) during the first quarter are summarized in the matrix below.

$$\begin{array}{c c} & \begin{array}{ccc} \text{Atl.} & \text{Chi.} & \text{N.Y.} \end{array} \\ \begin{array}{c} \text{Coats} \\ \text{Shirts} \\ \text{Pants} \\ \text{Ties} \end{array} & \begin{bmatrix} 40 & 63 & 18 \\ 85 & 56 & 42 \\ 6 & 18 & 8 \\ 7 & 10 & 8 \end{bmatrix} \end{array}$$

During this period the selling price of a coat was $200, of a shirt $40, of a pair of pants $50, and of a tie $30. Use matrix multiplication to find the total revenue received by each factory.

45. *Egg production* The following tables give the production of eggs (in millions) for 2000 and 2005 for selected southern states and the average prices in cents per dozen for these states for 2000 and 2005.

(a) Write the production data for 2000 and 2005 in the first table as matrix A. Write a matrix B, containing the price data from the second table.
(b) What is the order of the product $\frac{1}{12}AB^T$?
(c) Where are the entries in the product found in part (b) that give the total revenue from the production of eggs for each of these states for the years 2000 and 2005?

Production of Eggs

State	2000	2005
Alabama	2378	2071
Florida	2723	2980
Georgia	5114	4850
Mississippi	1581	1627
North Carolina	2490	2573
South Carolina	1245	1289
Virginia	824	823

Price per Dozen

State	2000	2005
Alabama	131.0	113.0
Florida	47.8	40.6
Georgia	86.8	84.3
Mississippi	118.0	125.0
North Carolina	107.0	116.0
South Carolina	64.2	57.8
Virginia	96.3	98.3

Source: National Agricultural Statistics Service, U.S. Department of Agriculture

46. *Area and population* Matrix A below gives the fraction of the earth's area and the projected fraction of its population for five continents in 2050. Matrix B gives the earth's area (in square miles) and its projected 2050 population. Find the area and population of each given continent by finding AB.

$$A = \begin{bmatrix} 0.162 & 0.047 \\ 0.119 & 0.086 \\ 0.066 & 0.065 \\ 0.298 & 0.582 \\ 0.202 & 0.215 \end{bmatrix} \begin{array}{l} \text{North America} \\ \text{South America} \\ \text{Europe} \\ \text{Asia} \\ \text{Africa} \end{array}$$

with column headers: Fraction of Area, Fraction of Population

$$B = \begin{bmatrix} 57,850,000 & 0 \\ 0 & 9,322,000,000 \end{bmatrix} \begin{array}{l} \text{Area} \\ \text{Population} \end{array}$$

with column headers: Area, Population

Source: U.S. Census Bureau

47. *Population dynamics* Suppose that, for a certain metropolitan area and the surrounding counties, during each 5-year period an average of 20% of the metropolitan population M moves to the surrounding counties and the rest remains. Similarly, suppose that in

the same period, an average of 30% of the surrounding counties' population S moves to the metropolitan area and the rest remains. This population dynamic can be represented as the following matrix

$$D = \begin{bmatrix} 80\% & 20\% \\ 30\% & 70\% \end{bmatrix} \begin{matrix} M \\ S \end{matrix} = \begin{bmatrix} 0.8 & 0.2 \\ 0.3 & 0.7 \end{bmatrix}$$

where row 1 shows how the metropolitan population M changed (80% remained in M and 20% moved to S), and row 2 shows how the population of the surrounding counties changed. Currently the population is evenly divided between the two areas, which can be represented by the row matrix

$$P = \begin{bmatrix} \% \text{ in } M & \% \text{ in } S \end{bmatrix} = \begin{bmatrix} 50\% & 50\% \end{bmatrix} = \begin{bmatrix} 0.5 & 0.5 \end{bmatrix}$$

(a) Form the product PD and interpret its entries.
(b) Predictions of this population distribution after 10 years and after 15 years could be found from what matrix products?
(c) Suppose that at some future time, the populations reach the point where 60% live in the metropolitan area and 40% live in the surrounding counties. Find the predicted distribution 5 years later.

48. *Nutrition* Suppose the weights (in grams) and lengths (in centimeters) of three groups of laboratory animals are given by matrix A, where column 1 gives the lengths and each row corresponds to one group.

$$A = \begin{bmatrix} 12.5 & 250 \\ 11.8 & 215 \\ 9.8 & 190 \end{bmatrix}$$

If the increase in both weight and length over the next 2 weeks is 20% for group I, 7% for group II, and 0% for group III, then the increases in the measures during the 2 weeks can be found by computing GA, where

$$G = \begin{bmatrix} 0.20 & 0 & 0 \\ 0 & 0.07 & 0 \\ 0 & 0 & 0 \end{bmatrix}$$

(a) What are the increases in respective weights and measures at the end of these 2 weeks?
(b) Find the matrix that gives the new weights and measures at the end of this period by computing

$$(I + G)A$$

where I is the 3×3 identity matrix.

Encoding messages **Multiplication by a matrix can be used to encode messages (and multiplication by its inverse can be used to decode messages). Given the code**

a	b	c	d	e	f	g	h	i	j
1	2	3	4	5	6	7	8	9	10

k	l	m	n	o	p	q	r	s	t
11	12	13	14	15	16	17	18	19	20

u	v	w	x	y	z	blank
21	22	23	24	25	26	27

and the code matrix

$$A = \begin{bmatrix} 5 & 9 \\ 6 & 11 \end{bmatrix}$$

complete Problems 49 and 50.

49. Use matrix A to encode the message "The die is cast."
50. Use matrix A to encode the message "To be or not to be."

51. *Oil refineries* When gasoline is refined from crude oil, each gallon of regular, mid-grade, and premium uses a different blend of two different grades of crude oil according to the following matrix.

		Gasoline Blends		
		Reg.	Mid.	Prem.
Crude Grade	Black	$\frac{3}{4}$	$\frac{2}{5}$	$\frac{1}{4}$
	Gold	$\frac{1}{4}$	$\frac{3}{5}$	$\frac{3}{4}$

In addition, the demand (in thousands of gallons) from a Houston refinery is 22 regular, 12 mid-grade, and 8 premium, and the demand from a Gulfport refinery is 30 regular, 20 mid-grade, and 11 premium.

(a) Make a 2×3 matrix B that contains the blending information and a 3×2 matrix D for the demands at each refinery. Then use a matrix product to find each refinery's need for each type of crude oil.
(b) If the cost of black crude is $3.17 per gallon and for gold crude is $3.32 per gallon, then the matrix

$$P = \begin{bmatrix} 3.17 & 3.32 \end{bmatrix}$$

represents these crude prices. Write a matrix product involving B, D, and P that could be used to find the total cost for crude oil at each refinery. Then find those total costs.

52. *Production* A manufacturer of small kitchen appliances has the following unit costs for labor and materials for three of its products: a blender, a mixer, and a food processor.

	Blender	Mixer	Food Proc.
Labor	$8.50	$5.50	$12.00
Materials	$6.00	$4.00	$15.00

Furthermore, the quarterly demand for each appliance is summarized as follows.

	1st Qtr	2nd Qtr	3rd Qtr	4th Qtr
Blender	1200	1500	1500	2000
Mixer	1200	1000	1000	1500
Food Proc.	500	500	400	1000

(a) Identify matrices and use their product to find the quarterly costs for labor and materials for these appliances. What are the first quarter's labor costs?

(b) From part (a), let C be the 2×3 cost matrix and let D be the 3×4 demand matrix. Let T be a 4×1 matrix in which each entry is a 1. Find the product CDT and tell what it represents.

53. *Accounting* The annual budget of the Magnum Company has the following expenses, in thousands of dollars, for selected departments.

	Mfg.	Office	Sales	Shp.	Act.	Mgt.
Supplies	0.7	8.5	10.2	1.1	5.6	3.6
Phone	0.5	0.2	6.1	1.3	0.2	1.0
Transp.	2.2	0.4	8.8	1.2	1.2	4.8
Salaries	251.8	63.4	81.6	35.2	54.3	144.2
Utilities	30.0	1.0	1.0	1.0	1.0	1.0
Materials	788.9	0	0	0	0	0

Mfg. = Manufacturing; Shp. = Shipping;
Act. = Accounting; Mgt. = Management

(a) Write a matrix B for these budget amounts.

(b) Write a matrix A so that BA would contain new budget figures that reflect an 11% increase in manufacturing, sales, and shipping, and a 5% decrease in the other departments.

54. *Accounting* Consider the original budget matrix in Problem 53. Assume there is a 20% increase in manufacturing, a 3% increase in office, a 5% increase in sales, a 20% increase in shipping, a 5% increase in accounting, and a 3% decrease in management. Find the new budget matrix by developing a matrix A to represent these departmental increases and then multiplying it from the left by the matrix B in Problem 53.

OBJECTIVES

3.3

- To use matrices to solve systems of linear equations with unique solutions
- To use matrices to solve systems of linear equations with nonunique solutions

Gauss-Jordan Elimination: Solving Systems of Equations

| APPLICATION PREVIEW |

The Walters Manufacturing Company makes three types of metal storage sheds. The company has three departments: stamping, painting, and packaging. The following table gives the number of hours each division requires for each shed.

	Shed		
Department	Type I	Type II	Type III
Stamping	2	3	4
Painting	1	2	1
Packaging	1	1	2

By using the information in the table and by solving a system of equations, we can determine how many of each type of shed can be produced if the stamping department has 3200 hours available, the painting department has 1700 hours, and the packaging department has 1300 hours. The set of equations used to solve this problem (in Example 2) is

$$\begin{cases} 2x_1 + 3x_2 + 4x_3 = 3200 \\ x_1 + 2x_2 + x_3 = 1700 \\ x_1 + x_2 + 2x_3 = 1300 \end{cases}$$

In this section, we will solve such systems by using matrices and the Gauss-Jordan elimination method.

Systems with Unique Solutions

In solving systems with the left-to-right elimination method used in Example 8 in Section 1.5, "Solutions of Systems of Linear Equations," we operated on the coefficients of the variables x, y, and z and on the constants. If we keep the coefficients of the variables x, y, and z in distinctive columns, we do not need to write the equations. In solving a system of linear equations with matrices, we first write the coefficients and constants from the system in the **augmented matrix.** For example, the augmented matrix associated with

$$\begin{cases} x + 2y + 3z = 6 \\ x \quad\quad - z = 0 \\ x - y - z = -4 \end{cases} \text{ is } \left[\begin{array}{ccc|c} 1 & 2 & 3 & 6 \\ 1 & 0 & -1 & 0 \\ 1 & -1 & -1 & -4 \end{array}\right]$$

In the augmented matrix, the numbers on the left side of the solid line form the **coefficient matrix,** with each column containing the coefficients of a variable (0 represents any missing variable). The column on the right side of the line (called the *augment*) contains the constants. Each row of the matrix gives the corresponding coefficients of an equation.

CHECKPOINT

1. (a) Write the augmented matrix for the following system of linear equations.

$$\begin{cases} 3x + 2y - z = 3 \\ x - y + 2z = 4 \\ 2x + 3y - z = 3 \end{cases}$$

(b) Write the coefficient matrix for the system.

We can use matrices to solve systems of linear equations by performing the same operations on the rows of a matrix to reduce it as we do on equations in a linear system. The three different operations we can use to reduce the matrix are called **elementary row operations** and are similar to the operations with equations that result in equivalent systems. These operations are

1. Interchange two rows.
2. Add a multiple of one row to another row.
3. Multiply a row by a nonzero constant.

When a new matrix results from one or more of these elementary row operations being performed on a matrix, the new matrix is said to be **equivalent** to the original because both these matrices represent equivalent systems of equations. Thus, if it can be shown that the augmented matrix

$$\left[\begin{array}{ccc|c} 1 & 2 & 3 & 6 \\ 1 & 0 & -1 & 0 \\ 1 & -1 & -1 & -4 \end{array}\right] \text{ is equivalent to } \left[\begin{array}{ccc|c} 1 & 0 & 0 & -0.5 \\ 0 & 1 & 0 & 4 \\ 0 & 0 & 1 & -0.5 \end{array}\right]$$

then the systems corresponding to these matrices have the same solution. That is,

$$\begin{cases} x + 2y + 3z = 6 \\ x \quad\quad - z = 0 \\ x - y - z = -4 \end{cases} \text{ has the same solution as } \begin{cases} x = -0.5 \\ y = 4 \\ z = -0.5 \end{cases}$$

Thus, if a system of linear equations has a unique solution, we can solve the system by reducing the associated matrix to one whose coefficient matrix is the identity matrix and then "reading" the values of the variables that give the solution.

The process that we use to solve a system of equations with matrices (called the **elimination method** or **Gauss-Jordan elimination method**) is a systematic procedure that uses row operations to attempt to reduce the coefficient matrix to an identity matrix.

For example, the system

$$\begin{cases} 2x + 5y + 4z = 4 \\ x + 4y + 3z = 1 \\ x - 3y - 2z = 5 \end{cases}$$

can be represented by the augmented matrix

$$\begin{bmatrix} 2 & 5 & 4 & | & 4 \\ 1 & 4 & 3 & | & 1 \\ 1 & -3 & -2 & | & 5 \end{bmatrix}$$

The following procedure (using the augmented matrix above) is used to reduce the augmented matrix for a system of equations to an equivalent matrix from which the solutions to the system may be found.

Gauss-Jordan Elimination Method

Goal (for Each Step)	Row Operation	Equivalent Matrix
1. Get a 1 in row 1, column 1.	Interchange row 1 and row 2.	$\begin{bmatrix} 1 & 4 & 3 & \| & 1 \\ 2 & 5 & 4 & \| & 4 \\ 1 & -3 & -2 & \| & 5 \end{bmatrix}$
2. Add multiples of row 1 *only* to the other rows to get zeros as the other entries of column 1.	Add -2 times row 1 to row 2; put the result in row 2. Add -1 times row 1 to row 3; put the result in row 3.	$\begin{bmatrix} 1 & 4 & 3 & \| & 1 \\ 0 & -3 & -2 & \| & 2 \\ 0 & -7 & -5 & \| & 4 \end{bmatrix}$
3. Use rows below row 1 to get a 1 in row 2, column 2.	Multiply row 2 by $-\frac{1}{3}$; put the result in row 2.	$\begin{bmatrix} 1 & 4 & 3 & \| & 1 \\ 0 & 1 & \frac{2}{3} & \| & -\frac{2}{3} \\ 0 & -7 & -5 & \| & 4 \end{bmatrix}$
4. Add multiples of row 2 *only* to the other rows to get zeros as the other entries in column 2.	Add -4 times row 2 to row 1; put the result in row 1. Add 7 times row 2 to row 3; put the result in row 3.	$\begin{bmatrix} 1 & 0 & \frac{1}{3} & \| & \frac{11}{3} \\ 0 & 1 & \frac{2}{3} & \| & -\frac{2}{3} \\ 0 & 0 & -\frac{1}{3} & \| & -\frac{2}{3} \end{bmatrix}$
5. Use rows below row 2 to get a 1 in row 3, column 3.	Multiply row 3 by -3; put the result in row 3.	$\begin{bmatrix} 1 & 0 & \frac{1}{3} & \| & \frac{11}{3} \\ 0 & 1 & \frac{2}{3} & \| & -\frac{2}{3} \\ 0 & 0 & 1 & \| & 2 \end{bmatrix}$
6. Add multiples of row 3 *only* to the other rows to get zeros as the other entries in column 3.	Add $-\frac{1}{3}$ times row 3 to row 1; put the result in row 1; Add $-\frac{2}{3}$ times row 3 to row 2; put the result in row 2.	$\begin{bmatrix} 1 & 0 & 0 & \| & 3 \\ 0 & 1 & 0 & \| & -2 \\ 0 & 0 & 1 & \| & 2 \end{bmatrix}$
7. Repeat the process until it cannot be continued.	All rows have been used. The matrix is in reduced form.	

The previous display shows a series of step-by-step goals for reducing a matrix and shows a series of row operations that reduces this 3×3 matrix. The reduction procedure and row operations apply regardless of the size of the system.

In the Gauss-Jordan method box, the systems of equations corresponding to the initial and the final augmented matrices are

$$\begin{array}{cc} \text{Initial} & \text{Final} \\ 2x + 5y + 4z = 4 & x + 0y + 0z = 3 \\ x + 4y + 3z = 1 \quad \text{and} & 0x + y + 0z = -2 \\ x - 3y - 2z = 5 & 0x + 0y + z = 2 \end{array}$$

Because the augmented matrices for these systems are equivalent, both systems have the same solution, $x = 3$, $y = -2$, and $z = 2$.

When a system of linear equations has a unique solution, the coefficient part of the reduced augmented matrix will be an identity matrix. Note that for this to occur, the coefficient matrix must be square; that is, the number of equations must equal the number of variables.

EXAMPLE　1　**Using the Gauss-Jordan Method**

Solve the system

$$
\begin{aligned}
x_1 + x_2 + x_3 + 2x_4 &= 6 \\
x_1 + 2x_2 \quad\quad\ + x_4 &= -2 \\
x_1 + x_2 + 3x_3 - 2x_4 &= 12 \\
x_1 + x_2 - 4x_3 + 5x_4 &= -16
\end{aligned}
$$

Solution

First note that there is a variable missing in the second equation. When we form the augmented matrix, we must insert a zero in this place so that each column represents the coefficients of one variable.

To solve this system, we must reduce the augmented matrix.

$$
\left[\begin{array}{cccc|c}
1 & 1 & 1 & 2 & 6 \\
1 & 2 & 0 & 1 & -2 \\
1 & 1 & 3 & -2 & 12 \\
1 & 1 & -4 & 5 & -16
\end{array}\right]
$$

The reduction process follows. The entry in row 1, column 1 is 1. To get zeros in the first column, add -1 times row 1 to row 2, and put the result in row 2; add -1 times row 1 to row 3 and put the result in row 3; and add -1 times row 1 to row 4 and put the result in row 4. These steps follow.

$$
\left[\begin{array}{cccc|c}
1 & 1 & 1 & 2 & 6 \\
1 & 2 & 0 & 1 & -2 \\
1 & 1 & 3 & -2 & 12 \\
1 & 1 & -4 & 5 & -16
\end{array}\right]
\begin{array}{c}
(-1)R_1 + R_2 \to R_2 \\
(-1)R_1 + R_3 \to R_3 \\
\hline
(-1)R_1 + R_4 \to R_4
\end{array}
\left[\begin{array}{cccc|c}
1 & 1 & 1 & 2 & 6 \\
0 & 1 & -1 & -1 & -8 \\
0 & 0 & 2 & -4 & 6 \\
0 & 0 & -5 & 3 & -22
\end{array}\right]
$$

The entry in row 2, column 2 is 1. To get zeros in the second column, add -1 times row 2 to row 1, and put the result in row 1.

$$
(-1)R_2 + R_1 \to R_1
\left[\begin{array}{cccc|c}
1 & 0 & 2 & 3 & 14 \\
0 & 1 & -1 & -1 & -8 \\
0 & 0 & 2 & -4 & 6 \\
0 & 0 & -5 & 3 & -22
\end{array}\right]
$$

The entry in row 3, column 3 is 2. To get a 1 in this position, multiply row 3 by $\frac{1}{2}$.

$$
\tfrac{1}{2}R_3 \to R_3
\left[\begin{array}{cccc|c}
1 & 0 & 2 & 3 & 14 \\
0 & 1 & -1 & -1 & -8 \\
0 & 0 & 1 & -2 & 3 \\
0 & 0 & -5 & 3 & -22
\end{array}\right]
$$

Using row 3, add -2 times row 3 to row 1 and put the result in row 1; add row 3 to row 2 and put the result in row 2; and add 5 times row 3 to row 4 and put the result in row 4.

$$
\begin{array}{c}
(-2)R_3 + R_1 \to R_1 \\
R_3 + R_2 \to R_2 \\
\hline
5R_3 + R_4 \to R_4
\end{array}
\left[\begin{array}{cccc|c}
1 & 0 & 0 & 7 & 8 \\
0 & 1 & 0 & -3 & -5 \\
0 & 0 & 1 & -2 & 3 \\
0 & 0 & 0 & -7 & -7
\end{array}\right]
$$

Multiplying $-\frac{1}{7}$ times row 4 and putting the result in row 4 gives a 1 in row 4, column 4.

$$-\tfrac{1}{7}R_4 \rightarrow R_4 \quad \begin{bmatrix} 1 & 0 & 0 & 7 & | & 8 \\ 0 & 1 & 0 & -3 & | & -5 \\ 0 & 0 & 1 & -2 & | & 3 \\ 0 & 0 & 0 & 1 & | & 1 \end{bmatrix}$$

Adding appropriate multiples of row 4 to the other rows gives

$$\begin{aligned} (-7)R_4 + R_1 \rightarrow R_1 \\ 3R_4 + R_2 \rightarrow R_2 \\ 2R_4 + R_3 \rightarrow R_3 \end{aligned} \quad \begin{bmatrix} 1 & 0 & 0 & 0 & | & 1 \\ 0 & 1 & 0 & 0 & | & -2 \\ 0 & 0 & 1 & 0 & | & 5 \\ 0 & 0 & 0 & 1 & | & 1 \end{bmatrix}$$

This corresponds to the system

$$\begin{aligned} x_1 & & & = 1 \\ & x_2 & & = -2 \\ & & x_3 & = 5 \\ & & & x_4 = 1 \end{aligned}$$

Thus the solution is $x_1 = 1$, $x_2 = -2$, $x_3 = 5$, and $x_4 = 1$. ∎

Calculator Note   Graphing calculators are especially useful in solving systems of equations because they can be used to perform the row reductions necessary to obtain a reduced matrix. On some calculators, a direct command will give a reduced form for the augmented matrix. Figure 3.8(a) shows the augmented matrix for the system of equations in Example 1, and Figure 3.8(b) shows the reduced form of the augmented matrix (which is the same as the reduced matrix found in Example 1). The steps used to solve a system of linear equations by finding the reduced matrix are shown in Appendix C, Section 3.3. ∎

Figure 3.8   (a)   (b)

CHECKPOINT   2. Solve the system.

$$\begin{cases} 3x + 2y - z = 3 \\ x - y + 2z = 4 \\ 2x + 3y - z = 3 \end{cases}$$

EXAMPLE 2   **Manufacturing | APPLICATION PREVIEW |**

The Walters Manufacturing Company needs to know how best to use the time available within its three manufacturing departments in the construction and packaging of the three types of metal storage sheds. Each one must be stamped, painted, and packaged. Table 3.6 shows the number of hours required for the processing of each type of shed. Using the information in the table, determine how many of each type of shed can be produced if the stamping department has 3200 hours available, the painting department has 1700 hours, and the packaging department has 1300 hours.

| TABLE 3.6 |

Department	Shed		
	Type I	Type II	Type III
Stamping	2	3	4
Painting	1	2	1
Packaging	1	1	2

Solution

If we let x_1 be the number of type I sheds, x_2 be the number of type II sheds, and x_3 be the number of type III sheds, we can develop the following equations.

$$\text{Stamping hours:} \quad 2x_1 + 3x_2 + 4x_3 = 3200$$
$$\text{Painting hours:} \quad 1x_1 + 2x_2 + 1x_3 = 1700$$
$$\text{Packaging hours:} \quad 1x_1 + 1x_2 + 2x_3 = 1300$$

The augmented matrix for this system of equations is

$$\begin{bmatrix} 2 & 3 & 4 & | & 3200 \\ 1 & 2 & 1 & | & 1700 \\ 1 & 1 & 2 & | & 1300 \end{bmatrix}$$

Reducing this augmented matrix proceeds as follows:

$$\begin{bmatrix} 2 & 3 & 4 & | & 3200 \\ 1 & 2 & 1 & | & 1700 \\ 1 & 1 & 2 & | & 1300 \end{bmatrix} \qquad \begin{bmatrix} 1 & 1 & 2 & | & 1300 \\ 1 & 2 & 1 & | & 1700 \\ 2 & 3 & 4 & | & 3200 \end{bmatrix}$$

$$\begin{array}{c} (-1)R_1 + R_2 \rightarrow R_2 \\ \overline{(-2)R_1 + R_3 \rightarrow R_3} \end{array} \begin{bmatrix} 1 & 1 & 2 & | & 1300 \\ 0 & 1 & -1 & | & 400 \\ 0 & 1 & 0 & | & 600 \end{bmatrix}$$

$$\begin{array}{c} (-1)R_2 + R_1 \rightarrow R_1 \\ \overline{(-1)R_2 + R_3 \rightarrow R_3} \end{array} \begin{bmatrix} 1 & 0 & 3 & | & 900 \\ 0 & 1 & -1 & | & 400 \\ 0 & 0 & 1 & | & 200 \end{bmatrix} \quad \begin{array}{c} (-3)R_3 + R_1 \rightarrow R_1 \\ \overline{R_3 + R_2 \rightarrow R_2} \end{array} \begin{bmatrix} 1 & 0 & 0 & | & 300 \\ 0 & 1 & 0 & | & 600 \\ 0 & 0 & 1 & | & 200 \end{bmatrix}$$

Thus the solution to the system is

$$x_1 = 300 \qquad x_2 = 600 \qquad x_3 = 200$$

The company should make 300 type I, 600 type II, and 200 type III sheds.

Systems with Nonunique Solutions

All the systems considered so far have unique solutions, but it is also possible for a system of linear equations to have an infinite number of solutions or no solution at all. Although coefficient matrices for systems with an infinite number of solutions or no solution will not reduce to identity matrices, row operations can be used to obtain a reduced form from which the solutions, if they exist, can be determined.

A matrix is said to be in **reduced form** when it is in the following form:

1. The first nonzero element in each row is 1.
2. Every column containing a first nonzero element for some row has zeros everywhere else.
3. The first nonzero element of each row is to the right of the first nonzero element of every row above it.
4. All rows containing zeros are grouped together below the rows containing nonzero entries.

The following matrices are in reduced form because they satisfy these conditions.

$$\begin{bmatrix} 1 & 0 & | & 4 \\ 0 & 1 & | & 2 \\ 0 & 0 & | & 0 \end{bmatrix} \quad \begin{bmatrix} 1 & 0 & 0 & | & 0 \\ 0 & 1 & 0 & | & 3 \\ 0 & 0 & 1 & | & 1 \\ 0 & 0 & 0 & | & 0 \end{bmatrix} \quad \begin{bmatrix} 1 & 4 & 0 & | & 1 \\ 0 & 0 & 1 & | & 2 \\ 0 & 0 & 0 & | & 0 \end{bmatrix}$$

The following matrices are *not* in reduced form.

$$\begin{bmatrix} 1 & ① & | & 0 \\ 0 & 1 & | & 3 \\ 0 & 0 & | & 0 \end{bmatrix} \quad \begin{bmatrix} 1 & 0 & | & 1 \\ 0 & ② & | & 1 \\ 0 & 0 & | & 0 \end{bmatrix} \quad \begin{bmatrix} 0 & 1 & | & 0 \\ 1 & 0 & | & 0 \\ 0 & 0 & | & 1 \end{bmatrix}$$

In the first two matrices, the circled element must be changed to obtain a reduced form. Can you see what row operations would transform each of these matrices into reduced form? The third matrix does not satisfy condition 3.

We can solve a system of linear equations by using row operations on the augmented matrix until the coefficient matrix is transformed to an equivalent matrix in reduced form. We begin by following the goals outlined in the Gauss-Jordan elimination method and in the Example 1 discussion.

EXAMPLE 3   ## Matrix Solution of a System

Solve the system

$$\begin{cases} x_1 + x_2 - x_3 + x_4 = 3 \\ x_2 + x_3 + x_4 = 1 \\ x_1 \qquad - 2x_3 + x_4 = 6 \\ 2x_1 - x_2 - 5x_3 - 3x_4 = -5 \end{cases}$$

Solution

Attempting to reduce the coefficient matrix of the associated augmented matrix to an identity matrix requires the following.

$$\begin{bmatrix} 1 & 1 & -1 & 1 & | & 3 \\ 0 & 1 & 1 & 1 & | & 1 \\ 1 & 0 & -2 & 1 & | & 6 \\ 2 & -1 & -5 & -3 & | & -5 \end{bmatrix} \xrightarrow[\substack{(-1)R_1 + R_3 \to R_3 \\ (-2)R_1 + R_4 \to R_4}]{} \begin{bmatrix} 1 & 1 & -1 & 1 & | & 3 \\ 0 & 1 & 1 & 1 & | & 1 \\ 0 & -1 & -1 & 0 & | & 3 \\ 0 & -3 & -3 & -5 & | & -11 \end{bmatrix}$$

$$\xrightarrow[\substack{(-1)R_2 + R_1 \to R_1 \\ R_2 + R_3 \to R_3 \\ 3R_2 + R_4 \to R_4}]{} \begin{bmatrix} 1 & 0 & -2 & 0 & | & 2 \\ 0 & 1 & 1 & 1 & | & 1 \\ 0 & 0 & 0 & 1 & | & 4 \\ 0 & 0 & 0 & -2 & | & -8 \end{bmatrix}$$

The entry in row 3, column 3 cannot be made 1 using rows *below* row 2. Moving to column 4, the entry in row 3, column 4 is a 1. Using row 3 gives

$$\xrightarrow[\substack{(-1)R_3 + R_2 \to R_2 \\ 2R_3 + R_4 \to R_4}]{} \begin{bmatrix} 1 & 0 & -2 & 0 & | & 2 \\ 0 & 1 & 1 & 0 & | & -3 \\ 0 & 0 & 0 & 1 & | & 4 \\ 0 & 0 & 0 & 0 & | & 0 \end{bmatrix}$$

The augmented matrix is now reduced; this matrix corresponds to the system

$$\begin{cases} x_1 - 2x_3 = 2 \\ x_2 + x_3 = -3 \\ x_4 = 4 \\ 0 = 0 \end{cases}$$

If we solve each of the equations for the leading variable (the variable corresponding to the first 1 in each row of the reduced form of a matrix) and let any non-leading variables equal any real number (x_3 in this case), we obtain the **general solution** of the system.

$$
\begin{aligned}
x_1 &= 2 + 2x_3 \\
x_2 &= -3 - x_3 \\
x_4 &= 4 \\
x_3 &= \text{any real number}
\end{aligned}
$$

The general solution gives the values of x_1 and x_2 dependent on the value of x_3, so we can get many different solutions of the system by specifying different values of x_3. For example, if $x_3 = 1$, then $x_1 = 4$, $x_2 = -4$, $x_3 = 1$, and $x_4 = 4$ is a solution of the system; if we let $x_3 = -2$, then $x_1 = -2$, $x_2 = -1$, $x_3 = -2$, and $x_4 = 4$ is another solution.   ■

We have seen two different possibilities for solutions of systems of linear equations. In Examples 1 and 2, there was only one solution, whereas in Example 3 we saw that there were infinitely many solutions, one for each possible value of x_3. A third possibility exists: that the system has no solution. Recall that these possibilities also existed for two equations in two unknowns, as discussed in Chapter 1, "Linear Equations and Functions."

EXAMPLE   4   A System with No Solution

Solve the system

$$
\begin{cases}
x + 2y - z = 3 \\
3x + y = 4 \\
2x - y + z = 2
\end{cases}
$$

Solution

The augmented matrix for this system is reduced as follows:

$$
\left[\begin{array}{ccc|c}
1 & 2 & -1 & 3 \\
3 & 1 & 0 & 4 \\
2 & -1 & 1 & 2
\end{array}\right]
\begin{array}{c}
(-3)R_1 + R_2 \to R_2 \\
\overline{(-2)R_1 + R_3 \to R_3}
\end{array}
\left[\begin{array}{ccc|c}
1 & 2 & -1 & 3 \\
0 & -5 & 3 & -5 \\
0 & -5 & 3 & -4
\end{array}\right]
$$

$$
-\tfrac{1}{5}R_2 \to R_2
\left[\begin{array}{ccc|c}
1 & 2 & -1 & 3 \\
0 & 1 & -\tfrac{3}{5} & 1 \\
0 & -5 & 3 & -4
\end{array}\right]
$$

$$
\begin{array}{c}
(-2)R_2 + R_1 \to R_1 \\
\overline{(5)R_2 + R_3 \to R_3}
\end{array}
\left[\begin{array}{ccc|c}
1 & 0 & \tfrac{1}{5} & 1 \\
0 & 1 & -\tfrac{3}{5} & 1 \\
0 & 0 & 0 & 1
\end{array}\right]
$$

The system of equations corresponding to the reduced matrix has $0 = 1$ as the third equation. This is clearly an impossibility, so there is no solution.   ■

Now that we have seen examples of each of the different solution possibilities for n equations in n variables, let us consider what we have learned. In all cases the solution procedure began by setting up and then reducing the augmented matrix. Once the matrix is reduced, we can write the corresponding reduced system of equations. The solutions, if they exist, are easily found from this reduced system. We summarize the possibilities in Table 3.7.

■ | **TABLE 3.7**

UNIQUE AND NONUNIQUE SOLUTIONS

Reduced Form of Augmented Matrix for *n* Equations in *n* Variables	Solution to System
1. Coefficient array is an identity matrix.	Unique solution (see Examples 1 and 2).
2. Coefficient array is *not* an identity matrix with either:	
(a) A row of 0s in the coefficient array with a nonzero entry in the augment.	(a) No solution (see Example 4).
(b) Or otherwise.	(b) Infinitely many solutions. Solve for lead variables in terms of non-lead variables; non-lead variables can equal any real number (see Example 3).

Calculator Note   Whether or not a unique solution exists, we can use a graphing calculator to reduce an augmented matrix and then find any solution that exists (or that no solution exists). For example, following is a system of equations along with the calculator screens for its augmented matrix and the reduced form of its augmented matrix.

$$\begin{cases} x + 2y - 2z = 4 \\ 2x + 5y \phantom{{}- 2z} = 3 \\ x + y - 6z = 9 \end{cases}$$

```
[A]
        [[1  2 -2  4]
         [2  5  0  3]
         [1  1 -6  9]]
```

```
rref([A])
        [[1  0 -10  14]
         [0  1   4  -5]
         [0  0   0   0]]
```

From the reduced matrix we obtain the following equations and general solution.

$$\begin{aligned} x - 10z &= 14 \\ y + 4z &= -5 \end{aligned} \qquad\qquad \begin{aligned} x &= 10z + 14 \\ y &= -4z - 5 \\ z &= \text{ any real number} \end{aligned}$$

Most calculators have a command (like rref([A]) above) that gives the reduced form of a matrix. See Appendix C, Section 3.3, for details.   ■

CHECKPOINT   For each system of equations, the reduced form of the augmented matrix is given. Give the solution to the system, if it exists.

3. $\begin{cases} 2x + 3y + 2z = 180 \\ -x + 2y + 4z = 180 \\ 2x + 6y + 5z = 270 \end{cases}$ $\quad\begin{bmatrix} 1 & 0 & 0 & | & 100 \\ 0 & 1 & 0 & | & -80 \\ 0 & 0 & 1 & | & 110 \end{bmatrix}$

4. $\begin{cases} x - 2y + 9z = 12 \\ 2x - y + 3z = 18 \\ x + y - 6z = 6 \end{cases}$ $\quad\begin{bmatrix} 1 & 0 & -1 & | & 8 \\ 0 & 1 & -5 & | & -2 \\ 0 & 0 & 0 & | & 0 \end{bmatrix}$

5. $\begin{cases} x - 4y + 3z = 4 \\ 2x - 2y + z = 6 \\ x + 2y - 2z = 4 \end{cases}$ $\quad\begin{bmatrix} 1 & 0 & -\frac{1}{3} & | & 0 \\ 0 & 1 & -\frac{5}{6} & | & 0 \\ 0 & 0 & 0 & | & 1 \end{bmatrix}$

Nonsquare Systems

Finally, we consider systems with fewer equations than variables. Because the coefficient matrix for such a system is not square, it cannot reduce to an identity matrix. Hence these systems of equations cannot have a unique solution but may have no solution or infinitely many solutions. Nevertheless, they are solved in the same manner as those considered so far but with the following two possible results.

1. If the reduced augmented matrix contains a row of 0s in the coefficient matrix with a nonzero number in the augment, the system has no solution.
2. Otherwise, the system has infinitely many solutions.

EXAMPLE 5   Investment

markhiggins/Shutterstock.com

A trust account manager has $500,000 to be invested in three different accounts. The accounts pay annual interest rates of 8%, 10%, and 14%, and the goal is to earn $49,000 a year. To accomplish this, assume that x dollars is invested at 8%, y dollars at 10%, and z dollars at 14%. Find how much should be invested in each account to satisfy the conditions.

Solution

The sum of the three investments is $500,000, so we have the equation

$$x + y + z = 500{,}000$$

The interest earned from the 8% investment is $0.08x$, the amount earned from the 10% investment is $0.10y$, and the amount earned from the 14% investment is $0.14z$, so the total amount earned from the investments is given by the equation

$$0.08x + 0.10y + 0.14z = 49{,}000$$

These two equations represent all the given information, so the system is

$$\begin{cases} x + y + z = 500{,}000 \\ 0.08x + 0.10y + 0.14z = 49{,}000 \end{cases}$$

We solve this system using matrices, as follows:

$$\begin{bmatrix} 1 & 1 & 1 & | & 500{,}000 \\ 0.08 & 0.10 & 0.14 & | & 49{,}000 \end{bmatrix} \xrightarrow{-0.08R_1 + R_2 \to R_2} \begin{bmatrix} 1 & 1 & 1 & | & 500{,}000 \\ 0 & 0.02 & 0.06 & | & 9{,}000 \end{bmatrix}$$

$$\xrightarrow{50R_2 \to R_2} \begin{bmatrix} 1 & 1 & 1 & | & 500{,}000 \\ 0 & 1 & 3 & | & 450{,}000 \end{bmatrix} \xrightarrow{-R_2 + R_1 \to R_1} \begin{bmatrix} 1 & 0 & -2 & | & 50{,}000 \\ 0 & 1 & 3 & | & 450{,}000 \end{bmatrix}$$

This matrix represents the equivalent system

$$\begin{cases} x - 2z = 50{,}000 \\ y + 3z = 450{,}000 \end{cases} \quad \text{so} \quad \begin{aligned} x &= 50{,}000 + 2z \\ y &= 450{,}000 - 3z \\ z &= \text{any real number} \end{aligned}$$

Because a negative amount cannot be invested, x, y, and z must all be nonnegative. Note that $x \ge 0$ when $z \ge 0$ and that $y \ge 0$ when $450{,}000 - 3z \ge 0$, or when $z \le 150{,}000$. Thus the amounts invested are

$$\begin{aligned} \$z \text{ at } 14\%, \quad &\text{where} \quad 0 \le z \le 150{,}000 \\ \$x \text{ at } 8\%, \quad &\text{where} \quad x = 50{,}000 + 2z \\ \$y \text{ at } 10\%, \quad &\text{where} \quad y = 450{,}000 - 3z \end{aligned}$$

There are many possible investment plans. One example would be with $z =$ $100,000, $x =$ $250,000, and $y =$ $150,000. Observe that the values for x and y depend on z, and once z is chosen, x will be between $50,000 and $350,000, and y will be between $0 and $450,000. ■

CHECKPOINT SOLUTIONS

1. (a) $\begin{bmatrix} 3 & 2 & -1 & | & 3 \\ 1 & -1 & 2 & | & 4 \\ 2 & 3 & -1 & | & 3 \end{bmatrix}$ (b) $\begin{bmatrix} 3 & 2 & -1 \\ 1 & -1 & 2 \\ 2 & 3 & -1 \end{bmatrix}$

2. $\begin{bmatrix} 3 & 2 & -1 & | & 3 \\ 1 & -1 & 2 & | & 4 \\ 2 & 3 & -1 & | & 3 \end{bmatrix}$ $\begin{array}{c} \text{Switch } R_1 \text{ and } R_2 \\ \text{Then } -3R_1 + R_2 \to R_2 \\ \hline -2R_1 + R_3 \to R_3 \end{array}$ $\begin{bmatrix} 1 & -1 & 2 & | & 4 \\ 0 & 5 & -7 & | & -9 \\ 0 & 5 & -5 & | & -5 \end{bmatrix}$

$\begin{array}{c} \text{Switch } R_2 \text{ and } R_3 \\ \text{Then } \frac{1}{5}R_2 \to R_2 \\ \hline R_2 + R_1 \to R_1 \\ -5R_2 + R_3 \to R_3 \end{array}$ $\begin{bmatrix} 1 & 0 & 1 & | & 3 \\ 0 & 1 & -1 & | & -1 \\ 0 & 0 & -2 & | & -4 \end{bmatrix}$

$\begin{array}{c} -\frac{1}{2}R_3 \to R_3 \\ \text{Then } R_3 + R_2 \to R_2 \\ \hline -R_3 + R_1 \to R_1 \end{array}$ $\begin{bmatrix} 1 & 0 & 0 & | & 1 \\ 0 & 1 & 0 & | & 1 \\ 0 & 0 & 1 & | & 2 \end{bmatrix}$ Thus $x = 1, y = 1, z = 2$.

3. $x = 100, y = -80, z = 110$
4. $x - z = 8, y - 5z = -2 \Rightarrow x = z + 8, y = 5z - 2, z =$ any real number
5. No solution

| EXERCISES | 3.3

In Problems 1 and 2, use the indicated row operation to change matrix A, where

$$A = \begin{bmatrix} 1 & -2 & -1 & | & -7 \\ 3 & 1 & 2 & | & 0 \\ 4 & 2 & 2 & | & 1 \end{bmatrix}$$

1. Add -3 times row 1 to row 2 of matrix A and place the result in row 2 to get 0 in row 2, column 1.
2. Add -4 times row 1 to row 3 of matrix A and place the result in row 3 to get 0 in row 3, column 1.

In Problems 3 and 4, write the augmented matrix associated with each system of linear equations.

3. $\begin{cases} x - 3y + 4z = 2 \\ 2x \quad\quad + 2z = 1 \\ x + 2y + z = 1 \end{cases}$ 4. $\begin{cases} x + 2y + 2z = 3 \\ x - 2y \quad\quad = 4 \\ y - z = 1 \end{cases}$

In each of Problems 5 and 6, the given matrix is an augmented matrix used in the solution of a system of linear equations. What is the solution of the system?

5. $\begin{bmatrix} 1 & 0 & 0 & | & 2 \\ 0 & 1 & 0 & | & \frac{1}{2} \\ 0 & 0 & 1 & | & -5 \end{bmatrix}$ 6. $\begin{bmatrix} 1 & 0 & 0 & | & -8 \\ 0 & 1 & 0 & | & 1 \\ 0 & 0 & 1 & | & \frac{1}{3} \end{bmatrix}$

In Problems 7–10, the given matrix is an augmented matrix representing a system of linear equations. Use the Gauss–Jordan elimination method (see Gauss–Jordan elimination method box and Example 1) to find the solution of the system.

7. $\begin{bmatrix} 1 & 1 & 2 & | & -1 \\ 0 & 3 & 1 & | & 7 \\ 0 & -2 & 4 & | & 0 \end{bmatrix}$

8. $\begin{bmatrix} 1 & 5 & 2 & | & 6 \\ 0 & -2 & 3 & | & 9 \\ 0 & 1 & 3 & | & 0 \end{bmatrix}$

9. $\begin{bmatrix} 1 & 2 & 5 & | & -4 \\ 2 & -2 & 4 & | & -2 \\ 0 & 1 & -3 & | & 7 \end{bmatrix}$

10. $\begin{bmatrix} 1 & 1 & 1 & | & 3 \\ 3 & -2 & 4 & | & 5 \\ 1 & 2 & 1 & | & 4 \end{bmatrix}$

In Problems 11–16, use row operations on augmented matrices to solve the given systems of linear equations.

11. $\begin{cases} x + y - z = 0 \\ x + 2y + 3z = -5 \\ 2x - y - 13z = 17 \end{cases}$ 12. $\begin{cases} x + 2y - z = 3 \\ 2x + 5y - 2z = 7 \\ -x + y + 5z = -12 \end{cases}$

13. $\begin{cases} 2x - 6y - 12z = 6 \\ 3x - 10y - 20z = 5 \\ 2x \qquad - 17z = -4 \end{cases}$ 14. $\begin{cases} -3x + 6y - 9z = 3 \\ x - y - 2z = 0 \\ 5x + 5y - 7z = 63 \end{cases}$

15. $\begin{cases} x - 2y + 3z + w = -2 \\ x - 3y + z - w = -7 \\ x - y \qquad = -2 \\ x \qquad + z + w = 2 \end{cases}$

16. $\begin{cases} x + 4y - 6z - 3w = 3 \\ x - y \qquad + 2w = -5 \\ x \qquad + z + w = 1 \\ y + z + w = 0 \end{cases}$

In each of Problems 17–20, a system of linear equations and a reduced matrix for the system are given. (a) Use the reduced matrix to find the general solution of the system, if one exists. (b) If multiple solutions exist, find two specific solutions.

17. $\begin{cases} x + 2y + 3z = 1 \\ 2x - y \quad = 3 \\ x + 2y + 3z = 2 \end{cases}$ $\begin{bmatrix} 1 & 0 & \frac{3}{5} & 0 \\ 0 & 1 & \frac{6}{5} & 0 \\ 0 & 0 & 0 & 1 \end{bmatrix}$

18. $\begin{cases} 2x + 3y + 4z = 2 \\ x + 2y + 2z = 1 \\ x + y + 2z = 2 \end{cases}$ $\begin{bmatrix} 1 & 0 & 2 & 0 \\ 0 & 1 & 0 & 0 \\ 0 & 0 & 0 & 1 \end{bmatrix}$

19. $\begin{cases} 2x + y - z = 7 \\ x - y - z = 4 \\ 3x + 3y - z = 10 \end{cases}$ $\begin{bmatrix} 1 & 0 & -\frac{2}{3} & \frac{11}{3} \\ 0 & 1 & \frac{1}{3} & -\frac{1}{3} \\ 0 & 0 & 0 & 0 \end{bmatrix}$

20. $\begin{cases} x - y + z = 3 \\ 3x \quad + 2z = 7 \\ x - 4y + 2z = 5 \end{cases}$ $\begin{bmatrix} 1 & 0 & \frac{2}{3} & \frac{7}{3} \\ 0 & 1 & -\frac{1}{3} & -\frac{2}{3} \\ 0 & 0 & 0 & 0 \end{bmatrix}$

21. How can you tell that a system of linear equations has no solution by just looking at its reduced matrix?
22. Describe the procedure for finding the general solution of a system of linear equations if its reduced matrix indicates that it has an infinite number of solutions.

The systems of equations in Problems 23–38 may have unique solutions, an infinite number of solutions, or no solution. Use matrices to find the general solution of each system, if a solution exists.

23. $\begin{cases} x + y + z = 0 \\ 2x - y - z = 0 \\ -x + 2y + 2z = 0 \end{cases}$ 24. $\begin{cases} 2x - y + 3z = 0 \\ x + 2y + 2z = 0 \\ x - 3y + z = 0 \end{cases}$

25. $\begin{cases} 3x + 2y + z = 0 \\ x + y + 2z = 2 \\ 2x + y - z = -1 \end{cases}$ 26. $\begin{cases} x + 3y + 2z = 2 \\ 2x - y - 2z = 1 \\ 3x + 2y \quad = 1 \end{cases}$

27. $\begin{cases} 2x + 2y + z = 2 \\ x - 2y + 2z = 1 \\ -x + 2y - 2z = -1 \end{cases}$ 28. $\begin{cases} 2x + y - z = 2 \\ x - y + 2z = 3 \\ x + y - z = 1 \end{cases}$

29. $\begin{cases} x - 3y + 3z = 7 \\ x + 2y - z = -2 \\ 3x + 2y + 4z = 5 \end{cases}$ 30. $\begin{cases} 3x + 2y - 4z = -12 \\ 3x - 3y + 2z = -15 \\ 4x + 6y + z = 0 \end{cases}$

31. $\begin{cases} 2x - 5y + z = -9 \\ x + 4y - 6z = 2 \\ 3x - 4y - 2z = -10 \end{cases}$ 32. $\begin{cases} 2x - y + z = 2 \\ 3x + y - 6z = -7 \\ x - y + 2z = 3 \end{cases}$

33. $\begin{cases} x + y + z = 3 \\ x - y + z = 4 \end{cases}$ 34. $\begin{cases} 3x + 2y + z = 3 \\ x - y - z = 2 \end{cases}$

35. $\begin{cases} 3x - 2y + 5z = 14 \\ 2x - 3y + 4z = 8 \end{cases}$ 36. $\begin{cases} x - 4y + z = -4 \\ 2x - 5y - 5z = -9 \end{cases}$

37. $\begin{cases} -0.6x_1 + 0.1x_2 + 0.4x_3 = 10 \\ 0.4x_1 - 0.7x_2 + 0.2x_3 = -26 \\ 0.2x_1 + 0.6x_2 - 0.5x_3 = 20 \end{cases}$

38. $\begin{cases} 0.1x_1 - 0.1x_2 - 0.3x_3 = 17 \\ 0.2x_1 + 0.3x_2 + 0.1x_3 = -9 \\ 0.3x_1 + 0.2x_2 - 0.5x_3 = 5 \end{cases}$

 In Problems 39–46, use technology to solve each system of equations, if a solution exists.

39. $\begin{cases} x_1 + 3x_2 + 2x_3 + 2x_4 = 3 \\ x_1 + x_2 + 3x_3 \quad = 4 \\ 2x_1 \quad + 2x_3 - 3x_4 = 4 \\ x_1 - 3x_2 \quad = 1 \end{cases}$

40. $\begin{cases} x_1 + x_2 + x_3 + 2x_4 = 1 \\ x_1 \quad - 3x_3 \quad = 2 \\ x_1 - 3x_2 \quad + x_4 = -2 \\ x_2 - 4x_3 + x_4 = 0 \end{cases}$

41. $\begin{cases} 3x + 2y + z - w = 3 \\ x - y - 2z + 2w = 2 \\ 2x + 3y - z + w = 1 \\ -x + y + 2z - 2w = -2 \end{cases}$

42. $\begin{cases} 2x_1 + 3x_2 - x_3 + 3x_4 + x_5 = 22 \\ 3x_1 + x_2 - 4x_3 + 3x_4 - x_5 = 0 \\ x_1 + x_2 + 3x_3 - 4x_4 + 2x_5 = 6 \\ x_1 + 2x_2 - 3x_3 + 2x_4 - 2x_5 = -6 \\ 2x_1 \quad + 4x_4 - 5x_5 = -7 \end{cases}$

43. $\begin{cases} x_1 + 2x_2 - x_3 + x_4 = 3 \\ x_1 + 3x_2 + 4x_3 + x_4 = -2 \\ 2x_1 + 5x_2 + 2x_3 + 2x_4 = 1 \\ 2x_1 + 3x_2 - 6x_3 + 2x_4 = 3 \end{cases}$

44. $\begin{cases} x_1 + 2x_2 + 3x_3 + 4x_4 = 2 \\ x_1 + 2x_2 + 4x_3 + 3x_4 = 2 \\ 2x_1 + 4x_2 + 6x_3 + 8x_4 = 4 \\ x_1 + 4x_2 + 3x_3 \qquad\quad = 4 \end{cases}$

45. $\begin{cases} x_1 + 3x_2 + 4x_3 - x_4 + 2x_5 = 1 \\ x_1 - x_2 - 2x_3 + x_4 \qquad = 3 \\ x_1 + 2x_2 + 3x_3 + x_4 + 4x_5 = 0 \\ 2x_1 + 2x_2 + 2x_3 \qquad + 2x_5 = 4 \end{cases}$

46. $\begin{cases} 2x_1 - x_2 + x_3 + 3x_4 + 3x_5 = 7 \\ x_1 + x_2 + x_3 + 2x_4 + 2x_5 = 0 \\ 2x_1 + x_2 - x_3 + x_4 + x_5 = -3 \\ 4x_1 - x_2 - 3x_3 + x_4 + x_5 = 1 \end{cases}$

47. Solve $\begin{cases} a_1 x + b_1 y = c_1 \\ a_2 x + b_2 y = c_2 \end{cases}$ for x. This gives a formula for solving two equations in two variables for x.

48. Solve $\begin{cases} a_1 x + b_1 y = c_1 \\ a_2 x + b_2 y = c_2 \end{cases}$ for y. This gives a formula for solving two equations in two variables for y.

APPLICATIONS

49. *Nutrition* A preschool has Campbell's Chunky Beef soup, which contains 2.5 g of fat and 15 mg of cholesterol per serving (cup), and Campbell's Chunky Sirloin Burger soup, which contains 7 g of fat and 15 mg of cholesterol per serving. By combining the soups, it is possible to get 10 servings of soup that will have 61 g of fat and 150 mg of cholesterol. How many cups of each soup should be used?

50. *Ticket sales* A 3500-seat theater sells tickets for $75 and $110. Each night the theater's expenses total $245,000. When all 3500 seats sell, the owners want ticket revenues to cover expenses plus earn a profit of 25% of expenses. How many tickets of each price should be sold to achieve this?

51. *Investment* A man has $235,000 invested in three properties. One earns 12%, one 10%, and one 8%. His annual income from the properties is $22,500 and the amount invested at 8% is twice that invested at 12%.
  (a) How much is invested in each property?
  (b) What is the annual income from each property?

52. *Loans* A bank lent $1.2 million for the development of three new products, with one loan each at 6%, 7%, and 8%. The amount lent at 8% was equal to the sum of the amounts lent at the other two rates, and the bank's annual income from the loans was $88,000. How much was lent at each rate?

53. *Car rental patterns* A car rental agency in a major city has a total of 2200 cars that it rents from three locations: Metropolis Airport, downtown, and at the smaller City Airport. Some weekly rental and return patterns are shown in the table (note that Airport means Metropolis Airport).

| | Rented from | | |
Returned to	AP	DT	CA
Airport (AP)	90%	10%	10%
Downtown (DT)	5%	80%	5%

At the beginning of a week, how many cars should be at each location so that same number of cars will be there at the end of the week (and hence at the start of the next week)?

54. *Nutrition* A psychologist studying the effects of nutrition on the behavior of laboratory rats is feeding one group a combination of three foods: I, II, and III. Each of these foods contains three additives, A, B, and C, that are being used in the study. Each additive is a certain percentage of each of the foods as follows:

| | Foods | | |
	I	II	III
Additive A	10%	30%	60%
Additive B	0%	4%	5%
Additive C	2%	2%	12%

If the diet requires 53 g per day of A, 4.5 g per day of B, and 8.6 g per day of C, find the number of grams per day of each food that must be used.

55. *Nutrition* The following table gives the calories, fat, and carbohydrates per ounce for three brands of cereal. How many ounces of each brand should be combined to get 443 calories, 5.7 g of fat, and 113.4 g of carbohydrates?

Cereal	Calories	Fat (g)	Carbohydrates (g)
All Fiber	50	0	22.0
Frosted Puffs	108	0.1	25.7
Natural			
Mixed Grain	127	5.5	18.0

56. *Investment* A brokerage house offers three stock portfolios. Portfolio I consists of 2 blocks of common stock and 1 municipal bond. Portfolio II consists of 4 blocks of common stock, 2 municipal bonds, and 3 blocks of preferred stock. Portfolio III consists of 7 blocks of common stock, 3 municipal bonds, and 3 blocks of preferred stock. A customer wants 21 blocks of common stock, 10 municipal bonds, and 9 blocks of preferred stock. How many units of each portfolio should be offered?

57. *Investment* Suppose that portfolios I and II in Problem 56 are unchanged and portfolio III consists of 2 blocks of common stock, 2 municipal bonds, and 3 blocks of preferred stock. A customer wants 12 blocks of common stock, 6 municipal bonds, and 6 blocks of preferred stock. How many units of each portfolio should be offered?

58. *Nutrition* Each ounce of substance A supplies 5% of the required nutrition a patient needs. Substance B supplies 15% of the required nutrition per ounce, and substance C supplies 12% of the required nutrition per ounce. If digestive restrictions require that substances A and C be given in equal amounts and that the amount of substance B be one-fifth of these other amounts, find the number of ounces of each substance that should be in the meal to provide 100% nutrition.

59. *Nutrition* A glass of skim milk supplies 0.1 mg of iron, 8.5 g of protein, and 1 g of carbohydrates. A quarter pound of lean red meat provides 3.4 mg of iron, 22 g of protein, and 20 g of carbohydrates. Two slices of whole-grain bread supply 2.2 mg of iron, 10 g of protein, and 12 g of carbohydrates. If a person on a special diet must have 12.1 mg of iron, 97 g of protein, and 70 g of carbohydrates, how many glasses of skim milk, how many quarter-pound servings of meat, and how many two-slice servings of whole-grain bread will supply this?

60. *Transportation* The King Trucking Company has an order for three products for delivery. The following table gives the particulars for the products.

	Type I	Type II	Type III
Unit volume (cubic feet)	10	8	20
Unit weight (pounds)	10	20	40
Unit value (dollars)	100	20	200

If the carrier can carry 6000 cu ft, can carry 11,000 lb, and is insured for $36,900, how many units of each type can be carried?

61. *Nutrition* A botanist can purchase plant food of four different types, I, II, III, and IV. Each food comes in the same size bag, and the following table summarizes the number of grams of each of three nutrients that each bag contains.

	Foods (grams)			
	I	II	III	IV
Nutrient A	5	5	10	5
Nutrient B	10	5	30	10
Nutrient C	5	15	10	25

The botanist wants to use a food that has these nutrients in a different proportion and determines that he will need a total of 10,000 g of A, 20,000 g of B, and 20,000 g of C. Find the number of bags of each type of food that should be ordered.

62. *Traffic flow* In the analysis of traffic flow, a certain city estimates the following situation for the "square" of its downtown district. In the following figure, the arrows indicate the flow of traffic. If x_1 represents the number of cars traveling between intersections A and B, x_2 represents the number of cars traveling between B and C, x_3 the number between C and D, and x_4 the number between D and A, we can formulate equations based on the principle that the number of vehicles entering an intersection equals the number leaving it. That is, for intersection A we obtain

$$200 + x_4 = 100 + x_1$$

(a) Formulate equations for the traffic at B, C, and D.
(b) Solve the system of these four equations.
(c) Can the entire traffic flow problem be studied and solved by counting only the x_4 cars that travel between A and D? Explain.

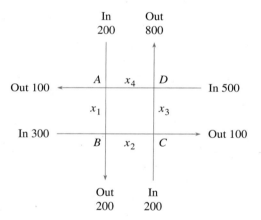

63. *Nutrition* Three different bacteria are cultured in one dish and feed on three nutrients. Each individual of species I consumes 1 unit of each of the first and second nutrients and 2 units of the third nutrient. Each individual of species II consumes 2 units of the first nutrient and 2 units of the third nutrient. Each individual of species III consumes 2 units of the first nutrient, 3 units of the second nutrient, and 5 units of the third nutrient. If the culture is given 5100 units of the first nutrient, 6900 units of the second nutrient, and 12,000 units of the third nutrient, how many of each species can be supported such that all of the nutrients are consumed?

64. *Irrigation* An irrigation system allows water to flow in the pattern shown in the figure below. Water flows into the system at A and exits at B, C, D, and E with the amounts shown. Using the fact that at each point the water entering equals the water leaving, formulate an equation for water flow at each of the five points and solve the system.

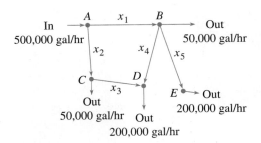

65. *Investment* An investment club has set a goal of earning 15% on the money they invest in stocks. The members are considering purchasing three possible stocks, with their cost per share (in dollars) and their projected growth per share (in dollars) summarized in the following table.

	Stocks		
	Computer (C)	Utility (U)	Retail (R)
Cost/share	30	44	26
Growth/share	6.00	6.00	2.40

   (a) If they have $392,000 to invest, how many shares of each stock should they buy to meet their goal?
   (b) If they buy 1000 shares of retail stock, how many shares of the other stocks do they buy? What if they buy 2000 shares of retail stock?

   (c) What is the minimum number of shares of computer stock they will buy, and what is the number of shares of the other stocks in this case?
   (d) What is the maximum number of shares of computer stock purchased, and what is the number of shares of the other stocks in this case?

66. *Investment* A trust account manager has $220,000 to be invested. The investment choices have current yields of 8%, 7%, and 10%. Suppose that the investment goal is to earn interest of $16,600, and risk factors make it prudent to invest some money in all three investments.
   (a) Find a general description for the amounts invested at the three rates.
   (b) If $10,000 is invested at 10%, how much will be invested at each of the other rates? What if $30,000 is invested at 10%?
   (c) What is the minimum amount that will be invested at 7%, and in this case how much will be invested at the other rates?
   (d) What is the maximum amount that will be invested at 7%, and in this case how much will be invested at the other rates?

67. *Investment* A brokerage house offers three stock portfolios. Portfolio I consists of 2 blocks of common stock and 1 municipal bond. Portfolio II consists of 4 blocks of common stock, 2 municipal bonds, and 3 blocks of preferred stock. Portfolio III consists of 2 blocks of common stock, 1 municipal bond, and 3 blocks of preferred stock. A customer wants 16 blocks of common stock, 8 municipal bonds, and 6 blocks of preferred stock. If the numbers of the three portfolios offered must be integers, find all possible offerings.

3.4

- To find the inverse of a square matrix
- To use inverse matrices to solve systems of linear equations
- To find determinants of certain matrices

Inverse of a Square Matrix; Matrix Equations

| APPLICATION PREVIEW |

Enigma Machine

During World War II, military commanders sent instructions that used simple substitution codes. These codes were easily broken, so they were further coded by using a coding matrix and matrix multiplication. The resulting coded messages, when received, could be unscrambled with a decoding matrix that was the inverse matrix of the coding matrix. In Section 3.2, "Multiplication of Matrices," we encoded messages by using the following code:

a	b	c	d	e	f	g	h	i	j	k	l
1	2	3	4	5	6	7	8	9	10	11	12

m	n	o	p	q	r	s	t	u	v	w	x
13	14	15	16	17	18	19	20	21	22	23	24

y	z	blank
25	26	27

and the encoding matrix

$$A = \begin{bmatrix} 3 & 5 \\ 4 & 6 \end{bmatrix}$$

which converts the numbers to the coded message (in pairs of numbers). To decode a message encoded by this matrix A, we find the inverse of matrix A, which is denoted A^{-1}, and multiply A^{-1} by the coded message. (See Example 4.) In this section, we will discuss how to find and apply the inverse of a given square matrix.

Inverse Matrices   If the product of A and B is the identity matrix, I, we say that B is the inverse of A (and A is the inverse of B). The matrix B is called the **inverse matrix** of A, denoted A^{-1}.

Inverse Matrices

> Two square matrices, A and B, are called **inverses** of each other if
> $$AB = I \quad \text{and} \quad BA = I$$
> In this case, $B = A^{-1}$ and $A = B^{-1}$.

EXAMPLE 1 Inverse Matrices

Is B the inverse of A if $A = \begin{bmatrix} 1 & 2 \\ 1 & 1 \end{bmatrix}$ and $B = \begin{bmatrix} -1 & 2 \\ 1 & -1 \end{bmatrix}$?

Solution

$$AB = \begin{bmatrix} 1 & 2 \\ 1 & 1 \end{bmatrix} \cdot \begin{bmatrix} -1 & 2 \\ 1 & -1 \end{bmatrix} = \begin{bmatrix} 1 & 0 \\ 0 & 1 \end{bmatrix} = I$$

$$BA = \begin{bmatrix} -1 & 2 \\ 1 & -1 \end{bmatrix} \cdot \begin{bmatrix} 1 & 2 \\ 1 & 1 \end{bmatrix} = \begin{bmatrix} 1 & 0 \\ 0 & 1 \end{bmatrix} = I$$

Thus B is the inverse of A, or $B = A^{-1}$. We also say A is the inverse of B, or $A = B^{-1}$. Thus $(A^{-1})^{-1} = A$. ∎

CHECKPOINT

1. Are the matrices A and B inverses if

$$A = \begin{bmatrix} 1 & 1 & -1 \\ 1 & -1 & 3 \\ 4 & 2 & 1 \end{bmatrix} \text{ and } B = \begin{bmatrix} 3.5 & 1.5 & -1 \\ -5.5 & -2.5 & 2 \\ -3 & -1 & 1 \end{bmatrix}?$$

We have seen how to use elementary row operations on augmented matrices to solve systems of linear equations. We can also find the inverse of a matrix by using elementary row operations.

If the inverse exists for a square matrix A, we find A^{-1} as follows.

Finding the Inverse of a Square Matrix

Procedure	Example
To find the inverse of the square matrix A:	Find the inverse of matrix $A = \begin{bmatrix} 1 & 2 \\ 1 & 1 \end{bmatrix}$.
1. Form the augmented matrix $[A \mid I]$, where A is the $n \times n$ matrix and I is the $n \times n$ identity matrix.	1. $\begin{bmatrix} 1 & 2 & \mid & 1 & 0 \\ 1 & 1 & \mid & 0 & 1 \end{bmatrix}$
2. Perform elementary row operations on $[A \mid I]$ until we have an augmented matrix of the form $[I \mid B]$—that is, until the matrix A on the left is transformed into the identity matrix. If A has no inverse, the reduction process on $[A \mid I]$ will yield a row of zeros in the left half of the augmented matrix.	2. $\begin{bmatrix} 1 & 2 & \mid & 1 & 0 \\ 1 & 1 & \mid & 0 & 1 \end{bmatrix}$ $\xrightarrow{-R_1 + R_2 \to R_2} \begin{bmatrix} 1 & 2 & \mid & 1 & 0 \\ 0 & -1 & \mid & -1 & 1 \end{bmatrix}$ $\begin{array}{c} 2R_2 + R_1 \to R_1 \\ \hline -R_2 \to R_2 \end{array} \begin{bmatrix} 1 & 0 & \mid & -1 & 2 \\ 0 & 1 & \mid & 1 & -1 \end{bmatrix}$
3. The matrix B (on the right) is the inverse of matrix A.	3. The inverse of A is $B = \begin{bmatrix} -1 & 2 \\ 1 & -1 \end{bmatrix}$. We verified this in Example 1.

EXAMPLE   2   Finding an Inverse Matrix

Find the inverse of matrix A.

$$A = \begin{bmatrix} 2 & 5 & 4 \\ 1 & 4 & 3 \\ 1 & -3 & -2 \end{bmatrix}$$

Solution

To find the inverse of matrix A, we reduce A in $[A \mid I]$ (the matrix A augmented with the identity matrix I). When the left side becomes an identity matrix, the inverse is in the augment.

$$\begin{bmatrix} 2 & 5 & 4 & | & 1 & 0 & 0 \\ 1 & 4 & 3 & | & 0 & 1 & 0 \\ 1 & -3 & -2 & | & 0 & 0 & 1 \end{bmatrix} \xrightarrow{\text{Switch } R_1 \text{ and } R_2} \begin{bmatrix} 1 & 4 & 3 & | & 0 & 1 & 0 \\ 2 & 5 & 4 & | & 1 & 0 & 0 \\ 1 & -3 & -2 & | & 0 & 0 & 1 \end{bmatrix}$$

$$\xrightarrow[{-R_1 + R_3 \to R_3}]{-2R_1 + R_2 \to R_2} \begin{bmatrix} 1 & 4 & 3 & | & 0 & 1 & 0 \\ 0 & -3 & -2 & | & 1 & -2 & 0 \\ 0 & -7 & -5 & | & 0 & -1 & 1 \end{bmatrix}$$

$$\xrightarrow{-\frac{1}{3}R_2 \to R_2} \begin{bmatrix} 1 & 4 & 3 & | & 0 & 1 & 0 \\ 0 & 1 & \frac{2}{3} & | & -\frac{1}{3} & \frac{2}{3} & 0 \\ 0 & -7 & -5 & | & 0 & -1 & 1 \end{bmatrix}$$

$$\xrightarrow[{7R_2 + R_3 \to R_3}]{-4R_2 + R_1 \to R_1} \begin{bmatrix} 1 & 0 & \frac{1}{3} & | & \frac{4}{3} & -\frac{5}{3} & 0 \\ 0 & 1 & \frac{2}{3} & | & -\frac{1}{3} & \frac{2}{3} & 0 \\ 0 & 0 & -\frac{1}{3} & | & -\frac{7}{3} & \frac{11}{3} & 1 \end{bmatrix}$$

$$\xrightarrow[{-3R_3 \to R_3}]{\substack{R_3 + R_1 \to R_1 \\ 2R_3 + R_2 \to R_2}} \begin{bmatrix} 1 & 0 & 0 & | & -1 & 2 & 1 \\ 0 & 1 & 0 & | & -5 & 8 & 2 \\ 0 & 0 & 1 & | & 7 & -11 & -3 \end{bmatrix}$$

The inverse we seek is

$$A^{-1} = \begin{bmatrix} -1 & 2 & 1 \\ -5 & 8 & 2 \\ 7 & -11 & -3 \end{bmatrix}$$

Calculator Note To see how a graphing calculator can be used to find the inverse of a matrix, see Appendix C, Section 3.4. For example, the inverse of the matrix

$$\begin{bmatrix} 1 & 2 & 4 \\ 3 & 1 & 3 \\ 5 & 2 & 4 \end{bmatrix}$$

is found by entering this matrix, using the inverse key or command, and converting the entries to fractions.

```
[A]⁻¹▸Frac
[[-1/4    0     1/4  ]
 [3/8    -2     9/8  ]
 [1/8     1    -5/8]]
■
```

so $A^{-1} = \begin{bmatrix} -\frac{1}{4} & 0 & \frac{1}{4} \\ \frac{3}{8} & -2 & \frac{9}{8} \\ \frac{1}{8} & 1 & -\frac{5}{8} \end{bmatrix}$

CHECKPOINT

2. Find the inverse of the matrix

$$A = \begin{bmatrix} 1 & 2 & 1 \\ 0 & 1 & 1 \\ 1 & 2 & 2 \end{bmatrix}$$

The technique of reducing $[A \mid I]$ can be used to find A^{-1} or to find that A^{-1} doesn't exist for any square matrix A. However, a special formula can be used to find the inverse of a 2×2 matrix, if the inverse exists.

Inverse of a 2 × 2 Matrix

If $A = \begin{bmatrix} a & b \\ c & d \end{bmatrix}$, then $A^{-1} = \dfrac{1}{ad - bc} \begin{bmatrix} d & -b \\ -c & a \end{bmatrix}$, provided $ad - bc \neq 0$.
If $ad - bc = 0$, then A^{-1} does not exist.

This result can be verified by direct calculation or by reducing $[A \mid I]$.

EXAMPLE 3 **Inverse of a 2 × 2 Matrix**

Find the inverse, if it exists, for each of the following.

(a) $A = \begin{bmatrix} 3 & 7 \\ 2 & 5 \end{bmatrix}$ (b) $B = \begin{bmatrix} 2 & -1 \\ -4 & 2 \end{bmatrix}$

Solution

(a) For A, $ad - bc = (3)(5) - (2)(7) = 1 \neq 0$, so A^{-1} exists.

$$A^{-1} = \frac{1}{1} \begin{bmatrix} 5 & -7 \\ -2 & 3 \end{bmatrix} = \begin{bmatrix} 5 & -7 \\ -2 & 3 \end{bmatrix}$$

(b) For B, $ad - bc = (2)(2) - (-4)(-1) = 4 - 4 = 0$, so B^{-1} does not exist.

EXAMPLE 4 **Decoding Messages** | **APPLICATION PREVIEW** |

In the Application Preview we recalled how to encode messages with

a	b	c	d	e	f	g	h	i	j	k	l
1	2	3	4	5	6	7	8	9	10	11	12

m	n	o	p	q	r	s	t	u	v	w	x
13	14	15	16	17	18	19	20	21	22	23	24

y	z	blank
25	26	27

and with the encoding matrix

$$A = \begin{bmatrix} 3 & 5 \\ 4 & 6 \end{bmatrix}$$

which converts the numbers to the coded message (in pairs of numbers).

To decode any message encoded by A, we must find the inverse of A and multiply A^{-1} by the coded message. Use the inverse of A to decode the coded message 96, 118, 65, 84, 131, 168, 55, 72.

Solution

We first find the inverse of matrix A.

$$A^{-1} = \frac{1}{18-20}\begin{bmatrix} 6 & -5 \\ -4 & 3 \end{bmatrix} = -\frac{1}{2}\begin{bmatrix} 6 & -5 \\ -4 & 3 \end{bmatrix} = \begin{bmatrix} -3 & 2.5 \\ 2 & -1.5 \end{bmatrix}$$

We can write the coded message numbers (in pairs) as columns of a matrix B and then find the product $A^{-1}B$.

$$A^{-1}B = \begin{bmatrix} -3 & 2.5 \\ 2 & -1.5 \end{bmatrix}\begin{bmatrix} 96 & 65 & 131 & 55 \\ 118 & 84 & 168 & 72 \end{bmatrix} = \begin{bmatrix} 7 & 15 & 27 & 15 \\ 15 & 4 & 10 & 2 \end{bmatrix}$$

Reading the numbers (down the respective columns) gives the result 7, 15, 15, 4, 27, 10, 15, 2, which is the message "good job."

Spreadsheet Note We can also find the inverse of a square matrix with Excel, if the inverse exists (See Appendix D, Section 3.4 and the Online Excel Guide). The following spreadsheet shows a matrix A and its inverse, A^{-1}.

=minverse(B1:D3)			
	A	**B**	**C**	**D**
1	Matrix A	−1	0	1
2		1	4	−3
3		1	−2	1
4				
5	Inverse A	0.5	0.5	1
6		1	0.5	0.5
7		1.5	0.5	1

Warning: Roundoff error can occur when technology is used to find the inverse of a matrix.

Matrix Equations   The system $\begin{cases} 2x + 5y + 4z = 4 \\ x + 4y + 3z = 1 \\ x - 3y - 2z = 5 \end{cases}$ can be written as either of the following matrix equations.

$$\begin{bmatrix} 2x + 5y + 4z \\ x + 4y + 3z \\ x - 3y - 2z \end{bmatrix} = \begin{bmatrix} 4 \\ 1 \\ 5 \end{bmatrix} \quad \text{or} \quad \begin{bmatrix} 2 & 5 & 4 \\ 1 & 4 & 3 \\ 1 & -3 & -2 \end{bmatrix}\begin{bmatrix} x \\ y \\ z \end{bmatrix} = \begin{bmatrix} 4 \\ 1 \\ 5 \end{bmatrix}$$

We can see that this second form of a matrix equation is equivalent to the first if we carry out the multiplication. With the system written in this second form, we could also solve the system by multiplying both sides of the equation by the inverse of the coefficient matrix.

EXAMPLE 5   **Solution with Inverse Matrices**

Use an inverse matrix to solve the system:

$$\begin{cases} 2x + 5y + 4z = 4 \\ x + 4y + 3z = 1 \\ x - 3y - 2z = 5 \end{cases}$$

Solution

To solve the system, we multiply both sides of the associated matrix equation, written above, by the inverse of the coefficient matrix, which we found in Example 2.

$$\begin{bmatrix} -1 & 2 & 1 \\ -5 & 8 & 2 \\ 7 & -11 & -3 \end{bmatrix}\begin{bmatrix} 2 & 5 & 4 \\ 1 & 4 & 3 \\ 1 & -3 & -2 \end{bmatrix}\begin{bmatrix} x \\ y \\ z \end{bmatrix} = \begin{bmatrix} -1 & 2 & 1 \\ -5 & 8 & 2 \\ 7 & -11 & -3 \end{bmatrix}\begin{bmatrix} 4 \\ 1 \\ 5 \end{bmatrix}$$

Note that we must be careful to multiply both sides *from the left* because matrix multiplication is not commutative. If we carry out the multiplications, we obtain

$$\begin{bmatrix} 1 & 0 & 0 \\ 0 & 1 & 0 \\ 0 & 0 & 1 \end{bmatrix}\begin{bmatrix} x \\ y \\ z \end{bmatrix} = \begin{bmatrix} 3 \\ -2 \\ 2 \end{bmatrix}, \quad \text{or} \quad \begin{bmatrix} x \\ y \\ z \end{bmatrix} = \begin{bmatrix} 3 \\ -2 \\ 2 \end{bmatrix}$$

which yields $x = 3, y = -2, z = 2$, the same solution as that found in the previous section.

Just as we wrote the system of three equations as a matrix equation of the form $AX = B$, this can be done in general. If A is an $n \times n$ matrix and if B and X are $n \times 1$ matrices, then

$$AX = B$$

is a **matrix equation.**

If the inverse of a matrix A exists, then we can use that inverse to solve the matrix equation for the matrix X. The general solution method follows.

$$AX = B$$

Multiplying both sides of the equation (from the left) by A^{-1} gives

$$A^{-1}(AX) = A^{-1}B$$
$$(A^{-1}A)X = A^{-1}B$$
$$IX = A^{-1}B$$
$$X = A^{-1}B$$

Thus inverse matrices can be used to solve systems of equations. Unfortunately, this method will work only if the solution to the system is unique. In fact, a system $AX = B$ has a unique solution if and only if A^{-1} exists. If the inverse of the coefficient matrix exists, the solution method above can be used to solve the system.

CHECKPOINT

3. Use inverse matrices to solve the system.

$$\begin{cases} 7x - 5y = 12 \\ 2x - 3y = \ \ 6 \end{cases}$$

Calculator Note   Because we often can easily find the inverse of a matrix with a graphing calculator, it is easy to use a graphing calculator to solve a system of linear equations by using the inverse of the coefficient matrix.

EXAMPLE 6   **Freight Logistics with Technology**

On-Time Freight carries three classes of cargo, I, II, and III, and sets their delivery rates according to the class. The following table gives the details of each class and On-Time's capacity limits.

	Class I	Class II	Class III	Limits
Volume (cubic feet)	25	20	50	15,000
Weight (pounds)	25	50	100	27,500
Insured value (dollars)	250	50	500	92,250

(a) Create a system of linear equations that could be used to find the number of units of each cargo class that should be hauled. Then use the inverse of the coefficient matrix to solve the system.

(b) Use the inverse from part (a) to find how to change the hauling decision if an additional 300 cubic feet of volume becomes available.

(c) What is the connection between column 1 of the inverse matrix used in parts (a) and (b) and the answer found in part (b)?

Solution

(a) Let x = the number of units of class I cargo

y = the number of units of class II cargo

z = the number of units of class III cargo

Then we can formulate the following system of equations:

$$\begin{aligned} 25x + 20y + 50z &= 15{,}000 \\ 25x + 50y + 100z &= 27{,}500 \\ 250x + 50y + 500z &= 92{,}250 \end{aligned}$$

The matrix equation for this system is $AX = B$, as follows:

$$AX = \begin{bmatrix} 25 & 20 & 50 \\ 25 & 50 & 100 \\ 250 & 50 & 500 \end{bmatrix} \begin{bmatrix} x \\ y \\ z \end{bmatrix} = \begin{bmatrix} 15{,}000 \\ 27{,}500 \\ 92{,}250 \end{bmatrix} = B$$

We use technology to find the inverse of the coefficient matrix, A. If we multiply both sides (from the left) by A^{-1}, we get $X = A^{-1}B$. (See Figure 3.9.)

```
[A]
  [[25  20  50 ]
   [25  50  100]
   [250 50  500]]
```

```
[B]
          [[15000]
           [27500]
           [92250]]
```

```
[A]⁻¹[B]
          [[254]
           [385]
           [19 ]]
```

Figure 3.9

Thus the solution is $x = 254$ units of class I cargo, $y = 385$ units of class II cargo, and $z = 19$ units of class III cargo.

(b) If an additional 300 cubic feet of cargo space becomes available, this changes only the first entry of B. The new B and the new solution, $A^{-1}B$, are as follows, along with $300\,A^{-1}$. (See Figure 3.10.)

```
[B]
          [[15300]
           [27500]
           [92250]]
```

```
[A]⁻¹[B]
          [[286]
           [405]
           [1  ]]
```

```
300*[A]⁻¹
          [[32   -12   -.8]
           [20    0    -2 ]
           [-18   6    1.2]]
```

Figure 3.10

(c) This new solution is the original $X = A^{-1}B$ plus 300 times column 1 of A^{-1}.

$$[\text{original } X] + 300\,[\text{column 1 of } A^{-1}] = \begin{bmatrix} 254 \\ 385 \\ 19 \end{bmatrix} + \begin{bmatrix} 32 \\ 20 \\ -18 \end{bmatrix} = \begin{bmatrix} 286 \\ 405 \\ 1 \end{bmatrix}$$

The effects of similar changes in weight or insured value also could be found by using the appropriate column of A^{-1}. Thus we see that the inverse is useful not only in solving the original problem, but also in adjusting that solution to changes in resource amounts. ∎

Spreadsheet Note   We can also use Excel to solve a system of linear equations, if a unique solution exists. We can solve such a system by finding the inverse of the coefficient matrix and multiplying this inverse times the matrix containing the constants. The spreadsheet that follows shows the solution of Example 5 found with Excel. See also Appendix D, Section 3.4 and the Online Excel Guide.

	A	B	C	D
1	Matrix A	2	5	4
2		1	4	3
3		1	−3	−2
4				
5	Inverse A	−1	2	1
6		−5	8	2
7		7	−11	−3
8				
9	Matrix B	4		
10		1		
11		5		
12				
13	Solution X	3		
14		−2		
15		2		

EXAMPLE 7 Venture Capital

Suppose a bank draws its venture capital funds from three main sources of income—business loans, auto loans, and home mortgages. The income from these sources for each of 3 years is given in Table 3.8, and the venture capital for these years is given in Table 3.9. If the bank uses a fixed percent of its income from each of the business loans (x), auto loans (y), and home mortgages (z) to get its venture capital funds, find the percent of income used for each of these sources of income.

| TABLE 3.8 |

INCOME FROM LOANS

	Business	Auto	Home
2010	68,210	23,324	57,234
2011	43,455	19,335	66,345
2012	58,672	15,654	69,334

| TABLE 3.9 |

	Venture Capital
2010	53,448.74
2011	43,447.50
2012	50,582.88

Solution

The matrix equation describing this problem is $AX = V$, or

$$\begin{bmatrix} 68,210 & 23,324 & 57,234 \\ 43,455 & 19,335 & 66,345 \\ 58,672 & 15,654 & 69,334 \end{bmatrix} \begin{bmatrix} x \\ y \\ z \end{bmatrix} = \begin{bmatrix} 53,448.74 \\ 43,447.50 \\ 50,582.88 \end{bmatrix}$$

Finding the inverse of matrix A and multiplying both sides of the matrix equation (from the left) by A^{-1} give the solution $X = A^{-1}V$:

$$\begin{bmatrix} x \\ y \\ z \end{bmatrix} = \begin{bmatrix} 0.47 \\ 0.23 \\ 0.28 \end{bmatrix}$$

Thus 47%, 23%, and 28% come from business, auto, and home loans, respectively. ■

Determinants Recall that the inverse of $A = \begin{bmatrix} a & b \\ c & d \end{bmatrix}$ can be found with the formula

$$A^{-1} = \frac{1}{ad - bc} \begin{bmatrix} d & -b \\ -c & a \end{bmatrix}$$

if $ad - bc \neq 0$.

The value $ad - bc$ used in finding the inverse of this 2×2 matrix is used so frequently that it is given a special name, the **determinant** of A (denoted *det A* or $|A|$).

Determinant of a 2 × 2 Matrix

$$\det \begin{bmatrix} a & b \\ c & d \end{bmatrix} = \begin{vmatrix} a & b \\ c & d \end{vmatrix} = ad - bc$$

EXAMPLE 8 Determinant of a 2 × 2 Matrix

Find det A if $A = \begin{bmatrix} 2 & 4 \\ 3 & -4 \end{bmatrix}$.

Solution

$$\det A = (2)(-4) - (3)(4) = -8 - 12 = -20$$
■

Calculator Note There are formulas for finding the determinants of square matrices of orders larger than 2×2, but for the matrices used in this text, graphing calculators make it easy to find determinants. (See Appendix C, Section 3.4.) ■

We have already seen that the inverse of a 2×2 matrix A does not exist if and only if det $A = 0$. In general, the inverse of an $n \times n$ matrix B does not exist if det $B = 0$. This also means that if the coefficient matrix of a system of linear equations has a determinant equal to 0, the system does not have a unique solution.

EXAMPLE 9 Solution with Technology

Consider the following matrix equation $AX = B$.

$$\begin{bmatrix} 2 & 3 & 0 & 1 & 3 \\ 1 & 0 & 2 & 3 & 1 \\ 0 & 1 & 0 & 2 & 3 \\ 1 & 0 & 2 & 2 & 1 \\ 1 & 0 & 0 & 0 & 3 \end{bmatrix} \begin{bmatrix} x_1 \\ x_2 \\ x_3 \\ x_4 \\ x_5 \end{bmatrix} = \begin{bmatrix} 16 \\ 2 \\ 9 \\ 3 \\ 10 \end{bmatrix}$$

(a) Use a calculator to find the determinant of A.

(b) Use the result from part (a) to determine whether $AX = B$ has a unique solution.

Solution

(a) Entering matrix A and using the determinant command gives det $A = 24$.

(b) Because A is the coefficient matrix for the system and det $A = 24$, the system has a unique solution. Using the inverse matrix gives the solution $x_1 = 1$, $x_2 = 2$, $x_3 = 0.5$, $x_4 = -1$, $x_5 = 3$. ∎

CHECKPOINT SOLUTIONS

1. Yes, because both AB and BA give the 3×3 identity matrix.

2. $$\left[\begin{array}{ccc|ccc} 1 & 2 & 1 & 1 & 0 & 0 \\ 0 & 1 & 1 & 0 & 1 & 0 \\ 1 & 2 & 2 & 0 & 0 & 1 \end{array}\right] \xrightarrow{-R_1 + R_3 \longrightarrow R_3} \left[\begin{array}{ccc|ccc} 1 & 2 & 1 & 1 & 0 & 0 \\ 0 & 1 & 1 & 0 & 1 & 0 \\ 0 & 0 & 1 & -1 & 0 & 1 \end{array}\right]$$

$$\xrightarrow{-2R_2 + R_1 \longrightarrow R_1} \left[\begin{array}{ccc|ccc} 1 & 0 & -1 & 1 & -2 & 0 \\ 0 & 1 & 1 & 0 & 1 & 0 \\ 0 & 0 & 1 & -1 & 0 & 1 \end{array}\right]$$

$$\begin{array}{c} R_3 + R_1 \rightarrow R_1 \\ \overline{-R_3 + R_2 \rightarrow R_2} \end{array} \left[\begin{array}{ccc|ccc} 1 & 0 & 0 & 0 & -2 & 1 \\ 0 & 1 & 0 & 1 & 1 & -1 \\ 0 & 0 & 1 & -1 & 0 & 1 \end{array}\right]$$

The inverse is $A^{-1} = \begin{bmatrix} 0 & -2 & 1 \\ 1 & 1 & -1 \\ -1 & 0 & 1 \end{bmatrix}$.

3. This system can be written

$$\begin{bmatrix} 7 & -5 \\ 2 & -3 \end{bmatrix} \begin{bmatrix} x \\ y \end{bmatrix} = \begin{bmatrix} 12 \\ 6 \end{bmatrix}$$

and for the coefficient matrix A, $ad - bc = -21 - (-10) = -11$. Thus A^{-1} exists,

$$A^{-1} = -\frac{1}{11} \begin{bmatrix} -3 & 5 \\ -2 & 7 \end{bmatrix} = \begin{bmatrix} \frac{3}{11} & -\frac{5}{11} \\ \frac{2}{11} & -\frac{7}{11} \end{bmatrix}$$

so multiplying by A^{-1} *from the left* gives the solution.

$$\begin{bmatrix} \frac{3}{11} & -\frac{5}{11} \\ \frac{2}{11} & -\frac{7}{11} \end{bmatrix} \begin{bmatrix} 7 & -5 \\ 2 & -3 \end{bmatrix} \begin{bmatrix} x \\ y \end{bmatrix} = \begin{bmatrix} \frac{3}{11} & -\frac{5}{11} \\ \frac{2}{11} & -\frac{7}{11} \end{bmatrix} \begin{bmatrix} 12 \\ 6 \end{bmatrix}$$

$$\begin{bmatrix} 1 & 0 \\ 0 & 1 \end{bmatrix} \begin{bmatrix} x \\ y \end{bmatrix} = \begin{bmatrix} \frac{6}{11} \\ -\frac{18}{11} \end{bmatrix}$$

Thus the solution is $x = \frac{6}{11}$, $y = -\frac{18}{11}$.

| EXERCISES | 3.4

1. If A is a 3×3 matrix and B is its inverse, what does the product AB equal?

2. If $C = \begin{bmatrix} 2 & -4 & 12 \\ 0 & 6 & -12 \\ 1 & -2 & 3 \end{bmatrix}$ and

   $D = \dfrac{1}{6}\begin{bmatrix} 1 & 2 & 4 \\ 2 & 1 & -4 \\ 1 & 0 & -2 \end{bmatrix}$, are C and D inverse matrices?

3. If $A = \begin{bmatrix} 1 & 2 & 1 \\ 0 & 0 & 3 \\ 1 & 0 & 1 \end{bmatrix}$ and $B = \begin{bmatrix} 0 & -\frac{1}{3} & 1 \\ \frac{1}{2} & 0 & -\frac{1}{2} \\ 0 & \frac{1}{3} & 0 \end{bmatrix}$,

   does $B = A^{-1}$?

4. If $D = \begin{bmatrix} 0 & 2 & -6 \\ -3 & 0 & 3 \\ 0 & -2 & 0 \end{bmatrix}$ and

   $C = -\dfrac{1}{3}\begin{bmatrix} 2 & 4 & 2 \\ 0 & 0 & 6 \\ 2 & 0 & 2 \end{bmatrix}$, does $C = D^{-1}$?

In Problems 5–10, find the inverse matrix for each matrix that has an inverse.

5. $\begin{bmatrix} 4 & 7 \\ 1 & 2 \end{bmatrix}$ 6. $\begin{bmatrix} 4 & 5 \\ 7 & 9 \end{bmatrix}$ 7. $\begin{bmatrix} 2 & -1 \\ -4 & 2 \end{bmatrix}$

8. $\begin{bmatrix} 3 & 12 \\ 1 & 4 \end{bmatrix}$ 9. $\begin{bmatrix} 4 & 7 \\ 2 & 1 \end{bmatrix}$ 10. $\begin{bmatrix} 6 & -4 \\ -1 & 1 \end{bmatrix}$

In Problems 11–14, find the inverse of matrix A and check it by calculating AA^{-1}.

11. $A = \begin{bmatrix} 3 & 0 & 0 \\ 0 & 3 & 0 \\ 0 & 0 & 3 \end{bmatrix}$ 12. $A = \begin{bmatrix} 4 & 0 & 0 \\ 0 & 3 & 0 \\ 0 & 0 & 3 \end{bmatrix}$

13. $A = \begin{bmatrix} 0 & 1 & 0 \\ 1 & 1 & 0 \\ 0 & 1 & 1 \end{bmatrix}$ 14. $A = \begin{bmatrix} 0 & 2 & 1 \\ 3 & 0 & 1 \\ 1 & 1 & 1 \end{bmatrix}$

In Problems 15–20, find the inverse matrix for each matrix that has an inverse.

15. $\begin{bmatrix} 3 & 1 & 2 \\ 1 & 2 & 3 \\ 1 & 1 & 1 \end{bmatrix}$ 16. $\begin{bmatrix} 1 & 2 & 3 \\ -1 & 5 & 6 \\ -1 & 3 & 3 \end{bmatrix}$

17. $\begin{bmatrix} 1 & 3 & 5 \\ -1 & -1 & 2 \\ 1 & 5 & 12 \end{bmatrix}$ 18. $\begin{bmatrix} 1 & -1 & 4 \\ -1 & 0 & -2 \\ -1 & -3 & 4 \end{bmatrix}$

19. $\begin{bmatrix} 1 & 2 & 4 \\ 1 & -1 & -3 \\ 2 & 1 & 1 \end{bmatrix}$ 20. $\begin{bmatrix} 3 & 4 & -1 \\ 4 & 2 & 2 \\ 2 & 6 & -4 \end{bmatrix}$

21. Find the inverse of

   $C = \begin{bmatrix} 0 & -1 & 0 & 1 & 0 \\ 1 & 1.5 & -1 & -1.5 & -0.5 \\ 0.5 & 1.75 & -1 & -1.25 & -0.25 \\ -0.5 & -1 & 1 & 1 & 0 \\ 0 & 0.5 & 0 & -0.5 & 0.5 \end{bmatrix}$

22. Find the inverse of $B = \begin{bmatrix} 2 & 3 & 0 & 1 & 3 \\ 1 & 0 & 2 & 3 & 1 \\ 0 & 1 & 0 & 2 & 3 \\ 1 & 0 & 2 & 2 & 1 \\ 1 & 0 & 0 & 0 & 3 \end{bmatrix}$.

In each of Problems 23–26, the inverse of matrix A is given. Use the inverse to solve for X.

23. $A^{-1} = \begin{bmatrix} 3 & 2 \\ 1 & 1 \end{bmatrix}$ Solve $AX = \begin{bmatrix} 3 \\ 2 \end{bmatrix}$.

24. $A^{-1} = \begin{bmatrix} 1 & -2 \\ 1 & 3 \end{bmatrix}$ Solve $AX = \begin{bmatrix} 5 \\ -1 \end{bmatrix}$.

25. $A^{-1} = \begin{bmatrix} 3 & 2 & 1 \\ 1 & 1 & 2 \\ 1 & 2 & 1 \end{bmatrix}$ Solve $AX = \begin{bmatrix} 3 \\ -1 \\ 2 \end{bmatrix}$.

26. $A^{-1} = \begin{bmatrix} 3 & 0 & -3 \\ 1 & 1 & 2 \\ 1 & 2 & 1 \end{bmatrix}$ Solve $AX = \begin{bmatrix} -1 \\ 2 \\ 3 \end{bmatrix}$.

27. Use the inverse found in Problem 13 to solve

   $\begin{bmatrix} 0 & 1 & 0 \\ 1 & 1 & 0 \\ 0 & 1 & 1 \end{bmatrix}\begin{bmatrix} x \\ y \\ z \end{bmatrix} = \begin{bmatrix} 1 \\ 2 \\ 3 \end{bmatrix}$

28. Use the inverse found in Problem 14 to solve

   $\begin{bmatrix} 0 & 2 & 1 \\ 3 & 0 & 1 \\ 1 & 1 & 1 \end{bmatrix}\begin{bmatrix} x \\ y \\ z \end{bmatrix} = \begin{bmatrix} 1 \\ 0 \\ 4 \end{bmatrix}$

In Problems 29–32, use inverse matrices to solve each system of linear equations.

29. $\begin{cases} x + 2y = 4 \\ 3x + 4y = 10 \end{cases}$ 30. $\begin{cases} 3x - 4y = 11 \\ 2x + 3y = -4 \end{cases}$

31. $\begin{cases} 2x + y = 4 \\ 3x + y = 5 \end{cases}$ 32. $\begin{cases} 5x - 2y = 6 \\ 3x + 3y = 12 \end{cases}$

In Problems 33–38, use inverse matrices to find the solution of the systems of equations.

33. $\begin{cases} x + y + z = 3 \\ 2x + y + z = 4 \\ 2x + 2y + z = 5 \end{cases}$

34. $\begin{cases} 2x - y - 2z = 2 \\ 3x - y + z = -3 \\ x + y - z = 7 \end{cases}$

35. $\begin{cases} x + y + 2z = 8 \\ 2x + y + z = 7 \\ 2x + 2y + z = 10 \end{cases}$

36. $\begin{cases} x - 2y + z = 0 \\ 2x + y - 2z = 2 \\ 3x + 2y - 3z = 2 \end{cases}$

37. $\begin{cases} -x_2 + x_4 = 0.7 \\ x + x_2 - x_3 - 1.5x_4 - 0.5x_5 = -1.6 \\ 0.5x_1 + 1.75x_2 - x_3 - 1.25x_4 - 0.25x_5 = 1.275 \\ -0.5x_1 - x_2 + x_3 + x_4 = 1.15 \\ 0.5x_2 - 0.5x_4 + 0.5x_5 = -0.15 \end{cases}$

38. $\begin{cases} 2x_1 + 3x_2 + x_4 + 3x_5 = 0 \\ x_1 + 2x_3 + 3x_4 + x_5 = 27 \\ x_2 + 2x_4 + 3x_5 = -15 \\ x_1 + 2x_3 + 2x_4 + x_5 = 24 \\ x_2 + 3x_5 = -24 \end{cases}$

In Problems 39–46, (a) evaluate each determinant, and (b) use the determinant to decide whether each matrix has an inverse. Use technology in Problems 43–46.

39. $\begin{vmatrix} 1 & 2 \\ 3 & 4 \end{vmatrix}$

40. $\begin{vmatrix} 4 & 5 \\ -1 & -2 \end{vmatrix}$

41. $\begin{vmatrix} 3 & -1 \\ 12 & -4 \end{vmatrix}$

42. $\begin{vmatrix} -1 & 2 \\ 4 & -8 \end{vmatrix}$

43. $\begin{vmatrix} 3 & 2 & 1 \\ -1 & 0 & 2 \\ 0 & 1 & 1 \end{vmatrix}$

44. $\begin{vmatrix} 1 & 2 & 2 \\ 3 & 0 & 1 \\ -1 & 0 & -2 \end{vmatrix}$

45. $\begin{vmatrix} 0 & 1 & 2 \\ 3 & 1 & 1 \\ 4 & -1 & 3 \end{vmatrix}$

46. $\begin{vmatrix} 3 & 1 & 4 & 2 \\ -1 & 2 & 0 & 5 \\ 4 & 3 & 0 & -1 \\ 0 & 4 & 2 & 1 \end{vmatrix}$

APPLICATIONS

Decoding **In Problems 47–50, use the code from the Application Preview and the given encoding matrix A to decode the given message.**

47. If the code matrix is

$$A = \begin{bmatrix} 5 & 9 \\ 6 & 11 \end{bmatrix}$$

decode the message

49, 59, 133, 161, 270, 327, 313, 381

48. If the code matrix is

$$A = \begin{bmatrix} 3 & 5 \\ 1 & 2 \end{bmatrix}$$

decode the message

157, 59, 73, 29, 147, 58, 63, 24, 119, 44

49. If the code matrix is

$$A = \begin{bmatrix} 0 & 2 & 1 \\ 3 & 0 & 1 \\ 1 & 1 & 1 \end{bmatrix}$$

decode the message

47, 22, 34, 28, 87, 46, 63, 66, 55, 56, 44, 43, 17, 14, 15

(Because A and A^{-1} are 3×3 matrices, use triples of numbers.)

50. If the code matrix is

$$A = \begin{bmatrix} 1 & 2 & 1 \\ 5 & 8 & 2 \\ 7 & 11 & 3 \end{bmatrix}$$

decode the message

49, 165, 231, 49, 154, 220, 39, 162, 226

51. *Competition* A product is made by only two competing companies. Suppose Company X retains two-thirds of its customers and loses one-third to Company Y each year, and Company Y retains three-quarters of its customers and loses one-quarter to Company X each year. We can represent the number of customers each company had last year by

$$\begin{bmatrix} x_0 \\ y_0 \end{bmatrix}$$

where x_0 is the number Company X had and y_0 is the number Company Y had. Then the number that each will have this year can be represented by

$$\begin{bmatrix} x \\ y \end{bmatrix} = \begin{bmatrix} \frac{2}{3} & \frac{1}{4} \\ \frac{1}{3} & \frac{3}{4} \end{bmatrix} \begin{bmatrix} x_0 \\ y_0 \end{bmatrix}$$

If Company X has 1900 customers and Company Y has 1700 customers this year, how many customers did each have last year?

52. *Demographics* Suppose that a government study showed that 90% of urban families remained in an urban area in the next generation (and 10% moved to a rural area), whereas 70% of rural families remained in a rural area in the next generation (and 30% moved to an urban area). This means that if $\begin{bmatrix} u_0 \\ r_0 \end{bmatrix}$ represents the

current percents of urban families, u_0, and of rural families, r_0, then

$$\begin{bmatrix} u \\ r \end{bmatrix} = \begin{bmatrix} 0.90 & 0.30 \\ 0.10 & 0.70 \end{bmatrix} \begin{bmatrix} u_0 \\ r_0 \end{bmatrix}$$

represents the percents of urban families, u, and rural families, r, one generation from now. Currently the population is 60% urban and 40% rural. Find the percents in each group one generation before this one.

In Problems 53–63, set up each system of equations and then solve it by using inverse matrices.

53. *Medication* Medication A is given every 4 hours and medication B is given twice per day, and the ratio of the dosage of A to the dosage of B is always 5 to 8.
   (a) For patient I, the total intake of the two medications is 50.6 mg per day. Find the dosage of each administration of each medication for patient I.
   (b) For patient II, the total intake of the two medications is 92 mg per day. Find the dosage of each administration of each medication for patient II.

54. *Transportation* The Ace Freight Company has an order for two products to be delivered to two stores of a company. The table gives information regarding the two products.

	Product I	Product II
Unit volume (cu ft)	20	30
Unit weight (lb)	100	400

   (a) If truck A can carry 2350 cu ft and 23,000 lb, how many of each product can it carry?
   (b) If truck B can carry 2500 cu ft and 24,500 lb, how many of each product can it carry?

55. *Investment* One safe investment pays 10% per year, and a more risky investment pays 18% per year. A woman has $145,600 to invest and would like to have an income of $20,000 per year from her investments. How much should she invest at each rate?

56. *Nutrition* A biologist has a 40% solution and a 10% solution of the same plant nutrient. How many cubic centimeters of each solution should be mixed to obtain 25 cc of a 28% solution?

57. *Manufacturing* A manufacturer of table saws has three models, Deluxe, Premium, and Ultimate, which must be painted, assembled, and packaged for shipping. The table gives the number of hours required for each of these operations for each type of table saw.
   (a) If the manufacturer has 96 hours available per day for painting, 156 hours for assembly, and 37 hours for packaging, how many of each type of saw can be produced each day?
   (b) If 8 more hours of painting time become available, find the new production strategy, and tell how it is related to the inverse matrix used in part (a).

	Deluxe	Premium	Ultimate
Painting	1.6	2	2.4
Assembly	2	3	4
Packaging	0.5	0.5	1

58. *Transportation* Ace Trucking Company has an order for three products, A, B, and C, for delivery. The table gives the volume in cubic feet, the weight in pounds, and the value for insurance in dollars for a unit of each of the products.
   (a) If the carrier can carry 8000 cu ft and 12,400 lb and is insured for $52,600, how many units of each product can be carried?
   (b) If the insured value increases by $6400, find the new delivery scheme and tell how it is related to the inverse matrix used in (a).

	Product A	Product B	Product C
Unit volume (cu ft)	24	20	40
Weight (lb)	40	30	60
Value ($)	150	180	200

59. *Investment* A trust account manager has $1,000,000 to be invested in three different accounts. The accounts pay 6%, 8%, and 10%, and the goal is to earn $86,000 with the amount invested at 10% equal to the sum of the other two investments. To accomplish this, assume that x dollars are invested at 8%, y dollars at 10%, and z dollars at 6%. Find how much should be invested in each account to satisfy the conditions.

60. *Investment* A company offers three mutual fund plans for its employees. Plan I consists of 4 blocks of common stock and 2 municipal bonds. Plan II consists of 8 blocks of common stock, 4 municipal bonds, and 6 blocks of preferred stock. Plan III consists of 14 blocks of common stock, 6 municipal bonds, and 6 blocks of preferred stock. An employee wants to combine these plans so that she has 84 blocks of common stock, 40 municipal bonds, and 36 blocks of preferred stock. How many units of each plan does she need?

61. *Attendance* Suppose that during the first 2 weeks of a controversial art exhibit, the daily number of visitors to the gallery turns out to be the sum of the numbers of visitors on the previous 3 days. We represent the numbers of visitors on 3 successive days by

$$N = \begin{bmatrix} n_t \\ n_{t+1} \\ n_{t+2} \end{bmatrix}$$

   (a) Find the matrix M such that

$$MN = \begin{bmatrix} n_{t+1} \\ n_{t+2} \\ n_t + n_{t+1} + n_{t+2} \end{bmatrix}$$

(b) If the numbers of visitors on 3 successive days are given by

$$\begin{bmatrix} 191 \\ 346 \\ 645 \end{bmatrix}$$

use M^{-1} to find the number of visitors 1 day earlier (before the 191-visitor day).

62. **Bee ancestry** Because a female bee comes from a fertilized egg and a male bee comes from an unfertilized egg, the number (n_{t+2}) of ancestors of a male bee $t + 2$ generations before the present generation is the sum of the number of ancestors t and $t + 1$ generations $(n_t$ and $n_{t+1})$ before the present. If the numbers of ancestors of a male bee in a given generation t and in the previous generation are given by

$$N = \begin{bmatrix} n_t \\ n_{t+1} \end{bmatrix}$$

then there is a matrix M such that the numbers of ancestors in the two generations preceding generation t are given by

$$MN = \begin{bmatrix} 0 & 1 \\ 1 & 1 \end{bmatrix} \begin{bmatrix} n_t \\ n_{t+1} \end{bmatrix} = \begin{bmatrix} n_{t+1} \\ n_t + n_{t+1} \end{bmatrix}$$

For a given male bee, the numbers of ancestors 5 and 6 generations back are given by

$$\begin{bmatrix} 8 \\ 13 \end{bmatrix}.$$

Find the numbers of ancestors 4 and 5 generations back by multiplying both sides of

$$MN = \begin{bmatrix} 8 \\ 13 \end{bmatrix}$$

by the inverse of M.

63. **Bacteria growth** The population of a colony of bacteria grows in such a way that the population size at any hour t is the sum of the populations of the 3 previous hours. Suppose that the matrix

$$N = \begin{bmatrix} n_t \\ n_{t+1} \\ n_{t+2} \end{bmatrix}$$

describes the population sizes for 3 successive hours.

(a) Write matrix M so that MN gives the population sizes for 3 successive hours beginning 1 hour later—that is, such that

$$MN = \begin{bmatrix} n_{t+1} \\ n_{t+2} \\ n_t + n_{t+1} + n_{t+2} \end{bmatrix}$$

(b) If the populations at the ends of 3 successive 1-hour periods were 200 at the end of the first hour, 370 at the end of the second hour, and 600 at the end of the third hour, what was the population 1 hour before it was 200? Use M^{-1}.

OBJECTIVES

- To interpret Leontief technology matrices
- To use Leontief models to solve input-output problems

3.5

Applications of Matrices: Leontief Input-Output Models

■ | APPLICATION PREVIEW |■

Suppose we consider a simple economy as being based on three commodities: agricultural products, manufactured goods, and fuels. Suppose further that production of 10 units of agricultural products requires 5 units of agricultural products, 2 units of manufactured goods, and 1 unit of fuels; that production of 10 units of manufactured goods requires 1 unit of agricultural products, 5 units of manufactured products, and 3 units of fuels; and that production of 10 units of fuels requires 1 unit of agricultural products, 3 units of manufactured goods, and 4 units of fuels.

Table 3.10 summarizes this information in terms of production of 1 unit. The first column represents the units of agricultural products, manufactured goods, and fuels, respectively, that are needed to produce 1 unit of agricultural products. Column 2 represents the units required to produce 1 unit of manufactured goods, and column 3 represents the units required to produce 1 unit of fuels.

■ | TABLE 3.10 |

	Outputs		
Inputs	Agricultural Products	Manufactured Goods	Fuels
Agricultural products	0.5	0.1	0.1
Manufactured goods	0.2	0.5	0.3
Fuels	0.1	0.3	0.4

From Table 3.10 we can form matrix A, which is called a technology matrix or a Leontief matrix.

$$A = \begin{bmatrix} 0.5 & 0.1 & 0.1 \\ 0.2 & 0.5 & 0.3 \\ 0.1 & 0.3 & 0.4 \end{bmatrix}$$

The Leontief input-output model is named for Wassily Leontief. The model Leontief developed was useful in predicting the effects on the economy of price changes or shifts in government spending.*

Leontief's work divided the economy into 500 sectors, which, in a subsequent article in *Scientific American* (October 1951), were reduced to a more manageable 42 departments of production. We can examine the workings of input-output analysis with a very simplified view of the economy. (We will do this in Example 2 with the economy described above.)

In this section, we will interpret Leontief technology matrices for simple economies and will solve input-output problems for these economies by using Leontief models.

In Table 3.10, we note that the sum of the units of agricultural products, manufactured goods, and fuels required to produce 1 unit of fuels (column 3) does not add up to 1 unit. This is because not all commodities or industries are represented in the model. In particular, it is customary to omit labor from models of this type.

EXAMPLE 1   Leontief Model

Use Table 3.10 to answer the following questions.

(a) How many units of agricultural products and of fuels are required to produce 100 units of manufactured goods?
(b) Production of which commodity is least dependent on the other two?
(c) If fuel costs rise, which two industries will be most affected?

Solution
(a) Referring to column 2, manufactured goods, we see that 1 unit requires 0.1 unit of agricultural products and 0.3 unit of fuels. Thus 100 units of manufactured goods require 10 units of agricultural products and 30 units of fuels.
(b) Looking down the columns, we see that 1 unit of agricultural products requires 0.3 unit of the other two commodities; 1 unit of manufactured goods requires 0.4 unit of the other two; and 1 unit of fuels requires 0.4 unit of the other two. Thus production of agricultural products is least dependent on the others.
(c) A rise in the cost of fuels would most affect those industries that use the larger amounts of fuels. One unit of agricultural products requires 0.1 unit of fuels, whereas a unit of manufactured goods requires 0.3 unit, and a unit of fuels requires 0.4 of its own units. Thus manufacturing and the fuel industry would be most affected by a cost increase in fuels. ■

*Leontief's work dealt with a massive analysis of the American economy. He was awarded a Nobel Prize in economics in 1973 for his study.

CHECKPOINT

The following technology matrix for a simple economy describes the relationship of certain industries to each other in the production of 1 unit of product.

$$
\begin{array}{cc}
 & \begin{array}{cccc} \text{Ag} & \text{Mfg} & \text{Fuels} & \text{Util} \end{array} \\
\begin{array}{l} \text{Agriculture} \\ \text{Manfacturing} \\ \text{Fuels} \\ \text{Utilities} \end{array} &
\begin{bmatrix}
0.32 & 0.06 & 0.09 & 0.06 \\
0.11 & 0.41 & 0.19 & 0.31 \\
0.31 & 0.14 & 0.18 & 0.20 \\
0.18 & 0.26 & 0.21 & 0.25
\end{bmatrix}
\end{array}
$$

1. Which industry is most dependent on its own goods for its operation?
2. How many units of fuels are required to produce 100 units of utilities?

Open Leontief Model

For a simplified model of the economy, such as that described with Table 3.10, not all information is contained within the technology matrix. In particular, each industry has a gross production. The **gross production matrix** for the economy can be represented by the column matrix

$$
X = \begin{bmatrix} x_1 \\ x_2 \\ x_3 \end{bmatrix}
$$

where x_1 is the gross production of agricultural products, x_2 is the gross production of manufactured goods, and x_3 is the gross production of fuels.

The amounts of the gross productions used within the economy by the various industries are given by AX. Those units of gross production not used by these industries are called **final demands** or **surpluses** and may be considered as being available for consumers, the government, or export. If we place these surpluses in a column matrix D, then they can be represented by the equation

$$
X - AX = D, \text{ or } (I - A)X = D
$$

where I is an identity matrix of appropriate size. This matrix equation is called the **technological equation** for an **open Leontief model.** This is called an open model because some of the goods from the economy are "open," or available to those outside the economy.

Open Leontief Model

The technological equation for an open Leontief model is

$$
(I - A)X = D
$$

EXAMPLE   2

Gross Outputs | APPLICATION PREVIEW |

Technology matrix A represents a simple economy with an agricultural industry, a manufacturing industry, and a fuels industry (as introduced in Table 3.10). If we wish to have surpluses of 85 units of agricultural products, 65 units of manufactured goods, and 0 units of fuels, what should the gross outputs be?

$$
A = \begin{bmatrix}
0.5 & 0.1 & 0.1 \\
0.2 & 0.5 & 0.3 \\
0.1 & 0.3 & 0.4
\end{bmatrix}
$$

Solution

Let X be the matrix of gross outputs for the industries and let D be the column matrix of each industry's surpluses. Then the technological equation is $(I - A)X = D$. We begin by finding the matrix $I - A$.

$$
I - A = \begin{bmatrix}
1 & 0 & 0 \\
0 & 1 & 0 \\
0 & 0 & 1
\end{bmatrix} - \begin{bmatrix}
0.5 & 0.1 & 0.1 \\
0.2 & 0.5 & 0.3 \\
0.1 & 0.3 & 0.4
\end{bmatrix} = \begin{bmatrix}
0.5 & -0.1 & -0.1 \\
-0.2 & 0.5 & -0.3 \\
-0.1 & -0.3 & 0.6
\end{bmatrix}
$$

Hence we must solve the matrix equation

$$\begin{bmatrix} 0.5 & -0.1 & -0.1 \\ -0.2 & 0.5 & -0.3 \\ -0.1 & -0.3 & 0.6 \end{bmatrix} \begin{bmatrix} x_1 \\ x_2 \\ x_3 \end{bmatrix} = \begin{bmatrix} 85 \\ 65 \\ 0 \end{bmatrix}$$

The augmented matrix is

$$\begin{bmatrix} 0.5 & -0.1 & -0.1 & | & 85 \\ -0.2 & 0.5 & -0.3 & | & 65 \\ -0.1 & -0.3 & 0.6 & | & 0 \end{bmatrix}$$

If we reduce by the methods of Section 3.3, "Gauss-Jordan Elimination: Solving Systems of Equations," we obtain

$$\begin{bmatrix} 1 & 0 & 0 & | & 300 \\ 0 & 1 & 0 & | & 400 \\ 0 & 0 & 1 & | & 250 \end{bmatrix}$$

so the gross outputs for the industries are

Agriculture:	$x_1 = 300$
Manufacturing:	$x_2 = 400$
Fuels:	$x_3 = 250$

In general, the technological equation for the open Leontief model can be solved by using the inverse of $I - A$. That is,

$$(I - A)X = D \qquad \text{has the solution} \qquad X = (I - A)^{-1}D$$

Technology Note

If we have the technology matrix A and the surplus matrix D, we can solve the technological equation for an open Leontief model with a calculator or computer by defining matrices I, A, and D and evaluating $X = (I - A)^{-1}D$. Figure 3.11 shows the solution of Example 2 using a graphing calculator.

```
[A]   [[.5   .1   .1]        ([I]-[A])⁻¹*[D]
       [.2   .5   .3]                    [[300]
       [.1   .3   .4]]                    [400]
[D]                                       [250]]
      [[85]
       [65]
       [0 ]]
```

Figure 3.11

EXAMPLE 3   Production

A primitive economy with a lumber industry and a power industry has the following technology matrix.

$$A = \begin{matrix} & \text{Lumber} & \text{Power} \\ \begin{bmatrix} 0.1 & 0.2 \\ 0.2 & 0.4 \end{bmatrix} & \begin{matrix} \text{Lumber} \\ \text{Power} \end{matrix} \end{matrix}$$

(a) If surpluses of 30 units of lumber and 70 units of power are desired, find the gross production of each industry.

(b) If an additional 5 units of surplus power were required, how much additional output would be required from each industry?

Solution

(a) Let x be the gross production of lumber, and let y be the gross production of power. Then

$$I - A = \begin{bmatrix} 0.9 & -0.2 \\ -0.2 & 0.6 \end{bmatrix}, \quad X = \begin{bmatrix} x \\ y \end{bmatrix}, \quad \text{and} \quad D = \begin{bmatrix} 30 \\ 70 \end{bmatrix}$$

We must solve the matrix equation $(I - A)X = D$ for X, and we can do this by using

$$X = (I - A)^{-1}D$$

We can find $(I - A)^{-1}$ with the formula from Section 3.4: "Inverse of a Square Matrix; Matrix Equations" or with a graphing calculator.

$$(I - A)^{-1} = \frac{1}{0.54 - 0.04}\begin{bmatrix} 0.6 & 0.2 \\ 0.2 & 0.9 \end{bmatrix} = 2\begin{bmatrix} 0.6 & 0.2 \\ 0.2 & 0.9 \end{bmatrix} = \begin{bmatrix} 1.2 & 0.4 \\ 0.4 & 1.8 \end{bmatrix}$$

Then we can find the gross production of each industry:

$$X = (I - A)^{-1}D = \begin{bmatrix} 1.2 & 0.4 \\ 0.4 & 1.8 \end{bmatrix}\begin{bmatrix} 30 \\ 70 \end{bmatrix} = \begin{bmatrix} 64 \\ 138 \end{bmatrix}$$

Hence the gross productions are

$$\text{Lumber: } x = 64$$
$$\text{Power: } y = 138$$

(b) If 5 more units of surplus power were required, then the new gross productions would be

$$(I - A)^{-1}\begin{bmatrix} 30 \\ 70 + 5 \end{bmatrix} = \begin{bmatrix} 1.2 & 0.4 \\ 0.4 & 1.8 \end{bmatrix}\begin{bmatrix} 30 \\ 75 \end{bmatrix} = \begin{bmatrix} 66 \\ 147 \end{bmatrix}$$

Thus, for 5 additional units of power, the increased production required from each industry would be

$$\begin{bmatrix} \text{Lumber} \\ \text{Power} \end{bmatrix} = \begin{bmatrix} 66 \\ 147 \end{bmatrix} - \begin{bmatrix} 64 \\ 138 \end{bmatrix} = \begin{bmatrix} 2 \\ 9 \end{bmatrix} \quad \text{which is} \quad 5\begin{bmatrix} \text{Col 2 of} \\ (I - A)^{-1} \end{bmatrix} = 5\begin{bmatrix} 0.4 \\ 1.8 \end{bmatrix} = \begin{bmatrix} 2 \\ 9 \end{bmatrix} \quad \blacksquare$$

The relationship observed in part (b) of Example 3 is true in general about $(I - A)^{-1}$. Namely, the entries in column j of $(I - A)^{-1}$ are the increased amounts needed from each industry to satisfy an increase of 1 unit of surplus from industry j.

EXAMPLE 4   **Open Economy**

The economy of a developing nation is based on agricultural products, steel, and coal. An output of 1 ton of agricultural products requires inputs of 0.1 ton of agricultural products, 0.02 ton of steel, and 0.05 ton of coal. An output of 1 ton of steel requires inputs of 0.01 ton of agricultural products, 0.13 ton of steel, and 0.18 ton of coal. An output of 1 ton of coal requires inputs of 0.01 ton of agricultural products, 0.20 ton of steel, and 0.05 ton of coal. Write the technology matrix for this economy. Find the necessary gross productions to provide surpluses of 2350 tons of agricultural products, 4552 tons of steel, and 911 tons of coal.

Solution

The technology matrix for the economy is

$$\begin{matrix} & \text{Ag} & \text{Steel} & \text{Coal} \\ \begin{bmatrix} 0.1 & 0.01 & 0.01 \\ 0.02 & 0.13 & 0.20 \\ 0.05 & 0.18 & 0.05 \end{bmatrix} & \begin{matrix} \text{Ag} \\ \text{Steel} \\ \text{Coal} \end{matrix} \end{matrix}$$

The technological equation for this economy is $(I - A)X = D$, or

$$\left(\begin{bmatrix} 1 & 0 & 0 \\ 0 & 1 & 0 \\ 0 & 0 & 1 \end{bmatrix} - \begin{bmatrix} 0.1 & 0.01 & 0.01 \\ 0.02 & 0.13 & 0.20 \\ 0.05 & 0.18 & 0.05 \end{bmatrix} \right) X = \begin{bmatrix} 2350 \\ 4552 \\ 911 \end{bmatrix}$$

Thus the solution is

Thus the necessary gross productions of the industries are

$$X = \begin{bmatrix} 2700 \\ 5800 \\ 2200 \end{bmatrix} \begin{matrix} \text{Ag} \\ \text{Steel} \\ \text{Coal} \end{matrix}$$

CHECKPOINT

3. Suppose a primitive economy has a wood products industry and a minerals industry, with technology matrix A (open Leontief model).

$$A = \begin{bmatrix} 0.12 & 0.11 \\ 0.09 & 0.15 \end{bmatrix} \begin{matrix} \text{Wood products} \\ \text{Minerals} \end{matrix}$$

with column labels W and M.

If surpluses of 1738 units of wood products and 1332 units of minerals are desired, find the gross production of each industry.

Closed Leontief Model

The model we have considered is referred to as an open Leontief model because not all inputs and outputs were incorporated within the technology matrix. If a model is developed in which all inputs and outputs are used within the system, then such a model is called a **closed Leontief model**. In such a model, labor (and perhaps other factors) must be included. Labor is included by considering a new industry, households, which produces labor. When such a closed model is developed, all outputs are used within the system, and the sum of the entries in each column equals 1. In this case, there is no surplus, so $D = 0$, and we have the following:

Closed Leontief Model

The technological equation for a closed Leontief model is

$$(I - A)X = 0$$

where 0 is a zero column matrix.

For closed models, the technological equation does *not* have a unique solution, so the matrix $(I - A)^{-1}$ does *not* exist and hence cannot be used to find the solution.

EXAMPLE 5   Closed Economy

The following closed Leontief model with technology matrix A might describe the economy of the entire country, with x_1 equal to the government budget, x_2 the value of industrial output (profit-making organizations), x_3 the budget of nonprofit organizations, and x_4 the households budget.

$$A = \begin{array}{c} \\ \end{array} \begin{array}{cccc} \text{G} & \text{I} & \text{N} & \text{H} \end{array} \\ A = \begin{bmatrix} 0.4 & 0.2 & 0.1 & 0.3 \\ 0.2 & 0.2 & 0.2 & 0.1 \\ 0.2 & 0 & 0.2 & 0.1 \\ 0.2 & 0.6 & 0.5 & 0.5 \end{bmatrix} \begin{array}{l} \text{Government} \\ \text{Industry} \\ \text{Nonprofit} \\ \text{Households} \end{array}$$

Find the total budgets (or outputs) x_1, x_2, x_3, and x_4.

Solution

This is a closed Leontief model; therefore, we solve the technological equation $(I - A)X = 0$.

$$\left(\begin{bmatrix} 1 & 0 & 0 & 0 \\ 0 & 1 & 0 & 0 \\ 0 & 0 & 1 & 0 \\ 0 & 0 & 0 & 1 \end{bmatrix} - \begin{bmatrix} 0.4 & 0.2 & 0.1 & 0.3 \\ 0.2 & 0.2 & 0.2 & 0.1 \\ 0.2 & 0 & 0.2 & 0.1 \\ 0.2 & 0.6 & 0.5 & 0.5 \end{bmatrix} \right) X = \begin{bmatrix} 0 \\ 0 \\ 0 \\ 0 \end{bmatrix}$$

or

$$\begin{bmatrix} 0.6 & -0.2 & -0.1 & -0.3 \\ -0.2 & 0.8 & -0.2 & -0.1 \\ -0.2 & 0 & 0.8 & -0.1 \\ -0.2 & -0.6 & -0.5 & 0.5 \end{bmatrix} \begin{bmatrix} x_1 \\ x_2 \\ x_3 \\ x_4 \end{bmatrix} = \begin{bmatrix} 0 \\ 0 \\ 0 \\ 0 \end{bmatrix}$$

The augmented matrix for this system is

$$\begin{bmatrix} 0.6 & -0.2 & -0.1 & -0.3 & 0 \\ -0.2 & 0.8 & -0.2 & -0.1 & 0 \\ -0.2 & 0 & 0.8 & -0.1 & 0 \\ -0.2 & -0.6 & -0.5 & 0.5 & 0 \end{bmatrix}$$

Reducing this matrix with row operations, we obtain

$$\begin{bmatrix} 1 & 0 & 0 & -\frac{55}{82} & 0 \\ 0 & 1 & 0 & -\frac{15}{41} & 0 \\ 0 & 0 & 1 & -\frac{12}{41} & 0 \\ 0 & 0 & 0 & 0 & 0 \end{bmatrix}$$

See Figure 3.12 for this reduction with a graphic calculator.

```
rref([I]-[A]▶Fr
ac
[[1   0   0   -55/82]
 [0   1   0   -15/41]
 [0   0   1   -12/41]
 [0   0   0    0    ]]
```

Figure 3.12

The system of equations that corresponds to this augmented matrix is

$$\begin{aligned} x_1 - \tfrac{55}{82}x_4 &= 0 & & & x_1 &= \tfrac{55}{82}x_4 \\ x_2 - \tfrac{15}{41}x_4 &= 0 & \text{or} & & x_2 &= \tfrac{15}{41}x_4 \\ x_3 - \tfrac{12}{41}x_4 &= 0 & & & x_3 &= \tfrac{12}{41}x_4 \\ & & & & x_4 &= \text{households budget} \end{aligned}$$

Note that the economy satisfies the given equation if the government budget is $\frac{55}{82}$ times the households budget, if the value of industrial output is $\frac{15}{41}$ times the households budget, and if the budget of nonprofit organizations is $\frac{12}{41}$ times the households budget. The dependency here is expected because industrial output is limited by labor supply.

CHECKPOINT

4. For a closed Leontief model:
   (a) What is the sum of the column entries of the technology matrix?
   (b) State the technological equation.

We have examined two types of input-output models as they pertain to the economy as a whole. Since Leontief's original work with the economy, various other applications of input-output models have been developed. Consider the following parts-listing problem.

EXAMPLE 6 Manufacturing

A storage shed consists of 4 walls and a roof. The walls and roof are made from stamped aluminum panels and are reinforced with 4 braces, each of which is held with 6 bolts. The final assembly joins the walls to each other and to the roof, using a total of 20 more bolts. The parts listing for these sheds can be described by the following matrix.

$$Q = \begin{bmatrix} S & W & R & P & Br & Bo \\ 0 & 0 & 0 & 0 & 0 & 0 \\ 4 & 0 & 0 & 0 & 0 & 0 \\ 1 & 0 & 0 & 0 & 0 & 0 \\ 0 & 1 & 1 & 0 & 0 & 0 \\ 0 & 4 & 4 & 0 & 0 & 0 \\ 20 & 24 & 24 & 0 & 0 & 0 \end{bmatrix} \begin{matrix} \text{Sheds} \\ \text{Walls} \\ \text{Roofs} \\ \text{Panels} \\ \text{Braces} \\ \text{Bolts} \end{matrix}$$

This matrix is a type of input-output matrix, with the rows representing inputs that are used directly to produce the items that head the columns. We note that the entries here are quantities used rather than proportions used. Also, the columns containing all zeros indicate primary assembly items because they are not made from other parts.

Thus to produce a shed requires 4 walls, 1 roof, and 20 bolts, and to produce a roof requires 1 aluminum panel, 4 braces, and 24 bolts.

Suppose that an order is received for 4 completed sheds and spare parts including 2 walls, 1 roof, 8 braces, and 24 bolts. How many of each of the assembly items are required to fill the order?

Solution

If matrix D represents the order and matrix X represents the gross production, we have

$$D = \begin{bmatrix} 4 \\ 2 \\ 1 \\ 0 \\ 8 \\ 24 \end{bmatrix} \begin{matrix} \text{Sheds} \\ \text{Walls} \\ \text{Roofs} \\ \text{Panels} \\ \text{Braces} \\ \text{Bolts} \end{matrix} \qquad X = \begin{bmatrix} x_1 \\ x_2 \\ x_3 \\ x_4 \\ x_5 \\ x_6 \end{bmatrix} = \begin{bmatrix} \text{total sheds required} \\ \text{total walls required} \\ \text{total roofs required} \\ \text{total panels required} \\ \text{total braces required} \\ \text{total bolts required} \end{bmatrix}$$

Then X must satisfy $X - QX = D$, which is the technological equation for an open Leontief model.

We can find X by solving the system $(I - Q)X = D$, which is represented by the augmented matrix

$$\begin{bmatrix} 1 & 0 & 0 & 0 & 0 & 0 & | & 4 \\ -4 & 1 & 0 & 0 & 0 & 0 & | & 2 \\ -1 & 0 & 1 & 0 & 0 & 0 & | & 1 \\ 0 & -1 & -1 & 1 & 0 & 0 & | & 0 \\ 0 & -4 & -4 & 0 & 1 & 0 & | & 8 \\ -20 & -24 & -24 & 0 & 0 & 1 & | & 24 \end{bmatrix}$$

Although this matrix is quite large, it is easily reduced and yields

$$\left[\begin{array}{cccccc|c} 1 & 0 & 0 & 0 & 0 & 0 & 4 \\ 0 & 1 & 0 & 0 & 0 & 0 & 18 \\ 0 & 0 & 1 & 0 & 0 & 0 & 5 \\ 0 & 0 & 0 & 1 & 0 & 0 & 23 \\ 0 & 0 & 0 & 0 & 1 & 0 & 100 \\ 0 & 0 & 0 & 0 & 0 & 1 & 656 \end{array}\right]$$

This matrix tells us that the order will have 4 complete sheds. The 18 walls from the matrix include the 16 from the complete sheds, and the 5 roofs include the 4 from the complete sheds. The 23 panels, 100 braces, and 656 bolts are the total number of *primary assembly items* (bolts, braces, and panels) required to fill the order.

The inverse of $I - Q$ exists, so it could be used directly or with technology to find the solution to the parts-listing problem of Example 6.

CHECKPOINT SOLUTIONS

1. Manufacturing
2. Under the "Util" column and across from the "Fuels" row is 0.20, indicating that producing 1 unit of utilities requires 0.20 unit of fuels. Thus producing 100 units of utilities requires 20 units of fuels.
3. Let x = the gross production of wood products
   y = the gross production of minerals
   We must solve $(I - A)X = D$.

$$\left(\begin{bmatrix} 1 & 0 \\ 0 & 1 \end{bmatrix} - \begin{bmatrix} 0.12 & 0.11 \\ 0.09 & 0.15 \end{bmatrix} \right) \begin{bmatrix} x \\ y \end{bmatrix} = \begin{bmatrix} 1738 \\ 1332 \end{bmatrix}$$

$$\begin{bmatrix} 0.88 & -0.11 \\ -0.09 & 0.85 \end{bmatrix} \begin{bmatrix} x \\ y \end{bmatrix} = \begin{bmatrix} 1738 \\ 1332 \end{bmatrix}$$

$$\begin{bmatrix} 0.88 & -0.11 \\ -0.09 & 0.85 \end{bmatrix}^{-1} = \frac{1}{(0.88)(0.85) - (0.09)(0.11)} \begin{bmatrix} 0.85 & 0.11 \\ 0.09 & 0.88 \end{bmatrix}$$

Hence

$$\begin{bmatrix} x \\ y \end{bmatrix} = \frac{1}{0.7381} \begin{bmatrix} 0.85 & 0.11 \\ 0.09 & 0.88 \end{bmatrix} \begin{bmatrix} 1738 \\ 1332 \end{bmatrix} = \begin{bmatrix} 2200 \\ 1800 \end{bmatrix}$$

4. (a) The sum of the column entries is 1.
   (b) $(I - A)X = 0$.

| EXERCISES | 3.5

1. The following technology matrix for a simple economy describes the relationship of certain industries to each other in the production of 1 unit of product.

	A	M	F	U	
	0.36	0.03	0.10	0.04	Agriculture
	0.06	0.42	0.25	0.33	Manufacturing
	0.18	0.15	0.10	0.41	Fuels
	0.10	0.20	0.31	0.15	Utilities

   (a) For each 100 units of manufactured products produced, how many units of fuels are required?
   (b) How many units of utilities are required to produce 40 units of agricultural products?

2. For the economy in Problem 1, what industry is most dependent on utilities?

The following technology matrix describes the relationship of certain industries within the economy to each other. (A&F, agriculture and food; RM, raw materials; M, manufacturing; F, fuels industry; U, utilities; SI, service industries)

A&F	RM	M	F	U	SI	
0.410	0.008	0	0.002	0	0.006	A&F
0.025	0.493	0.190	0.024	0.030	0.150	RM
0.015	0.006	0.082	0.009	0.001	0.116	M
0.097	0.096	0.040	0.053	0.008	0.093	F
0.028	0.129	0.039	0.058	0.138	0.409	U
0.043	0.008	0.010	0.012	0.002	0.095	SI

Use this matrix in Problems 3–10.

3. For each 1000 units of raw materials produced, how many units of agricultural and food products were required?

4. For each 1000 units of raw materials produced, how many units of service were required?

5. How many units of fuels were required to produce 1000 units of manufactured goods?

6. How many units of fuels were required to produce 1000 units of power (utilities' goods)?

7. Which industry is most dependent on its own goods for its operations? Which industry is least dependent on its own goods?

8. Which industry is most dependent on the fuels industry?

9. Which three industries would be most affected by a rise in the cost of raw materials?

10. Which industry would be most affected by a rise in the cost of manufactured goods?

11. Suppose a primitive economy consists of two industries, farm products and farm machinery. Suppose also that its technology matrix is

$$A = \begin{bmatrix} 0.5 & 0.1 \\ 0.1 & 0.3 \end{bmatrix} \begin{matrix} \text{Products} \\ \text{Machinery} \end{matrix}$$

with column headings P and M.

If surpluses of 96 units of farm products and 8 units of farm machinery are desired, find the gross production of each industry.

12. Suppose an economy has two industries, agriculture and minerals. Suppose further that the technology matrix for this economy is A.

$$A = \begin{bmatrix} 0.3 & 0.1 \\ 0.1 & 0.2 \end{bmatrix} \begin{matrix} \text{Agriculture} \\ \text{Minerals} \end{matrix}$$

with column headings A and M.

If surpluses of 60 agricultural units and 70 mineral units are desired, find the gross production for each industry.

13. An economy is based on two industries: utilities and manufacturing. The technology matrix for these industries is A.

$$A = \begin{bmatrix} 0.3 & 0.15 \\ 0.3 & 0.4 \end{bmatrix} \begin{matrix} \text{Utilities} \\ \text{Manufacturing} \end{matrix}$$

with column headings U and M.

If surpluses of 80 units of utilities output and 180 units of manufacturing are desired, find the gross production of each industry.

14. A primitive economy has a mining industry and a fishing industry, with technology matrix A.

$$A = \begin{bmatrix} 0.25 & 0.05 \\ 0.05 & 0.40 \end{bmatrix} \begin{matrix} \text{Mining} \\ \text{Fishing} \end{matrix}$$

with column headings M and F.

If surpluses of 147 units of mining output and 26 units of fishing output are desired, find the gross production of each industry.

15. Suppose the economy of an underdeveloped country has an agricultural industry and an oil industry, with technology matrix A.

$$A = \begin{bmatrix} 0.4 & 0.2 \\ 0.2 & 0.1 \end{bmatrix} \begin{matrix} \text{Agricultural products} \\ \text{Oil products} \end{matrix}$$

with column headings A and O.

(a) If surpluses of 0 units of agricultural products and 610 units of oil products are desired, find the gross production of each industry.

(b) Find the additional production needed from each industry for 1 more unit of oil products surplus.

16. Suppose a simple economy with only an agricultural industry and a steel industry has the following technology matrix.

$$A = \begin{bmatrix} 0.3 & 0.2 \\ 0.1 & 0.4 \end{bmatrix} \begin{matrix} \text{Agriculture} \\ \text{Steel} \end{matrix}$$

with column headings A and S.

(a) If surpluses of 15 units of agricultural products and 35 units of steel are desired, find the gross production of each industry.

(b) Find the additional production needed from each industry for 1 more unit of agricultural surplus.

17. One sector of an economy consists of a mining industry and a manufacturing industry, with technology matrix A.

$$A = \begin{bmatrix} 0.2 & 0.1 \\ 0.6 & 0.3 \end{bmatrix} \begin{matrix} \text{Mining} \\ \text{Manufacturing} \end{matrix}$$

with column headings M and Mfg.

(a) Surpluses of 36 units of mining output and 278 units of manufacturing output are desired. Find the gross production of each industry.

(b) Find the additional production needed from each industry for 1 more unit of mining surplus.

18. An underdeveloped country has an agricultural industry and a manufacturing industry, with technology matrix A.

$$A = \begin{bmatrix} 0.20 & 0.20 \\ 0.20 & 0.45 \end{bmatrix} \begin{matrix} \text{Agriculture} \\ \text{Manufacturing} \end{matrix}$$

with column headings A and M.

(a) Surpluses of 8 units of agricultural products and 620 units of manufactured products are desired. Find the gross production of each industry.

(b) Find the additional production needed from each industry for 1 more unit of manufacturing surplus.

19. A simple economy has an electronic components industry and a computer industry. Each unit of electronic components output requires inputs of 0.3 unit of elec-

tronic components and 0.2 unit of computers. Each unit of computer industry output requires inputs of 0.6 unit of electronic components and 0.2 unit of computers.
(a) Write the technology matrix for this simple economy.
(b) If surpluses of 648 units of electronic components and 16 units of computers are desired, find the gross production of each industry.

20. An economy has an agricultural industry and a textile industry. Each unit of agricultural output requires 0.4 unit of agricultural input and 0.1 unit of textiles input. Each unit of textiles output requires 0.1 unit of agricultural input and 0.2 unit of textiles input.
(a) Write the technology matrix for this economy.
(b) If surpluses of 5 units of agricultural products and 195 units of textiles are desired, find the gross production of each industry.

21. A primitive economy consists of a fishing industry and an oil industry. A unit of fishing industry output requires 0.30 unit of fishing industry input and 0.35 unit of oil industry input. A unit of oil industry output requires inputs of 0.04 unit of fishing products and 0.10 unit of oil products.
(a) Write the technology matrix for this primitive economy.
(b) If surpluses of 20 units of fishing products and 1090 units of oil products are desired, find the gross production of each industry.

22. An economy has a manufacturing industry and a banking industry. Each unit of manufacturing output requires inputs of 0.5 unit of manufacturing and 0.2 unit of banking. Each unit of banking output requires inputs of 0.3 unit each of manufacturing and banking.
(a) Write the technology matrix for this economy.
(b) If surpluses of 141 units of manufacturing and 106 units of banking are desired, find the gross production of each industry.

Interdepartmental costs **Within a company there is a (micro)economy that is monitored by the accounting procedures. In terms of the accounts, the various departments "produce" costs, some of which are internal and some of which are direct costs. Problems 23–26 show how an open Leontief model can be used to determine departmental costs.**

23. Suppose the development department of a firm charges 10% of its total monthly costs to the promotional department, and the promotional department charges 5% of its total monthly costs to the development department. The direct costs of the development department are $20,400, and the direct costs of the promotional department are $9,900. The solution to the matrix equation

$$\begin{bmatrix} 20{,}400 \\ 9{,}900 \end{bmatrix} + \begin{bmatrix} 0 & 0.05 \\ 0.1 & 0 \end{bmatrix}\begin{bmatrix} x \\ y \end{bmatrix} = \begin{bmatrix} x \\ y \end{bmatrix}$$

for the column matrix $\begin{bmatrix} x \\ y \end{bmatrix}$ gives the total costs for each department. Note that this equation can be written in the form

$$D + AX = X, \quad \text{or} \quad X - AX = D$$

which is the form for an open economy. Find the total costs for each department in this (micro)economy.

24. Suppose the shipping department of a firm charges 20% of its total monthly costs to the printing department and that the printing department charges 10% of its total monthly costs to the shipping department. If the direct costs of the shipping department are $16,500 and the direct costs of the printing department are $11,400, find the total costs for each department.

25. Suppose the engineering department of a firm charges 20% of its total monthly costs to the computer department, and the computer department charges 25% of its total monthly costs to the engineering department. If during a given month the direct costs are $11,750 for the engineering department and $10,000 for the computer department, what are the total costs of each department?

26. The sales department of an auto dealership charges 10% of its total monthly costs to the service department, and the service department charges 20% of its total monthly costs to the sales department. During a given month, the direct costs are $88,200 for sales and $49,000 for service. Find the total costs of each department.

27. Suppose that an economy has three industries, fishing, agriculture, and mining, and that matrix A is the technology matrix for this economy.

	F	A	M	
$A =$	0.5	0.1	0.1	Fishing
	0.3	0.5	0.2	Agriculture
	0.1	0.3	0.4	Mining

If surpluses of 110 units of fishing output and 50 units each of agricultural and mining goods are desired, find the gross production of each industry.

28. Suppose that an economy has the same technology matrix as the economy in Problem 27. If surpluses of 180 units of fishing output, 90 units of agricultural goods, and 40 units of mining goods are desired, find the gross production of each industry.

29. Suppose that the economy of a small nation has an electronics industry, a steel industry, and an auto industry, with the following technology matrix.

	E	S	A	
$A =$	0.6	0.2	0.2	Electronics
	0.1	0.4	0.5	Steel
	0.1	0.2	0.2	Autos

If the nation wishes to have surpluses of 100 units of electronics production, 272 units of steel production, and 200 automobiles, find the gross production of each industry.

30. Suppose an economy has the same technology matrix as that in Problem 29. If surpluses of 540 units of electronics, 30 units of steel, and 140 autos are desired, find the gross production for each industry.

31. Suppose that a simple economy has three industries, service, manufacturing, and agriculture, and that matrix A is the technology matrix for this economy.

$$A = \begin{bmatrix} & \text{S} & \text{M} & \text{A} \\ 0.4 & 0.1 & 0.1 \\ 0.2 & 0.5 & 0.2 \\ 0.2 & 0.1 & 0.3 \end{bmatrix} \begin{array}{l} \text{Service} \\ \text{Manufacturing} \\ \text{Agriculture} \end{array}$$

If surpluses of 24 units of service output, 62 units of manufactured goods, and 32 units of agricultural goods are desired, find the gross production of each industry.

32. Suppose that an economy has the same technology matrix as the economy in Problem 31. If surpluses of 14 units of manufactured goods and 104 units of agricultural goods are desired, find the gross production of each industry.

Problems 33–38 refer to closed Leontief models.

33. Suppose the technology matrix for a closed model of a simple economy is given by

$$A = \begin{bmatrix} & \text{P} & \text{M} & \text{H} \\ 0.5 & 0.1 & 0.2 \\ 0.1 & 0.3 & 0 \\ 0.4 & 0.6 & 0.8 \end{bmatrix} \begin{array}{l} \text{Products} \\ \text{Machinery} \\ \text{Households} \end{array}$$

Find the gross productions for the industries.

34. Suppose the technology matrix for a closed model of a simple economy is given by matrix A. Find the gross productions for the industries.

$$A = \begin{bmatrix} & \text{G} & \text{I} & \text{H} \\ 0.4 & 0.1 & 0.3 \\ 0.4 & 0.3 & 0.2 \\ 0.2 & 0.6 & 0.5 \end{bmatrix} \begin{array}{l} \text{Government} \\ \text{Industry} \\ \text{Households} \end{array}$$

35. Suppose the technology matrix for a closed model of a simple economy is given by matrix A. Find the gross productions for the industries.

$$A = \begin{bmatrix} & \text{G} & \text{I} & \text{H} \\ 0.4 & 0.2 & 0.2 \\ 0.2 & 0.3 & 0.3 \\ 0.4 & 0.5 & 0.5 \end{bmatrix} \begin{array}{l} \text{Government} \\ \text{Industry} \\ \text{Households} \end{array}$$

36. Suppose the technology matrix for a closed model of an economy is given by matrix A. Find the gross productions for the industries.

$$A = \begin{bmatrix} & \text{S} & \text{M} & \text{H} \\ 0.2 & 0.1 & 0.1 \\ 0.6 & 0.5 & 0.1 \\ 0.2 & 0.4 & 0.8 \end{bmatrix} \begin{array}{l} \text{Shipping} \\ \text{Manufacturing} \\ \text{Households} \end{array}$$

37. A closed model for an economy has a manufacturing industry, utilities industry, and households industry. Each unit of manufacturing output uses 0.5 unit of manufacturing input, 0.4 unit of utilities input, and 0.1 unit of households input. Each unit of utilities output requires 0.4 unit of manufacturing input, 0.5 unit of utilities input, and 0.1 unit of households input. Each unit of household output requires 0.3 unit each of manufacturing and utilities input and 0.4 unit of households input.
    (a) Write the technology matrix for this closed model of the economy.
    (b) Find the gross production for each industry.

38. A closed model for an economy identifies government, the profit sector, the nonprofit sector, and households as its industries. Each unit of government output requires 0.3 unit of government input, 0.2 unit of profit sector input, 0.2 unit of nonprofit sector input, and 0.3 unit of households input. Each unit of profit sector output requires 0.2 unit of government input, 0.3 unit of profit sector input, 0.1 unit of nonprofit sector input, and 0.4 unit of households input. Each unit of nonprofit sector output requires 0.1 unit of government input, 0.1 unit of profit sector input, 0.2 unit of nonprofit sector input, and 0.6 unit of households input. Each unit of households output requires 0.05 unit of government input, 0.1 unit of profit sector input, 0.1 unit of nonprofit sector input, and 0.75 unit of households input.
    (a) Write the technology matrix for this closed model of the economy.
    (b) Find the gross production for each industry.

39. For the storage shed in Example 6, find the number of each primary assembly item required to fill an order for 24 sheds, 12 braces, and 96 bolts.

40. Card tables are made by joining 4 legs and a top using 4 bolts. The legs are each made from a steel rod. The top has a frame made from 4 steel rods. A cover and 4 special clamps that brace the top and hold the legs are joined to the frame using a total of 8 bolts. The parts-listing matrix for the card table assembly is given by

$$A = \begin{bmatrix} \text{CT} & \text{L} & \text{T} & \text{R} & \text{Co} & \text{Cl} & \text{B} \\ 0 & 0 & 0 & 0 & 0 & 0 & 0 \\ 4 & 0 & 0 & 0 & 0 & 0 & 0 \\ 1 & 0 & 0 & 0 & 0 & 0 & 0 \\ 0 & 1 & 4 & 0 & 0 & 0 & 0 \\ 0 & 0 & 1 & 0 & 0 & 0 & 0 \\ 0 & 0 & 4 & 0 & 0 & 0 & 0 \\ 4 & 0 & 8 & 0 & 0 & 0 & 0 \end{bmatrix} \begin{array}{l} \text{Card table} \\ \text{Legs} \\ \text{Top} \\ \text{Rods} \\ \text{Cover} \\ \text{Clamps} \\ \text{Bolts} \end{array}$$

If an order is received for 10 card tables, 4 legs, 1 top, 1 cover, 6 clamps, and 12 bolts, how many of each primary assembly item are required to fill the order?

41. A sawhorse is made from 2 pairs of legs and a top joined with 4 nails. The top is a 2 × 4-in. board 3 ft long. Each pair of legs is made from two 2 × 4-in.

boards 3 ft long, a brace, and a special clamp, with the brace and the clamp joined using 8 nails. The parts-listing matrix for the sawhorse is given by

$$A = \begin{matrix} & \text{SH} & \text{T} & \text{LP} & 2\times4 & \text{B} & \text{C} & \text{N} \\ & \begin{bmatrix} 0 & 0 & 0 & 0 & 0 & 0 & 0 \\ 1 & 0 & 0 & 0 & 0 & 0 & 0 \\ 2 & 0 & 0 & 0 & 0 & 0 & 0 \\ 0 & 1 & 2 & 0 & 0 & 0 & 0 \\ 0 & 0 & 1 & 0 & 0 & 0 & 0 \\ 0 & 0 & 1 & 0 & 0 & 0 & 0 \\ 4 & 0 & 8 & 0 & 0 & 0 & 0 \end{bmatrix} & \begin{matrix} \text{Sawhorse} \\ \text{Top} \\ \text{Leg pair} \\ 2\times4\text{s} \\ \text{Brace} \\ \text{Clamp} \\ \text{Nails} \end{matrix} \end{matrix}$$

How many of each primary assembly item are required to fill an order for 10 sawhorses, 6 extra 2×4s, 6 extra clamps, and 100 nails?

42. A log carrier has a body made from a 4-ft length of reinforced cloth having a patch on each side and a dowel slid through each end to act as handles. The parts-listing matrix for the log carrier is given by

$$A = \begin{matrix} & \text{LC} & \text{B} & \text{H} & \text{C} & \text{P} \\ & \begin{bmatrix} 0 & 0 & 0 & 0 & 0 \\ 1 & 0 & 0 & 0 & 0 \\ 2 & 0 & 0 & 0 & 0 \\ 0 & 1 & 0 & 0 & 0 \\ 0 & 2 & 0 & 0 & 0 \end{bmatrix} & \begin{matrix} \text{Log carrier} \\ \text{Body} \\ \text{Handles} \\ \text{Cloth} \\ \text{Patch} \end{matrix} \end{matrix}$$

How many of each primary assembly item are required to fill an order for 500 log carriers and 20 handles?

KEY TERMS AND FORMULAS

Section	Key Terms	Formulas

3.1	Matrices
	    Entries
	    Order
	    Square, row, column, and zero matrices
	Transpose
	Sum of two matrices
	Negative of a matrix
	Scalar multiplication
		A^T

3.2	Matrix product Identity matrix	2×2 is $\begin{bmatrix} 1 & 0 \\ 0 & 1 \end{bmatrix}$

3.3	Augmented matrix
	Coefficient matrix
	Elementary row operations
	Solving systems of equations
	    Gauss-Jordan elimination method
	Nonunique solutions
	    Reduced form	

3.4	Inverse matrices Matrix equations Determinants	$AX = B$ $\begin{vmatrix} a & b \\ c & d \end{vmatrix} = ad - bc$

3.5	Technology matrix
	Leontief input-output model
	Gross production matrix
	    Final demands (surpluses)
	Leontief model
	Technological equation
	    Open
	    Closed
		$(I - A)X = D$
		$(I - A)X = 0$

REVIEW EXERCISES

Use the matrices below as needed to complete Problems 1–25.

$$A = \begin{bmatrix} 4 & 4 & 2 & -5 \\ 6 & 3 & -1 & 0 \\ 0 & 0 & -3 & 5 \end{bmatrix} \quad B = \begin{bmatrix} 2 & -5 & -11 & 8 \\ 4 & 0 & 0 & 4 \\ -2 & -2 & 1 & 9 \end{bmatrix}$$

$$C = \begin{bmatrix} 4 & -2 \\ 5 & 0 \\ 6 & 0 \\ 1 & 3 \end{bmatrix} \quad D = \begin{bmatrix} 3 & 5 \\ 1 & 2 \end{bmatrix} \quad E = \begin{bmatrix} 1 & 1 \\ 1 & 1 \\ 4 & 6 \\ 0 & 5 \end{bmatrix}$$

$$F = \begin{bmatrix} -1 & 6 \\ 4 & 11 \end{bmatrix} \quad G = \begin{bmatrix} 2 & -5 \\ -1 & 3 \end{bmatrix} \quad I = \begin{bmatrix} 1 & 0 \\ 0 & 1 \end{bmatrix}$$

1. Find a_{12} in matrix A.
2. Find b_{23} in matrix B.
3. Which of the matrices, if any, are 3×4?
4. Which of the matrices, if any, are 2×4?
5. Which matrices are square?
6. Write the negative of matrix B.
7. If a matrix is added to its negative, what kind of matrix results?
8. Two matrices can be added if they have the same _____.

Perform the indicated operations in Problems 9–25.

9. $A + B$ 10. $C - E$ 11. $D^T - I$
12. $3C$ 13. $4I$ 14. $-2F$
15. $4D - 3I$ 16. $F + 2D$ 17. $3A - 5B$
18. AC 19. CD 20. DF
21. FD 22. FI 23. IF
24. DG^T 25. $(DG)F$

In Problems 26–28, the reduced matrix for a system of equations is given. (a) Identify the type of solution for the system (unique solution, no solution, or infinitely many solutions). Explain your reasoning. (b) For each system that has a solution, find it. If the system has infinitely many solutions, find two different specific solutions.

26. $\begin{bmatrix} 1 & 0 & -2 & | & 6 \\ 0 & 1 & 3 & | & 7 \\ 0 & 0 & 0 & | & 0 \end{bmatrix}$ 27. $\begin{bmatrix} 1 & 0 & -4 & | & 0 \\ 0 & 1 & 3 & | & 0 \\ 0 & 0 & 0 & | & 1 \end{bmatrix}$

28. $\begin{bmatrix} 1 & 0 & 0 & | & 0 \\ 0 & 1 & 0 & | & -10 \\ 0 & 0 & 1 & | & 14 \end{bmatrix}$

29. Given the following augmented matrix representing a system of linear equations, find the solution.

$$\begin{bmatrix} 1 & 1 & 2 & | & 5 \\ 4 & 0 & 1 & | & 5 \\ 2 & 1 & 1 & | & 5 \end{bmatrix}$$

In Problems 30–36, solve each system using matrices.

30. $\begin{cases} x - 2y = 4 \\ -3x + 10y = 24 \end{cases}$

31. $\begin{cases} x + y + z = 4 \\ 3x + 4y - z = -1 \\ 2x - y + 3z = 3 \end{cases}$

32. $\begin{cases} -x + y + z = 3 \\ 3x - z = 1 \\ 2x - 3y - 4z = -2 \end{cases}$

33. $\begin{cases} x + y - 2z = 5 \\ 3x + 2y + 5z = 10 \\ -2x - 3y + 15z = 2 \end{cases}$

34. $\begin{cases} x - y = 3 \\ x + y + 4z = 1 \\ 2x - 3y - 2z = 7 \end{cases}$

35. $\begin{cases} x - 3y + z = 4 \\ 2x - 5y - z = 6 \end{cases}$

36. $\begin{cases} x_1 + x_2 + x_3 + x_4 = 3 \\ x_1 - 2x_2 + x_3 - 4x_4 = -5 \\ x_1 - x_3 + x_4 = 0 \\ x_2 + x_3 + x_4 = 2 \end{cases}$

37. Are D and G inverse matrices if

$$D = \begin{bmatrix} 3 & 5 \\ 1 & 2 \end{bmatrix} \quad \text{and} \quad G = \begin{bmatrix} 2 & -5 \\ -1 & 3 \end{bmatrix}?$$

In Problems 38–40, find the inverse of each matrix.

38. $\begin{bmatrix} 7 & -1 \\ -10 & 2 \end{bmatrix}$ 39. $\begin{bmatrix} 1 & 0 & 2 \\ 3 & 4 & -1 \\ 1 & 1 & 0 \end{bmatrix}$

40. $\begin{bmatrix} 3 & 3 & 2 \\ -1 & 4 & 2 \\ 2 & 5 & 3 \end{bmatrix}$

In Problems 41–43, solve each system of equations by using inverse matrices.

41. $\begin{cases} x + 2z = 5 \\ 3x + 4y - z = 2 \\ x + y = -3 \end{cases}$ (See Problem 39.)

42. $\begin{cases} 3x + 3y + 2z = 1 \\ -x + 4y + 2z = -10 \\ 2x + 5y + 3z = -6 \end{cases}$ (See Problem 40.)

43. $\begin{cases} x + 3y + z = 0 \\ x + 4y + 3z = 2 \\ 2x - y - 11z = -12 \end{cases}$

44. Does the following matrix have an inverse?

$$\begin{bmatrix} 1 & 2 & 4 \\ 2 & 0 & -4 \\ 1 & 0 & -2 \end{bmatrix}$$

In Problems 45 and 46:
    (a) **Find the determinant of the matrix.**
    (b) **Use it to decide whether the matrix has an inverse.**

45. $\begin{bmatrix} 4 & 4 \\ -2 & 2 \end{bmatrix}$

46. $\begin{bmatrix} 1 & 2 & 3 \\ 4 & -1 & 8 \\ 6 & 3 & 14 \end{bmatrix}$

APPLICATIONS

The Burr Cabinet Company manufactures bookcases and filing cabinets at two plants, A and B. Matrix M gives the production for the two plants during June, and matrix N gives the production for July. Use them in Problems 47–49.

$$M = \begin{matrix} & A & B \\ & \begin{bmatrix} 150 & 80 \\ 280 & 300 \end{bmatrix} & \begin{matrix} \text{Bookcases} \\ \text{Files} \end{matrix} \end{matrix} \qquad N = \begin{matrix} A & B \\ \begin{bmatrix} 100 & 60 \\ 200 & 400 \end{bmatrix} \end{matrix}$$

$$S = \begin{bmatrix} 120 & 80 \\ 180 & 300 \end{bmatrix} \qquad P = \begin{bmatrix} 1000 & 800 \\ 600 & 1200 \end{bmatrix}$$

47. *Production* Write the matrix that represents total production at the two plants for the 2 months.
48. *Production* If matrix P represents the inventories at the plants at the beginning of June and matrix S represents shipments from the plants during June, write the matrix that represents the inventories at the end of June.
49. *Production* If the company sells its bookcases to wholesalers for $100 and its filing cabinets for $120, for which month was the value of production higher: (a) at plant A? (b) at plant B?

A small church choir is made up of men and women who wear choir robes in the sizes shown in matrix A.

$$A = \begin{matrix} & \text{Men} & \text{Women} \\ & \begin{bmatrix} 1 & 14 \\ 12 & 10 \\ 8 & 3 \end{bmatrix} & \begin{matrix} \text{Small} \\ \text{Medium} \\ \text{Large} \end{matrix} \end{matrix}$$

$$B = \begin{matrix} & S & M & L \\ & \begin{bmatrix} 25 & 40 & 45 \\ 10 & 10 & 10 \end{bmatrix} & \begin{matrix} \text{Robes} \\ \text{Hoods} \end{matrix} \end{matrix}$$

Matrix B contains the prices (in dollars) of new robes and hoods according to size. Use these matrices in Problems 50 and 51.

50. *Cost* Find the product BA, and label the rows and columns to show what each entry represents.
51. *Cost* To find a matrix that gives the cost of new robes and the cost of new hoods, find

$$BA \begin{bmatrix} 1 \\ 1 \end{bmatrix}$$

52. *Manufacturing* Two departments of a firm, A and B, need different amounts of the same products. The following table gives the amounts of the products needed by the two departments.

	Steel	Plastic	Wood
Department A	30	20	10
Department B	20	10	20

These three products are supplied by two suppliers, Ace and Kink, with the unit prices given in the following table.

	Ace	Kink
Steel	300	280
Plastic	150	100
Wood	150	200

    (a) Use matrix multiplication to find how much these two orders will cost at the two suppliers. The result should be a 2×2 matrix.
    (b) From which supplier should each department make its purchase?

53. *Investment* Over the period of time 2002–2011, Maura's actual return (per dollar of stock) was 0.013469 per month, Ward's actual return was 0.013543 per month, and Goldsmith's actual return was 0.006504. Under certain assumptions, including that whatever underlying process generated the past set of observations will continue to hold in the present and near future, we can estimate the expected return for a stock portfolio containing these assets in some combination.
    Suppose we have a portfolio that has 20% of our total wealth in Maura, 30% in Ward, and 50% in Goldsmith stock. Use the following steps to estimate the portfolio's historical return, which can be used to estimate the future return.
    (a) Write a 1×3 matrix that defines the decimal part of our total wealth in Maura, in Ward, and in Goldsmith.
    (b) Write a 3×1 matrix that gives the monthly returns from each of these companies.
    (c) Find the historical return of the portfolio by computing the product of these two matrices.
    (d) What is the expected monthly return of the stock portfolio?

54. *Investment* A woman has $50,000 to invest. She has decided to invest all of it by purchasing some shares of stock in each of three companies: a fast-food chain that sells for $50 per share and has an expected growth of 11.5% per year, a software company that sells for $20 per share and has an expected growth of 15% per year, and a pharmaceutical company that sells for $80 per share and has an expected growth of 10% per year. She plans to buy twice as many shares of stock in the fast-food chain as in the pharmaceutical company. If her goal is 12% growth per year, how many shares of each stock should she buy?

55. *Nutrition* A biologist is growing three different types of slugs (types A, B, and C) in the same laboratory environment. Each day, the slugs are given a nutrient mixture that contains three different ingredients (I, II, and III). Each type A slug requires 1 unit of I, 3 units of II, and 1 unit of III per day. Each type B slug requires 1 unit of I, 4 units of

II, and 2 units of III per day. Each type C slug requires 2 units of I, 10 units of II, and 6 units of III per day.
(a) If the daily mixture contains 2000 units of I, 8000 units of II, and 4000 units of III, find the number of slugs of each type that can be supported.
(b) Is it possible to support 500 type A slugs? If so, how many of the other types are there?
(c) What is the maximum number of type A slugs possible? How many of the other types are there in this case?

56. *Transportation* An airline company has three types of aircraft that carry three types of cargo. The payload of each type is summarized in the table below.

Units Carried	Plane Type		
	Passenger	Transport	Jumbo
First-class mail	100	100	100
Passengers	150	20	350
Air freight	20	65	35

(a) Suppose that on a given day the airline must move 1100 units of first-class mail, 460 units of air freight, and 1930 passengers. How many aircraft of each type should be scheduled? Use inverse matrices.
(b) How should the schedule from part (a) be adjusted to accommodate 730 more passengers?
(c) What column of the inverse matrix used in part (a) can be used to answer part (b)?

57. *Economy models* An economy has a shipping industry and an agricultural industry with technology matrix A.

$$A = \begin{bmatrix} S & A \\ 0.1 & 0.2 \\ 0.2 & 0.4 \end{bmatrix} \begin{matrix} \\ \text{Shipping} \\ \text{Agriculture} \end{matrix}$$

(a) Surpluses of 4720 tons of shipping output and 40 tons of agricultural output are desired. Find the gross production of each industry.
(b) Find the additional production needed from each industry for 1 more unit of agricultural surplus.

58. *Economy models* A simple economy has a shoe industry and a cattle industry. Each unit of shoe output requires inputs of 0.1 unit of shoes and 0.2 unit of cattle products. Each unit of cattle products output requires inputs of 0.1 unit of shoes and 0.05 unit of cattle products.
(a) Write the technology matrix for this simple economy.
(b) If surpluses of 850 units of shoes and 275 units of cattle products are desired, find the gross production of each industry.

59. *Economy models* A look at the industrial sector of an economy can be simplified to include three industries: the mining industry, the manufacturing industry, and the fuels industry. The technology matrix for this sector of the economy is given by

$$A = \begin{bmatrix} M & Mf & F \\ 0.4 & 0.2 & 0.2 \\ 0.2 & 0.4 & 0.2 \\ 0.1 & 0.2 & 0.2 \end{bmatrix} \begin{matrix} \text{Mining} \\ \text{Manufacturing} \\ \text{Fuels} \end{matrix}$$

Find the gross production of each industry if surpluses of 72 units of mined goods, 40 units of manufactured goods, and 220 units of fuels are desired.

60. *Economy models* Suppose a closed Leontief model for a nation's economy has the following technology matrix.

$$A = \begin{bmatrix} G & A & M & H \\ 0.4 & 0.2 & 0.2 & 0.2 \\ 0.2 & 0.4 & 0.1 & 0.2 \\ 0.2 & 0.1 & 0.3 & 0.1 \\ 0.2 & 0.3 & 0.4 & 0.5 \end{bmatrix} \begin{matrix} \text{Government} \\ \text{Agriculture} \\ \text{Manufacturing} \\ \text{Households} \end{matrix}$$

Find the gross production of each industry.

---

3 CHAPTER TEST

In Problems 1–6, perform the indicated matrix operations with the following matrices.

$$A = \begin{bmatrix} 1 & -2 \\ 3 & 2 \\ 4 & 1 \end{bmatrix} \quad B = \begin{bmatrix} 2 & -2 & 1 \\ 3 & 1 & 5 \end{bmatrix}$$

$$C = \begin{bmatrix} 3 & -4 & -1 \\ 2 & 2 & -1 \end{bmatrix} \quad D = \begin{bmatrix} 1 & 2 & 4 \\ 3 & 5 & 41 \\ 3 & 2 & 3 \end{bmatrix}$$

1. $A^T + B$ 2. $B - C$ 3. CD
4. DA 5. BA 6. ABD

7. Find the inverse of the matrix $\begin{bmatrix} 1 & 3 \\ 2 & 4 \end{bmatrix}$.

8. Find the inverse of the matrix

$$\begin{bmatrix} 1 & 2 & 4 \\ 1 & 2 & 2 \\ 1 & 1 & 4 \end{bmatrix}$$

9. If $AX = B$ and

$$A^{-1} = \begin{bmatrix} 1 & 2 & 0 \\ 3 & 1 & 2 \\ 4 & 1 & 1 \end{bmatrix} \quad \text{and} \quad B = \begin{bmatrix} 3 \\ 1 \\ 2 \end{bmatrix}$$

find the matrix X.

10. Solve

$$\begin{cases} x - y + 2z = 4 \\ x + 4y + z = 4 \\ 2x + 2y + 4z = 10 \end{cases}$$

11. Solve

$$\begin{cases} x - y + 2z = 4 \\ x + 4y + z = 4 \\ 2x + 3y + 3z = 8 \end{cases}$$

12. Solve

$$\begin{cases} x - y + 3z = 4 \\ x + 5y + 2z = 3 \\ 2x + 4y + 5z = 8 \end{cases}$$

13. Use an inverse matrix to solve

$$\begin{cases} x + y + 2z = 4 \\ x + 2y + z + w = 4 \\ 2x + 5y + 4z + 2w = 10 \\ 2y + z + 2w = 0 \end{cases}$$

14. Solve

$$\begin{cases} x - y + 2z - w = 4 \\ x + 4y + z + w = 4 \\ 2x + 2y + 4z + 2w = 10 \\ - y + z + 2w = 2 \end{cases}$$

15. Suppose that the solution of an investment problem involving a system of linear equations is given by

$$B = 75{,}000 - 3H \quad \text{and} \quad E = 20{,}000 + 2H$$

where B represents the dollars invested in Barton Bank stocks, H is the dollars invested in Heath Healthcare stocks, and E is the dollars invested in Electronics Depot stocks.
(a) If $10,000 is invested in the Heath Healthcare stocks, how much is invested in the other two stocks?
(b) What is the dollar range that could be invested in the Heath Healthcare stocks?
(c) What is the minimum amount that could be invested in the Electronics Depot stocks? How much is invested in the other two stocks in this case?

16. In an ecological model, matrix A gives the fractions of several types of plants consumed by the herbivores in the ecosystem. Similarly, matrix B gives the fraction of each type of herbivore that is consumed by the carnivores in the system. Each row of matrix A refers to a type of plant, and each column refers to a kind of herbivore. Similarly, each row of matrix B is a kind of herbivore and each column is a kind of carnivore.

Herbivores

$$A = \begin{bmatrix} 0.2 & 0.1 & 0.4 \\ 0.3 & 0.3 & 0.1 \\ 0.2 & 0.1 & 0.1 \\ 0.1 & 0.2 & 0.5 \\ 0.4 & 0.4 & 0 \end{bmatrix} \text{ Plants}$$

Carnivores

$$B = \begin{bmatrix} 0.1 & 0.1 & 0.2 \\ 0.2 & 0 & 0.4 \\ 0.1 & 0.5 & 0.1 \end{bmatrix} \text{ Herbivores}$$

The matrix AB gives the fraction of each plant that is consumed by each carnivore.
(a) Find AB.
(b) What fraction of plant type 1 (row 1) is consumed by each carnivore?
(c) Identify the plant type that each carnivore consumes the most.

17. A furniture manufacturer produces four styles of chairs and has orders for 1000 of style A, 4000 of style B, 2000 of style C, and 1000 of style D. The following table lists the numbers of units of raw materials the manufacturer needs for each style. Suppose wood costs $5 per unit, nylon costs $3 per unit, velvet costs $4 per unit, and springs cost $4 per unit.

	Wood	Nylon	Velvet	Springs
Style A	10	5	0	0
Style B	5	0	20	10
Style C	5	20	0	10
Style D	5	10	10	10

(a) Form a 1×4 matrix containing the number of units of each style ordered.
(b) Use matrix multiplication to determine the total number of units of each raw material needed.
(c) Write a 4×1 matrix representing the costs of the raw materials.
(d) Use matrix multiplication to find the 1×1 matrix that represents the total investment to fill the orders.
(e) Use matrix multiplication to determine the cost of materials for each style of chair.

18. Complete parts (a) and (b) by using the code discussed in Sections 3.2 and 3.4 (where a is 1, ..., z is 26, and blank is 27), and the coding matrix is

$$A = \begin{bmatrix} 8 & 5 \\ 3 & 2 \end{bmatrix}$$

(a) Encode the message "Less is more," the motto of architect Mies van der Rohe.
(b) Decode the message 138, 54, 140, 53, 255, 99, 141, 54, 201, 76, 287, 111.

19. A young couple with a $120,000 inheritance wants to invest all this money. They plan to diversify their investments, choosing some of each of the following types of stock.

Type	Cost/Share	Expected Total Growth/Share
Growth	$ 30	$ 4.60
Blue-chip	100	11.00
Utility	50	5.00

Their strategy is to have the total investment in growth stocks equal to the sum of the other investments, and their goal is a 13% growth for their investment. How many shares of each type of stock should they purchase?

20. Suppose an economy has two industries, agriculture and minerals, and the economy has the technology matrix

$$A = \begin{bmatrix} 0.4 & 0.2 \\ 0.1 & 0.3 \end{bmatrix} \begin{matrix} \text{Ag} \\ \text{M} \end{matrix}$$

with columns labeled Ag and M.

   (a) If surpluses of 100 agriculture units and 140 minerals units are desired, find the gross production of each industry.
   (b) How many additional units must each industry produce to have 4 more units of agricultural surplus?
   (c) How many additional units must each industry produce for 1 more unit of minerals surplus?

21. Suppose the technology matrix for a closed model of a simple economy is given by matrix A. Find the gross productions of the industries.

$$A = \begin{bmatrix} 0.4 & 0.3 & 0.4 \\ 0.2 & 0.4 & 0.2 \\ 0.4 & 0.3 & 0.4 \end{bmatrix} \begin{matrix} \text{Profit} \\ \text{Nonprofit} \\ \text{Households} \end{matrix}$$

with columns labeled P, NP, H.

Use the following information in Problems 22 and 23. The national economy of Swiziland has four products: agricultural products, machinery, fuel, and steel. Producing 1 unit of agricultural products requires 0.2 unit of agricultural products, 0.3 unit of machinery, 0.2 unit of fuel, and 0.1 unit of steel. Producing 1 unit of machinery requires 0.1 unit of agricultural products, 0.2 unit of machinery, 0.2 unit of fuel, and 0.4 unit of steel. Producing 1 unit of fuel requires 0.1 unit of agricultural products, 0.2 unit of machinery, 0.3 unit of fuel, and 0.2 unit of steel. Producing 1 unit of steel requires 0.1 unit of agricultural products, 0.2 unit of machinery, 0.3 unit of fuel, and 0.2 unit of steel.

22. Create the technology matrix for this economy.

23. Determine how many units of each product will give surpluses of 1700 units of agriculture products, 1900 units of machinery, 900 units of fuel, and 300 units of steel.

24. A simple closed economy has the technology matrix A. Find the total outputs of the four sectors of the economy.

$$A = \begin{bmatrix} 0.25 & 0.25 & 0.3 & 0.1 \\ 0.3 & 0.25 & 0.2 & 0.4 \\ 0.15 & 0.2 & 0.1 & 0.3 \\ 0.3 & 0.3 & 0.4 & 0.2 \end{bmatrix} \begin{matrix} \text{Agriculture} \\ \text{Steel} \\ \text{Fuel} \\ \text{Households} \end{matrix}$$

with columns labeled Ag, S, F, H.

I. Taxation

Federal income tax allows a deduction for any state income tax paid during the year. In addition, the state of Alabama allows a deduction from its state income tax for any federal income tax paid during the year. The federal corporate income tax rate is equivalent to a flat rate of 34% if the taxable federal income is between $335,000 and $10,000,000, and the Alabama rate is 5% of the taxable state income.*

Both the Alabama and the federal taxable income for a corporation are $1,000,000 *before* either tax is paid. Because each tax is deductible on the other return, the taxable income will differ for the state and federal taxes. One procedure often used by tax accountants to find the tax due in this and similar situations is called *iteration* and is described by the first five steps below.[†]

1. Make an estimate of the federal taxes due by assuming no state tax is due, deduct this estimated federal tax due from the state taxable income, and calculate an estimate of the state taxes due on the basis of this assumption.
2. Deduct the estimated state tax due as computed in (1) from the federal taxable income, and calculate a new estimate of the federal tax due under this assumption.
3. Deduct the new estimated federal income tax due as computed in (2) from the state taxable income, and calculate a new estimate of the state taxes due on the basis of these calculations.
4. Repeat the process in (2) and (3) to get a better estimate of the taxes due to both governments.
5. Continue this process until the federal tax changes from one repetition to another by less than $1. What federal tax is due? What state tax is due?

To find the tax due each government directly, we can solve a matrix equation.

6. Create two linear equations that describe this taxation situation, convert the system to a matrix equation, and solve the system to see exactly what tax is due to each government.
7. What is the effective rate that this corporation pays to each government?

*Source: Federal Income Tax Tables and Alabama Income Tax Instructions.
[†]Performing these steps with an electronic spreadsheet is described by Kenneth H. Johnson in "A Simplified Calculation of Mutually Dependent Federal and State Tax Liabilities," in *The Journal of Taxation,* December 1994.

II. Company Profits after Bonuses and Taxes

A company earns $800,000 profit before paying bonuses and taxes. Suppose that a bonus of 2% is paid to each employee after all taxes are paid, that state taxes of 6% are paid on the profit after the bonuses are paid, and that federal taxes are 34% of the profit that remains after bonuses and state taxes are paid.

1. How much profit remains after all taxes and bonuses are paid? Give your answer to the nearest dollar.
2. If the employee bonuses are increased to 3%, employees would receive 50% more bonus money. How much more profit would this cost the company than the 2% bonuses?
3. Use a calculator or spreadsheet to determine the loss of profit associated with bonuses of 4%, 5%, etc., up to 10%, and make a management decision about what bonuses to give in order to balance employee morale with loss of profit.
4. Use technology and the data points found above to create an equation that models the company's profit after expenses as a function of the employee bonus percent.

4

CHAPTER

Weldon Schloneger/Shutterstock.com

Inequalities and Linear Programming

Most companies seek to maximize profits subject to the limitations imposed by product demand and available resources (such as raw materials and labor) or to minimize production costs subject to the need to fill customer orders. If the relationships among the various resources, production requirements, costs, and profits are all linear, then these activities may be planned (or programmed) in the best possible (optimal) way by using **linear programming.** Because linear programming provides the best possible solution to problems involving allocation of limited resources among various activities, its impact has been tremendous.

In this chapter, we introduce and discuss this important method. The chapter topics and applications include the following.

Prerequisite Problem Type	For Section	Answer	Section for Review
(a) Solve $3x - 2y \geq 4$ for y. (b) Solve $2x + 4y = 60$ for y.	4.1	(a) $y \leq \frac{3}{2}x - 2$ (b) $y = 15 - \frac{1}{2}x$	1.1 Linear equations and inequalities
Graph the equation $y = \frac{3}{2}x - 2$.	4.1		1.3 Graphing linear equations
Solve the systems: (a) $\begin{cases} x + 2y = 10 \\ 2x + y = 14 \end{cases}$ (b) $\begin{cases} x + 0.5y = 16 \\ x + y = 24 \end{cases}$	4.1 4.2	(a) $x = 6, \; y = 2$ (b) $x = 8, \; y = 16$	1.5 Systems of linear equations
Write the system in an augmented matrix: $\begin{cases} x + 2y + s_1 = 10 \\ 2x + y + s_2 = 14 \\ -2x - 3y + f = 0 \end{cases}$	4.3 4.4 4.5	$\begin{bmatrix} 1 & 2 & 1 & 0 & 0 & 10 \\ 2 & 1 & 0 & 1 & 0 & 14 \\ -2 & -3 & 0 & 0 & 1 & 0 \end{bmatrix}$	3.3 Gauss-Jordan elimination
Write a matrix equivalent to matrix A with the entry in row 1, column 2 equal to 1 and with all other entries in column 2 equal to 0. First multiply row 1 by $\frac{1}{2}$. $A = \begin{bmatrix} 1 & 2 & 1 & 0 & 0 & 10 \\ 2 & 1 & 0 & 1 & 0 & 14 \\ -2 & -3 & 0 & 0 & 1 & 0 \end{bmatrix}$	4.3 4.4 4.5	$\begin{bmatrix} \frac{1}{2} & 1 & \frac{1}{2} & 0 & 0 & 5 \\ \frac{3}{2} & 0 & -\frac{1}{2} & 1 & 0 & 9 \\ -\frac{1}{2} & 0 & \frac{3}{2} & 0 & 1 & 15 \end{bmatrix}$	3.3 Gauss-Jordan elimination

- To graph linear inequalities in two variables
- To solve systems of linear inequalities in two variables

Linear Inequalities in Two Variables

▎| APPLICATION PREVIEW |

CDF Appliances has assembly plants in Atlanta and Fort Worth, where the company produces a variety of kitchen appliances, including a 12-cup coffee maker and a cappuccino machine. At the Atlanta plant, 160 of the coffee makers and 200 of the cappuccino machines can be assembled each hour. At the Fort Worth plant, 800 of the coffee makers and 200 of the cappuccino machines can be assembled each hour. CDF Appliances expects orders for at least 64,000 of the coffee makers and at least 40,000 of the cappuccino machines. At each plant the number of assembly hours available for these two appliances is limited (constrained) by each plant's capacity and the need to fill the orders. Finding the assembly hours for each plant that satisfy all these constraints at the same time is called solving the system of inequalities. (See Example 4.)

One Linear Inequality in Two Variables

Before we look at systems of inequalities, we will discuss solutions of one inequality in two variables, such as $y < x$. The solutions of this inequality are the ordered pairs (x, y) that satisfy the inequality. Thus $(1, 0), (3, 2), (0, -1),$ and $(-2, -5)$ are solutions of $y < x$, but $(3, 7), (-4, -3),$ and $(2, 2)$ are not.

The graph of $y < x$ consists of all points in which the y-coordinate is less than the x-coordinate. The graph of the region $y < x$ can be found by graphing the line $y = x$ (as a dashed line, because the given inequality does not include $y = x$). This line separates the xy-plane into two **half-planes**, $y < x$ and $y > x$. We can determine which half-plane is the solution region by selecting as a **test point** any point *not on the line*; let's choose $(2, 0)$. Because the coordinates of this test point satisfy the inequality $y < x$, the half-plane containing this point is the solution region for $y < x$. (See Figure 4.1.) If the coordinates of the test point do not satisfy the inequality, then the other half-plane is the solution region. For example, say we had chosen $(0, 4)$ as our test point. Its coordinates do not satisfy $y < x$, so the half-plane that does *not* contain $(0, 4)$ is the solution region. (Note that we get the same region.)

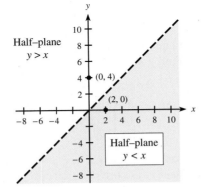

Figure 4.1

EXAMPLE 1   Graphing an Inequality

Graph the inequality $4x - 2y \leq 6$.

Solution

First we graph the line $4x - 2y = 6$, or (equivalently) $y = 2x - 3$, as a solid line, because points lying on the line satisfy the given inequality. Next we pick a test point that is not on the line. If we use $(0, 0)$, we see that its coordinates satisfy $4x - 2y \leq 6$—that is, $y \geq 2x - 3$. Hence the **solution region** is the line $y = 2x - 3$ and the half-plane that contains the test point $(0, 0)$. See Figure 4.2.

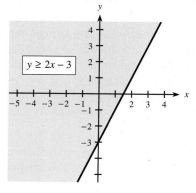

Figure 4.2

Figure 4.3

Calculator Note Graphing calculators can also be used to shade the solution region of an inequality. Details are shown in Appendix C, Section 4.1. Figure 4.3 shows a graphing calculator window for the solution region for $y \geq 2x - 3$.

Systems of Linear Inequalities If we have two or more inequalities in two variables, we can find the solutions that satisfy all the inequalities. We call the inequalities a **system of inequalities,** and the solution of the system can be found by finding the intersection of the solution sets of all the inequalities.

The solution set of the system of inequalities can be found by graphing the inequalities on the same set of axes and noting their points of intersection.

EXAMPLE 2   Graphical Solution of a System of Inequalities

Graph the solution of the system

$$\begin{cases} 3x - 2y \geq 4 \\ x + y - 3 > 0 \end{cases}$$

Solution

Begin by graphing the equations $3x - 2y = 4$ and $x + y = 3$ (from $x + y - 3 = 0$) by the intercept method: Find y when $x = 0$ and find x when $y = 0$.

$3x - 2y = 4$		$x + y = 3$	
x	y	x	y
0	-2	0	3
4/3	0	3	0

We graph $3x - 2y = 4$ as a solid line and $x + y = 3$ as a dashed line (see Figure 4.4(a)). We use any point not on either line as a test point; let's use $(0, 0)$. Note that the coordinates of $(0, 0)$ do not satisfy either $3x - 2y \geq 4$ or $x + y - 3 > 0$. Thus the solution region for each individual inequality is the half-plane that does not contain the point $(0, 0)$. Figure 4.4(b) indicates the half-plane solution for each inequality with arrows pointing from the line into the desired half-plane (away from the test point). The points that satisfy both of these inequalities lie in the intersection of the two individual solution regions, shown in Figure 4.4(c). This solution region is the graph of the solution of this system of inequalities.

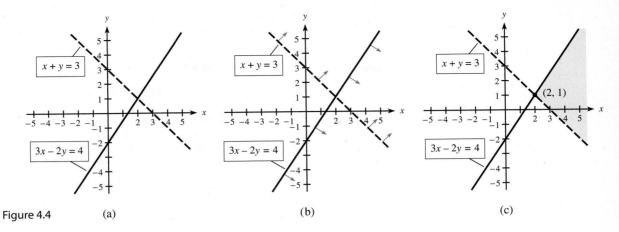

Figure 4.4   (a)   (b)   (c)

The point (2, 1) in Figure 4.4(c), where the two regions form a "corner," can be found by solving the *equations* $3x - 2y = 4$ and $x + y = 3$ simultaneously.

EXAMPLE 3   ## Graphical Solution of a System of Inequalities

Graph the solution of the system

$$\begin{cases} x + 2y \le 10 \\ 2x + y \le 14 \\ x \ge 0, y \ge 0 \end{cases}$$

Solution

The two inequalities $x \ge 0$ and $y \ge 0$ restrict the solution to Quadrant I (and the axes bounding Quadrant I).

We seek points in the first quadrant (on or above $y = 0$ and on or to the right of $x = 0$) that satisfy $x + 2y \le 10$ *and* $2x + y \le 14$. Note that the test point $(0, 0)$ satisfies both of these inequalities. Thus the solution region lies in Quadrant I and toward the origin from the lines $x + 2y = 10$ and $2x + y = 14$. (See Figure 4.5.) We can observe from the graph that the points $(0, 0)$, $(7, 0)$, and $(0, 5)$ are corners of the solution region. The corner $(6, 2)$ is found by solving the *equations* $y = 5 - \frac{1}{2}x$ and $y = 14 - 2x$ simultaneously as follows:

$$5 - \frac{1}{2}x = 14 - 2x$$

$$\frac{3}{2}x = 9$$

$$x = 6$$

$$y = 2$$

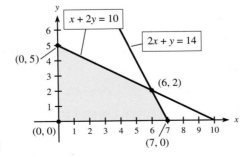

Figure 4.5

We will see that the corners of the solution region are important in solving linear programming problems.

Many applications restrict the variables to be nonnegative (such as $x \geq 0$ and $y \geq 0$ in Example 3). As we noted, the effect of this restriction is to limit the solution to Quadrant I and the axes bounding Quadrant I.

EXAMPLE 4   Manufacturing Constraints | APPLICATION PREVIEW |

CDF Appliances has assembly plants in Atlanta and Fort Worth, where the company produces a variety of kitchen appliances, including a 12-cup coffee maker and a cappuccino machine. At the Atlanta plant, 160 of the coffee makers and 200 of the cappuccino machines can be assembled each hour. At the Fort Worth plant, 800 of the coffee makers and 200 of the cappuccino machines can be assembled each hour. CDF Appliances expects orders for at least 64,000 of the coffee makers and at least 40,000 of the cappuccino machines. At each plant, the number of assembly hours available for these two appliances is constrained by each plant's capacity and the need to fill the orders. Write the system of inequalities that describes these assembly plant constraints, and graph the solution region for the system.

Solution

Let x be the number of assembly hours at the Atlanta plant, and let y be the number of assembly hours at the Fort Worth plant. The production capabilities of each facility and the anticipated orders are summarized in the following table.

	Atlanta	Fort Worth	Needed
Coffee maker	160/hr	800/hr	At least 64,000
Cappuccino machine	200/hr	200/hr	At least 40,000

This table and the fact that both x and y must be nonnegative give the following constraints.

$$160x + 800y \geq 64{,}000$$
$$200x + 200y \geq 40{,}000$$
$$x \geq 0, y \geq 0$$

The solution is restricted to Quadrant I and the axes that bound Quadrant I. The equation $160x + 800y = 64{,}000$ can be graphed with x- and y-intercepts:

$$x\text{-intercept: } y = 0 \quad \text{gives} \quad 160x = 64{,}000 \quad \text{or} \quad x = 400$$
$$y\text{-intercept: } x = 0 \quad \text{gives} \quad 800y = 64{,}000 \quad \text{or} \quad y = 80$$

The test point $(0, 0)$ does not satisfy $160x + 800y \geq 64{,}000$, so the region lies above the line (see Figure 4.6(a)). In like manner, the region satisfying $200x + 200y \geq 40{,}000$ lies above the line $200x + 200y = 40{,}000$, and the solution region for this system is shown in Figure 4.6(b).

The corner (150, 50) is found by solving simultaneously as follows.

$$\begin{cases} 160x + 800y = 64{,}000 \\ 200x + 200y = 40{,}000 \end{cases} \quad \text{is equivalent to} \quad \begin{cases} x + 5y = 400 & (1) \\ x + y = 200 & (2) \end{cases}$$

Finding equation (1) minus equation (2) gives one equation in one variable and allows us to complete the solution.

$$4y = 200, \quad \text{so} \quad y = 200/4 = 50 \quad \text{and} \quad x = 200 - y = 150$$

Any point in the shaded region of Figure 4.6(b) represents a possible number of assembly hours at each plant that would fill the orders.

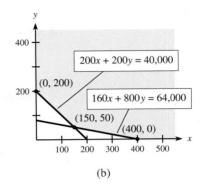

Figure 4.6   (a)   (b)

EXAMPLE 5   Land Management

A farm co-op has 6000 acres available to plant with corn and soybeans. Each acre of corn requires 9 gallons of fertilizer/herbicide and 3/4 hour of labor to harvest. Each acre of soybeans requires 3 gallons of fertilizer/herbicide and 1 hour of labor to harvest. The co-op has available at most 40,500 gallons of fertilizer/herbicide and at most 5250 hours of labor for harvesting. The number of acres of each crop is limited (constrained) by the available resources: land, fertilizer/herbicide, and labor for harvesting. Write the system of inequalities that describes the constraints and graph the solution region for the system.

Solution

If x represents the number of acres of corn and y represents the number of acres of soybeans, then both x and y must be nonnegative and we have the following constraints.

$$
\begin{array}{llll}
\text{Land acres:} & x + y \leq 6{,}000 & (1) \\
\text{Fertilizer/herbicide gallons:} & 9x + 3y \leq 40{,}500 & (2) \\
\text{Labor hours:} & \dfrac{3}{4}x + y \leq 5{,}250 & (3) \\
& x \geq 0, y \geq 0 &
\end{array}
$$

The intercepts of the lines associated with the inequalities are

$(6000, 0)$ and $(0, 6000)$ for the line $x + y = 6000$ (from Inequality (1))

$(4500, 0)$ and $(0, 13{,}500)$ for the line $9x + 3y = 40{,}500$ (from Inequality (2))

$(7000, 0)$ and $(0, 5250)$ for the line $\dfrac{3}{4}x + y = 5250$ (from Inequality (3))

The solution region is shaded in Figure 4.7, with three of the corners at $(0, 0)$, $(4500, 0)$, and $(0, 5250)$. The corner $(3750, 2250)$ is found by solving simultaneously.

$$\begin{cases} 9x + 3y = 40{,}500 & (4) \\ x + y = 6{,}000 & (5) \end{cases}$$

$$\begin{cases} 9x + 3y = 40{,}500 & (4) \\ -(3x + 3y = 18{,}000) & [3 \times \text{Eq. } (5)] \end{cases}$$
$$\overline{\qquad 6x \qquad\quad = 22{,}500}$$

$$x = \frac{22{,}500}{6} = 3750$$

$$y = 6000 - x = 2250$$

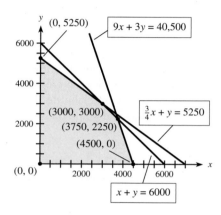

Figure 4.7

The corner $(3000, 3000)$ is found similarly by solving simultaneously with $x + y = 6000$ and $\frac{3}{4}x + y = 5250$.

Any point in the shaded region of Figure 4.7 represents a possible number of acres of corn and of soybeans that the co-op could plant, treat with fertilizer/herbicide, and harvest.

CHECKPOINT

1. Graph the region determined by the inequalities

$$2x + 3y \le 12$$
$$4x + 2y \le 16$$
$$x \ge 0, y \ge 0$$

2. Determine the corners of the region.

Calculator Note

Graphing calculators can also be used in the graphical solution of a system of inequalities. See Appendix C, Section 4.1 and Example 6 for details.

 EXAMPLE 6

Finding a Solution Region with a Graphing Calculator

Use a graphing calculator to find the following.

(a) Find the region determined by the inequalities below.

$$5x + 2y \le 54$$
$$2x + 4y \le 60$$
$$x \ge 0, y \ge 0$$

(b) Find the corners of this region.

Solution

(a) We first write the inequalities as equations, solved for y.

$$5x + 2y = 54 \Rightarrow y = 27 - \frac{5}{2}x$$

$$2x + 4y = 60 \Rightarrow y = 15 - \frac{1}{2}x$$

Figure 4.8

Graphing these equations with a graphing calculator and using shading shows the region satisfying the inequalities (see Figure 4.8).

(b) Finding the x- and y-intercepts and using the command INTERSECT with pairs of lines that form the borders of this region will give the points where the boundaries intersect. These points, (0, 0), (0, 15), (6, 12), and (10.8, 0), can also be found algebraically. These points are the corners of the solution region. These corners will be important to us in the graphical solutions of linear programming problems in the next section.

CHECKPOINT SOLUTIONS

1.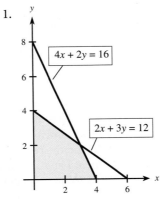

2. The graph shows corners at (0, 0), (0, 4), and (4, 0). A corner also occurs where $2x + 3y = 12$ and $4x + 2y = 16$ intersect. The point of intersection is $x = 3$, $y = 2$, so (3, 2) is a corner.

| EXERCISES | 4.1

In Problems 1–6, graph each inequality.

1. $y \leq 2x - 1$

2. $y \geq 4x - 5$

3. $\dfrac{x}{2} + \dfrac{y}{4} < 1$

4. $x - \dfrac{y}{3} < \dfrac{-2}{3}$

5. $0.4x \geq 0.8$

6. $\dfrac{-y}{8} > \dfrac{1}{4}$

In Problems 7–12, the graph of the boundary equations for each system of inequalities is shown with that system. Locate the solution region and find the corners.

7. $\begin{cases} x + 4y \leq 60 \\ 4x + 2y \leq 100 \\ x \geq 0, y \geq 0 \end{cases}$

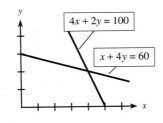

8. $\begin{cases} 4x + 3y \leq 240 \\ 5x - y \leq 110 \\ x \geq 0, y \geq 0 \end{cases}$

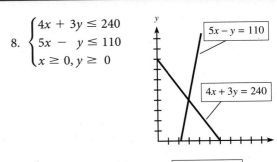

9. $\begin{cases} -3x + 4y \leq 18 \\ 2x + y \geq 10 \\ x + y \leq 15 \\ x \geq 0, y \geq 0 \end{cases}$

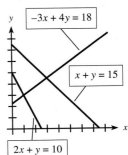

10.
$$\begin{cases} x + y \le 25 \\ 4x + y \le 40 \\ 3x + 8y \ge 88 \\ x \ge 0, y \ge 0 \end{cases}$$

11.
$$\begin{cases} x + 3y \ge 6 \\ 2x + 4y \ge 10 \\ 3x + y \ge 5 \\ x \ge 0, y \ge 0 \end{cases}$$

12.
$$\begin{cases} x + 4y \ge 10 \\ 4x + 2y \ge 10 \\ x + y \ge 4 \\ x \ge 0, y \ge 0 \end{cases}$$

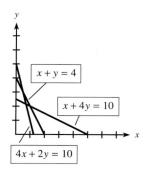

In Problems 13–26, graph the solution of each system of inequalities.

13.
$$\begin{cases} y < 2x \\ y > x - 1 \end{cases}$$

14.
$$\begin{cases} y > 3x - 4 \\ y < 2x + 3 \end{cases}$$

15.
$$\begin{cases} 2x + y < 3 \\ x - 2y \ge -1 \end{cases}$$

16.
$$\begin{cases} 3x + y > 4 \\ x - 2y < -1 \end{cases}$$

17.
$$\begin{cases} x + 5y \le 200 \\ 2x + 3y \le 134 \\ x \ge 0, y \ge 0 \end{cases}$$

18.
$$\begin{cases} -x + y \le 2 \\ x + 2y \le 10 \\ 3x + y \le 15 \\ x \ge 0, y \ge 0 \end{cases}$$

19.
$$\begin{cases} x + 2y \le 48 \\ x + y \le 30 \\ 2x + y \le 50 \\ x \ge 0, y \ge 0 \end{cases}$$

20.
$$\begin{cases} 3x + y \le 9 \\ 3x + 2y \le 12 \\ x + 2y \le 8 \\ x \ge 0, y \ge 0 \end{cases}$$

21.
$$\begin{cases} x + 2y \ge 19 \\ 3x + 2y \ge 29 \\ x \ge 0, y \ge 0 \end{cases}$$

22.
$$\begin{cases} 4x + y \ge 12 \\ x + y \ge 9 \\ x + 3y \ge 15 \\ x \ge 0, y \ge 0 \end{cases}$$

23.
$$\begin{cases} x + 3y \ge 3 \\ 2x + 3y \ge 5 \\ 2x + y \ge 3 \\ x \ge 0, y \ge 0 \end{cases}$$

24.
$$\begin{cases} x + 2y \ge 10 \\ 2x + y \ge 11 \\ x + y \ge 9 \\ x \ge 0, y \ge 0 \end{cases}$$

25.
$$\begin{cases} x + 2y \ge 20 \\ -3x + 2y \le 4 \\ x \ge 12 \\ x \ge 0, y \ge 0 \end{cases}$$

26.
$$\begin{cases} 3x + 2y \ge 75 \\ -3x + 5y \ge 30 \\ y \le 40 \\ x \ge 0, y \ge 0 \end{cases}$$

APPLICATIONS

27. *Management* The Wellbuilt Company produces two types of wood chippers, economy and deluxe. The deluxe model requires 3 hours to assemble and 1/2 hour to paint, and the economy model requires 2 hours to assemble and 1 hour to paint. The maximum number of assembly hours available is 24 per day, and the maximum number of painting hours available is 8 per day.
    (a) Write the system of inequalities that describes the constraints on the number of each type of wood chipper produced. Begin by identifying what x and y represent.
    (b) Graph the solution of the system of inequalities and find the corners of the solution region.

28. *Learning environments* An experiment that involves learning in animals requires placing white mice and rabbits into separate, controlled environments, environment I and environment II. The maximum amount of time available in environment I is 500 minutes, and the maximum amount of time available in environment II is 600 minutes. The white mice must spend 10 minutes in environment I and 25 minutes in environment II, and the rabbits must spend 15 minutes in environment I and 15 minutes in environment II.
    (a) Write a system of inequalities that describes the constraints on the number of each type of animal used in the experiment. Begin by identifying what x and y represent.
    (b) Graph the solution of the system of inequalities and find the corners of the solution region.

29. *Manufacturing* A company manufactures two types of electric hedge trimmers, one of which is cordless. The cord-type trimmer requires 2 hours to make, and the cordless model requires 4 hours. The company has only 800 work hours to use in manufacturing each day, and the packaging department can package only 300 trimmers per day.
    (a) Write the inequalities that describe the constraints on the number of each type of hedge trimmer produced. Begin by identifying what x and y represent.
    (b) Graph the region determined by these constraint inequalities.

30. *Manufacturing* Sierra Wood Products manufactures two high-quality products, rockers and bookshelf units. Its profit is $30 per rocker and $42 per bookshelf unit. Next week's production will be constrained by two limited resources, labor and wood. The labor available next week is expected to be at most 930 hours, and the amount of wood available is expected to be at most 2400 board feet. Each rocker requires 4 labor hours and

8 board feet of wood. Each bookshelf unit requires 3 labor hours and 12 board feet of wood.

(a) Write the inequalities that describe the constraints on the number of each product produced next week. Begin by identifying what x and y represent.

(b) Graph the region determined by these constraint inequalities.

31. *Advertising* Apex Motors manufactures luxury cars and sport utility vehicles. The most likely customers are high-income men and women, and company managers want to initiate an advertising campaign targeting these groups. They plan to run 1-minute spots on business/investment programs, where they can reach 7 million women and 4 million men from their target groups. They also plan 1-minute spots during sporting events, where they can reach 2 million women and 12 million men from their target groups. Apex feels that the ads must reach at least 30 million women and at least 28 million men who are prospective customers.

(a) Write the inequalities that describe the constraints on the number of each type of 1-minute spots needed to reach these target groups.

(b) Graph the region determined by these constraint inequalities.

32. *Manufacturing* The Video Star Company makes two different models of DVD players, which are assembled on two different assembly lines. Line 1 can assemble 30 units of the Star model and 40 units of the Prostar model per hour, and Line 2 can assemble 150 units of the Star model and 40 units of the Prostar model per hour. The company needs to produce at least 270 units of the Star model and 200 units of the Prostar model to fill an order.

(a) Write the inequalities that describe the production constraints on the number of each type of DVD player needed to fill the order.

(b) Graph the region determined by these constraint inequalities.

33. *Politics* A candidate wishes to use a combination of radio and television advertisements in her campaign. Research has shown that each 1-minute spot on television reaches 0.09 million people and each 1-minute spot on radio reaches 0.006 million. The candidate feels she must reach at least 2.16 million people, and she must buy a total of at least 80 minutes of advertisements.

(a) Write the inequalities that relate the number of each type of advertising to her needs.

(b) Graph the region determined by these constraint inequalities.

34. *Nutrition* In a hospital ward, the patients can be grouped into two general categories depending on their condition and the amount of solid foods they require in their diet. A combination of two diets is used for solid foods because they supply essential nutrients for recovery. The following table summarizes the patient groups and their minimum daily requirements.

	Diet A	Diet B	Daily Requirement
Group 1	4 oz per serving	1 oz per serving	26 oz
Group 2	2 oz per serving	1 oz per serving	18 oz

(a) Write the inequalities that describe how many servings of each diet are needed to provide the nutritional requirements.

(b) Graph the region determined by these constraint inequalities.

35. *Manufacturing* A sausage company makes two different kinds of hot dogs, regular and all beef. Each pound of all-beef hot dogs requires 0.75 lb of beef and 0.2 lb of spices, and each pound of regular hot dogs requires 0.18 lb of beef, 0.3 lb of pork, and 0.2 lb of spices. Suppliers can deliver at most 1020 lb of beef, at most 600 lb of pork, and at least 500 lb of spices.

(a) Write the inequalities that describe how many pounds of each type of hot dog can be produced.

(b) Graph the region determined by these constraint inequalities.

36. *Manufacturing* A cereal manufacturer makes two different kinds of cereal, Senior Citizen's Feast and Kids Go. Each pound of Senior Citizen's Feast requires 0.6 lb of wheat and 0.2 lb of vitamin-enriched syrup, and each pound of Kids Go requires 0.4 lb of wheat, 0.2 lb of sugar, and 0.2 lb of vitamin-enriched syrup. Suppliers can deliver at most 2800 lb of wheat, at most 800 lb of sugar, and at least 1000 lb of the vitamin-enriched syrup.

(a) Write the inequalities that describe how many pounds of each type of cereal can be made.

(b) Graph the region determined by these constraint inequalities.

- To use graphical methods to find the optimal value of a linear function subject to constraints

Linear Programming: Graphical Methods

| APPLICATION PREVIEW |

Many practical problems in business and economics seek to optimize some function (such as cost or profit) subject to complex relationships among capital, raw materials, labor, and so forth. Consider the following example.

A farm co-op has 6000 acres available to plant with corn and soybeans. Each acre of corn requires 9 gallons of fertilizer/herbicide and 3/4 hour of labor to harvest. Each acre of soybeans requires 3 gallons of fertilizer/herbicide and 1 hour of labor to harvest. The co-op has available at most 40,500 gallons of fertilizer/herbicide and at most 5250 hours of labor for harvesting. If the profits per acre are $60 for corn and $40 for soybeans, how many acres of each crop should the co-op plant to maximize their profit? What is the maximum profit?

The farm co-op's maximum profit can be found by using a mathematical technique called linear programming. (See Example 1.) Linear programming can be used to solve problems such as this if the limits on the variables (called constraints) can be expressed as linear inequalities and if the function that is to be maximized or minimized (called the objective function) is a linear function.

Feasible Regions and Solutions

Linear programming is widely used by businesses for problems that involve many variables (sometimes more than 100). In this section we begin our study of this important technique by considering problems involving two variables. With two variables we can use graphical methods to help solve the problem. The constraints form a system of linear inequalities in two variables that we can solve by graphing. The solution of the system of constraint inequalities determines a region, any point of which may yield the *optimal* (maximum or minimum) value for the objective function.* Hence any point in the region determined by the constraints is called a **feasible solution,** and the region itself is called the **feasible region.** In a linear programming problem, we seek the feasible solution that maximizes (or minimizes) the objective function.

EXAMPLE   1   Maximizing Profit | APPLICATION PREVIEW |

A farm co-op has 6000 acres available to plant with corn and soybeans. Each acre of corn requires 9 gallons of fertilizer/herbicide and 3/4 hour of labor to harvest. Each acre of soybeans requires 3 gallons of fertilizer/herbicide and 1 hour of labor to harvest. The co-op has available at most 40,500 gallons of fertilizer/herbicide and at most 5250 hours of labor for harvesting. If the profits per acre are $60 for corn and $40 for soybeans, how many acres of each crop should the co-op plant to maximize their profit? What is the maximum profit?

Solution

We begin by letting x equal the number of acres of corn and y equal the number of acres of soybeans. Because the profit P is $60 for each of the x acres of corn and $40 for each of the y acres of soybeans, the function that describes the co-op's profit is given by

$$\text{Profit} = P = 60x + 40y \quad (\text{in dollars})$$

The constraints for this farm co-op application were developed in Example 5 of Section 4.1.

---

*The region determined by the constraints must be *convex* for the optimal to exist. A convex region is one such that for any two points in the region, the segment joining those points lies entirely within the region. We restrict our discussion to convex regions.

Combining the profit equation and the constraints found earlier gives the linear programming problem

$$\text{Maximize Profit} \quad P = 60x + 40y$$
$$\text{Subject to: } x + y \leq 6{,}000$$
$$9x + 3y \leq 40{,}500$$
$$\frac{3}{4}x + y \leq 5{,}250$$
$$x \geq 0, y \geq 0$$

The solution of the system of inequalities, or constraints, forms the feasible region shaded in Figure 4.9(a). *Any* point inside the shaded region or on its boundary is a feasible (possible) solution of the problem. For example, point A (1000, 2000) is in the feasible region, and at this point the profit is $P = 60(1000) + 40(2000) = 140{,}000$ dollars.

To find the maximum value of $P = 60x + 40y$, we cannot possibly evaluate P at every point in the feasible region. However, many points in the feasible region may correspond to the same value of P. For example, at point A in Figure 4.9(a), the value of P is 140,000 and the profit function becomes

$$60x + 40y = 140{,}000 \quad \text{or} \quad y = \frac{140{,}000 - 60x}{40} = 3500 - \frac{3}{2}x$$

The graph of this function is a line with slope $m = -3/2$ and y-intercept 3500. Many points in the feasible region lie on this line (see Figure 4.9(b)), and their coordinates all result in a profit $P = 140{,}000$. Any point in the feasible region that results in profit P satisfies

$$P = 60x + 40y \quad \text{or} \quad y = \frac{P - 60x}{40} = \frac{P}{40} - \frac{3}{2}x$$

In this form we can see that different P-values change the y-intercept for the line but the slope is always $m = -3/2$, so the lines for different P-values are parallel. Figure 4.9(b) shows the feasible region and the lines representing the objective function for $P = 140{,}000$, $P = 315{,}000$, and $P = 440{,}000$. Note that the line corresponding to $P = 315{,}000$ intersects the feasible region at the corner point (3750, 2250). Values of P less than 315,000 give lines that pass through the feasible region, but represent a profit less than \$315,000 (such as the line for $P = 140{,}000$ through point A). Similarly, values of P greater than 315,000 give lines that miss the feasible region, and hence cannot be solutions of the problem.

Thus, the farm co-op's maximum profit, subject to the constraints (i.e., the solution of the co-op's linear programming problem), is $P = \$315{,}000$ when $x = 3750$ and $y = 2250$. That is, when the co-op plants 3750 acres of corn and 2250 acres of soybeans, it achieves maximum profit of \$315,000.

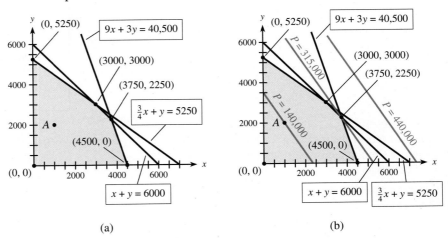

Figure 4.9   (a)   (b)

Notice in Example 1 that the objective function was maximized at one of the "corners" (vertices) of the feasible region. This is not a coincidence; it turns out that a corner will always lie on the objective function line corresponding to the optimal value.

Solving Graphically   The feasible region in Figure 4.9 is an example of a **closed and bounded region** because it is entirely enclosed by, and includes, the lines associated with the constraints.

Solutions of Linear Programming Problems

1. When the feasible region for a linear programming problem is closed and bounded, the objective function has a maximum value and a minimum value.

2. When the feasible region is not closed and bounded, the objective function may have a maximum only, a minimum only, or no solution.

3. If a linear programming problem has a solution, then the optimal (maximum or minimum) value of an objective function occurs at a corner of the feasible region determined by the constraints.

4. If the objective function has its optimal value at two corners, then it also has that optimal value at any point on the line (boundary) connecting those two corners.

Thus, for a closed and bounded region, we can find the maximum or minimum value of the objective function by evaluating the function at each of the corners of the feasible region formed by the solution of the constraint inequalities. If the feasible region is not closed and bounded, we must check to make sure the objective function has an optimal value.

The steps involved in solving a linear programming problem are as follows.

Linear Programming (Graphical Method)

Procedure	Example
To find the optimal value of a function subject to constraints:	Find the maximum and minimum values of $C = 2x + 3y$ subject to the constraints $$\begin{cases} x + 2y \le 10 \\ 2x + \ y \le 14 \\ x \ge 0, y \ge 0 \end{cases}$$
1. Write the objective function and constraint inequalities from the problem.	1. Objective function: $C = 2x + 3y$ Constraints: $\quad\quad x + 2y \le 10$ $\quad\quad\quad\quad\quad\ 2x + \ y \le 14$ $\quad\quad\quad\quad\quad\ x \ge 0, y \ge 0$
2. Graph the solution of the constraint system. (a) If the feasible region is closed and bounded, proceed to Step 3. (b) If the region is not closed and bounded, check whether an optimal value exists. If not, state this. If so, proceed to Step 3.	2. The constraint region is closed and bounded. See Figure 4.10. Figure 4.10
3. Find the corners of the resulting feasible region. This may require simultaneous solution of two or more pairs of boundary equations.	3. Corners are $(0, 0)$, $(0, 5)$, $(6, 2)$, $(7, 0)$.
4. Evaluate the objective function at each corner of the feasible region determined by the constraints.	4. At $(0, 0)$, $C = 2x + 3y = 2(0) + 3(0) = 0$ At $(0, 5)$, $C = 2x + 3y = 2(0) + 3(5) = 15$ At $(6, 2)$, $C = 2x + 3y = 2(6) + 3(2) = 18$ At $(7, 0)$, $C = 2x + 3y = 2(7) + 3(0) = 14$
5. If two corners give the optimal value of the objective function, then all points on the boundary line joining these two corners also optimize the function.	5. The function is maximized at $x = 6$, $y = 2$. The maximum value is $C = 18$. The function is minimized at $x = 0$, $y = 0$. The minimum value is $C = 0$.

EXAMPLE 2 Maximizing Revenue

STANDARD   PLUSH

Chairco manufactures two types of chairs, standard and plush. Standard chairs require 2 hours to construct and finish, and plush chairs require 3 hours to construct and finish. Upholstering takes 1 hour for standard chairs and 3 hours for plush chairs. There are 240 hours per day available for construction and finishing, and 150 hours per day are available for upholstering. If the revenue for standard chairs is $89 and for plush chairs is $133.50, how many of each type should be produced each day to maximize revenue?

Solution

Let x be the number of standard chairs produced each day, and let y be the number of plush chairs produced. Then the daily revenue function is given by $R = 89x + 133.5y$. There are constraints for construction and finishing (no more than 240 hours/day) and for upholstering (no more than 150 hours/day). Thus we have the following.

$$\text{Construction/finishing constraint:} \quad 2x + 3y \leq 240$$
$$\text{Upholstering constraint:} \quad x + 3y \leq 150$$

Because all quantities must be nonnegative, we also have the constraints $x \geq 0$ and $y \geq 0$. Thus we seek to solve the following problem.

$$\text{Maximize } R = 89x + 133.5y \text{ subject to}$$
$$2x + 3y \leq 240$$
$$x + 3y \leq 150$$
$$x \geq 0, y \geq 0$$

The feasible set is the closed and bounded region shaded in Figure 4.11. The corners of the feasible region are $(0, 0)$, $(120, 0)$, $(0, 50)$, and $(90, 20)$. All of these are obvious except $(90, 20)$, which can be found by solving $2x + 3y = 240$ and $x + 3y = 150$ simultaneously. Testing the objective function at the corners gives the following.

At $(0, 0)$, $\quad R = 89x + 133.5y = 89(0) + 133.5(0) = 0$
At $(120, 0)$, $\quad R = 89(120) + 133.5(0) = 10{,}680$
At $(0, 50)$, $\quad R = 89(0) + 133.5(50) = 6675$
At $(90, 20)$, $\quad R = 89(90) + 133.5(20) = 10{,}680$

Maximum at two corners

Figure 4.11

Thus the maximum revenue of $10,680 occurs at either the point $(120, 0)$ or the point $(90, 20)$. This means that the revenue function will be maximized not only at these two corner points but also at any point on the segment joining them. Since the number of each type of chair must be an integer, Chairco has maximum revenue of $10,680 at any pair of integer values along the segment joining $(120, 0)$ and $(90, 20)$. For example, the point $(105, 10)$ is on this segment, and the revenue at this point is also $10,680:

$$89x + 133.5y = 89(105) + 133.5(10) = 10{,}680$$

CHECKPOINT

1. Find the maximum and minimum values of the objective function $f = 4x + 3y$ on the shaded region in the figure, determined by the following constraints.

$$\begin{cases} 2x + 3y \leq 12 \\ 4x - 2y \leq 8 \\ x \geq 0, y \geq 0 \end{cases}$$

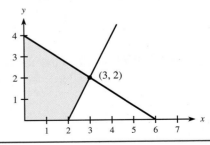

The examples so far have involved closed and bounded regions. Similar procedures apply for an unbounded region, but optimal solutions are no longer guaranteed.

EXAMPLE 3   Minimization

Find the maximum and minimum values (if they exist) of $C = x + y$ subject to the constraints

$$3x + 2y \geq 12$$
$$x + 3y \geq 11$$
$$x \geq 0, y \geq 0$$

Solution

The graph of the constraint system is shown in Figure 4.12(a). Note that the feasible region is not closed and bounded, so we must check whether optimal values exist. This check is done by graphing $C = x + y$ for selected values of C and noting the trend. Figure 4.12(b) shows the solution region with graphs of $C = x + y$ for $C = 3$, $C = 5$, and $C = 8$. Note that the objective function has a minimum but no maximum.

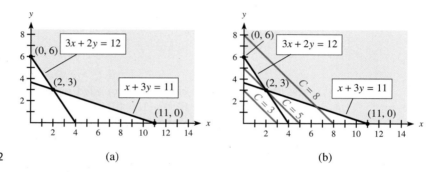

Figure 4.12   (a)   (b)

The corners $(0, 6)$ and $(11, 0)$ can be identified from the graph. The third corner, $(2, 3)$, can be found by solving the equations $3x + 2y = 12$ and $x + 3y = 11$ simultaneously.

$$
\begin{array}{r}
3x + 2y = 12 \\
-3x - 9y = -33 \\
\hline
-7y = -21 \quad \Rightarrow y = 3 \quad \text{and} \quad x = 2
\end{array}
$$

Examining the value of C at each corner point, we have

$$
\begin{aligned}
\text{At } (0, 6), \quad & C = x + y = 0 + 6 = 6 \\
\text{At } (11, 0), \quad & C = x + y = 11 + 0 = 11 \\
\text{At } (2, 3), \quad & C = x + y = 2 + 3 = 5
\end{aligned}
$$

Thus, we conclude the following:

Minimum value of $C = x + y$ is 5 at $(2, 3)$.
Maximum value of $C = x + y$ does not exist.

Note that C can be made arbitrarily large in the feasible region.

CHECKPOINT

2. Find the maximum and minimum values (if they exist) of the objective function $g = 3x + 4y$ subject to the following constraints.

$$x + 2y \geq 12, \quad x \geq 0$$
$$3x + 4y \geq 30, \quad y \geq 2$$

EXAMPLE **4**   **Minimizing Production Costs**

Two chemical plants, one at Macon and one at Jonesboro, produce three types of fertilizer, low phosphorus (LP), medium phosphorus (MP), and high phosphorus (HP). At each plant, the fertilizer is produced in a single production run, so the three types are produced in fixed proportions. The Macon plant produces 1 ton of LP, 2 tons of MP, and 3 tons of HP in a single operation, and it charges $600 for what is produced in one operation, whereas one operation of the Jonesboro plant produces 1 ton of LP, 5 tons of MP, and 1 ton of HP, and it charges $1000 for what it produces in one operation. If a customer needs 100 tons of LP, 260 tons of MP, and 180 tons of HP, how many production runs should be ordered from each plant to minimize costs?

Solution

If x represents the number of operations requested from the Macon plant and y represents the number of operations requested from the Jonesboro plant, then we seek to minimize cost

$$C = 600x + 1000y$$

The following table summarizes production capabilities and requirements.

	Macon Plant	Jonesboro Plant	Requirements
Units of LP	1	1	100
Units of MP	2	5	260
Units of HP	3	1	180

Using the number of operations requested and the fact that requirements must be met or exceeded, we can formulate the following constraints.

$$\begin{cases} x + y \geq 100 \\ 2x + 5y \geq 260 \\ 3x + y \geq 180 \\ x \geq 0, y \geq 0 \end{cases}$$

Graphing this system gives the feasible set shown in Figure 4.13. The objective function has a minimum even though the feasible set is not closed and bounded. The corners are $(0, 180)$, $(40, 60)$, $(80, 20)$, and $(130, 0)$, where $(40, 60)$ is obtained by solving $x + y = 100$ and $3x + y = 180$ simultaneously, and where $(80, 20)$ is obtained by solving $x + y = 100$ and $2x + 5y = 260$ simultaneously.

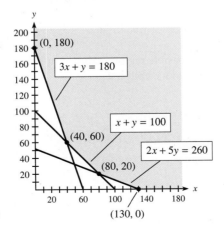

Figure 4.13

Evaluating $C = 600x + 1000y$ at each corner, we obtain

$$
\begin{array}{ll}
\text{At } (0, 180), & C = 600(0) + 1000(180) = 180{,}000 \\
\text{At } (40, 60), & C = 600(40) + 1000(60) = 84{,}000 \\
\text{At } (80, 20), & C = 600(80) + 1000(20) = 68{,}000 \\
\text{At } (130, 0), & C = 600(130) + 1000(0) = 78{,}000
\end{array}
$$

Thus, by placing orders requiring 80 production runs from the Macon plant and 20 production runs from the Jonesboro plant, the customer's needs will be satisfied at a minimum cost of $68,000.

EXAMPLE 5   Maximization Subject to Constraints with Graphing Calculators

Use a graphing calculator to maximize $f = 5x + 11y$ subject to the constraints

$$
\begin{array}{l}
5x + 2y \le 54 \\
2x + 4y \le 60 \\
x \ge 0, y \ge 0
\end{array}
$$

Solution

The feasible region (with dark shading) is shown in Figure 4.14. The boundaries intersect at $(0, 0)$, $(0, 15)$, $(6, 12)$ and $(10.8, 0)$. These corners can be found with INTERSECT and/or TRACE. (See Appendix C, Section 4.2, for details.) These corners can also be found algebraically. Testing the objective function at each corner gives the values of f shown below.

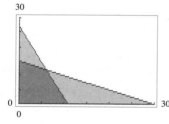

Figure 4.14

$$
\begin{array}{ll}
\text{At } (0, 0), & f = 5(0) + 11(0) = 0 \\
\text{At } (0, 15), & f = 5(0) + 11(15) = 165 \\
\text{At } (6, 12), & f = 5(6) + 11(12) = 162 \\
\text{At } (10.8, 0), & f = 5(10.8) + 11(0) = 54
\end{array}
$$

The maximum value is $f = 165$ at $x = 0, y = 15$.

CHECKPOINT SOLUTIONS

1. The values of $f = 4x + 3y$ at the corners are found as follows.

$$
\begin{array}{ll}
\text{At } (0, 0), & f = 4(0) + 3(0) = 0 \\
\text{At } (2, 0), & f = 4(2) + 3(0) = 8 \\
\text{At } (3, 2), & f = 4(3) + 3(2) = 18 \\
\text{At } (0, 4), & f = 4(0) + 3(4) = 12
\end{array}
$$

The maximum value of f is 18 at $x = 3, y = 2$, and the minimum value is $f = 0$ at $x = 0, y = 0$.

2. The graph of the feasible region is shown in Figure 4.15. The values of $g = 3x + 4y$ at the corners are found as follows:

$$
\begin{array}{ll}
\text{At } (0, 7.5), & g = 3(0) + 4(7.5) = 30 \\
\text{At } (6, 3), & g = 3(6) + 4(3) = 30 \\
\text{At } (8, 2), & g = 3(8) + 4(2) = 32
\end{array}
$$

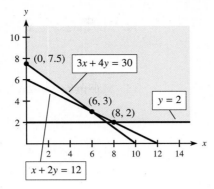

Figure 4.15

The minimum value of g is 30 at both $(0, 7.5)$ and $(6, 3)$. Thus any point on the border joining $(0, 7.5)$ and $(6, 3)$ will give the minimum value 30. For example, $(2, 6)$ is on this border and gives the value $6 + 24 = 30$. The maximum value of g does not exist; g can be made arbitrarily large on this feasible region.

| EXERCISES | 4.2

In Problems 1–4, use the given feasible region determined by the constraint inequalities to find the maximum and minimum of the given objective function (if they exist).

1. $C = 9x + 10y$

2. $C = 2x + 7y$

3. $f = 5x + 2y$

4. $f = 4x + 5y$

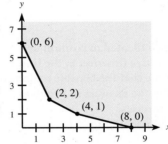

In each of Problems 5–8, the graph of the feasible region is shown. Find the corners of each feasible region, and then find the maximum and minimum of the given objective function (if they exist).

5. $f = 3x + 2y$

6. $f = 5x + 8y$

7. $g = 2x + 3y$

8. $g = x + 3y$

In Problems 9–12, find the indicated maximum or minimum value of the objective function in the linear programming problem. Note that the feasible regions for these problems are found in the answers to Problems 19, 20, 23, and 24 in the 4.1 Exercises.

9. Maximize $f = 30x + 50y$ subject to
$$x + 2y \le 48$$
$$x + y \le 30$$
$$2x + y \le 50$$
$$x \ge 0, y \ge 0$$

10. Maximize $f = 7x + 10y$ subject to
$$3x + y \le 9$$
$$3x + 2y \le 12$$
$$x + 2y \le 8$$
$$x \ge 0, y \ge 0$$

11. Minimize $g = 100x + 22y$ subject to
$$x + 3y \ge 3$$
$$2x + 3y \ge 5$$
$$2x + y \ge 3$$
$$x \ge 0, y \ge 0$$

12. Minimize $g = 12x + 8y$ subject to
$$x + 2y \ge 10$$
$$2x + y \ge 11$$
$$x + y \ge 9$$
$$x \ge 0, y \ge 0$$

In Problems 13–24, solve the following linear programming problems. Restrict $x \ge 0$ and $y \ge 0$.

13. Maximize $f = 3x + 4y$ subject to
$$x + y \le 6$$
$$2x + y \le 10$$
$$y \le 4$$

14. Maximize $f = x + 3y$ subject to
$$x + 4y \le 12$$
$$y \le 2$$
$$x + y \le 9$$

15. Maximize $f = 2x + 6y$ subject to
$$x + y \le 7$$
$$2x + y \le 12$$
$$x + 3y \le 15$$

16. Maximize $f = 4x + 2y$ subject to
$$x + 2y \le 20$$
$$x + y \le 12$$
$$4x + y \le 36$$

17. Minimize $g = 7x + 6y$ subject to
$$5x + 2y \ge 16$$
$$3x + 7y \ge 27$$

18. Minimize $g = 22x + 17y$ subject to
$$8x + 5y \ge 100$$
$$12x + 25y \ge 360$$

19. Minimize $g = 3x + y$ subject to
$$4x + y \ge 11$$
$$3x + 2y \ge 12$$

20. Minimize $g = 50x + 70y$ subject to
$$11x + 15y \ge 225$$
$$x + 3y \ge 27$$

21. Maximize $f = x + 2y$ subject to
$$x + y \ge 4$$
$$2x + y \le 8$$
$$y \le 4$$

22. Maximize $f = 3x + 5y$ subject to
$$2x + 4y \ge 8$$
$$3x + y \le 7$$
$$y \le 4$$

23. Minimize $g = 40x + 25y$ subject to
$$x + y \ge 100$$
$$-x + y \le 20$$
$$-2x + 3y \ge 30$$

24. Minimize $g = 3x + 8y$ subject to
$$4x - 5y \ge 50$$
$$-x + 2y \ge 4$$
$$x + y \le 80$$

APPLICATIONS

25. *Manufacturing* The Wellbuilt Company produces two types of wood chippers, economy and deluxe. The deluxe model requires 3 hours to assemble and $\frac{1}{2}$ hour to paint, and the economy model requires 2 hours to assemble and 1 hour to paint. The maximum number of assembly hours available is 24 per day, and the maximum number of painting hours available is 8 per day. If the profit on the deluxe model is $15 per unit and the profit on the economy model is $12 per unit, how many units of each model will maximize profit? (See Problem 27 in the 4.1 Exercises.)

26. *Learning environments* An experiment involving learning in animals requires placing white mice and rabbits into separate, controlled environments, environment I and environment II. The maximum amount of time available in environment I is 500 minutes, and the maximum amount of time available in environment II is 600 minutes. The white mice must spend 10 minutes in environment I and 25 minutes in environment II, and the rabbits must spend 15 minutes in environment I and 15 minutes in environment II. Find the maximum possible number of animals that can be used in the experiment, and find the number of white mice and the number of rabbits that can be used. (See Problem 28 in the 4.1 Exercises.)

27. *Manufacturing* A company manufactures two types of electric hedge trimmers, one of which is cordless. The cord-type trimmer requires 2 hours to make, and the cordless model requires 4 hours. The company has only 800 work hours to use in manufacturing each day, and the packaging department can package only 300 trimmers per day. If the company sells the cord-type model for $22.50 and the cordless model for $45.00, how many of each type should it produce per day to maximize its sales? (See Problem 29 in the 4.1 Exercises.)

28. *Manufacturing* Sierra Wood Products manufactures two high-quality products, rockers and bookshelf units. Its profit is $30 per rocker and $42 per bookshelf unit. Next week's production will be constrained by two limited resources, labor and wood. The labor available next week is expected to be at most 930 hours, and the amount of wood available is expected to be at most 2400 board feet. Each rocker requires 4 labor hours and 8 board feet of wood. Each bookshelf unit requires 3 labor hours and 12 board feet of wood. Find how many rockers and bookshelf units should be produced next week to maximize Sierra's profit. Find the maximum profit. (See Problem 30 in the 4.1 Exercises.)

29. *Politics* A candidate wishes to use a combination of radio and television advertisements in her campaign. Research has shown that each 1-minute spot on television reaches 0.09 million people and that each 1-minute spot on radio reaches 0.006 million. The candidate feels she must reach at least 2.16 million people, and she must buy a total of at least 80 minutes of advertisements. How many minutes of each medium should be used to minimize costs if television costs $500/minute and radio costs $100/minute? (See Problem 33 in the 4.1 Exercises.)

30. *Nutrition* In a hospital ward, the patients can be grouped into two general categories depending on their condition and the amount of solid foods they require in their diet. A combination of two diets is used for solid foods because they supply essential nutrients for recovery, but each diet has an amount of a substance deemed detrimental. The following table summarizes the patient group, minimum diet requirements, and the amount of the detrimental substance. How many servings from each diet should be given each day in order to minimize the intake of this detrimental substance? (See Problem 34 in the 4.1 Exercises.)

	Diet A	Diet B	Daily Requirement
Group 1	4 oz per serving	1 oz per serving	26 oz
Group 2	2 oz per serving	1 oz per serving	18 oz
Detrimental substance	0.18 oz per serving	0.09 oz per serving	

31. *Production scheduling* Newjet, Inc. manufactures inkjet printers and laser printers. The company has the capacity to make 70 printers per day, and it has 120 hours of labor per day available. It takes 1 hour to make an inkjet printer and 3 hours to make a laser printer. The profits are $40 per inkjet printer and $60 per laser printer. Find the number of each type of printer that should be made to give maximum profit, and find the maximum profit.

32. *Production scheduling* At one of its factories, a jeans manufacturer makes two styles: #891 and #917. Each pair of style-891 takes 10 minutes to cut out and 20 minutes to assemble and finish. Each pair of style-917 takes 10 minutes to cut out and 30 minutes to assemble and finish. The plant has enough workers to provide at most 7500 minutes per day for cutting and at most 19,500 minutes per day for assembly and finishing. The profit on each pair of style-891 is $6.00 and the profit on each pair of style-917 is $7.50. How many pairs of each style should be produced per day to obtain maximum profit? Find the maximum daily profit.

33. *Nutrition* A privately owned lake contains two types of game fish, bass and trout. The owner provides two types of food, A and B, for these fish. Bass require 2 units of food A and 4 units of food B, and trout require 5 units of food A and 2 units of food B. If the owner has 800 units of each food, find the maximum number of fish that the lake can support.

34. *Nutrition* In a zoo, there is a natural habitat containing several feeding areas. One of these areas serves as a feeding area for two species, I and II, and it is supplied each day with 120 pounds of food A, 110 pounds of food B, and 57 pounds of food C. Each individual of species I requires 5 lb of A, 5 lb of B, and 2 lb of C, and each individual of species II requires 6 lb of A, 4 lb of B, and 3 lb of C. Find the maximum number of these species that can be supported.

Shadow prices—land management **For Problems 35 and 36, refer to the farm co-op application in Example 1. Rework that linear programming problem with the indicated changes in one constraint and answer the questions.**

35. (a) If one more acre of land became available (for a total of 6001 acres), how would this change the co-op's planting strategy and its maximum profit?

   (b) Repeat part (a) if 8 more acres of land were available.

   (c) Based on parts (a) and (b), what is the profit value of each additional acre of land? This value is called the **shadow price** of an acre of land.

36. (a) If one more gallon of fertilizer/herbicide became available (for a total of 40,501 gallons), how would this change the co-op's planting strategy and its maximum profit?

   (b) Repeat part (a) if 8 more gallons of fertilizer/herbicide were available.

   (c) Based on parts (a) and (b), what is the profit value of each additional gallon of fertilizer/herbicide (that is, the shadow price of a gallon of fertilizer/herbicide)?

37. *Manufacturing* Two factories produce three different types of kitchen appliances. The following table summarizes the production capacity, the number of each type of appliance ordered, and the daily operating costs for the factories. How many days should each factory operate to fill the orders at minimum cost? Find the minimum cost.

	Factory 1	Factory 2	Number Ordered
Appliance 1	80/day	20/day	1600
Appliance 2	10/day	10/day	500
Appliance 3	20/day	70/day	2000
Daily cost	$10,000	$20,000	

38. *Nutrition* In a laboratory experiment, two separate foods are given to experimental animals. Each food contains essential ingredients, A and B, for which the animals have a minimum requirement, and each food also has an ingredient C, which can be harmful to the animals. The following table summarizes this information.

	Food 1	Food 2	Required
Ingredient A	10 units/g	3 units/g	49 units
Ingredient B	6 units/g	12 units/g	60 units
Ingredient C	3 units/g	1 unit/g	

How many grams of foods 1 and 2 should be given to the animals in order to satisfy the requirements for A and B while minimizing the amount of ingredient C ingested?

39. *Manufacturing* The Janie Gioffre Drapery Company makes three types of draperies at two different locations. At location I, it can make 10 pairs of deluxe drapes, 20 pairs of better drapes, and 13 pairs of standard drapes per day. At location II, it can make 20 pairs of deluxe, 50 pairs of better, and 6 pairs of standard per day. The company has orders for 2000 pairs of deluxe drapes, 4200 pairs of better drapes, and 1200 pairs of standard drapes. If the daily costs are $500 per day at location I and $800 per day at location II, how many days should Janie schedule at each location in order to fill the orders at minimum cost? Find the minimum cost.

40. *Nutrition* Two foods contain only proteins, carbohydrates, and fats. Food A costs $1 per pound and contains 30% protein and 50% carbohydrates. Food B costs $1.50 per pound and contains 20% protein and 75% carbohydrates. What combination of these two foods provides at least 1 pound of protein, $2\frac{1}{2}$ pounds of carbohydrates, and $\frac{1}{4}$ pound of fat at the lowest cost?

41. *Manufacturing* A sausage company makes two different kinds of hot dogs, regular and all beef. Each pound of all-beef hot dogs requires 0.75 lb of beef and 0.2 lb of spices, and each pound of regular hot dogs requires 0.18 lb of beef, 0.3 lb of pork, and 0.2 lb of spices. Suppliers can deliver at most 1020 lb of beef, at most 600 lb of pork, and at least 500 lb of spices. If the profit is $0.60 on each pound of all-beef hot dogs and $0.40 on each pound of regular hot dogs, how many pounds of each should be produced to obtain maximum profit? What is the maximum profit?

42. *Manufacturing* A cereal manufacturer makes two different kinds of cereal, Senior Citizen's Feast and Kids Go. Each pound of Senior Citizen's Feast requires 0.6 lb of wheat and 0.2 lb of vitamin-enriched syrup, and each pound of Kids Go requires 0.4 lb of wheat, 0.2 lb of sugar, and 0.2 lb of vitamin-enriched syrup. Suppliers can deliver at most 2800 lb of wheat, at most 800 lb of sugar, and at least 1000 lb of the vitamin-enriched syrup. If the profit is $0.90 on each pound of Senior Citizen's Feast and $1.00 on each pound of Kids Go, find the number of pounds of each cereal that should be produced to obtain maximum profit. Find the maximum profit.

43. *Shipping costs* TV Circuit has 30 large-screen televisions in a warehouse in Erie and 60 large-screen televisions in a warehouse in Pittsburgh. Thirty-five are needed in a store in Blairsville, and 40 are needed in a store in Youngstown. It costs $18 to ship from Pittsburgh to Blairsville and $22 to ship from Pittsburgh to Youngstown, whereas it costs $20 to ship from Erie to Blairsville and $25 to ship from Erie to Youngstown. How many televisions should be shipped from each warehouse to each store to minimize the shipping cost? *Hint:* If the number shipped from Pittsburgh to Blairsville is represented by x, then the number shipped from Erie to Blairsville is represented by $35 - x$.

44. *Construction* A contractor builds two types of homes. The Carolina requires one lot, $160,000 capital, and 160 worker-days of labor, whereas the Savannah requires one lot, $240,000 capital, and 160 worker-days of labor. The contractor owns 300 lots and has $48,000,000 available capital and 43,200 worker-days of labor. The profit on the Carolina is $40,000 and the profit on the Savannah is $50,000. Find how many of each type of home should be built to maximize profit. Find the maximum possible profit.

45. *Management* A bank has two types of branches. A satellite branch employs 3 people, requires $100,000 to construct and open, and generates an average daily revenue of $10,000. A full-service branch employs 6 people, requires $140,000 to construct and open, and generates an average daily revenue of $18,000. The bank has up to $2.98 million available to open new branches, and has decided to limit the new branches to a maximum of 25 and to hire at most 120 new employees.

   (a) How many branches of each type should the bank open in order to maximize the average daily revenue? Find the maximum average daily revenue.

   (b) At the optimal solution from part (a), analyze the bank's constraints (number of new branches, number of new employees, and budget) to determine the "Amount Available," "Amount Used," and "Amount Not Used (Slack)."

   (c) Obtaining additional quantities of which constraint items would have the potential to increase the bank's average daily revenue? Explain.

(d) Obtaining more of which constraint item would not increase average daily revenue? Explain.

46. *Manufacturing* A company manufactures two different sizes of boat lifts. Each size requires some time in the welding and assembly department and some time in the parts and packaging department. The smaller lift requires $\frac{3}{4}$ hour in welding and assembly and $1\frac{2}{3}$ hours in parts and packaging. The larger lift requires $1\frac{1}{2}$ hours in welding and assembly and 1 hour in parts and packaging. The factory has 156 hours/day available in welding and assembly and 174 hours/day available in parts and packaging. Furthermore, daily demand for the lifts is at most 90 large and at most 100 small, and profits are $50 for each large lift and $30 for each small lift.

   (a) How many of each type of boat lift should be manufactured each day in order to maximize the profit? Find the maximum profit.

   (b) At the optimal solution in part (a), analyze the company's constraints (welding and assembly hours, parts and packaging hours, and demand) to determine the "Amount Available," "Amount Used," and "Amount Not Used (Slack)."

   (c) Obtaining additional quantities of which constraint items would have the potential to increase the company's profit? Explain.

   (d) Obtaining more of which constraint item would not increase profit? Explain.

OBJECTIVE

4.3

- To use the simplex method to maximize functions subject to constraints

The Simplex Method: Maximization

▮ | APPLICATION PREVIEW | ▮

The Solar Technology Company manufactures three different types of hand calculators and classifies them as scientific, business, and graphing according to their calculating capabilities. The three types have production requirements given by the following table.

	Scientific	Business	Graphing
Electronic circuit components	5	7	10
Assembly time (hours)	1	3	4
Cases	1	1	1

The firm has a monthly limit of 90,000 circuit components, 30,000 hours of labor, and 9000 cases. If the profit is $6 for each scientific, $13 for each business, and $20 for each graphing calculator, the number of each that should be produced to yield maximum profit and the amount of that maximum possible profit can be found by using the simplex method of linear programming. (See Example 3.)

The Simplex Method

The graphical method for solving linear programming problems is practical only when there are two variables. The method discussed in this section, the **simplex method,** is especially useful if there are more than two variables in a problem. This method gives a systematic way of moving from one feasible corner of the convex region to another in such a way that the value of the objective function increases until an optimal value is reached or it is discovered that no solution exists.

The simplex method was developed by George Dantzig in 1947. One of the earliest applications of the method was to the scheduling problem that arose in connection with the Berlin airlift, begun in 1948. Since then, linear programming and the simplex method have been used to solve optimization problems in a wide variety of businesses. In fact, in a recent survey of Fortune 500 firms, 85% of the respondents indicated that they use linear programming.

In 1984, N. Karmarkar, a researcher at Bell Labs, developed a new method (that uses interior points rather than corner points) for solving linear programming problems. When the number of variables is very large, Karmarkar's method is more efficient than the simplex method. However, the simplex method is just as effective for many applications and is still widely used.

In discussing the simplex method, we initially restrict ourselves to **standard maximization problems,** which satisfy the following conditions.

1. The objective function is to be maximized.
2. All variables are nonnegative.
3. The constraints are of the form

$$a_1x_1 + a_2x_2 + \cdots + a_nx_n \le b$$

where $b > 0$.

These conditions may seem to restrict the types of problems unduly, but in applied situations where the objective function is to be maximized, the constraints often satisfy conditions 2 and 3.

Before outlining a procedure for the simplex method, let us develop the procedure and investigate its rationale by seeing how the simplex method compares with the graphical method.

EXAMPLE 1   Maximizing Profit

A farm co-op has 6000 acres available to plant with corn and soybeans. Each acre of corn requires 9 gallons of fertilizer/herbicide and 3/4 hour of labor to harvest. Each acre of soybeans requires 3 gallons of fertilizer/herbicide and 1 hour of labor to harvest. The co-op has available at most 40,500 gallons of fertilizer/herbicide and at most 5250 hours of labor for harvesting. If the profits per acre are $60 for corn and $40 for soybeans, how many acres of each crop should the co-op plant in order to maximize their profit? What is the maximum profit?

Solution

This application was solved graphically in Example 1 in Section 4.2. As we saw there, with $x =$ the number of acres of corn and $y =$ the number of acres of soybeans, the farm co-op linear programming problem is

Maximize profit $\quad P = 60x + 40y$

subject to $\qquad\qquad x + \ y \le 6{,}000 \qquad$ (Land constraint)

$\qquad\qquad\qquad 9x + 3y \le 40{,}500 \qquad$ (Fertilizer/herbicide constraint)

$\qquad\qquad\qquad \dfrac{3}{4}x + \ y \le 5{,}250 \qquad$ (Labor hours constraint)

Note that $x \ge 0$ and $y \ge 0$. Because variables must be nonnegative in the simplex method, we shall no longer state these conditions.

The simplex method uses matrix methods on systems of equations, so we convert each constraint inequality to an equation by using a new variable, called a **slack variable.** We can think of each slack variable as representing the amount of the constraint left unused. In the land constraint, $x + y$ represents the total number of acres planted, and this number cannot exceed the 6000 acres available. Thus, if we let s_1 represent the unused (unplanted) acres of land, then $s_1 \geq 0$ and

$$x + y \leq 6000 \quad \text{becomes} \quad x + y + s_1 = 6000$$

Similarly, if s_2 represents the unused gallons of fertilizer/herbicide, then $s_2 \geq 0$ and

$$9x + 3y \leq 40{,}500 \quad \text{becomes} \quad 9x + 3y + s_2 = 40{,}500$$

And if s_3 represents the unused hours of labor, then $s_3 \geq 0$ and

$$\frac{3}{4}x + y \leq 5250 \quad \text{becomes} \quad \frac{3}{4}x + y + s_3 = 5250$$

Notice in each constraint that the expressions in x and y represent the amount of that resource that is used and that the slack variable represents the amount not used.

Previously, when we used matrices with systems of equations we arranged the equations with all the variables on the left side of the equation and the constants on the right. If we write the objective function in this form

$$P = 60x + 40y \quad \text{becomes} \quad -60x - 40y + P = 0$$

and then the following system of equations describes this problem.

$$\begin{cases} x & + & y & + & s_1 & & & & & = & 6{,}000 \\ 9x & + & 3y & & & + & s_2 & & & = & 40{,}500 \\ \frac{3}{4}x & + & y & & & & & + & s_3 & = & 5{,}250 \\ -60x & - & 40y & & & & & & + P & = & 0 \end{cases}$$

We seek to maximize P in the last equation subject to the constraints in the first three equations.

We can place this system of equations in a matrix called a **simplex matrix** or a **simplex tableau.** Note that the objective function is in the last (bottom) row of this matrix with all variables on the left side and that the rows above the function row correspond to the constraints.

$$A = \begin{bmatrix} x & y & s_1 & s_2 & s_3 & P & \\ 1 & 1 & 1 & 0 & 0 & 0 & 6{,}000 \\ 9 & 3 & 0 & 1 & 0 & 0 & 40{,}500 \\ \frac{3}{4} & 1 & 0 & 0 & 1 & 0 & 5{,}250 \\ -60 & -40 & 0 & 0 & 0 & 1 & 0 \end{bmatrix} \begin{array}{l} \text{Land constraint} \\ \text{Fertilizer/herbicide constraint} \\ \text{Labor hours constraint} \\ \text{Objective function (maximum profit)} \end{array}$$

From the graph in Figure 4.16, we know that $(0, 0)$ is a feasible solution giving a value of 0 for P. Because the origin is always a feasible solution of the type of linear programming problems we are considering, the simplex method begins there and systematically moves to new corners while increasing the value of P.

Corners	$P = 60x + 40y$
$(0, 0)$	$P = 0$
$(4500, 0)$	$P = 270{,}000$
$(3750, 2250)$	$P = 315{,}000$
$(3000, 3000)$	$P = 300{,}000$
$(0, 5250)$	$P = 210{,}000$

Figure 4.16

Note that if $x = 0$ and $y = 0$, then all 6000 acres of land are unused $(s_1 = 6000)$, all 40,500 gallons of fertilizer/herbicide are unused $(s_2 = 40,500)$, all 5250 labor hours are unused $(s_3 = 5250)$, and profit is $P = 0$. From rows 1, 2, 3, and 4 of matrix A, we can read these values of s_1, s_2, s_3, and P, respectively.

Recall that the last row still corresponds to the objective function $P = 60x + 40y$. If we seek to improve (that is, increase the value of) $P = 60x + 40y$ by changing the value of only one of the variables, then because the coefficient of x is larger, the rate of increase is greatest by increasing x.

In general, we can find the variable that will improve the objective function most rapidly by looking for the *most negative* value in the last row (the objective function row) of the simplex matrix. The column that contains this value is called the **pivot column.**

The simplex matrix A is shown again below with the x-column indicated as the pivot column.

$$
A = \left[\begin{array}{cccccc|c}
x & y & s_1 & s_2 & s_3 & P & \\
\boxed{1} & 1 & 1 & 0 & 0 & 0 & 6{,}000 \\
\boxed{9} & 3 & 0 & 1 & 0 & 0 & 40{,}500 \\
\tfrac{3}{4} & 1 & 0 & 0 & 1 & 0 & 5{,}250 \\
-60 & -40 & 0 & 0 & 0 & 1 & 0
\end{array}\right]
\begin{array}{l}
6000 \div 1 = 6000 \\
40{,}500 \div 9 = 4500 \text{ smallest} \\
5250 \div \left(\tfrac{3}{4}\right) = 5250\left(\tfrac{4}{3}\right) = 7000
\end{array}
$$

⌐— Most negative entry; pivot column

The amount by which x can be increased is limited by the constraining equations (rows 1, 2, and 3 of the simplex matrix). As the graph in Figure 4.16 shows, the constraints limit x to no larger than $x = 4500$. Note that when the positive coefficients in the pivot column (the x-column) of the simplex matrix are divided into the constants in the augment, the *smallest* quotient is $40{,}500 \div 9 = 4500$. This smallest quotient identifies the **pivot row.** The **pivot entry** (or **pivot**) is the entry in both the pivot column and the pivot row. The 9 (circled) in row 2, column 1 of matrix A is the pivot entry. Notice that the smallest quotient, 4500, represents the amount that x can be increased (while $y = 0$), and the point $(4500, 0)$ corresponds to a corner adjoining $(0, 0)$ on the constraint region (see Figure 4.16).

To continue this solution method, we use row operations with the pivot row of the simplex matrix to simulate moving to another corner of the constraint region. We multiply the second row by $\frac{1}{9}$ to convert the pivot entry to 1, and then add multiples of row 2 to each of the remaining rows to make all elements of the pivot column, except the pivot element, equal to 0.

$$
A = \left[\begin{array}{cccccc|c}
x & y & s_1 & s_2 & s_3 & P & \\
1 & 1 & 1 & 0 & 0 & 0 & 6{,}000 \\
\boxed{9} & 3 & 0 & 1 & 0 & 0 & 40{,}500 \\
\tfrac{3}{4} & 1 & 0 & 0 & 1 & 0 & 5{,}250 \\
-60 & -40 & 0 & 0 & 0 & 1 & 0
\end{array}\right]
\xrightarrow{\frac{1}{9}R_2 \to R_2}
\left[\begin{array}{cccccc|c}
x & y & s_1 & s_2 & s_3 & P & \\
1 & 1 & 1 & 0 & 0 & 0 & 6{,}000 \\
\boxed{1} & \tfrac{1}{3} & 0 & \tfrac{1}{9} & 0 & 0 & 4{,}500 \\
\tfrac{3}{4} & 1 & 0 & 0 & 1 & 0 & 5{,}250 \\
-60 & -40 & 0 & 0 & 0 & 1 & 0
\end{array}\right]
$$

$$
\begin{array}{c}
-R_2 + R_1 \to R_1 \\
-\tfrac{3}{4}R_2 + R_3 \to R_3 \\
\hline
60R_2 + R_4 \to R_4
\end{array}
\left[\begin{array}{cccccc|c}
x & y & s_1 & s_2 & s_3 & P & \\
0 & \tfrac{2}{3} & 1 & -\tfrac{1}{9} & 0 & 0 & 1{,}500 \\
1 & \tfrac{1}{3} & 0 & \tfrac{1}{9} & 0 & 0 & 4{,}500 \\
0 & \tfrac{3}{4} & 0 & -\tfrac{1}{12} & 1 & 0 & 1{,}875 \\
0 & -20 & 0 & \tfrac{20}{3} & 0 & 1 & 270{,}000
\end{array}\right] = B
$$

This "transforms" the simplex matrix A into the simplex matrix B. Recall that this transformation was based on holding $y = 0$ and increasing x as much as possible so the resulting point would be feasible—that is, moving from $(0, 0)$ to $(4500, 0)$ on the graph in Figure 4.16. At the point $(4500, 0)$ the profit is $P = 60x + 40y = 60(4500) + 40(0) = 270{,}000$, and the resources used (and not used, or slack) are as follows.

Land: $\qquad x + y + s_1 = 6000 \Rightarrow 4500 + 0 + s_1 = 6000 \Rightarrow s_1 = 1500$

Fertilizer/herbicide: $\quad 9x + 3y + s_2 = 40{,}500 \Rightarrow 40{,}500 + 0 + s_2 = 40{,}500 \Rightarrow s_2 = 0$

Labor hours: $\qquad \dfrac{3}{4}x + y + s_3 = 5250 \Rightarrow 3375 + 0 + s_3 = 5250 \Rightarrow s_3 = 1875$

Let's see how these values $(x = 4500, y = 0, s_1 = 1500, s_2 = 0, s_3 = 1875, \text{ and } P = 270{,}000)$ can be found in matrix B.

Notice that the columns of B that correspond to the variables x, s_1, and s_3 and to the objective function P are all different, but each contains a single entry of 1 and the other entries are 0. Variables with columns of this type (but *not* the objective function) are called **basic variables.** Similarly, the columns for variables y and s_2 do not have this special form and these columns correspond to **nonbasic variables.** Notice also that the bottom row of B represents

$$-20y + \frac{20}{3}s_2 + P = 270{,}000, \quad \text{so} \quad P = 270{,}000 + 20y - \frac{20}{3}s_2$$

depends on y and s_2 (the nonbasic variables). If these nonbasic variables equal 0 (that is, $y = 0$ and $s_2 = 0$), then rows 1, 2, 3, and 4 of matrix B allow us to read the values of s_1, x, s_3, and P, respectively.

$$s_1 = 1500, \quad x = 4500, \quad s_3 = 1875, \quad P = 270{,}000$$

These solution values correspond to the feasible solution at the corner $(4500, 0)$ in Figure 4.16 and are called a **basic feasible solution.**

We also see that the value of $P = 270{,}000 + 20y - \frac{20}{3}s_2$ can be increased by increasing the value of y while holding the value of s_2 at 0. In matrix B, we can see this fact by observing that the most negative number in the last row (objective function row) occurs in the y-column. This means the y-column is the new pivot column.

The amount of increase in y is limited by the constraints. In matrix B we can discover the limitations on y by dividing the coefficient of y (if positive) into the constant term in the augment of each row and choosing the smallest nonnegative quotient. This identifies the pivot row, and hence the pivot entry, circled in matrix B.

$$B = \begin{bmatrix} x & y & s_1 & s_2 & s_3 & P & \\ 0 & \boxed{\tfrac{2}{3}} & 1 & -\tfrac{1}{9} & 0 & 0 & 1{,}500 \\ 1 & \tfrac{1}{3} & 0 & \tfrac{1}{9} & 0 & 0 & 4{,}500 \\ 0 & \tfrac{3}{4} & 0 & -\tfrac{1}{12} & 1 & 0 & 1{,}875 \\ 0 & -20 & 0 & \tfrac{20}{3} & 0 & 1 & 270{,}000 \end{bmatrix}$$

$1500 \div \left(\tfrac{2}{3}\right) = 1500\left(\tfrac{3}{2}\right) = 2250 \quad$ smallest

$4500 \div \left(\tfrac{1}{3}\right) = 4500\left(\tfrac{3}{1}\right) = 13{,}500$

$1875 \div \left(\tfrac{3}{4}\right) = 1875\left(\tfrac{4}{3}\right) = 2500$

$\uparrow$ Largest negative; pivot column

The smallest quotient is 2250; note that if we move to a corner adjoining $(4500, 0)$ on the feasible region in Figure 4.16, the largest y-value is 2250 [at the point $(3750, 2250)$].

Let us transform the simplex matrix B by multiplying row 1 by $\frac{3}{2}$ to convert the pivot entry to 1, and then adding multiples of row 1 to the other rows to make all other entries in the y-column (pivot column) equal to 0. The new simplex matrix is C.

$$B = \begin{bmatrix} x & y & s_1 & s_2 & s_3 & P & \\ 0 & \boxed{\tfrac{2}{3}} & 1 & -\tfrac{1}{9} & 0 & 0 & 1{,}500 \\ 1 & \tfrac{1}{3} & 0 & \tfrac{1}{9} & 0 & 0 & 4{,}500 \\ 0 & \tfrac{3}{4} & 0 & -\tfrac{1}{12} & 1 & 0 & 1{,}875 \\ 0 & -20 & 0 & \tfrac{20}{3} & 0 & 1 & 270{,}000 \end{bmatrix} \xrightarrow{\tfrac{3}{2}R_1 \to R_1} \begin{bmatrix} x & y & s_1 & s_2 & s_3 & P & \\ 0 & \boxed{1} & \tfrac{3}{2} & -\tfrac{1}{6} & 0 & 0 & 2{,}250 \\ 1 & \tfrac{1}{3} & 0 & \tfrac{1}{9} & 0 & 0 & 4{,}500 \\ 0 & \tfrac{3}{4} & 0 & -\tfrac{1}{12} & 1 & 0 & 1{,}875 \\ 0 & -20 & 0 & \tfrac{20}{3} & 0 & 1 & 270{,}000 \end{bmatrix}$$

$$\begin{array}{c} -\tfrac{1}{3}R_1 + R_2 \to R_2 \\ -\tfrac{3}{4}R_1 + R_3 \to R_3 \\ \hline 20R_1 + R_4 \to R_4 \end{array} \begin{bmatrix} x & y & s_1 & s_2 & s_3 & P & \\ 0 & 1 & \tfrac{3}{2} & -\tfrac{1}{6} & 0 & 0 & 2{,}250 \\ 1 & 0 & -\tfrac{1}{2} & \tfrac{1}{6} & 0 & 0 & 3{,}750 \\ 0 & 0 & -\tfrac{9}{8} & \tfrac{1}{24} & 1 & 0 & 187.5 \\ 0 & 0 & 30 & \tfrac{10}{3} & 0 & 1 & 315{,}000 \end{bmatrix} = C$$

In this new simplex matrix C, the basic variables (corresponding to the columns with a single entry of 1) are x, y, and s_3, the nonbasic variables are s_1 and s_2, and the last row (the objective function row) corresponds to

$$30s_1 + \frac{10}{3}s_2 + P = 315{,}000 \quad \text{or} \quad P = 315{,}000 - 30s_1 - \frac{10}{3}s_2$$

From the objective function we see that any increase in s_1 or s_2 will cause a *decrease* in P. Observing this or noting that all entries in the last row are nonnegative tells us that we have found the optimal value of the objective function and it occurs when $s_1 = 0$ and $s_2 = 0$. Using this, rows 1, 2, 3, and 4 of matrix C give the values for y, x, s_3, and P, respectively.

$$y = 2250, \quad x = 3750, \quad s_3 = 187.5, \quad P = 315{,}000, \quad \text{with} \quad s_1 = 0 \quad \text{and} \quad s_2 = 0$$

This corresponds to the corner (3750, 2250) on the graph and to the maximum value of $P = 315{,}000$ at this corner (see Figure 4.16).

Just as we found graphically, these values mean that the co-op should plant $x = 3750$ acres of corn and $y = 2250$ acres of soybeans for a maximum profit of \$315,000. And this planting scheme results in $s_1 = 0$ unused acres of land, $s_2 = 0$ unused gallons of fertilizer/herbicide, and $s_3 = 187.5$ unused hours of labor.   ∎

As we review the simplex solution in Example 1, we observe that each of the basic feasible solutions corresponded to a corner (x, y) of the feasible region and that two of the five variables x, y, s_1, s_2, and s_3 were equal to 0 at each feasible solution.

At $(0, 0)$: x and y were equal to 0.
At $(4500, 0)$: y and s_2 were equal to 0.
At $(3750, 2250)$: s_1 and s_2 were equal to 0.

See Figure 4.17 for an illustration of how the simplex method moved us from corner to corner until the optimal solution was obtained.

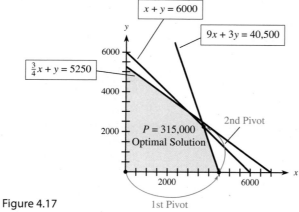

Pivoting Summary

1st Pivot:
from: (0, 0) where $P = 0$
to: (4500, 0) where $P = 270{,}000$

2nd Pivot:
from: (4500, 0) where $P = 270{,}000$
to: (3750, 2250) where $P = 315{,}000$
The Optimal Solution

Figure 4.17

Recall from Example 1 that at each step in the simplex method we can identify the *basic variables* directly from the simplex matrix by noting that their columns contain a *single entry of 1* with all other entries being zero. (Check this.) The remaining columns identify the *nonbasic variables*, and at each feasible solution (that is, at each step in the simplex method) the nonbasic variables were set equal to zero. With the nonbasic variables equal to zero, the values of the basic variables and the objective function can be read from the rows of the simplex matrix.

The Simplex Method: Tasks and Procedure

The simplex method involves a series of decisions and operations using matrices. It involves three major tasks.

Simplex Method Tasks

Task A: Setting up the matrix for the simplex method.

Task B: Determining necessary operations and implementing those operations to reach a solution.

Task C: Reading the solution from the simplex matrix.

From Example 1, it should be clear that the pivot selection and row operations of Task B are designed to move the system to the corner that achieves the most rapid increase in the function and at the same time is sensitive to the nonnegative limitations on the variables. The procedure that combines these three tasks to maximize a function is given next.

Linear Programming (Simplex Method)

Procedure	Example

To use the simplex method to solve linear programming problems:

Maximize $f = 2x + 3y$ subject to
$$x + 2y \le 10$$
$$2x + y \le 14$$

1. Use a different slack variable to write each constraint inequality as an equation, with positive constants on the right side.

1. $x + 2y \le 10$ becomes $x + 2y + s_1 = 10$.
$2x + y \le 14$ becomes $2x + y + s_2 = 14$.
Maximize f in $-2x - 3y + f = 0$.

2. Set up the simplex matrix. It contains the system of constraint equations with the objective function in the last row with all variables on the left and coefficient 1 for f.

2.
$$
\begin{array}{ccccc}
x & y & s_1 & s_2 & f \\
\end{array}
$$
$$
\left[\begin{array}{ccccc|c}
1 & 2 & 1 & 0 & 0 & 10 \\
2 & 1 & 0 & 1 & 0 & 14 \\
\hline
-2 & -3 & 0 & 0 & 1 & 0
\end{array}\right]
$$

3. Find the pivot entry:
   (a) The pivot column has the most negative number in the last row. (If a tie occurs, use either column.)

3. (a)
$$
\left[\begin{array}{ccccc|c}
1 & \boxed{2} & 1 & 0 & 0 & 10 \\
2 & \boxed{1} & 0 & 1 & 0 & 14 \\
\hline
-2 & \boxed{-3} & 0 & 0 & 1 & 0
\end{array}\right]
$$
$\uparrow$ Most negative entry; pivot column

   (b) The positive coefficient in the pivot column that gives the smallest nonnegative quotient when divided into the constant in the constraint rows of the augment is the pivot entry. If there is a tie, either coefficient may be chosen. If there are no positive coefficients in the pivot column, no solution exists. Stop.

   (b) Row 1 quotient: $\dfrac{10}{2} = 5$

   Row 2 quotient: $\dfrac{14}{1} = 14$

   Therefore, pivot row is row 1.

$$
\left[\begin{array}{ccccc|c}
1 & ② & 1 & 0 & 0 & 10 \\
2 & 1 & 0 & 1 & 0 & 14 \\
\hline
-2 & -3 & 0 & 0 & 1 & 0
\end{array}\right]
$$
Pivot entry is 2, circled.

4. Use row operations with only the row containing the pivot entry to make the pivot entry a 1 and all other entries in the pivot column zeros. This process is called **pivoting**. This makes the variable corresponding to the pivot column a basic variable.

4. Row operations:
Multiply row 1 by $\frac{1}{2}$.
Add -1 times new row 1 to row 2.
Add 3 times new row 1 to row 3.

Result:
$$
\left[\begin{array}{ccccc|c}
\frac{1}{2} & 1 & \frac{1}{2} & 0 & 0 & 5 \\
\frac{3}{2} & 0 & -\frac{1}{2} & 1 & 0 & 9 \\
\hline
-\frac{1}{2} & 0 & \frac{3}{2} & 0 & 1 & 15
\end{array}\right]
$$
Indicators

(continued)

Linear Programming (Simplex Method) (continued)

Procedure	Example
5. The numerical entries in the last row are the indicators of what to do next.	5. $-\frac{1}{2}$ is negative, so we identify a new pivot column and reduce again.

5. (a) If there is a negative indicator, return to Step 3.
   (b) If all indicators are positive or zero, an optimum value has been obtained for the objective function.
   (c) In a complete solution, the variables that have positive entries in the last row are nonbasic variables.

$$\begin{bmatrix} \frac{1}{2} & 1 & \frac{1}{2} & 0 & 0 & 5 \\ \frac{3}{2} & 0 & -\frac{1}{2} & 1 & 0 & 9 \\ -\frac{1}{2} & 0 & \frac{3}{2} & 0 & 1 & 15 \end{bmatrix}$$
$5 \div \frac{1}{2} = 10$
$9 \div \frac{3}{2} = 6^*$

Pivot column   *6 is smaller quotient.

The new pivot entry is $\frac{3}{2}$ (circled). Now reduce, using the new pivot row, to obtain:

$$\begin{bmatrix} 0 & 1 & \frac{2}{3} & -\frac{1}{3} & 0 & 2 \\ 1 & 0 & -\frac{1}{3} & \frac{2}{3} & 0 & 6 \\ 0 & 0 & \frac{4}{3} & \frac{1}{3} & 1 & 18 \end{bmatrix}$$

Indicators all 0 or positive, so the solution is complete.
Nonbasic variables: s_1 and s_2. Basic variables: x and y.

6. After setting the nonbasic variables equal to 0, read the values of the basic variables and the objective function from the rows of the matrix.

6. f is maximized at 18 when $y = 2$, $x = 6$, $s_1 = 0$, and $s_2 = 0$. (This same example was solved graphically in the Procedure/Example in Section 4.2.)

As we look back over our work, we can observe the following:

1. Steps 1 and 2 complete Task A (setting up the simplex matrix).
2. Steps 3–5 complete Task B (pivoting to obtain the final matrix).
3. Step 6 completes Task C (reading the optimal solution).

EXAMPLE 2   Simplex Method Tasks

Complete Tasks A, B, and C to find the maximum value of $f = 4x + 3y$ subject to

$$x + 2y \leq 8$$
$$2x + y \leq 10$$

Solution

Task A: Introducing the slack variables gives the system of equations

$$\begin{cases} x + 2y + s_1 & = 8 \\ 2x + y & + s_2 & = 10 \\ -4x - 3y & + f = 0 \end{cases}$$

Writing this in a matrix with the objective function in the last row gives

$$A = \begin{bmatrix} x & y & s_1 & s_2 & f & \\ 1 & 2 & 1 & 0 & 0 & 8 \\ 2 & 1 & 0 & 1 & 0 & 10 \\ -4 & -3 & 0 & 0 & 1 & 0 \end{bmatrix}$$
$8/1 = 8$
$10/2 = 5^*$

Most negative   *Smallest quotient

Note that in this initial simplex matrix A, variables x and y are nonbasic (so set to 0) and this corresponds to the basic feasible solution $x = 0$, $y = 0$ and $s_1 = 8$, $s_2 = 10$, $f = 0$.

Task B: The most negative entry in the last row is -4 (indicated by the arrow), so the pivot column is column 1. The smallest quotient formed by dividing the positive coefficients from column 1 into the constants in the augment is 5 (indicated by the asterisk), so row 2 is the pivot row. Thus the pivot entry is in row 2, column 1 (circled in matrix A).

Next use row operations with row 2 only to make the pivot entry equal 1 and all other entries in column 1 equal zero. The row operations are

(a) Multiply row 2 by $\frac{1}{2}$ to get a 1 as the new pivot entry.
(b) Add -1 times the new row 2 to row 1 to get a 0 in row 1 above the pivot entry.
(c) Add 4 times the new row 2 to row 3 to get a 0 in row 3 below the pivot entry.

This gives the simplex matrix B, which has nonbasic variables $y = 0$ and $s_2 = 0$ and corresponds to the basic feasible solution $y = 0$, $s_2 = 0$ and $x = 5$, $s_1 = 3$, $f = 20$.

$$B = \begin{bmatrix} x & y & s_1 & s_2 & f & \\ 0 & \frac{3}{2} & 1 & -\frac{1}{2} & 0 & 3 \\ 1 & \frac{1}{2} & 0 & \frac{1}{2} & 0 & 5 \\ 0 & -1 & 0 & 2 & 1 & 20 \end{bmatrix} \begin{matrix} 3 \div \frac{3}{2} = 2^* \\ 5 \div \frac{1}{2} = 10 \end{matrix}$$

$\uparrow$
Most negative   *Smallest quotient

The last row contains a negative entry, so the solution is not optimal and we locate another pivot column to continue. The pivot column is indicated with an arrow, and the smallest quotient is indicated with an asterisk. The new pivot entry is circled.

The row operations using this pivot row are

(a) Multiply row 1 by $\frac{2}{3}$ to get a 1 as the new pivot element.
(b) Add $-\frac{1}{2}$ times the new row 1 to row 2 to get a 0 in row 2 below the pivot element.
(c) Add the new row 1 to row 3 to get a 0 in row 3 below the pivot element.

This gives

$$C = \begin{bmatrix} x & y & s_1 & s_2 & f & \\ 0 & 1 & \frac{2}{3} & -\frac{1}{3} & 0 & 2 \\ 1 & 0 & -\frac{1}{3} & \frac{2}{3} & 0 & 4 \\ 0 & 0 & \frac{2}{3} & \frac{5}{3} & 1 & 22 \end{bmatrix}$$

Because there are no negative indicators in the last row, the solution is complete.

Task C: s_1 and s_2 are nonbasic variables, so they equal zero. Thus f is maximized at 22 when $y = 2$, $x = 4$, $s_1 = 0$, and $s_2 = 0$.

EXAMPLE 3   Manufacturing | APPLICATION PREVIEW |

The Solar Technology Company manufactures three different types of hand calculators and classifies them as scientific, business, and graphing according to their calculating capabilities. The three types have production requirements given by the following table.

	Scientific	Business	Graphing
Electronic circuit components	5	7	10
Assembly time (hours)	1	3	4
Cases	1	1	1

The firm has a monthly limit of 90,000 circuit components, 30,000 hours of labor, and 9000 cases. If the profit is $6 for each scientific, $13 for each business, and $20 for each graphing calculator, how many of each should be produced to yield the maximum profit? What is the maximum profit?

Solution

Let x_1 be the number of scientific calculators produced, x_2 the number of business calculators produced, and x_3 the number of graphing calculators produced. Then the problem is to maximize the profit $f = 6x_1 + 13x_2 + 20x_3$ subject to

Inequalities	Equations with Slack Variables
$5x_1 + 7x_2 + 10x_3 \leq 90{,}000$	$5x_1 + 7x_2 + 10x_3 + s_1 \qquad\qquad = 90{,}000$
$x_1 + 3x_2 + 4x_3 \leq 30{,}000$	$x_1 + 3x_2 + 4x_3 + \quad s_2 \qquad = 30{,}000$
$x_1 + x_2 + x_3 \leq 9000$	$x_1 + x_2 + x_3 + \qquad\quad s_3 = 9000$

The slack variables can be interpreted as follows: s_1 is the number of unused circuit components, s_2 is the number of unused hours of labor, and s_3 is the number of unused calculator cases. The simplex matrix, with the first pivot entry circled, is shown below.

Slack variables

$$
\begin{array}{ccccccc|c}
x_1 & x_2 & x_3 & s_1 & s_2 & s_3 & f & \\
5 & 7 & 10 & 1 & 0 & 0 & 0 & 90{,}000 \\
1 & 3 & \boxed{4} & 0 & 1 & 0 & 0 & 30{,}000 \\
1 & 1 & 1 & 0 & 0 & 1 & 0 & 9000 \\
\hline
-6 & -13 & -20 & 0 & 0 & 0 & 1 & 0
\end{array}
$$

$90{,}000/10 = 9000$
$30{,}000/4 = 7500^*$
$9000/1 = 9000$

↑ Most negative

*Smallest quotient

We now use row operations to change the pivot entry to 1 and create zeros elsewhere in the pivot column. The row operations are

1. Multiply row 2 by $\frac{1}{4}$ to convert the pivot entry to 1.
2. Using the new row 2,
   (a) Add -10 times new row 2 to row 1.
   (b) Add -1 times new row 2 to row 3.
   (c) Add 20 times new row 2 to row 4.

The result is the second simplex matrix.

Slack variables

$$
\begin{array}{ccccccc|c}
x_1 & x_2 & x_3 & s_1 & s_2 & s_3 & f & \\
\frac{5}{2} & -\frac{1}{2} & 0 & 1 & -\frac{5}{2} & 0 & 0 & 15{,}000 \\
\frac{1}{4} & \frac{3}{4} & 1 & 0 & \frac{1}{4} & 0 & 0 & 7500 \\
\boxed{\frac{3}{4}} & \frac{1}{4} & 0 & 0 & -\frac{1}{4} & 1 & 0 & 1500 \\
\hline
-1 & 2 & 0 & 0 & 5 & 0 & 1 & 150{,}000
\end{array}
$$

$15{,}000 \div \frac{5}{2} = 6000$
$7500 \div \frac{1}{4} = 30{,}000$
$1500 \div \frac{3}{4} = 2000^*$

↑ Most negative

*Smallest quotient

We check the last row indicators. Because there is an entry that is negative, we repeat the simplex process. Again the pivot entry is circled, and we apply row operations similar to those above. What are the row operations this time? The resulting matrix is

$$
\begin{array}{ccccccc|c}
x_1 & x_2 & x_3 & s_1 & s_2 & s_3 & f & \\
0 & -\frac{4}{3} & 0 & 1 & -\frac{5}{3} & -\frac{10}{3} & 0 & 10{,}000 \\
0 & \frac{2}{3} & 1 & 0 & \frac{1}{3} & -\frac{1}{3} & 0 & 7000 \\
1 & \frac{1}{3} & 0 & 0 & -\frac{1}{3} & \frac{4}{3} & 0 & 2000 \\
\hline
0 & \frac{7}{3} & 0 & 0 & \frac{14}{3} & \frac{4}{3} & 1 & 152{,}000
\end{array}
$$

Checking the last row, we see that all the entries in this row are 0 or positive, so the solution is complete. From the final simplex matrix we see that the nonbasic variables are x_2, s_2, and s_3, and with these equal to zero we determine all the solution values:

$$x_2 = 0, s_2 = 0, s_3 = 0 \quad \text{and} \quad x_1 = 2000, x_3 = 7000, s_1 = 10{,}000, f = 152{,}000$$

Thus the numbers of calculators that should be produced are

$$x_1 = 2000 \text{ scientific calculators}$$
$$x_2 = 0 \text{ business calculators}$$
$$x_3 = 7000 \text{ graphing calculators}$$

in order to obtain a maximum profit of $152,000 for the month. Note also that the slack variables tell us that with this optimal solution there were $s_1 = 10{,}000$ unused circuit components, $s_2 = 0$ unused labor hours, and $s_3 = 0$ unused calculator cases.

CHECKPOINT

1. Write the following constraints as equations by using slack variables.

$$3x_1 + x_2 + x_3 \le 9$$
$$2x_1 + x_2 + 3x_3 \le 8$$
$$2x_1 + x_2 \qquad \le 5$$

2. Set up the simplex matrix to maximize $f = 2x_1 + 5x_2 + x_3$ subject to the constraints discussed in Problem 1.

Using the simplex matrix from Problem 2, perform the following.

3. Find the first pivot entry.
4. Use row operations to make the variable of the first pivot entry basic.
5. Find the second pivot entry and make a second variable basic.
6. Find the solution.

Spreadsheet Note

As our discussion indicates, the simplex method is quite complicated, even when the number of variables is relatively small (2 or 3). For this reason, computer software packages are often used to solve linear programming problems. The steps for solving linear programming problems with Excel are shown in Appendix D, Section 4.3, and the Online Excel Guide.

The following Excel screen shows entries for beginning to solve the linear programming problem that we solved "by hand" with the simplex method in Example 3.

	A	B	C
1	Variables		
2			
3	# scientific calculators (x)	0	
4	# business calculators (y)	0	
5	# graphing calculators (z)	0	
6			
7	Objective		
8			
9	Maximize profit	= 6*B3 + 13*B4 + 20*B5	
10			
11	Constraints		
12		Amount used	Maximum
13	Circuit components	= 5*B3 + 7*B4 + 10*B5	90000
14	Labor hours	= B3 + 3*B4 + 4*B5	30000
15	Cases	= B3 + B4 + B5	9000

The screen below gives the solution. Step-by-step instructions are found in Appendix D, Section 4.3, and the Online Excel Guide.

	A	B	C
1	Variables		
2			
3	# scientific calculators (x)	2000	
4	# business calculators (y)	0	
5	# graphing calculators (z)	7000	
6			
7	Objective		
8			
9	Maximize profit	152000	
10			
11	Constraints		
12		Amount used	Maximum
13	Circuit components	80000	90000
14	Labor hours	30000	30000
15	Cases	9000	9000

This screen indicates that the profit is maximized at $152,000 when 2000 scientific and 7000 graphing calculators are produced. Note that under "Constraints," the difference between the columns labeled "Maximum" and "Amount used" gives the amount of each resource that was unused—that is, the value of each slack variable: $s_1 = 10,000$, $s_2 = 0$, and $s_3 = 0$. Note that this is the same solution found in Example 3. ▪

Nonunique Solutions: Multiple Solutions and No Solution

As we've seen with graphical methods, a linear programming problem can have multiple solutions when the optimal value for the objective function occurs at two adjacent corners of the feasible region. Consider the following problem.

Maximize $f = 2x + y$ subject to

$$x + \frac{1}{2}y \le 16$$
$$x + y \le 24$$
$$x \ge 0, y \ge 0$$

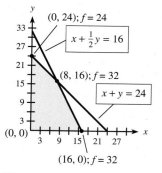

Figure 4.18

From Figure 4.18, we can see that the maximum value of f is $f = 32$ at the two corners (8, 16) and (16, 0). This means that $f = 32$ at any point on the segment joining those corners. Thus this problem has infinitely many solutions. Let's examine how we can discover these multiple solutions with the simplex method.

The simplex matrix for this problem (with the slack variables introduced) is

$$\begin{array}{ccccc} x & y & s_1 & s_2 & f \\ \left[\begin{array}{ccccc|c} \boxed{1} & \frac{1}{2} & 1 & 0 & 0 & 16 \\ 1 & 1 & 0 & 1 & 0 & 24 \\ \hline -2 & -1 & 0 & 0 & 1 & 0 \end{array}\right] \end{array}$$

The most negative value in the last row is -2, so the x-column is the pivot column. The smallest quotient occurs in row 1; the pivot entry (circled) is 1. Making x a basic variable gives the following transformed simplex matrix.

$$\begin{array}{ccccc} x & y & s_1 & s_2 & f \\ \left[\begin{array}{ccccc|c} 1 & \frac{1}{2} & 1 & 0 & 0 & 16 \\ 0 & \frac{1}{2} & -1 & 1 & 0 & 8 \\ \hline 0 & 0 & 2 & 0 & 1 & 32 \end{array}\right] \end{array}$$

This simplex matrix has no negative indicators, so the optimal value of f has been found ($f = 32$ when $x = 16, y = 0$). Note that one of the nonbasic variables (y) has a zero indicator. When this occurs, we can use the column with the 0 indicator as our pivot column and often obtain a new solution that has the same value for the objective function. In this final tableau, if we used the y-column as the pivot column, then we could find the second solution (at $x = 8, y = 16$) that gives the same optimal value of f. You will be asked to do this in Problem 39 of the exercises for this section.

Multiple Solutions

When the simplex matrix for the optimal value of f has a nonbasic variable with a zero indicator in its column, there may be multiple solutions giving the *same* optimal value for f. We can discover whether another solution exists by using the column of that nonbasic variable as the pivot column.

Spreadsheet Note   Note that with Excel, multiple solutions may be found by using different initial values for the variables when the problem is entered into Excel.

No Solution   It is also possible for a linear programming problem to have an unbounded solution (and thus no maximum value for f).

EXAMPLE 4   Simplex Method When No Maximum Exists

Maximize $f = 2x_1 + x_2 + 3x_3$ subject to

$$\begin{aligned} x_1 - 3x_2 + x_3 &\le 3 \\ x_1 - 6x_2 + 2x_3 &\le 6 \end{aligned}$$

if a maximum exists.

Solution
The simplex matrix for this problem (after introduction of slack variables) is

$$\begin{array}{cccccc} x_1 & x_2 & x_3 & s_1 & s_2 & f \\ \left[\begin{array}{ccc|ccc|c} 1 & -3 & \boxed{1} & 1 & 0 & 0 & 3 \\ 1 & -6 & 2 & 0 & 1 & 0 & 6 \\ \hline -2 & -1 & -3 & 0 & 0 & 1 & 0 \end{array}\right] \end{array}$$

We see that the x_3 column has the most negative number, so we use that column as the pivot column.

We see that the smallest quotient is 3. Both coefficients give this quotient, so we can use either coefficient as the pivot entry. Using the element in row 1, we can make x_3 basic.

The new simplex matrix is

$$
\begin{array}{c}
\begin{array}{ccccccc} x_1 & x_2 & x_3 & s_1 & s_2 & f \end{array} \\
\left[\begin{array}{cccccc|c}
1 & -3 & 1 & 1 & 0 & 0 & 3 \\
-1 & 0 & 0 & -2 & 1 & 0 & 0 \\
\hline
1 & -10 & 0 & 3 & 0 & 1 & 9
\end{array}\right]
\end{array}
$$

The most negative value in the last row of this matrix is -10, so the pivot column is the x_2-column. But there are no positive coefficients in the x_2-column; what does this mean? Even if we could pivot using the x_2-column, the variables x_1 and s_1 would remain equal to 0. And the relationships among the remaining variables x_2, x_3, and s_2 would be the same.

$$-3x_2 + x_3 = 3 \quad \text{or} \quad x_3 = 3 + 3x_2$$
$$s_2 = 0$$

As x_2 is increased, x_3 also increases because all variables are nonnegative. This means that no matter how much we increase x_2, all other variables remain nonnegative. Furthermore, as we increase x_2 (and hence x_3), the value of f also increases. That is, there is no maximum value for f. ∎

This example indicates that when a linear programming problem has an unbounded solution (and thus no maximum value for f), this is identified by the following condition in the simplex method.

No Solution

If, after the pivot column has been found, there are no positive coefficients in that column, no maximum solution exists.

Some difficulties can arise in using the simplex method to solve linear programming problems. These "difficulties" are discussed in more advanced courses, and we shall not encounter them in this text.

Shadow Prices Finally, we note that one of the most powerful aspects of the simplex method is that it not only solves the given problem but also tells how to adapt the given solution if the situation changes. In particular, from the final simplex matrix (final tableau), the solution to the problem can be read, and there is information about the amount of change in the objective function if 1 additional unit of a resource becomes available (this change is called the **shadow price** of the resource) and how this additional resource changes the optimal solution values.

For example, if one more acre of land became available in the Example 1 application (for a total of 6001 acres), it can be shown that if the co-op planted 3749.5 acres of corn and 2251.5 acres of soybeans, the profit would increase by \$30. That is, the shadow price of land is \$30/acre (or the marginal profit value of the land is \$30/acre). The following simplex matrix C is the final one from Example 1 (where $x =$ acres of corn, $y =$ acres of soybeans, and $s_1 =$ the slack variable for the land constraint). The bottom entry in the s_1-column of C is the shadow price for land. Furthermore, if the s_1-column is added to the last column in C, then matrix D results. The solution obtained from D gives the new planting scheme and the new maximum profit if one more acre of land is planted ($x = 3749.5$ acres of corn and $y = 2251.5$ acres of soybeans for a new maximum profit of $P = \$315,030$).

$$
C = \begin{array}{c}
\begin{array}{cccccc} x & y & s_1 & s_2 & s_3 & P \end{array} \\
\left[\begin{array}{cccccc|c}
0 & 1 & \frac{3}{2} & -\frac{1}{6} & 0 & 0 & 2{,}250 \\
1 & 0 & -\frac{1}{2} & \frac{1}{6} & 0 & 0 & 3{,}750 \\
0 & 0 & -\frac{9}{8} & \frac{1}{24} & 1 & 0 & 187.5 \\
\hline
0 & 0 & 30 & \frac{10}{3} & 0 & 1 & 315{,}000
\end{array}\right]
\end{array}
\quad
D = \begin{array}{c}
\begin{array}{cccccc} x & y & s_1 & s_2 & s_3 & P \end{array} \\
\left[\begin{array}{cccccc|c}
0 & 1 & \frac{3}{2} & -\frac{1}{6} & 0 & 0 & 2{,}251.5 \\
1 & 0 & -\frac{1}{2} & \frac{1}{6} & 0 & 0 & 3{,}749.5 \\
0 & 0 & -\frac{9}{8} & \frac{1}{24} & 1 & 0 & 186\frac{3}{8} \\
\hline
0 & 0 & 30 & \frac{10}{3} & 0 & 1 & 315{,}030
\end{array}\right]
\end{array}
$$

Additional material on shadow prices appears in the second Extended Application/Group Project at the end of this chapter.

CHECKPOINT SOLUTIONS

1. $3x_1 + x_2 + x_3 + s_1 = 9$
   $2x_1 + x_2 + 3x_3 + s_2 = 8$
   $2x_1 + x_2 + s_3 = 5$

2. $\begin{bmatrix} 3 & 1 & 1 & 1 & 0 & 0 & 0 & 9 \\ 2 & 1 & 3 & 0 & 1 & 0 & 0 & 8 \\ 2 & 1 & 0 & 0 & 0 & 1 & 0 & 5 \\ \hline -2 & -5 & -1 & 0 & 0 & 0 & 1 & 0 \end{bmatrix}$

3. The first pivot entry is the 1 in row 3, column 2.

4. $\begin{bmatrix} 1 & 0 & 1 & 1 & 0 & -1 & 0 & 4 \\ 0 & 0 & 3 & 0 & 1 & -1 & 0 & 3 \\ 2 & 1 & 0 & 0 & 0 & 1 & 0 & 5 \\ \hline 8 & 0 & -1 & 0 & 0 & 5 & 1 & 25 \end{bmatrix}$

5. The second pivot entry is the 3 in row 2, column 3.

$\begin{bmatrix} 1 & 0 & 0 & 1 & -\frac{1}{3} & -\frac{2}{3} & 0 & 3 \\ 0 & 0 & 1 & 0 & \frac{1}{3} & -\frac{1}{3} & 0 & 1 \\ 2 & 1 & 0 & 0 & 0 & 1 & 0 & 5 \\ \hline 8 & 0 & 0 & 0 & \frac{1}{3} & \frac{14}{3} & 1 & 26 \end{bmatrix}$

6. All indicators are 0 or positive, so f is maximized at 26 when $x_1 = 0$, $x_2 = 5$, and $x_3 = 1$. Note also that $s_1 = 3$, $s_2 = 0$, and $s_3 = 0$.

| EXERCISES | 4.3

1. Convert the constraint inequalities $3x + 5y \le 15$ and $3x + 6y \le 20$ to equations containing slack variables.
2. Convert the constraint inequalities $2x + y \le 4$ and $3x + 2y \le 8$ to equations containing slack variables.

In Problems 3–6, set up the simplex matrix used to solve each linear programming problem. Assume all variables are nonnegative.

3. Maximize $f = 3x + 7y$ subject to

$$2x + 5y \le 400$$
$$x + 2y \le 175$$

4. Maximize $f = x + 3y$ subject to

$$5x + y \le 50$$
$$x + 2y \le 50$$

5. Maximize $f = 2x + 5y + 2z$ subject to

$$2x + 7y + 9z \le 100$$
$$6x + 5y + z \le 145$$
$$x + 2y + 7z \le 90$$

6. Maximize $f = 3x + 5y + 11z$ subject to
   $$2x + 3y + 4z \le 60$$
   $$x + 4y + z \le 48$$
   $$5x + y + z \le 48$$

7. Just by looking at a simplex matrix, how can you tell the number of slack variables?
8. In a simplex matrix, what tells you whether or not the solution is complete?

In Problems 9–18, a simplex matrix for a standard maximization problem is given.

(a) Write the values of *all* the variables (use $x_1, x_2, x_3, \dots$ and $s_1, s_2, s_3, \dots$) and of the objective function f.

(b) Indicate whether or not the solution from part (a) is complete (optimal).

(c) If the solution is not complete, find the next pivot or indicate that no solution exists. When a new pivot can be found, state *all* row operations with that pivot (that is, row operations that make that pivot equal to 1, and then make other entries in the pivot column equal to 0). Do not perform the row operations.

9. $\begin{bmatrix} 10 & 27 & 1 & 0 & 0 & 0 & 200 \\ 4 & 51 & 0 & 1 & 0 & 0 & 400 \\ 15 & 27 & 0 & 0 & 1 & 0 & 350 \\ \hline -8 & -7 & 0 & 0 & 0 & 1 & 0 \end{bmatrix}$

10. $\begin{bmatrix} 5 & 5 & 7 & 1 & 0 & 0 & 0 & 12 \\ 4 & 0 & 6 & 0 & 1 & 0 & 0 & 48 \\ 0 & 1 & 1 & 0 & 0 & 1 & 0 & 8 \\ \hline -1 & -3 & -1 & 0 & 0 & 0 & 1 & 0 \end{bmatrix}$

11. $\begin{bmatrix} 2 & 0 & 1 & -\frac{3}{4} & 0 & 14 \\ 3 & 1 & 0 & \frac{1}{3} & 0 & 45 \\ \hline -6 & 0 & 0 & 3 & 1 & 75 \end{bmatrix}$

12. $\begin{bmatrix} 0 & 4 & 1 & -\frac{1}{5} & 0 & 2 \\ 1 & 2 & 0 & 1 & 0 & 4 \\ 0 & 2 & 0 & 2 & 1 & 12 \end{bmatrix}$

13.
$$\begin{bmatrix} 1 & 4 & 0 & 0 & \frac{3}{4} & 4 & 0 & | & 24 \\ 0 & -2 & 0 & 1 & -\frac{5}{8} & -2 & 0 & | & 16 \\ 0 & 3 & 1 & 0 & 2 & 6 & 0 & | & 21 \\ \hline 0 & 4 & 0 & 0 & 2 & \frac{1}{2} & 1 & | & 780 \end{bmatrix}$$

14.
$$\begin{bmatrix} 2 & 1 & 1 & 1 & 0 & 0 & 0 & | & 12 \\ -2 & 0 & -1 & -2 & 0 & 1 & 0 & | & 5 \\ 4 & 0 & 2 & -1 & 1 & 0 & 0 & | & 6 \\ \hline -2 & 0 & 5 & 7 & 0 & 0 & 1 & | & 30 \end{bmatrix}$$

15.
$$\begin{bmatrix} 4 & 4 & 1 & 0 & 0 & 2 & 0 & | & 12 \\ 2 & 4 & 0 & 1 & 0 & -1 & 0 & | & 4 \\ -3 & -11 & 0 & 0 & 1 & -1 & 0 & | & 6 \\ \hline -3 & -3 & 0 & 0 & 0 & 4 & 1 & | & 150 \end{bmatrix}$$

16.
$$\begin{bmatrix} 1 & 0 & -3 & 4 & -4 & 0 & 0 & | & 12 \\ 0 & 1 & -4 & 2 & 5 & 0 & 0 & | & 100 \\ 0 & 0 & -1 & -6 & -3 & 1 & 0 & | & 40 \\ \hline 0 & 0 & 6 & -1 & -3 & 0 & 1 & | & 380 \end{bmatrix}$$

17.
$$\begin{bmatrix} 4 & -1 & 0 & 1 & -5 & 0 & 0 & | & 5 \\ 1 & 0 & 1 & 0 & 1 & 0 & 0 & | & 12 \\ 3 & -3 & 0 & 0 & -2 & 1 & 0 & | & 6 \\ \hline -2 & -5 & 0 & 0 & 10 & 0 & 1 & | & 120 \end{bmatrix}$$

18.
$$\begin{bmatrix} 0 & 20 & -6 & 1 & 0 & -3 & 0 & | & 4 \\ 0 & 5 & -6 & 0 & 1 & -2 & 0 & | & 2 \\ 1 & -1 & 0 & 0 & 0 & 4 & 0 & | & 6 \\ \hline 0 & -9 & -12 & 0 & 0 & 10 & 1 & | & 20 \end{bmatrix}$$

In Problems 19–24, a simplex matrix is given. In each case the solution is complete, so identify the maximum value of f and a set of values of the variables that gives this maximum value. If multiple solutions may exist, indicate this and locate the next pivot.

19.
$$\begin{bmatrix} 1 & 0 & \frac{3}{4} & -\frac{3}{4} & 0 & | & 11 \\ 0 & 1 & \frac{5}{12} & \frac{11}{12} & 0 & | & 9 \\ \hline 0 & 0 & 2 & 4 & 1 & | & 20 \end{bmatrix}$$

20.
$$\begin{bmatrix} 0 & 4 & 1 & -\frac{1}{5} & 0 & | & 2 \\ 1 & 2 & 0 & 1 & 0 & | & 4 \\ \hline 0 & 2 & 0 & 2 & 1 & | & 12 \end{bmatrix}$$

21.
$$\begin{bmatrix} 4 & 1 & 0 & 0 & \frac{3}{4} & 4 & 0 & | & 14 \\ -2 & 0 & 0 & 1 & -\frac{8}{5} & -2 & 0 & | & 6 \\ 3 & 0 & 1 & 0 & 2 & 6 & 0 & | & 11 \\ \hline 4 & 0 & 0 & 0 & 2 & \frac{1}{2} & 1 & | & 525 \end{bmatrix}$$

22.
$$\begin{bmatrix} 0 & 1 & 0 & -3 & -1 & -4 & 0 & | & 12 \\ 1 & 0 & 0 & -2 & -1 & -5 & 0 & | & 16 \\ 0 & 0 & 1 & -1 & 2 & 1 & 0 & | & 22 \\ \hline 0 & 0 & 0 & 4 & 1 & 2 & 1 & | & 150 \end{bmatrix}$$

23.
$$\begin{bmatrix} 1 & 0 & 3 & 0 & 6 & 0 & | & 50 \\ 0 & 0 & 4 & 1 & -4 & 0 & | & 6 \\ 0 & 1 & -2 & 0 & 2 & 0 & | & 10 \\ \hline 0 & 0 & 9 & 0 & 0 & 1 & | & 100 \end{bmatrix}$$

24.
$$\begin{bmatrix} 0 & 1 & 2 & 1 & 0 & 0 & | & 20 \\ 1 & 0 & 6 & 1 & 0 & 0 & | & 50 \\ 0 & 0 & -1 & -2 & 1 & 0 & | & 10 \\ \hline 0 & 0 & 4 & 0 & 0 & 1 & | & 88 \end{bmatrix}$$

In Problems 25–38, use the simplex method to maximize the given functions. Assume all variables are nonnegative.

25. Maximize $f = 3x + 10y$ subject to
$$14x + 7y \le 35$$
$$5x + 5y \le 50$$

26. Maximize $f = 7x + 10y$ subject to
$$14x + 14y \le 98$$
$$8x + 10y \le 100$$

27. Maximize $f = 2x + 3y$ subject to
$$x + 2y \le 10$$
$$x + y \le 7$$

28. Maximize $f = 5x + 30y$ subject to
$$2x + 10y \le 96$$
$$x + 10y \le 90$$

29. Maximize $f = 2x + y$ subject to
$$-x + y \le 2$$
$$x + 2y \le 10$$
$$3x + y \le 15$$

30. Maximize $f = 2x + 6y$ subject to
$$2x + 5y \le 30$$
$$x + 5y \le 25$$
$$x + y \le 11$$

31. Maximize $f = 7x + 10y + 4z$ subject to
$$3x + 5y + 4z \le 30$$
$$3x + 2y \quad\ \le 4$$
$$x + 2y \quad\ \le 8$$

32. Maximize $f = 64x + 36y + 38z$ subject to
$$4x + 2y + 2z \le 40$$
$$8x + 10y + 5z \le 90$$
$$4x + 4y + 3z \le 30$$

33. Maximize $f = 20x + 12y + 12z$ subject to
$$x + \quad\ z \le 40$$
$$x + y \quad\ \le 30$$
$$y + z \le 40$$

34. Maximize $f = 10x + 5y + 4z$ subject to
$$2x + y + z \le 50$$
$$x + 3y \quad\ \le 20$$
$$y + z \le 15$$

35. Maximize $f = 10x + 8y + 5z$ subject to
$$2x + y + z \le 40$$
$$x + 2y \quad\ \le 10$$
$$y + 3z \le 80$$

36. Maximize $f = x + 3y + z$ subject to
$$x + 4y \quad\ \le 12$$
$$3x + 6y + 4z \le 48$$
$$y + z \le 8$$

37. Maximize $f = 24x_1 + 30x_2 + 18x_3 + 18x_4$ subject to

$$12x_1 + 16x_2 + 20x_3 + 8x_4 \le 880$$
$$5x_1 + 10x_2 + 10x_3 + 5x_4 \le 460$$
$$10x_1 - 5x_2 + 8x_3 + 5x_4 \le 280$$

38. Maximize $f = 8x_1 + 17x_2 + 24x_3 + 31x_4 + 36x_5$ subject to

$$x_1 + x_2 + 5x_3 + 3x_4 + 2x_5 \le 5000$$
$$2x_1 + x_2 + 4x_3 + 4x_4 + 2x_5 \le 6000$$
$$3x_1 + x_2 + 5x_3 + 2x_4 + 3x_5 \le 7000$$

Problems 39–44 involve linear programming problems that have nonunique solutions.

The simplex matrices shown in Problems 39 and 40 indicate that an optimal solution has been found but that a second solution is possible. Find the second solution.

39. $\begin{bmatrix} 1 & \frac{1}{2} & 1 & 0 & 0 & 16 \\ 0 & \frac{1}{2} & -1 & 1 & 0 & 8 \\ \hline 0 & 0 & 2 & 0 & 1 & 32 \end{bmatrix}$

40. $\begin{bmatrix} 1 & 2 & 0 & 1 & 0 & 40 \\ 0 & 1 & 1 & 2 & 0 & 15 \\ \hline 0 & 0 & 0 & 4 & 1 & 90 \end{bmatrix}$

In Problems 41–44, use the simplex method to maximize each function (whenever possible) subject to the given constraints. If there is no solution, indicate this; if multiple solutions exist, find two of them.

41. Maximize $f = 3x + 2y$ subject to

$$x - 10y \le 10$$
$$-x + y \le 40$$

42. Maximize $f = 10x + 15y$ subject to

$$-5x + y \le 24$$
$$2x - 3y \le 9$$

43. Maximize $f = 3x + 12y$ subject to

$$2x + y \le 120$$
$$x + 4y \le 200$$

44. Maximize $f = 8x + 6y$ subject to

$$4x + 3y \le 24$$
$$10x + 9y \le 198$$

APPLICATIONS

45. *Manufacturing* Newjet Inc. manufactures two types of printers, an inkjet printer and a laser printer. The company can make a total of 60 printers per day, and it has 120 labor-hours per day available. It takes 1 labor-hour to make an inkjet printer and 3 labor-hours to make a laser printer. The profits are $40 per inkjet printer and $60 per laser printer.
    (a) Write the simplex matrix to maximize the daily profit.
    (b) Find the maximum profit and the number of each type of printer that will give the maximum profit.

46. *Construction* A contractor builds two types of homes. The Carolina requires one lot, $160,000 capital, and 160 worker-days of labor, and the Savannah requires one lot, $240,000 capital, and 160 worker-days of labor. The contractor owns 300 lots and has $48,000,000 available capital and 43,200 worker-days of labor. The profit on the Carolina is $40,000 and the profit on the Savannah is $50,000.
    (a) Write the simplex matrix to maximize the profit.
    (b) Use the simplex method to find how many of each type of home should be built to maximize profit, and find the maximum possible profit.

47. *Production scheduling* At one of its factories, a jeans manufacturer makes two styles: #891 and #917. Each pair of style-891 takes 10 minutes to cut out and 20 minutes to assemble and finish. Each pair of style-917 takes 10 minutes to cut out and 30 minutes to assemble and finish. The plant has enough workers to provide at most 7500 minutes per day for cutting and at most 19,500 minutes per day for assembly and finishing. The profit on each pair of style-891 is $6.00 and the profit on each pair of style-917 is $7.50. How many pairs of each style should be produced per day to obtain maximum profit? Find the maximum daily profit.

48. *Budget utilization* A car rental agency has a budget of $1.8 million to purchase at most 100 new cars. The agency will purchase either compact cars at $15,000 each or luxury cars at $30,000 each. From past rental patterns, the agency decides to purchase at most 50 luxury cars and expects an annual profit of $7500 per compact car and $11,000 per luxury car. How many of each type of car should be purchased in order to obtain the maximum profit while satisfying budgetary and other planning constraints? Find the maximum profit.

49. *Manufacturing* The Standard Steel Company produces two products, railroad car wheels and axles. Production requires processing in two departments: the smelting department (department A) and the machining department (department B). Department A has 50 hours available per week, and department B has 43 hours available per week. Manufacturing one axle requires 4 hours in department A and 3 hours in department B, and manufacturing one wheel requires 3 hours in department A and 5 hours in department B. The profits are $300 per axle and $300 per wheel. Find the maximum possible profit and the number of axles and wheels that will maximize the profit.

50. *Experimentation* An experiment involves placing the males and females of a laboratory animal species in two

separate controlled environments. There is a limited time available in these environments, and the experimenter wishes to maximize the number of animals subject to the constraints described.

	Males	Females	Time Available
Environment A	20 min	25 min	800 min
Environment B	20 min	15 min	600 min

How many males and how many females will maximize the total number of animals?

51. *Production scheduling* Happy Valley Ice Cream Company is planning its production for next week. Demand for Happy Valley's premium and light ice creams continues to outpace the company's production capacities. Two resources used in ice cream production are in short supply for next week. The mixing machines will be available for only 140 hours, and only 28,000 gallons of high-grade milk will be available. One hundred gallons of premium ice cream requires 0.3 hour of mixing and 90 gallons of milk. One hundred gallons of light ice cream requires 0.5 hour of mixing and 70 gallons of milk. If Happy Valley earns a profit of $100 per hundred gallons on both of its ice creams, how many hundreds of gallons of premium and of light ice cream should Happy Valley produce next week to maximize profit? How much profit will result?

52. *Shipping* A produce wholesaler has determined that it takes $\frac{1}{2}$ hour of labor to sort and pack a crate of tomatoes and that it takes $1\frac{1}{4}$ hours to sort and pack a crate of peaches. The crate of tomatoes weighs 60 pounds, and the crate of peaches weighs 50 pounds. The wholesaler has 2500 hours of labor available each week and can ship 120,000 pounds per week. If profits are $1 per crate of tomatoes and $2 per crate of peaches, how many crates of each should be sorted, packed, and shipped to maximize overall profit? What is the maximum profit?

53. *Advertising* Tire Corral has $6000 available per month for advertising. Newspaper ads cost $100 each and can occur a maximum of 21 times per month. Radio ads cost $300 each and can occur a maximum of 28 times per month at this price. Each newspaper ad reaches 6000 men over 20 years of age, and each radio ad reaches 8000 of these men. The company wants to maximize the number of ad exposures to this group. How many of each ad should it purchase? What is the maximum possible number of exposures?

54. *Manufacturing* A bicycle manufacturer makes a ten-speed and a regular bicycle. The ten-speed requires 2 units of steel and 6 units of aluminum in its frame and 12 special components for the hub, sprocket, and gear assembly. The regular bicycle requires 5 units each of steel and aluminum for its frame and 5 of the special

components. Shipments are such that steel is limited to 100 units per day, aluminum is limited to 120 units per day, and the special components are limited to 180 units per day. If the profits are $30 on each ten-speed and $20 on each regular bike, how many of each should be produced to yield the maximum profit? What is the maximum profit?

 Problems 55–64 involve three or more variables. Solve them with the simplex method, Excel, or some other technology.

55. *Advertising* The total advertising budget for a firm is $200,000. The following table gives the costs per ad package for each medium and the number of exposures per ad package (with all numbers in thousands).

	Medium 1	Medium 2	Medium 3
Cost/package	10	4	5
Exposures/ package	3100	2000	2400

If the maximum numbers of medium 1, medium 2, and medium 3 packages that can be purchased are 18, 10, and 12, respectively, how many of each ad package should be purchased to maximize the number of ad exposures?

56. *Advertising* The Laposata Pasta Company has $12,000 available for advertising. The following table gives the costs per ad and the numbers of people exposed to its ads for three different media (with numbers in thousands).

Ad Packages	Newspaper	Radio	TV
Cost	2	2	4
Total audience	30	21	54
Working mothers	6	12	8

If the total available audience is 420,000, and if the company wishes to maximize the number of exposures to working mothers, how many ads of each type should it purchase?

57. *Manufacturing* A firm has decided to discontinue production of an unprofitable product. This will create excess capacity, and the firm is considering one or more of three possible new products: A, B, and C. The available weekly hours in the plant will be 477 hours in tool and die, 350 hours on the drill presses, and 150 hours on lathes. The hours of production required in each of these areas are as follows for each of the products.

	Tool and Die	Drill Press	Lathe
A	9	5	3
B	3	4	0
C	0.5	0	2

Furthermore, the sales department foresees no limitations on the sale of products A and C but anticipates sales of only 20 or fewer per week for product B. If the unit profits expected are $30 for A, $9 for B, and $15 for C, how many of each should be produced to maximize overall profit? What is the maximum profit?

58. *Medicine*   A medical clinic performs three types of medical tests that use the same machines. Tests A, B, and C take 15 minutes, 30 minutes, and 1 hour, respectively, with respective profits of $30, $50, and $100. The clinic has four machines available. One person is qualified to do test A, two to do test B, and one to do test C. If the clinic has a rush of customers for these tests, how many of each type should it schedule in a 12-hour day to maximize its profit?

59. *Manufacturing*   A manufacturer of blenders produces three different sizes: Regular, Special, and Kitchen Magic. The production of each type requires the materials and amounts given in the following table. Suppose the manufacturer is opening a new plant and anticipates weekly supplies of 90,000 electrical components, 12,000 units of aluminum, and 9000 containers. The unit profits are $3 for the Regular, $4 for the Special, and $8 for the Kitchen Magic. How many of each type of blender should be produced to maximize overall profit? What is the maximum possible profit?

	Regular	Special	Kitchen Magic
Electrical components	5	12	24
Units of aluminum	1	2	4
Blending containers	1	1	1

60. *Construction*   A contractor builds three types of houses: the Aries, the Belfair, and the Wexford. Each house requires one lot, and the following table gives the number of labor-hours and the amount of capital needed for each type of house, as well as the profit on the sale of each house. There are 12 lots, 47,500 labor-hours, and $3,413,000 available for the contractor's use.
    (a) Building how many of each type of house will maximize his profit?
    (b) What is the maximum possible profit?

	Aries	Belfair	Wexford
Labor-hours	3,000	3,700	5,000
Capital	$205,000	$279,600	$350,000
Profit	$20,000	$25,000	$30,000

61. *Revenue*   A woman has a building with 26 one-bedroom apartments, 40 two-bedroom apartments, and 60 three-bedroom apartments available to rent to students. She has set the rent at $500 per month for the one-bedroom

units, $800 per month for the two-bedroom units, and $1150 per month for the three-bedroom units. She must rent to one student per bedroom, and zoning laws limit her to at most 250 students in this building. There are enough students available to rent all the apartments.
    (a) How many of each type of apartment should she rent to maximize her revenue?
    (b) What is the maximum possible revenue?

62. *Manufacturing*   Patio Iron makes wrought iron outdoor dining tables, chairs, and stools. Each table uses 8 feet of a standard width wrought iron, 4 hours of labor for cutting and assembly, and 2 hours of labor for detail and finishing work. Each chair uses 6 feet of the wrought iron, 2 hours of cutting and assembly labor, and 1.5 hours of detail and finishing labor. Each stool uses 1 foot of the wrought iron, 1.5 hours for cutting and assembly, and 0.5 hour for detail and finishing work, and the daily demand for stools is at most 16. Each day Patio Iron has available at most 108 feet of wrought iron, 50 hours for cutting and assembly, and 40 hours for detail and finishing. If the profits are $60 for each dining table, $48 for each chair, and $36 for each stool, how many of each item should be made each day to maximize profit? Find the maximum profit.

63. *Manufacturing*   At one of its factories, a manufacturer of television sets makes one or more of four models of HD sets: a 20-in. LCD, a 42-in. LCD, a 42-in. plasma, and a 50-in. plasma. The assembly and testing time requirements for each model are shown in the following table, together with the maximum amounts of time available per week for assembly and testing. In addition to these constraints, the supplier of cabinet units indicated that it would supply no more than 200 units per week and that of these, no more than 40 could be for the 20-in. LCD model.

	20-in. LCD	42-in. LCD	42-in. Plasma	50-in. Plasma	Total Available
Assembly time (hours)	7	10	12	15	2000
Test time (hours)	2	2	4	5	500
Profit (dollars)	46	60	75	100	

Use the profit for each television shown in the table to find the number of sets of each type that should be produced to obtain the maximum profit for the week. Find the maximum profit.

64. *Investment analysis*   Conglomo Corporation is considering investing in other smaller companies, and it can purchase any fraction of each company. Each investment by Conglomo requires a partial payment now and a final payment 1 year from now. For each investment, the following table summarizes the amount of

each payment (in millions of dollars) and the projected 5-year profit (also in millions of dollars).

	Company 1	Company 2	Company 3	Company 4	Company 5
Paid now	13.2	63.6	6.0	6.0	34.8
Paid in 1 year	3.6	7.2	6.0	1.2	40.8
Projected profit	15.6	19.2	19.2	16.8	46.8

This table may be interpreted as follows: if Conglomo purchases one-fifth of Company 4, then it pays $\frac{1}{5}(6.0) = \$1.2$ million now and $\frac{1}{5}(1.2) = \$0.24$ million $= \$240,000$ after 1 year, and the one-fifth share has a projected 5-year profit of $\frac{1}{5}(16.8) = \$3.36$ million. Conglomo has available $48 million for investment now and $24 million for investment 1 year from now. What fraction of each smaller company should Conglomo purchase in order to maximize the projected 5-year profit? What is the maximum profit? *Hint:* If x_1 represents the fraction of Company 1 that is purchased, then $x_1 \leq 1$ is a constraint.

OBJECTIVES

4.4

- To formulate the dual for minimization problems
- To solve minimization problems using the simplex method on the dual

The Simplex Method: Duality and Minimization

| APPLICATION PREVIEW |

A beef producer is considering two different types of feed. Each feed contains some or all of the necessary ingredients for fattening beef. Brand 1 feed costs 20 cents per pound and brand 2 costs 30 cents per pound. Table 4.1 contains all the relevant data about nutrition and cost of each brand and the minimum requirements per unit of beef. The producer would like to determine how much of each brand to buy in order to satisfy the nutritional requirements for Ingredients A and B at minimum cost. (See Example 3.)

| TABLE 4.1 |

	Brand 1	Brand 2	Minimum Requirement
Ingredient A	3 units/lb	5 units/lb	40 units
Ingredient B	4 units/lb	3 units/lb	46 units
Cost per pound	20¢	30¢	

In this section, we will use the simplex method to solve minimization problems such as this one.

Dual Problems   We have solved both maximization and minimization problems using graphical methods, but the simplex method, as discussed in the previous section, applies only to maximization problems. Now let us turn our attention to extending the use of the simplex method to solve minimization problems. Such problems might arise when a company seeks to minimize its production costs yet fill customers' orders or purchase items necessary for production.

As with maximization problems, we shall consider only **standard minimization problems,** in which the constraints satisfy the following conditions.

1. All variables are nonnegative.
2. The constraints are of the form

$$a_1 y_1 + a_2 y_2 + \cdots + a_n y_n \geq b \quad \text{where } b \text{ is positive.}$$

Because the simplex method specifically seeks to increase the objective function, it does not apply to minimization problems. However, associated with each minimization problem there is a related maximization problem called the **dual problem** or **dual.**

EXAMPLE   1   A Minimization Problem and Its Dual

Given the problem

$$\text{Minimize } g = 11y_1 + 7y_2$$
$$\text{subject to } \quad y_1 + 2y_2 \geq 10$$
$$3y_1 + \quad y_2 \geq 15$$

find the dual maximization problem.

Solution

First, we write a matrix A that has a form similar to the simplex matrix, but without slack variables and with positive coefficients for the variables in the last row (and with the function name in the augment).

The matrix for the dual problem is formed by interchanging the rows and columns of matrix A. Matrix B is the result of this procedure, and recall that B is the **transpose** of A.

Minimization $\qquad\qquad$ Dual

$$A = \begin{bmatrix} 1 & 2 & | & 10 \\ 3 & 1 & | & 15 \\ \hline 11 & 7 & | & g \end{bmatrix} \qquad B = \begin{bmatrix} 1 & 3 & | & 11 \\ 2 & 1 & | & 7 \\ \hline 10 & 15 & | & g \end{bmatrix}$$

Note that row 1 of A becomes column 1 of B, row 2 of A becomes column 2 of B, and row 3 of A becomes column 3 of B.

In the same way that we formed matrix A, we can now "convert back" from matrix B to the maximization problem that is the dual of the original minimization problem. We state this dual problem, using different letters to emphasize that this is a different problem from the original.

$$\text{Maximize } f = 10x_1 + 15x_2$$
$$\text{subject to } \quad x_1 + 3x_2 \leq 11$$
$$2x_1 + \quad x_2 \leq 7$$

Next let's see how the solutions of these problems are related. The following box shows the solution of the Example 1 minimization problem and its dual maximization problem.

Comparison of a Minimization Problem and Its Dual

Maximization Problem—Simplex Method

1.
$$\begin{array}{cccccc} x_1 & x_2 & s_1 & s_2 & f & \\ \begin{bmatrix} 1 & ③ & 1 & 0 & 0 & | & 11 \\ 2 & 1 & 0 & 1 & 0 & | & 7 \\ \hline -10 & -15 & 0 & 0 & 1 & | & 0 \end{bmatrix} \end{array}$$

2.
$$\begin{bmatrix} \frac{1}{3} & 1 & \frac{1}{3} & 0 & 0 & | & \frac{11}{3} \\ \frac{5}{3} & 0 & -\frac{1}{3} & 1 & 0 & | & \frac{10}{3} \\ \hline -5 & 0 & 5 & 0 & 1 & | & 55 \end{bmatrix}$$

3.
$$\begin{bmatrix} 0 & 1 & \frac{2}{5} & -\frac{1}{5} & 0 & | & 3 \\ 1 & 0 & -\frac{1}{5} & \frac{3}{5} & 0 & | & 2 \\ \hline 0 & 0 & 4 & 3 & 1 & | & 65 \end{bmatrix}$$

Maximum $f = 65$ occurs at $x_1 = 2$, $x_2 = 3$.

Minimization Problem—Graphical Method

Corners:

$A = (0, 15)$
$B = (4, 3)$ $\quad \left\{ \begin{array}{l} \text{obtained by solving} \\ \text{simultaneously} \end{array} \right.$
$C = (10, 0)$

$g = 11y_1 + 7y_2;$
At A, $g = 105$
At B, $g = 65$
At C, $g = 110$

Minimum $g = 65$ occurs at $y_1 = 4$, $y_2 = 3$.

In comparing the solutions of the minimization problem and its dual, the first thing to note is that the maximum value of f in the maximization problem and the minimum value of g in the minimization problem are the same. Furthermore, looking at the final simplex matrix, we can also find the values of y_1 and y_2 that give the minimum value of g by looking at the last (bottom) entries in the slack variable columns of the matrix.

$$
\begin{array}{c}
\begin{array}{ccccc} x_1 & y_2 & s_1 & s_2 & f \end{array} \\
\left[\begin{array}{ccccc|c}
0 & 1 & \frac{2}{5} & -\frac{1}{5} & 0 & 3 \\
1 & 0 & -\frac{1}{5} & \frac{3}{5} & 0 & 2 \\
\hline
0 & 0 & 4 & 3 & 1 & 65
\end{array}\right]
\end{array}
$$

These values give the values of y_1 and y_2 in the minimization problem.

Duality and Solving   From Example 1 we see that the given minimization problem and its dual maximization problem are very closely related. Furthermore, when problems exhibit this relationship, the simplex method can be used to solve them both. This fact was proved by John von Neumann, and it is summarized by the Principle of Duality.

Principle of Duality

1. When a standard minimization problem and its dual have a solution, the maximum value of the function to be maximized is the same value as the minimum value of the function to be minimized.
2. When the simplex method is used to solve the maximization problem, the values of the variables that solve the corresponding minimization problem are *the last entries in the columns corresponding to the slack variables.*

EXAMPLE **2**   ## Minimization with the Simplex Method

Given the problem

$$
\begin{array}{rl}
\text{Minimize } & 18y_1 + 12y_2 = g \\
\text{subject to } & 2y_1 + y_2 \geq 8 \\
& 6y_1 + 6y_2 \geq 36
\end{array}
$$

(a)   State the dual of this minimization problem.
(b)   Solve this minimization problem by first solving the dual maximization problem.

Solution

(a)   The dual of this minimization problem will be a maximization problem. To form the dual, first write the matrix A (without slack variables and with positive coefficients for the variables in the last row) for the given problem.

$$
A = \left[\begin{array}{cc|c}
2 & 1 & 8 \\
6 & 6 & 36 \\
\hline
18 & 12 & g
\end{array}\right]
$$

Next, transpose matrix A to yield matrix B.

$$
B = \left[\begin{array}{cc|c}
2 & 6 & 18 \\
1 & 6 & 12 \\
\hline
8 & 36 & g
\end{array}\right]
$$

Then write the dual maximization problem, renaming the variables and the function.

Dual problem

$$
\begin{array}{rl}
\text{Maximize } & f = 8x_1 + 36x_2 \\
\text{subject to } & 2x_1 + 6x_2 \leq 18 \\
& x_1 + 6x_2 \leq 12
\end{array}
$$

(b) To solve the given minimization problem, we use the simplex method on its dual maximization problem. The complete simplex matrix for each step is given, and each pivot entry is circled.

1.
$$\begin{bmatrix} 2 & 6 & 1 & 0 & 0 & 18 \\ 1 & ⑥ & 0 & 1 & 0 & 12 \\ -8 & -36 & 0 & 0 & 1 & 0 \end{bmatrix}$$
2.
$$\begin{bmatrix} ① & 0 & 1 & -1 & 0 & 6 \\ \frac{1}{6} & 1 & 0 & \frac{1}{6} & 0 & 2 \\ -2 & 0 & 0 & 6 & 1 & 72 \end{bmatrix}$$

3. $x_1 \quad x_2 \quad s_1 \quad s_2 \quad f$
$$\begin{bmatrix} 1 & 0 & 1 & -1 & 0 & 6 \\ 0 & 1 & -\frac{1}{6} & \frac{2}{6} & 0 & 1 \\ 0 & 0 & 2 & 4 & 1 & 84 \end{bmatrix}$$

The solution of the maximization problem is $f = 84$ (at $x_1 = 6$, $x_2 = 1$). By the Principle of Duality, $g = 84$ is the minimum value of the objective function $g = 18y_1 + 12y_2$, and the values that give this minimum are the last entries in the slack variable columns, $y_1 = 2$ and $y_2 = 4$. ■

CHECKPOINT

Perform the following steps to begin the process of finding the minimum value of $g = y_1 + 4y_2$, subject to the following constraints.

$$2y_1 + 4y_2 \geq 18$$
$$y_1 + 5y_2 \geq 15$$

1. Form the matrix associated with the minimization problem.
2. Find the transpose of this matrix.
3. State the dual problem by using the matrix from Problem 2.
4. Write the simplex matrix for the dual of this problem.
5. The dual of this minimization problem has the following solution matrix. What is the solution of the minimization problem?

$$\begin{bmatrix} 1 & 0 & \frac{5}{6} & -\frac{1}{6} & 0 & \frac{1}{6} \\ 0 & 1 & -\frac{2}{3} & \frac{1}{3} & 0 & \frac{2}{3} \\ 0 & 0 & 5 & 2 & 1 & 13 \end{bmatrix}$$

EXAMPLE 3 Purchasing | APPLICATION PREVIEW |

A beef producer is considering two different types of feed. Each feed contains some or all of the necessary ingredients for fattening beef. Brand 1 feed costs 20 cents per pound and brand 2 costs 30 cents per pound. How much of each brand should the producer buy in order to satisfy the nutritional requirements for ingredients A and B at minimum cost? Table 4.2 contains all the relevant data about nutrition and cost of each brand and the minimum requirements per unit of beef.

| TABLE 4.2 |

	Brand 1	Brand 2	Minimum Requirement
Ingredient A	3 units/lb	5 units/lb	40 units
Ingredient B	4 units/lb	3 units/lb	46 units
Cost per pound	20¢	30¢	

Solution

Let y_1 be the number of pounds of brand 1, and let y_2 be the number of pounds of brand 2. Then we can formulate the problem as follows:

$$\text{Minimize cost } C = 20y_1 + 30y_2$$
$$\text{subject to} \quad 3y_1 + 5y_2 \geq 40$$
$$4y_1 + 3y_2 \geq 46$$

The original linear programming problem is usually called the **primal problem.** If we write this in an augmented matrix, without the slack variables, then we can use the transpose to find the dual problem.

Primal
$$\begin{bmatrix} 3 & 5 & 40 \\ 4 & 3 & 46 \\ 20 & 30 & C \end{bmatrix}$$

Dual
(with function renamed)
$$\begin{bmatrix} 3 & 4 & 20 \\ 5 & 3 & 30 \\ 40 & 46 & f \end{bmatrix}$$

Thus the dual maximization problem is

$$\text{Maximize } f = 40x_1 + 46x_2$$
$$\text{subject to} \quad 3x_1 + 4x_2 \leq 20$$
$$5x_1 + 3x_2 \leq 30$$

The simplex matrix for this maximization problem, with slack variables included, is

1. $$\begin{bmatrix} 3 & \textcircled{4} & 1 & 0 & 0 & 20 \\ 5 & 3 & 0 & 1 & 0 & 30 \\ -40 & -46 & 0 & 0 & 1 & 0 \end{bmatrix}$$

Solving the problem gives

2. $$\begin{bmatrix} \frac{3}{4} & 1 & \frac{1}{4} & 0 & 0 & 5 \\ \textcircled{\frac{11}{4}} & 0 & -\frac{3}{4} & 1 & 0 & 15 \\ -\frac{11}{2} & 0 & \frac{23}{2} & 0 & 1 & 230 \end{bmatrix}$$
3. $$\begin{bmatrix} 0 & 1 & \frac{5}{11} & -\frac{3}{11} & 0 & \frac{10}{11} \\ 1 & 0 & -\frac{3}{11} & \frac{4}{11} & 0 & \frac{60}{11} \\ 0 & 0 & 10 & 2 & 1 & 260 \end{bmatrix}$$

The solution to this problem is

$$y_1 = 10 \text{ lb of brand 1}$$
$$y_2 = 2 \text{ lb of brand 2}$$
$$\text{Minimum cost} = 260 \text{ cents or \$2.60 per unit of beef}$$

In a more extensive study of linear programming, the duality relationship that we have used in this section as a means of solving minimization problems can be shown to have more properties than we have mentioned.

Spreadsheet Note When we use Excel, minimization problems are solved in a manner similar to maximization problems. Because of the constraints, the Solver for this problem has different directions on the inequality symbols; Solver is also set to find the minimum (min) rather than the maximum (max) value of the objective function. (For details on using the Excel Solver, see Appendix D, Section 4.3, and the Online Excel Guide.)

The solution to the minimization problem in Example 3, found with Solver and shown on the next page, is that cost is minimized at 260 cents when 10 lb of brand 1 and 2 lb of brand 2 are used. This is the same solution we found "by hand" with the simplex method.

	A	B	C
1	Variables		
2			
3	Pounds Brand 1	10	
4	Pounds Brand 2	2	
5			
6	Objective		
7			
8	Minimize cost	260	
9			
10	Constraints		
11		Amount in feeds	Required
12	Ingredient A	40	40
13	Ingredient B	46	46

CHECKPOINT SOLUTIONS

1. $\begin{bmatrix} 2 & 4 & | & 18 \\ 1 & 5 & | & 15 \\ \hline 1 & 4 & | & g \end{bmatrix}$ 2. $\begin{bmatrix} 2 & 1 & | & 1 \\ 4 & 5 & | & 4 \\ \hline 18 & 15 & | & g \end{bmatrix}$

3. Find the maximum value of $f = 18x_1 + 15x_2$ subject to the constraints

$$2x_1 + x_2 \le 1$$
$$4x_1 + 5x_2 \le 4$$

4. The simplex matrix for this dual problem is

$$\begin{bmatrix} 2 & 1 & 1 & 0 & 0 & | & 1 \\ 4 & 5 & 0 & 1 & 0 & | & 4 \\ \hline -18 & -15 & 0 & 0 & 1 & | & 0 \end{bmatrix}$$

5. The minimum value is $g = 13$ when $y_1 = 5$ and $y_2 = 2$.

| EXERCISES | 4.4

In Problems 1–4, complete the following.
(a) Form the matrix associated with each given minimization problem and find its transpose.
(b) Write the dual maximization problem. Be sure to rename the variables.

1. Minimize $g = 4y_1 + 5y_2$ subject to

$$5y_1 + 2y_2 \ge 16$$
$$y_1 + 2y_2 \ge 8$$

2. Minimize $g = 3y_1 + 2y_2$ subject to

$$3y_1 + y_2 \ge 6$$
$$3y_1 + 4y_2 \ge 12$$

3. Minimize $g = 7y_1 + 3y_2$ subject to

$$y_1 + 2y_2 \ge 30$$
$$y_1 + 4y_2 \ge 50$$

4. Minimize $g = 9y_1 + 10y_2$ subject to

$$y_1 + 2y_2 \ge 21$$
$$3y_1 + 2y_2 \ge 27$$

In Problems 5 and 6, suppose a primal minimization problem and its dual maximization problem were solved by using the simplex method on the dual problem, and the final simplex method is given.
(a) Find the solution of the minimization problem. Use y_1, y_2, y_3 as the variables and g as the function.
(b) Find the solution of the maximization problem. Use x_1, x_2, x_3 as the variables and f as the function.

5. $\begin{bmatrix} 1 & -\frac{2}{5} & 0 & 3 & -\frac{3}{5} & 0 & 0 & | & 15 \\ 0 & -\frac{3}{5} & 0 & -2 & -\frac{11}{5} & 1 & 0 & | & 13 \\ 0 & -\frac{4}{5} & 1 & -1 & -\frac{2}{5} & 0 & 0 & | & 29 \\ \hline 0 & 2 & 0 & 7 & 4 & 0 & 1 & | & 452 \end{bmatrix}$

6. $\begin{bmatrix} 0 & 0 & 1 & \frac{2}{5} & \frac{5}{3} & \frac{4}{15} & 0 & | & 16 \\ 1 & 0 & 0 & -\frac{1}{5} & \frac{11}{3} & \frac{1}{5} & 0 & | & 19 \\ 0 & 1 & 0 & \frac{3}{5} & -\frac{2}{3} & \frac{2}{3} & 0 & | & 22 \\ 0 & 0 & 0 & 12 & 15 & 20 & 1 & | & 554 \end{bmatrix}$

In Problems 7–10, write the dual maximization problem, and then solve both the primal and dual problems with the simplex method.

7. Minimize $g = 2y_1 + 10y_2$ subject to

$$2y_1 + y_2 \geq 11$$
$$y_1 + 3y_2 \geq 11$$
$$y_1 + 4y_2 \geq 16$$

8. Minimize $g = 8y_1 + 4y_2$ subject to

$$3y_1 - 2y_2 \geq 6$$
$$2y_1 + y_2 \geq 11$$

9. Minimize $g = 3y_1 + y_2$ subject to

$$4y_1 + y_2 \geq 11$$
$$3y_1 + 2y_2 \geq 12$$
$$3y_1 + y_2 \geq 6$$

10. Minimize $g = 2y_1 + 5y_2$ subject to

$$4y_1 + y_2 \geq 12$$
$$y_1 + y_2 \geq 9$$
$$y_1 + 3y_2 \geq 15$$

Use the simplex method in Problems 11–14.

11. Minimize $g = 8x + 7y + 12z$ subject to

$$x + y + z \geq 3$$
$$y + 2z \geq 2$$
$$x \geq 2$$

12. Minimize $g = 12y_1 + 8y_2 + 10y_3$ subject to

$$y_1 + 2y_3 \geq 10$$
$$y_1 + y_2 \geq 12$$
$$2y_1 + 2y_2 + y_3 \geq 8$$

13. Minimize $g = 12y_1 + 48y_2 + 8y_3$ subject to

$$y_1 + 3y_2 \geq 1$$
$$4y_1 + 6y_2 + y_3 \geq 3$$
$$4y_2 + y_3 \geq 1$$

14. Minimize $g = 20x + 30y + 36z$ subject to

$$x + 2y + 3z \geq 48$$
$$2x + 2y + 3z \geq 70$$
$$2x + 3y + 4z \geq 96$$

In Problems 15 and 16, a primal maximization problem is given.
(a) Form the dual minimization problem.
(b) Solve both the primal and dual problems with the simplex method.

15. Maximize $f = 40x_1 + 20x_2$ subject to

$$3x_1 + 2x_2 \leq 120$$
$$x_1 + x_2 \leq 50$$

16. Maximize $f = 28x_1 + 12x_2$ subject to

$$7x_1 + 12x_2 \leq 50$$
$$2x_1 + 6x_2 \leq 100$$

In Problems 17–20, you may want to use Excel or some other technology.

17. Minimize $g = 40y_1 + 90y_2 + 30y_3$ subject to

$$y_1 + 2y_2 + y_3 \geq 16$$
$$y_1 + 5y_2 + 2y_3 \geq 18$$
$$2y_1 + 5y_2 + 3y_3 \geq 38$$

18. Minimize $w = 48y_1 + 20y_2 + 8y_3$ subject to

$$4y_1 + 2y_2 + y_3 \geq 30$$
$$12y_1 + 4y_2 + 3y_3 \geq 60$$
$$2y_1 + 3y_2 + y_3 \geq 40$$

19. Minimize $g = 50y_1 + 20y_2 + 30y_3 + 80y_4$ subject to

$$40y_1 + 20y_2 + 15y_3 + 50y_4 \geq 50$$
$$3y_1 + 2y_2 + 5y_4 \geq 6$$
$$2y_1 + 2y_2 + 4y_3 + 4y_4 \geq 10$$
$$2y_1 + 4y_2 + y_3 + 5y_4 \geq 8$$

20. Minimize $g = 200y_1 + 100y_2 + 200y_3 + 40y_4$ subject to

$$3y_1 + 2y_2 + y_3 + y_4 \geq 88$$
$$2y_1 + 2y_2 + y_3 \geq 86$$
$$2y_1 + 4y_2 + y_3 \geq 100$$
$$5y_1 + 5y_2 + y_3 \geq 100$$

APPLICATIONS

21. *Production scheduling* CDF Appliances has assembly plants in Atlanta and Fort Worth where it produces a variety of kitchen appliances, including a 12-cup coffee maker and a cappuccino machine. In each hour at the Atlanta plant, 160 of the coffee makers and 200 of the cappuccino machines can be assembled, and the hourly cost is $700. In each hour at the Fort Worth plant, 800 of the coffee makers and 200 of the cappuccino machines can be assembled, and the hourly cost is $2100. CDF Appliances expects orders each week for at least 64,000 of the coffee makers and at least 40,000 of the cappuccino machines. How many hours per week should each plant be operated in order to provide inventory for the orders at minimum cost? Find the minimum cost.

22. *Manufacturing* Nekita Corporation assembles cell phones and camera cell phones at two different factories within the same city. During each hour at the first factory, 15 cell phones and 30 camera cell phones can be assembled at a cost of $100/hour. During each hour

at the second factory, 10 cell phones and 60 camera cell phones can be assembled at a cost of $150/hour. If Nekita expects weekly orders for at least 15,000 cell phones and at least 45,000 camera cell phones, how many hours per week should it schedule at each location to be able to fill the orders at minimum cost? What is the minimum cost?

23. *Manufacturing* The Video Star Company makes two different models of DVD players, which are assembled on two different assembly lines. Line 1 can assemble 30 units of the Star model and 40 units of the Prostar model per hour, and line 2 can assemble 150 units of the Star model and 40 units of the Prostar model per hour. The company needs to produce at least 270 units of the Star model and 200 units of the Prostar model to fill an order. If it costs $200 per hour to run line 1 and $400 per hour to run line 2, how many hours should each line be run to fill the order at the minimum cost? What is the minimum cost?

24. *Nutrition* A pork producer is considering two types of feed that contain the necessary ingredients for the nutritional requirements for fattening hogs. Red Star Brand contains 9 units of ingredient A and 12 units of ingredient B, and Blue Chip Brand contains 15 units of ingredient A and 9 units of ingredient B. The nutritional requirements for the hogs are at least 120 units of ingredient A and at least 138 units of ingredient B.
    (a) If Red Star Brand costs 50 cents per pound and Blue Chip Brand costs 75 cents, how many pounds of each brand should be bought to satisfy the nutritional requirements at the minimum cost?
    (b) What is the minimum cost?

25. *Production* A small company produces two products, I and II, at three facilities, A, B, and C. It has orders for 2000 of product I and 1200 of product II. The production capacities and costs per week to operate the three facilities are summarized in the following table.

	A	B	C
I	200	200	400
II	100	200	100
Cost/week	$1000	$3000	$4000

How many weeks should each facility operate to fill the company's orders at a minimum cost, and what is the minimum cost?

26. *Nutrition* In a hospital ward, the patients can be grouped into two general categories depending on their conditions and the amounts of solid foods they require in their diet. A combination of two diets is used for solid foods because they supply essential nutrients for recovery, but each diet has an amount of a substance deemed detrimental. For each patient group, the fol-

lowing table summarizes the diet requirements and the amounts of the detrimental substance. How many servings from each diet should be given each day in order to minimize the intake of this detrimental substance?

	Diet A	Diet B	Required Daily
Group 1	4 oz per serving	1 oz per serving	26 oz
Group 2	2 oz per serving	1 oz per serving	18 oz
Detrimental substance	0.18 oz per serving	0.07 oz per serving	

27. *Production* Two factories produce three different types of kitchen appliances. The following table summarizes the production capacities, the numbers of each type of appliance ordered, and the daily operating costs for the factories. How many days should each factory operate to fill the orders at minimum cost?

	Factory 1	Factory 2	Number Ordered
Appliance 1	80/day	20/day	1600
Appliance 2	10/day	10/day	500
Appliance 3	50/day	20/day	1900
Daily cost	$10,000	$20,000	

28. *Nutrition* In a laboratory experiment, two separate foods are given to experimental animals. Each food contains essential ingredients, A and B, for which the animals have minimum requirements, and each food also has an ingredient C, which can be harmful to the animals. The following table summarizes this information.

	Food 1	Food 2	Required
Ingredient A	10 units/g	3 units/g	49 units
Ingredient B	6 units/g	12 units/g	60 units
Ingredient C	3 units/g	1 unit/g	

How many grams of foods 1 and 2 will satisfy the requirements for A and B and minimize the amount of ingredient C that is ingested?

29. *Politics* A political candidate wishes to use a combination of radio and TV advertisements in her campaign. Research has shown that each 1-minute spot on TV reaches 0.9 million people and that each 1-minute spot on radio reaches 0.6 million. The candidate feels she must reach 63 million people, and she must buy at least 90 minutes of advertisements. How many minutes of each medium should be used if TV costs $500 per

minute, radio costs $100 per minute, and the candidate wishes to minimize costs?

30. **Production** The James MacGregor Mining Company owns three mines: I, II, and III. Three grades of ore, A, B, and C, are mined at these mines. For each grade of ore, the number of tons per week available from each mine and the number of tons per week required to fill orders are given in the following table.

		I	II	III	Required Tons/Week
Ore Grades	A	10	10	10	90
	B	0	10	10	50
	C	10	0	10	60
Cost/day		$6000	$8000	$12,000	

Find the number of days the company should operate each mine so that orders are filled at minimum cost. Find the minimum cost.

31. **Supply costs** DeTurris Office Supplies presently carries reams of laser printer paper in three different grades: recycled, satin white, and glossy white. Three wholesalers offer special purchase packages consisting of different numbers of reams of these three grades, as shown in the following table. DeTurris Office Supplies needs at least 230 reams of the recycled paper, 240 reams of the satin white paper, and 210 reams of the glossy white paper.
   (a) How many of each package should DeTurris buy to minimize its cost?
   (b) What is the minimum possible cost?

	Recycled	Satin White	Glossy White	Package Cost
Georgia package	10	5	6	$120
Union package	5	8	6	140
Pacific package	6	6	6	126

32. **Dieting** A dieting company offers three foods, A, B, and C, and groups its customers into two groups according to their nutritional needs. The following table gives the percent of the daily nutritional requirements that a serving of each food provides and the number of ounces of detrimental substances in each food. Determine the combination of food types that will provide at least 100% of the daily requirements *and* will minimize the detrimental substances. What is the minimum amount of the detrimental substance?

	Food A	Food B	Food C	Daily Requirement
Group I	30% per serving	10% per serving	20% per serving	100%
Group II	10% per serving	20% per serving	40% per serving	100%
Detrimental substances	0.1 oz per serving	0.2 oz per serving	0.25 oz per serving	

33. **Nutrition** A hospital wishes to provide at least 24 units of nutrient A and 16 units of nutrient B in a meal, while minimizing the cost of the meal. If three types of food are available, with the nutritional values and costs (per ounce) given in the following table,
   (a) What is the minimum possible cost?
   (b) How many ounces of each food should be served to minimize cost? Find two solutions that give the minimum cost.

	Units of Nutrient A	Units of Nutrient B	Cost
Food I	2	1	1
Food II	2	5	5
Food III	2	1	2

34. **Pollution** Three factories each dump waste water containing three different types of pollutants into a river. State regulations require the factories to treat their waste in order to reduce pollution levels. The following table shows the possible percent reduction of each pollutant at each site and the cost per ton to process the waste.

	Factory 1	Factory 2	Factory 3
Pollutant 1	75%	45%	20%
Pollutant 2	65%	30%	15%
Pollutant 3	10%	15%	5%
Cost/ton	$50	$20	$8

If the state requires a reduction of at least 65 tons per day of pollutant 1, at least 40 tons per day of pollutant 2, and at least 20 tons per day of pollutant 3, find the number of tons of waste that must be treated each day at each site so that the state's requirements are satisfied and the treatment costs are minimized. Find the minimum cost.

35. **Scheduling** Package Express delivers packages and overnight mailers. At each of several decentralized

delivery depots in one district, Package Express hires a number of full- and part-time unskilled employees (so one-half of an employee is an individual who works half a day for 5 days). Each employee works the same shift (or part of a shift) for 5 consecutive days. Thus, if x_1 is the number of employees who begin work on Monday, then those same x_1 employees work Monday through Friday. The following table shows the minimum number of unskilled workers needed at a depot on each day of the week.

Mon.	Tues.	Wed.	Thurs.	Fri.	Sat.	Sun.
20	16	16	20	22	12	17

How many unskilled employees should begin their shifts on each day of the week in order to staff a depot properly but minimize the total number of these workers that Package Express needs? *Hint*: The total number of workers on Monday is the sum of those who begin their shifts on any of the days Thursday through Monday. Total numbers of workers on other days are found similarly.

 36. *Scheduling*   Each nurse works 8 consecutive hours at the Beaver Medical Center. The center has the following staffing requirements for each 4-hour work period.

Work Period	Nurses Needed
1 (7–11)	40
2 (11–3)	20
3 (3–7)	30
4 (7–11)	40
5 (11–3)	20
6 (3–7)	10

(a) If y_1 represents the number of nurses starting in period 1, y_2 the number starting in period 2, and so on, write the linear programming problem that will minimize the total number of nurses needed. (Note that the nurses who begin work in period 6 work periods 6 and 1 for their 8-hour shift.)

(b) Solve the problem in (a).

OBJECTIVES   **4.5**

- To solve maximization problems with mixed constraints
- To solve minimization problems with mixed constraints

The Simplex Method with Mixed Constraints

| APPLICATION PREVIEW |

The Laser Company manufactures two models of home theater systems, the Star and the Allstar, at two plants, located in Ashville and in Cleveland. The maximum daily output at the Ashville plant is 900, and the profits there are $200 per unit of the Allstar and $100 per unit of the Star. The maximum daily output at the Cleveland plant is 800, and the profits there are $210 per unit of the Allstar and $80 per unit of the Star. In addition, restrictions at the Ashville plant mean that the number of units of the Star model cannot exceed 100 more than the number of units of the Allstar model produced. If the company gets a rush order for 800 units of the Allstar model and 600 units of the Star model, finding the number of units of each model that should be produced at each location to fill the order and obtain the maximum profit is a mixed constraint linear programming problem (see Example 3).

Mixed Constraints and Maximization

In the previous two sections, we used the simplex method to solve two different types of standard linear programming problems. These types are summarized as follows.

	Maximization Problems	**Minimization Problems**
Function	Maximized	Minimized
Variables	Nonnegative	Nonnegative
Constraints	$a_1x_1 + a_2x_2 + \cdots + a_nx_n \leq b \ (b \geq 0)$	$c_1y_1 + c_2y_2 + \cdots + c_ny_n \geq d \ (d \geq 0)$
Simplex method	Applied directly	Applied to dual

In this section we will show how to apply the simplex method to mixed constraint linear programming problems that do not exactly fit either of these types. The term *mixed constraint* is used because some inequalities describing the constraints contain "≤" and some contain "≥" signs.

We begin by considering maximization problems with constraints that have a form different from those noted in the preceding table. This can happen in one of the following ways.

1. If a constraint has the form $a_1x_1 + a_2x_2 + \cdots + a_nx_n \leq b$, where $b < 0$, such as with
$$x - 2y \leq -8$$
2. If a constraint has the form $a_1x_1 + a_2x_2 + \cdots + a_nx_n \geq b$, where $b \geq 0$, such as with
$$2x - 3y \geq 6$$

Note that in the latter case, multiplying both sides of the inequality by (-1) changes it as follows:

$$a_1x_1 + a_2x_2 + \cdots + a_nx_n \geq b \text{ becomes } -a_1x_1 - a_2x_2 - \cdots - a_nx_n \leq -b$$

That is,

$$2x - 3y \geq 6 \text{ becomes } -2x + 3y \leq -6$$

Thus we see that the two possibilities for mixed constraints are actually one: constraints that have the form $a_1x_1 + a_2x_2 + \cdots + a_nx_n \leq b$, where b is any constant. We call these **less than or equal to constraints** and denote them as **≤ constraints.**

EXAMPLE 1 Maximization with Mixed Constraints

Maximize $f = x + 2y$ subject to

$$\begin{aligned} x + y &\leq 13 \\ 2x - 3y &\geq 6 \\ x \geq 0, y &\geq 0 \end{aligned}$$

Solution

We begin by expressing all constraints as ≤ constraints. In this case, we multiply $2x - 3y \geq 6$ by (-1) to obtain $-2x + 3y \leq -6$. We can now use slack variables to write the inequalities as equations and form the simplex matrix.

$$\begin{aligned} x + y + s_1 &= 13 \\ -2x + 3y + s_2 &= -6 \\ -x - 2y + f &= 0 \end{aligned} \quad \text{gives}$$

x_1	y_2	s_1	s_2	f	
1	1	1	0	0	13
−2	3	0	1	0	−6
−1	−2	0	0	1	0

The −6 in the upper portion of the last column is a problem. If we compute values for the variables x, y, s_1, and s_2 that are associated with this matrix, we get $s_2 = -6$. This violates the condition of the simplex method that all variables be nonnegative. In order to use the simplex method, we must change the sign of any negative entry that appears in the upper portion of the last column (above the line separating the objective function from the constraints). If the problem has a solution, there will always be another negative entry in the same row as this negative entry, but in a different column. We choose this column as the pivot column, because pivoting with it will give a positive entry in the last column.

x	y	s_1	s_2	f	
1	1	1	0	0	13
−2	3	0	1	0	−6	← Negative in last column
−1	−2	0	0	1	0

↑
Pivot column (negative entry in the same row as the negative entry in the last column)

Once we have identified the pivot column, we choose the pivot entry by forming *all* quotients and choosing the entry that gives the *smallest positive quotient*. Often this will mean pivoting by a negative number, which is the case in this problem.

$$\begin{array}{ccccc} x & y & s_1 & s_2 & f \\ \end{array}$$

$$\left[\begin{array}{ccccc|c} 1 & 1 & 1 & 0 & 0 & 13 \\ \boxed{-2} & 3 & 0 & 1 & 0 & -6 \\ \hline -1 & -2 & 0 & 0 & 1 & 0 \end{array}\right] \quad \begin{array}{l} 13/1 = 13 \\ (-6)/(-2) = 3^* \end{array}$$

↑
Pivot entry circled   *Smallest positive quotient

Pivoting with this entry gives the following matrix.

$$\begin{array}{ccccc} x & y & s_1 & s_2 & f \\ \end{array}$$

$$\left[\begin{array}{ccccc|c} 0 & \frac{5}{2} & 1 & \frac{1}{2} & 0 & 10 \\ 1 & -\frac{3}{2} & 0 & -\frac{1}{2} & 0 & 3 \\ \hline 0 & -\frac{7}{2} & 0 & -\frac{1}{2} & 1 & 3 \end{array}\right] \Big\} \text{No negatives}$$

↑
Most negative

This new matrix has no negatives in the upper portion of the last column, so we proceed with the simplex method as we have used it previously. The new pivot column is found from the most negative entry in the last row (indicated), and the pivot is found from the smallest positive quotient (circled). Using this pivot completes the solution.

$$\begin{array}{ccccc} x & y & s_1 & s_2 & f \\ \end{array}$$

$$\left[\begin{array}{ccccc|c} 0 & 1 & \frac{2}{5} & \frac{1}{5} & 0 & 4 \\ 1 & 0 & \frac{3}{5} & -\frac{1}{5} & 0 & 9 \\ \hline 0 & 0 & \frac{7}{5} & \frac{1}{5} & 1 & 17 \end{array}\right]$$

We see that when $x = 9$ and $y = 4$, then the maximum value of $f = x + 2y$ is 17. ▪

CHECKPOINT

1. Write the simplex matrix to maximize $f = 4x + y$ subject to the constraints

$$\begin{aligned} x + 2y &\le 12 \\ 3x - 4y &\ge 6 \\ x \ge 0, y &\ge 0 \end{aligned}$$

2. Using the matrix from Problem 1, find the maximum value of $f = 4x + y$ subject to the constraints.

Mixed Constraints and Minimization

If mixed constraints occur in a minimization problem, the simplex method does not apply to the dual problem. However, the same techniques used in Example 1 can be slightly modified and applied to minimization problems with mixed constraints. If our objective is to minimize f, then we alter the problem so as to maximize $-f$ subject to "$\le$ constraints" and then proceed as in Example 1.

EXAMPLE 2

Minimization with Mixed Constraints

Minimize the function $f = 3x + 4y$ subject to the constraints

$$\begin{aligned} x + y &\ge 20 \\ x + 2y &\ge 25 \\ -5x + y &\le 4 \\ x \ge 0, y &\ge 0 \end{aligned}$$

Solution

Because of the mixed constraints, we seek to maximize $-f = -3x - 4y$ subject to

$$-x - y \leq -20$$
$$-x - 2y \leq -25$$
$$-5x + y \leq 4$$

The simplex matrix for this problem is

$$
\begin{array}{cccccc}
x & y & s_1 & s_2 & s_3 & -f \\
\left[\begin{array}{cccccc|c}
-1 & -1 & 1 & 0 & 0 & 0 & -20 \\
-1 & -2 & 0 & 1 & 0 & 0 & -25 \\
-5 & 1 & 0 & 0 & 1 & 0 & 4 \\
\hline
3 & 4 & 0 & 0 & 0 & 1 & 0
\end{array}\right]
\end{array}
\quad \leftarrow \text{Negatives}
$$

In this case, there are two negative entries in the upper portion of the last column. When this happens, we can start with either one; we choose -20 (row 1). In row 1 (to the left of -20), we find negative entries in columns 1 and 2. We can choose our pivot column as either of these columns; we choose column 1. Once this choice is made, the pivot is determined from the quotients.

$$
\begin{array}{cccccc}
x & y & s_1 & s_2 & s_3 & -f \\
\left[\begin{array}{cccccc|c}
\boxed{-1} & -1 & 1 & 0 & 0 & 0 & -20 \\
-1 & -2 & 0 & 1 & 0 & 0 & -25 \\
-5 & 1 & 0 & 0 & 1 & 0 & 4 \\
\hline
3 & 4 & 0 & 0 & 0 & 1 & 0
\end{array}\right]
\end{array}
\quad
\begin{array}{l}
-20/(-1) = 20^* \\
-25/(-1) = 25 \\
4/(-5) = -4/5
\end{array}
$$

$\uparrow$
Pivot column (pivot entry circled)   *Smallest positive quotient

Pivoting with this entry gives the following matrix.

$$
\begin{array}{cccccc}
x & y & s_1 & s_2 & s_3 & -f \\
\left[\begin{array}{cccccc|c}
1 & 1 & -1 & 0 & 0 & 0 & 20 \\
0 & \boxed{-1} & -1 & 1 & 0 & 0 & -5 \\
0 & 6 & -5 & 0 & 1 & 0 & 104 \\
\hline
0 & 1 & 3 & 0 & 0 & 1 & -60
\end{array}\right]
\end{array}
\quad \leftarrow \text{Negative}
$$

$\uparrow$
Pivot column

Now there is only one negative in the upper portion of the last column. Looking for negatives in this same row, we see that we can choose either column 2 or column 3 for our pivot column. We choose column 2, and the pivot is circled. Pivoting gives the following matrix.

$$
\begin{array}{cccccc}
x & y & s_1 & s_2 & s_3 & -f \\
\left[\begin{array}{cccccc|c}
1 & 0 & -2 & 1 & 0 & 0 & 15 \\
0 & 1 & 1 & -1 & 0 & 0 & 5 \\
0 & 0 & -11 & 6 & 1 & 0 & 74 \\
\hline
0 & 0 & 2 & 1 & 0 & 1 & -65
\end{array}\right]
\end{array}
$$

At this point we have all positives in the upper portion of the last column, so the simplex method can be applied. (The negative value in the lower portion is acceptable because $-f$ is our function.) Looking at the indicators, we see that the solution is complete.

From the matrix we have $x = 15$, $y = 5$, and $-f = -65$. Thus the solution is $x = 15$ and $y = 5$, which gives the minimum value for the function $f = 3x + 4y = 65$. ∎

A careful review of these examples allows us to summarize the key procedural steps for solving linear programming problems with mixed constraints.

Summary: Simplex Method for Mixed Constraints

1. If the problem is to minimize f, then maximize $-f$.
2. a. Make all constraints $\leq$ constraints by multiplying both sides of any $\geq$ constraints by (-1).
   b. Use slack variables and form the simplex matrix.
3. In the simplex matrix, scan the *upper portion* of the last column for any negative entries.
   a. If there are no negative entries, apply the simplex method.
   b. If there are negative entries, go to Step 4.
4. When there is a negative value in the upper portion of the last column, proceed as follows:
   a. Select any negative entry in the same row and use its column as the pivot column.
   b. In the pivot column, compute all quotients for the entries above the line and determine the pivot from the *smallest positive quotient*.
   c. After completing the pivot operations, return to Step 3.

EXAMPLE 3

Production Scheduling for Maximum Profit | APPLICATION PREVIEW |

The Laser Company manufactures two models of home theater systems, the Star and the Allstar, at two plants, located in Ashville and in Cleveland. The maximum daily output at the Ashville plant is 900, and the profits there are $200 per unit of the Allstar and $100 per unit of the Star. The maximum daily output at the Cleveland plant is 800, and the profits there are $210 per unit of the Allstar and $80 per unit of the Star. In addition, restrictions at the Ashville plant mean that the number of units of the Star model cannot exceed 100 more than the number of units of the Allstar model produced. If the company gets a rush order for 800 units of the Allstar model and 600 units of the Star model, how many units of each model should be produced at each location to fill the order and obtain the maximum profit?

Solution

The following table identifies the variables x and y and relates other important facts in the problem. In particular, we see that only variables x and y are required.

	Ashville Plant	**Total Needed**	**Cleveland Plant**
Allstar	x produced (profit = $200 each)	800	$800 - x$ produced (profit = $210 each)
Star	y produced (profit = $100 each)	600	$600 - y$ produced (profit = $80 each)
Capacity	900	–	800

We wish to maximize profit, and from the table we see that total profit is given by

$$P = 200x + 100y + 210(800 - x) + 80(600 - y)$$

or

$$P = 216,000 - 10x + 20y$$

We can read capacity constraints from the table.

$$x + y \leq 900 \quad (\text{Ashville})$$
$$(800 - x) + (600 - y) \leq 800 \quad \text{or} \quad x + y \geq 600 \quad (\text{Cleveland})$$

An additional Ashville plant constraint from the statement of the problem is

$$y \leq x + 100 \quad \text{or} \quad -x + y \leq 100$$

Thus our problem is

$$\text{Maximize } P = 216{,}000 - 10x + 20y$$
$$\text{subject to} \quad x + y \le 900$$
$$x + y \ge 600$$
$$-x + y \le 100$$
$$x \ge 0,\, y \ge 0$$

We must express $x + y \ge 600$ as a $\le$ constraint; multiplying both sides by (-1) gives $-x - y \le -600$. The simplex matrix is

$$
\begin{array}{cccccc}
x & y & s_1 & s_2 & s_3 & P \\
\end{array}
$$

$$
\left[
\begin{array}{cccccc|c}
1 & 1 & 1 & 0 & 0 & 0 & 900 \\
\boxed{-1} & -1 & 0 & 1 & 0 & 0 & -600 \\
-1 & 1 & 0 & 0 & 1 & 0 & 100 \\
10 & -20 & 0 & 0 & 0 & 1 & 216{,}000
\end{array}
\right]
\quad \leftarrow \text{ Negative}
$$

$\uparrow$ Pivot column

The negative in the upper portion of the last column is indicated. In row 2 we find negatives in both column 1 and column 2, so either of these may be our pivot column. Our choice is indicated, and the pivot entry is circled. The matrix that results from the pivot operations follows.

$$
\begin{array}{cccccc}
x & y & s_1 & s_2 & s_3 & P \\
\end{array}
$$

$$
\left[
\begin{array}{cccccc|c}
0 & 0 & 1 & 1 & 0 & 0 & 300 \\
1 & 1 & 0 & -1 & 0 & 0 & 600 \\
0 & \boxed{2} & 0 & -1 & 1 & 0 & 700 \\
0 & -30 & 0 & 10 & 0 & 1 & 210{,}000
\end{array}
\right]
$$

$\uparrow$ Pivot column

No entry in the upper portion of the last column is negative, so we can proceed with the simplex method. From the indicators we see that column 2 is the pivot column (indicated above), and the pivot entry is circled. The simplex matrix that results from pivoting follows.

$$
\begin{array}{cccccc}
x & y & s_1 & s_2 & s_3 & P \\
\end{array}
$$

$$
\left[
\begin{array}{cccccc|c}
0 & 0 & 1 & \boxed{1} & 0 & 0 & 300 \\
1 & 0 & 0 & -\frac{1}{2} & -\frac{1}{2} & 0 & 250 \\
0 & 1 & 0 & -\frac{1}{2} & \frac{1}{2} & 0 & 350 \\
0 & 0 & 0 & -5 & 15 & 1 & 220{,}500
\end{array}
\right]
$$

$\uparrow$ Pivot column

The new pivot column is indicated, and the pivot entry is circled. The pivot operation yields the following matrix.

$$
\begin{array}{cccccc}
x & y & s_1 & s_2 & s_3 & P \\
\end{array}
$$

$$
\left[
\begin{array}{cccccc|c}
0 & 0 & 1 & 1 & 0 & 0 & 300 \\
1 & 0 & \frac{1}{2} & 0 & -\frac{1}{2} & 0 & 400 \\
0 & 1 & \frac{1}{2} & 0 & \frac{1}{2} & 0 & 500 \\
0 & 0 & 5 & 0 & 15 & 1 & 222{,}000
\end{array}
\right]
$$

This matrix shows that the solution is complete. We see that $x = 400$ (so $800 - x = 400$), $y = 500$ (so $600 - y = 100$), and $P = \$222{,}000$.

Thus the company should operate the Ashville plant at capacity and produce 400 units of the Allstar model and 500 units of the Star model. The remainder of the order, 400 units of the Allstar model and 100 units of the Star model, should be produced at the Cleveland plant. This production schedule gives maximum profit $P = \$222{,}000$. ∎

Spreadsheet Note   When using Excel to solve a linear programming problem with mixed constraints, it is not necessary to convert the form of the inequalities. They can simply be entered in their "mixed" form, and the objective function can be maximized or minimized with Solver. ∎

CHECKPOINT SOLUTIONS

1.
$$\left[\begin{array}{ccccc|c} 1 & 2 & 1 & 0 & 0 & 12 \\ \boxed{-3} & 4 & 0 & 1 & 0 & -6 \\ \hline -4 & -1 & 0 & 0 & 1 & 0 \end{array}\right]$$

2.
$$\left[\begin{array}{ccccc|c} 0 & \boxed{\frac{10}{3}} & 1 & \frac{1}{3} & 0 & 10 \\ 1 & -\frac{4}{3} & 0 & -\frac{1}{3} & 0 & 2 \\ \hline 0 & -\frac{19}{3} & 0 & -\frac{4}{3} & 1 & 8 \end{array}\right] \rightarrow \left[\begin{array}{ccccc|c} 0 & 1 & \frac{3}{10} & \boxed{\frac{1}{10}} & 0 & 3 \\ 1 & 0 & \frac{2}{5} & -\frac{1}{5} & 0 & 6 \\ \hline 0 & 0 & \frac{19}{10} & -\frac{7}{10} & 1 & 27 \end{array}\right]$$
$$\rightarrow \left[\begin{array}{ccccc|c} 0 & 10 & 3 & 1 & 0 & 30 \\ 1 & 2 & 1 & 0 & 0 & 12 \\ \hline 0 & 7 & 4 & 0 & 1 & 48 \end{array}\right]$$

The maximum value is $f = 48$ at $x = 12$, $y = 0$, $s_1 = 0$, and $s_2 = 30$.

| EXERCISES | 4.5

In Problems 1–4, express each inequality as a ≤ constraint.

1. $3x - y \geq 5$
2. $4x - 3y \geq 6$
3. $y \geq 40 - 6x$
4. $x \geq 60 - 8y$

In Problems 5–8, complete both of the following.
(a) **State the given problem in a form from which the simplex matrix can be formed (that is, as a maximization problem with ≤ constraints).**
(b) **Form the simplex matrix, and circle the first pivot entry.**

5. Maximize $f = 2x + 3y$ subject to
$$\begin{aligned} 7x + 4y &\leq 28 \\ -3x + y &\geq 2 \\ x \geq 0, y &\geq 0 \end{aligned}$$

6. Maximize $f = 5x + 11y$ subject to
$$\begin{aligned} x - 3y &\geq 3 \\ -x + y &\leq 1 \\ x &\leq 10 \\ x \geq 0, y &\geq 0 \end{aligned}$$

7. Minimize $g = 3x + 8y$ subject to
$$\begin{aligned} 4x - 5y &\leq 50 \\ x + y &\leq 80 \\ -x + 2y &\geq 4 \\ x \geq 0, y &\geq 0 \end{aligned}$$

8. Minimize $g = 40x + 25y$ subject to
$$\begin{aligned} x + y &\leq 100 \\ -x + y &\leq 20 \\ -2x + 3y &\geq 6 \\ x \geq 0, y &\geq 0 \end{aligned}$$

In Problems 9 and 10, a final simplex matrix for a minimization problem is given. In each case, find the solution.

9.
$$\begin{array}{cccccccc} x & y & z & s_1 & s_2 & s_3 & -f & \\ \left[\begin{array}{ccccccc|c} 0 & 1 & 0 & \frac{7}{3} & \frac{1}{3} & -\frac{2}{3} & 0 & 8 \\ 0 & 0 & 1 & \frac{2}{3} & -\frac{1}{3} & \frac{8}{3} & 0 & 12 \\ 1 & 0 & 0 & -\frac{4}{3} & \frac{2}{3} & \frac{4}{3} & 0 & 6 \\ \hline 0 & 0 & 0 & 4 & \frac{4}{3} & 2 & 1 & -120 \end{array}\right] \end{array}$$

10.
$$\begin{array}{cccccccc} x & y & z & s_1 & s_2 & s_3 & -f & \\ \left[\begin{array}{ccccccc|c} 1 & 0 & 0 & \frac{2}{5} & -\frac{2}{5} & 0 & 0 & 50 \\ 0 & 0 & 1 & \frac{1}{5} & \frac{1}{5} & \frac{11}{5} & 0 & 12 \\ 0 & 1 & 0 & 1 & -\frac{8}{5} & \frac{14}{5} & 0 & 30 \\ \hline 0 & 0 & 0 & 3 & 1 & 4 & 1 & -1200 \end{array}\right] \end{array}$$

In Problems 11–18, use the simplex method to find the optimal solution. Assume all variables are nonnegative.

11. Maximize $f = 4x + y$ subject to
$$\begin{aligned} 5x + 2y &\leq 84 \\ -3x + 2y &\geq 4 \end{aligned}$$

12. Maximize $f = x + 2y$ subject to

$$-x + 2y \leq 60$$
$$-7x + 4y \geq 20$$

13. Minimize $f = 2x + 3y$ subject to

$$x \geq 5$$
$$y \leq 13$$
$$-x + y \geq 2$$

14. Minimize $f = 3x + 2y$ subject to

$$x \leq 20$$
$$y \leq 20$$
$$x + y \geq 21$$

15. Minimize $f = 3x + 2y$ subject to

$$-x + y \leq 10$$
$$x + y \geq 20$$
$$x + y \leq 35$$

16. Minimize $f = 4x + y$ subject to

$$-x + y \leq 4$$
$$3x + y \geq 12$$
$$x + y \leq 20$$

17. Maximize $f = 2x + 5y$ subject to

$$-x + y \leq 10$$
$$x + y \leq 30$$
$$-2x + y \geq -24$$

18. Maximize $f = 3x + 2y$ subject to

$$-x + 2y \leq 20$$
$$-3x + 2y \leq -36$$
$$x + y \leq 22$$

In Problems 19–26, use the simplex method or Excel or some other technology. Assume all variables are non-negative.

19. Minimize $f = x + 2y + 3z$ subject to

$$x + z \leq 20$$
$$x + y \geq 30$$
$$y + z \leq 20$$

20. Maximize $f = -x + 2y + 4z$ subject to

$$x + y + z \leq 40$$
$$-x + y + z \geq 20$$
$$x + y - z \geq 10$$

21. Maximize $f = 2x - y + 4z$ subject to

$$x + y + z \leq 8$$
$$x - y + z \geq 4$$
$$x + y - z \geq 2$$

22. Maximize $f = 5x + 2y + z$ subject to

$$2x + 3y + z \leq 30$$
$$x - 2y + z \geq 20$$
$$2x + 5y + 2z \geq 25$$

23. Minimize $f = 10x + 30y + 35z$ subject to

$$x + y + z \leq 250$$
$$x + y + 2z \geq 150$$
$$2x + y + z \leq 180$$

24. Minimize $f = x + 2y + z$ subject to

$$x + 3y + 2z \geq 40$$
$$x + y + z \geq 30$$
$$x + y + z \leq 100$$

25. Maximize $f = 25x_1 + 25x_2 + 25x_3 + 20x_4 + 20x_5 + 20x_6$ subject to

$$x_1 + x_4 \leq 100$$
$$x_2 + x_5 \leq 20$$
$$x_3 + x_6 \leq 30$$
$$0.8x_2 \geq 0.2x_1 + 0.2x_3$$
$$0.9x_5 \geq 0.1x_4 + 0.1x_6$$
$$0.9x_6 \geq 0.1x_4 + 0.1x_5$$

26. Minimize $g = 480x_1 + 460x_2 + 440x_3 + 420x_4 + 530y_1 + 510y_2 + 490y_3 + 470y_4 - 9500$ subject to

$$x_1 + y_1 \geq 30$$
$$x_1 + x_2 + y_1 + y_2 \geq 90$$
$$x_1 + x_2 + x_3 + y_1 + y_2 + y_3 \geq 165$$
$$x_1 + x_2 + x_3 + x_4 + y_1 + y_2 + y_3 + y_4 \geq 190$$
$$x_1 \leq 40, x_2 \leq 40, x_3 \leq 40, x_4 \leq 40$$

APPLICATIONS

27. *Production* A sausage company makes two different kinds of hot dogs, regular and all beef. Each pound of all-beef hot dogs requires 0.75 lb of beef and 0.2 lb of spices, and each pound of regular hot dogs requires 0.18 lb of beef, 0.3 lb of pork, and 0.2 lb of spices. Suppliers can deliver at most 1020 lb of beef, at most 600 lb of pork, and at least 500 lb of spices. If the profit is $0.60 on each pound of all-beef hot dogs and $0.40 on each pound of regular hot dogs, how many pounds of each should be produced to obtain maximum profit? What is the maximum profit?

28. *Manufacturing* A cereal manufacturer makes two different kinds of cereal, Senior Citizen's Feast and Kids Go. Each pound of Senior Citizen's Feast requires 0.6 lb of wheat and 0.2 lb of vitamin-enriched syrup, and each pound of Kids Go requires 0.4 lb of wheat, 0.2 lb of sugar, and 0.2 lb of vitamin-enriched syrup. Suppliers can deliver at most 2800 lb of wheat, at most 800 lb of sugar, and at least 1000 lb of the vitamin-enriched

syrup. If the profit is $0.90 on each pound of Senior Citizen's Feast and $1.00 on each pound of Kids Go, find the number of pounds of each cereal that should be produced to obtain maximum profit. Find the maximum profit.

29. *Water purification* Nolan Industries manufactures water filters/purifiers that attach to a kitchen faucet. Each purifier consists of a housing unit that attaches to the faucet and a 60-day filter (sold separately) that is inserted into the housing. Past records indicate that on average the number of filters produced per week should be at least 400. It takes 20 minutes to make and assemble each filter and 40 minutes for each housing. The manufacturing facility has at most 20,000 minutes per week for making and assembling these units, but due to certain parts supply constraints, the number of housing units per week can be at most 400. If manufacturing costs (for material and labor) are $6.60 for each filter and $8.35 for each housing unit, how many of each should be produced to minimize weekly costs? Find the minimum cost.

30. *Manufacturing* Johnson City Cooperage manufactures 30-gallon and 55-gallon fiber drums. Each 30-gallon drum takes 30 minutes to make, each 55-gallon drum takes 40 minutes to make, and the company has at most 10,000 minutes available each week. Also, workplace limitations and product demand indicate that the number of 55-gallon drums produced plus half the number of 30-gallon drums produced should be at least 160, and the number of 30-gallon drums should be at least twice the number of 55-gallon drums. If Johnson City Cooperage's manufacturing costs are $4 for each 30-gallon drum and $6 for each 55-gallon drum, how many of each drum should be made each week to satisfy the constraints at minimum cost? Find the minimum cost.

31. *Manufacturing* A company manufactures commercial heating system components and domestic furnaces at its factories in Monaca, Pennsylvania, and Hamburg, New York. At the Monaca plant, no more than 1000 units per day can be produced, and the number of commercial components cannot exceed 100 more than half the number of domestic furnaces. At the Hamburg plant, no more than 850 units per day can be produced. The profit on each commercial component is $400 at the Monaca plant and $390 at the Hamburg plant. The profit on each domestic furnace is $200 at the Monaca plant and $215 at the Hamburg plant. If there is a rush order for 500 commercial components and 750 domestic furnaces, how many of each should be produced at each plant in order to maximize profits? Find the maximum profit.

32. *Production scheduling* A manufacturer makes Portable Satellite Radios and Auto Satellite Radios at plants in Lakeland and Rockledge. At the Lakeland plant, at

most 1800 radios can be produced, and the production of the Auto Satellite Radios can be at most 200 fewer than the production of the Portable Satellite Radios. At the Rockledge plant, at most 1200 radios can be produced. The profits on the Portable Satellite Radios are $100 at Lakeland and $90 at Rockledge, and the profits on the Auto Satellite Radios are $70 at Lakeland and $75 at Rockledge. If the manufacturer gets a rush order for 1500 Portable Satellite Radios and 1300 Auto Satellite Radios, how many of each should be produced at each location so as to maximize profits? Find the maximum profit.

33. *Manufacturing* Refer to Problem 31. Suppose that the cost of each commercial component is $380 at the Monaca plant and $400 at the Hamburg plant. The cost of each domestic furnace is $200 at the Monaca plant and $185 at the Hamburg plant. If the same rush order for 500 commercial components and 750 domestic furnaces is received, how many of each should be produced at each location to minimize cost? Find the minimum cost.

34. *Manufacturing* Refer to Problem 32. Suppose the costs associated with Portable Satellite Radios are $50 at Lakeland and $60 at Rockledge, and the costs associated with Auto Satellite Radios are $40 at Lakeland and $25 at Rockledge. If the manufacturer gets the same rush order for 1500 units of Portable Satellite Radios and 1300 units of Auto Satellite Radios, how many units of each should be produced at each location in order to minimize costs? Find the minimum cost.

35. *Water purification* Three water purification facilities can handle at most 10 million gallons in a certain time period. Plant I leaves 20% of certain impurities, and costs $20,000 per million gallons. Plant II leaves 15% of these impurities and costs $30,000 per million gallons. Plant III leaves 10% impurities and costs $40,000 per million gallons. The desired level of impurities in the water from all three plants is at most 15%. If plant I and plant III combined must handle at least 6 million gallons, find the number of gallons each plant should handle so as to achieve the desired level of purity at minimum cost. Find the minimum cost.

36. *Chemical mixture* A chemical storage tank has a capacity of 200 tons. Currently the tank contains 50 tons of a mixture that has 10% of a certain active chemical and 1.8% of other inert ingredients. The owners of the tank want to replenish the supply in the tank and will purchase some combination of two available mixes. Mix 1 contains 70% of the active chemical and 3% of the inert ingredients; its cost is $100 per ton. Mix 2 contains 30% of the active chemical and 1% of the inert ingredients; its cost is $40 per ton. The desired final mixture should have at least 40% of the active chemical and at most 2% of the inert ingredients. How many tons of each mix should be purchased to obtain

the desired final mixture at minimum cost? Find the minimum cost. Note that at least 40% of the active chemical means

$$70\% \,(\text{mix } 1) + 30\% \,(\text{mix } 2) + 10\% \,(\text{mix on hand})$$
$$\geq 40\% \,(\text{mix } 1 + \text{mix } 2 + \text{mix on hand})$$

37. *Manufacturing* A ball manufacturer produces soccer balls, footballs, and volleyballs. The manager feels that restricting the types of balls produced could increase revenue. The following table gives the price of each ball, the raw materials cost, and the profit on each ball. The monthly profit must be at least $10,000, and the raw materials costs must be no more than $20,000. How many of each type of ball should be produced to maximize the revenue, and what is the maximum revenue?

	Raw Materials Cost	Price per Ball	Profit per Ball
Footballs	$10	$30	$10
Soccer balls	12	25	8
Volleyballs	8	20	8

38. *Land management* A farm co-op has two farms, one at Spring Run and one at Willow Bend, where it grows corn and soybeans. Differences between the farms affect the associated costs and yield of each crop, as shown in the following table.

	Corn		Soybeans	
	Yield (bu/acre)	Cost/Acre	Yield (bu/acre)	Cost/Acre
Spring Run	450	$110	360	$99
Willow Bend	585	$132	315	$88

Each farm has 100 acres available to plant, and the total desired yields are at least 46,800 bushels of corn and at least 42,300 bushels of soybeans. How many acres of each crop should be planted at each farm in order to achieve the desired crop yields at minimum cost? What is the minimum cost?

KEY TERMS AND FORMULAS

Section	Key Terms
4.1	Linear inequalities in two variables Graphs Systems Solution region
4.2	Linear programming Objective function Constraints Optimum values Feasible region Graphical solution
4.3	Simplex method (maximization) Standard maximization problem Slack variables Simplex matrix Pivot entry Basic and nonbasic variables Basic feasible solution Pivoting Nonunique solutions Shadow prices
4.4	Simplex method (minimization) Standard minimization problem Dual problem Transpose Primal problem
4.5	Simplex method with mixed constraints Creating $\leq$ constraints

REVIEW EXERCISES

In Problems 1–4, graph the solution set of each inequality or system of inequalities.

1. $2x + 3y \le 12$

2. $4x + 5y > 100$

3. $\begin{cases} x + 2y \le 20 \\ 3x + 10y \le 80 \\ x \ge 0, \; y \ge 0 \end{cases}$

4. $\begin{cases} 3x + y \ge 4 \\ x + y \ge 2 \\ -x + y \le 4 \\ x \qquad \le 5 \end{cases}$

In Problems 5–8, a function and the graph of a feasible region are given. In each case, find both the maximum and minimum values of the function, if they exist, and the point at which each occurs.

5. $f = -x + 3y$

6. $f = 6x + 4y$

7. $f = 7x - 6y$

8. $f = 9x + 10y$

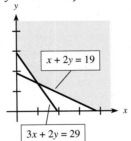

In Problems 9–14, solve the linear programming problems using graphical methods. Restrict $x \ge 0$ and $y \ge 0$.

9. Maximize $f = 5x + 6y$ subject to

$$x + 3y \le 24$$
$$4x + 3y \le 42$$
$$2x + y \le 20$$

10. Maximize $f = x + 4y$ subject to

$$7x + 3y \le 105$$
$$2x + 5y \le 59$$
$$x + 7y \le 70$$

11. Minimize $g = 5x + 3y$ subject to

$$3x + y \ge 12$$
$$x + y \ge 6$$
$$x + 6y \ge 11$$

12. Minimize $g = x + 5y$ subject to

$$8x + y \ge 85$$
$$x + y \ge 50$$
$$x + 4y \ge 80$$
$$x + 10y \ge 104$$

13. Maximize $f = 5x + 2y$ subject to

$$y \le 20$$
$$2x + y \le 32$$
$$-x + 2y \ge 4$$

14. Minimize $f = x + 4y$ subject to

$$y \le 30$$
$$3x + 2y \ge 75$$
$$-3x + 5y \ge 30$$

In Problems 15–18, use the simplex method to solve the linear programming problems. Assume all variables are nonnegative.

15. Maximize $f = 7x + 12y$ subject to the conditions in Problem 10.

16. Maximize $f = 3x + 4y$ subject to

$$x + 4y \le 160$$
$$x + 2y \le 100$$
$$4x + 3y \le 300$$

17. Maximize $f = 3x + 8y$ subject to the conditions in Problem 16.

18. Maximize $f = 3x + 2y$ subject to

$$x + 2y \le 48$$
$$x + y \le 30$$
$$2x + y \le 50$$
$$x + 10y \le 200$$

Problems 19 and 20 have nonunique solutions. If there is no solution, indicate this; if there are multiple solutions, find two different solutions. Use the simplex method, with $x \ge 0$, $y \ge 0$.

19. Maximize $f = 4x + 4y$ subject to

$$x + 5y \le 500$$
$$x + 2y \le 230$$
$$x + y \le 160$$

20. Maximize $f = 2x + 5y$ subject to

$$-4x + y \le 40$$
$$x - 7y \le 70$$

In Problems 21–24, form the dual and use the simplex method to solve the minimization problem. Assume all variables are nonnegative.

21. Minimize $g = 7y_1 + 6y_2$ subject to

$$5y_1 + 2y_2 \geq 16$$
$$3y_1 + 7y_2 \geq 27$$

22. Minimize $g = 3y_1 + 4y_2$ subject to

$$3y_1 + y_2 \geq 8$$
$$y_1 + y_2 \geq 6$$
$$2y_1 + 5y_2 \geq 18$$

23. Minimize $g = 2y_1 + y_2$ subject to the conditions in Problem 22.

24. Minimize $g = 12y_1 + 11y_2$ subject to

$$y_1 + y_2 \geq 100$$
$$2y_1 + y_2 \geq 140$$
$$6y_1 + 5y_2 \geq 580$$

Problems 25 and 26 involve mixed constraints. Solve each with the simplex method. Assume all variables are nonnegative.

25. Maximize $f = 3x + 5y$ subject to

$$x + y \geq 19$$
$$-x + y \geq 1$$
$$-x + 10y \leq 190$$

26. Maximize $f = 4x + 6y$ subject to

$$2x + 5y \leq 37$$
$$5x - y \leq 34$$
$$-x + 2y \geq 4$$

In Problems 27–34, use the simplex method. Assume all variables are nonnegative.

27. Maximize $f = 39x + 5y + 30z$ subject to

$$x + z \leq 7$$
$$3x + 5y \leq 30$$
$$3x + y \leq 18$$

28. Minimize $g = 12y_1 + 5y_2 + 2y_3$ subject to

$$y_1 + 2y_2 + y_3 \geq 60$$
$$12y_1 + 4y_2 + 3y_3 \geq 120$$
$$2y_1 + 3y_2 + y_3 \geq 80$$

29. Minimize $g = 25y_1 + 10y_2 + 4y_3$ subject to

$$7.5y_1 + 4.5y_2 + 2y_3 \geq 650$$
$$6.5y_1 + 3y_2 + 1.5y_3 \geq 400$$
$$y_1 + 1.5y_2 + 0.5y_3 \geq 200$$

30. Minimize $f = 10x + 3y$ subject to

$$-x + 10y \geq 5$$
$$4x + y \geq 62$$
$$x + y \leq 50$$

31. Minimize $f = 4x + 3y$ subject to

$$-x + y \geq 1$$
$$x + y \leq 45$$
$$10x + y \geq 45$$

32. Maximize $f = 88x_1 + 86x_2 + 100x_3 + 100x_4$ subject to

$$3x_1 + 2x_2 + 2x_3 + 5x_4 \leq 200$$
$$2x_1 + 2x_2 + 4x_3 + 5x_4 \leq 100$$
$$x_1 + x_2 + x_3 + x_4 \leq 200$$
$$x_1 \leq 40$$

33. Maximize $f = 8x_1 + 10x_2 + 12x_3 + 14x_4$ subject to

$$6x_1 + 3x_2 + 2x_3 + x_4 \geq 350$$
$$3x_1 + 2x_2 + 5x_3 + 6x_4 \leq 300$$
$$8x_1 + 3x_2 + 2x_3 + x_4 \leq 400$$
$$x_1 + x_2 + x_3 + x_4 \leq 100$$

34. Minimize $g = 10x_1 + 9x_2 + 12x_3 + 8x_4$ subject to

$$45x_1 + 58.5x_3 \geq 4680$$
$$36x_2 + 31.5x_4 \geq 4230$$
$$x_1 + x_2 \leq 100$$
$$x_3 + x_4 \leq 100$$

APPLICATIONS

35. *Manufacturing* A company manufactures backyard swing sets of two different sizes. The larger set requires 5 hours of labor to complete, the smaller set requires 2 hours, and there are 700 hours of labor available each week. The packaging department can package at most 185 swing sets per week. If the profit is $100 on each larger set and $50 on each smaller set, how many of each should be produced to yield the maximum profit? What is the maximum profit? Use graphical methods.

36. *Production* A company produces two different grades of steel, A and B, at two different factories, 1 and 2. The following table summarizes the production capabilities of the factories, the cost per day, and the number of units of each grade of steel that is required to fill orders.

	Factory 1	Factory 2	Required
Grade A steel	1 unit	2 units	80 units
Grade B steel	3 units	2 units	140 units
Cost per day	$5000	$6000	

How many days should each factory operate in order to fill the orders at minimum cost? What is the minimum cost? Use graphical methods.

Use the simplex method to solve Problems 37–45.

37. *Production* A small industry produces two items, I and II. It operates at capacity and makes a profit of $6 on each item I and $4 on each item II. The following table gives the hours required to produce each item and the hours available per day.

	I	II	Hours Available
Assembly	2 hours	1 hour	100
Packaging & inspection	1 hour	1 hour	60

Find the number of items that should be produced each day to maximize profits, and find the maximum daily profit.

38. *Production* Pinocchio Crafts makes two types of wooden crafts: Jacob's ladders and locomotive engines. The manufacture of these crafts requires both carpentry and finishing. Each Jacob's ladder requires 1 hour of finishing and $\frac{1}{2}$ hour of carpentry. Each locomotive engine requires 1 hour of finishing and 1 hour of carpentry. Pinocchio Crafts can obtain all the necessary raw materials, but only 120 finishing hours and 75 carpentry hours per week are available. Also, demand for Jacob's ladders is limited to at most 100 per week. If Pinocchio Crafts makes a profit of $3 on each Jacob's ladder and $5 on each locomotive engine, how many of each should it produce each week to maximize profits? What is the maximum profit?

39. *Profit* At its Jacksonville factory, Nolmaur Electronics manufactures 4 models of TV sets: LCD models in 27-, 32-, and 42-in. sizes and a 42-in. plasma model. The manufacturing and testing hours required for each model and available at the factory each week, as well as each model's profit, are shown in the following table.

	27-in. LCD	32-in. LCD	42-in. LCD	42-in. Plasma	Available Hours
Manufacturing (hr)	8	10	12	15	1870
Testing (hr)	2	4	4	4	530
Profit	$80	$120	$160	$200	

In addition, the supplier of the amplifier units can provide at most 200 units per week with at most 100 of these for both types of 42-in. models. The weekly demand for the 32-in. sets is at most 120. Nolmaur wants to determine the number of each type of set that should be produced each week to obtain maximum profit.

(a) Carefully identify the variables for Nolmaur's linear programming problem.

(b) Carefully state Nolmaur's linear programming problem.

(c) Solve this linear programming problem to determine Nolmaur's manufacturing plan and maximum profit.

40. *Nutrition* A nutritionist wants to find the least expensive combination of two foods that meet minimum daily vitamin requirements, which are 5 units of A and 30 units of B. Each ounce of food I provides 2 units of A and 1 unit of B, and each ounce of food II provides 10 units of A and 10 units of B. If food I costs 30 cents per ounce and food II costs 20 cents per ounce, find the number of ounces of each food that will provide the required vitamins and minimize the cost.

41. *Nutrition* A laboratory wishes to purchase two different feeds, A and B, for its animals. The following table summarizes the nutritional contents of the feeds, the required amounts of each ingredient, and the cost of each type of feed.

	Feed A	Feed B	Required
Carbohydrates	1 unit/lb	4 units/lb	40 units
Protein	2 units/lb	1 unit/lb	80 units
Cost	14¢/lb	16¢/lb	

How many pounds of each type of feed should the laboratory buy in order to satisfy its needs at minimum cost?

42. *Production* A company makes three products, I, II, and III, at three different factories. At factory A, it can make 10 units of each product per day. At factory B, it can make 20 units of II and 20 units of III per day. At factory C, it can make 20 units of I, 20 units of II, and 10 units of III per day. The company has orders for 200 units of I, 500 units of II, and 300 units of III. If the daily costs are $200 at A, $300 at B, and $500 at C, find the number of days that each factory should operate in order to fill the company's orders at minimum cost. Find the minimum cost.

43. *Profit* A company makes pancake mix and cake mix. Each pound of pancake mix uses 0.6 lb of flour and 0.1 lb of shortening. Each pound of cake mix uses 0.4 lb of flour, 0.1 lb of shortening, and 0.4 lb of sugar. Suppliers can deliver at most 6000 lb of flour, at least 500 lb of shortening, and at most 1200 lb of sugar. If the profit per pound is $0.35 for pancake mix and $0.25 for cake mix, how many pounds of each mix should be made to earn maximum profit? What is the maximum profit?

44. *Manufacturing* A company manufactures desks and computer tables at plants in Texas and Louisiana. At the Texas plant, production costs are $12 for each desk and $20 for each computer table, and the plant can produce at most 120 units per day. At the Louisiana plant, costs are $14 for each desk and $19 per computer table, and the plant can produce at most 150 units per day. The company gets a rush order for 130 desks and 130 computer tables at a time when the Texas plant is further limited by the fact that the number of computer tables it produces must be at least 10 more than the number of desks. How should production be scheduled at each location in order to fill the order at minimum cost? What is the minimum cost?

45. *Cost* Armstrong Industries makes two different grades of steel at its plants in Midland and Donora. Weekly demand is at least 500 tons for grade 1 steel and at least 450 tons for grade 2. Due to differences in the equipment and the labor force, production times and costs per ton for each grade of steel differ slightly at each location, as shown in the following table.

	Grade 1		Grade 2		
	Min/ Ton	Cost/ Ton	Min/ Ton	Cost/ Ton	Furnace Time/Week (in Minutes)
Midland	40	$100	42	$120	19,460
Donora	44	$110	45	$90	21,380

Find the number of tons of each grade of steel that should be made each week at each plant so that Armstrong meets demand at minimum cost. Find the minimum cost.

4   CHAPTER TEST

1. Maximize $f = 3x + 5y$ subject to the constraints determined by the shaded region shown in the figure.

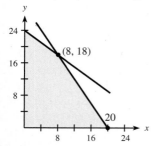

2. Following are three simplex matrices in various stages of the simplex method solution of a maximization problem.
   (a) Identify the matrix for which multiple solutions exist. Circle the pivot and specify all row operations with that pivot that are needed to find a second solution.
   (b) Identify the matrix for which no solution exists. Explain how you can tell there is no solution.
   (c) For the remaining matrix, find the basic feasible solution. Use the variables $x_1, x_2, \ldots$, the slack variables $s_1, s_2, \ldots$, and the objective function f, and tell whether these values give the optimal solution. If they do not, identify the next pivot.

$$A = \begin{bmatrix} 2 & 0 & -4 & 1 & -2 & 0 & 0 & 6 \\ -1 & 1 & 0 & 0 & 1 & 0 & 0 & 3 \\ 4 & 0 & -6 & 0 & -1 & 1 & 0 & 10 \\ -3 & 0 & -8 & 0 & 4 & 0 & 1 & 50 \end{bmatrix}$$

$$B = \begin{bmatrix} 0 & 1 & -2 & \frac{1}{4} & 0 & \frac{1}{5} & 0 & 12 \\ 0 & 0 & 4 & -\frac{3}{4} & 1 & -\frac{2}{5} & 0 & 20 \\ 1 & 0 & 3 & -\frac{5}{4} & 0 & \frac{4}{5} & 0 & 40 \\ 0 & 0 & 4 & 6 & 0 & -\frac{1}{5} & 1 & 170 \end{bmatrix}$$

$$C = \begin{bmatrix} 1 & 2 & 0 & 1 & 0 & -\frac{3}{2} & 0 & 40 \\ 0 & 1 & 0 & -2 & 1 & \frac{1}{2} & 0 & 15 \\ 0 & 3 & 1 & -1 & 0 & \frac{1}{4} & 0 & 60 \\ 0 & 0 & 0 & 4 & 0 & 6 & 1 & 220 \end{bmatrix}$$

3. Graph the solution region for each of the following.
   (a) $3x - 5y \le 30$ (b) $x > 2$ (c) $\begin{cases} 5y \ge 2x \\ x + y > 7 \\ 2y \le 5x \end{cases}$

4. Formulate the dual maximization problem associated with the following.
   Minimize $g = 2y_1 + 3y_2 + 5y_3$ subject to
   $$\begin{aligned} 3y_1 + 5y_2 + \ y_3 &\ge 100 \\ 4y_1 + 6y_2 + 3y_3 &\ge 120 \\ y_1 \ge 0, y_2 \ge 0, y_3 &\ge 0 \end{aligned}$$

5. Find the maximum and minimum values of $f = 5x + 2y$ (if they exist) subject to the constraints determined by the shaded region in the figure.

6. Use graphical methods to minimize $g = 3x + y$ subject to $5x - 4y \le 40$, $x + y \ge 80$, $2x - y \ge 4$, $x \ge 0$, and $y \ge 0$.

7. Express the following linear programming problem as a maximization problem with $\le$ constraints. Assume $x \ge 0, y \ge 0$.
   Minimize $g = 7x + 3y$ subject to
   $$\begin{aligned} -x + 4y &\ge \ 4 \\ x - \ y &\le \ 5 \\ 2x + 3y &\le 30 \end{aligned}$$

8. The final simplex matrix for a problem is as follows. Give the solutions to *both* the minimization problem and the dual maximization problem. Carefully label each solution.

$$\begin{bmatrix} 0 & 1 & -0.5 & 3 & -0.7 & 0 & 0 & 15 \\ 1 & 0 & -0.8 & -2 & -0.5 & 0 & 0 & 17 \\ 0 & 0 & -0.6 & -1 & -2.4 & 1 & 0 & 11 \\ 0 & 0 & 12 & 4 & 18 & 0 & 1 & 658 \end{bmatrix}$$

9. Use the simplex method to maximize $f = 70x + 5y$ subject to $x + 1.5y \le 150$, $x + 0.5y \le 90$, $x \ge 0$, and $y \ge 0$.

10. Maximize $f = 60x + 48y + 36z$ subject to

$$8x + 6y + z \leq 108$$
$$4x + 2y + 1.5z \leq 50$$
$$2x + 1.5y + 0.5z \leq 40$$
$$z \leq 16$$
$$x \geq 0, \quad y \geq 0, \quad z \geq 0$$

11. River Brewery is a microbrewery that produces an amber lager and an ale. Producing a barrel of lager requires 3 lb of corn and 2 lb of hops. Producing a barrel of ale requires 2 lb each of corn and hops. Profits are $35 from each barrel of lager and $30 from each barrel of ale. Suppliers can provide at most 1200 lb of corn and at most 1000 lb of hops per month. Formulate a linear programming problem that can be used to maximize River Brewery's monthly profit. Then solve it with the simplex method.

12. A marketing research group conducting a telephone survey must contact at least 150 wives and 120 husbands. It costs $3 to make a daytime call and (because of higher labor costs) $4 to make an evening call. On average, daytime calls reach wives 30% of the time, husbands 10% of the time, and neither of these 60% of the time, whereas evening calls reach wives 30% of the time, husbands 30% of the time, and neither of these 40% of the time. Staffing considerations mean that daytime calls must be less than or equal to half of the total calls made. Formulate a linear programming problem

that can be used to minimize the cost of completing the survey. Then solve it with any method from this chapter.

13. Lawn Rich, Inc. makes four different lawn care products that have fixed percents of phosphate, nitrogen, potash, and other minerals. The following table shows the percent of each of the four ingredients in each of Lawn Rich's products and the profit per ton for each product.

	Product 1	Product 2	Product 3	Product 4
% Phosphate	60	30	20	10
% Nitrogen	20	20	20	20
% Potash	9	6	15	18
% Other minerals	8	3	2	1
Profit/ton	$40	$50	$60	$70

A lawn care company buys in bulk from Lawn Rich and then blends the products for its own purposes. For the blend it desires, the lawn care company wants its Lawn Rich order to contain at least 35 tons of phosphate, at most 20 tons of nitrogen, at most 9 tons of potash, and at most 4 tons of other minerals. How many tons of each product should Lawn Rich produce to fulfill the customer's needs and maximize its own profit? What is the maximum profit?

I. Transportation

The Kimble Firefighting Equipment Company has two assembly plants: plant A in Atlanta and plant B in Buffalo. It has two distribution centers: center I in Pittsburgh and center II in Savannah. The company can produce at most 800 alarm valves per week at plant A and at most 1000 per week at plant B. Center I must have at least 900 alarm valves per week, and center II must have at least 600 alarm valves per week. The costs per unit for transportation from the plants to the centers follow.

Plant A to center I $2
Plant A to center II   3
Plant B to center I   4
Plant B to center II   1

What weekly shipping plan will meet the market demands and minimize the total cost of shipping the valves from the assembly plants to the distribution centers? What is the minimum transportation cost? Should the company eliminate the route with the most expensive unit shipment cost?

1. To assist the company in making these decisions, use linear programming with the following variables.

   y_1 = the number of units shipped from plant A to center I
   y_2 = the number of units shipped from plant A to center II
   y_3 = the number of units shipped from plant B to center I
   y_4 = the number of units shipped from plant B to center II

2. Form the constraint inequalities that give the limits for the plants and distribution centers, and form the total cost function that is to be minimized.
3. Solve the mixed constraint problem for the minimum transportation cost.
4. Determine whether any shipment route is unnecessary.

II. Slack Variables and Shadow Prices

Part A: With linear programming problems, one set of interesting questions deals with how the optimal solution changes if the constraint quantities change. Surprisingly, answers to these questions can be found in the final simplex tableau. In this investigation, we restrict ourselves to standard maximization problems and begin by reexamining the farm co-op application discussed in Example 1 in Section 4.3.

Farm Co-op Problem Statement

Maximize profit $P = 60x + 40y$ subject to

$$
\begin{aligned}
x + y &\leq 6000 & &\text{(Land constraint, in acres)} \\
9x + 3y &\leq 40{,}500 & &\text{(Fertilizer/herbicide constraint, in gallons)} \\
\tfrac{3}{4}x + y &\leq 5250 & &\text{(Labor constraint, in hours)}
\end{aligned}
$$

Initial Tableau

$$
A = \begin{array}{c}
\begin{array}{cccccc}
x & y & s_1 & s_2 & s_3 & P
\end{array} \\
\left[
\begin{array}{cccccc|c}
1 & 1 & 1 & 0 & 0 & 0 & 6{,}000 \\
9 & 3 & 0 & 1 & 0 & 0 & 40{,}500 \\
\frac{3}{4} & 1 & 0 & 0 & 1 & 0 & 5{,}250 \\
\hline
-60 & -40 & 0 & 0 & 0 & 1 & 0
\end{array}
\right]
\end{array}
$$

Final Tableau

$$
C = \begin{array}{c}
\begin{array}{cccccc}
x & y & s_1 & s_2 & s_3 & P
\end{array} \\
\left[
\begin{array}{cccccc|c}
0 & 1 & \frac{3}{2} & -\frac{1}{6} & 0 & 0 & 2{,}250 \\
1 & 0 & -\frac{1}{2} & \frac{1}{6} & 0 & 0 & 3{,}750 \\
0 & 0 & -\frac{9}{8} & \frac{1}{24} & 1 & 0 & 187.5 \\
\hline
0 & 0 & 30 & \frac{10}{3} & 0 & 1 & 315{,}000
\end{array}
\right]
\end{array}
$$

Notice in the initial tableau that the columns for the slack variables and the objective function form an identity matrix (here a 4×4 matrix), and the row operations of the simplex method transform this identity matrix into another matrix in the same columns of the final tableau. Call this matrix S.

1. (a) Identify S and calculate SA, where A is the initial tableau above. What do you notice when you compare the result of SA with the final tableau, C?
   (b) Look at the Solar Technology manufacturing application in Example 3 in Section 4.3 and identify the corresponding matrix S there. Then find S times the initial tableau and compare your result with the final tableau. What do you notice?

2. (a) In the farm co-op application above, if the number of gallons of fertilizer/herbicide were increased by h to $40{,}500 + h$, then the row 2 entry in the last column of A would become $40{,}500 + h$. Call this new initial tableau A_h. Find the effect this change in fertilizer/herbicide would have on the optimal solution by calculating SA_h. Describe the differences between C (the final tableau of the original co-op problem) and SA_h.
   (b) Repeat part (a) if the number of acres of land is changed by k.
   (c) Use the results of parts (a) and (b) to complete the following general statement, A.
   Statement A: If constraint i has slack variable s_i and the quantity of constraint i is changed by h, then the new optimal solution can be found by using

   $h \cdot$ (the ____ column) plus the ____ column as the new ____ column

(d) Based on your results so far (and similar calculations with other examples, if needed), decide whether the following statement is true or false.

"The process described in statement A for determining the new optimal solution applies for any increment of change in any constraint or combination of constraints as long as the last column of the new final tableau has *all* nonnegative entries."

(e) Apply these results to find the new optimal solution to the farm co-op application if the co-op obtained 16 additional acres of land and 48 more gallons of fertilizer/herbicide.

3. (a) In part 2(a), how much is the objective function changed in the new optimal solution?

(b) If $h = 1$ in part 2(a), how much would the objective function change and where in the final tableau is the value that gives this amount of change?

(c) Recall that the shadow price for a constraint measures the change in the objective function if one additional unit of the resource for that constraint becomes available. What is the shadow price for fertilizer/herbicide, and what does it tell us?

(d) Find the shadow prices for acres of land and labor hours and tell what each means.

(e) Complete the following general statement.

Statement B: The shadow price for constraint i is found in the final tableau as the _____ entry in the column for _____.

(f) From this example (and others if you check), notice that if a slack variable is nonzero, then the shadow price of the associated constraint will equal zero. Why do you think this is true?

Part B: Each week the Plush Seating Co. makes stuffed chairs (x) and love seats (y) by using hours of carpentry time (s_1), hours of assembly time (s_2), and hours of upholstery time (s_3) in order to maximize profit P, in dollars. Plush Seating's final tableau is shown below; use it and the results from part A to answer the questions that follow.

x	y	s_1	s_2	s_3	P	
1	0	$\frac{1}{3}$	-1	0	0	28
0	1	$-\frac{1}{3}$	2	0	0	8
0	0	$\frac{4}{3}$	-10	1	0	10
0	0	$\frac{8}{3}$	64	0	1	2816

1. Producing how many chairs and love seats will yield a maximum profit? Find the maximum profit.

2. How many hours of assembly time are left unused?

3. How many hours of upholstery time are left unused?

4. How much will profit increase if an extra hour of carpentry time becomes available? What is this amount of increase called?

5. How much will profit increase if an extra hour of upholstery time becomes available?

6. If 1 more hour of labor were available, where should Plush Seating use it? Explain why.

7. If each chair takes 2 hours of upholstery time and each love seat takes 6 hours, how many hours of upholstery time are available each week?

8. If Plush Seating could hire a part-timer to do 6 hours of carpentry and 1 hour of assembly, determine the new optimal solution.

9. Suppose that each worker can do any of the three jobs, and, rather than hiring a part-timer, managers want to reassign the extra upholstery hours. If they use 9 of those hours in carpentry and the other 1 in assembly, find the new optimal solution.

10. Find a way to reassign any number of the upholstery hours in a way different from that in Question 9, so that profit is improved even more than in Question 9.

5

CHAPTER

Exponential and Logarithmic Functions

Monkey Business Images/Shutterstock.com

In this chapter we study exponential and logarithmic functions, which provide models for many applications that at first seem remote and unrelated. In our study of these functions, we will examine their descriptions, their properties, their graphs, and the special inverse relationship between these two functions. We will see how exponential and logarithmic functions are applied to some of the concerns of social scientists, business managers, and life scientists.

The chapter topics and applications include the following.

Prerequisite Problem Type	For Section	Answer	Section for Review
Write the following with positive exponents: (a) x^{-3} (b) $\dfrac{1}{x^{-2}}$ (c) $\sqrt{x}$	**5.1** **5.2** **5.3**	(a) $\dfrac{1}{x^3}$ (b) x^2 (c) $x^{1/2}$	0.3, 0.4 Exponents and radicals
Simplify: (a) 2^0 (b) $x^0 \ (x \neq 0)$ (c) $49^{1/2}$ (d) 10^{-2}	**5.1** **5.2** **5.3**	(a) 1 (b) 1 (c) 7 (d) $\dfrac{1}{100}$	0.3, 0.4 Exponents
Answer true or false: (a) $\left(\dfrac{1}{2}\right)^x = 2^{-x}$ (b) $\sqrt{50} = 50^{1/2}$ (c) If $8 = 2^y$, then $y = 4$. (d) If $x^3 = 8$, then $x = 2$.	**5.1** **5.2**	(a) True (b) True (c) False; $y = 3$ (d) True	0.3, 0.4 Exponents and radicals
(a) If $f(x) = 2^{-2x}$, what is $f(-2)$? (b) If $f(x) = 2^{-2x}$, what is $f(1)$? (c) If $f(t) = (1 + 0.02)^t$, what is $f(0)$? (d) If $f(t) = 100(0.03)^{0.02t}$, what is $f(0)$? (e) If $f(x) = \dfrac{9.46}{1 + 53.08e^{-1.28x}}$, what is $f(5)$?	**5.1** **5.2** **5.3**	(a) 16 (b) $\dfrac{1}{4}$ (c) 1 (d) 3 (e) ≈ 8.693	1.2 Function notation

OBJECTIVES

5.1

- To graph exponential functions
- To evaluate exponential functions
- To model with exponential functions

Exponential Functions

▮ | APPLICATION PREVIEW | ▮

If $10,000 is invested at 6%, compounded monthly, then the future value S of the investment after x years is given by the exponential function

$$S = 10,000(1.005)^{12x}$$

(We will find the future value of the investment after 5 years in Example 2.)
   In this section we will evaluate and graph exponential functions, and we will model data with exponential functions.

Exponential Functions and Graphs

Suppose a culture of bacteria has the characteristic that each minute, every microorganism splits into two new organisms. We can describe the number of bacteria in the culture as a function of time. That is, if we begin the culture with one microorganism, we know that after 1 minute we will have two organisms, after 2 minutes, 4, and so on. Table 5.1 gives a few of the values that describe this growth. If x represents the number of minutes that have passed and y represents the number of organisms, the points (x, y) lie on the graph of the function with equation

$$y = 2^x$$

The equation $y = 2^x$ is an example of a special group of functions called **exponential functions**, defined as follows.

▮ | TABLE 5.1 | ▮

Minutes Passed	Number of Organisms
0	1
1	2
2	4
3	8
4	16

Exponential Functions

If a is a real number with $a > 0$ and $a \neq 1$, then the function

$$f(x) = a^x$$

is an **exponential function** with base a.

A table of some values satisfying $y = 2^x$ and the graph of this function are given in Figure 5.1. This function is said to model the growth of the number of organisms in the previous discussion, even though some points on the graph do not correspond to a time and a number of organisms. For example, time x could not be negative, and the number of organisms y could not be fractional.

x	$y = 2^x$
-3	$2^{-3} = \frac{1}{8}$
-2	$2^{-2} = \frac{1}{4}$
-1	$2^{-1} = \frac{1}{2}$
0	$2^0 = 1$
1	$2^1 = 2$
2	$2^2 = 4$
3	$2^3 = 8$

Figure 5.1

We defined rational powers of x in terms of radicals in Chapter 0, so 2^x makes sense for any rational power x. It can also be shown that the laws of exponents apply for irrational numbers. We will assume that if we graphed $y = 2^x$ for irrational values of x, those points would lie on the curve in Figure 5.1. Thus, in general, we can graph an exponential function by plotting easily calculated points, such as those in the table in Figure 5.1, and drawing a smooth curve through the points.

EXAMPLE   1   **Graphing an Exponential Function**

Graph $y = 10^x$.

Solution

A table of values and the graph are given in Figure 5.2.

x	y
-3	$10^{-3} = 1/1000$
-2	$10^{-2} = 1/100$
-1	$10^{-1} = 1/10$
0	$10^0 = 1$
1	$10^1 = 10$
2	$10^2 = 100$
3	$10^3 = 1000$

Figure 5.2

Calculator Note   We also could have used a graphing calculator to graph $y = 2^x$ and $y = 10^x$. Figure 5.3 shows graphs of $f(x) = 1.5^x$, $f(x) = 4^x$, and $f(x) = 20^x$ that were obtained using a graphing calculator. Note the viewing window for each graph in the figure. See Appendix C, Section 5.1, for details.

Figure 5.3

Note that the three graphs in Figure 5.3 and the graphs of $y = 2^x$ and $y = 10^x$ are similar. The graphs of $y = 2^x$ and $y = 10^x$ clearly approach, but do not touch, the negative x-axis. However, the graphs in Figure 5.3 appear as if they might eventually merge with the negative x-axis. By adjusting the viewing window, however, we would see that these graphs also approach, but do not touch, the negative x-axis. That is, the negative x-axis is an asymptote for these functions.

In fact, the shapes of the graphs of functions of the form $y = f(x) = a^x$, with $a > 1$, are similar to those in Figures 5.1, 5.2, and 5.3. Exponential functions of this type, and more generally of the form $f(x) = C(a^x)$, where $C > 0$ and $a > 1$, are called **exponential growth functions** because they are used to model growth in diverse applications. Their graphs have the basic shape shown in the following box.

Graphs of Exponential Growth Functions

Function: $y = f(x) = C(a^x)$ $(C > 0, a > 1)$
y-intercept: $(0, C)$
Graph shape:

Domain: All real numbers;   Range: $y > 0$.
Asymptote: The x-axis (negative half)

One exponential growth model concerns money invested at compound interest. Often we seek to evaluate rather than graph these functions.

EXAMPLE 2   Future Value of an Investment | APPLICATION PREVIEW |

If \$10,000 is invested at 6%, compounded monthly, then the future value of the investment S after x years is given by

$$S = 10,000(1.005)^{12x}$$

Find the future value of the investment after (a) 5 years and (b) 30 years.

Solution
These future values can be found with a calculator.

(a) $S = 10,000(1.005)^{12(5)} = 10,000(1.005)^{60} = \$13,488.50$ (nearest cent)
(b) $S = 10,000(1.005)^{12(30)} = 10,000(1.005)^{360} = \$60,225.75$ (nearest cent)

Note that the amount after 30 years is significantly more than the amount after 5 years, a result consistent with exponential growth models.

iStockphoto.com/Martin McElligott

1. Can any value of x give a negative value for y if $y = a^x$ and $a > 1$?
2. If $a > 1$, what asymptote does the graph of $y = a^x$ approach?

A special function that occurs frequently in economics and biology is $y = e^x$, where e is a fixed irrational number (approximately 2.71828 . . .). We will see how e arises when we discuss interest that is compounded continuously, and we will formally define e in Section 9.2, "Continuous Functions; Limits at Infinity."

Because $e > 1$, the graph of $y = e^x$ will have the same basic shape as other growth exponentials. We can calculate the y-coordinate for points on the graph of this function with a calculator. A table of some values (with y-values rounded to two decimal places) and the graph are shown in Figure 5.4.

x	$y = e^x$
-2	0.14
-1	0.37
0	1.00
1	2.72
2	7.39

Figure 5.4

Exponentials whose bases are between 0 and 1, such as $y = \left(\frac{1}{2}\right)^x$, have graphs different from those of the exponentials just discussed. Using the properties of exponents, we have

$$y = \left(\frac{1}{2}\right)^x = (2^{-1})^x = 2^{-x}$$

By using this technique, all exponentials of the form $y = b^x$, where $0 < b < 1$, can be rewritten in the form $y = a^{-x}$, where $a = \frac{1}{b} > 1$. Thus, graphs of equations of the form $y = a^{-x}$, where $a > 1$, and of the form $y = b^x$, where $0 < b < 1$, will have the same shape.

EXAMPLE 3   Graphing an Exponential Function

Graph $y = 2^{-x}$.

Solution
A table of values and the graph are given in Figure 5.5.

x	$y = 2^{-x}$
-3	$2^3 = 8$
-2	$2^2 = 4$
-1	$2^1 = 2$
0	$2^0 = 1$
1	$2^{-1} = \frac{1}{2}$
2	$2^{-2} = \frac{1}{4}$
3	$2^{-3} = \frac{1}{8}$

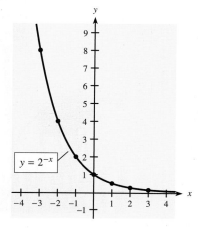

Figure 5.5

EXAMPLE   4   **Graphing an Exponential Function with Base *e***

Graph $y = e^{-2x}$.

Solution

Using a calculator to find the values of powers of e (to 2 decimal places), we get the graph shown in Figure 5.6.

x	$y = e^{-2x}$
-3	$e^6 = 403.43$
-2	$e^4 = 54.60$
-1	$e^2 = 7.39$
0	$e^0 = 1.00$
1	$e^{-2} = 0.14$
2	$e^{-4} = 0.02$

Figure 5.6

We can also use a graphing utility to graph exponential functions such as those in Examples 3 and 4. Additional examples of functions of this type would yield graphs with the same shape. **Exponential decay functions** have the form $y = a^{-x}$, where $a > 1$, or, more generally, the form $y = C(a^{-x})$, where $C > 0$ and $a > 1$. They model decay for various phenomena, and their graphs have the characteristics and shape shown in the following box.

Graphs of Exponential Decay Functions

Function: $y = f(x) = C(a^{-x})$ $(C > 0, a > 1)$ or
$\qquad\quad\ y = f(x) = C(b^x)$ $(C > 0, 0 < b < 1)$
y-intercept: $(0, C)$
Graph shape:

Domain: All real numbers;   Range: $y > 0$.
Asymptote: The x-axis (positive half)

Exponential decay functions can be used to describe various physical phenomena, such as the number of atoms of a radioactive element (radioactive decay), the lingering effect of an advertising campaign on new sales after the campaign ends, and the effect of inflation on the purchasing power of a fixed income.

EXAMPLE 5   **Purchasing Power and Inflation**

The purchasing power P of a fixed income of \$30,000 per year (such as a pension) after t years of 4% inflation can be modeled by

$$P = 30,000e^{-0.04t}$$

Find the purchasing power after (a) 5 years and (b) 20 years.

Solution

We can use a calculator to answer both parts.

(a) $P = 30,000e^{-0.04(5)} = 30,000e^{-0.2} = \$24,562$ (nearest dollar)

(b) $P = 30,000e^{-0.04(20)} = 30,000e^{-0.8} = \$13,480$ (nearest dollar)

Note that the impact of inflation over time significantly erodes purchasing power and provides some insight into the plight of elderly people who live on fixed incomes.

Exponential functions with base e often arise in natural ways. As we will see in Section 6.2, the growth of money that is compounded continuously is given by $S = Pe^{rt}$, where P is the original principal, r is the annual interest rate, and t is the time in years. Certain populations (of insects, for example) grow exponentially, and the number of individuals can be closely approximated by the equation $y = P_0e^{ht}$, where P_0 is the original population size, h is a constant that depends on the type of population, and y is the population size at any instant t. Also, the amount y of a radioactive substance is modeled by the exponential decay equation $y = y_0e^{-kt}$, where y_0 is the original amount and k is a constant that depends on the radioactive substance.

There are other important exponential functions that use base e but whose graphs are different from those we have discussed. For example, the standard normal probability curve (often referred to as a bell-shaped curve) is the graph of an exponential function with base e (see Figure 5.7). Later in this chapter we will study other exponential functions that model growth but whose graphs are also different from those discussed previously.

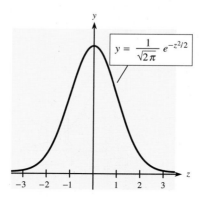

$$y = \frac{1}{\sqrt{2\pi}} \, e^{-z^2/2}$$

Figure 5.7   Standard normal probability curve

CHECKPOINT

3. True or false: The graph of $y = \left(\dfrac{1}{a}\right)^x$, with $a > 1$, is the same as the graph of $y = a^{-x}$.

4. True or false: The graph of $y = a^{-x}$, with $a > 1$, approaches the positive x-axis as an asymptote.

5. True or false: The graph of $y = 2^{-x}$ is the graph of $y = 2^x$ reflected about the y-axis.

Calculator Note   Graphing calculators allow us to investigate variations of the growth and decay exponentials. For example, we can examine the similarities and differences between the graphs of

$y = f(x) = a^x$ and those of $y = mf(x), y = f(kx)$, $y = f(x + h)$, and $y = f(x) + C$ for constants m, k, h, and C. We also can explore these similarities and differences for $y = f(x) = a^{-x}$. Figure 5.8 shows graphs of $y = f(x) = e^x$ and $y = mf(x) = me^x$ for $m = -6, -3, 2$, and 10.

From the graphs, we see that when $m > 0$, the shape of the graph is still that of a growth exponential. When $m < 0$, the shape is that of a growth exponential turned upside down, or reflected through the x-axis (making the range $y < 0$). In all cases, the asymptote is unchanged and is the negative x-axis. In each case, the y-intercept is $(0, m)$.

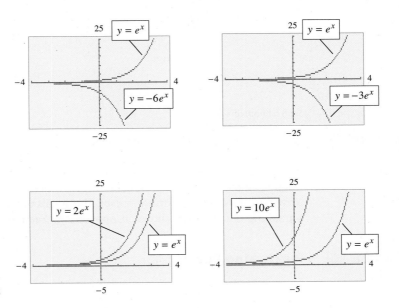

Figure 5.8

Because the outputs of exponential functions grow very rapidly, it is sometimes hard to find an appropriate window in which to show the graph of an exponential function on a graphing calculator. One way to find appropriate values of y-min and y-max when x-min and x-max are given is to use TABLE to find values of y for selected values of x. See Appendix C, Section 5.1 for details.

Figure 5.9(a) shows a table of values of $y = 1000e^{0.12x}$ that correspond to certain values of x, and Figure 5.9(b) shows the graph of this function in a window that uses the table values to set y-max equal to 3500, with y-min $= 0$.

Figure 5.9

Modeling with Exponential Functions

Many types of data can be modeled using an exponential growth function. Figure 5.10(a) shows a graph of amounts of carbon in the atmosphere due to emissions from the burning of fossil fuels. With curve-fitting tools available with some computer software or on graphing calculators, we can develop an equation that models, or approximates, these data. The model and its graph are shown in Figure 5.10(b).

$$E = 85.53\,e^{0.0309x}$$

Year (a)

Years Past 1850 (b)

Figure 5.10

Source: http://cdiac.ornl.gov/

Calculator Note The model in Figure 5.10(b) is an exponential growth function. As we have noted, functions of this type have the general form $y = C(a^x)$ with $a > 1$, and exponential decay functions have the general form $y = C(a^{-x})$ with $a > 1$ [or $y = C(b^x)$ with $0 < b < 1$]. Note that when technology is applied to model exponentials (either growth or decay), the model is written in an equivalent form $y = a*b^x$. The details of modeling exponential functions with a graphing calculator are shown in Appendix C, Section 5.1.

EXAMPLE   6   Purchasing Power

The purchasing power of $1 is calculated by assuming that the consumer price index (CPI) was $1 during 1983. It is used to show the values of goods that could be purchased for $1 in 1983. Table 5.2 gives the purchasing power of a 1983 dollar for the years 1968–2008.

(a) Use these data, with $x = 0$ in 1960, to find an exponential function that models the decay of the dollar.
(b) What does this model predict as the purchasing power of $1 in 2016?
(c) When will the purchasing power of a dollar fall below $0.20?

■ | TABLE 5.2 |

Year	Purchasing Power of $1	Year	Purchasing Power of $1	Year	Purchasing Power of $1
1968	2.873	1982	1.035	1996	0.637
1969	2.726	1983	1.003	1997	0.623
1970	2.574	1984	0.961	1998	0.613
1971	2.466	1985	0.928	1999	0.600
1972	2.391	1986	0.913	2000	0.581
1973	2.251	1987	0.880	2001	0.565
1974	2.029	1988	0.846	2002	0.556
1975	1.859	1989	0.807	2003	0.543
1976	1.757	1990	0.766	2004	0.529
1977	1.649	1991	0.734	2005	0.512
1978	1.532	1992	0.713	2006	0.500
1979	1.380	1993	0.692	2007	0.482
1980	1.215	1994	0.675	2008	0.464
1981	1.098	1995	0.656		

Source: U.S. Bureau of Labor Statistics

Solution

(a) From a scatter plot of the points, with $x = 0$ in 1960, it appears that an exponential decay model is appropriate (see Figure 5.11(a)). Using the function of the form $a*b^x$, the data can be modeled by the equation $y = 3.443(0.9556^x)$ with $x = 0$ in 1960. Figure 5.11(b) shows how the graph of the equation fits the data.

To write this equation with a base greater than 1, we can write 0.9556 as $1/(0.9556)^{-1} = 1.0465^{-1}$. Thus the model also could be written as

$$y = 3.443(1.0465^{-x})$$

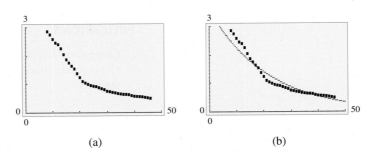

Figure 5.11   (a)   (b)

(b) Recall that we use an unrounded model in our calculations and graphs, unless otherwise instructed. For the year 2016, we use $x = 56$. Evaluating the function for $x = 56$ gives the purchasing power of $0.270.

(c) Evaluation from the graph or a table shows that the purchasing power is below $0.20 when x is 63, or in the year 2023, if the model remains valid.

Spreadsheet Note   A spreadsheet also can be used to create a scatter plot of the data in Table 5.2 and to develop an exponential model. Figure 5.12(a) shows an Excel scatter plot of the Table 5.2 data, and Figure 5.12(b) shows the scatter plot with Excel's base e exponential model. (Procedural details for using Excel are in Appendix D, Section 5.1, and in the Online Excel Guide.) Note that the model $y = 3.443(0.9556^x)$ is equivalent to $y = 3.443e^{-0.0454x}$ because $e^{-0.0454} \approx 0.9556$.

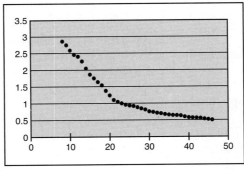

Figure 5.12   (a)   (b)

1. No, all values of y are positive.
2. The left side of the x-axis ($y = 0$)
3. True
4. True
5. True

| EXERCISES | 5.1

In Problems 1–4, use a calculator to evaluate each expression.

1. (a) $10^{0.5}$
   (b) $5^{-2.7}$
2. (a) $10^{3.6}$
   (b) $8^{-2.6}$
3. (a) $3^{1/3}$
   (b) e^2
4. (a) $2^{11/6}$
   (b) e^{-3}

In Problems 5–16, graph each function.

5. $y = 4^x$
6. $y = 8^x$
7. $y = 2(3^x)$
8. $y = 3(2^x)$
9. $y = \left(\dfrac{4}{5}\right)^x$
10. $y = \left(\dfrac{2}{3}\right)^x$
11. $y = 5^{-x}$
12. $y = 3^{x-1}$
13. $y = 2e^x$
14. $y = 3^{-x}$
15. $y = 3^{-2x}$
16. $y = 5e^{-x}$

17. (a) Find $b > 1$ to express $y = 3(\tfrac{2}{5})^x$ in the form $y = 3(b^{-x})$.
    (b) Are these functions growth exponentials or decay exponentials? Explain.
    (c) Check your result by graphing both functions.

18. (a) Find $b > 1$ to express $y = 8(\tfrac{5}{7})^x$ in the form $y = 8(b^{-x})$.
    (b) Are these functions growth exponentials or decay exponentials? Explain.
    (c) Check your result by graphing both functions.

19. (a) Graph $y = 2(1.5)^{-x}$.
    (b) Graph $2(\tfrac{2}{3})^x$.
    (c) Algebraically show why these graphs are identical.

20. (a) Graph $y = 2.5(3.25)^{-x}$.
    (b) Graph $y = 2.5(\tfrac{4}{13})^x$.
    (c) Algebraically show why these graphs are identical.

21. Given that $y = \left(\dfrac{4}{5}\right)^x$, write an equivalent equation in the form $y = b^{-x}$, with $b > 1$.

22. Given that $y = 2.5^{-x}$, write an equivalent equation in the form $y = b^x$, with $0 < b < 1$.

In Problems 23–26, use a graphing utility to graph the functions.

23. Given $f(x) = e^{-x}$. Graph $y = f(x)$ and $y = f(kx) = e^{-kx}$ for each k, where $k = 0.1, 0.5, 2$, and 5. Explain the effect that different values of k have on the graphs.

24. Given $f(x) = 2^{-x}$. Graph $y = f(x)$ and $y = mf(x) = m(2^{-x})$ for each m, where $m = -7, -2, 3$, and 8. Explain the effect that different values of m have on the graphs.

25. Given $f(x) = 4^x$. Graph $y = f(x)$ and $y = f(x) + C = 4^x + C$ for each C, where $C = -5, -2, 3$, and 6. Explain the effect that C has on the graphs.

26. Given $f(x) = 3^x$. Graph $y = f(x)$ and $y = f(x - h) = 3^{x-h}$ for each h, where $h = 4, 1, -2$, and -5. Explain the effect that h has on the graphs.

 For Problems 27 and 28, let $f(x) = c(1 + e^{-ax})$ with $a > 0$. Use a graphing utility to graph the functions.

27. (a) Fix $a = 1$ and graph $y = f(x) = c(1 + e^{-x})$ for $c = 10, 50$, and 100.
    (b) What effect does c have on the graphs?

28. (a) Fix $c = 50$ and graph $y = f(x) = 50(1 + e^{-ax})$ for $a = 0.1, 1$, and 10.
    (b) What effect does a have on the graphs?

APPLICATIONS

29. *Compound interest* If $1000 is invested for x years at 8%, compounded quarterly, the future value that will result is
$$S = 1000(1.02)^{4x}$$
What amount will result in 8 years?

30. *Compound interest* If $3200 is invested for x years at 8%, compounded quarterly, the interest earned is
$$I = 3200(1.02)^{4x} - 3200$$
What interest is earned in 5 years?

31. *Compound interest* We will show in the next chapter that if P is invested for n years at 10% compounded continuously, the future value of the investment is given by
$$S = Pe^{0.1n}$$
Use $P = 1000$ and graph this function for $0 \le n \le 20$.

32. *Compound interest* If $1000 is invested for x years at 10%, compounded continuously, the future value that results is
$$S = 1000e^{0.10x}$$
What amount will result in 5 years?

33. *Drug in the bloodstream* The percent concentration y of a certain drug in the bloodstream at any time t in minutes is given by the equation
$$y = 100(1 - e^{-0.462t})$$
Graph this equation for $0 \le t \le 10$. Write a sentence that interprets the graph.

34. *Bacterial growth* A single bacterium splits into two bacteria every half hour, so the number of bacteria in a culture quadruples every hour. Thus the equation by which a colony of 10 bacteria multiplies in t hours is given by
$$y = 10(4^t)$$
Graph this equation for $0 \le t \le 8$.

35. *Product reliability* A statistical study shows that the fraction of television sets of a certain brand that are still in service after x years is given by $f(x) = e^{-0.15x}$. Graph this equation for $0 \le x \le 10$. Write a sentence that interprets the graph.

36. *National health care expenditures* With U.S. Department of Health and Human Services data since 2000 and projected to 2018, the total public expenditures for health care H can be modeled by

$$H = 624e^{0.07t}$$

where t is the number of years after 2000 and H is in billions of dollars. Graph this equation with a graphing utility to show the graph through the year 2020.

Population growth **Use the following information to answer Problems 37–40. World population can be considered as growing according to the equation**

$$N = N_0(1 + r)^t$$

where N_0 is the number of individuals at time $t = 0$, r is the yearly rate of growth, and t is the number of years.

37. Sketch the graph for $t = 0$ to $t = 10$ when the growth rate is 2% and N_0 is 4.1 billion.
38. Sketch the graph for $t = 0$ to $t = 10$ when the growth rate is 3% and N_0 is 4.1 billion.
39. Repeat Problem 37 when the growth rate is 5%.
40. Repeat Problem 38 when the growth rate is 7%.

41. *Personal consumption* With data from the U.S. Bureau of Labor Statistics for selected years from 1988 and projected to 2018, the billions of dollars spent for personal consumption in the United States can be modeled by

$$P = 2969e^{0.051t}$$

where t is the number of years past 1985.
  (a) Is this model one of exponential growth or exponential decay? Explain.
  (b) Graph this equation with a graphing utility to show the graph from 1985 through the year 2020.

42. *Advertising and sales* Suppose that sales are related to advertising expenditures according to one of the following two models, where S_1 and S_n are sales and x is advertising, all in millions of dollars.

$$S_1 = 30 + 20x - 0.4x^2$$
$$S_n = 24.58 + 325.18(1 - e^{-x/14})$$

  (a) Graph both of these functions on the same set of axes. Use a graphing utility.
  (b) Do these two functions give approximately the same sales per million dollars of advertising for $0 \le x \le 20$?
  (c) How do these functions differ for $x > 20$? Which more realistically represents the relationship between sales and advertising expenditures after $20 million is spent on advertising? Why?

43. *Industrial consolidation* The following figure, from *Investor's Business Daily*, shows how quickly the U.S. metal processing industry is consolidating. The linear equation that is the best fit for the number of metal processors as a function of years after 1990 is

$y_1 = -329.6970x + 5392.1212$, and the best exponential fit is $y_2 = 9933.7353e^{-0.1672x}$. The linear equation gives a much better fit for the data points than the exponential equation. Why, then, is the exponential equation a more useful model to predict the number of metal processors in 2015?

44. **Modeling** *National debt* The following table gives the U.S. national debt for selected years from 1900 to 2009.
  (a) Using a function of the form $y = a*b^x$, with $x = 0$ in 1900 and y equal to the national debt in billions, model the data.
  (b) Use the model to predict the debt in 2015.
  (c) Predict when the debt will be $50 trillion ($50,000 billion).

Year	U.S. Debt ($billions)	Year	U.S. Debt ($billions)
1900	1.2	1975	533.2
1910	1.1	1985	1823.1
1920	24.2	1990	3233.3
1930	16.1	1996	5224.8
1940	43.0	2000	5674.2
1945	258.7	2005	7932.7
1955	272.8	2009	11,956.6
1965	313.8		

Source: Bureau of Public Debt, U.S. Treasury

  (d) Look at a graph of both the data and the model. What events may affect the accuracy of this model as a predictor of future public debt?

45. **Modeling** *Personal income* Total personal income in the United States (in billions of dollars) for selected years from 1960 to 2018 is given in the following table.

Year	1960	1970	1980	1990	2000	2008	2018
Personal Income	411.5	838.8	2307.9	4878.6	8429.7	12,100.7	19,129.6

Source: Bureau of Economic Analysis, U.S. Department of Commerce

  (a) These data can be modeled by an exponential function. Write the equation of this function, with x as the number of years past 1960.

(b) Does the model overestimate or underestimate the projected total personal income in 2018?

(c) In what year does the model predict the total personal income will reach $30 trillion?

46. **Modeling** *Daily shares traded on the NYSE* Selected data for the average daily shares traded (in thousands) on the New York Stock Exchange from 1900 to 2006 are given in the following table.

Year	Average	Year	Average	Year	Average
1900	505	1980	44,871	2000	1,041,578
1920	828	1985	109,169	2002	1,441,015
1940	751	1990	156,777	2003	1,398,400
1950	1980	1995	346,101	2004	1,457,000
1960	3042	1998	673,590	2005	1,602,000
1970	11,564	1999	809,183	2006	1,826,000

Source: New York Stock Exchange, *Fact Book*

(a) Use technology to create an exponential model for the data (with $x = 0$ in 1900).

(b) Use the model to predict the average daily shares traded in 2013.

(c) Examine a graph of both the data and the model. Comment on the fit of the model to the data.

47. **Modeling** *Consumer Price Index* The consumer price index (CPI) is calculated by averaging the prices of various items after assigning a weight to each item, where the average for 1984 was 100. The following table gives the consumer price indexes for selected years from 1940 through 2008, reflecting buying patterns of all urban consumers, with x representing years past 1900.

(a) Find an equation that models these data.

(b) Use the model to predict the consumer price index in 2013.

(c) According to the model, during what year will the consumer price index pass 300?

Year	Consumer Price Index	Year	Consumer Price Index
1940	14	1990	130.7
1950	24.1	2000	172.2
1960	29.6	2005	195.3
1970	38.8	2008	215.3
1980	82.4		

Source: U.S. Bureau of the Census

48. **Modeling** *Compound interest* The following table gives the value of an investment, after intervals ranging from 0 to 7 years, of $20,000 invested at 10%, compounded annually.

(a) Develop an exponential model for these data, accurate to four decimal places, with x in years and y in dollars.

(b) Use the model to find the amount to which $20,000 will grow in 30 years if it is invested at 10%, compounded annually.

Year	Amount Investment Grows To
0	20,000
1	22,000
2	24,200
3	26,620
4	29,282
5	32,210.20
6	35,431.22
7	38,974.34

49. **Modeling** *Students per computer* The following table gives the average number of students per computer in public schools for selected school years that ended in 1985 through 2006.

(a) Find an exponential model for these data. Let x be the number of years past 1980.

(b) Is this model an exponential growth function or an exponential decay function? Explain how you know.

(c) How many students per computer in public schools does this model predict for 2010?

Year	Students per Computer	Year	Students per Computer
1985	75	1995	10.5
1986	50	1996	10
1987	37	1997	7.8
1988	32	1998	6.1
1989	25	1999	5.7
1990	22	2000	5.4
1991	20	2001	5.0
1992	18	2002	4.9
1993	16	2004	4.4
1994	14	2006	3.9

Source: Quality Education Data, Inc., Denver, Colorado

OBJECTIVES

5.2

- To use and apply the definition of logarithmic functions
- To graph logarithmic functions
- To model logarithmic functions
- To use properties of logarithmic functions
- To use the change-of-base formula

Logarithmic Functions and Their Properties

| APPLICATION PREVIEW |

If P dollars is invested at an annual rate r, compounded continuously, then the future value of the investment after t years is given by

$$S = Pe^{rt}$$

A common question with investments such as this is "How long will it be before the investment doubles?" That is, when does $S = 2P$? (See Example 3.) The answer to this question gives an important formula, called a "doubling-time" formula. This requires the use of logarithmic functions.

Logarithmic Functions and Graphs

Before the development and easy availability of calculators and computers, certain arithmetic computations, such as $(1.37)^{13}$ and $\sqrt[16]{3.09}$, were difficult to perform. The computations could be performed relatively easily using **logarithms,** which were developed in the 17th century by John Napier, or by using a slide rule, which is based on logarithms. The use of logarithms as a computing technique has all but disappeared today, but the study of **logarithmic functions** is still very important because of the many applications of these functions.

For example, let us again consider the culture of bacteria described at the beginning of the previous section. If we know that the culture is begun with one microorganism and that each minute every microorganism present splits into two new ones, then we can find the number of minutes it takes until there are 1024 organisms by solving

$$1024 = 2^y$$

The solution of this equation may be written in the form

$$y = \log_2 1024$$

which is read "y equals the logarithm of 1024 to the base 2."

In general, we may express the equation $x = a^y$ $(a > 0, a \neq 1)$ in the form $y = f(x)$ by defining a **logarithmic function.**

Logarithmic Function

| TABLE 5.3 |

Logarithmic Form	Exponential Form
$\log_{10} 100 = 2$	$10^2 = 100$
$\log_{10} 0.1 = -1$	$10^{-1} = 0.1$
$\log_2 x = y$	$2^y = x$
$\log_a 1 = 0 \ (a > 0)$	$a^0 = 1$
$\log_a a = 1 \ (a > 0)$	$a^1 = a$

For $a > 0$ and $a \neq 1$, the **logarithmic function**

$$y = \log_a x \quad \text{(logarithmic form)}$$

has domain $x > 0$, base a, and is defined by

$$a^y = x \quad \text{(exponential form)}$$

From the definition, we know that $\log_3 81 = 4$ because $3^4 = 81$. In this case the logarithm, 4, is the exponent to which we have to raise the base 3 to obtain 81. In general, if $y = \log_a x$, then y is the exponent to which the base a must be raised to obtain x.

The a is called the **base** in both $\log_a x = y$ and $a^y = x$, and y is the *logarithm* in $\log_a x = y$ and the *exponent* in $a^y = x$. Thus **a logarithm is an exponent.**

Table 5.3 shows some logarithmic equations and their equivalent exponential forms.

EXAMPLE 1   **Logarithms and Exponential Forms**

(a)   Write $64 = 4^3$ in logarithmic form.
(b)   Write $\log_4 \left(\frac{1}{64}\right) = -3$ in exponential form.
(c)   If $4 = \log_2 x$, find x.
(d)   Evaluate: $\log_2 8$
(e)   Evaluate: $\log_5 \left(\frac{1}{25}\right)$

Solution

(a)   In $64 = 4^3$, the base is 4 and the exponent (or logarithm) is 3. Thus $64 = 4^3$ is equivalent to $3 = \log_4 64$.
(b)   In $\log_4 \left(\frac{1}{64}\right) = -3$, the base is 4 and the logarithm (or exponent) is -3. Thus $\log_4\left(\frac{1}{64}\right) = -3$ is equivalent to $4^{-3} = \frac{1}{64}$.
(c)   If $4 = \log_2 x$, then $2^4 = x$ and $x = 16$.
(d)   If $y = \log_2 8$, then $8 = 2^y$. Because $2^3 = 8$, $\log_2 8 = 3$.
(e)   If $y = \log_5 \left(\frac{1}{25}\right)$, then $\frac{1}{25} = 5^y$. Because $5^{-2} = \frac{1}{25}$, $\log_5 \left(\frac{1}{25}\right) = -2$.

EXAMPLE 2   **Graphing a Logarithmic Function**

Graph $y = \log_2 x$.

Solution

We may graph $y = \log_2 x$ by graphing $x = 2^y$. The table of values (found by substituting values of y and calculating x) and the graph are shown in Figure 5.13.

$x = 2^y$	y
$\frac{1}{8}$	-3
$\frac{1}{4}$	-2
$\frac{1}{2}$	-1
1	0
2	1
4	2
8	3

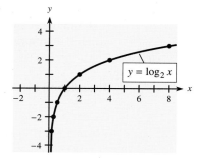

Figure 5.13

From the definition of logarithms, we see that every logarithm has a base. Most applications of logarithms involve logarithms to the base 10 (called **common logarithms**) or logarithms to the base e (called **natural logarithms**). In fact, logarithms to the base 10 and to the base e are the only ones that have function keys on calculators. Thus it is important to be familiar with their names and designations.

Common and Natural Logarithms	**Common logarithms:** $\log x$ means $\log_{10} x$.
	Natural logarithms: $\ln x$ means $\log_e x$.

Values of common and natural logarithmic functions are usually found with a calculator. For example, a calculator gives $\log 2 \approx 0.301$ and $\ln 2 \approx 0.693$.

EXAMPLE 3   **Doubling Time for an Investment** | APPLICATION PREVIEW |

If \$$P$ is invested for t years at interest rate r, compounded continuously, then the future value of the investment is given by $S = Pe^{rt}$. The doubling time for this investment can be found by solving for t in $S = Pe^{rt}$ when $S = 2P$. That is, we must solve $2P = Pe^{rt}$, or (equivalently) $2 = e^{rt}$. Express this equation in logarithmic form and then solve for t to find the doubling-time formula.

Solution

In logarithmic form, $2 = e^{rt}$ is equivalent to $\log_e 2 = rt$. Solving for t gives the doubling-time formula

$$t = \frac{\log_e 2}{r} = \frac{\ln 2}{r}$$

Note that if the interest rate is $r = 10\%$, compounded continuously, the time required for the investment to double is

$$t = \frac{\ln 2}{0.10} \approx \frac{0.693}{0.10} = \frac{69.3}{10} \approx 6.93$$

In general we can approximate the doubling time for an investment at $r\%$, compounded continuously, with $\frac{70}{r}$. (In economics, this is called the **Rule of 70.**)

EXAMPLE   **4**   **Market Share**

Suppose that after a company introduces a new product, the number of months m before its market share is s percent can be modeled by

$$m = 20 \ln \left(\frac{40}{40 - s} \right)$$

When will its product have a 35% share of the market?

Solution

A 35% market share means $s = 35$. Hence

$$m = 20 \ln \left(\frac{40}{40 - s} \right) = 20 \ln \left(\frac{40}{40 - 35} \right) = 20 \ln \left(\frac{40}{5} \right) = 20 \ln 8 \approx 41.6$$

Thus, the market share will be 35% after about 41.6 months.

EXAMPLE   **5**   **Graphing the Natural Logarithm**

Graph $y = \ln x$.

Solution

We can graph $y = \ln x$ by evaluating $y = \ln x$ for $x > 0$ (including some values $0 < x < 1$) with a calculator. The graph is shown in Figure 5.14.

x	$y = \ln x$
0.05	−3.000
0.10	−2.303
0.50	−0.693
1	0.000
2	0.693
3	1.099
5	1.609
10	2.303

Figure 5.14

Note that because $\ln x$ is a standard function on a graphing utility, such a utility could be used to obtain its graph. Note also that the graphs of $y = \log_2 x$ (Figure 5.13) and $y = \ln x$ (Figure 5.14) are very similar. The shapes of graphs of equations of the form $y = \log_a x$ with $a > 1$ are similar to these two graphs.

| Graphs of Logarithmic Functions | Equation: $y = \log_a x$ $(a > 1)$
x-intercept: $(1, 0)$
Domain: All positive reals
Range: All reals
Asymptote: y-axis (negative half) | 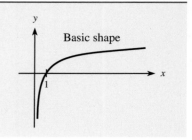 Basic shape |

CHECKPOINT

1. What asymptote does the graph of $y = \log_a x$ approach when $a > 1$?
2. For $a > 1$, does the equation $y = \log_a x$ represent the same function as the equation $x = a^y$?
3. For what values of x is $y = \log_a x$, $a > 0$, $a \neq 1$, defined?

Modeling with Logarithmic Functions

The basic shape of a logarithmic function is important for two reasons. First, when we graph a logarithmic function, we know that the graph should have this shape. Second, when data points have this basic shape, they suggest a logarithmic model.

 EXAMPLE 6   Life Expectancy

The expected life span of people in the United States depends on their year of birth (see the table and scatter plot, with $x = 0$ in 1900, in Figure 5.15). In Section 2.5, "Modeling; Fitting Curves to Data with Graphing Utilities," we modeled life span with a linear function and with a quadratic function. However, the scatter plot suggests that the best model may be logarithmic.

(a) Use technology to find a logarithmic equation that models the data.
(b) The National Center for Health Statistics projects the expected life span for people born in 2000 to be 77.0 and that for those born in 2010 to be 78.1. Use your model to project the life spans for those years.
(c) Could the expected life spans for 2015 and 2020, as given in the table, have been found with the model found in part (a)?

Year	Life Span (years)	Year	Life Span (years)
1920	54.1	1994	75.7
1930	59.7	1996	76.1
1940	62.9	1998	76.7
1950	68.2	1999	76.7
1960	69.7	2000	77.0
1970	70.8	2001	77.2
1975	72.6	2002	77.3
1980	73.7	2003	77.5
1987	75.0	2004	77.8
1988	74.9	2005	77.9
1989	75.2	2010	78.1
1990	75.4	2015	78.9
1992	75.8	2020	79.5

Source: National Center for Health Statistics

Figure 5.15

Solution

(a) A graphing calculator gives the logarithmic model

$$L(x) = 11.027 + 14.304 \ln x$$

where x is the number of years since 1900. Figure 5.16 shows the scatter plot and graph of the model.

Figure 5.16

(b) For the year 2000, the value of x is 100, so the projected life span is $L(100) = 76.9$. For 2010, the model gives 78.3 as the expected life span. These calculations closely approximate the projections from the National Center for Health Statistics.

(c) Yes, the values from the model match perfectly.

Properties of Logarithms

The definition of the logarithmic function and the previous examples suggest a special relationship between the logarithmic function $y = \log_a x$ and the exponential function $y = a^x \, (a > 0, a \neq 1)$. Because we can write $y = \log_a x$ in exponential form as $x = a^y$, we see that the connection between

$$y = \log_a x \quad \text{and} \quad y = a^x$$

is that x and y have been interchanged from one function to the other. This is true for the functional description and hence for the ordered pairs or coordinates that satisfy these functions. This is illustrated in Table 5.4 for the functions $y = \log x \, (y = \log_{10} x)$ and $y = 10^x$.

▪ **| TABLE 5.4 |**

$y = \log_{10} x = \log x$		$y = 10^x$	
Coordinates	Justification	Coordinates	Justification
$(1000, 3)$	$3 = \log 1000$	$(3, 1000)$	$1000 = 10^3$
$(100, 2)$	$2 = \log 100$	$(2, 100)$	$100 = 10^2$
$\left(\frac{1}{10}, -1\right)$	$-1 = \log \frac{1}{10}$	$\left(-1, \frac{1}{10}\right)$	$\frac{1}{10} = 10^{-1}$

In general we say that $y = f(x)$ and $y = g(x)$ are **inverse functions** if, whenever the pair (a, b) satisfies $y = f(x)$, the pair (b, a) satisfies $y = g(x)$. Furthermore, because the values of the x- and y-coordinates are interchanged for inverse functions, their graphs are reflections of each other about the line $y = x$.

Thus for $a > 0$ and $a \neq 1$, the logarithmic function $y = \log_a x$ (also written $x = a^y$) and the exponential function $y = a^x$ are inverse functions.

The logarithmic function $y = \log x$ is the inverse of the exponential function $y = 10^x$. Thus the graphs of $y = \log x$ and $y = 10^x$ are reflections of each other about the line $y = x$. Some values of x and y for these functions are given in Table 5.4, and their graphs are shown in Figure 5.17.

This inverse relationship is a consequence of the definition of the logarithmic function. We can use this definition to discover several other properties of logarithms.

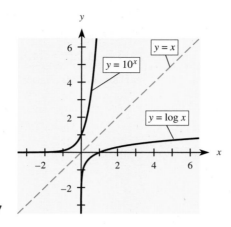

Figure 5.17

Because logarithms are exponents, the properties of logarithms can be derived from the properties of exponents. (The properties of exponents are discussed in Chapter 0, "Algebraic Concepts.") The following properties of logarithms are useful in simplifying expressions that contain logarithms.

Logarithmic Property I

If $a > 0$, $a \neq 1$, then $\log_a a^x = x$, for any real number x.

To prove this result, note that the exponential form of $y = \log_a a^x$ is $a^y = a^x$, so $y = x$. That is, $\log_a a^x = x$.

EXAMPLE 7 **Logarithmic Property I**

Use Property I to simplify each of the following.
(a) $\log_4 4^3$ (b) $\ln e^x$

Solution
(a) $\log_4 4^3 = 3$
Check: The exponential form is $4^3 = 4^3$. ✔

(b) $\ln e^x = \log_e e^x = x$
Check: The exponential form is $e^x = e^x$. ✔

We note that two special cases of Property I are used frequently; these are when $x = 1$ and $x = 0$.

Special Cases of Logarithmic Property I

Because $a^1 = a$, we have $\log_a a = 1$.
Because $a^0 = 1$, we have $\log_a 1 = 0$.

The logarithmic form of $y = a^{\log_a x}$ is $\log_a y = \log_a x$, so $y = x$. This means that $a^{\log_a x} = x$ and proves Property II.

Logarithmic Property II

If $a > 0$, $a \neq 1$, then $a^{\log_a x} = x$, for any positive real number x.

EXAMPLE 8 **Logarithmic Property II**

Use Property II to simplify each of the following.
(a) $2^{\log_2 4}$ (b) $e^{\ln x}$

Solution
(a) $2^{\log_2 4} = 4$
Check: The logarithmic form is $\log_2 4 = \log_2 4$. ✔

(b) $e^{\ln x} = x$

Check: The logarithmic form is $\log_e x = \ln x$. ✔

If $u = \log_a M$ and $v = \log_a N$, then their exponential forms are $a^u = M$ and $a^v = N$, respectively. Thus

$$\log_a (MN) = \log_a (a^u \cdot a^v) = \log_a (a^{u+v}) = u + v = \log_a M + \log_a N$$

and Property III is established.

Logarithmic Property III	If $a > 0$, $a \neq 1$, and M and N are positive real numbers, then $$\log_a (MN) = \log_a M + \log_a N$$

EXAMPLE 9   Logarithmic Property III

(a) Find $\log_2 (4 \cdot 16)$, if $\log_2 4 = 2$ and $\log_2 16 = 4$.
(b) Find $\ln 77$, if $\ln 7 = 1.9459$ and $\ln 11 = 2.3979$ (to 4 decimal places).

Solution

(a) $\log_2 (4 \cdot 16) = \log_2 4 + \log_2 16 = 2 + 4 = 6$
Check: $\log_2 (4 \cdot 16) = \log_2 (64) = 6$, because $2^6 = 64$. ✔

(b) $\ln 77 = \ln (7 \cdot 11) = \ln 7 + \ln 11 = 1.9459 + 2.3979 = 4.3438$
Check: Using a calculator, we can see that $e^{4.3438} \approx 77$. ✔

Logarithmic Property IV	If $a > 0$, $a \neq 1$, and M and N are positive real numbers, then $$\log_a (M/N) = \log_a M - \log_a N$$

The proof of this property is left to the student.

EXAMPLE 10   Logarithmic Property IV

(a) Evaluate $\log_3 \left(\frac{9}{27}\right)$.
(b) Find $\log_{10} \left(\frac{16}{5}\right)$, if $\log_{10} 16 = 1.2041$ and $\log_{10} 5 = 0.6990$ (to 4 decimal places).

Solution

(a) $\log_3 \left(\frac{9}{27}\right) = \log_3 9 - \log_3 27 = 2 - 3 = -1$
Check: $\log_3 \left(\frac{1}{3}\right) = -1$ because $3^{-1} = \frac{1}{3}$. ✔

(b) $\log_{10} \left(\frac{16}{5}\right) = \log_{10} 16 - \log_{10} 5 = 1.2041 - 0.6990 = 0.5051$
Check: Using a calculator, we can see that $10^{0.5051} \approx 3.2 = \frac{16}{5}$. ✔

Logarithmic Property V	If $a > 0$, $a \neq 1$, M is a positive real number, and N is any real number, then $$\log_a (M^N) = N \log_a M$$

The proof of this property is left to the student.

EXAMPLE 11   Logarithmic Property V

(a) Simplify $\log_3 (9^2)$.
(b) Simplify $\ln 8^{-4}$, if $\ln 8 = 2.0794$ (to 4 decimal places).

Solution

(a) $\log_3 (9^2) = 2 \log_3 9 = 2 \cdot 2 = 4$
(b) $\ln 8^{-4} = -4 \ln 8 = -4(2.0794) = -8.3176$

CHECKPOINT

4. Simplify:

(a) $6^{\log_6 x}$ (b) $\log_7 7^3$ (c) $\ln\left(\dfrac{1}{e^2}\right)$ (d) $\log 1$

5. If $\log_7 20 = 1.5395$ and $\log_7 11 = 1.2323$, find the following.

(a) $\log_7 220 = \log_7(20 \cdot 11)$ (b) $\log_7\left(\dfrac{11}{20}\right)$ (c) $\log_7 20^4$

Change of Base

With a calculator, we can directly evaluate only those logarithms with base 10 or base e. Also, logarithms with base 10 or base e are the only ones that are standard functions on a graphing calculator. Thus, if we had a way to express a logarithmic function with any base in terms of a logarithm with base 10 or base e, we would be able to evaluate the original logarithmic function and graph it with a graphing calculator.

In general, if we use the properties of logarithms, we can write

$$y = \log_b x \quad \text{in the form} \quad b^y = x$$

If we take the base a logarithm of both sides, we have

$$\log_a b^y = \log_a x$$
$$y \log_a b = \log_a x$$
$$y = \frac{\log_a x}{\log_a b}$$

This gives us the **change-of-base formula** from base b to base a.

Change-of-Base Formulas

If $a \neq 1$, $b \neq 1$, $a > 0$, $b > 0$, then

$$\log_b x = \frac{\log_a x}{\log_a b}$$

For calculation purposes, we can convert logarithms to base e or base 10.

Base e: $\log_b x = \dfrac{\ln x}{\ln b}$ Base 10: $\log_b x = \dfrac{\log x}{\log b}$

EXAMPLE 12   Change-of-Base Formula

Evaluate $\log_7 15$ by using a change-of-base formula.

Solution

$$\log_7 15 = \frac{\ln 15}{\ln 7} = \frac{2.70805}{1.94591} = 1.39166 \,(\text{approximately})$$

As a check, a calculator shows that $7^{1.39166} \approx 15.$ ✔

Calculator Note

The change-of-base formula expands the capability of graphing calculators so they can be used to evaluate logarithms and to graph logarithmic functions to any base. See Appendix C, Section 5.2, for details.

Figure 5.18(a) shows the graph of $y = \log_2 x = \dfrac{\ln x}{\ln 2}$. Note that it is exactly the same as the graph in Figure 5.13 in Example 2.

Figure 5.18(b) shows the graph of $y = \log_7 x = \dfrac{\ln x}{\ln 7}$.

Figure 5.18   (a)   (b)

Spreadsheet Note   The graph of a logarithm with any base b can be created with Excel by entering the formula "$= \log(x, b)$." See Appendix D, Section 5.2, and the Online Excel Guide for details. ▪

Natural logarithms, $y = \ln x$ (and the inverse exponentials with base e), have many practical applications, some of which are considered in the next section. Common logarithms, $y = \log x$, were widely used for computation before computers and calculators became popular. They also have several applications to scaling variables, where the purpose is to reduce the scale of variation when a natural physical variable covers a wide range.

EXAMPLE 13   **Richter Scale**

The Richter scale is used to measure the intensity of an earthquake. The magnitude on the Richter scale of an earthquake of intensity I is given by

$$R = \log(I/I_0)$$

where I_0 is a certain minimum intensity used for comparison.

(a) Find R if I is 15,800,000 times as great as I_0.
(b) As of 2010, the 1964 Alaskan earthquake was the most violent U.S. earthquake and the second strongest ever; it measured 9.2 on the Richter scale. Find the intensity of the 1964 Alaskan earthquake.

Solution

(a) If $I = 15{,}800{,}000 I_0$, then $I/I_0 = 15{,}800{,}000$. Hence

$$R = \log(15{,}800{,}000)$$
$$= 7.2 \text{ (approximated to 1 decimal place)}$$

(b) For $R = 9.2$, it follows that

$$9.2 = \log(I/I_0)$$

Rewriting this in exponential form gives

$$10^{9.2} = I/I_0$$

and from a calculator we obtain

$$I/I_0 = 1{,}580{,}000{,}000 \text{ (approximately)}$$

Thus the intensity is 1,580,000,000 times I_0.

Note that a Richter scale measurement that is 2 units larger means that the intensity is $10^2 = 100$ *times* greater. ▪

CHECKPOINT SOLUTIONS

1. The (negative) y-axis
2. Yes
3. $x > 0$ is the domain of $\log_a x$.

4. (a) x, by Property II
   (b) 3, by Property I
   (c) $\ln\left(\dfrac{1}{e^2}\right) = \ln\left(e^{-2}\right) = -2$, by Property I
   (d) 0, because $\log_a 1 = 0$ for any base a.

5. (a) By Property III,
   $\log_7(20 \cdot 11) = \log_7 20 + \log_7 11 = 1.5395 + 1.2323 = 2.7718$
   (b) By Property IV,
   $\log_7\left(\tfrac{11}{20}\right) = \log_7 11 - \log_7 20 = 1.2323 - 1.5395 = -0.3072$
   (c) By Property V,
   $\log_7 20^4 = 4\log_7 20 = 4(1.5395) = 6.1580$

| EXERCISES | 5.2

In Problems 1–4, use the definition of a logarithmic function to rewrite each equation in exponential form.

1. $4 = \log_2 16$
2. $4 = \log_3 81$
3. $\dfrac{1}{2} = \log_4 2$
4. $-2 = \log_3\left(\dfrac{1}{9}\right)$

In Problems 5–14, solve for x by writing the equation in exponential form.

5. $\log_3 x = 4$
6. $\log_4 x = -2$
7. $\log_{16} x = -\dfrac{1}{2}$
8. $\log_{25} x = \dfrac{1}{2}$
9. $\log_7(3x + 1) = 2$
10. $\log_3(7 - x) = 3$
11. $\log(4x - 7) = 2$
12. $\log(1.34 - x) = -1$
13. $\ln(2x + 5) = 2.2$ (to 3 decimal places)
14. $\ln(2 - x) = -1.4$ (to 3 decimal places)

In Problems 15–18, write the equation in logarithmic form.

15. $2^5 = 32$
16. $5^3 = 125$
17. $4^{-1} = \dfrac{1}{4}$
18. $9^{1/2} = 3$

In Problems 19 and 20, write the equation in logarithmic form and solve for x.

19. $e^{3x+5} = 0.55$ (to 3 decimal places)
20. $10^{2x+1} = 0.25$ (to 3 decimal places)

In Problems 21–26, graph each function.

21. $y = \log_3 x$
22. $y = \log_4 x$
23. $y = \ln x$
24. $y = \log_9 x$
25. $y = \log_2(-x)$
26. $y = \ln(-x)$

In Problems 27 and 28, use properties of logarithms or a definition to simplify each expression. Check each result with a change-of-base formula.

27. (a) $\log_3 27$ (b) $\log_5\left(\dfrac{1}{5}\right)$
28. (a) $\log_4 16$ (b) $\log_9 3$

29. If $f(x) = \ln(x)$, find $f(e^x)$.
30. If $f(x) = \ln(x)$, find $f(\sqrt{e})$.
31. If $f(x) = e^x$, find $f(\ln 3)$.
32. If $f(x) = 10^x$, find $f(\log 2)$.

In Problems 33 and 34, evaluate each logarithm by using properties of logarithms and the following facts.

$$\log_a x = 3.1 \quad \log_a y = 1.8 \quad \log_a z = 2.7$$

33. (a) $\log_a(xy)$ (b) $\log_a\left(\dfrac{x}{z}\right)$
    (c) $\log_a(x^4)$ (d) $\log_a \sqrt{y}$
34. (a) $\log_a(yz)$ (b) $\log_a\left(\dfrac{z}{y}\right)$
    (c) $\log_a(y^6)$ (d) $\log_a \sqrt[3]{z}$

Write each expression in Problems 35–38 as the sum or difference of two logarithmic functions containing no exponents.

35. $\log\left(\dfrac{x}{x+1}\right)$ 36. $\ln[(x+1)(4x+5)]$
37. $\log_7(x\sqrt[3]{x+4})$ 38. $\log_5\left(\dfrac{x^2}{\sqrt{x+4}}\right)$

Use the properties of logarithms to write each expression in Problems 39–42 as a single logarithm.

39. $\ln x - \ln y$ 40. $\log_3(x+1) + \log_3(x-1)$
41. $\log_5(x+1) + \dfrac{1}{2}\log_5 x$
42. $\log(2x+1) - \dfrac{1}{3}\log(x+1)$

In Problems 43–46, use a calculator to determine whether expression (a) is equivalent to expression (b). If they are equivalent, state what properties are being illustrated. If they are not equivalent, rewrite expression (a) so that they are equivalent.

43. (a) $\ln\sqrt{4 \cdot 6}$ (b) $\dfrac{1}{2}(\ln 4 + \ln 6)$

44. (a) $\log \dfrac{\sqrt{56}}{23}$ (b) $\dfrac{1}{2}\log 56 - \log 23$

45. (a) $\log \sqrt[3]{\dfrac{8}{5}}$ (b) $\dfrac{1}{3}\log 8 - \log 5$

46. (a) $\dfrac{\log_2 34}{17}$ (b) $\log_2 34 - \log_2 17$

47. (a) Given $f(x) = \ln x$, use a graphing utility to graph $f(x) = \ln x$ with $f(x - c) = \ln(x - c)$ for $c = -4, -2, 1,$ and 5.
    (b) For each c-value, identify the vertical asymptote and the domain of $y = \ln(x - c)$.
    (c) For each c-value, find the x-intercept of $y = \ln(x - c)$.
    (d) Write a sentence that explains precisely how the graphs of $y = f(x)$ and $y = f(x - c)$ are related.

48. Given $f(x) = \ln x$, use a graphing utility to graph $f(ax) = \ln(ax)$ for $a = -2, -1, -0.5, 0.2,$ and 3 with $f(x) = \ln x$. Explain the differences between the graphs
    (a) when $a > 0$ and when $a < 0$.
    (b) when $|a| > 1$ and when $0 < |a| < 1$.

In Problems 49 and 50, use a change-of-base formula to evaluate each logarithm.

49. (a) $\log_2 17$ (b) $\log_5 (0.78)$
50. (a) $\log_3 12$ (b) $\log_8 (0.15)$

In Problems 51–54, use a change-of-base formula to rewrite each logarithm. Then use a graphing utility to graph the function.

51. $y = \log_5 x$ 52. $y = \log_6 x$
53. $y = \log_{13} x$ 54. $y = \log_{16} x$
55. Prove logarithmic Property IV.
56. Prove logarithmic Property V.

APPLICATIONS

Richter scale Use the formula $R = \log(I/I_0)$ in Problems 57–60. (*Source:* Earthquake data from the U.S. Geological Survey.)

57. The largest earthquake in 2010 occurred offshore Bio-Bio, Chile, and measured 8.8 on the Richter scale. However, that year's most devastating quake was the 7.0 quake that struck Haiti, resulting in the deaths of more than 220,000 people. How many times more intense was the quake in Chile?

58. In May of 2008, an earthquake measuring 6.8 on the Richter scale struck near the east coast of Honshu, Japan. In March of 2011, a quake measuring 9.0 struck that same region. How many times more intense was the 2011 quake than the one in 2008?

59. The most destructive earthquake in the United States was the 1906 San Francisco earthquake that measured 7.8 on the Richter scale. This quake was the seventeenth most violent in the United States. Among the 40 most severe U.S. quakes, the only one that occurred east of

the Mississippi River shook Charleston, South Carolina in 1886 and measured 7.3. How many times more intense was the San Francisco quake?

60. The world's strongest earthquake struck Chile in 1960 and measured 9.5 on the Richter scale. The 2010 Chilean quake at 8.8 was the world's sixth largest. Find the ratio of their intensities.

Decibel readings **In Problems 61–64, use the fact that the loudness of sound (in decibels) perceived by the human ear depends on intensity levels according to**

$$L = 10 \log(I/I_0)$$

where I_0 is the threshold of hearing for the average human ear.

61. Find the loudness when I is 10,000 times I_0. This is the intensity level of the average voice.

62. A sound that causes pain has intensity about 10^{14} times I_0. Find the decibel reading for this threshold.

63. Graph the equation for loudness of sound in decibels. Use I/I_0 as the independent variable.

64. The background noise level of a relatively quiet room is about $L_1 = 32$ decibels and of a heated argument is about $L_2 = 66$ decibels. Find the ratio I_2/I_1 of the associated intensities.

pH levels **In Problems 65–68, use the following information. Chemists use the pH (hydrogen potential) of a solution to measure its acidity or basicity. The pH is given by the formula**

$$\text{pH} = -\log[\text{H}^+]$$

where $[\text{H}^+]$ is the concentration of hydrogen ions in moles per liter.

65. Most common solutions have pH ranges between 1 and 14. What values of $[\text{H}^+]$ are associated with these extremes?

66. Find the approximate pH of each of the following.
    (a) blood: $[\text{H}^+] = 3.98 \times 10^{-8}$ $= 0.0000000398$
    (b) beer: $[\text{H}^+] = 6.31 \times 10^{-5} = 0.0000631$
    (c) vinegar: $[\text{H}^+] = 6.3 \times 10^{-3} = 0.0063$

67. Sometimes pH is defined as the logarithm of the reciprocal of the concentration of hydrogen ions. Write an equation that represents this sentence, and explain how it and the equation given in the information preceding Problem 65 can both represent pH.

68. Find the approximate hydrogen ion concentration $[\text{H}^+]$ for each of the following.
    (a) apples: pH $= 3.0$ (b) eggs: pH $= 7.79$
    (c) water (neutral): pH $= 7.0$

Doubling time **In Problems 69 and 70, use the formula**

$$2 = \left(1 + \dfrac{r}{100n}\right)^{nt}$$

to find the doubling time t, in years, for an investment at $r\%$ compounded n times per year. Write each exponential

statement in logarithmic form. Then use a change-of-base formula to find the doubling time.

69. 8% compounded quarterly
70. 7.2% compounded monthly
71. *Women in the work force* For selected years from 1970 and projected to 2050, the number, in millions, of women in the work force is given by

$$w(x) = 37.6 \ln x - 81.2$$

where x is the number of years past 1950 (*Source:* U.S. Bureau of Labor Statistics).
(a) Graph this function for x representing 1960–2030.
(b) What does this model predict to be the number of women in the work force in 2030?
(c) Use the graph drawn in part (a) to estimate the year in which the number will reach 80 million.

72. *Life span update* In Example 6 we used data from 1920 to 2020 and found that the life span in the United States depended on the year of birth according to the equation

$$L(x) = 11.027 + 14.304 \ln x$$

where x is the number of years after 1900. Using data from 1920 to 1989, the model

$$\ell(x) = 11.616 + 14.144 \ln x$$

where x is the number of years after 1900, predicts life span as a function of birth year. Use both models to predict the life spans for people born in 1999 and in 2015. Did adding data from 1990 to 2020 give predictions that were quite different from or very similar to predictions based on the model found earlier?

73. **Modeling** *Poverty threshold* The following table gives the average poverty thresholds for one person for selected years 1990 to 2008. Use a logarithmic equation to model these data, with x as the number of years past 1980. What does this model predict for the poverty threshold in 2015?

Year	Income ($)	Year	Income ($)	Year	Income ($)
1990	6652	2000	8794	2003	9573
1995	7763	2001	9039	2004	9827
1998	8316	2002	9182	2005	10,160
1999	8501			2008	10,991

Source: U.S. Bureau of the Census

74. **Modeling** *Female workers* The percent of all workers 16 years and older that are female, for selected years from 1970 and projected to 2040, is given in the following table.
(a) Find the logarithmic function that models the percent as a function of the years, with x equal to the number of years past 1960.
(b) Visually determine whether this model is a good fit for the data.
(c) Use the model to predict the percent of females in the work force in 2045.

Year	Percent	Year	Percent
1970	38.1	2015	48.3
1980	42.5	2020	48.1
1990	45.2	2030	48.0
2000	46.6	2040	47.9
2010	47.9		

Source: Bureau of Labor Statistics

75. **Modeling** *Internet usage* The percent of the U.S. population that uses the Internet, during selected years from 2000, is given in the following table.
(a) Find the logarithmic function that models the percent as a function of the years, with x equal to the number of years after 1995.
(b) Visually determine whether this model is a good fit for the data.
(c) Use the model to predict the percent of Internet users in the United States in 2020.

Year	Percent	Year	Percent
2000	66.9	2005	78.6
2001	72.3	2006	77.6
2002	71.1	2007	79.0
2003	75.9	2008	80.0

Source: Digital Future Report, USC Annenberg

76. **Modeling** *U.S. households with cable/satellite TV* The following data represent the percent of U.S. households with cable/satellite TV for selected years from 1980 to 2009.
(a) Let $x = 0$ in 1970 and find a logarithmic equation that models the data.
(b) If this model remains valid, use it to predict the percent of U.S. households with cable TV in the year 2015.
(c) For what year after 2000 can we be sure this model is no longer valid?

Year	Percent
1980	22.6
1985	45.3
1990	58.6
1995	65.1
2000	77.9
2005	85.7
2006	86.2
2007	83.8
2008	88.2
2009	89.7

Source: Nielson Media Research

OBJECTIVES

5.3

- To solve exponential equations
- To solve exponential growth or decay equations when sufficient data are known
- To solve exponential equations representing demand, supply, total revenue, or total cost when sufficient data are known
- To model and solve problems involving Gompertz curves and logistic functions

Solutions of Exponential Equations: Applications of Exponential and Logarithmic Functions

▌| APPLICATION PREVIEW |

A company's sales decline following an advertising campaign so that the number of sales is $S = 2000(2^{-0.1x})$, where x is the number of days after the campaign ends. When should the company begin a new campaign? In other words, how many days will elapse before sales drop below 350 (see Example 3)?

In this section, we discuss applications of exponential and logarithmic functions to the solutions of problems involving exponential growth and decay, and supply and demand. With exponential decay, we consider various applications, including decay of radioactive materials and decay of sales following an advertising campaign. With exponential growth, we focus on population growth and growth that can be modeled by Gompertz curves and logistic functions. Finally, we consider applications of demand functions that can be modeled by exponential functions.

Solving Exponential Equations Using Logarithmic Properties

Questions such as the one in the Application Preview can be answered by solving an equation in which the variable appears in the exponent, called an **exponential equation.** Logarithmic properties are useful in converting an equation of this type to one that can be solved easily. In this section we limit our discussion and applications to equations involving a single exponential.

Solving Exponential Equations

Procedure	Example
To solve an exponential equation by using properties of logarithms:	Solve: $4(25^{2x}) = 312{,}500$
1. Isolate the exponential by rewriting the equation with a base raised to a power on one side.	1. $\dfrac{4(25^{2x})}{4} = \dfrac{312{,}500}{4}$ $\qquad 25^{2x} = 78{,}125$
2. Take the logarithm (either base e or base 10) of both sides.	2. We choose base e, although base 10 would work similarly. $\qquad \ln(25^{2x}) = \ln(78{,}125)$
3. Use a property of logarithms to remove the variable from the exponent.	3. Using logarithmic Property V gives $\qquad 2x \ln 25 = \ln(78{,}125)$
4. Solve for the variable.	4. Dividing both sides by $2 \ln 25$ gives $\qquad x = \dfrac{\ln(78{,}125)}{2 \ln 25} = 1.75$

In Step 2 we noted that using a logarithm base 10 would work similarly, and it gives the same result (try it). Unless the exponential in the equation has base e or base 10, the choice of a logarithm in Step 2 makes no difference. However, if the exponential in the equation has base e, then choosing a base e logarithm is slightly easier (see Examples 2 and 4), and similarly for choosing a base 10 logarithm when the equation has a base 10 exponential.

EXAMPLE 1 Solving an Exponential Equation

Solve the equation $6(4^{3x-2}) = 120$.

Solution

We first divide both sides by 6 to isolate the exponential.

$$4^{3x-2} = 20$$

Taking the logarithm, base 10, of both sides leads to the solution.

$$\log 4^{3x-2} = \log 20$$

$$(3x - 2)\log 4 = \log 20$$

$$3x - 2 = \frac{\log 20}{\log 4}$$

$$x = \frac{1}{3}\left(\frac{\log 20}{\log 4} + 2\right) \approx 1.387$$

An alternate method of solving the equation is to write $4^{3x-2} = 20$ in logarithmic form.

$$\log_4 20 = 3x - 2$$

$$x = \frac{\log_4 20 + 2}{3} \approx 1.387$$

The change-of-base formula can be used to verify that these solutions are the same.

Growth and Decay   Recall that **exponential decay models** are those that can be described by a function of the following form.

Decay Models $f(x) = C(a^{-x})$ with $a > 1$ and $C > 0$ or $f(x) = C(b^x)$ with $0 < b < 1$ and $C > 0$

Some applications that use exponential decay models are radioactive decay, demand curves, sales decay, and blood pressure in the aorta, illustrated in the following example.

EXAMPLE 2 Pressure in the Aorta

Medical research has shown that over short periods of time when the valves to the aorta of a normal adult close, the pressure in the aorta is a function of time and can be modeled by the equation

$$P = 95e^{-0.491t}$$

where t is in seconds. How long will it be before the pressure reaches 80?

Solution

Setting $P = 80$ and solving for t will give us the length of time before the pressure reaches 80.

$$80 = 95e^{-0.491t}$$

To solve this equation for t, we first isolate the exponential containing t by dividing both sides by 95.

$$\frac{80}{95} = e^{-0.491t}$$

Because e is the base of the exponential, we take the logarithm, base e, of both sides, then use logarithmic Property I to simplify the right-hand side of the expression.

$$\ln\left(\frac{80}{95}\right) = \ln e^{-0.491t} = -0.491t$$

Evaluating the left-hand side with a calculator gives $-0.172 = -0.491t$. Thus,

$$\frac{-0.172}{-0.491} = t \qquad \text{so} \qquad t = 0.35 \text{ second} \qquad \text{(approximately)}$$

EXAMPLE 3   Sales Decay | APPLICATION PREVIEW |

A company finds that its daily sales begin to fall after the end of an advertising campaign, and the decline is such that the number of sales is $S = 2000(2^{-0.1x})$, where x is the number of days after the campaign ends.

(a) How many sales will be made 10 days after the end of the campaign?
(b) If the company does not want sales to drop below 350 per day, when should it start a new campaign?

Solution

(a) If $x = 10$, sales are given by $S = 2000(2^{-1}) = 1000$.
(b) Setting $S = 350$ and solving for x will give us the number of days after the end of the campaign when sales will reach 350.

$$350 = 2000(2^{-0.1x})$$

$$\frac{350}{2000} = 2^{-0.1x} \qquad \text{so} \qquad 0.175 = 2^{-0.1x}$$

With the base 2 exponential isolated, we take logarithms of both sides. This time we choose base 10 logarithms and complete the solution as follows.

$$\log 0.175 = \log\left(2^{-0.1x}\right)$$

$$\log 0.175 = (-0.1x)(\log 2) \qquad \text{Property V}$$

$$\frac{\log 0.175}{\log 2} = -0.1x$$

$$-2.515 \approx -0.1x \qquad \text{so} \qquad x \approx 25.15$$

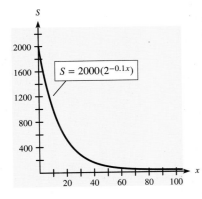

Thus sales will be 350 at day 25.15, and fall below 350 during the 26th day after the end of the campaign. If a new campaign isn't begun on or before the 26th day, sales will drop below 350. (See Figure 5.19.)

Figure 5.19

In business, economics, biology, and the social sciences, **exponential growth models** describe the growth of money, bacteria, or population.

| Growth Models | $f(x) = C(a^x)$ with $a > 1$ and $C > 0$ |

The function $y = P_0 e^{ht}$ can be used to model population growth for humans, insects, or bacteria.

EXAMPLE 4   Population

The population of a certain city was 30,000 in 1990 and 40,500 in 2000. If the formula $P = P_0 e^{ht}$ applies to the growth of the city's population, what should the population be in the year 2020?

Solution

We can first use the data from 1990 ($t = 0$) and 2000 ($t = 10$) to find the value of h in the formula. Letting $P_0 = 30{,}000$ and $P = 40{,}500$, we get

$$40{,}500 = 30{,}000e^{h(10)}$$
$$1.35 = e^{10h} \qquad \text{Isolate the exponential.}$$

Taking the natural logarithms of both sides and using logarithmic Property I give

$$\ln 1.35 = \ln e^{10h} = 10h$$
$$0.3001 = 10h \qquad \text{so} \qquad h \approx 0.0300$$

Thus the formula for this population is $P = P_0e^{0.03t}$. To predict the population for the year 2020, we set the most recent data point (for 2000) as $t = 0$, $P_0 = 40{,}500$, and find P for $t = 20$. This gives

$$P = 40{,}500e^{0.03(20)} = 40{,}500e^{0.6} = 40{,}500(1.8221) \approx 73{,}795$$

CHECKPOINT

1. Suppose the sales of a product, in dollars, are given by $S = 1000e^{-0.07x}$, where x is the number of days after the end of an advertising campaign.
   (a) What are sales 2 days after the end of the campaign?
   (b) How long will it be before sales are $300?

Economic and Management Applications

Sometimes cost, revenue, demand, and supply may also be modeled by exponential or logarithmic equations. For example, suppose the demand for a product is given by $p = 30(3^{-q/2})$, where q is the number of thousands of units demanded at a price of p dollars per unit. Then the graph of the demand curve is as given in Figure 5.20.

Figure 5.20

EXAMPLE 5   Demand

Suppose the demand function for q thousand units of a certain commodity is given by

$$p = 30(3^{-q/2})$$

(a) At what price per unit will the demand equal 4000 units?
(b) How many units, to the nearest thousand units, will be demanded if the price is $17.32?

Solution
(a) If 4000 units are demanded, then $q = 4$ and

$$p = 30(3^{-4/2}) = 30(0.1111) \approx 3.33 \text{ dollars}$$

(b) If $p = 17.32$, then $17.32 = 30(3^{-q/2})$

$$0.5773 = 3^{-q/2} \qquad \text{Isolate the exponential.}$$

$$\ln 0.5773 = \ln 3^{-q/2} = -\frac{q}{2}\ln 3$$

$$\frac{-2\ln 0.5773}{\ln 3} = q \quad \text{so} \quad 1.000 \approx q$$

The number of units demanded would be approximately 1000 units.

CHECKPOINT

2. Suppose the monthly demand for a product is given by $p = 400e^{-0.003x}$, where p is the price in dollars and x is the number of units. How many units will be demanded when the price is $100?

EXAMPLE 6   Total Revenue

Suppose the demand function for a commodity is given by $p = 100e^{-x/10}$, where p is the price per unit when x units are sold.

(a) What is the total revenue function for the commodity?
(b) What would be the total revenue if 30 units were demanded and supplied?

Solution
(a) The total revenue can be computed by multiplying the quantity sold and the price per unit. The demand function gives the price per unit when x units are sold, so the total revenue for x units is $R(x) = x \cdot p = x(100e^{-x/10})$. Thus the total revenue function is $R(x) = 100xe^{-x/10}$.
(b) If 30 units are sold, the total revenue is

$$R(30) = 100(30)e^{-30/10} \approx 100(30)(0.0498) = 149.40 \text{ (dollars)}$$

Gompertz Curves and Logistic Functions

Gompertz Curves

One family of curves that has been used to describe human growth and development, the growth of organisms in a limited environment, and the growth of many types of organizations is the family of **Gompertz curves**. These curves are graphs of equations of the form

$$N = Ca^{R^t}$$

where t represents the time, $R\ (0 < R < 1)$ is a constant that depends on the population, a represents the proportion of initial growth, C is the maximum possible number of individuals, and N is the number of individuals at a given time t.

For example, the equation $N = 100(0.03)^{0.2^t}$ could be used to predict the size of a deer herd introduced on a small island. Here the maximum number of deer C would be 100, the proportion of the initial growth a is 0.03, and R is 0.2. For this example, t represents time, measured in decades. The graph of this equation is given in Figure 5.21.

$N = 100(0.03)^{0.2^t}$

Figure 5.21

EXAMPLE 7   Organizational Growth

A hospital administrator predicts that the growth in the number of hospital employees will follow the Gompertz equation

$$N = 2000(0.6)^{0.5^t}$$

where t represents the number of years after the opening of a new facility.

(a) What is the number of employees when the facility opens?
(b) How many employees are predicted after 1 year of operation?

(c) Graph the curve.
(d) What is the maximum value of N that the curve will approach?

Solution

(a) The facility opens when $t = 0$, so $N = 2000(0.6)^{0.5^0} = 2000(0.6)^1 = 1200$.
(b) In 1 year, $t = 1$, so $N = 2000(0.6)^{0.5} = 2000\sqrt{0.6} \approx 1549$.
(c) The graph is shown in Figure 5.22.
(d) From the graph we can see that as larger values of t are substituted in the function, the values of N approach, but never reach, 2000. We say that the line $N = 2000$ (dashed) is an **asymptote** for this curve and that 2000 is the maximum possible value.

Figure 5.22

$N = 2000(0.6)^{0.5^t}$

EXAMPLE 8   Wildlife Populations

The Gompertz equation

$$N = 100(0.03)^{0.2^t}$$

predicts the size of a deer herd on a small island t decades from now. During what year will the deer population reach or exceed 70?

Solution

We solve the equation with $N = 70$.

$$70 = 100(0.03)^{0.2^t}$$
$$0.7 = 0.03^{0.2^t} \qquad \text{Isolate the exponential.}$$
$$\ln 0.7 = \ln 0.03^{0.2^t} = 0.2^t \ln 0.03$$
$$\frac{\ln 0.7}{\ln 0.03} = 0.2^t \qquad \text{Again, isolate the exponential.}$$
$$\ln\left(\frac{\ln 0.7}{\ln 0.03}\right) = t \ln 0.2 \qquad \text{Take the logarithm of both sides.}$$
$$\ln(0.10172) \approx t(-1.6094)$$
$$\frac{-2.2855}{-1.6094} \approx t \qquad \text{so} \qquad t \approx 1.42 \text{ decades}$$

The population will exceed 70 in just over 14 years, or during the 15th year.

Calculator Note Some graphing calculators have a SOLVER feature or program that can be used to solve an equation. Solution with such a feature or program may not be successful unless a reasonable guess at the solution (which can be seen from a graph) is chosen to start the process used to solve the equation. Figure 5.23 shows the equation from Example 8 and its solution with the SOLVER feature of a graphing calculator.

```
EQUATION SOLVER
eqn:0=100(.03)^(
.2^X)-70■
```

```
100(.03)^(.2^...=0
X=1.4201015868...
bound=(-1E99,1...
```

Figure 5.23

CHECKPOINT

3. Suppose the number of employees at a new regional hospital is predicted by the Gompertz curve

$$N = 3500(0.1)^{0.5^t}$$

where t is the number of years after the hospital opens.
(a) How many employees did the hospital have when it opened?
(b) What is the expected upper limit on the number of employees?

Logistic Functions

Gompertz curves describe situations in which growth is limited. There are other equations that model this phenomenon under different assumptions. Two examples are

(a) $y = c(1 - e^{-ax})$, $a > 0$ See Figure 5.24(a).

(b) $y = \dfrac{A}{1 + ce^{-ax}}$, $a > 0$ See Figure 5.24(b).

Figure 5.24   (a)   (b)

These equations have many applications. In general, both (a) and (b) can be used to model learning, sales of new products, and population growth, and (b) can be used to describe the spread of epidemics. The equation

$$y = \frac{A}{1 + ce^{-ax}}   a > 0$$

is called a **logistic function,** and the graph in Figure 5.24(b) is called a **logistic curve.**

EXAMPLE 9   **Blu-ray Players**

In recent years, Blu-ray players have been one of the most frequently purchased pieces of home electronics equipment. One company's revenues from the sales of Blu-ray players from 2006 to 2011 can be modeled by the logistic function

$$y = \frac{9.46}{1 + 53.08e^{-1.28x}}$$

where x is the number of years past 2005 and y is in millions of dollars.

(a) Graph this function.

(b) Use the function to estimate the sales revenue for 2011.

Solution

(a) The graph of this function is shown in Figure 5.25. Note that the graph is an S-shaped curve with a relatively slow initial rise, then a steep climb, followed by a leveling off. It is reasonable that sales would eventually level off. Very seldom will exponential growth continue indefinitely, so logistic functions often better represent many types of sales and organizational growth.

(b) For the 2011 estimate, use $x = 6$ in the function.

$$y = \frac{9.46}{1 + 53.08e^{-1.28(6)}} = \frac{9.46}{1 + 53.08e^{-7.68}} \approx 9.234$$

Thus the model estimates that in 2011, the sales revenue from Blu-ray players for this company was about \$9.234 million.   ◼

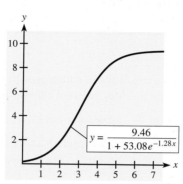

Figure 5.25

CHECKPOINT SOLUTIONS

1. (a) $S = 1000e^{-0.07(2)} = 1000e^{-0.14} \approx \$869.36$ Nearest cent

    (b) $$300 = 1000e^{-0.07x}$$
    $$0.3 = e^{-0.07x}$$
    $$\ln(0.3) = -0.07x$$
    $$\frac{\ln(0.3)}{-0.07} = x \approx 17$$ Nearest day

2. $$100 = 400e^{-0.003x}$$
    $$0.25 = e^{-0.003x}$$
    $$\ln(0.25) = -0.003x$$
    $$\frac{\ln(0.25)}{-0.003} = x \approx 462$$ Nearest unit

3. (a) $3500(0.1) = 350$

    (b) 3500

| EXERCISES | 5.3

In Problems 1–22, solve each equation. Give answers correct to 3 decimal places in Problems 1–12.

1. $8^{3x} = 32{,}768$

2. $7^{2x} = 823{,}543$

3. $0.13P = P(2^{-x})$

4. $0.05A = A(1.06)^{-x}$

5. $25{,}000 = 10{,}000(1.05)^{2x}$

6. $75{,}000 = 15{,}000(1.02)^{4x}$

7. $10{,}000 = 1500e^{0.10x}$

8. $2500 = 600e^{0.05x}$

9. $78 = 100 - 100e^{-0.01x}$

10. $500 = 600 - 600e^{-0.4x}$

11. $55 = \dfrac{60}{1 + 5e^{-0.6x}}$

12. $150 = \dfrac{200}{1 + 30e^{-0.3x}}$

13. $\log x = 5$

14. $\ln x = 8$

15. $\log_4(9x + 1) = 3$

16. $\log_5(x + 2) = 2$

17. $\ln x - \ln 5 = 10$

18. $\ln x + \ln 8 = 5$

19. $7 + \log(8x) = 25 - 2\log x$

20. $3\log x + 10 = \log(3x) + 14$

21. $\ln(x + 2) + \ln x = \ln(x + 12)$

22. $\log_4 x - \log_4(x + 3) = \log_4(x - 2)$

For Problems 23 and 24, let $f(x) = \dfrac{A}{1 + ce^{-x}}$. **Use a graphing utility to make the requested graphs.**

23. (a) Fix $A = 100$ and graph $y = f(x) = \dfrac{100}{1 + ce^{-x}}$

    for $c = 0.25, 1, 9,$ and 49.

    (b) What effect does c have on the graphs?

24. (a) Fix $c = 1$ and graph $y = f(x) = \dfrac{A}{1 + e^{-x}}$ for

    $A = 50, 100,$ and 150.

    (b) What effect does A have on the graphs?

APPLICATIONS

25. *Sales decay* The sales decay for a product is given by $S = 50{,}000e^{-0.8x}$, where S is the monthly sales and x is the number of months that have passed since the end of a promotional campaign.

    (a) What will be the sales 4 months after the end of the campaign?

    (b) How many months after the end of the campaign will sales drop below 1000, if no new campaign is initiated?

26. *Sales decay* The sales of a product decline after the end of an advertising campaign, with the sales decay given by $S = 100{,}000e^{-0.5x}$, where S represents the weekly sales and x represents the number of weeks since the end of the campaign.

    (a) What will be the sales for the tenth week after the end of the campaign?

    (b) During what week after the end of the campaign will sales drop below 400?

27. *Inflation* The purchasing power P (in dollars) of an annual amount of A dollars after t years of 5% inflation decays according to

    $$P = Ae^{-0.05t}$$

    (*Source: Viewpoints,* VALIC)

    (a) How long will it be before a pension of $60,000 per year has a purchasing power of $30,000?

    (b) How much pension A would be needed so that the purchasing power P is $50,000 after 15 years?

28. *Product reliability* A statistical study shows that the fraction of television sets of a certain brand that are still in service after x years is given by $f(x) = e^{-0.15x}$.

    (a) What fraction of the sets are still in service after 5 years?

    (b) After how many years will the fraction still in service be $1/10$?

29. *Radioactive half-life* An initial amount of 100 g of the radioactive isotope thorium-234 decays according to

    $$Q(t) = 100e^{-0.02828t}$$

    where t is in years. How long before half of the initial amount has disintegrated? This time is called the half-life of this isotope.

30. *Radioactive half-life* A breeder reactor converts stable uranium-238 into the isotope plutonium-239. The decay of this isotope is given by

    $$A(t) = A_0e^{-0.00002876t}$$

    where $A(t)$ is the amount of the isotope at time t, in years, and A_0 is the original amount.

    (a) If $A_0 = 500$ lb, how much will be left after a human lifetime (use $t = 80$ years)?

    (b) Find the half-life of this isotope.

31. *Population growth* If the population of a certain county was 100,000 in 1998 and 110,517 in 2008, and if the formula $y = P_0e^{ht}$ applies to the growth of the county's population, estimate the population of the county in 2023.

32. *Population growth* The population of a certain city grows according to the formula $y = P_0e^{0.03t}$. If the population was 250,000 in 2000, estimate the year in which the population reaches 350,000.

33. *Health care* For selected years from 2001 to 2015, the national health care expenditures H, in billions of dollars, can be modeled by

    $$H = 1403e^{0.0712t}$$

    where t is the number of years past 2000 (*Source:* U.S. Department of Health and Human Services).

    (a) When will national health care expenditures reach $4.0 trillion (that is, $4000 billion)?

    (b) How do you think a national health care plan would alter this model?

34. *U.S. debt* For selected years from 1900 to 2009, the national debt d, in billions of dollars, can be modeled by

    $$d = 1.669e^{0.0829t}$$

    where t is the number of years past 1900 (*Source:* Bureau of Public Debt, U.S. Treasury). How long will it be before the debt is predicted to reach $25 trillion (that is, $25,000 billion)? Do you think the Financial Crisis of 2008 and the subsequent federal stimulus bills have affected this model? Explain.

35. *Demand* The demand function for a certain commodity is given by $p = 100e^{-q/2}$.

    (a) At what price per unit will the quantity demanded equal 6 units?

    (b) If the price is $1.83 per unit, how many units will be demanded, to the nearest unit?

36. *Demand* The demand function for a product is given by $p = 3000e^{-q/3}$.

    (a) At what price per unit will the quantity demanded equal 6 units?

    (b) If the price is $149.40 per unit, how many units will be demanded, to the nearest unit?

37. *Supply* If the supply function for a product is given by $p = 100e^q/(q + 1)$, where q represents the number of hundreds of units, what will be the price when the producers are willing to supply 300 units?

38. *Supply* If the supply function for a product is given by $p = 200(2^q)$, where q represents the number of hundreds of units, what will be the price when the producers are willing to supply 500 units?

39. *Total cost* If the total cost function for a product is $C(x) = e^{0.1x} + 400$, where x is the number of items produced, what is the total cost of producing 30 units?

40. *Total cost* If the total cost for x units of a product is given by $C(x) = 400 \ln (x + 10) + 100$, what is the total cost of producing 100 units?

41. *Total revenue* If the demand function for a product is given by $p = 200e^{-0.02x}$, where p is the price per unit when x units are demanded, what is the total revenue when 100 units are demanded and supplied?

42. *Total revenue* If the demand function for a product is given by $p = 4000/\ln (x + 10)$, where p is the price per unit when x units are demanded, what is the total revenue when 40 units are demanded and supplied?

43. *Compound interest* If $8500 is invested at 11.5% compounded continuously, the future value S at any time t (in years) is given by

$$S = 8500e^{0.115t}$$

  (a) What is the amount after 18 months?
  (b) How long before the investment doubles?

44. *Compound interest* If $1000 is invested at 10% compounded continuously, the future value S at any time t (in years) is given by $S = 1000e^{0.1t}$.
  (a) What is the amount after 1 year?
  (b) How long before the investment doubles?

45. *Compound interest* If $5000 is invested at 9% per year compounded monthly, the future value S at any time t (in months) is given by $S = 5000(1.0075)^t$.
  (a) What is the amount after 1 year?
  (b) How long before the investment doubles?

46. *Compound interest* If $10,000 is invested at 1% per month, the future value S at any time t (in months) is given by $S = 10,000(1.01)^t$.
  (a) What is the amount after 1 year?
  (b) How long before the investment doubles?

Securities industry profits **The securities industry experienced dramatic growth in the last two decades. The following models for the industry's revenue R and expenses or costs C (both in billions of dollars) were developed as functions of the years past 1985 with data from the U.S. Securities and Exchange Commission.**

$$R(t) = 21.4e^{0.131t} \quad \text{and} \quad C(t) = 18.6e^{0.131t}$$

Use these models in Problems 47 and 48.

47. (a) Use the models to predict the profit for the securities industry in 2015.
  (b) How long before the profit found in part (a) is predicted to double?

(c) What happened since 2008 that probably would affect this prediction?

48. Use the models to find how long before the securities industry's profit reaches $500 billion.

49. *Purchasing power* The consumer price index (CPI) represents the change in prices of all goods and services. The CPI is based on a 1982 base of 100, which means that the CPI of 195.3 in 2005 indicates that goods that cost $100 in 1982 cost $195.30 in 2005. For selected years from 1945 to 2009, the CPI can be modeled by

$$P(x) = 14.06(1.042)^x$$

where x is the number of years from 1940.
  (a) Find $P(50)$ and $P(75)$, and explain what each means.
  (b) In what year will items costing $100 in 1982 cost $400, according to this model?

50. *Daily shares traded on the NYSE* For selected years from 1970 to 2006, the average daily shares traded (in thousands) on the New York Stock Exchange can be modeled by

$$N(t) = 63.599e^{0.0916t}$$

where t is the number of years past 1900 (*Source:* New York Stock Exchange, *Fact Book*).
  (a) Use the model to estimate the average daily shares traded in 2013.
  (b) Use the model to estimate when the average daily shares traded will reach 3 billion.

51. *Supply* Suppose the supply of x units of a product at price p dollars per unit is given by

$$p = 10 + 5 \ln (3x + 1)$$

How many units would be supplied when the price is $50 each?

52. *Demand* Say the demand function for a product is given by $p = 100/\ln (q + 1)$.
  (a) What will be the price if 19 units are demanded?
  (b) How many units, to the nearest unit, will be demanded if the price is $29.40?

GOMPERTZ CURVES AND LOGISTIC FUNCTIONS APPLICATIONS

53. *Sales growth* The president of a company predicts that sales will increase after she assumes office and that the number of monthly sales will follow the curve given by $N = 3000(0.2)^{0.6^t}$, where t represents the months since she assumed office.
  (a) What will be the sales when she assumes office?
  (b) What will be the sales after 3 months?
  (c) What is the expected upper limit on sales?
  (d) Graph the curve.

54. **Organizational growth** Because of a new market opening, the number of employees of a firm is expected to increase according to the equation $N = 1400(0.5)^{0.3^t}$, where t represents the number of years after the new market opens.
    (a) What is the level of employment when the new market opens?
    (b) How many employees should be working at the end of 2 years?
    (c) What is the expected upper limit on the number of employees?
    (d) Graph the curve.

55. **Organizational growth** Suppose that the equation $N = 500(0.02)^{0.7^t}$ represents the number of employees working t years after a company begins operations.
    (a) How many employees are there when the company opens (at $t = 0$)?
    (b) After how many years will at least 100 employees be working?

56. **Sales growth** A firm predicts that sales will increase during a promotional campaign and that the number of daily sales will be given by $N = 200(0.01)^{0.8^t}$, where t represents the number of days after the campaign begins. How many days after the beginning of the campaign would the firm expect to sell at least 60 units per day?

57. **Drugs in the bloodstream** The concentration y of a certain drug in the bloodstream t hours after an oral dosage (with $0 \le t \le 15$) is given by the equation

    $$y = 100(1 - e^{-0.462t})$$

    (a) What is y after 1 hour $(t = 1)$?
    (b) How long does it take for y to reach 50?

58. **Population growth** Suppose that the number y of otters t years after otters were reintroduced into a wild and scenic river is given by

    $$y = 2500 - 2490e^{-0.1t}$$

    (a) Find the population when the otters were reintroduced (at $t = 0$).
    (b) How long will it be before the otter population numbers 1500?

59. **Spread of disease** On a college campus of 10,000 students, a single student returned to campus infected by a disease. The spread of the disease through the student body is given by

    $$y = \frac{10,000}{1 + 9999e^{-0.99t}}$$

    where y is the total number infected at time t (in days).
    (a) How many are infected after 4 days?
    (b) The school will shut down if 50% of the students are ill. During what day will it close?

60. **Spread of a rumor** The number of people $N(t)$ in a community who are reached by a particular rumor at time t is given by the equation

    $$N(t) = \frac{50,500}{1 + 100e^{-0.7t}}$$

    (a) Find $N(0)$.
    (b) What is the upper limit on the number of people affected?
    (c) How long before 75% of the upper limit is reached?

61. **Market share** Suppose that the market share y (as a percent) that a company expects t months after a new product is introduced is given by $y = 40 - 40e^{-0.05t}$.
    (a) What is the market share after the first month (to the nearest percent)?
    (b) How long (to the nearest month) before the market share is 25%?

62. **Advertising** An advertising agency has found that when it promotes a new product in a certain market of 350,000, the number of people x who are aware of the product t days after the ad campaign is initiated is given by

    $$x = 350,000(1 - e^{-0.077t})$$

    (a) How many people (to the nearest thousand) are aware after 1 week?
    (b) How long (to the nearest day) before 300,000 are aware of the new product?

63. **Pollution** Pollution levels in a lake have been modeled by the equation

    $$x = 0.05 + 0.18e^{-0.38t}$$

    where x is the volume of pollutants (in cubic kilometers) and t is the time (in years).
    (a) Find the initial pollution levels; that is, find x when $t = 0$.
    (b) How long before x is 30% of that initial level?

64. **Fish length** Suppose that the length x (in centimeters) of an individual of a certain species of fish is given by

    $$x = 50 - 40e^{-0.05t}$$

    where t is its age in months.
    (a) Find the length after 1 year.
    (b) How long (to the nearest month) will it be until the length is 45 cm?

65. **U.S. civilian labor force** With U.S. Bureau of Labor Statistics data since 1950 and projected to 2040, the total civilian labor force age 16 years and older (in millions) can be modeled by

    $$L = \frac{197}{1 + 3.65e^{-0.037t}}$$

    where t is the number of years after 1940.
    (a) Use the model to estimate the size of the civilian labor force in 2015.
    (b) Use the model to estimate the year when the civilian labor force is predicted to reach 170 million.

66. *Chemical reaction* When two chemicals, A and B, react to form another chemical C (such as in the digestive process), this is a special case of the **law of mass action,** which is fundamental to studying chemical reaction rates. Suppose that chemical C is formed from A and B according to

$$x = \frac{120\left[1 - (0.6)^{3t}\right]}{4 - (0.6)^{3t}}$$

where x is the number of pounds of C formed in t minutes.

(a) How much of C is present when the reaction begins?
(b) How much of C is formed in 4 minutes?
(c) How long does it take to form 10 lb of C?

67. **Modeling** *Internet users* The following table gives the percent of the U.S. population with Internet connections for selected years from 2000 to 2008.

(a) Find the logistic function that models these data. Use x as the number of years past 2000.
(b) Use the model to predict the percent of the U.S. population with Internet connections in 2015.
(c) When does the model predict that more than 80.8% of the U.S. population will have Internet connections?

Year	Percent	Year	Percent
2000	66.9	2005	78.6
2001	72.3	2006	77.6
2002	71.1	2007	79.0
2003	75.9	2008	80.0

Source: 2009 Digital Future Report, University of Southern California

68. **Modeling** *Endangered species* The following table gives the numbers of species of plants in the U.S. that were endangered in various years from 1980 to 2009.

(a) Find the logistic function that models these data. Use x as the number of years past 1975.
(b) Use the model to predict the number of species of endangered plants in 2012.
(c) When does the model predict that 619 plant species will be endangered?

Year	Endangered Plant Species
1980	50
1985	93
1990	179
1995	432
2000	593
2003	599
2006	598
2009	601

Source: U.S. Fish and Wildlife Service

KEY TERMS AND FORMULAS

Section	Key Terms	Formulas
5.1	Exponential functions Growth functions Decay functions e	$f(x) = a^x \quad (a > 1)$ $f(x) = C(a^x) \quad (C > 0, a > 1)$ $f(x) = C(a^{-x}) \quad (C > 0, a > 1)$ $f(x) = C(b^x) \quad (C > 0, 0 < b < 1)$ $e \approx 2.71828$
5.2	Logarithmic function Common logarithm Natural logarithm Inverse functions Logarithmic Properties I–V	$y = \log_a x$, defined by $x = a^y$ $\log x = \log_{10} x$ $\ln x = \log_e x$ $\log_a a^x = x;$ $a^{\log_a x} = x;$ $\log_a (MN) = \log_a M + \log_a N;$ $\log_a (M/N) = \log_a M - \log_a N;$ $\log_a (M^N) = N(\log_a M)$

Section	Key Terms	Formulas
	Change-of-base formulas	$\log_b x = \dfrac{\log_a x}{\log_a b}$ $\log_b x = \dfrac{\ln x}{\ln b}$
5.3	Solving exponential equations Exponential growth and decay Decay models Growth models Gompertz curves Logistic functions	Isolate the exponential; take logarithm of both sides. $f(x) = Ca^{-x} \quad (a > 1, C > 0)$ $f(x) = Ca^{x} \quad (a > 1, C > 0)$ $N = Ca^{R^t}$ $y = \dfrac{A}{1 + ce^{-ax}} \quad (a > 0)$

REVIEW EXERCISES

1. Write each statement in logarithmic form.
   (a) $2^x = y$ (b) $3^y = 2x$
2. Write each statement in exponential form.
   (a) $\log_7\left(\dfrac{1}{49}\right) = -2$ (b) $\log_4 x = -1$

Graph the following functions.
3. $y = e^x$ 4. $y = e^{-x}$
5. $y = \log_2 x$ 6. $y = 2^x$
7. $y = \frac{1}{2}(4^x)$ 8. $y = \ln x$
9. $y = \log_4 x$ 10. $y = 3^{-2x}$
11. $y = \log x$ 12. $y = 10(2^{-x})$

In Problems 13–20 evaluate each logarithm without using a calculator. In Problems 13–17, check with the change-of-base formula.
13. $\log_5 1$ 14. $\log_2 8$

15. $\log_{25} 5$ 16. $\log_3\left(\dfrac{1}{3}\right)$

17. $\log_3 3^8$ 18. $\ln e$
19. $e^{\ln 5}$ 20. $10^{\log 3.15}$

In Problems 21–24, if $\log_a x = 1.2$ and $\log_a y = 3.9$, find each of the following by using the properties of logarithms.

21. $\log_a\left(\dfrac{x}{y}\right)$ 22. $\log_a \sqrt{x}$
23. $\log_a (xy)$ 24. $\log_a (y^4)$

In Problems 25 and 26, use the properties of logarithms to write each expression as the sum or difference of two logarithmic functions containing no exponents.

25. $\log (yz)$ 26. $\ln \sqrt{\dfrac{x + 1}{x}}$

27. Is it true that $\ln x + \ln y = \ln (x + y)$ for all positive values of x and y?
28. If $f(x) = \ln x$, find $f(e^{-2})$.
29. If $f(x) = 2^x + \log (7x - 4)$, find $f(2)$.
30. If $f(x) = e^x + \ln (x + 1)$, find $f(0)$.
31. If $f(x) = \ln (3e^x - 5)$, find $f(\ln 2)$.

In Problems 32 and 33, use a change-of-base formula to evaluate each logarithm.
32. $\log_9 2158$
33. $\log_{12} (0.0195)$

In Problems 34 and 35, rewrite each logarithm by using a change-of-base formula, then graph the function with a graphing utility.
34. $y = \log_{\sqrt{3}} x$
35. $f(x) = \log_{11} (2x - 5)$

In Problems 36–42, solve each equation.
36. $6^{4x} = 46{,}656$
37. $8000 = 250(1.07)^x$
38. $11{,}000 = 45{,}000e^{-0.05x}$
39. $312 = 300 + 300e^{-0.08x}$
40. $\log_3(4x - 5) = 3$
41. $\ln (2x - 1) - \ln 3 = \ln 9$
42. $3 + 2\log_2 x = \log_2(x + 3) + 5$

APPLICATIONS

43. *Medicare spending* The graph in the figure on the following page shows the projected federal spending for Medicare as a percent of the gross domestic product. If these expenditures were modeled as a function of time,

which of a growth exponential, a decay exponential, or a logarithm would be the best model? Justify your answer.

A Consuming Problem

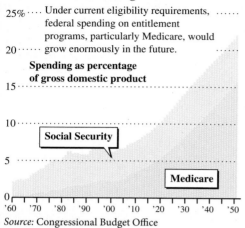

25% .... Under current eligibility requirements, ... federal spending on entitlement programs, particularly Medicare, would
20 ······ grow enormously in the future.

Spending as percentage of gross domestic product

Social Security

Medicare

'60 '70 '80 '90 '00 '10 '20 '30 '40 '50

Source: Congressional Budget Office

44. **Students per computer** The following figure shows the history of the number of students per computer in U.S. public schools. If this number of students were modeled by a function, do you think the best model would be linear, quadratic, exponential, or logarithmic? Explain.

Students per Computer in U.S. Public Schools

Source: MCH Strategic Data, Sweet Springs, MO. Reprinted by permission.

45. **Inflation** The purchasing power P of a $60,000 pension after t years of 3% annual inflation is modeled by

$$P(t) = 60{,}000(0.97)^t$$

(a) What is the purchasing power after 20 years?
(b) Graph this function for $t = 0$ to $t = 25$ with a graphing utility.

46. **Modeling** *Consumer credit* The data in the following table show the total consumer credit (in billions of dollars) that was outstanding in the United States for various years from 1980 to 2008.
(a) Find an exponential function that models these data. Use $x = 0$ in 1975.
(b) What does the model predict for the total consumer credit outstanding in 2015?

(c) In what year did the total consumer credit reach $5300 billion, according to the model?

Year	Amount (in billions)
1980	$349.4
1985	$593.2
1990	$789.1
1995	$1095.8
2000	$1560.2
2001	$1666.9
2002	$1725.7
2003	$2119.9
2004	$2232.3
2005	$2323.4
2006	$2415.0
2007	$2551.9
2008	$2592.1

Source: Federal Reserve

47. **Poverty threshold** The average poverty threshold for 1990–2008 for a single individual can be modeled by

$$y = -3130.3 + 4056.8 \ln x$$

where x is the number of years past 1980 and y is the annual income in dollars (*Source:* U.S. Bureau of the Census).
(a) What does the model predict as the poverty threshold in 2015?
(b) Graph this function for $x = 5$ to $x = 40$ with a graphing utility.

48. **Modeling** *Percent of paved roads* The following table shows various years from 1960 to 2008 and, for those years, the percents of U.S. roads and streets that were paved.
(a) Find a logarithmic equation that models these data. Use $x = 0$ in 1950.
(b) What percent of paved roads does the model predict for 2015?
(c) When does the model predict that 70% of U.S. roads and streets will be paved?

Year	Percent	Year	Percent
1960	34.7	1995	60.8
1965	39.4	2000	63.4
1970	44.5	2002	64.8
1975	48.3	2004	64.5
1980	53.7	2006	65.2
1985	54.7	2008	67.4
1990	58.4		

Source: U.S. Department of Transportation

49. *Stellar magnitude* The stellar magnitude M of a star is related to its brightness B as seen from earth according to

$$M = -\frac{5}{2} \log \left(B/B_0 \right)$$

where B_0 is a standard level of brightness (the brightness of the star Vega).
   (a) Find the magnitude of Venus if its brightness is 36.3 times B_0.
   (b) Find the brightness (as a multiple of B_0) of the North Star if its magnitude is 2.1.
   (c) If the faintest stars have magnitude 6, find their brightness (as a multiple of B_0).
   (d) Is a star with magnitude -1.0 brighter than a star with magnitude $+1.0$?

50. *Sales decay* The sales decay for a product is given by $S = 50{,}000e^{-0.1x}$, where S is the weekly sales (in dollars) and x is the number of weeks that have passed since the end of an advertising campaign.
   (a) What will sales be 6 weeks after the end of the campaign?
   (b) How many weeks will pass before sales drop below $15,000?

51. *Sales decay* The sales decay for a product is given by $S = 50{,}000e^{-0.6x}$, where S is the monthly sales (in dollars) and x is the number of months that have passed since the end of an advertising campaign. What will sales be 6 months after the end of the campaign?

52. *Compound interest* If $1000 is invested at 12%, compounded monthly, the future value S at any time t (in years) is given by

$$S = 1000(1.01)^{12t}$$

How long will it take for the amount to double?

53. *Compound interest* If $5000 is invested at 13.5%, compounded continuously, then the future value S at any time t (in years) is given by $S = 5000e^{0.135t}$.
   (a) What is the amount after 9 months?
   (b) How long will it be before the investment doubles?

54. *World population* With data from the International Data Base of the U.S. Bureau of the Census, the

accompanying figure shows a scatter plot of actual or projected world population (in billions) in 5-year increments from 1950 to 2050 ($x = 0$ in 1945). Which of the following functions would be the best model: exponential growth, exponential decay, logarithmic, or logistic? Explain.

55. *Advertising and sales* Because of a new advertising campaign, a company predicts that sales will increase and that the yearly sales will be given by the equation

$$N = 10{,}000(0.3)^{0.5^t}$$

where t represents the number of years after the start of the campaign.
   (a) What are the sales when the campaign begins?
   (b) What are the predicted sales for the third year?
   (c) What are the maximum predicted sales?

56. *Spread of a disease* The spread of a highly contagious virus in a high school can be described by the logistic function

$$y = \frac{5000}{1 + 1000e^{-0.8x}}$$

where x is the number of days after the virus is identified in the school and y is the total number of people who are infected by the virus in the first x days.
   (a) Graph the function for $0 \le x \le 15$.
   (b) How many students had the virus when it was first discovered?
   (c) What is the total number infected by the virus during the first 15 days?
   (d) In how many days will the total number infected reach 3744?

| **5** | **CHAPTER TEST** |

In Problems 1–4, graph the functions.
   1. $y = 5^x$ 2. $y = 3^{-x}$
   3. $y = \log_5 x$ 4. $y = \ln x$

In Problems 5–8, use technology to graph the functions.
   5. $y = 3^{0.5x}$ 6. $y = \ln(0.5x)$
   7. $y = e^{2x}$ 8. $y = \log_7 x$

In Problems 9–12, use a calculator to give a decimal approximation of the numbers to three decimal places.
   9. e^4 10. $3^{-2.1}$
   11. $\ln 4$ 12. $\log 21$
13. Use the definition of a logarithmic function to write $\log_7 x = 3.1$ in exponential form. Then find x to three decimal places.

14. Write $3^{2x} = 27$ in logarithmic form.

In Problems 15 and 16, solve each equation for x to 3 decimal places.

15. $3 + 6e^{-2x} = 7$ 16. $8 - \log_3(5x - 13) = 5$

In Problems 17–20, simplify the expressions, using properties or definitions of logarithms.

17. $\log_2 8$ 18. $e^{\ln x^4}$ 19. $\log_7 7^3$ 20. $\ln e^{x^2}$

21. Write $\ln (M \cdot N)$ as a sum involving M and N.

22. Write $\ln \left(\dfrac{x^3 - 1}{x + 2} \right)$ as a difference involving two binomials.

23. Write $\log_4 (x^3 + 1)$ as a base e logarithm using a change-of-base formula.

24. Solve for x: $47,500 = 1500(1.015)^{6x}$

25. The graph in the following figure shows the number of active workers who will be (or have been) supporting each Social Security beneficiary. What type of function might be an appropriate model for this situation?

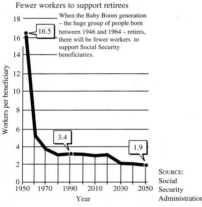

Fewer workers to support retirees

When the Baby Boom generation – the huge group of people born between 1946 and 1964 – retires, there will be fewer workers to support Social Security beneficiaries.

SOURCE: Social Security Administration

26. The graph in the figure shows the history of U.S. cellular telephone subscribership for selected years from 1986 to 2008. If these data were modeled by a smooth curve with years on the horizontal axis, what type of function might be appropriate? Explain.

U.S. Cellular Telephone Subscribership, 1986–2008

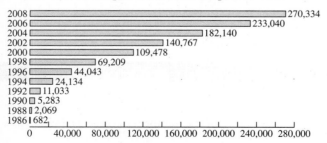

Source: The CTIA Semi-Annual Wireless Industry Indices. Used with the permission of CTIA—The Wireless Association:*

*Data may slightly from other sources.

27. The total national expenditures (in billions of dollars) for health services and supplies from 2000 and projected to 2018 can be modeled with the equation

$$E = 1327e^{0.062t}$$

where t is the number of years past 2000 (*Source:* U.S. Centers for Medicare & Medicaid Services).
(a) Find the predicted total expenditures for 2015.
(b) According to the model, how long will it take for the 2015 total expenditures to double?

28. A company plans to phase out one model of its product and replace it with a new model. An advertising campaign for the product being replaced just ended, and typically after such a campaign, monthly sales volume S (in dollars) decays according to

$$S = 22,000e^{-0.35t}$$

where t is in months. When the monthly sales volume for this product reaches \$2500, the company plans to discontinue production and launch the new model. How long will it be until this happens?

29. The total U.S. personal income I (in billions of dollars) from 1988 and projected to 2018 can be modeled by

$$I = \frac{70,290}{1 + 18.26e^{-0.058t}}$$

where t is the number of years past 1985 (*Source:* U.S. Department of Labor).
(a) What does the model predict for the total U.S. personal income in 2015?
(b) When will the total U.S. personal income reach \$25,000 billion?

30. *Modeling* The following table shows the receipts (in billions of dollars) for world tourism for selected years 1990–2007.
(a) From a scatter plot of the data (with $x = 0$ in 1980), indicate whether an exponential, logarithmic, or logistic model is most appropriate. Explain.
(b) Find the best-fitting model of the type found in part (a).
(c) What does the model predict receipts for world tourism will be in 2010?

Year	Receipts (in billions)	Year	Receipts (in billions)
1990	\$264	2000	\$473
1992	\$317	2002	\$474
1994	\$356	2003	\$524
1996	\$439	2004	\$623
1998	\$445	2007	\$735

Source: World Tourism Organization

I. Starbucks Stores (Modeling)

We all know that the number of Starbucks stores increased rapidly during 1992–2009. To
see how rapidly, observe the following table, which gives the number of U.S. stores and the
total number of stores during this period.

Year	Number of U.S. Stores	Total Stores
1992	113	127
1993	163	183
1994	264	300
1995	430	483
1996	663	746
1997	974	1121
1998	1321	1568
1999	1657	2028
2000	2119	2674
2001	2925	3817
2002	3756	5104
2003	4453	6193
2004	5452	7567
2005	7353	10,241
2006	8896	12,440
2007	10,684	15,011
2008	11,567	16,680
2009	11,128	16,635

Source: Starbucks.com

To investigate how the number of stores is likely to increase in the future and how the total
number of stores compares with the number of U.S. stores, complete the following.

1. Create a scatter plot of the points $(x, f(x))$, with x equal to the number of the years past
   1990 and $f(x)$ equal to the number of U.S. stores in the designated year.
2. Find an exponential function that models these data. Rewrite the function with base e.
3. How accurately does this model estimate the number of U.S. stores in 2000 and in 2006?
4. Find a logistic function that models the data. Does this model estimate the number of
   U.S. stores in 2000 and in 2006 better than the exponential model?
5. Graph the exponential model and the logistic model on the same axes as the scatter
   plot to determine whether the exponential or the logarithmic model is the better fit.
6. Find the exponential and the logistic functions that model the total number of Starbucks stores as a function of the number of years past 1992.
7. Which of the two models found in Question 6 is the better fit for the data?
8. Create a new column of data containing the ratio of total stores to U.S. stores by
   dividing the total number of stores by the number of U.S. stores in each row of the table.
9. Create a scatter plot with the number of years past 1990 as the inputs and the ratios
   found in Question 8 as the outputs.
10. Discuss the growth of the ratio of total stores to U.S. stores during 1992–2009. At
    what average rate is this ratio growing during 1992–2009?
11. Check the Internet to see whether the growth models developed previously remain
    accurate into the next decade.

II. Agricultural Business Management

A commercial vegetable and fruit grower carefully observes the relationship between the amount of fertilizer used on a certain variety of pumpkin and the extra revenue made from the sales of the resulting pumpkin crop. These observations are recorded in the following table.

Amount of fertilizer (pounds/acre)	0	250	500	750	1000	1250	1500	1750	2000
Extra revenue earned (dollars/acre)	0	96	145	172	185	192	196	198	199

The fertilizer costs 14¢ per pound. What would you advise the grower is the most profitable amount of fertilizer to use?

Check your advice by answering the following questions.

1. Is each pound of fertilizer equally effective?
2. Estimate the maximum amount of extra revenue that can be earned per acre by observing the data.
3. Graph the data points giving the extra revenue made from improved pumpkin sales as a function of the amount of fertilizer used. What does the graph tell you about the growth of the extra revenue as a function of the amount of fertilizer used?
4. Which of the following equations best models the graph you obtained in Question 3?

    (a) $N = Ca^{R^x}$ (b) $y = \dfrac{A}{1 + ce^{-ax}}$ (c) $y = c(1 - e^{-ax})$

    Determine a specific equation that fits the observed data. That is, find the value of the constants in the model you have chosen.
5. Graph the total cost of the fertilizer as a function of the amount of fertilizer used on the graph you created for Question 3. Determine an equation that models this relationship. For what amount of fertilizer is the extra revenue earned from pumpkin sales offset by the cost of the fertilizer?
6. Use the graphs or the equations you have created to estimate the maximum extra profit that can be made and the amount of fertilizer per acre that would result in that extra profit.

6

HamsterMan/Shutterstock.com

Mathematics of Finance

Regardless of whether or not your career is in business, understanding how interest is computed on investments and loans is important to you as a consumer. The proliferation of personal finance and money management software attests to this importance. The goal of this chapter is to provide some understanding of the methods used to determine the interest and future value (principal plus interest) resulting from savings plans and the methods used in repayment of debts.

The topics and applications discussed in this chapter include the following.

SECTIONS	APPLICATIONS
6.1 Simple Interest; Sequences **Arithmetic sequences**	Loans, return on an investment, duration of an investment
6.2 Compound Interest; **Geometric Sequences**	529 plans, future value, present value, comparing investments, doubling time
6.3 Future Values of Annuities **Ordinary annuities** **Annuities due**	Comparing investment plans, regular investments to reach a goal, time to reach a goal
6.4 Present Values of Annuities **Ordinary annuities** **Annuities due** **Deferred annuities**	Retirement planning, lottery prizes, court settlements, bond pricing
6.5 Loans and Amortization **Unpaid balance of a loan**	Home mortgages, buying a car, effect of paying an extra amount

Prerequisite Problem Type	For Section	Answer	Section for Review
What is $\dfrac{(-1)^n}{2n}$, if (a) $n = 1$? (b) $n = 2$? (c) $n = 3$?	**6.1**	(a) $-\frac{1}{2}$ (b) $\frac{1}{4}$ (c) $-\frac{1}{6}$	0.2 Signed numbers
(a) What is $(-2)^6$? (b) What is $\dfrac{\frac{1}{4}\left[1 - \left(\frac{1}{2}\right)^6\right]}{1 - \frac{1}{2}}$?	**6.2**	(a) 64 (b) $\frac{63}{128}$	0.2 Signed numbers
If $f(x) = \dfrac{1}{2x}$, what is (a) $f(2)$? (b) $f(4)$?	**6.1**	(a) $\frac{1}{4}$ (b) $\frac{1}{8}$	1.2 Function notation
Evaluate: $e^{(0.08)(20)}$	**6.2**	4.95303	5.1 Exponential functions
Evaluate: (a) $\dfrac{1 - (1.05)^{-16}}{0.05}$ (b) $5000 + 5000\left[\dfrac{1-(1.059)^{-9}}{0.059}\right]$	**6.3** **6.4**	(a) 10.83777 (b) 39,156.96575	0.3 Integral exponents
Solve: (a) $1100 = 1000 + 1000(0.058)t$ (b) $12{,}000 = P(1.03)^6$ (c) $850 = A_n\left[\dfrac{0.0065}{1 - (1.0065)^{-360}}\right]$	**6.1–6.5**	(a) $t \approx 1.72$ (b) $P \approx 10{,}049.81$ (c) $A_n \approx 118{,}076.79$	1.1 Linear equations
Solve: (a) $2 = (1.08)^n$ (b) $20{,}000 = 10{,}000e^{0.08t}$	**6.2**	(a) $n \approx 9.01$ (b) $t \approx 8.66$	5.3 Solutions of exponential equations

6.1

Simple Interest; Sequences

| APPLICATION PREVIEW |

Mary Spaulding purchased some Wind-Gen Electric stock for $6125.00. After 6 months, the stock had risen in value by $138.00 and had paid dividends totaling $144.14. One way to evaluate this investment and compare it with a bank savings plan is to find the simple interest rate that these gains represent. (See Example 3.)

In this section we begin our study of the mathematics of finance by considering simple interest. Simple interest forms the basis for all calculations involving interest that is paid on an investment or that is due on a loan. Also, we can evaluate short-term investments (such as in stocks or real estate) by calculating their simple interest rates.

Simple Interest   If a sum of money P (called the **principal**) is invested for a time period t (frequently in years) at an interest rate r per period, the **simple interest** is given by the following formula.

Simple Interest

The **simple interest** I is given by

$$I = Prt$$

where

$I =$ interest (in dollars)
$P =$ principal (in dollars)
$r =$ annual interest rate (written as a decimal)
$t =$ time (in years)*

Note that the time measurements for r and t must agree.

Simple interest is paid on investments involving time certificates issued by banks and on certain types of bonds, such as U.S. government bonds and municipal bonds. The interest for a given period is paid to the investor, and the principal remains the same.

If you borrow money from a friend or a relative, interest on your loan might be calculated with the simple interest formula. We'll consider some simple interest loans in this section, but interest on loans from banks and other lending institutions is calculated using methods discussed later.

EXAMPLE   1   Simple Interest

(a) If $8000 is invested for 2 years at an annual interest rate of 9%, how much interest will be received at the end of the 2-year period?
(b) If $4000 is borrowed for 39 weeks at an annual interest rate of 15%, how much interest is due at the end of the 39 weeks?

---

*Periods of time other than years can be used, as can other monetary systems.

Solution

(a) The interest is $I = Prt = \$8000(0.09)(2) = \$1440$.

(b) Use $I = Prt$ with $t = 39/52 = 0.75$ year. Thus

$$I = \$4000(0.15)(0.75) = \$450$$

Future Value

The **future amount of an investment,** or its **future value,** at the end of an interest period is the sum of the principal and the interest. Thus, in Example 1(a), the future value is

$$S = \$8000 + \$1440 = \$9440$$

Similarly, the **future amount of a loan,** or its **future value,** is the amount of money that must be repaid. In Example 1(b), the future value of the loan is the principal plus the interest, or

$$S = \$4000 + \$450 = \$4450$$

Future Value	If we use the letter S to denote the **future value** of an investment or a loan, then we have Future value of investment or loan: $\ S = P + I$ where P is the principal (in dollars) and I is the interest (in dollars).

The principal P of a loan is also called the **face value** or the **present value** of the loan.

EXAMPLE 2   Future Value and Present Value

(a) If \$2000 is borrowed for one-half year at a simple interest rate of 12% per year, what is the future value of the loan at the end of the half-year?

(b) An investor wants to have \$20,000 in 9 months. If the best available interest rate is 6.05% per year, how much must be invested now to yield the desired amount?

Solution

(a) The interest for the half-year period is $I = \$2000(0.12)(0.5) = \$120$. Thus the future value of the investment for the period is

$$S = P + I = \$2000 + \$120 = \$2120$$

(b) We know that $S = P + I = P + Prt$. In this case, we must solve for P, the present value. Also, the time 9 months is $(9/12)$ of a year.

$$\$20,000 = P + P(0.0605)(9/12) = P + 0.045375P$$
$$\$20,000 = 1.045375P$$
$$\frac{\$20,000}{1.045375} = P \ \ \text{so} \ \ P = \$19,131.89$$

EXAMPLE 3   Return on an Investment | APPLICATION PREVIEW |

Mary Spaulding bought Wind-Gen Electric stock for \$6125.00. After 6 months, the value of her shares had risen by \$138.00 and dividends totaling \$144.14 had been paid. Find the simple interest rate she earned on this investment if she sold the stock at the end of the 6 months.

Solution

To find the simple interest rate that Mary earned on this investment, we find the rate that would yield an amount of simple interest equal to all of Mary's gains (that is, equal to the rise in the stock's price plus the dividends she received). Thus the principal is $6125.00, the time is 1/2 year, and the interest earned is the total of all gains (that is, interest $I = \$138.00 + \$144.14 = \$282.14$). Using these values in $I = Prt$ gives

$$\$282.14 = (\$6125)r(0.5) = \$3062.5r$$

$$r = \frac{\$282.14}{\$3062.5} \approx 0.092 = 9.2\%$$

Thus Mary's return was equivalent to an annual simple interest rate of about 9.2%.

EXAMPLE 4 Duration of an Investment

If $1000 is invested at 5.8% simple interest, how long will it take to grow to $1100?

Solution
We use $P = \$1000$, $S = \$1100$, and $r = 0.058$ in $S = P + Prt$ and solve for t.

$$\$1100 = \$1000 + \$1000(0.058)t$$

$$\$100 = \$58t \quad \text{so} \quad \frac{\$100}{\$58} = t \quad \text{and} \quad t \approx 1.72 \text{ years}$$

CHECKPOINT

1. What is the simple interest formula?
2. If $8000 is invested at 6% simple interest for 9 months, find the future value of the investment.
3. If a $2500 investment grows to $2875 in 15 months, what simple interest rate was earned?

Sequences Let's look at the monthly future values of a $2000 investment that earns 1% simple interest for each of 5 months.

Month	Interest ($I = Prt$)	Future Value of the Investment
1	($2000)(0.01)(1) = $20	$2000 + $20 = $2020
2	($2000)(0.01)(1) = $20	$2020 + $20 = $2040
3	($2000)(0.01)(1) = $20	$2040 + $20 = $2060
4	($2000)(0.01)(1) = $20	$2060 + $20 = $2080
5	($2000)(0.01)(1) = $20	$2080 + $20 = $2100

These future values are outputs that result when the inputs are positive integers that correspond to the number of months of the investment. Outputs (such as these future values) that arise uniquely from positive integer inputs define a special type of function.

Sequence A function whose domain is the set of positive integers is called a **sequence function**. The set of function outputs of a sequence function

$$f(1) = a_1, f(2) = a_2, \ldots, f(n) = a_n, \ldots$$

forms an ordered list called a **sequence**. The outputs $a_1, a_2, a_3, \ldots$ are called **terms** of the sequence, with a_1 the first term, a_2 the second term, and so on.

Because calculations involving interest often result from using positive integer inputs, sequences are the basis for most of the financial formulas derived in this chapter.

EXAMPLE 5   Terms of a Sequence

Write the first four terms of the sequence whose nth term is $a_n = (-1)^n/(2n)$.

Solution

The first four terms of the sequence are as follows:

$$a_1 = \frac{(-1)^1}{2(1)} = -\frac{1}{2} \qquad a_2 = \frac{(-1)^2}{2(2)} = \frac{1}{4}$$

$$a_3 = \frac{(-1)^3}{2(3)} = -\frac{1}{6} \qquad a_4 = \frac{(-1)^4}{2(4)} = \frac{1}{8}$$

We usually write these terms in the form $-\frac{1}{2}, \frac{1}{4}, -\frac{1}{6}, \frac{1}{8}$.

Arithmetic Sequences   The sequence 2020, 2040, 2060, 2080, 2100, . . . can also be described in the following way:

$$a_1 = 2020, \quad a_n = a_{n-1} + 20 \quad \text{for } n > 1$$

This sequence is an example of a special kind of sequence called an **arithmetic sequence**. In such a sequence, each term after the first can be found by adding a constant to the preceding term. Thus we have the following definition.

Arithmetic Sequence

A sequence is called an **arithmetic sequence** (progression) if there exists a number d, called the **common difference,** such that

$$a_n = a_{n-1} + d \quad \text{for } n > 1$$

EXAMPLE 6   Arithmetic Sequences

Write the next three terms of each of the following arithmetic sequences.
(a) 1, 3, 5, . . .
(b) 9, 6, 3, . . .
(c) $\frac{1}{2}, \frac{5}{6}, \frac{7}{6}, \ldots$

Solution
(a) The common difference is 2, so the next three terms are 7, 9, 11.
(b) The common difference is -3, so the next three terms are $0, -3, -6$.
(c) The common difference is $\frac{1}{3}$, so the next three terms are $\frac{3}{2}, \frac{11}{6}, \frac{13}{6}$.

Because each term after the first term in an arithmetic sequence is obtained by adding d to the preceding term, the second term is $a_1 + d$, the third is $(a_1 + d) + d = a_1 + 2d, \ldots,$ and the nth term is $a_1 + (n - 1)d$. Thus we have the following formula.

nth Term of an Arithmetic Sequence

The **nth term of an arithmetic sequence** (progression) is given by

$$a_n = a_1 + (n - 1)d$$

where a_1 is the first term and d is the common difference between successive terms.

EXAMPLE 7 nth Terms of Arithmetic Sequences

(a) Find the 11th term of the arithmetic sequence with first term 3 and common difference -2.
(b) If the first term of an arithmetic sequence is 4 and the 9th term is 20, find the 75th term.

Solution

(a) The 11th term is $a_{11} = 3 + (11 - 1)(-2) = -17$.

(b) Substituting the values $a_1 = 4$, $a_n = 20$, and $n = 9$ in $a_n = a_1 + (n - 1)d$ gives $20 = 4 + (9 - 1)d$. Solving this equation gives $d = 2$. Therefore, the 75th term is $a_{75} = 4 + (75 - 1)(2) = 152$.

Sum of an Arithmetic Sequence

Consider the arithmetic sequence with first term a_1, common difference d, and nth term a_n. The first n terms of an arithmetic sequence can be written in two ways, as follows.

$$\text{From } a_1 \text{ to } a_n: \quad a_1, a_1 + d, a_1 + 2d, a_1 + 3d, \ldots, a_1 + (n - 1)d$$
$$\text{From } a_n \text{ to } a_1: \quad a_n, a_n - d, a_n - 2d, a_n - 3d, \ldots, a_n - (n - 1)d$$

If we let s_n represent the sum of the first n terms of the sequence just described, then we have the following equivalent forms for the sum.

$$s_n = a_1 + (a_1 + d) + (a_1 + 2d) + \cdots + [a_1 + (n - 1)d] \qquad (1)$$
$$s_n = a_n + (a_n - d) + (a_n - 2d) + \cdots + [a_n - (n - 1)d] \qquad (2)$$

If we add equations (1) and (2) term by term, we obtain

$$2s_n = (a_1 + a_n) + (a_1 + a_n) + (a_1 + a_n) + \cdots + (a_1 + a_n)$$

in which $(a_1 + a_n)$ appears as a term n times. Thus,

$$2s_n = n(a_1 + a_n) \qquad \text{so} \qquad s_n = \frac{n}{2}(a_1 + a_n)$$

Sum of an Arithmetic Sequence

The **sum of the first n terms of an arithmetic sequence** is given by the formula

$$s_n = \frac{n}{2}(a_1 + a_n)$$

where a_1 is the first term of the sequence and a_n is the nth term.

EXAMPLE 8   Sums of Arithmetic Sequences

Find the sum of

(a) the first 10 terms of the arithmetic sequence with first term 2 and common difference 4

(b) the first 91 terms of the arithmetic sequence $\frac{1}{4}, \frac{7}{12}, \frac{11}{12}, \ldots$.

Solution

(a) We are given the values $n = 10$, $a_1 = 2$, and $d = 4$. Thus the 10th term is $a_{10} = 2 + (10 - 1)4 = 38$, and the sum of the first 10 terms is

$$s_{10} = \frac{10}{2}(2 + 38) = 200$$

(b) The first term is $\frac{1}{4}$ and the common difference is $\frac{1}{3}$. Therefore, the 91st term is $a_{91} = \frac{1}{4} + (91 - 1)\left(\frac{1}{3}\right) = 30\frac{1}{4} = \frac{121}{4}$. The sum of the first 91 terms is

$$s_{91} = \frac{91}{2}\left(\frac{1}{4} + \frac{121}{4}\right) = \frac{91}{2}\left(\frac{122}{4}\right) = \frac{91(61)}{4} = \left(\frac{5551}{4}\right) = 1387\frac{3}{4}$$

CHECKPOINT

4. Of the following sequences, identify the arithmetic sequences.
   (a) $1, 4, 9, 16, \ldots$
   (b) $1, 4, 7, 10, \ldots$
   (c) $1, 2, 4, 8, \ldots$

5. Given the arithmetic sequence $-10, -6, -2, \ldots$, find
   (a) the 51st term
   (b) the sum of the first 51 terms.

Technology Note   Finally, we should note that many graphing calculators, some graphics software packages, and spreadsheets have the capability of defining sequence functions and then operating on them by finding additional terms, graphing the terms, or summing a fixed number of terms.

CHECKPOINT SOLUTIONS

1. $I = Prt$
2. $S = P + I = 8000 + 8000(0.06)(\frac{9}{12}) = \$8360$
3. $S = P + I$, so

$$2875 = 2500 + 2500r\left(\frac{15}{12}\right)$$

$$375 = 3125r \quad \text{so} \quad r = \frac{375}{3125} = 0.12, \quad \text{or} \quad 12\%$$

4. Only (b) is an arithmetic sequence; the common difference is 3.
5. (a) The common difference is $d = 4$. The 51st term $(n = 51)$ is

$$a_{51} = -10 + (51 - 1)4 = -10 + 50(4) = -10 + 200 = 190$$

   (b) For $a_1 = -10$ and $a_{51} = 190$, the sum of the first 51 terms is
   $$s_{51} = \tfrac{51}{2}(-10 + 190) = 4590.$$

| EXERCISES | 6.1

SIMPLE INTEREST

In Problems 1–4, find the requested value and tell what the other numbers represent.

1. Find r: $250 = 1000(r)(4)$
2. Find t: $1500 = 5000(0.05)(t)$
3. Find P: $9600 = P + P(0.05)(4)$
4. Find P: $11,800 = P + P(0.03)(6)$
5. $10,000 is invested for 6 years at an annual simple interest rate of 16%.
   (a) How much interest will be earned?
   (b) What is the future value of the investment at the end of the 6 years?
6. $800 is invested for 5 years at an annual simple interest rate of 14%.
   (a) How much interest will be earned?
   (b) What is the future value of the investment at the end of the 5 years?
7. $1000 is invested for 3 months at an annual simple interest rate of 12%.
   (a) How much interest will be earned?
   (b) What is the future value of the investment after 3 months?
8. $1800 is invested for 9 months at an annual simple interest rate of 15%.
   (a) How much interest will be earned?
   (b) What is the future value of the investment after 9 months?
9. If you borrow $800 for 6 months at 16% annual simple interest, how much must you repay at the end of the 6 months?

10. If you borrow $1600 for 2 years at 14% annual simple interest, how much must you repay at the end of the 2 years?
11. If you lend $3500 to a friend for 15 months at 8% annual simple interest, find the future value of the loan.
12. Mrs. Gonzalez lent $2500 to her son Luis for 7 months at 9% annual simple interest. What is the future value of this loan?
13. A couple bought some stock for $30 per share that pays an annual dividend of $0.90 per share. After 1 year the price of the stock was $33. Find the simple interest rate on the growth of their investment.
14. Jenny Reed bought SSX stock for $16 per share. The annual dividend was $1.50 per share, and after 1 year SSX was selling for $35 per share. Find the simple interest rate of growth of her money.
15. (a) To buy a Treasury bill (T-bill) that matures to $10,000 in 6 months, you must pay $9750. What rate does this earn?
    (b) If the bank charges a fee of $40 to buy a T-bill, what is the actual interest rate you earn?
16. Janie Christopher lent $6000 to a friend for 90 days at 12%. After 30 days, she sold the note to a third party for $6000. What interest rate did the third party receive? Use 360 days in a year.
17. A firm buys 12 file cabinets at $140 each, with the bill due in 90 days. How much must the firm deposit now to have enough to pay the bill if money is worth 12% per year? Use 360 days in a year.

18. A student has a savings account earning 9% simple interest. She must pay $1500 for first-semester tuition by September 1 and $1500 for second-semester tuition by January 1. How much must she earn in the summer (by September 1) in order to pay the first-semester bill on time and still have the remainder of her summer earnings grow to $1500 between September 1 and January 1?

19. If you want to earn 15% annual simple interest on an investment, how much should you pay for a note that will be worth $13,500 in 10 months?

20. What is the present value of an investment at 6% annual simple interest if it is worth $832 in 8 months?

21. If $5000 is invested at 8% annual simple interest, how long does it take to be worth $9000?

22. How long does it take for $8500 invested at 11% annual simple interest to be worth $13,000?

23. A retailer owes a wholesaler $500,000 due in 45 days. If the payment is 15 days late, there is a 1% penalty charge. The retailer can get a 45-day certificate of deposit (CD) paying 6% or a 60-day certificate paying 7%. Is it better to take the 45-day certificate and pay on time or to take the 60-day certificate and pay late with the penalty?

24. An investor owns several apartment buildings. The taxes on these buildings total $30,000 per year and are due before April 1. The late fee is 1/2% per month up to 6 months, at which time the buildings are seized by the authorities and sold for back taxes. If the investor has $30,000 available on March 31, will he save money by paying the taxes at that time or by investing the money at 8% and paying the taxes and the penalty on September 30?

25. Bill Casler bought a $2000, 9-month certificate of deposit (CD) that would earn 8% annual simple interest. Three months before the CD was due to mature, Bill needed his CD money, so a friend agreed to lend him money and receive the value of the CD when it matured.
    (a) What is the value of the CD when it matures?
    (b) If their agreement allowed the friend to earn a 10% annual simple interest return on his loan to Bill, how much did Bill receive from his friend?

26. Suppose you lent $5000 to friend 1 for 18 months at an annual simple interest rate of 9%. After 1 year you need money for an emergency and decide to sell the note to friend 2.
    (a) How much does friend 1 owe when the loan is due?
    (b) If your agreement with friend 2 means she earns simple interest at an annual rate of 12%, how much did friend 2 pay you for the note?

SEQUENCES

27. Write the first ten terms of the sequence defined by $a_n = 3n$.

28. Write the first seven terms of the sequence defined by $a_n = 2/n$.

29. Write the first six terms of the sequence whose nth term is $(-1)^n/(2n + 1)$.

30. Write the first five terms of the sequence whose nth term is $a_n = (-1)^n/(n^2)$.

31. Write the first four terms and the tenth term of the sequence whose nth term is

$$a_n = \frac{n - 4}{n(n + 2)}$$

32. Write the sixth term of the sequence whose nth term is

$$a_n = \frac{n(n - 1)}{n + 3}$$

ARITHMETIC SEQUENCES

In Problems 33–36, (a) identify d and a_1 and (b) write the next three terms.

33. $2, 5, 8, \ldots$

34. $3, 9, 15, \ldots$

35. $3, \frac{9}{2}, 6, \ldots$

36. $2, 2.75, 3.5, \ldots$

37. Find the 83rd term of the arithmetic sequence with first term 6 and common difference $-\frac{1}{2}$.

38. Find the 66th term of the arithmetic sequence with first term $\frac{1}{2}$ and common difference $-\frac{1}{3}$.

39. Find the 100th term of the arithmetic sequence with first term 5 and eighth term 19.

40. Find the 73rd term of the arithmetic sequence with first term 20 and tenth term 47.

41. Find the sum of the first 38 terms of the arithmetic sequence with first term 2 and 38th term 113.

42. Find the sum of the first 56 terms of the arithmetic sequence with first term 6 and 56th term 226.

43. Find the sum of the first 70 terms of the arithmetic sequence with first term 10 and common difference $\frac{1}{2}$.

44. Find the sum of the first 80 terms of the arithmetic sequence with first term 12 and common difference -3.

45. Find the sum of the first 150 terms of the arithmetic sequence $6, \frac{9}{2}, 3, \ldots$.

46. Find the sum of the first 200 terms of the arithmetic sequence $12, 9, 6, \ldots$.

APPLICATIONS

47. *Bee reproduction* A female bee hatches from a fertilized egg, whereas a male bee hatches from an unfertilized egg. Thus a female bee has a male parent and a female parent, whereas a male bee has only a female parent. Therefore, the number of ancestors of a male bee follows the *Fibonacci sequence*

$$1, 2, 3, 5, 8, 13, \ldots$$

Observe the pattern and write three more terms of the sequence.

48. *Salaries* Suppose you are offered a job with a relatively low starting salary but with a $3000 raise for each of the next 7 years. How much more than your starting salary would you be making in the eighth year?

49. *Profit* A new firm loses $4000 in its first month, but its profit increases by $800 in each succeeding month for the next year. What is its profit in the twelfth month?

50. *Pay raises* If you make $36,000 and get $2400 raises each year, in how many years will your salary double?

51. *Salaries* Suppose you are offered two identical jobs: one paying a starting salary of $40,000 with yearly raises of $2000 and one paying a starting salary of $36,000 with yearly raises of $2400. Which job will pay you more for your tenth year on the job?

52. *Profit* A new firm loses $4000 in its first month, but its profit increases by $800 in each succeeding month for the next year. What is its profit for the year?

53. *Pay raises* If you are an employee, would you rather be given a raise of $1000 at the end of each year (plan I) or a raise of $300 at the end of each 6-month period (plan II)? Consider the table for an employee whose base salary is $20,000 per year (or $10,000 per 6-month period), and answer parts (a)–(g).

Period (months)	Salary Received per 6-Month Period	
	Plan I	Plan II
0–6	$10,000	$10,000
6–12	10,000	10,300
12–18	10,500	10,600
18–24	10,500	10,900
24–30	11,000	11,200
30–36	11,000	11,500

(a) Find the sum of the raises for plan I for the first 3 years.
(b) Find the sum of the raises for plan II for the first 3 years.
(c) Which plan is better, and by how much?
(d) Find the sum of the raises in plan I for 5 years.
(e) Find the sum of the raises in plan II for 5 years.
(f) Which plan is better, and by how much?
(g) Do you want plan I or plan II?

54. *Pay raises* As an employee, would you prefer being given a $2400 raise each year for 5 years or a $400 raise each quarter for 5 years?

OBJECTIVES

- To find the future value of a compound interest investment and the amount of interest earned when interest is compounded at regular intervals or continuously
- To find the annual percentage yield (APY), or the effective annual interest rate, of money invested at compound interest
- To find the time it takes for an investment to reach a specified amount
- To find specified terms, and sums of specified numbers of terms, of geometric sequences

6.2

Compound Interest; Geometric Sequences

| APPLICATION PREVIEW |

A common concern for young parents is how they will pay for their children's college educations. To address this, there are an increasing number of college savings plans, such as the so-called "529 plans," which are tax-deferred.

Suppose Jim and Eden established such a plan for their baby daughter Maura. If this account earns 9.8% compounded quarterly and if their goal is to have $200,000 by Maura's 18th birthday, what would be the impact of having $10,000 in the account by Maura's 1st birthday? (See Example 3.)

A compound interest investment (such as Jim and Eden's account) is one in which interest is paid into the account at regular intervals. In this section we consider investments of this type and develop formulas that enable us to determine the impact of making a $10,000 investment in Maura's college tuition account by her 1st birthday.

Compound Interest   In the previous section we discussed simple interest. A second method of paying interest is the **compound interest** method, where the interest for each period is added to the principal before interest is calculated for the next period. With compound interest, both the interest added and the principal earn interest for the next period. With this method, the principal grows as the interest is added to it. Think of it like building a snowman. You start with a snowball the size of your fist (your investment), and as you roll the snowball around the yard, the snowball picks up additional snow (interest). The more you roll it, the snowball itself (principal) keeps growing and as it does, the amount of snow it picks up along the way (interest) also grows. This method is used in investments such as savings accounts and U.S. government series EE bonds.

An understanding of compound interest is important not only for people planning careers with financial institutions but also for anyone planning to invest money. To see how compound interest is computed, consider the following table, which tracks the annual growth of $20,000 invested for 3 years at 10% compounded annually. (Notice that the ending principal for each year becomes the beginning principal for the next year.)

Year	Beginning Principal = P	10% Annual Interest = I	Ending Principal = $P + I$
1	$20,000	0.10($20,000) = $2000	$22,000
2	$22,000	0.10($22,000) = $2200	$24,200
3	$24,200	0.10($24,200) = $2420	$26,620

Note that the future value for each year can be found by multiplying the beginning principal for that year by $1 + 0.10$, or 1.10. That is,

First year: $\$20,000(1.10) = \$22,000$
Second year: $[\$20,000(1.10)](1.10) = \$20,000(1.10)^2 = \$24,200$
Third year: $[\$20,000(1.10)^2](1.10) = \$20,000(1.10)^3 = \$26,620$

This suggests that if we maintained this investment for n years, the future value at the end of this time would be $\$20,000(1.10)^n$. Thus we have the following general formula.

Future Value (Annual Compounding)

If $\$P$ is invested at an interest rate of r per year, compounded annually, the future value S at the end of the nth year is

$$S = P(1 + r)^n$$

EXAMPLE 1   Annual Compounding

If $3000 is invested for 4 years at 9% compounded annually, how much interest is earned?

Solution

The future value is

$$S = \$3000(1 + 0.09)^4$$
$$= \$3000(1.4115816)$$
$$= \$4234.7448$$
$$= \$4234.74, \text{ to the nearest cent}$$

Because $3000 of this amount was the original investment, the interest earned is $4234.74 − $3000 = $1234.74.   ◼

Some accounts have the interest compounded semiannually, quarterly, monthly, or daily. Unless specifically stated otherwise, a stated interest rate, called the **nominal annual rate,** is the rate per year and is denoted by r. The interest rate *per period*, denoted by i, is the nominal rate divided by the number of interest periods per year. The interest periods are also called *conversion periods*, and the number of periods is denoted by n. Thus, if $100 is invested for 5 years at 6% compounded semiannually (twice a year), it has been invested for $n = 10$ periods (5 years × 2 periods per year) at $i = 3\%$ per period (6% per year ÷ 2 periods per year). The future value of an investment of this type is found using the following formula.

Future Value (Periodic Compounding)

If $P is invested for t years at a nominal interest rate r, compounded m times per year, then the total number of compounding periods is

$$n = mt$$

the interest rate per compounding period is

$$i = \frac{r}{m} \ \left(\text{expressed as a decimal}\right)$$

and the future value is

$$S = P(1 + i)^n = P\left(1 + \frac{r}{m}\right)^{mt}$$

EXAMPLE 2   Periodic Compounding

For each of the following investments, find the interest rate per period, i, and the number of compounding periods, n.

(a) 12% compounded monthly for 7 years
(b) 7.2% compounded quarterly for 11 quarters

Solution

(a) If the compounding is monthly and $r = 12\% = 0.12$, then $i = 0.12/12 = 0.01$. The number of compounding periods is $n = (7 \text{ yr})(12 \text{ periods/yr}) = 84$.
(b) $i = 0.072/4 = 0.018$, $n = 11$ (the number of quarters given)   ◼

Once we know i and n, we can calculate the future value from the formula with a calculator.

EXAMPLE **3**   **Future Value**   **| APPLICATION PREVIEW |**

Jim and Eden want to have $200,000 in Maura's college fund on her 18th birthday, and they want to know the impact on this goal of having $10,000 invested at 9.8%, compounded quarterly, on her 1st birthday. To advise Jim and Eden regarding this, find

(a) the future value of the $10,000 investment
(b) the amount of compound interest that the investment earns
(c) the impact this would have on their goal.

Solution

(a) For this situation, $i = 0.098/4 = 0.0245$ and $n = 4(17) = 68$. Thus the future value of the $10,000 is given by

$$S = P(1 + i)^n = \$10,000(1 + 0.0245)^{68} = \$10,000(5.18577) = \$51,857.70$$

(b) The amount of interest earned is $51,857.70 − $10,000 = $41,857.70.
(c) Thus $10,000 invested by Maura's 1st birthday grows to an amount that is slightly more than 25% of their goal. This rather large early investment has a substantial impact on their goal.

Technology Note   The steps for finding the future value of an investment with a calculator or with Excel are found in Appendices C and D, Section 6.2. See also the Online Excel Guide.

We saw previously that compound interest calculations are based on those for simple interest, except that interest payments are added to the principal. In this way, interest is earned on both principal and previous interest payments. Let's examine the effect of this compounding by comparing compound interest and simple interest. If the investment in Example 3 had been at simple interest, the interest earned would have been $Prt = \$10,000(0.098)(17) = \$16,660$. This is almost $25,200 less than the amount of compound interest earned. And this difference would have been magnified over a longer period of time. Try reworking Example 3's investment over 30 years and compare the compound interest earned with the simple interest earned. This comparison begins to shed some light on why Albert Einstein characterized compound interest as "the most powerful force in the Universe."

EXAMPLE **4**   **Present Value**

What amount must be invested now in order to have $12,000 after 3 years if money is worth 6% compounded semiannually?

Solution

We need to find the present value P, knowing that the future value is $S = \$12,000$. Use $i = 0.06/2 = 0.03$ and $n = 3(2) = 6$.

$$S = P(1 + i)^n$$

$$\$12,000 = P(1 + 0.03)^6 = P(1.03)^6 \approx P(1.1940523)$$

$$P = \frac{\$12,000}{1.1940523} = \$10,049.81, \text{ to the nearest cent}$$

EXAMPLE **5**   **Rate Earned**

As Figure 6.1 on the next page shows, three years after Google stock was first sold publicly, its share price had risen 650%. Google's 650% increase means that $10,000 invested in Google stock at its initial public offering (I.P.O.) was worth $65,000 three years later. What interest rate compounded annually does this represent? (For similar information and calculations regarding Microsoft's annual compounding performance, see Problem 33 in the exercises for this section.)

Figure 6.1

Source: Based on data from Google Finance

Solution

We use $P = \$10,000$, $S = \$65,000$, and $n = 3$ in the formula $S = P(1 + i)^n$, and solve for i.

$$\$65,000 = \$10,000(1 + i)^3$$
$$6.5 = (1 + i)^3$$

At this point we take the cube root (third root) of both sides (or, equivalently, raise both sides to the 1/3 power).

$$6.5^{(1/3)} = \left[(1 + i)^3\right]^{(1/3)}$$
$$1.8663 \approx 1 + i \quad \text{so} \quad 0.8663 \approx i$$

Thus, this investment earned about 86.63% compounded annually.

CHECKPOINT

1. If $5000 is invested at 6%, compounded quarterly, for 5 years, find
   (a) the number of compounding periods per year, m
   (b) the number of compounding periods for the investment, n
   (c) the interest rate for each compounding period, i
   (d) the future value of the investment.
2. Find the present value of an investment that is worth $12,000 after 5 years at 9% compounded monthly.

If we invest a sum of money, say $100, then the higher the interest rate, the greater the future value. Figure 6.2 shows a graphical comparison of the future values when $100 is invested at 5%, 8%, and 10%, all compounded annually over a period of 30 years. Note that higher interest rates yield consistently higher future values and have dramatically higher future values after 15–20 years. Note also that these graphs of the future values are growth exponentials.

Figure 6.2

Spreadsheet Note

Spreadsheets and financial calculators can also be used to investigate and analyze compound interest investments, such as tracking the future value of an investment or comparing investments with different interest rates.

Table 6.1 shows a portion of a spreadsheet that tracks the monthly growth of two investments, both compounded monthly and both with $P = \$1000$, but one at 6% (giving $i = 0.005$) and the other at 6.9% (giving $i = 0.00575$).

| TABLE 6.1 |

SECOND 12 MONTHS OF TWO INVESTMENTS AT DIFFERENT INTEREST RATES

	A	B	C
1	Month #	$ = 1000(1.005)^n	$ = 1000(1.00575)^n
2	22	$1115.97	$1134.44
3	23	$1121.55	$1140.96
4	24	$1127.16	$1147.52

Continuous Compounding

Because more frequent compounding means that interest is paid more often (and hence more interest on interest is earned), it would seem that the more frequently the interest is compounded, the larger the future value will become. To determine the interest that results from *continuous* compounding (compounding every instant), consider an investment of $1 for 1 year at a 100% interest rate. If the interest is compounded m times per year, the future value is given by

$$S = \left(1 + \frac{1}{m}\right)^m$$

Table 6.2 shows the future values that result as the number of compounding periods increases.

| TABLE 6.2 |

Compounded	Number of Periods per Year	Future Value of $1
Annually	1	$\left(1 + \frac{1}{1}\right)^1 = 2$
Monthly	12	$\left(1 + \frac{1}{12}\right)^{12} = 2.6130\ldots$
Daily	360 (business year)	$\left(1 + \frac{1}{360}\right)^{360} = 2.7145\ldots$
Hourly	8640	$\left(1 + \frac{1}{8640}\right)^{8640} = 2.71812\ldots$
Each minute	518,400	$\left(1 + \frac{1}{518,400}\right)^{518,400} = 2.71827\ldots$

Table 6.2 shows that as the number of periods per year increases, the future value increases, although not very rapidly. In fact, no matter how often the interest is compounded, the future value will never exceed $2.72. We say that as the number of periods increases, the future value approaches a limit, which is the number e:

$$e = 2.7182818 \ldots.$$

We discussed the number e and the function $y = e^x$ in Chapter 5, "Exponential and Logarithmic Functions." The discussion here shows one way the number we call e may be derived. We will define e more formally later.

Future Value (Continuous Compounding)

In general, if $\$P$ is invested for t years at a nominal rate r compounded continuously, then the future value is given by the exponential function

$$S = Pe^{rt}$$

EXAMPLE 6 Continuous Compounding

(a) Find the future value if $1000 is invested for 20 years at 8%, compounded continuously.

(b) What amount must be invested at 6.5%, compounded continuously, so that it will be worth $25,000 after 8 years?

Solution

(a) The future value is

$$S = \$1000e^{(0.08)(20)} = \$1000e^{1.6}$$
$$= \$1000(4.95303) \quad (\text{because } e^{1.6} \approx 4.95303)$$
$$= \$4953.03$$

(b) Solve for the present value P in $25{,}000 = Pe^{(0.065)(8)}$.

$$\$25{,}000 = Pe^{(0.065)(8)} = Pe^{0.52} = P(1.68202765)$$
$$\frac{\$25{,}000}{1.68202765} = P \quad \text{so} \quad P = \$14{,}863.01, \text{ to the nearest cent}$$

EXAMPLE 7 Comparing Investments

How much more will you earn if you invest $1000 for 5 years at 8% compounded continuously instead of at 8% compounded quarterly?

Solution

If the interest is compounded continuously, the future value at the end of the 5 years is

$$S = \$1000e^{(0.08)(5)} = \$1000e^{0.4} \approx \$1000(1.49182) = \$1491.82$$

If the interest is compounded quarterly, the future value at the end of the 5 years is

$$S = \$1000(1.02)^{20} \approx \$1000(1.485947) = \$1485.95, \text{ to the nearest cent}$$

Thus the extra interest earned by compounding continuously is

$$\$1491.82 - \$1485.95 = \$5.87$$

Annual Percentage Yield

As Example 7 shows, when we invest money at a given compound interest rate, the method of compounding affects the amount of interest we earn. As a result, a rate of 8% can earn more than 8% interest if compounding is more frequent than annually.

For example, suppose $1 is invested for 1 year at 8%, compounded semiannually. Then $i = 0.08/2 = 0.04$, $n = 2$, the future value is $S = \$1(1.04)^2 = \$1.0816$, and the interest earned for the year is $\$1.0816 - \$1 = \$0.0816$. Note that this amount of interest represents an annual percentage yield of 8.16%, so we say that 8% compounded semiannually has an **annual percentage yield (APY)**, or **effective annual rate**, of 8.16%. Similarly, if $1 is invested at 8% compounded continuously, then the interest earned is $\$1(e^{0.08}) - \$1 = \$0.0833$, for an APY of 8.33%.

Banks acknowledge this difference between stated nominal interest rates and annual percentage yields by posting both rates for their investments. Note that the annual percentage yield is equivalent to the stated rate when compounding is annual. In general, the annual percentage yield equals I/P, or just I if $P = \$1$. Hence we can calculate the APY with the following formulas.

Annual Percentage Yield (APY)	Let r represent the annual (nominal) interest rate for an investment. Then the **annual percentage yield (APY)*** is found as follows.

Periodic Compounding. If m is the number of compounding periods per year, then $i = r/m$ is the interest rate per period, and

$$\text{APY} = \left(1 + \frac{r}{m}\right)^m - 1 = (1 + i)^m - 1 \quad \text{(as a decimal)}$$

Continuous Compounding

$$\text{APY} = e^r - 1 \quad \text{(as a decimal)}$$

Thus, although we cannot directly compare two nominal rates with different compounding periods, we can compare their corresponding APYs.

EXAMPLE 8   Comparing Yields

Suppose a young couple such as Jim and Eden from our Application Preview found three different investment companies that offered college savings plans: (a) one at 10% compounded annually, (b) another at 9.8% compounded quarterly, and (c) a third at 9.65% compounded continuously. Find the annual percentage yield (APY) for each of these three plans to discover which plan is best.

Solution

(a) For annual compounding, the stated rate is the APY. Thus, APY = 10%.

(b) Because the number of periods per year is $m = 4$ and the nominal rate is $r = 0.098$, the rate per period is $i = r/m = 0.098/4 = 0.0245$. Thus,

$$\text{APY} = (1 + 0.0245)^4 - 1 = 1.10166 - 1 = 0.10166 = 10.166\%$$

(c) For continuous compounding and a nominal rate of 9.65%, we have

$$\text{APY} = e^{0.0965} - 1 = 1.10131 - 1 = 0.10131 = 10.131\%$$

Hence we see that of these three choices, 9.8% compounded quarterly is best. Furthermore, even 9.65% compounded continuously has a higher APY than 10% compounded annually. ■

CHECKPOINT

3. For each future value formula below, decide which is used for interest that is compounded periodically and which is used for interest that is compounded continuously.
   (a) $S = P(1 + i)^n$ (b) $S = Pe^{rt}$

4. If $5000 is invested at 6% compounded continuously for 5 years, find the future value of the investment.

5. Find the annual percentage yield of an investment that earns 7% compounded semi-annually.

EXAMPLE 9   Doubling Time

How long does it take an investment of $10,000 to double if it is invested at
(a) 8%, compounded annually
(b) 8%, compounded continuously?

---

*Note that the annual percentage yield is also called the **effective annual rate.**

Solution

(a) We solve for n in $\$20{,}000 = \$10{,}000(1 + 0.08)^n$.

$$2 = 1.08^n$$

Taking the logarithm, base e, of both sides of the equation gives

$$\ln 2 = \ln 1.08^n$$
$$\ln 2 = n \ln 1.08 \quad \text{Logarithm Property V}$$
$$n = \frac{\ln 2}{\ln 1.08} \approx 9.0 \ (\text{years})$$

(b) Solve for t in $\$20{,}000 = \$10{,}000 e^{0.08t}$.

$$2 = e^{0.08t} \qquad \text{Isolate the exponential.}$$
$$\ln 2 = \ln e^{0.08t} \qquad \text{Take "ln" of both sides.}$$
$$\ln 2 = 0.08t \qquad \text{Logarithm Property I}$$
$$t = \frac{\ln 2}{0.08} \approx 8.7 \ (\text{years})$$

Spreadsheet Note

To understand better the effect of compounding periods on an investment, we can use a spreadsheet to compare different compounding schemes. Table 6.3 shows a spreadsheet that tracks the growth at 5-year intervals of a $100 investment for quarterly compounding and continuous compounding (both at 10%).

| TABLE 6.3 |

COMPARISON OF TWO INVESTMENTS WITH DIFFERENT COMPOUNDING SCHEMES

	A	B	C
1	Year	S=100(1.025)^(4n)	S=100*exp(.10n)
2	5	163.86	164.87
3	10	268.51	271.83
4	15	439.98	448.17
5	20	720.96	738.91
6	25	1181.37	1218.25
7	30	1935.81	2008.55

Also, most spreadsheets (including Excel) and some calculators have built-in finance packages that can be used to solve the compound interest problems of this section and later sections of this chapter. See Appendix D, Section 6.2, and the Online Excel Guide for details.

CHECKPOINT

6. How long does it take $5000 to double if it is invested at 9% compounded monthly?

Geometric Sequences

If $\$P$ is invested at an interest rate of i per period, compounded at the end of each period, the future value at the end of each succeeding period is

$$P(1 + i), P(1 + i)^2, P(1 + i)^3, \ldots, P(1 + i)^n, \ldots$$

The future values for each of the succeeding periods form a sequence in which each term (after the first) is found by multiplying the previous term by the same number. Such a sequence is called a **geometric sequence.**

Geometric Sequence

A sequence is called a **geometric sequence** (progression) if there exists a number r, called the **common ratio,** such that

$$a_n = ra_{n-1} \quad \text{for } n > 1$$

Geometric sequences form the foundation for other applications involving compound interest.

EXAMPLE 10   **Geometric Sequences**

Write the next three terms of the following geometric sequences.
(a) $1, 3, 9, \ldots$ (b) $4, 2, 1, \ldots$ (c) $3, -6, 12, \ldots$

Solution
(a) The common ratio is 3, so the next three terms are $27, 81, 243$.
(b) The common ratio is $\frac{1}{2}$, so the next three terms are $\frac{1}{2}, \frac{1}{4}, \frac{1}{8}$.
(c) The common ratio is -2, so the next three terms are $-24, 48, -96$.

Because each term after the first in a geometric sequence is obtained by multiplying the previous term by r, the second term is $a_1 r$, the third is $a_1 r^2$, etc., and the nth term is $a_1 r^{n-1}$. Thus we have the following formula.

---

nth Term of a Geometric Sequence

The **nth term of a geometric sequence** (progression) is given by

$$a_n = a_1 r^{n-1}$$

where a_1 is the first term of the sequence and r is the common ratio.

EXAMPLE 11   **nth Term of a Geometric Sequence**

Find the seventh term of the geometric sequence with first term 5 and common ratio -2.

Solution
The seventh term is $a_7 = 5(-2)^{7-1} = 5(64) = 320$.

EXAMPLE 12   **Ball Rebounding**

A ball is dropped from a height of 125 feet. If it rebounds $\frac{3}{5}$ of the height from which it falls every time it hits the ground, how high will it bounce after it strikes the ground for the fifth time?

Solution
The first rebound is $\frac{3}{5}(125) = 75$ feet; the second rebound is $\frac{3}{5}(75) = 45$ feet. The heights of the rebounds form a geometric sequence with first term 75 and common ratio $\frac{3}{5}$. Thus the fifth term is

$$a_5 = 75\left(\frac{3}{5}\right)^4 = 75\left(\frac{81}{625}\right) = \frac{243}{25} = 9\frac{18}{25} \text{ feet}$$

Sum of a Geometric Sequence
Next we develop a formula for the sum of a geometric sequence, a formula that is important in our study of annuities. The sum of the first n terms of a geometric sequence is

$$s_n = a_1 + a_1 r + a_1 r^2 + \cdots + a_1 r^{n-1} \qquad (1)$$

If we multiply Equation (1) by r, we have

$$r s_n = a_1 r + a_1 r^2 + a_1 r^3 + \cdots + a_1 r^n \qquad (2)$$

Subtracting Equation (2) from Equation (1), we obtain

$$s_n - r s_n = a_1 + (a_1 r - a_1 r) + (a_1 r^2 - a_1 r^2) + \cdots + (a_1 r^{n-1} - a_1 r^{n-1}) - a_1 r^n$$

Thus

$$s_n(1 - r) = a_1 - a_1 r^n \qquad \text{so} \qquad s_n = \frac{a_1 - a_1 r^n}{1 - r} \quad \text{if } r \neq 1$$

This gives the following.

Sum of a Geometric Sequence	The **sum of the first n terms of the geometric sequence** with first term a_1 and common ratio r is $$s_n = \frac{a_1(1 - r^n)}{1 - r} \quad \text{provided that } r \neq 1$$

EXAMPLE 13   Sums of Geometric Sequences

(a) Find the sum of the first five terms of the geometric progression with first term 4 and common ratio -3.

(b) Find the sum of the first six terms of the geometric sequence $\frac{1}{4}, \frac{1}{8}, \frac{1}{16}, \dots$.

Solution

(a) We are given that $n = 5$, $a_1 = 4$, and $r = -3$. Thus

$$s_5 = \frac{4[1 - (-3)^5]}{1 - (-3)} = \frac{4[1 - (-243)]}{4} = 244$$

(b) We know that $n = 6$, $a_1 = \frac{1}{4}$, and $r = \frac{1}{2}$. Thus

$$s_6 = \frac{\frac{1}{4}[1 - (\frac{1}{2})^6]}{1 - \frac{1}{2}} = \frac{\frac{1}{4}(1 - \frac{1}{64})}{\frac{1}{2}} = \frac{1 - \frac{1}{64}}{2} = \frac{64 - 1}{128} = \frac{63}{128}$$

CHECKPOINT

7. Identify any geometric sequences among the following.
   (a) $1, 4, 9, 16, \dots$
   (b) $1, 4, 7, 10, \dots$
   (c) $1, 4, 16, 64, \dots$

8. (a) Find the 40th term of the geometric sequence $8, 6, \frac{9}{2}, \dots$.
   (b) Find the sum of the first 20 terms of the geometric sequence $2, 6, 18, \dots$.

CHECKPOINT SOLUTIONS

1. (a) $m = 4$ (b) $n = m \cdot t = 4 \cdot 5 = 20$ (c) $i = \dfrac{r}{m} = \dfrac{0.06}{4} = 0.015$
   (d) $S = P(1 + i)^n = \$5000(1 + 0.015)^{20} \approx \$6734.28$, to the nearest cent

2. $i = 0.09/12 = 0.0075$ and $n = (5)(12) = 60$

$$\$12{,}000 = P(1 + 0.0075)^{60} = P(1.5656810270)$$
$$P = \$12{,}000/1.565681027 = \$7664.40, \text{ to the nearest cent}$$

3. (a) Periodic compounding
   (b) Continuous compounding

4. $S = Pe^{rt} = \$5000e^{(0.06)(5)} = \$5000e^{0.3} \approx \$6749.29$, to the nearest cent

5. $i = 0.07/2 = 0.035$ and $m = 2$

$$\text{APY} = (1 + 0.035)^2 - 1 \approx 0.0712, \text{ or } 7.12\%$$

6. With $i = 0.09/12 = 0.0075$, we solve for n in

$$\$10{,}000 = \$5000(1 + 0.0075)^n$$
$$2 = (1.0075)^n$$
$$\ln(2) = \ln(1.0075)^n = n\ln(1.0075)$$
$$\frac{\ln(2)}{\ln(1.0075)} = n \quad \text{so} \quad n \approx 92.8 \text{ months}$$

7. Only sequence (c) is geometric with common ratio $r = 4$.

8. (a) $a_{40} = a_1 r^{40-1} = 8\left(\dfrac{3}{4}\right)^{39} \approx 0.0001$

(b) $s_{20} = \dfrac{a_1(1 - r^{20})}{1 - r} = \dfrac{2(1 - 3^{20})}{1 - 3} = -(1 - 3^{20})$

$$= 3^{20} - 1 = 3{,}486{,}784{,}400$$

| EXERCISES | 6.2

COMPOUND INTEREST

In Problems 1–4, find the requested value and identify each of the other values as the periodic rate, the number of periods, the principal, or the future value.

1. Find S: $S = 2000(1 + 0.02)^{24}$
2. Find S: $S = 15{,}000(1 + 0.005)^{360}$
3. Find P: $25{,}000 = P(1 + 0.03)^{48}$
4. Find P: $100{,}000 = P(1 + 0.06)^{25}$

For each investment situation in Problems 5–8, identify (a) the annual interest rate, (b) the length of the investment in years, (c) the periodic interest rate, and (d) the number of periods of the investment.

5. 8% compounded quarterly for 7 years
6. 12% compounded monthly for 3 years
7. 9% compounded monthly for 5 years
8. 10% compounded semiannually for 8 years
9. Find the future value if $8000 is invested for 10 years at 12% compounded annually.
10. What is the future value if $8600 is invested for 8 years at 10% compounded semiannually?
11. What are the future value and the interest earned if $3200 is invested for 5 years at 8% compounded quarterly?
12. What interest will be earned if $6300 is invested for 3 years at 12% compounded monthly?
13. What lump sum do parents need to deposit in an account earning 10%, compounded monthly, so that it will grow to $80,000 for their son's college tuition in 18 years?
14. What lump sum should be deposited in an account that will earn 9%, compounded quarterly, to grow to $300,000 for retirement in 25 years?
15. What present value amounts to $10,000 if it is invested for 10 years at 6% compounded annually?
16. What present value amounts to $300,000 if it is invested at 7%, compounded semiannually, for 15 years?
17. Find the future value if $5100 is invested for 4 years at 9% compounded continuously.
18. Find the interest that will result if $8000 is invested at 7%, compounded continuously, for 8 years.
19. What is the compound interest if $410 is invested for 10 years at 8% compounded continuously?
20. If $8000 is invested at 8.5% compounded continuously, find the future value after $4\frac{1}{2}$ years.

21. Grandparents want to make a gift of $100,000 for their grandchild's 20th birthday. How much would have to be invested on the day of their grandchild's birth if their investment could earn
    (a) 10.5% compounded continuously
    (b) 11% compounded continuously?
    (c) Describe the effect that this slight change in the interest rate makes over the 20 years of this investment.
22. Suppose an individual wants to have $200,000 available for her child's education. Find the amount that would have to be invested at 12%, compounded continuously, if the number of years until college is
    (a) 7 years   (b) 14 years.
    (c) Does leaving the money invested twice as long mean that only half as much is needed initially? Explain why or why not.
23. Which investment will earn more money, a $1000 investment for 5 years at 8% compounded annually or a $1000 investment for 5 years compounded continuously at 7%?
24. How much more interest will be earned if $5000 is invested for 6 years at 7% compounded continuously, instead of at 7% compounded quarterly?
25. Find the annual percentage yield for an investment at
    (a) 7.3% compounded monthly
    (b) 6% compounded continuously.
26. What is the annual percentage yield (or effective annual rate) for a nominal rate of (a) 8.4% compounded quarterly and (b) 10% compounded continuously?

In Problems 27 and 28, rank each interest rate and compounding scheme in order from highest yield to lowest yield.

27. 8% compounded quarterly, 8% compounded monthly, 8% compounded annually
28. 6% compounded continuously, 6% compounded semiannually, 6% compounded monthly
29. Two different investment companies offer college savings plans, one at 8.2% compounded continuously and the other at 8.4% compounded quarterly. Which is the better investment?
30. For life insurance policies, some of the premium pays for the cost of the insurance, and the remainder goes toward the cash value of the policy and earns interest like a savings account. Suppose that, on the cash value

of their policies, one insurance company pays 4.8% compounded monthly and another pays 4.82% compounded semiannually. Which company offers a higher yield?

31. The figure shows a graph of the future value of $100 at 8% compounded annually, along with the graph of $100 at 8% compounded continuously. Which is which? Explain.

32. The figure shows a graph of the future value of $350 at 6% compounded monthly, along with the graph of $350 at 6% compounded annually. Which is which? Explain.

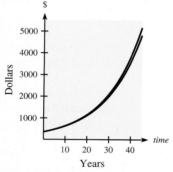

33. Microsoft's stock price peaked at 6118% of its I.P.O. price more than 13 years after the I.P.O. (*Source:* Bloomberg Financial Markets). Suppose that $10,000 invested in Microsoft at its I.P.O. price had been worth $600,000 (6000% of the I.P.O. price) after exactly 13 years. What interest rate, compounded annually, does this represent?

34. If $10,000 had been invested in the Sagamore Capital Opportunity Fund on September 30, 2000, it would have been worth $46,649.55 on September 30, 2010. What interest rate, compounded annually, did this investment earn?

35. How long (in years) would $700 have to be invested at 11.9%, compounded continuously, to earn $300 interest?

36. How long (in years) would $600 have to be invested at 8%, compounded continuously, to amount to $970?

37. At what nominal rate, compounded quarterly, would $20,000 have to be invested to amount to $26,425.82 in 7 years?

38. At what nominal rate, compounded annually, would $10,000 have to be invested to amount to $14,071 in 7 years?

39. For her 1st birthday, Polly's grandparents invested $1000 in an 18-year certificate for her that pays 8%

compounded annually. How much will the certificate be worth on Polly's 19th birthday?

40. To help their son buy a car on his 16th birthday, a boy's parents invest $7500 on his 10th birthday. If the investment pays 9% compounded continuously, how much is available on his 16th birthday?

41. (a) A 40-year-old man has $432,860 in an IRA account. He decides to make no additional contributions to the account but expects it to grow at 7.5% compounded annually. How much does he expect to have in the account when he retires at age 62?

    (b) How much more money would the man have if his investments earned 8.5% compounded annually?

42. (a) The purchase of Alaska cost the United States $7 million in 1869. If this money had been placed in a savings account paying 6% compounded annually, how much money would be available from this investment in 2010?

    (b) If the $7 million earned 7% compounded annually since 1869, how much would be available in 2010?

    (c) Do you think either amount would purchase Alaska in 2010? Explain in light of the value of Alaska's resources or perhaps the price per acre of land.

43. A couple needs $15,000 as a down payment for a home. If they invest the $10,000 they have at 8% compounded quarterly, how long will it take for the money to grow into $15,000?

44. How long does it take for an account containing $8000 to be worth $15,000 if the money is invested at 9% compounded monthly?

45. Mary Stahley invested $2500 in a 36-month certificate of deposit (CD) that earned 8.5% annual simple interest. When the CD matured, she invested the full amount in a mutual fund that had an annual growth equivalent to 18% compounded annually. How much was the mutual fund worth after 9 years?

46. Suppose Patrick Goldsmith deposited $1000 in an account that earned simple interest at an annual rate of 7% and left it there for 4 years. At the end of the 4 years, Patrick deposited the entire amount from that account into a new account that earned 7% compounded quarterly. He left the money in this account for 6 years. How much did he have after the 10 years?

In Problems 47 and 48, use a spreadsheet or financial program on a calculator or computer.

47. Track the future values of two investments of $5000, one at 6.3% compounded quarterly and another at 6.3% compounded monthly for each interest payment period for 10 years.

    (a) How long does it take each investment to be worth more than $7500?

    (b) What are the values of each investment after 3 years, 7 years, and 10 years?

48. Track the future values of two investments of $1000, one at 6.0% compounded semiannually and one at 6.6% compounded semiannually for each interest payment period for 25 years.

(a) How long before the difference between these investments is $50?

(b) How much sooner does the 6.6% investment reach $1500?

GEOMETRIC SEQUENCES

For each geometric sequence given in Problems 49 and 50, write the next three terms.

49. (a) 3, 6, 12, . . .
    (b) 81, 54, 36, . . .
50. (a) 4, 12, 36, . . .
    (b) 32, 40, 50, . . .

In Problems 51–60, write an expression that gives the requested term or sum.

51. The 13th term of the geometric sequence with first term 10 and common ratio 2

52. The 11th term of the geometric sequence with first term 6 and common ratio 3

53. The 16th term of the geometric sequence with first term 4 and common ratio $\frac{3}{2}$

54. The 20th term of the geometric sequence with first term 3 and common ratio -2

55. The sum of the first 17 terms of the geometric sequence with first term 6 and common ratio 3

56. The sum of the first 14 terms of the geometric sequence with first term 3 and common ratio 4

57. The sum of the first 35 terms of the geometric sequence 1, 3, 9, . . .

58. The sum of the first 14 terms of the geometric sequence 16, 64, 256, . . .

59. The sum of the first 18 terms of the geometric sequence 6, 4, $\frac{8}{3}$, . . .

60. The sum of the first 31 terms of the geometric sequence 9, -6, 4, . . .

APPLICATIONS

61. *Inflation* A house that 20 years ago was worth $160,000 has increased in value by 4% each year because of inflation. What is its worth today?

62. *Inflation* If inflation causes the cost of automobiles to increase by 3% each year, what should a car cost today if it cost $25,000 6 years ago?

63. *Population growth* Suppose a country has a population of 20 million and projects a growth rate of 2% per year for the next 20 years. What will the population of this country be in 10 years?

64. *Spread of AIDS* Suppose a country is so devastated by the AIDS epidemic that its population decreases by 0.5% each year for a 4-year period. If the population was originally 10 million, what is the population at the end of the 4-year period?

65. *Population growth* If the rate of growth of a population continues at 2%, in how many years will the population double?

66. *Population* If a population of 8 million begins to increase at a rate of 0.1% each month, in how many months will it be 10 million?

67. *Ball rebounding* A ball is dropped from a height of 128 feet. If it rebounds $\frac{3}{4}$ of the height from which it falls every time it hits the ground, how high will it bounce after it strikes the ground for the fourth time?

68. *Water pumping* A pump removes $\frac{1}{3}$ of the water in a container with every stroke. What amount of water is still in a container after 5 strokes if it originally contained 81 cm^3?

69. *Depreciation* A machine is valued at $10,000. If the depreciation at the end of each year is 20% of its value at the beginning of the year, find its value at the end of 4 years.

70. *Profit* Suppose a new business makes a $1000 profit in its first month and has its profit increase by 10% each month for the next 2 years. How much profit will the business earn in its 12th month?

71. *Bacterial growth* The size of a certain bacteria culture doubles each hour. If the number of bacteria present initially is 5000, how many would be present at the end of 6 hours?

72. *Bacterial growth* If a bacteria culture increases by 20% every hour and 2000 are present initially, how many will be present at the end of 10 hours?

73. *Profit* If changing market conditions cause a company earning $8,000,000 in 2005 to project a loss of 2% of its profit in each of the next 5 years, what profit does it project in 2010?

74. *Profit* Suppose a new business makes a $1000 profit in its first month and has its profit increase by 10% each month for the next 2 years. How much profit will it earn in its first year?

75. *Chain letters* Suppose you receive a chain letter with six names on it, and to keep the chain unbroken, you are to mail a dime to the person whose name is at the top, cross out the top name, add your name to the bottom, and mail it to five friends. If your friends mail out five letters each, and no one breaks the chain, you will eventually receive dimes. How many sets of mailings before your name is at the top of the list to receive dimes? How many dimes would you receive? (This is a geometric sequence with first term 5.)

76. *Chain letters* Mailing chain letters that involve sending money has been declared illegal because most people would receive nothing while a comparative few would profit. Suppose the chain letter in Problem 75 were to go through 12 unbroken progressions.
    (a) How many people would receive money?
    (b) How much money would these people receive as a group?

77. *Chain letters* How many letters would be mailed if the chain letter in Problem 75 went through 12 unbroken progressions?

- To compute the future values of ordinary annuities and annuities due
- To compute the payments required in order for ordinary annuities and annuities due to have specified future values
- To compute the payment required to establish a sinking fund
- To find how long it will take to reach a savings goal

Future Values of Annuities

| APPLICATION PREVIEW |

Twins graduate from college together and start their careers. Twin 1 invests $2000 at the end of each of 8 years in an account that earns 10%, compounded annually. After the initial 8 years, no additional contributions are made, but the investment continues to earn 10%, compounded annually. Twin 2 invests no money for 8 years but then contributes $2000 at the end of each year for a period of 36 years (to age 65) to an account that pays 10%, compounded annually. How much money does each twin have at age 65? (See Example 2 and Example 3.)

In this section we consider ordinary annuities and annuities due, and we develop a formula for each type of annuity that allows us to find its future value—that is, a formula for the value of the account after regular deposits have been made over a period of time.

Each twin's contributions form an annuity. An **annuity** is a financial plan characterized by regular payments. We can view an annuity as a savings plan in which the regular payments are contributions to the account, and then we can ask what the total value of the account will become (as in the Application Preview). Also, we can view an annuity as a payment plan (such as for retirement) in which regular payments are made from an account, often to an individual.

Ordinary Annuities   Most people save (or invest) money by depositing relatively small amounts at different times. If a depositor makes equal deposits at regular intervals, he or she is contributing to an annuity. The payments (deposits) may be made weekly, monthly, quarterly, yearly, or at any other interval of time. The sum of all payments plus all interest earned is called the **future amount of the annuity** or its **future value.**

In this text we will deal with annuities in which the payments begin and end on fixed dates, and we will deal first with annuities in which the payments are made at the end of each of the equal payment intervals. This type of annuity is called an **ordinary annuity** (and also an **annuity immediate**). The ordinary annuities we will consider have payment intervals that coincide with the compounding period of the interest.

Suppose you invested $100 at the end of each year for 5 years in an account that paid interest at 10%, compounded annually. How much money would you have in the account at the end of the 5 years?

Because you are making payments at the end of each period (year), this annuity is an ordinary annuity.

To find the future value of your annuity at the end of the 5 years, we compute the future value of each payment separately and add the amounts (see Figure 6.3). The $100 invested *at the end* of the first year will draw interest for 4 years, so it will amount to $100(1.10)^4$. Figure 6.3 shows similar calculations for years 2–4. The $100 invested at the end of the fifth year will draw no interest, so it will amount to $100.

Thus the future value of the annuity is given by

$$S = 100 + 100(1.10) + 100(1.10)^2 + 100(1.10)^3 + 100(1.10)^4$$

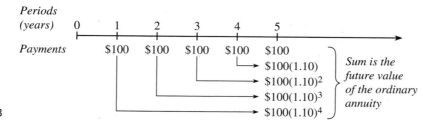

Figure 6.3

The terms of this sum are the first five values of the geometric sequence having $a_1 = 100$ and $r = 1.10$. Thus

$$S = \frac{100[1 - (1.10)^5]}{1 - 1.10} = \frac{100(-0.61051)}{-0.10} = 610.51$$

Thus the investment ($100 at the end of each year for 5 years, at 10%, compounded annually) would return $610.51.

Because every such annuity will take the same form, we can state that if a periodic payment R is made for n periods at an interest rate i *per period*, the **future amount of the annuity**, or its **future value**, will be given by

$$S = R \cdot \frac{1 - (1 + i)^n}{1 - (1 + i)} \qquad \text{or} \qquad S = R\left[\frac{(1 + i)^n - 1}{i}\right]$$

Future Value of an Ordinary Annuity	If R is deposited at the end of each period for n periods in an annuity that earns interest at a rate of i per period, the **future value of the annuity** will be $$S = R \cdot s_{\overline{n}|i} = R \cdot \left[\frac{(1 + i)^n - 1}{i}\right]$$ where $s_{\overline{n}|i}$ is read "s, n angle i" and represents the future value of an ordinary annuity of $1 per period for n periods with an interest rate of i per period.

The value of $s_{\overline{n}|i}$ can be computed directly with a calculator or found in Table I in Appendix A.

EXAMPLE 1   Future Value

Richard Lloyd deposits $200 at the end of each quarter in an account that pays 4%, compounded quarterly. How much money will he have in his account in $2\frac{1}{4}$ years?

Solution
The number of periods is $n = (4)(2.25) = 9$, and the rate *per period* is $i = 0.04/4 = 0.01$. At the end of $2\frac{1}{4}$ years the future value of the annuity will be

$$S = \$200 \cdot s_{\overline{9}|0.01} = \$200\left[\frac{(1 + 0.01)^9 - 1}{0.01}\right]$$
$$= \$200(9.368527) = \$1873.71, \text{ to the nearest cent}$$

Note that Table I in Appendix A also gives $s_{\overline{9}|0.01} = 9.368527$.

In the Application Preview, we described savings plans for twins. In the next two examples, we answer the questions posed in the Application Preview.

EXAMPLE 2   Future Value for Twin 2 | APPLICATION PREVIEW |

Twin 2 in the Application Preview invests $2000 at the end of each year for 36 years (until age 65) in an account that pays 10%, compounded annually. How much does twin 2 have at age 65?

Solution
This savings plan is an ordinary annuity with $i = 0.10$, $n = 36$, and $R = \$2000$. The future value (to the nearest dollar) is

$$S = R\left[\frac{(1 + i)^n - 1}{i}\right] = \$2000\left[\frac{(1.10)^{36} - 1}{0.10}\right] = \$598,254$$

EXAMPLE 3   Future Value for Twin 1 | APPLICATION PREVIEW |

Twin 1 invests $2000 at the end of each of 8 years in an account that earns 10%, compounded annually. After the initial 8 years, no additional contributions are made, but the investment continues to earn 10%, compounded annually, for 36 more years (until twin 1 is age 65). How much does twin 1 have at age 65?

Solution

We seek the future values of two different investments. The first is an ordinary annuity with $R = \$2000$, $n = 8$ periods, and $i = 0.10$. The second is a compound interest investment with $n = 36$ periods and $i = 0.10$ and whose principal (that is, its present value) is the future value of this twin's ordinary annuity.

We first find the future value of the ordinary annuity.

$$S = R\left[\frac{(1+i)^n - 1}{i}\right] = \$2000\left[\frac{(1+0.10)^8 - 1}{0.10}\right] \approx \$22{,}871.78$$

This amount is the principal of the compound interest investment. If no deposits or withdrawals were made for the next 36 years, the future value of this investment would be

$$S = P(1+i)^n = \$22{,}871.78(1+0.10)^{36} = \$707{,}028.03, \text{ to the nearest cent}$$

Thus, at age 65, twin 1's investment is worth about $707,028.

Looking back at Examples 2 and 3, we can extract the following summary and see which twin was the wiser.

	Contributions	Account Value at Age 65
Twin 1	$2000/year for 8 years = $16,000	$707,028
Twin 2	$2000/year for 36 years = $72,000	$598,254

Note that twin 1 contributed $56,000 less than twin 2 but had $108,774 more at age 65. This illustrates the powerful effect that time and compounding have on investments.

Calculator Note   Steps for finding the future value of an ordinary annuity with a graphing calculator are found in Appendix C, Section 6.3.

Figure 6.4 shows a comparison (each graphed as a smooth curve) of the future values of two annuities that are invested at 6% compounded monthly. One annuity has monthly payments of $100, and one has payments of $125. Note the impact of a slightly larger contribution on the future value of the annuity after 5 years, 10 years, 15 years, and 20 years. Of course, a slightly higher interest rate also can have a substantial impact over time; try a graphical comparison yourself.

Figure 6.4

Spreadsheet Note Excel can be used to find the future value of an ordinary annuity. See Appendix D, Section 6.3 or the Online Excel Guide. Excel also can be used to compare investments such as those compared graphically in Figure 6.4. Table 6.4 shows the future values at the end of every two years for the first 10 years of two ordinary annuities: one of $100 per month and a second of $125 per month and both at 6%, compounded monthly.

| TABLE 6.4 |

	A	B	C
1		Future Value for R = $100	Future Value for R = $125
2	End of Year #	at 6% compounded monthly	at 6% compounded monthly
3	2	2543.20	3178.99
4	4	5409.78	6762.23
5	6	8640.89	10,801.11
6	8	12,282.85	15,353.57
7	10	16,387.93	20,484.92

Sometimes we want to know how long it will take for an annuity to reach a desired future value.

EXAMPLE 4 **Time to Reach a Goal**

A small business invests $1000 at the end of each month in an account that earns 6% compounded monthly. How long will it take until the business has $100,000 toward the purchase of its own office building?

Solution

This is an ordinary annuity with $S = \$100{,}000$, $R = \$1000$, $i = 0.06/12 = 0.005$, and $n =$ the number of months. To answer the question of how long, solve for n.

Use $S = R\left[\dfrac{(1+i)^n - 1}{i}\right]$ and solve for n in $100{,}000 = 1000\left[\dfrac{(1+0.005)^n - 1}{0.005}\right]$.

This is an exponential equation. Hence, we isolate $(1.005)^n$, take the natural logarithm of both sides, and then solve for n as follows.

$$100{,}000 = \frac{1000}{0.005}\left[(1.005)^n - 1\right]$$
$$0.5 = (1.005)^n - 1$$
$$1.5 = (1.005)^n$$
$$\ln(1.5) = \ln\left[(1.005)^n\right] = n\left[\ln(1.005)\right]$$
$$n = \frac{\ln(1.5)}{\ln(1.005)} \approx 81.3$$

Because this investment is monthly, after 82 months the company will be able to purchase its own office building.

We can also find the periodic payment needed to obtain a specified future value.

EXAMPLE 5 **Payment for an Ordinary Annuity**

A young couple wants to save $50,000 over the next 5 years and then to use this amount as a down payment on a home. To reach this goal, how much money must they deposit at the end of each quarter in an account that earns interest at a rate of 5%, compounded quarterly?

Solution

This plan describes an ordinary annuity with a future value of $50,000 whose payment size, R, is to be determined. Quarterly compounding gives $n = 5(4) = 20$ and $i = 0.05/4 = 0.0125$.

$$S = R\left[\frac{(1 + i)^n - 1}{i}\right]$$

$$\$50{,}000 = R\left[\frac{(1 + 0.0125)^{20} - 1}{0.0125}\right] = R(22.56297854)$$

$$R = \frac{\$50{,}000}{22.56297854} = \$2216.02, \text{ to the nearest cent}$$

Sinking Funds

Just as the couple in Example 5 was saving for a future purchase, some borrowers, such as municipalities, may have a debt that must be paid in a single large sum on a specified future date. If these borrowers make periodic deposits that will produce that sum on a specified date, we say that they have established a **sinking fund.** If the deposits are all the same size and are made regularly, they form an ordinary annuity whose future value (on a specified date) is the amount of the debt. To find the size of these periodic deposits, we solve for R in the equation for the future value of an annuity:

$$S = R\left[\frac{(1 + i)^n - 1}{i}\right]$$

EXAMPLE 6   **Sinking Fund**

A company establishes a sinking fund to discharge a debt of $300,000 due in 5 years by making equal semiannual deposits, the first due in 6 months. If the deposits are placed in an account that pays 6%, compounded semiannually, what is the size of the deposits?

Solution

For this sinking fund, we want to find the payment size, R, given that the future value is $S = \$300{,}000$, $n = 2(5) = 10$, and $i = 0.06/2 = 0.03$. Thus we have

$$S = R\left[\frac{(1 + i)^n - 1}{i}\right]$$

$$\$300{,}000 = R\left[\frac{(1 + 0.03)^{10} - 1}{0.03}\right]$$

$$\$300{,}000 = R(11.463879)$$

$$\frac{\$300{,}000}{11.463879} = R \quad \text{so} \quad R = \$26{,}169.15$$

Thus the semiannual deposit is $26,169.15.

CHECKPOINT

1. Suppose that $500 is deposited at the end of every quarter for 6 years in an account that pays 8%, compounded quarterly.
   (a) What is the total number of payments (periods)?
   (b) What is the interest rate per period?
   (c) What formula is used to find the future value of the annuity?
   (d) Find the future value of the annuity.

2. A sinking fund of $100,000 is to be established with equal payments at the end of each half-year for 15 years. Find the amount of each payment if money is worth 10%, compounded semiannually.

Annuities Due

Deposits in savings accounts, rent payments, and insurance premiums are examples of **annuities due.** Unlike an ordinary annuity, an annuity due has the periodic payments made at the *beginning* of the period. The *term* of an annuity due is from the first payment to the end of one period after the last payment. Thus an annuity due draws interest for one period more than the ordinary annuity.

We can find the future value of an annuity due by treating each payment as though it were made at the *end* of the preceding period in an ordinary annuity. Then that amount, $Rs_{\overline{n}|i}$, remains in the account for one additional period (see Figure 6.5) and its future value is $Rs_{\overline{n}|i}(1 + i)$.

Figure 6.5

Thus the formula for the future value of an annuity due is as follows.

Future Value of an Annuity Due

$$S_{\text{due}} = Rs_{\overline{n}|i}(1 + i) = R\left[\frac{(1 + i)^n - 1}{i}\right](1 + i)$$

EXAMPLE 7   Future Value

Find the future value of an investment if $150 is deposited at the beginning of each month for 9 years and the interest rate is 7.2%, compounded monthly.

Solution

Because deposits are made at the *beginning* of each month, this is an annuity due with $R = \$150$, $n = 9(12) = 108$, and $i = 0.072/12 = 0.006$.

$$S_{\text{due}} = R\left[\frac{(1 + i)^n - 1}{i}\right](1 + i) = \$150\left[\frac{(1 + 0.006)^{108} - 1}{0.006}\right](1 + 0.006)$$

$$= \$150(151.3359308)(1.006) = \$22,836.59, \text{ to the nearest cent}$$

We can also use the formula for the future value of an annuity due to determine the payment size required to reach an investment goal.

EXAMPLE 8   Required Payment

Suppose a company wants to have $450,000 after $2\frac{1}{2}$ years to modernize its production equipment. How much of each previous quarter's profits should be deposited at the beginning of the current quarter to reach this goal, if the company's investment earns 6.8%, compounded quarterly?

Solution

We seek the payment size, R, for an annuity due with $S_{due} = \$450,000$, $n = (2.5)(4) = 10$, and $i = 0.068/4 = 0.017$.

$$S_{due} = R\left[\frac{(1 + i)^n - 1}{i}\right](1 + i)$$

$$\$450,000 = R\left[\frac{(1 + 0.017)^{10} - 1}{0.017}\right](1 + 0.017)$$

$$\$450,000 = R(10.80073308)(1.017) = (10.98434554)R$$

$$R = \frac{\$450,000}{10.98434554} = \$40,967.39, \text{ to the nearest cent}$$

Thus, the company needs to deposit about $40,967 at the beginning of each quarter for the next $2\frac{1}{2}$ years to reach its goal.

CHECKPOINT

3. Suppose $100 is deposited at the beginning of each month for 3 years in an account that pays 6%, compounded monthly.
   (a) What is the total number of payments (or periods)?
   (b) What is the interest rate per period?
   (c) What formula is used to find the future value of the annuity?
   (d) Find the future value.

CHECKPOINT SOLUTIONS

1. (a) $n = 4(6) = 24$ periods   (b) $i = 0.08/4 = 0.02$ per period

   (c) $S = R\left[\dfrac{(1 + i)^n - 1}{i}\right]$ for an ordinary annuity

   (d) $S = \$500\left[\dfrac{(1 + 0.02)^{24} - 1}{0.02}\right] = \$15,210.93$, to the nearest cent

2. Use $n = 2(15) = 30$, $i = 0.10/2 = 0.05$, and $S = \$100,000$ in the formula

   $$S = R\left[\frac{(1 + i)^n - 1}{i}\right]$$

   $$\$100,000 = R\left[\frac{(1 + 0.05)^{30} - 1}{0.05}\right] = R(66.4388475)$$

   $$\frac{\$100,000}{66.4388475} = R \text{ so } R = \$1505.14, \text{ to the nearest cent}$$

3. (a) $n = 3(12) = 36$ periods   (b) $i = 0.06/12 = 0.005$ per period

   (c) $S_{due} = R\left[\dfrac{(1 + i)^n - 1}{i}\right](1 + i)$ for an annuity due

   (d) $S_{due} = \$100\left[\dfrac{(1 + 0.005)^{36} - 1}{0.005}\right](1 + 0.005) = \$3953.28$, to the nearest cent

| EXERCISES | 6.3

ORDINARY ANNUITIES

In Problems 1–4, find the requested value (to the nearest dollar), and tell what each of the other values represents.

1. Find S: $S = 2500\left[\dfrac{(1 + 0.02)^{60} - 1}{0.02}\right]$

2. Find S: $S = 1000\left[\dfrac{(1 + 0.03)^{25} - 1}{0.03}\right]$

3. Find R: $80{,}000 = R\left[\dfrac{(1 + 0.04)^{30} - 1}{0.04}\right]$

4. Find R: $25{,}000 = R\left[\dfrac{(1 + 0.06)^{15} - 1}{0.06}\right]$

5. The figure shows a graph that compares the future values, at 8% compounded annually, of an annuity of $1000 per year and one of $1120 per year.
   (a) Decide which graph corresponds to which annuity.
   (b) Verify your conclusion to (a) by finding the value of each annuity and the difference between them at $t = 25$ years.

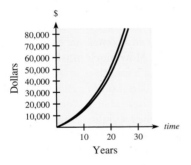

6. The figure shows a graph that compares the future values, at 9% compounded monthly, of an annuity of $50 per month and one of $60 per month.
   (a) Decide which graph corresponds to which annuity.
   (b) Use the graph to estimate (to the nearest 10 months) how long it will be before the larger annuity is $10,000 more than the smaller one.

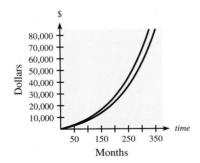

7. Find the future value of an annuity of $1300 paid at the end of each year for 5 years, if interest is earned at a rate of 6%, compounded annually.

8. Find the future value of an annuity of $5000 paid at the end of each year for 10 years, if it earns 9%, compounded annually.

9. Find the future value of an ordinary annuity of $80 paid quarterly for 3 years, if the interest rate is 8%, compounded quarterly.

10. Find the future value of an ordinary annuity of $300 paid quarterly for 5 years, if the interest rate is 12%, compounded quarterly.

11. The Weidmans want to save $40,000 in 2 years for a down payment on a house. If they make monthly deposits in an account paying 12%, compounded monthly, what is the size of the payments that are required to meet their goal?

12. A sinking fund is established to discharge a debt of $80,000 in 10 years. If deposits are made at the end of each 6-month period and interest is paid at the rate of 8%, compounded semiannually, what is the amount of each deposit?

13. If $2500 is deposited at the end of each quarter in an account that earns 5% compounded quarterly, after how many quarters will the account contain $80,000?

14. If $4000 is deposited at the end of each half year in an account that earns 6.2% compounded semiannually, how long will it be before the account contains $120,000?

15. When you establish a sinking fund, which interest rate is better? Explain.
    (a) 10%
    (b) 6%

16. If you set up a sinking fund, which interest rate is better? Explain.
    (a) 12% compounded monthly
    (b) 12% compounded annually

17. In this section's Application Preview, we considered the investment strategies of twins and found that starting early and stopping was a significantly better strategy than waiting, in terms of total contributions made as well as total value in the account at retirement. Suppose now that twin 1 invests $2000 at the end of each year for 10 years only (until age 33) in an account that earns 8%, compounded annually. Suppose that twin 2 waits until turning 40 to begin investing. How much must twin 2 put aside at the end of each year for the next 25 years in an account that earns 8% compounded annually in order to have the same amount as twin 1 at the end of these 25 years (when they turn 65)?

18. (a) Patty Stacey deposits $2000 at the end of each of 5 years in an IRA. If she leaves the money that has accumulated in the IRA account for 25 additional years, how much is in her account at the end of the 30-year period? Assume an interest rate of 9%, compounded annually.

(b) Suppose that Patty's husband delays starting an IRA for the first 10 years he works but then makes $2000 deposits at the end of each of the next 15 years. If the interest rate is 9%, compounded annually, and if he leaves the money in his account for 5 additional years, how much will be in his account at the end of the 30-year period?

(c) Does Patty or her husband have more IRA money?

ANNUITIES DUE

19. Find the future value of an annuity due of $100 each quarter for $2\frac{1}{2}$ years at 12%, compounded quarterly.

20. Find the future value of an annuity due of $1500 each month for 3 years if the interest rate is 12%, compounded monthly.

21. Find the future value of an annuity due of $200 paid at the beginning of each 6-month period for 8 years if the interest rate is 6%, compounded semiannually.

22. A house is rented for $3600 per quarter, with each quarter's rent payable in advance. If money is worth 8%, compounded quarterly, and the rent is deposited in an account, what is the future value of the rent for one year?

23. How much must be deposited at the beginning of each year in an account that pays 8%, compounded annually, so that the account will contain $24,000 at the end of 5 years?

24. What is the size of the payments that must be deposited at the beginning of each 6-month period in an account that pays 7.8%, compounded semiannually, so that the account will have a future value of $120,000 at the end of 15 years?

MISCELLANEOUS PROBLEMS

In Problems 25–40, (a) state whether the problem relates to an ordinary annuity or an annuity due, and then (b) solve the problem.

25. Parents agree to invest $500 (at 10%, compounded semiannually) for their son on the December 31 or June 30 following each semester that he makes the dean's list during his 4 years in college. If he makes the dean's list in each of the 8 semesters, how much money will his parents have to give him when he graduates?

26. Jake Werkheiser decides to invest $2000 in an IRA at the end of each year for the next 10 years. If he makes these investments, and if the certificates pay 12%, compounded annually, how much will he have at the end of the 10 years?

27. How much will have to be invested at the beginning of each year at 10%, compounded annually, to pay off a debt of $50,000 in 8 years?

28. If $1000 is deposited at the beginning of each quarter into an account that earns 8%, compounded quarterly, how long until the account contains $31,000?

29. A family wants to have a $200,000 college fund for their children at the end of 20 years. What contribution must be made at the end of each quarter if their investment pays 7.6%, compounded quarterly?

30. What payment must be put in an account at the end of each quarter to establish an ordinary annuity that has a future value of $50,000 in 14 years, if the investment pays 12%, compounded quarterly?

31. A couple has determined that they need $300,000 to establish an annuity when they retire in 25 years. How much money should they deposit at the end of each month in an investment plan that pays 10%, compounded monthly, so they will have the $300,000 in 25 years?

32. Sam deposits $500 at the end of every 6 months in an account that pays 8%, compounded semiannually. How much will he have at the end of 8 years?

33. Mr. Gordon plans to invest $300 at the end of each month in an account that pays 9%, compounded monthly. After how many months will the account be worth $50,000?

34. For 3 years, $400 is placed in a savings account at the beginning of each 6-month period. If the account pays interest at 10%, compounded semiannually, how much will be in the account at the end of the 3 years?

35. Grandparents plan to open an account on their grandchild's birthday and contribute each month until she goes to college. How much must they contribute at the beginning of each month in an investment that pays 12%, compounded monthly, if they want the balance to be $180,000 at the end of 18 years?

36. How much money should a couple deposit at the end of each month in an investment plan that pays 7.5%, compounded monthly, so they will have $800,000 in 30 years?

37. Jane Adele deposits $500 in an account at the beginning of each 3-month period for 9 years. If the account pays interest at the rate of 8%, compounded quarterly, how much will she have in her account after 9 years?

38. A company establishes a sinking fund to discharge a debt of $750,000 due in 8 years by making equal semiannual deposits, the first due in 6 months. If the investment pays 12%, compounded semiannually, what is the size of the deposits?

39. A sinking fund is established by a working couple so that they will have $60,000 to pay for part of their daughter's education when she enters college. If they make deposits at the end of each 3-month period for 10 years, and if interest is paid at 12%, compounded quarterly, what size deposits must they make?

40. A property owner has several rental units and wants to build more. How much of each month's rental income should be deposited at the beginning of each month in an account that earns 6.6%, compounded monthly, if the goal is to have $100,000 at the end of 4 years?

41. Suppose a recent college graduate's first job allows her to deposit $100 at the end of each month in a savings plan that earns 9%, compounded monthly. This savings plan continues for 8 years before new obligations make it impossible to continue. If the accrued amount remains in the plan for the next 15 years without deposits or withdrawals, how much money will be in the account 23 years after the plan began?

42. Suppose a young couple deposits $1000 at the end of each quarter in an account that earns 7.6%, compounded quarterly, for a period of 8 years. After the 8 years, they start a family and find they can contribute only $200 per quarter. If they leave the money from the first 8 years in the account and continue to contribute $200 at the end of each quarter for the next $18\frac{1}{2}$ years, how much will they have in the account (to help with their child's college expenses)?

43. A small business owner contributes $3000 at the end of each quarter to a retirement account that earns 8% compounded quarterly.
    (a) How long will it be until the account is worth $150,000?
    (b) Suppose when the account reaches $150,000, the business owner increases the contributions to $5000 at the end of each quarter. What will the total value of the account be after 15 more years?

44. A young executive deposits $300 at the end of each month for 8 years and then increases the deposits. If the account earns 7.2%, compounded monthly, how much (to the nearest dollar) should each new deposit be in order to have a total of $400,000 after 25 years?

 In Problems 45 and 46, use a spreadsheet or financial program on a calculator or computer.

45. Compare the future value of an ordinary annuity of $100 per month and that of an annuity due of $100 per month if each is invested at 7.2%, compounded monthly. Find the amount in each account at the end of each month for 10 years.
    (a) How much is contributed to each annuity?
    (b) Which account has more money after 10 years? Explain why.

46. Investigate the effect that small differences in payment size can have over time. Consider two ordinary annuities, both of which earn 8% compounded quarterly, one with payments of $100 at the end of each quarter and one with payments of $110 at the end of each quarter. Track the future value of each annuity at the end of each quarter for a period of 25 years.
    (a) How much is contributed to each annuity after 10 years, 20 years, and 25 years?
    (b) What is the difference in the future values after 10 years, 20 years, and 25 years? Why are these amounts more than the differences in the amounts contributed?

OBJECTIVES   6.4

- To compute the present values of ordinary annuities, annuities due, and deferred annuities
- To compute the payments from various annuities
- To find how long an annuity will last
- To apply present values to bond pricing

Present Values of Annuities

▌| APPLICATION PREVIEW |▐

If you wanted to receive, at retirement, $1000 at the end of each month for 16 years, what lump sum would you need to invest in an annuity that paid 9%, compounded monthly? (See Example 2.) We call this lump sum the present value of the annuity. Note that the annuity in this case is an account from which a person receives equal periodic payments (withdrawals).

In this section, we will find present values of annuities, compute payments from annuities, and find how long annuities will last.

We have discussed how contributing to an annuity program will result in a sum of money, and we have called that sum the future value of the annuity. Just as the term *annuity* is used to describe an account in which a person makes equal periodic payments (deposits), this term is also used to describe an account from which a person receives equal periodic payments (withdrawals). That is, if you invest a lump sum of money in an account today, so that at regular intervals you will receive a fixed sum of money, you have established an annuity. The single sum of money required to purchase an annuity that will provide these payments at regular intervals is the **present value** of the annuity.

Ordinary Annuities

Suppose we wish to invest a lump sum of money (denoted by A_n) in an annuity that earns interest at rate i per period in order to receive (withdraw) payments of size $R from this account at the end of each of n periods (after which time the account balance will be $0). Recall that receiving payments at the end of each period means that this is an ordinary annuity.

To find a formula for A_n, we can find the present value of each future payment and then add these present values (see Figure 6.6).

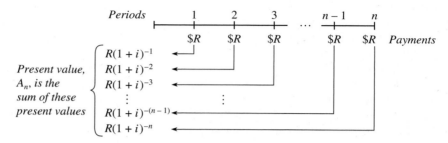

Figure 6.6

Figure 6.6 shows that we can express A_n as follows.

$$A_n = R(1 + i)^{-1} + R(1 + i)^{-2} + R(1 + i)^{-3} + \cdots + R(1 + i)^{-(n-1)} + R(1 + i)^{-n} \quad (1)$$

Multiplying both sides of equation (1) by $(1 + i)$ gives

$$(1 + i)A_n = R + R(1 + i)^{-1} + R(1 + i)^{-2} + \cdots + R(1 + i)^{-(n-2)} + R(1 + i)^{-(n-1)} \quad (2)$$

If we subtract Equation (1) from Equation (2), we obtain $iA_n = R - R(1 + i)^{-n}$. Then solving for A_n gives the following.

Present Value of an Ordinary Annuity

If a payment of $R is to be made at the end of each period for n periods from an account that earns interest at a rate of i per period, then the account is an **ordinary annuity,** and the **present value** is

$$A_n = R \cdot a_{\overline{n}|i} = R \cdot \left[\frac{1 - (1 + i)^{-n}}{i}\right]$$

where $a_{\overline{n}|i}$ represents the present value of an ordinary annuity of $1 per period for n periods, with an interest rate of i per period.

The values of $a_{\overline{n}|i}$ can be computed directly with a calculator or found in Table II in Appendix A.

EXAMPLE 1 **Present Value**

What is the present value of an annuity of $1500 payable at the end of each 6-month period for 2 years if money is worth 8%, compounded semiannually?

Solution

We are given that $R = \$1500$ and $i = 0.08/2 = 0.04$. Because a payment is made twice a year for 2 years, the number of periods is $n = (2)(2) = 4$. Thus,

$$A_n = R \cdot a_{\overline{4}|0.04} = \$1500\left[\frac{1 - (1 + 0.04)^{-4}}{0.04}\right] = \$1500(3.629895) \approx \$5444.84$$

If we had used Table II in Appendix A, we would have seen that $a_{\overline{4}|0.04}$, the present value of an ordinary annuity of $1 per period for 4 periods with an interest rate of $0.04 = 4\%$ per period, is 3.629895, and we would have obtained the same present value, $5444.84. ∎

EXAMPLE **2**   **Present Value** **| APPLICATION PREVIEW |**

Find the lump sum that one must invest in an annuity in order to receive $1000 at the end of each month for the next 16 years, if the annuity pays 9%, compounded monthly.

Solution

The sum we seek is the present value of an ordinary annuity, A_n, with $R = \$1000$, $i = 0.09/12 = 0.0075$, and $n = (16)(12) = 192$.

$$A_n = R\left[\frac{1 - (1 + i)^{-n}}{i}\right]$$

$$= \$1000\left[\frac{1 - (1.0075)^{-192}}{0.0075}\right] = \$1000(101.5727689) = \$101,572.77$$

Thus the required lump sum, to the nearest dollar, is $101,573.

Technology Note   The steps for finding the present value of an ordinary annuity with a calculator and with Excel are found in Appendices C and D, Section 6.4. See also the Online Excel Guide.

It is important to note that all annuities involve both periodic payments and a lump sum of money. It is whether this lump sum is in the present or in the future that distinguishes problems that use formulas for present values of annuities from those that use formulas for future values of annuities. In Example 2, the lump sum was needed now (in the present) to generate the $1000 payments, so we used the present value formula.

Figure 6.7 shows a graph that compares the present value of an annuity of $1000 per year at an interest rate of 6%, compounded annually, with the same annuity at an interest rate of 10%, compounded annually. Note the impact that the higher interest rate has on the present value needed to establish such an annuity for a longer period of time. Specifically, at 6% interest, a present value of more than $12,500 is needed to generate 25 years of $1000 payments, but at an interest rate of 10%, the necessary present value is less than $10,000.

Figure 6.7

Spreadsheet Note   The analysis shown graphically in Figure 6.7 can also be done with a spreadsheet, as Table 6.5 shows for years 5, 10, 15, 20, and 25.

| TABLE 6.5 |

PRESENT VALUE GIVING $R = \$1000$ FOR N YEARS

	A	B	C
1	Year number	at 6% compounded annually	at 10% compounded annually
2	5	$4212.36	$3790.79
3	10	$7360.09	$6144.57
4	15	$9712.25	$7606.08
5	20	$11469.92	$8513.56
6	25	$12783.36	$9077.04

Our graphical and spreadsheet comparisons in Figure 6.7 and Table 6.5 and those from other sections emphasize the truth of the saying "Time is money." We have seen that, given enough time, relatively small differences in contributions or in interest rates can result in substantial differences in amounts (both present and future values).

EXAMPLE 3 Payments from an Annuity

Suppose that a couple plans to set up an ordinary annuity with a $100,000 inheritance they received. What is the size of the quarterly payments they will receive for the next 6 years (while their children are in college) if the account pays 7%, compounded quarterly?

Solution

The $100,000 is the amount the couple has now, so it is the present value of an ordinary annuity whose payment size, R, we seek. Using present value $A_n = \$100,000$, $n = 6(4) = 24$, and $i = 0.07/4 = 0.0175$, we solve for R.

$$A_n = R\left[\frac{1 - (1 + i)^{-n}}{i}\right]$$

$$\$100,000 = R\left[\frac{1 - (1 + 0.0175)^{-24}}{0.0175}\right]$$

$$\$100,000 = R(19.46068565)$$

$$R = \frac{\$100,000}{19.46068565} \approx \$5138.57$$

CHECKPOINT

1. Suppose an annuity pays $2000 at the end of each 3-month period for $3\frac{1}{2}$ years and money is worth 4%, compounded quarterly.
   (a) What is the total number of periods?
   (b) What is the interest rate per period?
   (c) What formula is used to find the present value of the annuity?
   (d) Find the present value.
2. An inheritance of $400,000 will provide how much at the end of each year for the next 20 years, if money is worth 7%, compounded annually?

EXAMPLE 4 Number of Payments from an Annuity

An inheritance of $250,000 is invested at 9%, compounded monthly. If $2500 is withdrawn at the end of each month, how long will it be until the account balance is $0?

Solution

The regular withdrawals form an ordinary annuity with present value $A_n = \$250,000$, payment $R = \$2500$, $i = 0.09/12 = 0.0075$, and $n =$ the number of months.

Use $A_n = R\left[\dfrac{1 - (1 + i)^{-n}}{i}\right]$ and solve for n in $250,000 = 2500\left[\dfrac{1 - (1.0075)^{-n}}{0.0075}\right]$.

This is an exponential equation, and to solve it we isolate $(1.0075)^{-n}$ and then take the natural logarithm of both sides.

$$\frac{250,000(0.0075)}{2500} = 1 - (1.0075)^{-n}$$

$$0.75 = 1 - (1.0075)^{-n}$$

$$(1.0075)^{-n} = 0.25$$

$$\ln\left[(1.0075)^{-n}\right] = \ln(0.25) \quad \Rightarrow \quad -n\left[\ln(1.0075)\right] = \ln(0.25)$$

$$-n = \frac{\ln(0.25)}{\ln(1.0075)} \approx -185.5, \quad \text{so} \quad n \approx 185.5$$

Thus, the account balance will be $0 in 186 months.

Bond Pricing

Bonds represent a relatively safe investment similar to a bank certificate of deposit (CD), but unlike CDs (and like stocks), bonds can be traded. And, as is also true of stocks, the trading or market price of a bond may fluctuate.

Most commonly, bonds are issued by the government, corporations, or municipalities for periods of 10 years or longer. Bonds actually constitute a loan in which the issuer of the bond is the borrower, the bond holders (or purchasers) are the lenders, and the interest payments to the bond holders are called **coupons.** In the simplest case, a bond's issue price, or **par value,** is the same as its **maturity value,** and the coupons are paid semiannually.

For example, if a corporation plans to issue $5000 bonds at 6% semiannually, then the maturity value is $5000, the **coupon rate** is 6%, and each semiannual coupon payment will be

$$(\$5000)(0.06/2) = (\$5000)(0.03) = \$150$$

The coupons are paid at the end of every 6 months and constitute an ordinary annuity. At maturity, the bond holder receives the final coupon payment of $150 plus the $5000 maturity value of the bond.

Because the amount of the coupon is fixed by the coupon rate for the entire term of the bond, the market price of the bond is strongly influenced by current interest rates. If a $5000 bond pays a 6% coupon rate, but market interest rates are higher than that, an investor will typically invest in the bond only if the bond's price makes its rate of return comparable to the market rate. The rate of return that the investor requires in order to buy the bond is called the **yield rate.**

EXAMPLE 5   ### Bond Pricing

Suppose a 15-year corporate bond has a maturity value of $10,000 and coupons at 5% paid semiannually. If an investor wants to earn a yield of 7.2% compounded semiannually, what should he or she pay for this bond?

Solution

Each semiannual coupon payment is

$$(\$10,000)(0.05/2) = (\$10,000)(0.025) = \$250$$

Since the desired rate of return is 7.2% semiannually and the bond is for 15 years, we set $i = 0.072/2 = 0.036$ and $n = (15)(2) = 30$.

Then the market price of this bond is the sum of the present values found in (1) and (2) below.

(1) the principal (or present value) of a compound interest investment at $i = 0.036$ for $n = 30$ periods with future value $S = \$10,000$

$$S = P(1 + i)^n$$
$$\$10,000 = P(1 + 0.036)^{30} = P(1.036)^{30}$$
$$P = \frac{\$10,000}{(1.036)^{30}} \approx \$3461.05 \quad (\text{nearest cent})$$

(2) the present value of the ordinary annuity formed by the coupon payments of $R = \$250$ at $i = 0.036$ for $n = 30$ periods

$$A_n = R\left[\frac{1 - (1 + i)^{-n}}{i}\right]$$

$$A_n = \$250\left[\frac{1 - (1.036)^{-30}}{0.036}\right] \approx \$4540.94 \quad (\text{nearest cent})$$

Thus, to earn the desired 7.2% yield, the market price an investor should pay for this bond is

$$\text{Price} = \$3461.05 + \$4540.94 = \$8001.99$$

Note that in Example 5 the bond's market price is less than its maturity value. In this case the bond is said to be **selling at a discount.** This has to be the case in order for the yield rate to exceed the coupon rate. Similarly, if the yield rate is lower than the coupon rate, then the market price of the bond will exceed its maturity value. When this happens, the bond is said to be **selling at a premium.** In general, the market price of a bond moves in the opposite direction from current yield rates.

Annuities Due   Recall that an annuity due is one in which payments are made at the beginning of each period. This means that the present value of an annuity due of n payments (denoted $A_{(n,\text{due})}$) of R at interest rate i per period can be viewed as an initial payment of R plus the payment program for an ordinary annuity of $n - 1$ payments of R at interest rate i per period (see Figure 6.8).

Present Value of an Annuity Due

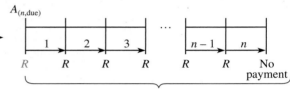

Figure 6.8   Present value of ordinary annuity with $n - 1$ payments, A_{n-1} Present value of annuity due with n payments, $R + A_{n-1}$

From Figure 6.8, we have

$$A_{(n,\text{due})} = R + A_{n-1} = R + R\left[\frac{1 - (1 + i)^{-(n-1)}}{i}\right]$$

$$= R\left[1 + \frac{1 - (1 + i)^{-(n-1)}}{i}\right] = R\left[\frac{i}{i} + \frac{1 - (1 + i)^{-(n-1)}}{i}\right]$$

$$= R\left[\frac{(1 + i) - (1 + i)^{-(n-1)}}{i}\right] = R(1 + i)\left[\frac{1 - (1 + i)^{-n}}{i}\right]$$

Thus we have the following formula for the present value of an annuity due.

Present Value of an Annuity Due	If a payment of R is to be made at the beginning of each period for n periods from an account that earns interest rate i per period, then the account is an **annuity due,** and its **present value** is given by $$A_{(n,\text{due})} = R\left[\frac{1 - (1 + i)^{-n}}{i}\right](1 + i) = Ra_{\overline{n}|i}(1 + i)$$ where $a_{\overline{n}|i}$ denotes the present value of an ordinary annuity of $1 per period for n periods at interest rate i per period.

EXAMPLE 6   Lottery Prize

A lottery prize worth $1,200,000 is awarded in payments of $10,000 at the beginning of each month for 10 years. Suppose money is worth 7.8%, compounded monthly. What is the *real* value of the prize?

Solution

The *real* value of this prize is its present value when it is awarded. That is, it is the present value of an annuity due with $R = \$10,000$, $i = 0.078/12 = 0.0065$, and $n = 12(10) = 120$.

Thus

$$A_{(120,\text{due})} = \$10,000\left[\frac{1 - (1 + 0.0065)^{-120}}{0.0065}\right](1 + 0.0065)$$

$$= \$10,000(83.1439199)(1.0065) = \$836,843.55, \text{ to the nearest cent.}$$

This means the lottery operator needs this amount to generate the 120 monthly payments of $10,000 each.

EXAMPLE 7   Court Settlement Payments

Suppose that a court settlement results in a $750,000 award. If this is invested at 9%, compounded semiannually, how much will it provide at the beginning of each half-year for a period of 7 years?

Solution

Because payments are made at the beginning of each half-year, this is an annuity due. We seek the payment size, R, and use the present value $A_{(n,\text{due})} = \$750,000$, $n = 2(7) = 14$, and $i = 0.09/2 = 0.045$.

$$A_{(n,\text{due})} = R\left[\frac{1 - (1 + i)^{-n}}{i}\right](1 + i)$$

$$\$750,000 = R\left[\frac{1 - (1 + 0.045)^{-14}}{0.045}\right](1 + 0.045)$$

$$\$750,000 \approx R(10.22282528)(1.045) \approx R(10.682852)$$

$$R = \frac{\$750,000}{10.682852} = \$70,205.97, \text{ to the nearest cent}$$

CHECKPOINT

3. What lump sum will be needed to generate payments of $5000 at the beginning of each quarter for a period of 5 years if money is worth 7%, compounded quarterly?

Deferred Annuities

A **deferred annuity** is one in which the first payment is made not at the beginning or end of the first period, but at some later date. An annuity that is deferred for k periods and then has payments of $R per period at the end of each of the next n periods is an ordinary deferred annuity and can be illustrated by Figure 6.9.

Deferred Annuity

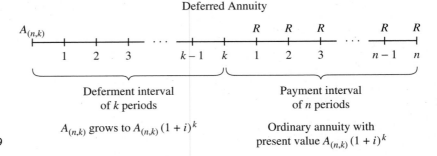

Figure 6.9

We now consider how to find the present value of such a deferred annuity when the interest rate is i per period. If payment is deferred for k periods, then the present value deposited now, denoted by $A_{(n,k)}$, is a compound interest investment for these k periods, and its future value is $A_{(n,k)}(1 + i)^k$. This amount then becomes the present value of the ordinary annuity for the next n periods. From Figure 6.9, we see that we have two equivalent expressions for the amount at the beginning of the first payment period.

$$A_{(n,k)}(1 + i)^k = R\left[\frac{1 - (1 + i)^{-n}}{i}\right]$$

Multiplying both sides by $(1 + i)^{-k}$ gives the following.

| **Present Value of a Deferred Annuity** | The **present value of a deferred annuity** of R per period for n periods, deferred for k periods with interest rate i per period, is given by $$A_{(n,k)} = R\left[\frac{1 - (1 + i)^{-n}}{i}\right](1 + i)^{-k} = Ra_{\overline{n}|i}(1 + i)^{-k}$$ |

EXAMPLE 8 Present Value of a Deferred Annuity

A deferred annuity is purchased that will pay $10,000 per quarter for 15 years after being deferred for 5 years. If money is worth 6% compounded quarterly, what is the present value of this annuity?

Solution

We use $R = \$10,000$, $n = 4(15) = 60$, $k = 4(5) = 20$, and $i = 0.06/4 = 0.015$ in the formula for the present value of a deferred annuity.

$$A_{(60,20)} = R\left[\frac{1 - (1 + i)^{-60}}{i}\right](1 + i)^{-20}$$

$$= \$10,000\left[\frac{1 - (1.015)^{-60}}{0.015}\right](1.015)^{-20}$$

$$= \$292,386.85, \text{ to the nearest cent}$$

EXAMPLE 9 Lottery Prize Payments

Suppose a lottery prize of $50,000 is invested by a couple for future use as their child's college fund. The family plans to use the money as 8 semiannual payments at the end of each 6-month period after payments are deferred for 10 years. How much would each payment be if the money can be invested at 8.6% compounded semiannually?

Solution

We seek the payment R for a deferred annuity with $n = 8$ payment periods, deferred for $k = 2(10) = 20$ periods, $i = 0.086/2 = 0.043$, and $A_{(n,k)} = \$50,000$.

$$A_{(n,k)} = R\left[\frac{1 - (1 + i)^{-n}}{i}\right](1 + i)^{-k}$$

$$\$50,000 = R\left[\frac{1 - (1.043)^{-8}}{0.043}\right](1.043)^{-20} = R(6.650118184)(0.4308378316)$$

$$\$50,000 = R(2.865122499)$$

$$R = \frac{\$50,000}{2.865122499} = \$17,451.26, \text{ to the nearest cent}$$

In Example 9, note the effect of the deferral time. The family receives $8(\$17,451.26) = \$139,610.08$ from the original $50,000 investment.

CHECKPOINT

4. Suppose an annuity at 6% compounded semiannually will pay $5000 at the end of each 6-month period for 5 years with the first payment deferred for 10 years.
   (a) What is the number of payment periods and the number of deferral periods?
   (b) What is the interest rate per period?
   (c) What formula is used to find the present value of this annuity?
   (d) Find the present value of this annuity.

CHECKPOINT SOLUTIONS

1. (a) $n = 3.5(4) = 14$
   (b) $i = 0.04/4 = 0.01$
   (c) $A_n = R\left[\dfrac{1 - (1 + i)^{-n}}{i}\right]$ for an ordinary annuity
   (d) $A_n = \$2000\left[\dfrac{1 - (1.01)^{-14}}{0.01}\right] = \$26{,}007.41$, to the nearest cent

2. We seek R for an ordinary annuity with $A_n = \$400{,}000$, $n = 20$, and $i = 0.07$.

   $$A_n = R\left[\frac{1 - (1 + i)^{-n}}{i}\right]$$

   $$\$400{,}000 = R\left[\frac{1 - (1.07)^{-20}}{0.07}\right] = R(10.59401425)$$

   $$R = \frac{\$400{,}000}{10.59401425} = \$37{,}757.17, \text{ to the nearest cent}$$

3. With payments at the beginning of each quarter, we seek the present value $A_{(n,\text{due})}$ with $n = 4(5) = 20$, $i = 0.07/4 = 0.0175$, and $R = \$5000$. Hence,

   $$A_{(20,\text{due})} = R\left[\frac{1 - (1 + i)^{-n}}{i}\right](1 + i)$$

   $$= \$5000\left[\frac{1 - (1 + 0.0175)^{-20}}{0.0175}\right](1 + 0.0175)$$

   $$= \$5000(16.752881)(1.0175) = \$85{,}230.28, \text{ to the nearest cent}$$

4. (a) $n = 5(2) = 10$ payment periods, and $k = 10(2) = 20$ deferral periods
   (b) $0.06/2 = 0.03$
   (c) $A_{(n,k)} = R\left[\dfrac{1 - (1 + i)^{-n}}{i}\right](1 + i)^{-k}$ for a deferred annuity
   (d) $A_{(n,k)} = \$5000\left[\dfrac{1 - (1.03)^{-10}}{0.03}\right](1.03)^{-20} = \$23{,}614.83$, to the nearest cent

| EXERCISES | 6.4

ORDINARY ANNUITIES

In Problems 1–4, find the requested value (to the nearest dollar), and tell what each of the other values represents.

1. Find A_n: $A_n = 1300\left[\dfrac{1 - (1 + 0.04)^{-30}}{0.04}\right]$

2. Find A_n: $A_n = 2550\left[\dfrac{1 - (1 + 0.01)^{-120}}{0.01}\right]$

3. Find R: $135{,}000 = R\left[\dfrac{1 - (1 + 0.005)^{-360}}{0.005}\right]$

4. Find R: $25{,}000 = R\left[\dfrac{1 - (1 + 0.02)^{-20}}{0.02}\right]$

5. Find the present value of an annuity of $6000 paid at the end of each 6-month period for 8 years if the interest rate is 8%, compounded semiannually.

6. Find the present value of an annuity that pays $3000 at the end of each 6-month period for 6 years if the interest rate is 6%, compounded semiannually.

7. Suppose a state lottery prize of $5 million is to be paid in 20 payments of $250,000 each at the end of each of the next 20 years. If money is worth 10%, compounded annually, what is the present value of the prize?

8. How much is needed in an account that earns 8.4% compounded monthly in order to withdraw $1000 at the end of each month for 20 years?

9. With a present value of $135,000, what is the size of the withdrawals that can be made at the end of each quarter for the next 10 years if money is worth 6.4%, compounded quarterly?

10. If $88,000 is invested in an annuity that earns 5.8%, compounded quarterly, what payments will it provide at the end of each quarter for the next $5\frac{1}{2}$ years?

11. A personal account earmarked as a retirement supplement contains $242,400. Suppose $200,000 is used to establish an annuity that earns 6%, compounded quarterly, and pays $4500 at the end of each quarter. How long will it be until the account balance is $0?

12. A professional athlete invested $2.5 million of a bonus in an account that earns 6.8%, compounded semiannually. If $120,000 is to be withdrawn at the end of each six months, how long will it be until the account balance is $0?

13. Suppose that a 25-year government bond has a maturity value of $1000 and a coupon rate of 6%, with coupons paid semiannually. Find the market price of the bond if the yield rate is 5% compounded semiannually. Is this bond selling at a discount or at a premium?

14. Suppose that a 10-year corporate bond has a maturity value of $25,000 and a coupon rate of 7%, with coupons paid semiannually. Find the market price of the bond if the yield rate is 8% compounded semiannually. Is this bond selling at a discount or at a premium?

15. The figure shows a graph that compares the present values of two ordinary annuities of $1000 annually, one at 8% compounded annually and one at 10% compounded annually.
    (a) Determine which graph corresponds to the 8% rate and which to the 10% rate.
    (b) Use the graph to estimate the difference between the present values of these annuities for 25 years.
    (c) Write a sentence that explains this difference.

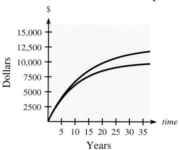

16. The figure shows a graph that compares the present values of two ordinary annuities of $800 quarterly, one at 6% compounded quarterly and one at 9% compounded quarterly.
    (a) Determine which graph corresponds to the 6% rate and which to the 9% rate.
    (b) Use the graph to estimate the difference between the present values of these annuities for 25 years (100 quarters).
    (c) Write a sentence that explains this difference.

ANNUITIES DUE

17. Explain the difference between an ordinary annuity and an annuity due.

18. Is there any difference between the present values in parts (a) and (b)? Explain.
    (a) An annuity due that pays $1000 at the beginning of each year for 10 years
    (b) Taking $1000 now and establishing an ordinary annuity that pays $1000 at the end of each year for 9 years

19. Find the present value of an annuity due that pays $3000 at the beginning of each quarter for the next 7 years. Assume that money is worth 5.8%, compounded quarterly.

20. Find the present value of an annuity due that pays $25,000 every 6 months for the next $2\frac{1}{2}$ years if money is worth 6.2%, compounded semiannually.

21. What amount must be set aside now to generate payments of $50,000 at the beginning of each year for the next 12 years if money is worth 5.92%, compounded annually?

22. Suppose an annuity will pay $15,000 at the beginning of each year for the next 7 years. How much money is needed to start this annuity if it earns 7.3%, compounded annually?

23. A year-end bonus of $25,000 will generate how much money at the beginning of each month for the next year, if it can be invested at 6.48%, compounded monthly?

24. A couple inherits $89,000. How much can this generate at the beginning of each month over the next 5 years, if money is worth 6.3%, compounded monthly?

MISCELLANEOUS PROBLEMS FOR ORDINARY ANNUITIES AND ANNUITIES DUE

In Problems 25–38, (a) decide whether the problem relates to an ordinary annuity or an annuity due, and then (b) solve the problem.

25. An insurance settlement of $1.5 million must replace Trixie Eden's income for the next 40 years. What income will this settlement provide at the end of each month if it is invested in an annuity that earns 8.4%, compounded monthly?

26. A trust will provide $10,000 to a county library at the beginning of each 3-month period for the next $2\frac{1}{2}$ years. If money is worth 7.4%, compounded quarterly, find the amount in the trust when it begins.

27. A company wants to have $40,000 at the beginning of each 6-month period for the next $4\frac{1}{2}$ years. If an annuity is set up for this purpose, how much must be invested now if the annuity earns 6.68%, compounded semiannually?

28. Is it more economical to buy an automobile for $29,000 cash or to pay $8000 down and $3000 at the end of each quarter for 2 years, if money is worth 8% compounded quarterly?

29. Dr. Jane Kodiak plans to sell her practice to an HMO. The HMO will pay her $1.5 million now or will make a $500,000 partial payment now and make additional payments of $140,000 at the end of each year for the next 10 years. If money is worth 6.5%, compounded annually, is it better to take $1.5 million now or $500,000 now and $140,000 at the end of each year for the next 10 years? Justify your choice.

30. As a result of a court settlement, an accident victim is awarded $1.2 million. The attorney takes one-third of this amount, another third is used for immediate expenses, and the remaining third is used to set up an annuity. What amount will this annuity pay at the beginning of each quarter for the next 5 years if the annuity earns 7.6%, compounded quarterly?

31. Recent sales of some real estate and record profits make it possible for a manufacturer to set aside $800,000 in a fund to be used for modernization and remodeling. How much can be withdrawn from this fund at the beginning of each half-year for the next 3 years if the fund earns 7.7%, compounded semiannually?

32. A $2.4 million state lottery pays $10,000 at the beginning of each month for 20 years. How much money must the state actually have in hand to set up the payments for this prize if money is worth 6.3%, compounded monthly?

33. A used piece of rental equipment has $2\frac{1}{2}$ years of useful life remaining. When rented, the equipment brings in $800 per month (paid at the beginning of the month). If the equipment is sold now and money is worth 4.8%, compounded monthly, what must the selling price be to recoup the income that the rental company loses by selling the equipment "early"?

34. As a result of a court settlement, a financial firm agreed to pay $13.4 million to Ford Motor Company, with $10 million of it going to a Ford charitable trust (*Source: The New York Times*). If the trust invested this money at 6.3%, compounded annually, how much could be awarded to worthwhile organizations at the end of each year for the next 20 years?

35. As the contestant with the longest winning streak in the history of *Jeopardy*, Ken Jennings won more than $2.5 million. Suppose he invested $1.5 million in an ordinary annuity that earned 7.2%, compounded monthly. How much would he receive at the end of each month for the next 20 years?

36. Suppose Becky has her choice of $10,000 at the end of each month for life or a single prize of $1.5 million. She is 35 years old and her life expectancy is 40 more years.
    (i) Find the present value of the annuity if money is worth 7.2%, compounded monthly.
    (ii) If she takes the $1.5 million, spends $700,000 of it, and invests the remainder at 7.2% compounded monthly, what amount will she receive at the end of each month for the next 40 years?

37. Juanita Domingo's parents want to establish a college trust for her. They want to make 16 quarterly withdrawals of $2000, with the first withdrawal 3 months from now. If money is worth 7.2%, compounded quarterly, how much must be deposited now to provide for this trust?

38. A retiree inherits $93,000 and invests it at 6.6%, compounded monthly, in an annuity that provides an amount at the end of each month for the next 12 years. Find the monthly amount.

39. A 10-year Emmaco Corporate bond has a par value of $10,000 with coupons at 7.8% paid semiannually.
    (a) If this bond is bought to yield 10% compounded semiannually, find its price.
    (b) Suppose that after this bond has been held for 2 years, the desired yield is 8% compounded semiannually. Find the selling price.

40. Kodicom, Inc. has 15-year bonds with a $5000 maturity value and a quoted coupon rate of 12% paid semiannually. The current yield is 10% compounded semiannually.
    (a) Compute the price of these bonds.
    (b) Suppose that with 12 years remaining until maturity, the yield rate drops to 8% compounded semiannually. Find the new price of these bonds.

For each of Problems 41 and 42, answer the following questions.

(a) **How much is in the account after the last deposit is made?**

(b) **How much was deposited?**

(c) **What is the amount of each withdrawal?**

(d) **What is the total amount withdrawn?**

41. Suppose an individual makes an initial investment of $2500 in an account that earns 7.8%, compounded monthly, and makes additional contributions of $100 at the end of each month for a period of 12 years. After these 12 years, this individual wants to make withdrawals at the end of each month for the next 5 years (so that the account balance will be reduced to $0).

42. Suppose that Nam Banh deposits his $12,500 bonus in an account that earns 8%, compounded quarterly, and makes additional deposits of $500 at the end of each quarter for the next $22\frac{1}{2}$ years, until he retires. To supplement his retirement, Nam wants to make withdrawals at the end of each quarter for the next 12 years (at which time the account balance will be $0).

43. A young couple wants to have a college fund that will pay $30,000 at the end of each half-year for 8 years.
    (a) If they can invest at 8%, compounded semiannually, how much do they need to invest at the end of each 6-month period for the next 18 years in order to begin making their college withdrawals 6 months after their last investment?
    (b) Suppose 8 years after beginning the annuity payments, they receive an inheritance of $38,000 that they contribute to the account, and they continue to make their regular payments as found in part (a). How many college withdrawals will they be able to make before the account balance is $0?

44. A recent college graduate begins a savings plan at age 27 by investing $400 at the end of each month in an account that earns 7.5%, compounded monthly.
    (a) If this plan is followed for 10 years, how much should the monthly contributions be for the next

28 years in order to be able to withdraw $10,000 at the end of each month from the account for the next 25 years?
    (b) What is the total amount contributed?
    (c) What is the total amount withdrawn?

DEFERRED ANNUITIES

45. Find the present value of an annuity of $2000 per year at the end of each of 8 years after being deferred for 6 years, if money is worth 7% compounded annually.

46. Find the present value of an annuity of $2000, at the end of each quarter for 5 years after being deferred for 3 years, if money is worth 8% compounded quarterly.

47. The terms of a single parent's will indicate that a child will receive an ordinary annuity of $16,000 per year from age 18 to age 24 (so the child can attend college) and that the balance of the estate goes to a niece. If the parent dies on the child's 14th birthday, how much money must be removed from the estate to purchase the annuity? (Assume an interest rate of 6%, compounded annually.)

48. On his 48th birthday, a man wants to set aside enough money to provide an income of $1500 at the end of each month from his 60th birthday to his 65th birthday. If he earns 6%, compounded monthly, how much will this supplemental retirement plan cost him on his 48th birthday?

49. The semiannual tuition payment at a major university is expected to be $30,000 for the 4 years beginning 18 years from now. What lump sum payment should the university accept now, in lieu of tuition payments beginning 18 years, 6 months from now? Assume that money is worth 7%, compounded semiannually, and that tuition is paid at the end of each half-year for 4 years.

50. A grateful alumnus wishes to provide a scholarship of $2000 per year for 5 years to his alma mater, with the first scholarship awarded on his 60th birthday. If money is worth 6%, compounded annually, how much money must he donate on his 50th birthday?

51. Danny Metzger's parents invested $1600 when he was born. This money is to be used for Danny's college education and is to be withdrawn in four equal annual payments beginning when Danny is age 19. Find the amount that will be available each year, if money is worth 6%, compounded annually.

52. Carol Goldsmith received a trust fund inheritance of $10,000 on her 30th birthday. She plans to use the money to supplement her income with 20 quarterly payments beginning on her 60th birthday. If money is worth 7.6% compounded quarterly, how much will each quarterly payment be?

53. According to *Sports Illustrated*, Peyton Manning of the NFL's Indianapolis Colts made over $10 million from product endorsements in 2010 (over and above his

Colts salary). Suppose Manning set aside a $ 7.5 million in a fund that earns 9.6%, compounded monthly. If he deferred this amount for 15 years, how much per month would it provide for the 40 years after the deferral period?

54. A couple received a $134,000 inheritance the year they turned 48 and invested it in a fund that earns 7.7% compounded semiannually. If this amount is deferred for 14 years (until they retire), how much will it provide at the end of each half-year for the next 20 years after they retire?

 In Problems 55 and 56, use a spreadsheet or financial program on a calculator or computer.

55. Suppose a couple have $100,000 at retirement that they can invest in an ordinary annuity that earns 7.8%, compounded monthly. Track the balance in this annuity account until it reaches $0, if the couple receive the following monthly payments.
 (a) $1000   (b) $2500

56. Suppose you invested $250,000 in an annuity that earned interest compounded monthly. This annuity paid $3000 at the end of each month. Experiment with the following different interest rates (compounded monthly) to see how long it will be, with each rate, until this annuity has an account balance of $0.
 (a) 6.5%   (b) 9%

- To find the regular payments required to amortize a debt
- To find the amount that can be borrowed for a specified payment
- To develop an amortization schedule
- To find the unpaid balance of a loan
- To find the effect of paying an extra amount

Loans and Amortization

▮ | APPLICATION PREVIEW | ▮

Chuckie and Angelica have been married for 4 years and are ready to buy their first home. They have saved $30,000 for a down payment, and their budget can accommodate a monthly mortgage payment of $1200.00. They want to know in what price range they can purchase a home if the rate for a 30-year loan is 7.8% compounded monthly. (See Example 3.)

When businesses, individuals, or families (such as Chuckie and Angelica) borrow money to make a major purchase, four questions commonly arise:

1. What will the payments be?
2. How much can be borrowed and still fit a budget?
3. What is the payoff amount of the loan before the final payment is due?
4. What is the total of all payments needed to pay off the loan?

In this section we discuss the most common way that consumers and businesses discharge debts—regular payments of fixed size made on a loan (called amortization)—and determine ways to answer Chuckie and Angelica's question (Question 2) and the other three questions posed above.

Amortization   Just as we invest money to earn interest, banks and lending institutions lend money and collect interest for its use. Federal law now requires that the full cost of any loan and the **true annual percentage rate (APR)** be disclosed with the loan. Because of this law, loans now are usually paid off by a series of partial payments with interest charged on the unpaid balance at the end of each payment period.

This type of loan is usually repaid by making all payments (including principal and interest) of equal size. This process of repaying the loan is called **amortization.**

When a bank makes a loan of this type, it is purchasing from the borrower an ordinary annuity that pays a fixed return each payment period. The lump sum the bank gives to the borrower (the principal of the loan) is the present value of the ordinary annuity, and each payment the bank receives from the borrower is a payment from the annuity. Hence, to find the size of these periodic payments, we solve for R in the formula for the present value of an ordinary annuity,

$$A_n = R\left[\frac{1 - (1 + i)^{-n}}{i}\right]$$

which yields the following algebraically equivalent formula.

Amortization Formula	If the debt of $\$A_n$, with interest at a rate of i per period, is amortized by n equal periodic payments (each payment being made at the end of a period), the size of each payment is

$$R = A_n \cdot \left[\frac{i}{1 - (1 + i)^{-n}}\right]$$

EXAMPLE 1   Payments to Amortize a Debt

A debt of $1000 with interest at 16%, compounded quarterly, is to be amortized by 20 quarterly payments (all the same size) over the next 5 years. What will the size of these payments be?

Solution

The amortization of this loan is an ordinary annuity with present value $1000. Therefore, $A_n = \$1000$, $n = 20$, and $i = 0.16/4 = 0.04$. Thus we have

$$R = A_n\left[\frac{i}{1 - (1 + i)^{-n}}\right] = \$1000\left[\frac{0.04}{1 - (1.04)^{-20}}\right]$$

$$= \$1000(0.07358175) = \$73.58, \text{ to the nearest cent}$$

EXAMPLE 2   Buying a Home

A man buys a house for $200,000. He makes a $50,000 down payment and agrees to amortize the rest of the debt with quarterly payments over the next 10 years. If the interest on the debt is 12%, compounded quarterly, find (a) the size of the quarterly payments, (b) the total amount of the payments, and (c) the total amount of interest paid.

Solution

(a) We know that $A_n = \$200,000 - \$50,000 = \$150,000$, $n = 4(10) = 40$, and $i = 0.12/4 = 0.03$. Thus, for the quarterly payment, we have

$$R = \$150,000\left[\frac{0.03}{1 - (1.03)^{-40}}\right]$$

$$= (\$150,000)(0.043262378) = \$6489.36, \text{ to the nearest cent}$$

(b) The man made 40 payments of $6489.36, so his payments totaled

$$(40)(\$6489.36) = \$259,574.40$$

plus the $50,000 down payment, or $309,574.40.

(c) Of the $309,574.40 paid, $200,000 was for payment of the house. The remaining $109,574.40 was the total amount of interest paid.

Technology Note   The steps for finding the payment size to amortize a debt with a calculator or Excel are found in Appendices C and D, Section 6.5. See also the Online Excel Guide.

EXAMPLE 3   Affordable Home | APPLICATION PREVIEW |

Chuckie and Angelica have $30,000 for a down payment, and their budget can accommodate a monthly mortgage payment of $1200.00. What is the most expensive home they can buy if they can borrow money for 30 years at 7.8%, compounded monthly?

Solution

We seek the amount that Chuckie and Angelica can borrow, or A_n, knowing that $R = \$1200$, $n = 30(12) = 360$, and $i = 0.078/12 = 0.0065$. We can use these values in the amortization formula and solve for A_n (or use the formula for the present value of an ordinary annuity).

$$R = A_n \left[\frac{i}{1 - (1 + i)^{-n}} \right]$$

$$\$1200 = A_n \left[\frac{0.0065}{1 - (1.0065)^{-360}} \right]$$

$$A_n = \$1200 \left[\frac{1 - (1.0065)^{-360}}{0.0065} \right]$$

$$A_n = \$1200(138.9138739) = \$166,696.65, \text{ to the nearest cent}$$

Thus, if they borrow $166,697 (to the nearest dollar) and put down $30,000, the most expensive home they can buy would cost $166,697 + $30,000 = $196,697. ■

CHECKPOINT

1. A debt of $25,000 is to be amortized with equal quarterly payments over 6 years, and money is worth 7%, compounded quarterly.
   (a) Find the total number of payments.
   (b) Find the interest rate per period.
   (c) Write the formula used to find the size of each payment.
   (d) Find the amount of each payment.
2. A new college graduate determines that she can afford a car payment of $400 per month. If the auto manufacturer is offering a special 2.1% financing rate, compounded monthly for 5 years, how much can she borrow and still have a $400 monthly payment?

Amortization Schedule

We can construct an **amortization schedule** that summarizes all the information regarding the amortization of a loan.

For example, a loan of $10,000 with interest at 10% could be repaid in 5 equal annual payments of size

$$R = \$10,000 \left[\frac{0.10}{1 - (1 + 0.10)^{-5}} \right] = \$10,000(0.263797) = \$2637.97$$

Each time this $2637.97 payment is made, some is used to pay the interest on the unpaid balance, and some is used to reduce the principal. For the first payment, the unpaid balance is $10,000, so the interest payment is 10% of $10,000, or $1000. The remaining $1637.97 is applied to the principal. Hence, after this first payment, the unpaid balance is $10,000 − $1637.97 = $8362.03.

For the second payment of $2637.97, the amount used for interest is 10% of $8362.03, or $836.20; the remainder, $1801.77, is used to reduce the principal.

This information for these two payments and for the remaining payments is summarized in the following amortization schedule.

Period	Payment	Interest	Balance Reduction	Unpaid Balance
				10000.00
1	2637.97	1000.00	1637.97	8362.03
2	2637.97	836.20	1801.77	6560.26
3	2637.97	656.03	1981.94	4578.32
4	2637.97	457.83	2180.14	2398.18
5	2638.00	239.82	2398.18	0.00
Total	13189.88	3189.88	10000.00	

Note that the last payment was increased by 3¢ so that the balance was reduced to $0 at the end of the 5 years. Such an adjustment is normal in amortizing a loan.

Spreadsheet Note   The preceding amortization schedule involves only a few payments. For loans involving more payments, a spreadsheet program is an excellent tool to develop an amortization schedule. The spreadsheet requires the user to understand the interrelationships among the columns. The accompanying spreadsheet output in Table 6.6 shows the amortization schedule for the first, sixth, twelfth, eighteenth, and twenty-fourth monthly payments on a $100,000 loan amortized for 30 years at 6%, compounded monthly. It is interesting to observe how little the unpaid balance changes during these first 2 years—and, consequently, how much of each payment is devoted to paying interest due rather than to reducing the debt. In fact, the column labeled "Total Interest" shows a running total of how much has been paid toward interest. We see that after 12 payments of $599.55, a total of $7194.60 has been paid, and $5966.59 of this has been interest payments. ∎

TABLE 6.6						
	A	**B**	**C**	**D**	**E**	**F**
1	Payment Number	Payment Amount	Interest	Balance Reduction	Unpaid Balance	Total Interest
2	0	0	0	0	$100,000.00	$0.00
3	1	$599.55	$500.00	$99.55	$99,900.45	$500.00
4	6	$599.55	$497.49	$102.06	$99,395.18	$2,992.48
5	12	$599.55	$494.39	$105.16	$98,771.99	$5,966.59
6	18	$599.55	$491.19	$108.36	$98,129.87	$8,921.77
7	24	$599.55	$487.90	$111.65	$97,468.25	$11,857.45

Unpaid Balance of a Loan   Many people who borrow money, such as for a car or a home, do not pay on the loan for its entire term. Rather, they pay off the loan early by making a final lump sum payment. The unpaid balance found in the amortization schedule is the "payoff amount" of the loan and represents the lump sum payment that must be made to complete payment on the loan. When the number of payments is large, we may wish to find the unpaid balance of a loan without constructing an amortization schedule.

Recall that calculations for amortization of a debt are based on the present value formula for an ordinary annuity. Because of this, the **unpaid balance of a loan** (also called the **payoff amount** and the **outstanding principal of the loan**) is the present value needed to generate all the remaining payments.

Unpaid Balance or Payoff Amount of a Loan

For a loan of n payments of R per period at interest rate i per period, the **unpaid balance,** or **payoff amount,** after k payments have been made is the present value of an ordinary annuity with $n - k$ payments. That is, with $n - k$ payments remaining,

$$\text{Unpaid balance} = A_{n-k} = R\left[\frac{1 - (1 + i)^{-(n-k)}}{i}\right]$$

EXAMPLE 4   Unpaid Balance

In Example 2, we found that the monthly payment for a loan of $150,000 at 12%, compounded quarterly, for 10 years is $6489.36 (to the nearest cent). Find the unpaid balance immediately after the 15th payment.

Solution

The unpaid balance after the 15th payment is the present value of the annuity with $40 - 15 = 25$ payments remaining. Thus we use $R = \$6489.36$, $i = 0.03$, and $n - k = 25$ in the formula for the unpaid balance of a loan.

$$A_{n-k} = R\left[\frac{1 - (1 + i)^{-(n-k)}}{i}\right] = \$6489.36\left[\frac{1 - (1.03)^{-25}}{0.03}\right]$$

$$= (\$6489.36)(17.4131477) = \$113,000.18, \text{ to the nearest cent}$$

CHECKPOINT

3. A 42-month auto loan has monthly payments of $411.35. If the interest rate is 8.1%, compounded monthly, find the unpaid balance immediately after the 24th payment.

Figure 6.10

The curve in Figure 6.10 shows the unpaid balance of a $100,000 loan at 6%, compounded monthly, for 30 years (with monthly payments of $599.55, as in Table 6.6). In the figure, the straight line represents how the unpaid balance would decrease if each payment diminished the debt by the same amount. Note how the curve decreases slowly at first and more rapidly as the unpaid balance nears zero. The reason for this behavior is that when the unpaid balance is large, much of each payment is devoted to interest. Similarly, when the debt decreases, more of each payment goes toward the principal. An interesting question then is what would be the effect of paying an extra amount (directly toward the principal) with each payment.

EXAMPLE 5   Effect of Paying an Extra Amount

Consider the loan in Table 6.6: $100,000 borrowed at 6% compounded monthly for 30 years, with monthly payments of $599.55. As Table 6.6 shows, the unpaid balance after 24 monthly payments is $97,468.25. Suppose that from this point the borrower decides to pay $650 per month.

(a) How many more payments must be made?
(b) How much would this save over the life of the loan?

Solution

(a) Use $A_n = R\left[\dfrac{1 - (1 + i)^{-n}}{i}\right]$ with $A_n = \$97,468.25$, $R = \$650$, $i = 0.06/12 = 0.005$, and solve for n (by first isolating the exponential $(1.005)^{-n}$).

$$97{,}468.25 = 650\left[\frac{1 - (1.005)^{-n}}{0.005}\right] \tag{1}$$

$$\frac{(97{,}468.25)(0.005)}{650} = 1 - (1.005)^{-n}$$

$$(1.005)^{-n} = 1 - \frac{(97{,}468.25)(0.005)}{650}$$

$$\ln\left[(1.005)^{-n}\right] = \ln(0.2502442308)$$
$$-n\left[\ln(1.005)\right] = \ln(0.2502442308)$$

$$n = \frac{\ln(0.2502442308)}{-\ln(1.005)} \approx 277.8$$

Figure 6.11

(b) For the purposes of determining the savings, assume $n = 277.8$ payments of $650 were made. Thus the total paid with each method is as follows.

Paying Extra: $(24 \text{ payments of } \$599.55) + (277.8 \text{ payments of } \$650) = \$194,959.20$
Paying $599.55: $(360 \text{ payments of } \$599.55) = \$215,838.00$

Hence by increasing the payments slightly, the borrower saved

$$\$215,838.00 - \$194,959.20 = \$20,878.80$$

Calculator Note   Notice in Example 5 that we could have solved Equation (1) graphically by finding where $y_1 = 97,468.25$ and $y_2 = 650\left[\dfrac{1 - (1.005)^{-x}}{0.005}\right]$ intersect (see Figure 6.11).

CHECKPOINT SOLUTIONS

1. (a) $n = 6(4) = 24$ payments
   (b) $i = 0.07/4 = 0.0175$ per period
   (c) $R = A_n\left[\dfrac{i}{1 - (1 + i)^{-n}}\right]$
   (d) $R = \$25,000\left[\dfrac{0.0175}{1 - (1.0175)^{-24}}\right] = \$1284.64$, to the nearest cent

2. Use $R = A_n\left[\dfrac{i}{1 - (1 + i)^{-n}}\right]$ with $i = 0.021/12 = 0.00175$, $n = 60$, and $R = \$400$.

$$\$400 = A_n\left[\dfrac{0.00175}{1 - (1.00175)^{-60}}\right] = A_n(0.0175715421)$$

$$A_n = \dfrac{\$400}{0.0175715421} \approx \$22,764.08, \text{ to the nearest cent}$$

3. Use $R = \$411.35$, $i = 0.081/12 = 0.00675$, and $n - k = 42 - 24 = 18$.

$$A_{n-k} = R\left[\dfrac{1 - (1 + i)^{-(n-k)}}{i}\right] = \$411.35\left[\dfrac{1 - (1.00675)^{-18}}{0.00675}\right]$$

$$= \$6950.13, \text{ to the nearest cent}$$

| EXERCISES | 6.5

1. Answer parts (a) and (b) with respect to loans for 10 years and 25 years. Assume the same interest rate.
   (a) Which loan results in more of each payment being directed toward principal? Explain.
   (b) Which loan results in a lower periodic payment? Explain.
2. When a debt is amortized, which interest rate is better for the borrower, 10% or 6%? Explain.
3. A debt of $8000 is to be amortized with 8 equal semiannual payments. If the interest rate is 12%, compounded semiannually, what is the size of each payment?

4. A loan of $10,000 is to be amortized with 10 equal quarterly payments. If the interest rate is 6%, compounded quarterly, what is the periodic payment?
5. A recent graduate's student loans total $18,000. If these loans are at 4.2%, compounded quarterly, for 10 years, what are the quarterly payments?
6. For equipment upgrades a business borrowed $400,000 at 8%, compounded semiannually, for 5 years. What are the semiannual payments?

7. A homeowner planning a kitchen remodeling can afford a $200 monthly payment. How much can the homeowner borrow for 5 years at 6%, compounded monthly, and still stay within the budget?

8. AdriAnne and Anna's Auto Repair wants to add a new service bay. How much can they borrow at 5%, compounded quarterly for $4\frac{1}{2}$ years, if the desired quarterly payment is $6000?

In Problems 9–12, develop an amortization schedule for the loan described.

9. $100,000 for 3 years at 9% compounded annually

10. $30,000 for 5 years at 7% compounded annually

11. $20,000 for 1 year at 12% compounded quarterly

12. $50,000 for $2\frac{1}{2}$ years at 10% compounded semiannually

13. A $10,000 loan is to be amortized for 10 years with quarterly payments of $334.27. If the interest rate is 6%, compounded quarterly, what is the unpaid balance immediately after the sixth payment?

14. A debt of $8000 is to be amortized with 8 equal semiannual payments of $1288.29. If the interest rate is 12%, compounded semiannually, find the unpaid balance immediately after the fifth payment.

15. When Maria Acosta bought a car $2\frac{1}{2}$ years ago, she borrowed $14,000 for 48 months at 8.1% compounded monthly. Her monthly payments are $342.44, but she'd like to pay off the loan early. How much will she owe just after her payment at the $2\frac{1}{2}$-year mark?

16. Six and a half years ago, a small business borrowed $50,000 for 10 years at 9%, compounded semiannually, in order to update some equipment. Now the company would like to pay off this loan. Find the payoff amount just after the company makes the 14th semiannual payment of $3843.81.

Problems 17–20 describe a debt to be amortized. In each problem, find:

(a) the size of each payment.

(b) the total amount paid over the life of the loan.

(c) the total interest paid over the life of the loan.

17. A man buys a house for $350,000. He makes a $150,000 down payment and amortizes the rest of the debt with semiannual payments over the next 10 years. The interest rate on the debt is 12%, compounded semiannually.

18. Sean Lee purchases $20,000 worth of supplies for his restaurant by making a $3000 down payment and amortizing the rest with quarterly payments over the next 5 years. The interest rate on the debt is 16%, compounded quarterly.

19. John Fare purchased $10,000 worth of equipment by making a $2000 down payment and promising to pay the remainder of the cost in semiannual payments over the next 4 years. The interest rate on the debt is 10%, compounded semiannually.

20. A woman buys an apartment house for $1,250,000 by making a down payment of $250,000 and amortizing the rest of the debt with semiannual payments over the next 10 years. The interest rate on the debt is 8%, compounded semiannually.

21. A man buys a car for $36,000. If the interest rate on the loan is 12%, compounded monthly, and if he wants to make monthly payments of $900 for 36 months, how much must he put down?

22. A woman buys a car for $40,000. If the interest rate on the loan is 12%, compounded monthly, and if she wants to make monthly payments of $700 for 3 years, how much must she have for a down payment?

23. A couple purchasing a home budget $1800 per month for their loan payment. If they have $20,000 available for a down payment and are considering a 25-year loan, how much can they spend on the home at each of the following rates?
   (a) 6.9% compounded monthly
   (b) 7.5% compounded monthly

24. A developer wants to buy a certain parcel of land. The developer feels she can afford payments of $44,000 each half-year for the next 7 years. How much can she borrow and hold to this budget at each of the following interest rates?
   (a) 8.9% compounded semiannually
   (b) 7.3% compounded semiannually

25. A couple who borrow $90,000 for 30 years at 7.2%, compounded monthly, must make monthly payments of $610.91.
   (a) Find their unpaid balance after 1 year.
   (b) During that first year, how much interest do they pay?

26. A company that purchases a piece of equipment by borrowing $250,000 for 10 years at 6%, compounded monthly, has monthly payments of $2775.51.
   (a) Find the unpaid balance on this loan after 1 year.
   (b) During that first year, how much interest does the company pay?

27. A recent college graduate buys a new car by borrowing $18,000 at 8.4%, compounded monthly, for 5 years. She decides to pay an extra $15 per payment.
   (a) What is the monthly payment required by the loan, and how much does she decide to pay each month?
   (b) How many payments (that include the extra $15) will she make?
   (c) How much will she save by paying the extra $15?

28. A young couple buying their first home borrow $85,000 for 30 years at 7.2%, compounded monthly, and make payments of $576.97. After 3 years, they are able to make a one-time payment of $2000 along with their 36th payment.
   (a) Find the unpaid balance immediately after they pay the extra $2000 and their 36th payment.

(b) How many regular payments of $576.97 will amortize the unpaid balance from part (a)?

(c) How much will the couple save over the life of the loan by paying the extra $2000?

A debt of $100,000 is amortized at 6%, compounded monthly, over 25 years with 300 monthly payments of $644.30 each. Figure 6.12 includes two graphs: one shows the total amount paid (in monthly payments) as a function of time (in months), and the other shows the amount paid toward the principal of the debt as a function of time. Use this figure to complete Problems 29 and 30.

Figure 6.12

29. (a) Correctly label each graph.
   (b) Draw a vertical segment whose length represents the total amount of interest paid on the debt after 250 months.

30. Draw a vertical segment whose length represents the outstanding principal of the debt (or the payoff amount of the loan) after 150 months.

31. What difference does 0.5% make on a loan? To answer this question, find (to the nearest dollar) the monthly payment and total interest paid over the life of the loan for each of the following.
   (a) An auto loan of $15,000 at 8.0% versus 8.5%, compounded monthly, for 4 years.
   (b) A mortgage loan of $80,000 at 6.75% versus 7.25%, compounded monthly, for 30 years.
   (c) In each of these 0.5% differences, what seems to have the greatest effect on the borrower: amount borrowed, interest rate, or duration of the loan? Explain.

32. Some banks now have biweekly mortgages (that is, with payments every other week). Compare a 20-year, $100,000 loan at 8.1% by finding the payment size and the total interest paid over the life of the loan under each of the following conditions.
   (a) Payments are monthly, and the rate is 8.1%, compounded monthly.
   (b) Payments are biweekly, and the rate is 8.1%, compounded biweekly.

33. Many banks charge points on mortgage loans. Each point is the equivalent of a 1% charge on the amount borrowed and is paid before the loan is made as part of the closing costs of buying a home (closing costs include points, title fees, attorney's fees, assessor's fees, and so on).
   (a) If $100,000 is borrowed for 25 years, for each of the following, find the payment size and the total paid over the life of the loan (including points).
      (i) $7\frac{1}{2}$%, compounded monthly, with 0 points
      (ii) $7\frac{1}{4}$%, compounded monthly, with 1 point
      (iii) 7%, compounded monthly, with 2 points
   (b) Which loan in part (a) has the lowest total cost over the life of the loan?

34. Time-share sales provide an opportunity for vacationers to own a resort condo for 1 week (or more) each year forever. The owners may use their week at their own condo or trade the week and vacation elsewhere. Time-share vacation sales usually require payment in full or financing through the time-share company, and interest rates are usually in the 13% to 18% range. Suppose the cost to buy a 1-week time share in a 3-bedroom condo is $21,833. Also suppose a 10% down payment is required, with the balance financed for 15 years at 16.5%, compounded monthly.
   (a) Find the monthly payment.
   (b) Determine the total cost over the life of the loan.
   (c) Suppose maintenance fees for this condo are $400 per year. Find the annual cost of the condo over the life of the loan. Assume that the annual maintenance fees remain constant.
   (d) Use part (c) and the 10% down payment to determine the average annual cost for having this vacation condo for 1 week over the life of the loan.

35. During four years of college, Nolan MacGregor's student loans are $4000, $3500, $4400, and $5000 for freshman year through senior year, respectively. Each loan amount gathers interest of 1%, compounded quarterly, while Nolan is in school and 3%, compounded quarterly, during a 6-month grace period after graduation.
   (a) What is the loan balance after the grace period? Assume the freshman year loan earns 1% interest for 3/4 year during the first year, then for 3 full years until graduation. Make similar assumptions for the loans for the other years.
   (b) After the grace period, the loan is amortized over the next 10 years at 3%, compounded quarterly. Find the quarterly payment.
   (c) If Nolan decides to pay an additional $90 per payment, how many payments of this size will amortize the debt?
   (d) How much will Nolan save by paying the extra $90 with each payment?

36. Clark and Lana take a 30-year home mortgage of $121,000 at 7.8%, compounded monthly. They make their regular monthly payments for 5 years, then decide to pay $1000 per month.
    (a) Find their regular monthly payment.
    (b) Find the unpaid balance when they begin paying the $1000.
    (c) How many payments of $1000 will it take to pay off the loan?
    (d) How much interest will they save by paying the loan in this way?

Use a spreadsheet or financial program on a calculator or computer to complete Problems 37 and 38.
37. Develop an amortization schedule for a 4-year car loan if $16,700 is borrowed at 8.2%, compounded monthly.
38. Develop an amortization schedule for a 10-year mortgage loan of $80,000 at 7.2%, compounded monthly.

KEY TERMS AND FORMULAS

Section	Key Terms	Formulas
6.1	Simple interest	$I = Prt$
	Future value of a simple interest investment or loan	$S = P + I$
	Sequence function	
	Arithmetic sequence	$a_n = a_{n-1} + d \quad (n > 1)$
	Common difference	d
	nth term of	$a_n = a_1 + (n - 1)d$
	Sum of first n terms	$s_n = \dfrac{n}{2}(a_1 + a_n)$
6.2	Future value of compound interest investment	
	Periodic compounding	$S = P(1 + i)^n = P\left(1 + \dfrac{r}{m}\right)^{mt}$
	Continuous compounding	$S = Pe^{rt}$
	Annual percentage yield	
	Periodic compounding	$\text{APY} = \left(1 + \dfrac{r}{m}\right)^m - 1$
		$\quad\quad = (1 + i)^m - 1$
	Continuous compounding	$\text{APY} = e^r - 1$
	Geometric sequence	$a_n = ra_{n-1} \quad (n > 1)$
	Common ratio	r
	nth term of	$a_n = a_1 r^{n-1}$
	Sum of first n terms	$s_n = \dfrac{a_1(1 - r^n)}{1 - r} \quad (\text{if } r \neq 1)$
6.3	Future values of annuities	
	Ordinary annuity	$S = R\left[\dfrac{(1 + i)^n - 1}{i}\right]$
	Required payment into an ordinary annuity	
	Sinking fund	
	Annuity due	$S_{\text{due}} = R\left[\dfrac{(1 + i)^n - 1}{i}\right](1 + i)$

Section	Key Terms	Formulas

6.4	Present values of annuities
	  Ordinary annuity
	    Bond pricing
		$A_n = R\left[\dfrac{1 - (1 + i)^{-n}}{i}\right]$

	Annuity due	$A_{(n,\text{due})} = R\left[\dfrac{1 - (1 + i)^{-n}}{i}\right](1 + i)$
	Deferred annuity	$A_{(n,k)} = R\left[\dfrac{1 - (1 + i)^{-n}}{i}\right](1 + i)^{-k}$

6.5	True annual percentage
	  rate (APR)
	Amortization (Loan amount is the
	  same as present value of an
	  ordinary annuity)
		$R = A_n\left[\dfrac{i}{1 - (1 + i)^{-n}}\right]$

	Unpaid balance ($n - k$ payments left) Amortization schedule	$A_{n-k} = R\left[\dfrac{1 - (1 + i)^{-(n-k)}}{i}\right]$

REVIEW EXERCISES

1. Find the first 4 terms of the sequence with nth term

$$a_n = \frac{1}{n^2}$$

2. Identify any arithmetic sequences and find the common differences.
   (a) $12, 7, 2, -3, \ldots$ (b) $1, 3, 6, 10, \ldots$
   (c) $\frac{1}{6}, \frac{1}{3}, \frac{1}{2}, \frac{2}{3}, \ldots$

3. Find the 80th term of the arithmetic sequence with first term -2 and common difference 3.

4. Find the 36th term of the arithmetic sequence with third term 10 and eighth term 25.

5. Find the sum of the first 60 terms of the arithmetic sequence $\frac{1}{3}, \frac{1}{2}, \frac{2}{3}, \ldots$

6. Identify any geometric sequences and their common ratios.
   (a) $\frac{1}{4}, 2, 16, 128, \ldots$ (b) $16, -12, 9, -\frac{27}{4}, \ldots$
   (c) $4, 16, 36, 64, \ldots$

7. Find the fourth term of the geometric sequence with first term 64 and eighth term $\frac{1}{2}$.

8. Find the sum of the first 16 terms of the geometric sequence $\frac{1}{9}, \frac{1}{3}, 1, \ldots$.

APPLICATIONS

Finance **Identify which of the following formulas applies to each situation in Problems 9–14.**

$$I = Prt \qquad S = P(1 + i)^n \qquad S = Pe^{rt}$$

$$S = R\left[\frac{(1 + i)^n - 1}{i}\right] \qquad A_n = R\left[\frac{1 - (1 + i)^{-n}}{i}\right]$$

9. The future value of a series of payments, with interest compounded when the payments are made

10. The simple interest earned on an investment

11. The present value of a series of payments, with interest compounded when the payments are made

12. The future value of an investment that earns interest compounded periodically

13. The regular payment size needed to amortize a debt, when interest is compounded when the payments are made

14. The future value of an investment that earns interest compounded continuously

15. *Loans* If $8000 is borrowed at 12% simple interest for 3 years, what is the future value of the loan at the end of the 3 years?

16. *Loan rate* Mary Toy borrowed $2000 from her parents and repaid them $2100 after 9 months. What simple interest rate did she pay?

17. *Tuition* How much summer earnings must a college student deposit on August 31 in order to have $3000 for tuition and fees on December 31 of the same year, if the investment earns 6% simple interest?

18. *Contest payments* Suppose the winner of a contest receives $10 on the first day of the month, $20 on the second day, $30 on the third day, and so on for a 30-day month. What is the total won?

19. *Salaries* Suppose you are offered two identical jobs: one paying a starting salary of $40,000 with yearly raises of $2000 and one paying a starting salary of $36,000 with yearly raises of $2500. Which job will pay more money over a 10-year period?

20. *Investments* An investment is made at 8%, compounded quarterly, for 10 years.
    (a) Find the number of periods.
    (b) Find the interest rate per period.

21. *Future value* Write the formula for the future value of a compound interest investment, if interest is compounded
    (a) periodically   (b) continuously.

22. *Comparing rates* Which compounding method, at 6%, earns more money?
    (a) semiannually   (b) monthly

23. *Interest* If $1000 is invested for 4 years at 8%, compounded quarterly, how much interest will be earned?

24. *Savings goal* How much must one invest now in order to have $18,000 in 4 years if the investment earns 5.4%, compounded monthly?

25. *Future value* What is the future value if $1000 is invested for 6 years at 8%, compounded continuously?

26. *College fund* A couple received an inheritance and plan to invest some of it for their grandchild's college education. How much must they invest if they would like the fund to have $100,000 after 15 years, and their investment earns 10.31%, compounded continuously?

27. *Investments* If $15,000 is invested at 6%, compounded quarterly, how long will it be before it grows to $25,000?

28. *Investment rates* (a) If an initial investment of $35,000 grows to $257,000 in 15 years, what annual interest rate, continuously compounded, was earned? (b) What is the annual percentage yield on this investment?

29. *Comparing yields* Find the annual percentage yield equivalent to a nominal rate of 7.2% (a) compounded quarterly and (b) compounded continuously.

30. *Chess legend* Legend has it that when the king of Persia wanted to reward the inventor of chess with whatever he desired, the inventor asked for one grain of wheat on the first square of the chessboard, with the number of grains doubled on each square thereafter for the remaining 63 squares. Find the number of grains on the 64th square. (The sum of all the grains of wheat on all the squares would cover Alaska more than 3 inches deep with wheat!)

31. *Chess legend* If, in Problem 30, the king granted the inventor's wish for *half* a chessboard, how many grains would the inventor receive?

32. *Annuity* Find the future value of an ordinary annuity of $800 paid at the end of every 6-month period for 10 years, if it earns interest at 12%, compounded semiannually.

33. *Sinking fund* How much would have to be invested at the end of each year at 6%, compounded annually, to pay off a debt of $80,000 in 10 years?

34. *Annuity* Find the future value of an annuity due of $800 paid at the beginning of every 6-month period for 10 years, if it earns interest at 12%, compounded semiannually.

35. *Construction fund* A company wants to have $250,000 available in $4\frac{1}{2}$ years for new construction. How much must be deposited at the beginning of each quarter to reach this goal if the investment earns 10.2%, compounded quarterly?

36. *Time to reach a goal* If $1200 is deposited at the end of each quarter in an account that earns 7.2%, compounded quarterly, how long will it be until the account is worth $60,000?

37. *Annuity* What lump sum would have to be invested at 9%, compounded semiannually, to provide an annuity of $10,000 at the end of each half-year for 10 years?

38. *Cruise fund* A couple wish to set up an annuity that will provide 6 monthly payments of $3000 while they take an extended cruise. How much of a $15,000 inheritance must be set aside if they plan to leave in 5 years and want the first payment before they leave? Assume that money is worth 7.8%, compounded monthly.

39. *Powerball lottery* Winners of lotteries receive the jackpot distributed over a period of years, usually 20 or 25 years. The winners of the Powerball lottery on July 29, 1998, elected to take a one-time cash payout rather than receive the $295.7 million jackpot in 25 annual payments beginning on the date the lottery was won.
    (a) How much money would the winners have received at the beginning of each of the 25 years?
    (b) If the value of money was 5.91%, compounded annually, what one-time payout did they receive in lieu of the annual payments?

40. *Payment from an annuity* A recent college graduate's gift from her grandparents is $20,000. How much will this provide at the end of each month for the next 12 months while the graduate travels? Assume that money is worth 6.6%, compounded monthly.

41. *Payment from an annuity* An IRA of $250,000 is rolled into an annuity that pays a retired couple at the beginning of each quarter for the next 20 years. If the annuity earns 6.2%, compounded quarterly, how much will the couple receive each quarter?

42. *Duration of an annuity* A retirement account that earns 6.8%, compounded semiannually, contains $488,000. How long can $40,000 be withdrawn at the end of each half-year until the account balance is $0?

43. *Amortization* A debt of $1000 with interest at 12%, compounded monthly, is amortized by 12 monthly payments (of equal size). What is the size of each payment?

44. *Loan pay-off* A debt of $8000 is amortized with eight semiannual payments of $1288.29 each. If money is worth 12%, compounded semiannually, find the unpaid balance after five payments have been made.

45. *Cash value* A woman paid $90,000 down for a house and agreed to pay 18 quarterly payments of $4500 each. If money is worth 4%, compounded quarterly, how much would the house have cost if she had paid cash?

46. *Amortization schedule* Complete the next two lines of the amortization schedule for a $100,000 loan for 30 years at 7.5%, compounded monthly, with monthly payments of $699.22.

Payment Number	Payment Amount	Interest	Balance Reduction	Unpaid Balance
56	$699.22	$594.67	$104.55	$95,042.20

MISCELLANEOUS FINANCIAL PROBLEMS

47. If an initial investment of $2500 grows to $38,000 in 18 years, what annual interest rate, compounded annually, did this investment earn?

48. How much must be deposited at the end of each month in an account that earns 8.4%, compounded monthly, if the goal is to have $40,000 after 10 years?

49. What is the future value if $1000 is invested for 6 years at 8% (a) simple interest and (b) compounded semiannually?

50. Quarterly payments of $500 are deposited in an account that pays 8%, compounded quarterly. How much will have accrued in the account at the end of 4 years if each payment is made at the end of each quarter?

51. If $8000 is invested at 7%, compounded continuously, how long will it be before it grows to $22,000?

52. An investment broker bought some stock at $87.89 per share and sold it after 3 months for $105.34 per share. What was the annual simple interest rate earned on this transaction?

53. Suppose that a 30-year municipal bond has a maturity value of $5000 and a coupon rate of 8%, with coupons paid semiannually. Find the market price of the bond if the current yield rate is 10% compounded semiannually. Is this bond selling at a discount or at a premium?

54. A $5000 Mauranol, Inc. corporate bond matures in 10 years and has a coupon rate of 7.2% paid semiannually.
    (a) If the yield rate is 8% compounded semiannually, find the bond's market price.
    (b) Three years later the yield rate is 5.8%. If the bond holder wishes to sell at this time, what is the bond's current market price?
    (c) If you bought a $5000 Mauranol, Inc. bond at the price in part (a), collected 3 years of coupons, and sold at the price in part (b), what amount would you have earned on your original investment?
    (d) Suppose you made a single investment with principal equal to the amount paid in part (a), and after 3 years you received a single lump sum return equal to the amount from part (c). What interest rate compounded semiannually would you have earned?

55. Kevin Patrick paid off the loan he took out to buy his car, but once the loan was paid, he continued to deposit $400 on the first of each month in an account that paid 5.4%, compounded monthly. After four years of making these deposits, Kevin was ready to buy a new car. How much did he have in the account?

56. A young couple receive an inheritance of $72,000 that they want to set aside for a college fund for their two children. How much will this provide at the end of each half-year for a period of 9 years if it is deferred for 11 years and can be invested at 7.3%, compounded semiannually?

57. A bank is trying to decide whether to advertise some new 18-month certificates of deposit (CDs) at 6.52%, compounded quarterly, or at 6.48%, compounded continuously. Which rate is a better investment for the consumer who buys such a CD? Which rate is better for the bank?

58. A divorce settlement of $40,000 is paid in $1000 payments at the end of each of 40 months. What is the present value of this settlement if money is worth 12%, compounded monthly?

59. If $8000 is invested at 12%, compounded continuously, for 3 years, what is the total interest earned at the end of the 3 years?

60. A couple borrowed $184,000 to buy a condominium. Their loan was for 25 years and money is worth 6%, compounded monthly.
    (a) Find their monthly payment size.
    (b) Find the total amount they would pay over 25 years.
    (c) Find the total interest they would pay over 25 years.
    (d) Find the unpaid balance after 7 years.

61. Suppose a salesman invests his $12,500 bonus in a fund that earns 10.8%, compounded monthly. Suppose also that he makes contributions of $150 at the end of each month to this fund.
    (a) Find the future value after $12\frac{1}{2}$ years.
    (b) If after the $12\frac{1}{2}$ years, the fund is used to set up an annuity, how much will it pay at the end of each month for the next 10 years?

62. Three years from now, a couple plan to spend 4 months traveling in China, Japan, and Southeast Asia. When they take their trip, they would like to withdraw $10,000 at the beginning of each month to cover their expenses for that month. Starting now, how much must they deposit at the beginning of each month for the next 3 years so that the account will provide the money they want while they are traveling? Assume that such an account pays 6.6%, compounded monthly.

63. At age 22, Aruam Sdlonyer receives a $4000 IRA from her parents. At age 30, she decides that at age 67 she'd like to have a retirement fund that would pay $20,000 at the end of each month for 20 years. Suppose all investments earn 8.4%, compounded monthly. How much does Aruam need to deposit at the end of each month from ages 30 to 67 to realize her goal?

64. A company borrows $2.6 million for 15 years at 5.6%, compounded quarterly. After 2 years of regular payments, the company's profits are such that management feels they can increase the quarterly payments to $70,000 each. How long will it take to pay off the loan, and how much interest will be saved?

6   CHAPTER TEST

1. If $8000 is invested at 7%, compounded continuously, how long will it be before it grows to $47,000?

2. How much must you put aside at the end of each half-year if, in 6 years, you want to have $12,000, and the current interest rate is 6.2%, compounded semiannually?

3. To buy a municipal bond that matures to $10,000 in 9 months, you must pay $9510. What simple interest rate is earned?

4. A debt of $280,000 is amortized with 40 equal semiannual payments of $14,357.78. If interest is 8.2%, compounded semiannually, find the unpaid balance of the debt after 25 payments have been made.

5. If an investment of $1000 grew to $13,500 in 9 years, what interest rate, compounded annually, did this investment earn?

6. A couple borrowed $97,000 at 7.2%, compounded monthly, for 25 years to purchase a condominium.
   (a) Find their monthly payment.
   (b) Over the 25 years, how much interest will they pay?

7. If you borrow $2500 for 15 months at 4% simple interest, how much money must you repay after the 15 months?

8. Suppose you invest $100 at the end of each month in an account that earns 6.9%, compounded monthly. What is the future value of the account after $5\frac{1}{2}$ years?

9. Find the annual percentage yield (the effective annual rate) for an investment that earns 8.4%, compounded monthly.

10. An accountant wants to withdraw $3000 from an investment at the beginning of each quarter for the next 15 years. How much must be deposited originally if the investment earns 6%, compounded quarterly? Assume that after the 15 years, the balance is zero.

11. If $10,000 is invested at 7%, compounded continuously, what is the value of the investment after 20 years?

12. A collector made a $10,000 down payment for a classic car and agreed to make 18 quarterly payments of $1500 at the end of each quarter. If money is worth 8%, compounded quarterly, how much would the car have cost if the collector had paid cash?

13. What amount must you invest in an account that earns 6.8%, compounded quarterly, if you want to have $9500 after 5 years?

14. If $1500 is deposited at the end of each half-year in a retirement account that earns 8.2%, compounded semiannually, how long will it be before the account contains $500,000?

15. A couple would like to have $50,000 at the end of $4\frac{1}{2}$ years. They can invest $10,000 now and make additional contributions at the end of each quarter over the $4\frac{1}{2}$ years. If the investment earns 7.7%, compounded quarterly, what size payments will enable them to reach their goal?

16. A woman makes $3000 contributions at the end of each half-year to a retirement account for a period of 8 years. For the next 20 years, she makes no additional contributions and no withdrawals.
   (a) If the account earns 7.5%, compounded semiannually, find the value of the account after the 28 years.
   (b) If this account is used to set up an annuity that pays her an amount at the beginning of each 6-month period for the next 20 years, how much will each payment be?

17. Maxine deposited $400 at the beginning of each month for 15 years in an account that earned 6%, compounded monthly. Find the value of the account after the 15 years.

18. Grandparents plan to establish a college trust for their youngest grandchild. How much is needed now so the trust, which earns 6.4%, compounded quarterly, will provide $4000 at the end of each quarter for 4 years after being deferred for 10 years?

19. The following sequence is arithmetic: 298.8, 293.3, 287.8, 282.3, ...
   (a) If you were not told that this sequence was arithmetic, how could you tell that it was?
   (b) Find the 51st term of this sequence.
   (c) Find the sum of the first 51 terms.

20. A 400-milligram dose of heart medicine is taken daily. During each 24-hour period, the body eliminates 40% of this drug (so that 60% remains in the body). Thus

the amount of drug in the bloodstream just after the 31st dose is given by

$$400 + 400(0.6) + 400(0.6)^2 + 400(0.6)^3 + \ldots$$
$$+ 400(0.6)^{29} + 400(0.6)^{30}$$

Find the level of the drug in the bloodstream at this time.

21. Suppose that a 10-year corporate bond has a maturity value of $10,000 and a coupon rate of 10%, with coupons paid semiannually. Find the market price of the bond if the current yield rate is 6% compounded semiannually. Is this bond selling at a discount or at a premium?

22. If you took a home mortgage loan of $150,000 for 30 years at 8.4%, compounded monthly, your monthly payments would be $1142.76. Suppose after 2 years you had an additional $2000. Would you save more over the life of the loan by paying an extra $2000 with your 24th payment or by paying $1160 per month beginning with the 25th payment? To help you answer this question, complete the following.

(a) Find the unpaid balance after 24 payments (both including and not including the $2000 payment).

(b) Determine how long it takes to pay off the loan with the regular $1142.76 payments and the additional $2000 payment. Then find the total interest paid.

(c) Determine how long it takes to pay off the loan without the additional $2000 payment, but with monthly payments of $1160 from the 25th payment. Then find the total interest paid.

(d) Which payment method costs less?

I. Mail Solicitation Home Equity Loan: Is This a Good Deal?

Discover® offers a home equity line of credit that lowers the total of the monthly payments on several hypothetical loans by $366.12. (See the following table.)

The home equity loan payment is based on "10.49% APR annualized over a 10-year term." This means the loan is amortized at 10.49% with monthly payments.

(a) Using this interest rate and monthly payments for the 10 years, how much money will still be owed at the end of the 10 years?
(b) How much is paid during the 10 years?
(c) How much would the payment have to be to have the debt paid in the 10 years?
(d) How long would it take to pay off the debts under the original plan if interest were 15% on each loan?

Loan Type	Current Monthly Payment Example		Discover Home Equity	
	Loan Amount	Monthly Payment	Loan Amount	Monthly Payment
Bank cards	$10,000	$186,000	PAID OFF	NONE
Auto loan	$12,500	$320.03	PAID OFF	NONE
Department store cards	$2,500	$78.63	PAID OFF	NONE
Discover home equity line of credit			$25,000	$218.54
Total	$25,000	$584.66	$25,000	$218.54

Source: Discover Loan Center mailer

II. Profit Reinvestment

T. C. Hardware Store wants to construct a new building at a second location. If construction could begin immediately, the cost would be $500,000. At this time, however, the owners do not have the required 20% down payment, so they plan to invest $2000 per month of their profits until they have the necessary amount. They can invest their money in an annuity account that pays 6%, compounded monthly, but they are concerned about the 3% average inflation rate in the construction industry. They would like you to give them some projections about how 3% inflation will affect the time required to accrue the down payment and the building's eventual cost. They would also like to know how their projected profits, after the new building is complete, will affect their schedule for paying off the mortgage loan.

Specifically, the owners would like you to prepare a report that answers the following questions.

1. If the 3% annual inflation rate is accurate, how long will it take to get the down payment? *Hint:* Assume inflation is compounded monthly. Then the required down payment will be 20% of

$$500,000\left(1 + \frac{0.03}{12}\right)^n$$

where n is in months. Thus you must find n such that this amount equals the future value of the owners' annuity. The solution to the resulting equation is difficult to obtain by algebraic methods but can be found with a graphing utility.

2. If the 3% annual inflation rate is accurate (compounded monthly), what will T. C. Hardware's projected construction costs be (to the nearest hundred dollars) when it has its down payment?

3. If T. C. Hardware borrows 80% of its construction costs and amortizes that amount at 7.8%, compounded monthly, for 15 years, what will its monthly payment be?

4. Finally, the owners believe that 2 years after this new building is begun (that is, after 2 years of payments on the loan), their profits will increase enough so that they'll be able to make double mortgage payments each month until the loan is paid. Under these assumptions, how long will it take T. C. Hardware to pay off the loan?

III. Purchasing a Home

Buying a home is the biggest single investment or purchase that most individuals make. This project is designed to give you some insight into the home-buying process and the associated costs.

Find all the costs associated with buying a home by making a 20% down payment and borrowing 80% of the cost of the home.

1. Decide how much your home will cost (and how much you'll have to put down and how much to mortgage). Call a realtor to determine the cost of a home in your area (this could be a typical starter home, an average home for the area, or your dream house). Ask the realtor to identify and estimate all the closing costs associated with buying your home. Closing costs include your down payment, attorney's fees, title fees, and so on.

2. Call at least three different banks to determine mortgage loan rates for 15 years, 25 years, and 30 years and the costs associated with obtaining your loan. These associated costs of a loan are paid at closing and include an application fee, an appraisal fee, points, and so on.

3. For each bank and each different loan duration, develop a summary that contains
   (a) an itemization and explanation of all closing costs and the total amount due at closing
   (b) the monthly payment
   (c) the total amount paid over the life of the loan
   (d) the amortization schedule for each loan (use a spreadsheet or financial software package).

4. For each duration (15 years, 25 years, and 30 years), identify which bank gives the best loan rate and explain why you think it is best. Be sure to consider what is best for someone who is likely to remain in the home for 7 years or less compared with someone who is likely to stay 20 years or more.

9

CHAPTER

Derivatives

Contax66/Shutterstock.com

If a firm receives $30,000 in revenue during a 30-day month, its average revenue per day is $30,000/30 = $1000. This does not necessarily mean the actual revenue was $1000 on any one day, just that the average was $1000 per day. Similarly, if a person drove 50 miles in one hour, the average velocity was 50 miles per hour, but the driver could still have received a speeding ticket for traveling 70 miles per hour.

The smaller the time interval, the nearer the average velocity will be to the instantaneous velocity (the speedometer reading). Similarly, changes in revenue over a smaller number of units can give information about the instantaneous rate of change of revenue. The mathematical bridge from average rates of change to instantaneous rates of change is the limit.

This chapter is concerned with *limits* and *rates of change*. We will see that the *derivative* of a function can be used to determine instantaneous rates of change.

The topics and applications discussed in this chapter include the following.

Prerequisite Problem Type	For Section	Answer	Section for Review
If $f(x) = \dfrac{x^2 - x - 6}{x + 2}$, then find (a) $f(-3)$ (b) $f(-2.5)$ (c) $f(-2.1)$ (d) $f(-2)$	**9.1–9.9**	(a) -6 (b) -5.5 (c) -5.1 (d) undefined	1.2 Function notation
Factor: (a) $x^2 - x - 6$ (b) $x^2 - 4$ (c) $x^2 + 3x + 2$	**9.1** **9.7**	(a) $(x + 2)(x - 3)$ (b) $(x - 2)(x + 2)$ (c) $(x + 1)(x + 2)$	0.6 Factoring
Write as a power: (a) $\sqrt{t}$ (b) $\dfrac{1}{x}$ (c) $\dfrac{1}{\sqrt[3]{x^2 + 1}}$	**9.4–9.8**	(a) $t^{1/2}$ (b) x^{-1} (c) $(x^2 + 1)^{-1/3}$	0.3, 0.4 Exponents and radicals
Simplify: (a) $\dfrac{4(x + h)^2 - 4x^2}{h}$, if $h \neq 0$ (b) $(2x^3 + 3x + 1)(2x) + (x^2 + 4)(6x^2 + 3)$ (c) $\dfrac{x(3x^2) - x^3(1)}{x^2}$, if $x \neq 0$	**9.3** **9.5** **9.7**	(a) $8x + 4h$ (b) $10x^4 + 33x^2 + 2x + 12$ (c) $2x$	0.5 Simplifying algebraic expressions
Simplify: (a) $\dfrac{x^2 - x - 6}{x + 2}$ if $x \neq -2$ (b) $\dfrac{x^2 - 4}{x - 2}$ if $x \neq 2$	**9.1** **9.7**	(a) $x - 3$ (b) $x + 2$	0.7 Simplifying fractions
If $f(x) = 3x^2 + 2x$, find $\dfrac{f(x + h) - f(x)}{h}$, if $h \neq 0$	**9.3**	$6x + 3h + 2$	1.2 Function notation
Find the slope of the line passing through $(1, 2)$ and $(2, 4)$.	**9.3**	2	1.3 Slopes
Write the equation of the line passing through $(1, 5)$ with slope 8.	**9.3** **9.4** **9.6**	$y = 8x - 3$	1.3 Point-slope equation of a line

Limits

▮ | APPLICATION PREVIEW | ▮

Although everyone recognizes the value of eliminating any and all particulate pollution from smokestack emissions of factories, company owners are concerned about the cost of removing this pollution. Suppose that USA Steel has shown that the cost C of removing p percent of the particulate pollution from the emissions at one of its plants is

$$C = C(p) = \frac{7300p}{100 - p}$$

To investigate the cost of removing as much of the pollution as possible, we can evaluate the limit as p (the percent) approaches 100 from values less than 100. (See Example 6.) Using a limit is important in this case, because this function is undefined at $p = 100$ (it is impossible to remove 100% of the pollution).

In various applications we have seen the importance of the slope of a line as a rate of change. In particular, the slope of a linear total cost, total revenue, or profit function for a product tells us the marginals or rates of change of these functions. When these functions are not linear, how do we define marginals (and slope)?

We can get an idea about how to extend the concept of slope (and rate of change) to functions that are not linear. Observe that for many curves, if we take a very close (or "zoom-in") view near a point, the curve appears straight. See Figure 9.1. We can think of the slope of the "straight" line as the slope of the curve. The mathematical process used to obtain this "zoom-in" view is the process of taking limits. The concept of limit is essential to the study of calculus.

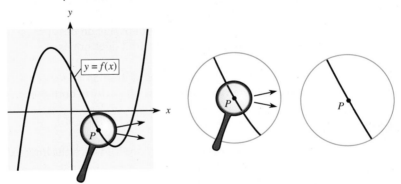

Figure 9.1   When we zoom in near point P, the curve appears straight.

Concept of a Limit   We have used the notation $f(c)$ to indicate the value of a function $f(x)$ at $x = c$. If we need to discuss a value that $f(x)$ approaches as x approaches c, we use the idea of a *limit*. For example, if

$$f(x) = \frac{x^2 - x - 6}{x + 2}$$

then we know that $x = -2$ is not in the domain of $f(x)$, so $f(-2)$ does not exist even though $f(x)$ exists for every value of $x \neq -2$. Figure 9.2 shows the graph of $y = f(x)$ with an open circle where $x = -2$. The open circle indicates that $f(-2)$ does not exist but shows that points near $x = -2$ have functional values that lie on the line on either side of the open circle. Even though $f(-2)$ is not defined, the figure shows that as x approaches -2 from either side of -2, the graph approaches the open circle at $(-2, -5)$ and the values of $f(x)$ approach -5. Thus -5 is the limit of $f(x)$ as x approaches -2, and we write

$$\lim_{x \to -2} f(x) = -5, \quad \text{or} \quad f(x) \to -5 \quad \text{as} \quad x \to -2$$

▮ | TABLE 9.1 | ▮

Left of –2	
x	$f(x) = \dfrac{x^2 - x - 6}{x + 2}$
–3.000	–6.000
–2.500	–5.500
–2.100	–5.100
–2.010	–5.010
–2.001	–5.001

Right of –2	
x	$f(x) = \dfrac{x^2 - x - 6}{x + 2}$
–1.000	–4.000
–1.500	–4.500
–1.900	–4.900
–1.990	–4.990
–1.999	–4.999

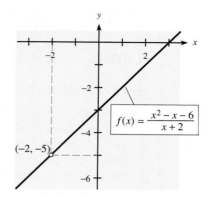

Figure 9.2

This conclusion is fairly obvious from the graph, but it is not so obvious from the equation for $f(x)$.

We can use the values near $x = -2$ in Table 9.1 to help verify that $f(x) \to -5$ as $x \to -2$. Note that to the left of -2, the values of $f(x)$ get very close to -5 as x gets very close to -2, and to the right of -2, the values of $f(x)$ get very close to -5 as x gets very close to -2. Hence, Table 9.1 and Figure 9.2 indicate that the value of $f(x)$ approaches -5 as x approaches -2 from both sides of $x = -2$.

From our discussion of the graph in Figure 9.2 and Table 9.1, we see that as x approaches -2 from either side of -2, the limit of the function is the value L that the function approaches. This limit L is not necessarily the value of the function at $x = -2$. This leads to our intuitive definition of **limit**.

Limit

Let $f(x)$ be a function defined on an open interval containing c, except perhaps at c. Then

$$\lim_{x \to c} f(x) = L$$

is read "the **limit** of $f(x)$ as x approaches c equals L." The number L exists if we can make values of $f(x)$ as close to L as we desire by choosing values of x sufficiently close to c. When the values of $f(x)$ do not approach a single finite value L as x approaches c, we say the limit does not exist.

As the definition states, a limit as $x \to c$ can exist only if the function approaches a single finite value as x approaches c from both the left and right of c.

EXAMPLE 1   Limits

Figure 9.3 shows three functions for which the limit exists as x approaches 2. Use this figure to find the following.

(a) $\lim\limits_{x \to 2} f(x)$ and $f(2)$ (if it exists)

(b) $\lim\limits_{x \to 2} g(x)$ and $g(2)$ (if it exists)

(c) $\lim\limits_{x \to 2} h(x)$ and $h(2)$ (if it exists)

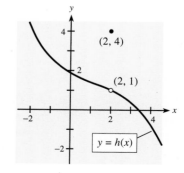

Figure 9.3   (a)   (b)   (c)

Solution

(a) From the graph in Figure 9.3(a), we see that as x approaches 2 from both the left and the right, the graph approaches the point $(2, 3)$. Thus $f(x)$ approaches the single value 3. That is,

$$\lim_{x \to 2} f(x) = 3$$

The value of $f(2)$ is the y-coordinate of the point on the graph at $x = 2$. Thus $f(2) = 3$.

(b) Figure 9.3(b) shows that as x approaches 2 from both the left and the right, the graph approaches the open circle at $(2, -1)$. Thus

$$\lim_{x \to 2} g(x) = -1$$

The figure also shows that at $x = 2$ there is no point on the graph. Thus $g(2)$ is undefined.

(c) Figure 9.3(c) shows that

$$\lim_{x \to 2} h(x) = 1$$

The figure also shows that at $x = 2$ there is a point on the graph at $(2, 4)$. Thus $h(2) = 4$, and we see that $\lim_{x \to 2} h(x) \neq h(2)$.

As Example 1 shows, the limit of the function as x approaches c may or may not be the same as the value of the function at $x = c$.

In Example 1 we saw that the limit as x approaches 2 meant the limit as x approaches 2 from both the left and the right. We can also consider limits only from the left or only from the right; these are called **one-sided limits**.

One-Sided Limits

> **Limit from the Right:** $\lim_{x \to c^+} f(x) = L$
>
> means the values of $f(x)$ approach the value L as $x \to c$ but $x > c$.
>
> **Limit from the Left:** $\lim_{x \to c^-} f(x) = M$
>
> means the values of $f(x)$ approach the value M as $x \to c$ but $x < c$.

Note that when one or both one-sided limits fail to exist, then the limit does not exist. Also, when the one-sided limits differ, such as if $L \neq M$ above, then the values of $f(x)$ do not approach a *single* value as x approaches c, and $\lim_{x \to c} f(x)$ does not exist.

EXAMPLE 2   One-Sided Limits

Using the functions graphed in Figure 9.4, determine why the limit as $x \to 2$ does not exist for

(a) $f(x)$.

(b) $g(x)$.

(c) $h(x)$.

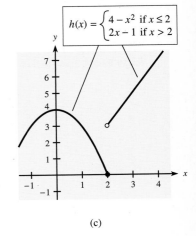

(a)   (b)   (c)

Figure 9.4

Solution

(a) As $x \to 2$ from the left side and the right side of $x = 2$, $f(x)$ increases without bound, which we denote by saying that $f(x)$ approaches $+\infty$ as $x \to 2$. In this case, $\lim_{x \to 2} f(x)$ does not exist [denoted by $\lim_{x \to 2} f(x)$ DNE] because $f(x)$ does not approach a finite value as $x \to 2$. In this case, we write

$$f(x) \to +\infty \text{ as } x \to 2$$

The graph has a vertical asymptote at $x = 2$.

(b) As $x \to 2$ from the left, $g(x)$ approaches $-\infty$, and as $x \to 2$ from the right, $g(x)$ approaches $+\infty$, so $g(x)$ does not approach a finite value as $x \to 2$. Therefore, the limit does not exist. The graph of $y = g(x)$ has a vertical asymptote at $x = 2$. In this case we summarize by writing

$$\lim_{x \to 2^-} g(x) \text{ DNE} \quad \text{or} \quad g(x) \to -\infty \text{ as } x \to 2^-$$
$$\lim_{x \to 2^+} g(x) \text{ DNE} \quad \text{or} \quad g(x) \to +\infty \text{ as } x \to 2^+$$

and

$$\lim_{x \to 2} g(x) \text{ DNE}$$

(c) As $x \to 2$ from the left, the graph approaches the point at $(2, 0)$, so $\lim_{x \to 2^-} h(x) = 0$. As $x \to 2$ from the right, the graph approaches the open circle at $(2, 3)$, so $\lim_{x \to 2^+} h(x) = 3$. Because these one-sided limits differ, $\lim_{x \to 2} h(x)$ does not exist.

Examples 1 and 2 illustrate the following two important facts regarding limits.

The Limit

1. The limit is said to exist only if the following conditions are satisfied:
    (a) The limit L is a finite value (real number).
    (b) The limit as x approaches c from the left equals the limit as x approaches c from the right. That is, we must have

    $$\lim_{x \to c^-} f(x) = \lim_{x \to c^+} f(x)$$

    Figure 9.4 and Example 2 illustrate cases where $\lim_{x \to c} f(x)$ does not exist.

2. The limit of a function as x approaches c is independent of the value of the function at c. When $\lim_{x \to c} f(x)$ exists, the value of the function at c may be (i) the same as the limit, (ii) undefined, or (iii) defined but different from the limit (see Figure 9.3 and Example 1).

CHECKPOINT

1. Can $\lim_{x \to c^-} f(x)$ exist if $f(c)$ is undefined?
2. Does $\lim_{x \to c^-} f(x)$ exist if $f(c) = 0$?
3. Does $f(c) = 1$ if $\lim_{x \to c} f(x) = 1$?
4. If $\lim_{x \to c^-} f(x) = 0$, does $\lim_{x \to c} f(x)$ exist?

Properties of Limits; Algebraic Evaluation

We have seen that the value of the limit of a function as $x \to c$ will not always be the same as the value of the function at $x = c$. However, there are many functions for which the limit and the functional value agree [see Figure 9.3(a)], and for these functions we can easily evaluate limits.

Properties of Limits

If k is a constant, $\lim_{x \to c} f(x) = L$, and $\lim_{x \to c} g(x) = M$, then the following are true.

I. $\lim_{x \to c} k = k$

II. $\lim_{x \to c} x = c$

III. $\lim_{x \to c} [f(x) \pm g(x)] = L \pm M$

IV. $\lim_{x \to c} [f(x) \cdot g(x)] = LM$

V. $\lim_{x \to c} \dfrac{f(x)}{g(x)} = \dfrac{L}{M}$ if $M \neq 0$

VI. $\lim_{x \to c} \sqrt[n]{f(x)} = \sqrt[n]{\lim_{x \to c} f(x)} = \sqrt[n]{L}$, provided that $L > 0$ when n is even.

If f is a polynomial function, then Properties I–IV imply that $\lim\limits_{x \to c} f(x)$ can be found by evaluating $f(c)$. Moreover, if h is a rational function whose denominator is not zero at $x = c$, then Property V implies that $\lim\limits_{x \to c} h(x)$ can be found by evaluating $h(c)$. The following summarizes these observations and recalls the definitions of polynomial and rational functions.

Function	Definition	Limit
Polynomial function	The function $$f(x) = a_n x^n + a_{n-1} x^{n-1} + \cdots + a_1 x + a_0,$$ where $a_n \neq 0$ and n is a positive integer, is called a **polynomial function** of degree n.	$\lim\limits_{x \to c} f(x) = f(c)$ for all values c (by Properties I–IV)
Rational function	The function $$h(x) = \frac{f(x)}{g(x)}$$ where both $f(x)$ and $g(x)$ are polynomial functions, is called a **rational function**.	$\lim\limits_{x \to c} h(x) = \lim\limits_{x \to c} \frac{f(x)}{g(x)} = \frac{f(c)}{g(c)}$ when $g(c) \neq 0$ (by Property V)

EXAMPLE   3   Limits

Find the following limits, if they exist.

(a) $\lim\limits_{x \to -1} (x^3 - 2x)$ (b) $\lim\limits_{x \to 4} \dfrac{x^2 - 4x}{x - 2}$

Solution

(a) Note that $f(x) = x^3 - 2x$ is a polynomial, so

$$\lim\limits_{x \to -1} f(x) = f(-1) = (-1)^3 - 2(-1) = 1$$

Figure 9.5(a) shows the graph of $f(x) = x^3 - 2x$.

(b) Note that this limit has the form

$$\lim\limits_{x \to c} \frac{f(x)}{g(x)}$$

where $f(x)$ and $g(x)$ are polynomials and $g(c) \neq 0$. Therefore, we have

$$\lim\limits_{x \to 4} \frac{x^2 - 4x}{x - 2} = \frac{4^2 - 4(4)}{4 - 2} = \frac{0}{2} = 0$$

Figure 9.5(b) shows the graph of $g(x) = \dfrac{x^2 - 4x}{x - 2}$.

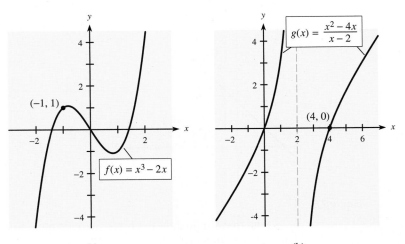

Figure 9.5   (a)   (b)

We have seen that we can use Property V to find the limit of a rational function $f(x)/g(x)$ as long as the denominator is *not* zero. If the limit of the denominator of $f(x)/g(x)$ *is* zero, then there are two possible cases.

Rational Functions: Evaluating Limits of the Form $\lim\limits_{x \to c} \dfrac{f(x)}{g(x)}$ **where** $\lim\limits_{x \to c} g(x) = 0$	**Type I.** If $\lim\limits_{x \to c} f(x) = 0$ and $\lim\limits_{x \to c} g(x) = 0$, then $\lim\limits_{x \to c} \dfrac{f(x)}{g(x)}$ has the **0/0 indeterminate form** at $x = c$. We can factor $x - c$ from $f(x)$ and $g(x)$, reduce the fraction, and then find the limit of the resulting expression, if it exists.
	Type II. If $\lim\limits_{x \to c} f(x) \neq 0$ and $\lim\limits_{x \to c} g(x) = 0$, then $\lim\limits_{x \to c} \dfrac{f(x)}{g(x)}$ does not exist. In this case, the values of $f(x)/g(x)$ become unbounded as x approaches c; the line $x = c$ is a vertical asymptote.

EXAMPLE 4   0/0 Indeterminate Form

Evaluate the following limits, if they exist.

(a) $\lim\limits_{x \to 2} \dfrac{x^2 - 4}{x - 2}$ 　　　　 (b) $\lim\limits_{x \to 1} \dfrac{x^2 - 3x + 2}{x^2 - 1}$

Solution

(a) This limit has the 0/0 indeterminate form at $x = 2$ because both the numerator and denominator equal zero when $x = 2$. Thus we can factor $x - 2$ from both the numerator and the denominator and reduce the fraction. (We can divide by $x - 2$ because $x - 2 \neq 0$ while $x \to 2$.)

$$\lim_{x \to 2} \frac{x^2 - 4}{x - 2} = \lim_{x \to 2} \frac{(x - 2)(x + 2)}{x - 2} = \lim_{x \to 2} (x + 2) = 4$$

Figure 9.6(a) shows the graph of $f(x) = (x^2 - 4)/(x - 2)$. Note the open circle at $(2, 4)$.

(b) By substituting 1 for x in $(x^2 - 3x + 2)/(x^2 - 1)$, we see that the expression has the 0/0 indeterminate form at $x = 1$, so $x - 1$ is a factor of both the numerator and the denominator. (We can then reduce the fraction because $x - 1 \neq 0$ while $x \to 1$.)

$$\lim_{x \to 1} \frac{x^2 - 3x + 2}{x^2 - 1} = \lim_{x \to 1} \frac{(x - 1)(x - 2)}{(x - 1)(x + 1)} = \lim_{x \to 1} \frac{x - 2}{x + 1}$$

$$= \frac{1 - 2}{1 + 1} = \frac{-1}{2} \quad (\text{by Property V})$$

Figure 9.6(b) shows the graph of $g(x) = (x^2 - 3x + 2)/(x^2 - 1)$. Note the open circle at $(1, -\frac{1}{2})$.

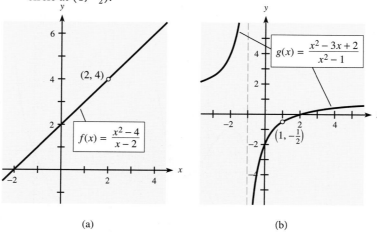

Figure 9.6 　　　　(a) 　　　　　　　　　　(b)

Note that although both problems in Example 4 had the 0/0 indeterminate form, they had different answers.

EXAMPLE   5   **Limit with $a/0$ Form**

Find $\lim\limits_{x \to 1} \dfrac{x^2 + 3x + 2}{x - 1}$, if it exists.

Solution

Substituting 1 for x in the function results in $6/0$, so this limit has the form $a/0$, with $a \neq 0$, and is like the Type II form discussed previously. Hence the limit does not exist. Because the numerator is not zero when $x = 1$, we know that $x - 1$ is *not* a factor of the numerator, and we cannot divide numerator and denominator as we did in Example 4. Table 9.2 confirms that this limit does not exist, because the values of the expression become unbounded as x approaches 1.

TABLE 9.2			
Left of $x = 1$		**Right of $x = 1$**	
x	$\dfrac{x^2 + 3x + 2}{x - 1}$	x	$\dfrac{x^2 + 3x + 2}{x - 1}$
0	−2	2	12
0.5	−7.5	1.5	17.5
0.7	−15.3	1.2	35.2
0.9	−55.1	1.1	65.1
0.99	−595.01	1.01	605.01
0.999	−5995.001	1.001	6005.001
0.9999	−59,995.0001	1.0001	60,005.0001
$\lim\limits_{x \to 1^-} \dfrac{x^2 + 3x + 2}{x - 1}$ DNE		$\lim\limits_{x \to 1^+} \dfrac{x^2 + 3x + 2}{x - 1}$ DNE	
$(f(x) \to -\infty$ as $x \to 1^-)$		$(f(x) \to +\infty$ as $x \to 1^+)$	

The left-hand and right-hand limits do not exist. Thus $\lim\limits_{x \to 1} \dfrac{x^2 + 3x + 2}{x - 1}$ does not exist.

In Example 5, even though the left-hand and right-hand limits do not exist (see Table 9.2), knowledge that the functional values are unbounded (that is, that they become infinite) is helpful in graphing. The graph is shown in Figure 9.7. We see that $x = 1$ is a vertical asymptote.

Figure 9.7

EXAMPLE   6   **Cost-Benefit** | APPLICATION PREVIEW |

USA Steel has shown that the cost C of removing p percent of the particulate pollution from the smokestack emissions at one of its plants is

$$C = C(p) = \frac{7300p}{100 - p}$$

Investigate the cost of removing as much of the pollution as possible.

© iStockphoto.com/Stefan Baum

Solution

First note that the costs of removing 90% and 99% of the pollution are found as follows:

Removing 90%: $C(90) = \dfrac{7300(90)}{100 - 90} = \dfrac{657,000}{10} = 65,700$ (dollars)

Removing 99%: $C(99) = \dfrac{7300(99)}{100 - 99} = \dfrac{722,700}{1} = 722,700$ (dollars)

The cost of removing 100% of the pollution is undefined because the denominator of the function is 0 when $p = 100$. To see what the cost approaches as p approaches 100 from values smaller than 100, we evaluate $\lim\limits_{x \to 100^-} \dfrac{7300p}{100 - p}$. This limit has the Type II form for rational functions. Thus $\dfrac{7300\,p}{100 - p} \to +\infty$ as $x \to 100^-$, which means that as the amount of pollution that is removed approaches 100%, the cost increases without bound. (That is, it is impossible to remove 100% of the pollution.)

CHECKPOINT

5. Evaluate the following limits (if they exist).

(a) $\lim\limits_{x \to -3} \dfrac{2x^2 + 5x - 3}{x^2 - 9}$ (b) $\lim\limits_{x \to 5} \dfrac{x^2 - 3x - 3}{x^2 - 8x + 1}$ (c) $\lim\limits_{x \to -3/4} \dfrac{4x}{4x + 3}$

In Problems 6–9, assume that f, g, and h are polynomials.

6. Does $\lim\limits_{x \to c} f(x) = f(c)$?

7. Does $\lim\limits_{x \to c} \dfrac{g(x)}{h(x)} = \dfrac{g(c)}{h(c)}$?

8. If $g(c) = 0$ and $h(c) = 0$, can we be certain that

(a) $\lim\limits_{x \to c} \dfrac{g(x)}{h(x)} = 0$?   (b) $\lim\limits_{x \to c} \dfrac{g(x)}{h(x)}$ exists?

9. If $g(c) \neq 0$ and $h(c) = 0$, what can be said about $\lim\limits_{x \to c} \dfrac{g(x)}{h(x)}$ and $\lim\limits_{x \to c} \dfrac{h(x)}{g(x)}$?

Limits of Piecewise Defined Functions

As we noted in Section 2.4, "Special Functions and Their Graphs," many applications are modeled by piecewise defined functions. To see how we evaluate a limit involving a piecewise defined function, consider the following example.

EXAMPLE 7   Limits of a Piecewise Defined Function

Find $\lim\limits_{x \to 1^-} f(x)$, $\lim\limits_{x \to 1^+} f(x)$, and $\lim\limits_{x \to 1} f(x)$, if they exist, for

$$f(x) = \begin{cases} x^2 + 1 & \text{if } x \leq 1 \\ x + 2 & \text{if } x > 1 \end{cases}$$

| TABLE 9.3 |

Left of 1	
x	$f(x) = x^2 + 1$
0.1	1.01
0.9	1.81
0.99	1.98
0.999	1.998
0.9999	1.9998

Right of 1	
x	$f(x) = x + 2$
1.2	3.2
1.01	3.01
1.001	3.001
1.0001	3.0001
1.00001	3.00001

Solution

Because $f(x)$ is defined by $x^2 + 1$ when $x < 1$,

$$\lim_{x \to 1^-} f(x) = \lim_{x \to 1^-} (x^2 + 1) = 2$$

Because $f(x)$ is defined by $x + 2$ when $x > 1$,

$$\lim_{x \to 1^+} f(x) = \lim_{x \to 1^+} (x + 2) = 3$$

And because

$$2 = \lim_{x \to 1^-} f(x) \neq \lim_{x \to 1^+} f(x) = 3$$

$\lim\limits_{x \to 1} f(x)$ does not exist.

Table 9.3 and Figure 9.8 show these results numerically and graphically.

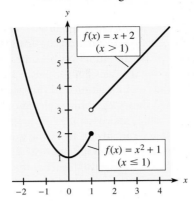

$f(x) = x + 2$
$(x > 1)$

$f(x) = x^2 + 1$
$(x \le 1)$

Figure 9.8

Calculator Note We have used graphical, numerical, and algebraic methods to understand and evaluate limits. Graphing calculators can be especially effective when exploring limits graphically or numerically. See Appendix C, Section 9.1, for details.

EXAMPLE 8   Limits: Graphically, Numerically, and Algebraically

Consider the following limits.

(a) $\lim\limits_{x \to 5} \dfrac{x^2 + 2x - 35}{x^2 - 6x + 5}$ (b) $\lim\limits_{x \to -1} \dfrac{2x}{x + 1}$

Investigate each limit by using the following methods.

(i) Graphically: Graph the function with a graphing calculator and trace near the limiting x-value.
(ii) Numerically: Use the table feature of a graphing calculator to evaluate the function very close to the limiting x-value.
(iii) Algebraically: Use properties of limits and algebraic techniques.

Solution

(a) $\lim\limits_{x \to 5} \dfrac{x^2 + 2x - 35}{x^2 - 6x + 5}$

(i) Figure 9.9(a) shows the graph of $y = (x^2 + 2x - 35)/(x^2 - 6x + 5)$. Tracing near $x = 5$ shows y-values getting close to 3.
(ii) Figure 9.9(b) shows a table for $y_1 = (x^2 + 2x - 35)/(x^2 - 6x + 5)$ with x-values approaching 5 from both sides (note that the function is undefined at $x = 5$). Again, the y-values approach 3 as x approaches 5 from both sides.

Both (i) and (ii) strongly suggest $\lim\limits_{x \to 5} \dfrac{x^2 + 2x - 35}{x^2 - 6x + 5} = 3$.

(iii) Algebraic evaluation of this limit confirms what the graph and the table suggest.

$$\lim_{x \to 5} \frac{x^2 + 2x - 35}{x^2 - 6x + 5} = \lim_{x \to 5} \frac{(x + 7)(x - 5)}{(x - 1)(x - 5)} = \lim_{x \to 5} \frac{x + 7}{x - 1} = \frac{12}{4} = 3$$

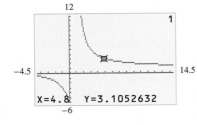

Figure 9.9   (a)   (b)

(b) $\displaystyle\lim_{x\to-1}\frac{2x}{x+1}$

 (i) Figure 9.10(a) shows the graph of $y = 2x/(x+1)$; it indicates a break in the graph near $x = -1$. Evaluation confirms that the break occurs at $x = -1$ and also suggests that the function becomes unbounded near $x = -1$. In addition, we can see that as x approaches -1 from opposite sides, the function is headed in different directions. All this suggests that the limit does not exist.

 (ii) Figure 9.10(b) shows a graphing calculator table of values for $y_1 = 2x/(x+1)$ and with x-values approaching $x = -1$ from both sides. The table reinforces our preliminary conclusion from the graph that the limit does not exist, because the function is unbounded near $x = -1$.

 (iii) Algebraically we see that this limit has the form $-2/0$. Thus $\displaystyle\lim_{x\to-1}\frac{2x}{x+1}$ DNE.

Figure 9.10   (a)   (b)

We could also use the graphing and table features of spreadsheets to explore limits.

CHECKPOINT SOLUTIONS

1. Yes. For example, Figure 9.2 and Table 9.1 show that this is possible for $f(x) = \dfrac{x^2 - x - 6}{x + 2}$. Remember that $\displaystyle\lim_{x\to c} f(x)$ does not depend on $f(c)$.

2. Not necessarily. Figure 9.4(c) shows the graph of $y = h(x)$ with $h(2) = 0$, but $\displaystyle\lim_{x\to 2} h(x)$ does not exist.

3. Not necessarily. Figure 9.3(c) shows the graph of $y = h(x)$ with $\displaystyle\lim_{x\to 2} h(x) = 1$ but $h(2) = 4$.

4. Not necessarily. For example, Figure 9.4(c) shows the graph of $y = h(x)$ with $\displaystyle\lim_{x\to 2^-} h(x) = 0$, but with $\displaystyle\lim_{x\to 2^+} h(x) = 2$, so the limit does not exist. Recall that if $\displaystyle\lim_{x\to c^-} f(x) = \lim_{x\to c^+} f(x) = L$, then $\displaystyle\lim_{x\to c} f(x) = L$.

5. (a) $\displaystyle\lim_{x\to-3}\frac{2x^2 + 5x - 3}{x^2 - 9} = \lim_{x\to-3}\frac{(2x-1)(x+3)}{(x+3)(x-3)} = \lim_{x\to-3}\frac{2x-1}{x-3} = \frac{-7}{-6} = \frac{7}{6}$

 (b) $\displaystyle\lim_{x\to 5}\frac{x^2 - 3x - 3}{x^2 - 8x + 1} = \frac{7}{-14} = -\frac{1}{2}$

 (c) Substituting $x = -3/4$ gives $-3/0$, so $\displaystyle\lim_{x\to-3/4}\frac{4x}{4x+3}$ does not exist.

6. Yes, Properties I–IV yield this result.

7. Not necessarily. If $h(c) \neq 0$, then this is true. Otherwise, it is not true.

8. For both (a) and (b), $g(x)/h(x)$ has the $0/0$ indeterminate form at $x = c$. In this case we can make no general conclusion about the limit. It is possible for the limit to exist (and be zero or nonzero) or not to exist. Consider the following $0/0$ indeterminate forms.

 (i) $\displaystyle\lim_{x\to 0}\frac{x^2}{x} = \lim_{x\to 0} x = 0$ (ii) $\displaystyle\lim_{x\to 0}\frac{x(x+1)}{x} = \lim_{x\to 0}(x+1) = 1$

 (iii) $\displaystyle\lim_{x\to 0}\frac{x}{x^2} = \lim_{x\to 0}\frac{1}{x}$, which does not exist

9. $\displaystyle\lim_{x\to c}\frac{g(x)}{h(x)}$ does not exist and $\displaystyle\lim_{x\to c}\frac{h(x)}{g(x)} = 0$

| EXERCISES | 9.1

In Problems 1–6, a graph of $y = f(x)$ is shown and a c-value is given. For each problem, use the graph to find the following, whenever they exist.

(a) $\lim\limits_{x \to c} f(x)$ and   (b) $f(c)$

1. $c = 4$

2. $c = 6$

3. $c = 20$

4. $c = -10$

5. $c = -8$

6. $c = -2$

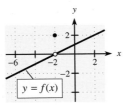

In Problems 7–10, use the graph of $y = f(x)$ and the given c-value to find the following, whenever they exist.

(a) $\lim\limits_{x \to c^-} f(x)$ (b) $\lim\limits_{x \to c^+} f(x)$
(c) $\lim\limits_{x \to c} f(x)$ (d) $f(c)$

7. $c = -10$

8. $c = 2$

9. $c = -4\frac{1}{2}$

10. $c = 2$

In Problems 11–14, complete each table and predict the limit, if it exists.

11. $f(x) = \dfrac{2 - x - x^2}{x - 1}$

$\lim\limits_{x \to 1} f(x) = ?$

x	$f(x)$
0.9	
0.99	
0.999	
1.001	
1.01	
1.1	

12. $f(x) = \dfrac{2x + 1}{\frac{1}{4} - x^2}$

$\lim\limits_{x \to -0.5} f(x) = ?$

x	$f(x)$
−0.51	
−0.501	
−0.5001	
−0.4999	
−0.499	
−0.49	

13. $f(x) = \begin{cases} 5x - 1 & \text{for } x < 1 \\ 8 - 2x - x^2 & \text{for } x \ge 1 \end{cases}$

$\lim\limits_{x \to 1} f(x) = ?$

x	$f(x)$
0.9	
0.99	
0.999	
1.001	
1.01	
1.1	

14. $f(x) = \begin{cases} 4 - x^2 & \text{for } x \le -2 \\ x^2 + 2x & \text{for } x > -2 \end{cases}$

$\lim\limits_{x \to -2} f(x) = ?$

x	$f(x)$
−2.1	
−2.01	
−2.001	
−1.999	
−1.99	

In Problems 15–38, use properties of limits and algebraic methods to find the limits, if they exist.

15. $\lim\limits_{x \to -35} (34 + x)$ **16.** $\lim\limits_{x \to 80} (82 - x)$

17. $\lim\limits_{x \to -1} (4x^3 - 2x^2 + 2)$

18. $\lim\limits_{x \to 3} (2x^3 - 12x^2 + 5x + 3)$

19. $\lim\limits_{x \to -1/2} \dfrac{4x - 2}{4x^2 + 1}$ **20.** $\lim\limits_{x \to -1/3} \dfrac{1 - 3x}{9x^2 + 1}$

21. $\lim\limits_{x \to 3} \dfrac{x^2 - 9}{x - 3}$ **22.** $\lim\limits_{x \to -4} \dfrac{x^2 - 16}{x + 4}$

23. $\lim\limits_{x \to 7} \dfrac{x^2 - 8x + 7}{x^2 - 6x - 7}$ **24.** $\lim\limits_{x \to -5} \dfrac{x^2 + 8x + 15}{x^2 + 5x}$

25. $\lim\limits_{x \to 10} \dfrac{3x^2 - 30x}{x^2 - 100}$

26. $\lim\limits_{x \to -6} \dfrac{2x^2 - 72}{3x^2 + 18x}$

27. $\lim\limits_{x \to -2} \dfrac{x^2 + 4x + 4}{x^2 + 3x + 2}$

28. $\lim\limits_{x \to 10} \dfrac{x^2 - 8x - 20}{x^2 - 11x + 10}$

29. $\lim\limits_{x \to 3} f(x)$, where $f(x) = \begin{cases} 10 - 2x & \text{if } x < 3 \\ x^2 - x & \text{if } x \geq 3 \end{cases}$

30. $\lim\limits_{x \to 5} f(x)$, where $f(x) = \begin{cases} 7x - 10 & \text{if } x < 5 \\ 25 & \text{if } x \geq 5 \end{cases}$

31. $\lim\limits_{x \to -1} f(x)$, where $f(x) = \begin{cases} x^2 + \dfrac{4}{x} & \text{if } x \leq -1 \\ 3x^3 - x - 1 & \text{if } x > -1 \end{cases}$

32. $\lim\limits_{x \to 2} f(x)$, where $f(x) = \begin{cases} \dfrac{x^3 - 4}{x - 3} & \text{if } x \leq 2 \\ \dfrac{3 - x^2}{x} & \text{if } x > 2 \end{cases}$

33. $\lim\limits_{x \to 2} \dfrac{x^2 + 6x + 9}{x - 2}$

34. $\lim\limits_{x \to 5} \dfrac{x^2 - 6x + 8}{x - 5}$

35. $\lim\limits_{x \to -1} \dfrac{x^2 + 5x + 6}{x + 1}$

36. $\lim\limits_{x \to 3} \dfrac{x^2 + 2x - 3}{x - 3}$

37. $\lim\limits_{h \to 0} \dfrac{(x + h)^3 - x^3}{h}$

38. $\lim\limits_{h \to 0} \dfrac{2(x + h)^2 - 2x^2}{h}$

In Problems 39–42, graph each function with a graphing calculator and use it to predict the limit. Check your work either by using the table feature of the calculator or by finding the limit algebraically.

39. $\lim\limits_{x \to 10} \dfrac{x^2 - 19x + 90}{3x^2 - 30x}$

40. $\lim\limits_{x \to -3} \dfrac{x^4 + 3x^3}{2x^4 - 18x^2}$

41. $\lim\limits_{x \to -1} \dfrac{x^3 - x}{x^2 + 2x + 1}$

42. $\lim\limits_{x \to 5} \dfrac{x^2 - 7x + 10}{x^2 - 10x + 25}$

In Problems 43–46, use the table feature of a graphing calculator to predict each limit. Check your work by using either a graphical or an algebraic approach.

43. $\lim\limits_{x \to -2} \dfrac{x^4 - 4x^2}{x^2 + 8x + 12}$

44. $\lim\limits_{x \to -4} \dfrac{x^3 + 4x^2}{2x^2 + 7x - 4}$

45. $\lim\limits_{x \to 4} f(x)$, where $f(x) = \begin{cases} 12 - \dfrac{3}{4}x & \text{if } x \leq 4 \\ x^2 - 7 & \text{if } x > 4 \end{cases}$

46. $\lim\limits_{x \to 7} f(x)$, where $f(x) = \begin{cases} 2 + x - x^2 & \text{if } x \leq 7 \\ 13 - 9x & \text{if } x > 7 \end{cases}$

47. Use values 0.1, 0.01, 0.001, 0.0001, and 0.00001 with your calculator to approximate

$$\lim\limits_{a \to 0} (1 + a)^{1/a}$$

to three decimal places. This limit equals the special number e that is discussed in Section 5.1, "Exponential Functions," and Section 6.2, "Compound Interest; Geometric Sequences."

48. (a) If $\lim\limits_{x \to 2^+} f(x) = 5$, $\lim\limits_{x \to 2^-} f(x) = 5$, and $f(2) = 0$, find $\lim\limits_{x \to 2} f(x)$, if it exists. Explain your conclusions.

(b) If $\lim\limits_{x \to 0^+} f(x) = 3$, $\lim\limits_{x \to 0^-} f(x) = 0$, and $f(0) = 0$, find $\lim\limits_{x \to 0} f(x)$, if it exists. Explain your conclusions.

49. If $\lim\limits_{x \to 3} f(x) = 4$ and $\lim\limits_{x \to 3} g(x) = -2$, find

(a) $\lim\limits_{x \to 3} [f(x) + g(x)]$

(b) $\lim\limits_{x \to 3} [f(x) - g(x)]$

(c) $\lim\limits_{x \to 3} [f(x) \cdot g(x)]$

(d) $\lim\limits_{x \to 3} \dfrac{g(x)}{f(x)}$

50. If $\lim\limits_{x \to -2} f(x) = 6$ and $\lim\limits_{x \to -2} g(x) = 3$, find

(a) $\lim\limits_{x \to -2} [5f(x) - 4g(x)]$

(b) $\lim\limits_{x \to -2} [g(x)]^2$

(c) $\lim\limits_{x \to -2} [4 - xf(x)]$

(d) $\lim\limits_{x \to -2} \left[\dfrac{f(x)}{g(x)} \right]$

51. If $\lim\limits_{x \to 2} [f(x) + g(x)] = 5$ and $\lim\limits_{x \to 2} g(x) = 11$, find

(a) $\lim\limits_{x \to 2} f(x)$

(b) $\lim\limits_{x \to 2} \{[f(x)]^2 - [g(x)]^2\}$

(c) $\lim\limits_{x \to 2} \dfrac{3g(x)}{f(x) - g(x)}$

52. If $\lim\limits_{x \to 5} [f(x) - g(x)] = 8$ and $\lim\limits_{x \to 5} g(x) = 2$, find

(a) $\lim\limits_{x \to 5} f(x)$

(b) $\lim\limits_{x \to 5} \{[g(x)]^2 - f(x)\}$

(c) $\lim\limits_{x \to 5} \left[\dfrac{2xg(x)}{4 - f(x)} \right]$

APPLICATIONS

53. *Revenue* The total revenue for a product is given by

$$R(x) = 1600x - x^2$$

where x is the number of units sold. What is $\lim\limits_{x \to 100} R(x)$?

54. *Profit* If the profit function for a product is given by

$$P(x) = 92x - x^2 - 1760$$

find $\lim\limits_{x \to 40} P(x)$.

55. *Sales and training* The average monthly sales volume (in thousands of dollars) for a firm depends on the number of hours x of training of its sales staff, according to

$$S(x) = \dfrac{4}{x} + 30 + \dfrac{x}{4}, \quad 4 \leq x \leq 100$$

(a) Find $\lim\limits_{x \to 4^+} S(x)$.

(b) Find $\lim\limits_{x \to 100^-} S(x)$.

56. *Sales and training* During the first 4 months of employment, the monthly sales S (in thousands of dollars) for a new salesperson depend on the number of hours x of training, as follows:

$$S = S(x) = \dfrac{9}{x} + 10 + \dfrac{x}{4}, \quad x \geq 4$$

(a) Find $\lim\limits_{x \to 4^+} S(x)$.

(b) Find $\lim\limits_{x \to 10} S(x)$.

57. *Advertising and sales* Suppose that the daily sales S (in dollars) t days after the end of an advertising campaign are

$$S = S(t) = 400 + \frac{2400}{t + 1}$$

(a) Find $S(0)$.   (b) Find $\lim\limits_{t \to 7} S(t)$.
(c) Find $\lim\limits_{t \to 14} S(t)$.

58. *Advertising and sales* Sales y (in thousands of dollars) are related to advertising expenses x (in thousands of dollars) according to

$$y = y(x) = \frac{200x}{x + 10}, \quad x \geq 0$$

(a) Find $\lim\limits_{x \to 10} y(x)$.   (b) Find $\lim\limits_{x \to 0^+} y(x)$.

59. *Productivity* During an 8-hour shift, the rate of change of productivity (in units per hour) of children's phonographs assembled after t hours on the job is

$$r(t) = \frac{128(t^2 + 6t)}{(t^2 + 6t + 18)^2}, \quad 0 \leq t \leq 8$$

(a) Find $\lim\limits_{t \to 4} r(t)$.   (b) Find $\lim\limits_{t \to 8} r(t)$.
(c) Is the rate of productivity higher near the lunch break (at $t = 4$) or near quitting time (at $t = 8$)?

60. *Revenue* If the revenue for a product is $R(x) = 100x - 0.1x^2$, and the average revenue per unit is

$$\overline{R}(x) = \frac{R(x)}{x}, \quad x > 0$$

find (a) $\lim\limits_{x \to 100} \dfrac{R(x)}{x}$ and   (b) $\lim\limits_{x \to 0^+} \dfrac{R(x)}{x}$

61. *Cost-benefit* Suppose that the cost C of obtaining water that contains p percent impurities is given by

$$C(p) = \frac{120,000}{p} - 1200$$

(a) Find $\lim\limits_{p \to 100^-} C(p)$, if it exists. Interpret this result.
(b) Find $\lim\limits_{p \to 0^+} C(p)$, if it exists.
(c) Is complete purity possible? Explain.

62. *Cost-benefit* Suppose that the cost C of removing p percent of the particulate pollution from the smokestacks of an industrial plant is given by

$$C(p) = \frac{730,000}{100 - p} - 7300$$

(a) Find $\lim\limits_{p \to 80} C(p)$
(b) Find $\lim\limits_{p \to 100^-} C(p)$ if it exists.
(c) Can 100% of the particulate pollution be removed? Explain.

63. *Federal income tax* Use the tax rate schedule for single taxpayers, and create a table of values that could be used to find the following limits, if they exist. Let x represent the amount of taxable income, and let $T(x)$ represent the tax due.

(a) $\lim\limits_{x \to 34,000^-} T(x)$ (b) $\lim\limits_{x \to 34,000^+} T(x)$
(c) $\lim\limits_{x \to 34,000} T(x)$

Schedule X—Single

If taxable income is over—	But not over—	The tax is:
$0	$8375	10% of the amount over $0
$8375	$34,000	$837.50 plus 15% of the amount over 8375
$34,000	$82,400	$4681.25 plus 25% of the amount over 34,000
$82,400	$171,850	$16,781.25 plus 28% of the amount over 82,400
$171,850	$373,650	$41,827.25 plus 33% of the amount over 171,850
$373,650	no limit	$108,421.25 plus 35% of the amount over 373,650

Source: Internal Revenue Service

64. *Parking costs* The Ace Parking Garage charges $5.00 for parking for 2 hours or less and $1.50 for each extra hour or part of an hour after the 2-hour minimum. The parking charges for the first 5 hours could be written as a function of the time as follows:

$$f(t) = \begin{cases} \$5.00 & \text{if } 0 < t \leq 2 \\ \$6.50 & \text{if } 2 < t \leq 3 \\ \$8.00 & \text{if } 3 < t \leq 4 \\ \$9.50 & \text{if } 4 < t \leq 5 \end{cases}$$

(a) Find $\lim\limits_{t \to 1} f(t)$, if it exists.
(b) Find $\lim\limits_{t \to 2} f(t)$, if it exists.

65. *Municipal water rates* The Corner Water Corp. of Shippenville, Pennsylvania has the following rates per 1000 gallons of water used.

Usage (x)	Cost per 1000 Gallons (C(x))
First 10,000 gallons	$15.96
Next 110,000 gallons	13.56
Over 120,000 gallons	Additional 11.04

If Corner Water has a monthly service fee of $12.76, write a function $C = C(x)$ that models the charges (where x is thousands of gallons) and find $\lim\limits_{x \to 10} C(x)$ (that is, as usage approaches 10,000 gallons).

66. *Airport parking* Long-term parking at Savannah Airport is free for the first half-hour and costs $1.00 for each hour or part of an hour thereafter. If $C = C(t)$ is the charge for t hours in Savannah's long-term parking, create a table of values for parking costs close to $t = 1/2$ and $t = 2$ and use them to find the following limits, if they exist.

(a) $\lim\limits_{t \to 0.5^-} C(t)$ (b) $\lim\limits_{t \to 0.5^+} C(t)$
(c) $\lim\limits_{t \to 0.5} C(t)$ (d) $\lim\limits_{t \to 2} C(t)$

Dow Jones Industrial Average **The graph in the figure shows the Dow Jones Industrial Average (DJIA) on a particularly tumultuous day in August 2011. Use the graph for Problems 67 and 68, with *t* as the time of day and *D(t)* as the DJIA at time *t*.**

67. Estimate $\lim\limits_{t\to 9.30\text{AM}^+} D(t)$, if it exists. Explain what this limit corresponds to.

68. Estimate $\lim\limits_{t\to 4.00\text{PM}^-} D(t)$, if it exists. Explain what this limit corresponds to.

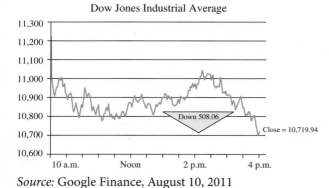

Dow Jones Industrial Average

Down 508.06

Close = 10,719.94

Source: Google Finance, August 10, 2011

Union participation **The table shows the percent of U.S. workers in unions for selected years from 1930 to 2008.**

Year	Percent	Year	Percent
1930	11.6	1975	25.5
1935	13.2	1980	21.9
1940	26.9	1985	18.0
1945	35.5	1990	16.1
1950	31.5	1995	14.9
1955	33.2	2000	13.5
1960	31.4	2005	12.5
1965	28.4	2008	12.4
1970	27.3		

Source: Bureau of Labor Statistics

Assume these data can be modeled with the function

$$U(t) = \frac{0.085t^3 - 24.2t^2 + 2200t - 44{,}000}{14.0t - 23.2}$$

where *U(t)* is the percent of U.S. workers in unions and *t* is the number of years past 1900. Use the table and the function in Problems 69 and 70.

69. (a) Find $\lim\limits_{t\to 115} U(t)$, if it exists.
   (b) What does this limit predict?
   (c) Does this prediction seem plausible? Explain.

70. (a) Find $\lim\limits_{t\to 50} U(t)$, if it exists.
   (b) What does this limit estimate?
   (c) Is the equation accurate as $t \to 50$? Explain.

OBJECTIVES

9.2

- To determine whether a function is continuous or discontinuous at a point
- To determine where a function is discontinuous
- To find limits at infinity and horizontal asymptotes

Continuous Functions; Limits at Infinity

■| APPLICATION PREVIEW |■

Suppose that a friend of yours and her husband have a taxable income of $137,300 and she tells you that she doesn't want to make any more money because that would put them in a higher tax bracket. She makes this statement because the tax rate schedule for married taxpayers filing a joint return (shown in the table) appears to have a jump in taxes for taxable income at $137,300.

Schedule Y-1—If your filing status is Married filing jointly or Qualifying widow(er)

If taxable income is over—	But not over—	The tax is:
$0	$16,750	10% of the amount over $0
$16,750	$68,000	$1,675.00 plus 15% of the amount over $16,750
$68,000	$137,300	$9,362.50 plus 25% of the amount over $68,000
$137,300	$209,250	$26,687.50 plus 28% of the amount over $137,300
$209,250	$373,650	$46,833.50 plus 33% of the amount over $209,250
$373,650	no limit	$101,085.50 plus 35% of the amount over $373,650

Source: Internal Revenue Service

To see whether the couple's taxes would jump to some higher level, we will write the function that gives income tax for married taxpayers as a function of taxable income and show that the function is continuous (see Example 3). That is, we will see that the tax paid does not jump at \$137,300 even though the tax on income above \$137,300 is collected at a higher rate. In this section, we will show how to determine whether a function is continuous, and we will investigate some different types of discontinuous functions.

Continuous Functions

We have found that $f(c)$ is the same as the limit as $x \to c$ for any polynomial function $f(x)$ and any real number c. Any function for which this special property holds is called a **continuous function.** The graphs of such functions can be drawn without lifting the pencil from the paper, and graphs of others may have holes, vertical asymptotes, or jumps that make it impossible to draw them without lifting the pencil. In general, we define continuity of a function at the value $x = c$ as follows.

Continuity at a Point

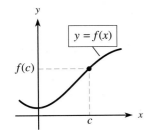

The function f is **continuous at $x = c$** if *all* of the following conditions are satisfied.

1. $f(c)$ exists   2. $\lim\limits_{x \to c} f(x)$ exists   3. $\lim\limits_{x \to c} f(x) = f(c)$

The figure at the left illustrates these three conditions.
If one or more of the conditions above do not hold, we say the function is **discontinuous at $x = c$.**

If a function is discontinuous at one or more points, it is called a **discontinuous function.** Figure 9.11 shows graphs of some functions that are discontinuous at $x = 2$.

(a) $f(x) = \dfrac{1}{x - 2}$

$\lim\limits_{x \to 2} f(x)$ and $f(2)$ do not exist.

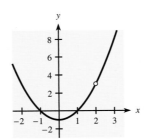

(b) $f(x) = \dfrac{x^3 - 2x^2 - x + 2}{x - 2}$

$f(2)$ does not exist.

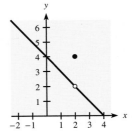

(c) $f(x) = \begin{cases} 4 - x & \text{if } x \neq 2 \\ 4 & \text{if } x = 2 \end{cases}$

$\lim\limits_{x \to 2} f(x) = 2 \neq 4 = f(2)$

Figure 9.11

In the previous section, we saw that if f is a polynomial function, then $\lim\limits_{x \to c} f(x) = f(c)$ for every real number c, and also that $\lim\limits_{x \to c} h(x) = h(c)$ if $h(x) = \dfrac{f(x)}{g(x)}$ is a rational function and $g(c) \neq 0$. Thus, by definition, we have the following.

Polynomial and Rational Functions	Every polynomial function is continuous for all real numbers. Every rational function is continuous at all values of x except those that make the denominator 0.

EXAMPLE 1 Discontinuous Functions

For what values of x, if any, are the following functions continuous?

(a) $h(x) = \dfrac{3x + 2}{4x - 6}$ (b) $f(x) = \dfrac{x^2 - x - 2}{x^2 - 4}$

Solution

(a) This is a rational function, so it is continuous for all values of x except for those that make the denominator, $4x - 6$, equal to 0. Because $4x - 6 = 0$ at $x = 3/2$, $h(x)$ is continuous for all real numbers except $x = 3/2$. Figure 9.12(a) shows a vertical asymptote at $x = 3/2$.

(b) This is a rational function, so it is continuous everywhere except where the denominator is 0. To find the zeros of the denominator, we factor $x^2 - 4$.

$$f(x) = \frac{x^2 - x - 2}{x^2 - 4} = \frac{x^2 - x - 2}{(x - 2)(x + 2)}$$

Because the denominator is 0 for $x = 2$ and for $x = -2$, $f(2)$ and $f(-2)$ do not exist (recall that division by 0 is undefined). Thus the function is continuous except at $x = 2$ and $x = -2$. The graph of this function (see Figure 9.12(b)) shows a hole at $x = 2$ and a vertical asymptote at $x = -2$.

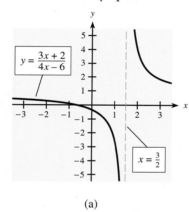

Figure 9.12   (a)   (b)

CHECKPOINT	1. Find any x-values where the following functions are discontinuous.

(a) $f(x) = x^3 - 3x + 1$ (b) $g(x) = \dfrac{x^3 - 1}{(x - 1)(x + 2)}$

If the pieces of a piecewise defined function are polynomials, the only values of x where the function might be discontinuous are those at which the definition of the function changes.

EXAMPLE 2 Piecewise Defined Functions

Determine the values of x, if any, for which the following functions are discontinuous.

(a) $g(x) = \begin{cases} (x + 2)^3 + 1 & \text{if } x \le -1 \\ 3 & \text{if } x > -1 \end{cases}$ (b) $f(x) = \begin{cases} 4 - x^2 & \text{if } x < 2 \\ x - 2 & \text{if } x \ge 2 \end{cases}$

$$g(x) = \begin{cases} (x+2)^3 + 1 \text{ if } x \leq -1 \\ 3 \qquad\qquad \text{ if } x > -1 \end{cases}$$

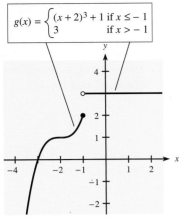

Figure 9.13

$$f(x) = \begin{cases} 4 - x^2 \text{ if } x < 2 \\ x - 2 \ \ \text{ if } x \geq 2 \end{cases}$$

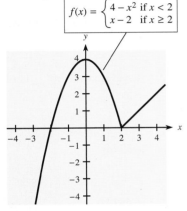

Figure 9.14

Solution

(a) $g(x)$ is a piecewise defined function in which each part is a polynomial. Thus, to see whether a discontinuity exists, we need only check the value of x for which the definition of the function changes—that is, at $x = -1$. Note that $x = -1$ satisfies $x \leq -1$, so $g(-1) = (-1 + 2)^3 + 1 = 2$. Because $g(x)$ is defined differently for $x < -1$ and $x > -1$, we use left- and right-hand limits.

For $x \rightarrow -1^-$, we know that $x < -1$, so $g(x) = (x + 2)^3 + 1$:

$$\lim_{x \to -1^-} g(x) = \lim_{x \to -1^-} [(x + 2)^3 + 1] = (-1 + 2)^3 + 1 = 2$$

Similarly, for $x \rightarrow -1^+$, we know that $x > -1$, so $g(x) = 3$:

$$\lim_{x \to -1^+} g(x) = \lim_{x \to -1^+} 3 = 3$$

Because the left- and right-hand limits differ, $\lim_{x \to -1} g(x)$ does not exist, so $g(x)$ is discontinuous at $x = -1$. This result is confirmed by examining the graph of g, shown in Figure 9.13.

(b) As with $g(x)$, $f(x)$ is continuous everywhere except perhaps at $x = 2$, where the definition of $f(x)$ changes. Because $x = 2$ satisfies $x \geq 2$, $f(2) = 2 - 2 = 0$. The left- and right-hand limits are

Left: $\quad \lim_{x \to 2^-} f(x) = \lim_{x \to 2^-} (4 - x^2) = 4 - 2^2 = 0$

Right: $\quad \lim_{x \to 2^+} f(x) = \lim_{x \to 2^+} (x - 2) = 2 - 2 = 0$

Because the right- and left-hand limits are equal, we conclude that $\lim_{x \to 2} f(x) = 0$. The limit is equal to the functional value, or:

$$\lim_{x \to 2} f(x) = f(2)$$

so we conclude that f is continuous at $x = 2$ and thus f is continuous for all values of x. This result is confirmed by the graph of f, shown in Figure 9.14. ∎

EXAMPLE 3 Taxes | APPLICATION PREVIEW |

The tax rate schedule for married taxpayers filing a joint return (shown in the table) appears to have a jump in taxes for taxable income at $137,300.

Schedule Y-1—If your filing status is Married filing jointly or Qualifying widow(er)

If taxable income is over—	But not over—	The tax is:
$0	$16,750	10% of the amount over $0
$16,750	$68,000	$1,675.00 plus 15% of the amount over $16,750
$68,000	$137,300	$9,362.50 plus 25% of the amount over $68,000
$137,300	$209,250	$26,687.50 plus 28% of the amount over $137,300
$209,250	$373,650	$46,833.50 plus 33% of the amount over $209,250
$373,650	no limit	$101,085.50 plus 35% of the amount over $373,650

Source: Internal Revenue Service

(a) Use the table and write the function that gives income tax for married taxpayers as a function of taxable income, x.

(b) Is the function in part (a) continuous at $x = 137,300$?

(c) A married friend of yours and her husband have a taxable income of $137,300, and she tells you that she doesn't want to make any more money because doing so would put her in a higher tax bracket. What would you tell her to do if she is offered a raise?

Solution

(a) The function that gives the tax due for married taxpayers is

$$T(x) = \begin{cases} 0.10x & \text{if } 0 \le x \le 16,750 \\ \$1675.00 + 0.15(x - 16,750) & \text{if } 16,750 < x \le 68,000 \\ \$9362.50 + 0.25(x - 68,000) & \text{if } 68,000 < x \le 137,300 \\ \$26,687.50 + 0.28(x - 137,300) & \text{if } 137,300 < x \le 209,250 \\ \$46,833.50 + 0.33(x - 209,250) & \text{if } 209,250 < x \le 373,650 \\ \$101,085.50 + 0.35(x - 373,650) & \text{if } x > 373,650 \end{cases}$$

(b) If this function is continous at $x = 137,300$, there is no jump in taxes at $137,300. We examine the three conditions for continuity at $x = 137,300$

(i) $T(137,300) = 26,687.50$, so $T(137,300)$ exists.

(ii) Because the function is piecewise defined near $137,300$, we evaluate $\lim\limits_{x \to 137,300} T(x)$ by evaluating one-sided limits:

From the left, we evaluate $\lim\limits_{x \to 137,300^-} T(x)$:

$$\lim\limits_{x \to 137,300^-} [9362.50 + 0.25(x - 68,000)] = 26,687.50$$

From the right, we evaluate $\lim\limits_{x \to 137,300^+} T(x)$:

$$\lim\limits_{x \to 137,300^+} [26,687.50 + 0.28(x - 137,300)] = 26,687.50$$

Because these one-sided limits agree, the limit exists and is

$$\lim\limits_{x \to 137,300} T(x) = 26,687.50.$$

(iii) Because $\lim\limits_{x \to 137,300} T(x) = T(137,300) = 26,687.50$, the function is continuous at $137,300$.

(c) If your friend earned more than $137,300, she and her husband would pay taxes at a higher rate on the money earned *above* the $137,300, but it would not increase the tax rate on any income *up to* $137,300. Thus she should take any raise that is offered. ∎

CHECKPOINT

2. If $f(x)$ and $g(x)$ are polynomials, $h(x) = \begin{cases} f(x) & \text{if } x \le a \\ g(x) & \text{if } x > a \end{cases}$ is continuous everywhere except perhaps at _____.

Limits at Infinity

We have seen that the graph of $y = 1/x$ has a vertical asymptote at $x = 0$ (shown in Figure 9.15(a)). By graphing $y = 1/x$ and evaluating the function for very large x-values, we can see that $y = 1/x$ never becomes negative for positive x-values regardless of how large the x-value is. Although no value of x makes $1/x$ equal to 0, it is easy to see that $1/x$ approaches 0 as x gets very large. This is denoted by

$$\lim\limits_{x \to +\infty} \frac{1}{x} = 0$$

and means that the line $y = 0$ (the x-axis) is a horizontal asymptote for $y = 1/x$. We also see that $y = 1/x$ approaches 0 as x decreases without bound, and we denote this by

$$\lim\limits_{x \to -\infty} \frac{1}{x} = 0$$

These limits for $f(x) = 1/x$ can also be established with numerical tables.

x	$f(x) = 1/x$	x	$f(x) = 1/x$
100	0.01	−100	−0.01
100,000	0.00001	−100,000	−0.00001
100,000,000	0.00000001	−100,000,000	−0.00000001
↓	↓	↓	↓
$+\infty$	0	$-\infty$	0
$\displaystyle\lim_{x \to +\infty} \frac{1}{x} = 0$		$\displaystyle\lim_{x \to -\infty} \frac{1}{x} = 0$	

(a)

(b)

Figure 9.15

We can use the graph of $y = 2/x^2$ in Figure 9.15(b) to see that the x-axis ($y = 0$) is a horizontal asymptote and that

$$\lim_{x \to +\infty} \frac{2}{x^2} = 0 \quad \text{and} \quad \lim_{x \to -\infty} \frac{2}{x^2} = 0$$

By using graphs and/or tables of values, we can generalize the results for the functions shown in Figure 9.15 and conclude the following.

Limits at Infinity

If c is any constant, then

1. $\displaystyle\lim_{x \to +\infty} c = c$ and $\displaystyle\lim_{x \to -\infty} c = c$.

2. $\displaystyle\lim_{x \to +\infty} \frac{c}{x^p} = 0$, where $p > 0$.

3. $\displaystyle\lim_{x \to -\infty} \frac{c}{x^n} = 0$, where $n > 0$ is any integer.

In order to use these properties for finding the limits of rational functions as x approaches $+\infty$ or $-\infty$, we first divide each term of the numerator and denominator by the highest power of x present and then determine the limit of the resulting expression.

EXAMPLE 4   Limits at Infinity

Find each of the following limits, if they exist.

(a) $\displaystyle\lim_{x \to +\infty} \frac{2x - 1}{x + 2}$ (b) $\displaystyle\lim_{x \to -\infty} \frac{x^2 + 3}{1 - x}$

Solution

(a) The highest power of x present is x^1, so we divide each term in the numerator and denominator by x and then use the properties for limits at infinity.

$$\lim_{x \to +\infty} \frac{2x - 1}{x + 2} = \lim_{x \to +\infty} \frac{\dfrac{2x}{x} - \dfrac{1}{x}}{\dfrac{x}{x} + \dfrac{2}{x}} = \lim_{x \to +\infty} \frac{2 - \dfrac{1}{x}}{1 + \dfrac{2}{x}}$$

$$= \frac{2 - 0}{1 + 0} = 2 \quad \text{(by Properties 1 and 2)}$$

Figure 9.16(a) shows the graph of this function with the y-coordinates of the graph approaching 2 as x approaches $+\infty$ and as x approaches $-\infty$. That is, $y = 2$ is a horizontal asymptote. Note also that there is a discontinuity (vertical asymptote) where $x = -2$.

(b) We divide each term in the numerator and denominator by x^2 and then use the properties.

$$\lim_{x \to -\infty} \frac{x^2 + 3}{1 - x} = \lim_{x \to -\infty} \frac{\dfrac{x^2}{x^2} + \dfrac{3}{x^2}}{\dfrac{1}{x^2} - \dfrac{x}{x^2}} = \lim_{x \to -\infty} \frac{1 + \dfrac{3}{x^2}}{\dfrac{1}{x^2} - \dfrac{1}{x}}$$

This limit does not exist because the numerator approaches 1 and the denominator approaches 0 through positive values. Thus

$$\frac{x^2 + 3}{1 - x} \to +\infty \text{ as } x \to -\infty$$

The graph of this function, shown in Figure 9.16(b), has y-coordinates that increase without bound as x approaches $-\infty$ and that decrease without bound as x approaches $+\infty$. (There is no horizontal asymptote.) Note also that there is a vertical asymptote at $x = 1$.

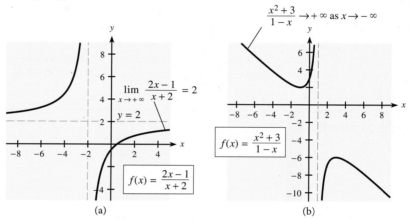

Figure 9.16   (a)   (b)

In our work with limits at infinity, we have mentioned horizontal asymptotes several times. The connection between these concepts follows.

Limits at Infinity and Horizontal Asymptotes

If $\lim_{x \to \infty} f(x) = b$ or $\lim_{x \to -\infty} f(x) = b$, where b is a constant, then the line $y = b$ is a horizontal asymptote for the graph of $y = f(x)$. Otherwise, $y = f(x)$ has no horizontal asymptotes.

CHECKPOINT

3. (a) Evaluate $\displaystyle\lim_{x \to +\infty} \frac{x^2 - 4}{2x^2 - 7}$.

    (b) What does part (a) say about horizontal asymptotes for $f(x) = (x^2 - 4)/(2x^2 - 7)$?

Calculator Note

We can use the graphing and table features of a graphing calculator to help locate and investigate discontinuities and limits at infinity (horizontal asymptotes). A graphing calculator can be used to focus our attention on a possible discontinuity and to support or suggest appropriate algebraic calculations. See Appendix C, Section 9.2, for details.

EXAMPLE 5   Limits with Technology

Use a graphing utility to investigate the continuity of the following functions.

(a) $f(x) = \dfrac{x^2 + 1}{x + 1}$ (b) $g(x) = \dfrac{x^2 - 2x - 3}{x^2 - 1}$

(c) $h(x) = \dfrac{|x + 1|}{x + 1}$ (d) $k(x) = \begin{cases} \dfrac{-x^2}{2} - 2x & \text{if } x \le -1 \\ \dfrac{x}{2} + 2 & \text{if } x > -1 \end{cases}$

Solution

(a) Figure 9.17(a) shows that $f(x)$ has a discontinuity (vertical asymptote) near $x = -1$. Because $f(-1)$ DNE, we know that $f(x)$ is not continuous at $x = -1$.

(b) Figure 9.17(b) shows that $g(x)$ is discontinuous (vertical asymptote) near $x = 1$, and this looks like the only discontinuity. However, the denominator of $g(x)$ is zero at $x = 1$ and $x = -1$, so $g(x)$ must have discontinuities at both of these x-values. Evaluating or using the table feature confirms that $x = -1$ is a discontinuity (a hole, or missing point). The figure also shows a horizontal asymptote; evaluation of $\lim\limits_{x \to \infty} g(x)$ confirms this is the line $y = 1$.

(c) Figure 9.17(c) shows a discontinuity (jump) at $x = -1$. We also see that $h(-1)$ DNE, which confirms the observations from the graph.

(d) The graph in Figure 9.17(d) appears to be continuous. The only "suspicious" x-value is $x = -1$, where the formula for $k(x)$ changes. Evaluating $k(-1)$ and examining a table near $x = -1$ indicates that $k(x)$ is continuous there. Algebraic evaluations of the two one-sided limits confirm this.

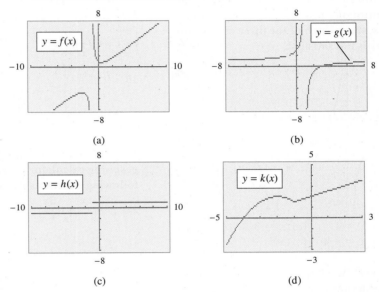

Figure 9.17

(a)   (b)

(c)   (d)

Continous Functions and Limits at Infinity

- The following information is useful in discussing continuity of functions.

  A. A polynomial function is continuous everywhere.

  B. A rational function is a function of the form $\dfrac{f(x)}{g(x)}$, where $f(x)$ and $g(x)$ are polynomials.

   1. If $g(x) \neq 0$ at any value of x, the function is continuous everywhere.

   2. If $g(c) = 0$, the function is discontinuous at $x = c$.

    (a) If $g(c) = 0$ and $f(c) \neq 0$, then there is a vertical asymptote at $x = c$.

    (b) If $g(c) = 0$ and $\lim\limits_{x \to c} \dfrac{f(x)}{g(x)} = L$, then the graph has a missing point at (c, L).

  C. A piecewise defined function may have a discontinuity at any x-value where the function changes its formula. One-sided limits must be used to see whether the limit exists.

- The following steps are useful when we are evaluating limits at infinity for a rational function $f(x) = p(x)/q(x)$.

   1. Divide both $p(x)$ and $q(x)$ by the highest power of x found in either polynomial.

   2. Use the properties of limits at infinity to complete the evaluation.

CHECKPOINT SOLUTIONS

1. (a) This is a polynomial function, so it is continuous at all values of x (discontinuous at none).
   (b) This is a rational function. It is discontinuous at $x = 1$ and $x = -2$ because these values make its denominator 0.

2. $x = a$

3. (a) $\displaystyle\lim_{x \to +\infty} \frac{x^2 - 4}{2x^2 - 7} = \lim_{x \to +\infty} \frac{1 - \dfrac{4}{x^2}}{2 - \dfrac{7}{x^2}} = \frac{1 - 0}{2 - 0} = \frac{1}{2}$

   (b) The line $y = 1/2$ is a horizontal asymptote.

| EXERCISES | 9.2

In Problems 1 and 2, refer to the figure. For each given x-value, use the figure to determine whether the function is continuous or discontinuous at that x-value. If the function is discontinuous, state which of the three conditions that define continuity is not satisfied.

1. (a) $x = -5$ (b) $x = 1$ (c) $x = 3$ (d) $x = 0$
2. (a) $x = 2$ (b) $x = -4$ (c) $x = -2$ (d) $x = 5$

In Problems 3–8, determine whether each function is continuous or discontinuous at the given x-value. Examine the three conditions in the definition of continuity.

3. $f(x) = \dfrac{x^2 - 4}{x - 2}, \quad x = -2$

4. $y = \dfrac{x^2 - 9}{x + 3}, \quad x = 3$

5. $y = \dfrac{x^2 - x - 12}{x^2 + 3x}, \quad x = -3$

6. $f(x) = \dfrac{x^2 - 6x + 8}{x^2 + x - 20}, \quad x = 4$

7. $f(x) = \begin{cases} x - 3 & \text{if } x \le 2 \\ 4x - 7 & \text{if } x > 2 \end{cases}, \quad x = 2$

8. $f(x) = \begin{cases} x^2 + 1 & \text{if } x \le 1 \\ 2x^2 - 1 & \text{if } x > 1 \end{cases}, \quad x = 1$

In Problems 9–16, determine whether the given function is continuous. If it is not, identify where it is discontinuous and which condition fails to hold. You can verify your conclusions by graphing each function with a graphing utility.

9. $f(x) = 4x^2 - 1$

10. $y = 5x^2 - 2x$

11. $g(x) = \dfrac{4x^2 + 3x + 2}{x + 2}$

12. $y = \dfrac{4x^2 + 4x + 1}{x + 1/2}$

13. $y = \dfrac{x}{x^2 + 1}$

14. $y = \dfrac{2x - 1}{x^2 + 3}$

15. $f(x) = \begin{cases} 3 & \text{if } x \le 1 \\ x^2 + 2 & \text{if } x > 1 \end{cases}$

16. $f(x) = \begin{cases} x^3 + 10 & \text{if } x \le -2 \\ 2 & \text{if } x > -2 \end{cases}$

In Problems 17–20, use the trace and table features of a graphing calculator to investigate whether each of the following functions has any discontinuities.

17. $y = \dfrac{x^2 - 5x - 6}{x + 1}$

18. $y = \dfrac{x^2 - 5x + 4}{x - 4}$

19. $f(x) = \begin{cases} x - 4 & \text{if } x \le 3 \\ x^2 - 8 & \text{if } x > 3 \end{cases}$

20. $f(x) = \begin{cases} x^2 + 4 & \text{if } x \ne 4 \\ 8 & \text{if } x = 4 \end{cases}$

Each of Problems 21–24 contains a function and its graph. For each problem, answer parts (a) and (b).
(a) Use the graph to determine, as well as you can,
   (i) vertical asymptotes. (ii) $\displaystyle\lim_{x \to +\infty} f(x)$.
   (iii) $\displaystyle\lim_{x \to -\infty} f(x)$. (iv) horizontal asymptotes.
(b) Check your conclusions in (a) by using the functions to determine items (i)–(iv) analytically.

21. $f(x) = \dfrac{8}{x + 2}$

22. $f(x) = \dfrac{x - 3}{x - 2}$

23. $f(x) = \dfrac{2(x + 1)^3(x + 5)}{(x - 3)^2(x + 2)^2}$

24. $f(x) = \dfrac{4x^2}{x^2 - 4x + 4}$

In Problems 25–32, complete (a) and (b).
(a) Use analytic methods to evaluate each limit.
(b) What does the result from part (a) tell you about
    horizontal asymptotes?
You can verify your conclusions by graphing the functions with a graphing calculator.

25. $\displaystyle\lim_{x \to +\infty} \dfrac{3}{x + 1}$ 26. $\displaystyle\lim_{x \to -\infty} \dfrac{4}{x^2 - 2x}$

27. $\displaystyle\lim_{x \to +\infty} \dfrac{x^3 - 1}{x^3 + 4}$ 28. $\displaystyle\lim_{x \to -\infty} \dfrac{3x^2 + 2}{x^2 - 4}$

29. $\displaystyle\lim_{x \to -\infty} \dfrac{5x^3 - 4x}{3x^3 - 2}$ 30. $\displaystyle\lim_{x \to +\infty} \dfrac{4x^2 + 5x}{x^2 - 4x}$

31. $\displaystyle\lim_{x \to +\infty} \dfrac{3x^2 + 5x}{6x + 1}$ 32. $\displaystyle\lim_{x \to -\infty} \dfrac{5x^3 - 8}{4x^2 + 5x}$

In Problems 33 and 34, use a graphing calculator to complete (a) and (b).
(a) Graph each function using a window with
    $0 \le x \le 300$ and $-2 \le y \le 2$. What does the graph
    indicate about $\displaystyle\lim_{x \to +\infty} f(x)$?
(b) Use the table feature with x-values larger than 10,000 to investigate $\displaystyle\lim_{x \to +\infty} f(x)$. Does the table support your conclusions in part (a)?

33. $f(x) = \dfrac{x^2 - 4}{3 + 2x^2}$ 34. $f(x) = \dfrac{5x^3 - 7x}{1 - 3x^3}$

In Problems 35 and 36, complete (a)–(c). Use analytic methods to find (a) any points of discontinuity and (b) limits as $x \to +\infty$ and $x \to -\infty$. (c) Then explain why, for these functions, a graphing calculator is better as a support tool for the analytic methods than as the primary tool for investigation.

35. $f(x) = \dfrac{1000x - 1000}{x + 1000}$ 36. $f(x) = \dfrac{3000x}{4350 - 2x}$

For Problems 37 and 38, let

$$f(x) = \dfrac{a_n x^n + a_{n-1}x^{n-1} + \cdots + a_1 x + a_0}{b_m x^m + b_{m-1}x^{m-1} + \cdots + b_1 x + b_0}$$

be a rational function.

37. If $m = n$, show that $\displaystyle\lim_{x \to \infty} f(x) = \dfrac{a_n}{b_n}$, and hence that
    $y = \dfrac{a_n}{b_n}$ is a horizontal asymptote.

38. (a) If $m > n$, show that $\displaystyle\lim_{x \to \infty} f(x) = 0$ and hence that
    $y = 0$ is a horizontal asymptote.
    (b) If $m < n$, find $\displaystyle\lim_{x \to \infty} f(x)$. What does this say about
    horizontal asymptotes?

APPLICATIONS

39. *Sales volume* Suppose that the weekly sales volume (in thousands of units) for a product is given by

$$y = \dfrac{32}{(p + 8)^{2/5}}$$

where p is the price in dollars per unit. Is this function continuous
(a) for all values of p?   (b) at $p = 24$?
(c) for all $p \ge 0$?
(d) What is the domain for this application?

40. *Worker productivity* Suppose that the average number of minutes M that it takes a new employee to assemble one unit of a product is given by

$$M = \dfrac{40 + 30t}{2t + 1}$$

where t is the number of days on the job. Is this function continuous
(a) for all values of t?   (b) at $t = 14$?
(c) for all $t \ge 0$?
(d) What is the domain for this application?

41. *Demand* Suppose that the demand for a product is defined by the equation

$$p = \dfrac{200{,}000}{(q + 1)^2}$$

where p is the price and q is the quantity demanded.
(a) Is this function discontinuous at any value of q? What value?
(b) Because q represents quantity, we know that $q \ge 0$. Is this function continuous for $q \ge 0$?

42. *Advertising and sales* The sales volume y (in thousands of dollars) is related to advertising expenditures x (in thousands of dollars) according to

$$y = \dfrac{200x}{x + 10}$$

(a) Is this function discontinuous at any points?
(b) Advertising expenditures x must be nonnegative. Is this function continuous for these values of x?

43. *Annuities* If an annuity makes an infinite series of equal payments at the end of the interest periods, it is called a **perpetuity**. If a lump sum investment of A_n is needed to result in n periodic payments of R when the interest rate per period is i, then

$$A_n = R\left[\dfrac{1 - (1 + i)^{-n}}{i}\right]$$

(a) Evaluate $\lim\limits_{n\to\infty} A_n$ to find a formula for the lump sum payment for a perpetuity.

(b) Find the lump sum investment needed to make payments of $100 per month in perpetuity if interest is 12%, compounded monthly.

44. **Response to adrenalin** Experimental evidence suggests that the response y of the body to the concentration x of injected adrenalin is given by

$$y = \frac{x}{a + bx}$$

where a and b are experimental constants.
(a) Is this function continuous for all x?
(b) On the basis of your conclusion in part (a) and the fact that in reality $x \geq 0$ and $y \geq 0$, must a and b be both positive, be both negative, or have opposite signs?

45. **Cost-benefit** Suppose that the cost C of removing p percent of the impurities from the waste water in a manufacturing process is given by

$$C(p) = \frac{9800p}{101 - p}$$

Is this function continuous for all those p-values for which the problem makes sense?

46. **Pollution** Suppose that the cost C of removing p percent of the particulate pollution from the exhaust gases at an industrial site is given by

$$C(p) = \frac{8100p}{100 - p}$$

Describe any discontinuities for $C(p)$. Explain what each discontinuity means.

47. **Pollution** The percent p of particulate pollution that can be removed from the smokestacks of an industrial plant by spending C dollars is given by

$$p = \frac{100C}{7300 + C}$$

Find the percent of the pollution that could be removed if spending C were allowed to increase without bound. Can 100% of the pollution be removed? Explain.

48. **Cost-benefit** The percent p of impurities that can be removed from the waste water of a manufacturing process at a cost of C dollars is given by

$$p = \frac{100C}{8100 + C}$$

Find the percent of the impurities that could be removed if cost were no object (that is, if cost were allowed to increase without bound). Can 100% of the impurities be removed? Explain.

49. **Federal income tax** The tax owed by a married couple filing jointly and their tax rates can be found in the following tax rate schedule.

Schedule Y-1—If your filing status is Married filing jointly or Qualifying widow(er)

If taxable income is over—	But not over—	The tax is:
$0	$16,750	10% of the amount over $0
$16,750	$68,000	$1,675.00 plus 15% of the amount over $16,750
$68,000	$137,300	$9,362.50 plus 25% of the amount over $68,000
$137,300	$209,250	$26,687.50 plus 28% of the amount over $137,300
$209,250	$373,650	$46,833.50 plus 33% of the amount over $209,250
$373,650	no limit	$101,085.50 plus 35% of the amount over $373,650

Source: Internal Revenue Service

From this schedule, the tax rate $R(x)$ is a function of taxable income x, as follows.

$$R(x) = \begin{cases} 0.10 & \text{if} & 0 \leq x \leq 16,750 \\ 0.15 & \text{if} & 16,750 < x \leq 68,000 \\ 0.25 & \text{if} & 68,000 < x \leq 137,300 \\ 0.28 & \text{if} & 137,300 < x \leq 209,250 \\ 0.33 & \text{if} & 209,250 < x \leq 373,650 \\ 0.35 & \text{if} & x > 373,650 \end{cases}$$

Identify any discontinuities in $R(x)$.

50. **Calories and temperature** Suppose that the number of calories of heat required to raise 1 gram of water (or ice) from $-40°C$ to $x°C$ is given by

$$f(x) = \begin{cases} \frac{1}{2}x + 20 & \text{if } -40 \leq x < 0 \\ x + 100 & \text{if } 0 \leq x \end{cases}$$

(a) What can be said about the continuity of the function $f(x)$?
(b) What happens to water at $0°C$ that accounts for the behavior of the function at $0°C$?

51. **Electrical usage costs** The monthly charge in dollars for x kilowatt-hours (kWh) of electricity used by a residential consumer of Excelsior Electric Membership Corporation from November through June is given by the function

$$C(x) = \begin{cases} 10 + 0.094x & \text{if} & 0 \leq x \leq 100 \\ 19.40 + 0.075(x - 100) & \text{if} & 100 < x \leq 500 \\ 49.40 + 0.05(x - 500) & \text{if} & x > 500 \end{cases}$$

(a) What is the monthly charge if 1100 kWh of electricity is consumed in a month?

(b) Find $\lim_{x \to 100} C(x)$ and $\lim_{x \to 500} C(x)$, if the limits exist.

(c) Is C continuous at $x = 100$ and at $x = 500$?

52. **Postage costs** First-class postage for a standard letter is 44 cents for the first ounce or part of an ounce that a letter weighs plus an additional 20 cents for each additional ounce or part of an ounce. Use the table or graph of the postage function, $f(x)$, to determine the following.

(a) $\lim_{x \to 2.5} f(x)$

(b) $f(2.5)$

(c) Is $f(x)$ continuous at 2.5?

(d) $\lim_{x \to 4} f(x)$

(e) $f(4)$

(f) Is $f(x)$ continuous at 4?

Weight x	Postage $f(x)$
$0 < x \leq 1$	\$0.44
$1 < x \leq 2$	0.64
$2 < x \leq 3$	0.84
$3 < x \leq 4$	1.04
$4 < x \leq 5$	1.24

Postage Function

53. **Modeling U.S. Work force** Since 1950 the U.S. work force has seen the arrival of the Baby Boomers and the changing role of women, among other influences. The data in the table show the millions of men and women in the U.S. work force for selected years from 1950 and projected to 2050. Complete the following to explore the dynamics of the changing roles of men and women in the work force.

(a) With x representing the number of years past 1950, use the data in the table to find a linear model for the number of men in the work force, $m(x)$, and a model for the number of women in the work force, $w(x)$.

(b) Use the results from part (a) to find the function $r(x)$ that gives the ratio of men to women in the U.S. work force.

(c) Find $\lim_{x \to 0} r(x)$ and $\lim_{x \to 100} r(x)$, and interpret their meanings.

(d) Find $\lim_{x \to \infty} r(x)$ and interpret its meaning.

Year	Work force (in millions)	
	Men	Women
1950	43.8	18.4
1960	46.4	23.2
1970	51.2	31.5
1980	61.5	45.5
1990	69.0	56.8
2000	75.2	65.7
2010	82.2	75.5
2015	84.2	78.6
2020	85.4	79.3
2030	88.5	81.6
2040	94.0	86.5
2050	100.3	91.5

Source: U.S. Bureau of Labor Statistics

54. **Students per computer** By using data from Quality Education Data Inc., Denver, CO, the number of students per computer in U.S. public schools (1984–2006) can be modeled with the function

$$f(x) = \frac{330 - 6x}{2x - 4.5}$$

where x is the number of years past the school year ending in 1981.

(a) Is this function continuous for school years from 1985 onward?

(b) Find the long-range projection of this model by finding $\lim_{x \to \infty} f(x)$. Explain what this tells us about the validity of the model.

- To define and find average rates of change
- To define the derivative as a rate of change
- To use the definition of derivative to find derivatives of functions
- To use derivatives to find slopes of tangents to curves

9.3

Rates of Change and Derivatives

| APPLICATION PREVIEW |

In Chapter 1, "Linear Equations and Functions," we studied linear revenue functions and defined the marginal revenue for a product as the rate of change of the revenue function. For linear revenue functions, this rate is also the slope of the line that is the graph of the revenue function. In this section, we will define marginal revenue as the rate of change of the revenue function, even when the revenue function is not linear.

Thus, if an oil company's revenue (in thousands of dollars) is given by

$$R = 100x - x^2, \ x \geq 0$$

where x is the number of thousands of barrels of oil sold per day, we can find and interpret the marginal revenue when 20,000 barrels are sold (see Example 4).

We will discuss the relationship between the *instantaneous rate of change* of a function at a given point and the slope of the line tangent to the graph of the function at that point. We will see how the derivative of a revenue function can be used to find both the slope of its tangent line and its marginal revenue.

Average Rates of Change

For linear functions, we have seen that the slope of the line measures the average rate of change of the function and can be found from any two points on the line. However, for a function that is not linear, the slope between different pairs of points no longer always gives the same number, but it can be interpreted as an **average rate of change.**

Average Rate of Change

The **average rate of change** of a function $y = f(x)$ from $x = a$ to $x = b$ is defined by

$$\text{Average rate of change} = \frac{f(b) - f(a)}{b - a}$$

The figure shows that this average rate is the same as the slope of the segment (or secant line) joining the points $(a, f(a))$ and $(b, f(b))$.

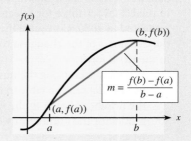

EXAMPLE 1 **Total Cost**

Suppose a company's total cost in dollars to produce x units of its product is given by

$$C(x) = 0.01x^2 + 25x + 1500$$

Find the average rate of change of total cost for the second 100 units produced (from $x = 100$ to $x = 200$).

Solution

The average rate of change of total cost from $x = 100$ to $x = 200$ units is

$$\frac{C(200) - C(100)}{200 - 100} = \frac{[0.01(200)^2 + 25(200) + 1500] - [0.01(100)^2 + 25(100) + 1500]}{100}$$

$$= \frac{6900 - 4100}{100} = \frac{2800}{100} = 28 \text{ dollars per unit}$$

EXAMPLE 2   Elderly in the Work Force

Figure 9.18 shows the percents of elderly men and of elderly women in the work force in selected years from 1950 to 2008. For these years, find and interpret the average rate of change of the percent of (a) elderly men in the work force and (b) elderly women in the work force.

Elderly in the Labor Force, 1950–2008

Figure 9.18   *Source:* Bureau of the Census, U.S. Department of Commerce

Solution

(a) From 1950 to 2008, the annual average rate of change in the percent of elderly men in the work force is

$$\frac{\text{Change in men's percent}}{\text{Change in years}} = \frac{21.5 - 45.8}{2008 - 1950} = \frac{-24.3}{58} \approx -0.419 \text{ percentage points per year}$$

This means that from 1950 to 2008, *on average*, the percent of elderly men in the work force dropped by 0.419 percentage points per year.

(b) Similarly, the average rate of change for women is

$$\frac{\text{Change in women's percent}}{\text{Change in years}} = \frac{13.3 - 9.7}{2008 - 1950} = \frac{3.6}{58} \approx 0.062 \text{ percentage points per year}$$

In like manner, this means that from 1950 to 2008, *on average*, the percent of elderly women in the work force increased by 0.062 percentage points each year.

Instantaneous Rates of Change: Velocity

Another common rate of change is velocity. For instance, if we travel 200 miles in our car over a 4-hour period, we know that we averaged 50 mph. However, during that trip there may have been times when we were traveling on an Interstate at faster than 50 mph and times when we were stopped at a traffic light. Thus, for the trip we have not only an average velocity but also instantaneous velocities (or instantaneous speeds as displayed on the speedometer). Let's see how average velocity can lead us to instantaneous velocity.

Suppose a ball is thrown straight upward at 64 feet per second from a spot 96 feet above ground level. The equation that describes the height y of the ball after x seconds is

$$y = f(x) = 96 + 64x - 16x^2$$

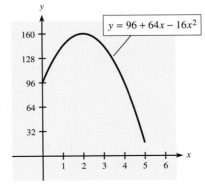

Figure 9.19

Figure 9.19 shows the graph of this function for $0 \le x \le 5$. The average velocity of the ball over a given time interval is the change in the height divided by the length of time that has passed. Table 9.4 on the next page shows some average velocities over time intervals beginning at $x = 1$.

■ | TABLE 9.4 |

AVERAGE VELOCITIES

Time (seconds)			Height (feet)			Average Velocity (ft/sec)
Beginning	Ending	Change (Δx)	Beginning	Ending	Change (Δy)	($\Delta y/\Delta x$)
1	2	1	144	160	16	16/1 = 16
1	1.5	0.5	144	156	12	12/0.5 = 24
1	1.1	0.1	144	147.04	3.04	3.04/0.1 = 30.4
1	1.01	0.01	144	144.3184	0.3184	0.3184/0.01 = 31.84

In Table 9.4, the smaller the time interval, the more closely the average velocity approximates the instantaneous velocity at $x = 1$. Thus the instantaneous velocity at $x = 1$ is closer to 31.84 feet per second than to 30.4 feet per second.

If we represent the change in time by h, then the average velocity from $x = 1$ to $x = 1 + h$ approaches the instantaneous velocity at $x = 1$ as h approaches 0. (Note that h can be positive or negative.) This is illustrated in the following example.

EXAMPLE 3 **Velocity**

Suppose a ball is thrown straight upward so that its height $f(x)$ (in feet) is given by the equation

$$f(x) = 96 + 64x - 16x^2$$

where x is time (in seconds).
(a) Find the average velocity from $x = 1$ to $x = 1 + h$.
(b) Find the instantaneous velocity at $x = 1$.

Solution
(a) Let h represent the change in x (time) from 1 to $1 + h$. Then the corresponding change in $f(x)$ (height) is

$$f(1 + h) - f(1) = [96 + 64(1 + h) - 16(1 + h)^2] - [96 + 64 - 16]$$
$$= 96 + 64 + 64h - 16(1 + 2h + h^2) - 144$$
$$= 16 + 64h - 16 - 32h - 16h^2 = 32h - 16h^2$$

The average velocity V_{av} is the change in height divided by the change in time.

$$V_{av} = \frac{f(1 + h) - f(1)}{1 + h - 1} = \frac{32h - 16h^2}{h} = 32 - 16h$$

(b) The instantaneous velocity V is the limit of the average velocity as h approaches 0.

$$V = \lim_{h \to 0} V_{av} = \lim_{h \to 0} (32 - 16h) = 32 \text{ feet per second}$$ ■

Note that average velocity is found over a time interval. Instantaneous velocity is usually called **velocity,** and it can be found at any time x, as follows.

Velocity

Suppose that an object moving in a straight line has its position y at time x given by $y = f(x)$. Then the **velocity** function for the object at time x is

$$V = \lim_{h \to 0} \frac{f(x + h) - f(x)}{h}$$

provided that this limit exists.

The instantaneous rate of change of any function (commonly called *rate of change*) can be found in the same way we find velocity. The function that gives this instantaneous rate of change of a function f is called the **derivative** of f.

Derivative	If f is a function defined by $y = f(x)$, then the **derivative** of $f(x)$ at any value x, denoted $f'(x)$, is

$$f'(x) = \lim_{h \to 0} \frac{f(x + h) - f(x)}{h}$$

if this limit exists. If $f'(c)$ exists, we say that f is **differentiable** at c.

The following procedure illustrates how to find the derivative of a function $y = f(x)$ at any value x.

Derivative Using the Definition

Procedure	Example
To find the derivative of $y = f(x)$ at any value x:	Find the derivative of $f(x) = 4x^2$.

1. Let h represent the change in x from x to $x + h$.

    1. The change in x from x to $x + h$ is h.

2. The corresponding change in $y = f(x)$ is

    $$f(x + h) - f(x)$$

    2. The change in $f(x)$ is
    $$\begin{aligned} f(x + h) - f(x) &= 4(x + h)^2 - 4x^2 \\ &= 4(x^2 + 2xh + h^2) - 4x^2 \\ &= 4x^2 + 8xh + 4h^2 - 4x^2 \\ &= 8xh + 4h^2 \end{aligned}$$

3. Form the difference quotient $\dfrac{f(x + h) - f(x)}{h}$ and simplify.

    3. $\dfrac{f(x + h) - f(x)}{h} = \dfrac{8xh + 4h^2}{h}$
    $$= 8x + 4h$$

4. Find $\lim\limits_{h \to 0} \dfrac{f(x + h) - f(x)}{h}$ to determine $f'(x)$, the derivative of $f(x)$.

    4. $f'(x) = \lim\limits_{h \to 0} \dfrac{f(x + h) - f(x)}{h}$
    $$f'(x) = \lim_{h \to 0} (8x + 4h) = 8x$$

Note that in the example above, we could have found the derivative of the function $f(x) = 4x^2$ at a particular value of x, say $x = 3$, by evaluating the derivative formula at that value:

$$f'(x) = 8x \quad \text{so} \quad f'(3) = 8(3) = 24$$

In addition to $f'(x)$, the derivative at any point x may be denoted by

$$\frac{dy}{dx}, \quad y', \quad \frac{d}{dx} f(x), \quad D_x y, \quad \text{or} \quad D_x f(x)$$

We can, of course, use variables other than x and y to represent functions and their derivatives. For example, we can represent the derivative of the function $p = 2q^2 - 1$ by dp/dq.

CHECKPOINT	1. Find the average rate of change of $f(x) = 30 - x - x^2$ over $[1, 4]$.

2. For the function $y = f(x) = x^2 - x + 1$, find

    (a) $f(x + h) - f(x)$.

    (b) $\dfrac{f(x + h) - f(x)}{h}$.

    (c) $f'(x) = \lim\limits_{h \to 0} \dfrac{f(x + h) - f(x)}{h}$.

    (d) $f'(2)$.

For linear functions, we defined the **marginal revenue** for a product as the rate of change of the total revenue function for the product. If the total revenue function for a product is not linear, we define the marginal revenue for the product as the instantaneous rate of change, or the derivative, of the revenue function.

Marginal Revenue

Suppose that the total revenue function for a product is given by $R = R(x)$, where x is the number of units sold. Then the **marginal revenue** at x units is

$$\overline{MR} = R'(x) = \lim_{h \to 0} \frac{R(x + h) - R(x)}{h}$$

provided that the limit exists.

Note that the marginal revenue (derivative of the revenue function) can be found by using the steps in the Procedure/Example box on the preceding page. These steps can also be combined, as they are in Example 4.

EXAMPLE   4   Revenue | APPLICATION PREVIEW |

Suppose that an oil company's revenue (in thousands of dollars) is given by the equation

$$R = R(x) = 100x - x^2, \ x \geq 0$$

where x is the number of thousands of barrels of oil sold each day.

(a) Find the function that gives the marginal revenue at any value of x.
(b) Find the marginal revenue when 20,000 barrels are sold (that is, at $x = 20$).

Solution
(a) The marginal revenue function is the derivative of $R(x)$.

$$R'(x) = \lim_{h \to 0} \frac{R(x + h) - R(x)}{h} = \lim_{h \to 0} \frac{[100(x + h) - (x + h)^2] - (100x - x^2)}{h}$$

$$= \lim_{h \to 0} \frac{100x + 100h - (x^2 + 2xh + h^2) - 100x + x^2}{h}$$

$$= \lim_{h \to 0} \frac{100h - 2xh - h^2}{h} = \lim_{h \to 0} (100 - 2x - h) = 100 - 2x$$

Thus, the marginal revenue function is $\overline{MR} = R'(x) = 100 - 2x$.
(b) The function found in part (a) gives the marginal revenue at *any* value of x. To find the marginal revenue when 20 units are sold, we evaluate $R'(20)$.

$$R'(20) = 100 - 2(20) = 60$$

Hence the marginal revenue at $x = 20$ is 60 thousand dollars per thousand barrels of oil. Because the marginal revenue is used to approximate the revenue from the sale of one additional unit, we interpret $R'(20) = 60$ to mean that the expected revenue from the sale of the next thousand barrels (after 20,000) will be approximately $60,000. [*Note:* The actual revenue from this sale is $R(21) - R(20) = 1659 - 1600 = 59$ thousand dollars.]

Tangent to a Curve   Just as average rates of change are connected with slopes, so are instantaneous rates (derivatives). In fact, the slope of the graph of a function at any point is the same as the derivative at that point. To show this, we define the slope of a curve at a point on the curve as the slope of the line tangent to the curve at the point.

In geometry, a **tangent** to a circle is defined as a line that has one point in common with the circle. [See Figure 9.20(a).] This definition does not apply to all curves, as Figure 9.20(b) shows. Many lines can be drawn through the point A that touch the curve only at A. One of the lines, line l, looks like it is tangent to the curve.

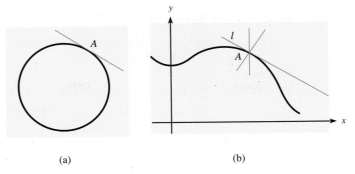

Figure 9.20   (a)   (b)

In Figure 9.21, the line l represents the tangent line to the curve at point A and shows that secant lines $(s_1, s_2,$ etc.) through A approach line l as the second points $(Q_1, Q_2,$ etc.) approach A. (For points and secant lines to the left of A, there would be a similar figure and conclusion.) This means that as we choose points on the curve closer and closer to A (from both sides of A), the limiting position of the secant lines through A is the **tangent line** to the curve at A.

Figure 9.21

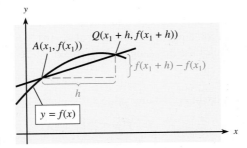

Figure 9.22

From Figure 9.22, we see that the slope of an arbitrary secant line through $A(x_1, f(x_1))$ and $Q(x_1 + h, f(x_1 + h))$ is given by

$$m_{AQ} = \frac{f(x_1 + h) - f(x_1)}{h}$$

Thus, as Q approaches A, the slope of the secant line AQ approaches the **slope of the tangent line** at A, and we have the following.

Slope of the Tangent

The **slope of the tangent** to the graph of $y = f(x)$ at point $A(x_1, f(x_1))$ is

$$m = \lim_{h \to 0} \frac{f(x_1 + h) - f(x_1)}{h}$$

if this limit exists. That is, $m = f'(x_1)$, the derivative at $x = x_1$.

EXAMPLE 5 **Slope of the Tangent**

Find the slope of $y = f(x) = x^2$ at the point $A(2, 4)$.

Solution

The formula for the slope of the tangent to $y = f(x)$ at $(2, 4)$ is

$$m = f'(2) = \lim_{h \to 0} \frac{f(2 + h) - f(2)}{h}$$

Thus for $f(x) = x^2$, we have

$$m = f'(2) = \lim_{h \to 0} \frac{(2 + h)^2 - 2^2}{h}$$

Taking the limit immediately would result in both the numerator and the denominator approaching 0. To avoid this, we simplify the fraction before taking the limit.

$$m = \lim_{h \to 0} \frac{4 + 4h + h^2 - 4}{h} = \lim_{h \to 0} \frac{4h + h^2}{h} = \lim_{h \to 0} (4 + h) = 4$$

Thus the slope of the tangent to $y = x^2$ at $(2, 4)$ is 4 (see Figure 9.23).

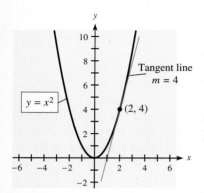

Figure 9.23

The statement "the slope of the tangent to the curve at $(2, 4)$ is 4" is frequently simplified to the statement "the slope of the curve at $(2, 4)$ is 4." Knowledge that the slope is a positive number on an interval tells us that the function is increasing on that interval, which means that a point moving along the graph of the function rises as it moves to the right on that interval. If the derivative (and thus the slope) is negative on an interval, the curve is decreasing on the interval; that is, a point moving along the graph falls as it moves to the right on that interval.

EXAMPLE 6 **Tangent Line**

Given $y = f(x) = 3x^2 + 2x + 11$, find

(a) the derivative of $f(x)$ at any point $(x, f(x))$.
(b) the slope of the tangent to the curve at $(1, 16)$.
(c) the equation of the line tangent to $y = 3x^2 + 2x + 11$ at $(1, 16)$.

Solution

(a) The derivative of $f(x)$ at any value x is denoted by $f'(x)$ and is

$$y' = f'(x) = \lim_{h \to 0} \frac{f(x + h) - f(x)}{h}$$

$$= \lim_{h \to 0} \frac{[3(x + h)^2 + 2(x + h) + 11] - (3x^2 + 2x + 11)}{h}$$

$$= \lim_{h \to 0} \frac{3(x^2 + 2xh + h^2) + 2x + 2h + 11 - 3x^2 - 2x - 11}{h}$$

$$= \lim_{h \to 0} \frac{6xh + 3h^2 + 2h}{h} = \lim_{h \to 0} (6x + 3h + 2) = 6x + 2$$

(b) The derivative is $f'(x) = 6x + 2$, so the slope of the tangent to the curve at $(1, 16)$ is $f'(1) = 6(1) + 2 = 8$.

(c) The equation of the tangent line uses the given point $(1, 16)$ and the slope $m = 8$. Using $y - y_1 = m(x - x_1)$ gives $y - 16 = 8(x - 1)$, or $y = 8x + 8$.

The discussion in this section indicates that the derivative of a function has several interpretations.

Interpretations of the Derivative	For a given function, each of the following means "find the **derivative.**"
	1. Find the **velocity** of an object moving in a straight line.
	2. Find the **instantaneous rate of change** of a function.
	3. Find the **marginal revenue** for a given revenue function.
	4. Find the **slope of the tangent** to the graph of a function.

That is, all the terms printed in boldface are mathematically the same, and the answers to questions about any one of them give information about the others.

Note in Figure 9.23 that near the point of tangency at (2, 4), the tangent line and the function look coincident. In fact, if we graphed both with a graphing calculator and repeatedly zoomed in near the point (2, 4), the two graphs would eventually appear as one. Try this for yourself. Thus the derivative of $f(x)$ at the point where $x = a$ can be approximated by finding the slope between $(a, f(a))$ and a second point that is nearby.

In addition, we know that the slope of the tangent to $f(x)$ at $x = a$ is defined by

$$f'(a) = \lim_{h \to 0} \frac{f(a + h) - f(a)}{h}$$

Hence we could also estimate $f'(a)$—that is, the slope of the tangent at $x = a$—by evaluating

$$\frac{f(a + h) - f(a)}{h} \quad \text{when } h \approx 0 \text{ and } h \neq 0$$

EXAMPLE   7   Approximating the Slope of the Tangent Line

(a) Let $f(x) = 2x^3 - 6x^2 + 2x - 5$. Use $\dfrac{f(a + h) - f(a)}{h}$ and two values of h to make estimates of the slope of the tangent to $f(x)$ at $x = 3$ on opposite sides of $x = 3$.

(b) Use the following table of values of x and $g(x)$ to estimate $g'(3)$.

x	1	1.9	2.7	2.9	2.999	3	3.002	3.1	4	5
$g(x)$	1.6	4.3	11.4	10.8	10.513	10.5	10.474	10.18	6	−5

Solution

The table feature of a graphing calculator can facilitate the following calculations.

(a) We can use $h = 0.0001$ and $h = -0.0001$ as follows:

With $h = 0.0001$: $f'(3) \approx \dfrac{f(3 + 0.0001) - f(3)}{0.0001} = \dfrac{f(3.0001) - f(3)}{0.0001} \approx 20$

With $h = -0.0001$: $f'(3) \approx \dfrac{f(3 + (-0.0001)) - f(3)}{-0.0001} = \dfrac{f(2.9999) - f(3)}{-0.0001} \approx 20$

(b) We use the given table and measure the slope between (3, 10.5) and another point that is nearby (the closer, the better). Using (2.999, 10.513), we obtain

$$g'(3) \approx \frac{y_2 - y_1}{x_2 - x_1} = \frac{10.5 - 10.513}{3 - 2.999} = \frac{-0.013}{0.001} = -13$$

Calculator Note   Most graphing calculators have a feature called the **numerical derivative** (usually denoted by nDer or nDeriv) that can approximate the derivative of a function at a point. See the steps used in Appendix C, Section 9.3. On most calculators this feature uses a calculation similar to our method in part (a) of Example 7 and produces the same estimate. The numerical derivative of $f(x) = 2x^3 - 6x^2 + 2x - 5$ with respect to x at $x = 3$ can be found as follows on many graphing calculators:

$$\text{nDeriv}(2x^3 - 6x^2 + 2x - 5, x, 3) = 20$$

Differentiability and Continuity

So far we have talked about how the derivative is defined, what it represents, and how to find it. However, there are functions for which derivatives do not exist at every value of x. Figure 9.24 shows some common cases where $f'(c)$ does not exist but where $f'(x)$ exists for all other values of x. These cases occur where there is a discontinuity, a corner, or a vertical tangent line.

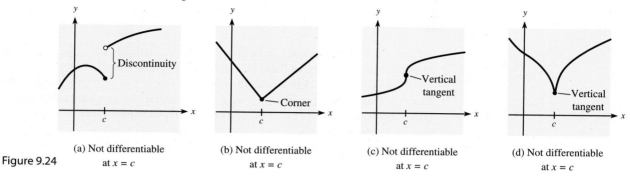

Figure 9.24

(a) Not differentiable at $x = c$

(b) Not differentiable at $x = c$

(c) Not differentiable at $x = c$

(d) Not differentiable at $x = c$

From Figure 9.24 we see that a function may be continuous at $x = c$ even though $f'(c)$ does not exist. Thus continuity does not imply differentiability at a point. However, differentiability does imply continuity.

Differentiability Implies Continuity

If a function f is differentiable at $x = c$, then f is continuous at $x = c$.

CHECKPOINT

3. Which of the following are given by $f'(c)$?
   (a) The slope of the tangent when $x = c$
   (b) The y-coordinate of the point where $x = c$
   (c) The instantaneous rate of change of $f(x)$ at $x = c$
   (d) The marginal revenue at $x = c$, if $f(x)$ is the revenue function
4. Must a graph that has no discontinuity, corner, or cusp at $x = c$ be differentiable at $x = c$?

Calculator Note

We can use a graphing calculator to explore the relationship between secant lines and tangent lines. For example, if the point (a, b) lies on the graph of $y = x^2$, then the equation of the secant line to $y = x^2$ from $(1, 1)$ to (a, b) has the equation

$$y - 1 = \frac{b - 1}{a - 1}(x - 1), \quad \text{or} \quad y = \frac{b - 1}{a - 1}(x - 1) + 1$$

Figure 9.25 illustrates the secant lines for three different choices for the point (a, b).

Figure 9.25   (a)   (b)   (c)

We see that as the point (a, b) moves closer to $(1, 1)$, the secant line looks more like the tangent line to $y = x^2$ at $(1, 1)$. Furthermore, (a, b) approaches $(1, 1)$ as $a \to 1$, and the slope of the secant approaches the following limit.

$$\lim_{a \to 1} \frac{b - 1}{a - 1} = \lim_{a \to 1} \frac{a^2 - 1}{a - 1} = \lim_{a \to 1} (a + 1) = 2$$

This limit, 2, is the slope of the tangent line at $(1, 1)$. That is, the derivative of $y = x^2$ at $(1, 1)$ is 2. [Note that a graphing calculator's calculation of the numerical derivative of $f(x) = x^2$ with respect to x at $x = 1$ gives $f'(1) = 2$.]

CHECKPOINT SOLUTIONS

1. $\dfrac{f(4) - f(1)}{4 - 1} = \dfrac{10 - 28}{3} = \dfrac{-18}{3} = -6$

2. (a) $f(x + h) - f(x) = [(x + h)^2 - (x + h) + 1] - (x^2 - x + 1)$
$$= x^2 + 2xh + h^2 - x - h + 1 - x^2 + x - 1$$
$$= 2xh + h^2 - h$$

   (b) $\dfrac{f(x + h) - f(x)}{h} = \dfrac{2xh + h^2 - h}{h}$
$$= 2x + h - 1$$

   (c) $f'(x) = \lim\limits_{h \to 0} \dfrac{f(x + h) - f(x)}{h} = \lim\limits_{h \to 0} (2x + h - 1)$
$$= 2x - 1$$

   (d) $f'(x) = 2x - 1$, so $f'(2) = 3$.

3. Parts (a), (c), and (d) are given by $f'(c)$. The y-coordinate where $x = c$ is given by $f(c)$.

4. No. Figure 9.24(c) shows such an example.

| EXERCISES | 9.3

In Problems 1–4, for each given function find the average rate of change over each specified interval.

1. $f(x) = x^2 + x - 12$ over (a) $[0, 5]$ and (b) $[-3, 10]$
2. $f(x) = 6 - x - x^2$ over (a) $[-1, 2]$ and (b) $[1, 10]$
3. For $f(x)$ given by the table, over (a) $[2, 5]$ and (b) $[3.8, 4]$

x	0	2	2.5	3	3.8	4	5
$f(x)$	14	20	22	19	17	16	30

4. For $f(x)$ given in the table, over (a) $[3, 3.5]$ and (b) $[2, 6]$

x	1	2	3	3.5	3.7	6
$f(x)$	40	25	18	15	18	38

5. Given $f(x) = 2x - x^2$, find the average rate of change of $f(x)$ over each of the following pairs of intervals.
   (a) $[2.9, 3]$ and $[2.99, 3]$ (b) $[3, 3.1]$ and $[3, 3.01]$
   (c) What do the calculations in parts (a) and (b) suggest the instantaneous rate of change of $f(x)$ at $x = 3$ might be?

6. Given $f(x) = x^2 + 3x + 7$, find the average rate of change of $f(x)$ over each of the following pairs of intervals.
   (a) $[1.9, 2]$ and $[1.99, 2]$
   (b) $[2, 2.1]$ and $[2, 2.01]$
   (c) What do the calculations in parts (a) and (b) suggest the instantaneous rate of change of $f(x)$ at $x = 2$ might be?

7. In the Procedure/Example box in this section, we were given $f(x) = 4x^2$ and found $f'(x) = 8x$. Find
   (a) the instantaneous rate of change of $f(x)$ at $x = 4$.
   (b) the slope of the tangent to the graph of $y = f(x)$ at $x = 4$.

(c) the point on the graph of $y = f(x)$ at $x = 4$.

8. In Example 6 in this section, we were given $f(x) = 3x^2 + 2x + 11$ and found $f'(x) = 6x + 2$. Find
   (a) the instantaneous rate of change of $f(x)$ at $x = 6$.
   (b) the slope of the tangent to the graph of $y = f(x)$ at $x = 6$.
   (c) the point on the graph of $y = f(x)$ at $x = 6$.

9. Let $f(x) = 3x^2 - 2x$.
   (a) Use the definition of derivative and the Procedure/ Example box in this section to verify that $f'(x) = 6x - 2$.
   (b) Find the instantaneous rate of change of $f(x)$ at $x = -1$.
   (c) Find the slope of the tangent to the graph of $y = f(x)$ at $x = -1$.
   (d) Find the point on the graph of $y = f(x)$ at $x = -1$.

10. Let $f(x) = 9 - \dfrac{1}{2} x^2$.
    (a) Use the definition of derivative and the Procedure/ Example box in this section to verify that $f'(x) = -x$.
    (b) Find the instantaneous rate of change of $f(x)$ at $x = 2$.
    (c) Find the slope of the tangent to the graph of $y = f(x)$ at $x = 2$.
    (d) Find the point on the graph of $y = f(x)$ at $x = 2$.

In Problems 11–14, the tangent line to the graph of $f(x)$ at $x = 1$ is shown. On the tangent line, P is the point of tangency and A is another point on the line.
(a) Find the coordinates of the points P and A.

(b) Use the coordinates of P and A to find the slope of the tangent line.

(c) Find $f'(1)$.

(d) Find the instantaneous rate of change of $f(x)$ at P.

11.

12.

13.

14.

For each function in Problems 15–18, find

(a) the derivative, by using the definition.

(b) the instantaneous rate of change of the function at any value and at the given value.

(c) the slope of the tangent at the given value.

15. $f(x) = 5x^2 + 6x - 11$; $x = -2$

16. $f(x) = 16x^2 - 4x + 2$; $x = 1$

17. $p(q) = 2q^2 + q + 5$; $q = 10$

18. $p(q) = 2q^2 - 4q + 5$; $q = 2$

For each function in Problems 19–22, approximate $f'(a)$ in the following ways.

(a) Use the numerical derivative feature of a graphing calculator.

(b) Use $\dfrac{f(a + h) - f(a)}{h}$ with $h = 0.0001$.

(c) Graph the function on a graphing calculator. Then zoom in near the point until the graph appears straight, pick two points, and find the slope of the line you see.

19. $f'(2)$ for $f(x) = 3x^4 - 7x - 5$

20. $f'(-1)$ for $f(x) = 2x^3 - 11x + 9$

21. $f'(4)$ for $f(x) = (2x - 1)^3$

22. $f'(3)$ for $f(x) = \dfrac{3x + 1}{2x - 5}$

In Problems 23 and 24, use the given tables to approximate $f'(a)$ as accurately as you can.

23.

x	12.0	12.99	13	13.1	$a = 13$
$f(x)$	1.41	17.42	17.11	22.84	

24.

x	-7.4	-7.50	-7.51	-7	$a = -7.5$
$f(x)$	22.12	22.351	22.38	24.12	

In the figures given in Problems 25 and 26, at each point A and B draw an approximate tangent line and then use it to complete parts (a) and (b).

(a) Is $f'(x)$ greater at point A or at point B? Explain.

(b) Estimate $f'(x)$ at point B.

25.

26.

In Problems 27 and 28, a point (a, b) on the graph of $y = f(x)$ is given, and the equation of the line tangent to the graph of $f(x)$ at (a, b) is given. In each case, find $f'(a)$ and $f(a)$.

27. $(4, -11)$; $7x - 3y = 61$

28. $(-1, 6)$; $x + 10y = 59$

29. If the instantaneous rate of change of $f(x)$ at $(2, -4)$ is 5, write the equation of the line tangent to the graph of $f(x)$ at $x = 2$.

30. If the instantaneous rate of change of $g(x)$ at $(-1, -2)$ is $1/2$, write the equation of the line tangent to the graph of $g(x)$ at $x = -1$.

Because the derivative of a function represents both the slope of the tangent to the curve and the instantaneous rate of change of the function, it is possible to use information about one to gain information about the other. In Problems 31 and 32, use the graph of the function $y = f(x)$ given in Figure 9.26.

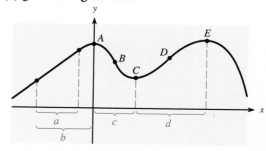

Figure 9.26

31. (a) Over what interval(s) (*a*) through (*d*) is the rate of change of $f(x)$ positive?
    (b) Over what interval(s) (*a*) through (*d*) is the rate of change of $f(x)$ negative?
    (c) At what point(s) *A* through *E* is the rate of change of $f(x)$ equal to zero?
32. (a) At what point(s) *A* through *E* does the rate of change of $f(x)$ change from positive to negative?
    (b) At what point(s) *A* through *E* does the rate of change of $f(x)$ change from negative to positive?
33. Given the graph of $y = f(x)$ in Figure 9.27, determine for which *x*-values *A, B, C, D,* or *E* the function is
    (a) continuous.   (b) differentiable.
34. Given the graph of $y = f(x)$ in Figure 9.27, determine for which *x*-values *F, G, H, I,* or *J* the function is
    (a) continuous.   (b) differentiable.

Figure 9.27

In Problems 35–38, (a) find the slope of the tangent to the graph of $f(x)$ at any point, (b) find the slope of the tangent at the given point, (c) write the equation of the line tangent to the graph of $f(x)$ at the given point, and (d) graph both $f(x)$ and its tangent line (use a graphing utility if one is available).

35. $f(x) = x^2 + x$; $(2, 6)$
36. $f(x) = x^2 + 3x$; $(-1, -2)$
37. $f(x) = x^3 + 3$; $(1, 4)$
38. $f(x) = 5x^3 + 2$; $(-1, -3)$

APPLICATIONS

39. *Total cost* Suppose total cost in dollars from the production of *x* printers is given by
$$C(x) = 0.0001x^3 + 0.005x^2 + 28x + 3000$$
Find the average rate of change of total cost when production changes
    (a) from 100 to 300 printers.
    (b) from 300 to 600 printers.
    (c) Interpret the results from parts (a) and (b).
40. *Average velocity* If an object is thrown upward at 64 feet per second from a height of 20 feet, its height *S* after *x* seconds is given by
$$S(x) = 20 + 64x - 16x^2$$
What is the average velocity in the
    (a) first 2 seconds after it is thrown?
    (b) next 2 seconds?
41. *Demand* If the demand for a product is given by
$$D(p) = \frac{1000}{\sqrt{p}} - 1$$

what is the average rate of change of demand when *p* increases from
    (a) 1 to 25?
    (b) 25 to 100?
42. *Revenue* If the total revenue function for a blender is
$$R(x) = 36x - 0.01x^2$$
where *x* is the number of units sold, what is the average rate of change in revenue $R(x)$ as *x* increases from 10 to 20 units?
43. *Total cost* Suppose the figure shows the total cost graph for a company. Arrange the average rates of change of total cost from *A* to *B*, *B* to *C*, and *A* to *C* from smallest to greatest, and explain your choice.

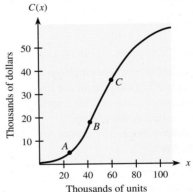

44. *Foreign-born population* The figure shows the percent of the U.S. population that was foreign-born for selected years from 1900 through 2008.
    (a) Use the figure to find the average rate of change in the percent of the U.S. population that was foreign-born from 1960 to 2008. Interpret your result.
    (b) From the figure, determine for which two consecutive data points the average rate of change in the percent of foreign-born was (i) closest to zero and (ii) furthest from zero.

**Foreign-Born Population Percent:
1900–2008**

Source: U.S. Bureau of the Census

45. *Marginal revenue* The revenue function for a sound system is
$$R(x) = 300x - x^2 \text{ dollars}$$
where *x* denotes the number of units sold.
    (a) What is the function that gives marginal revenue?
    (b) What is the marginal revenue if 50 units are sold, and what does it mean?
    (c) What is the marginal revenue if 200 units are sold, and what does it mean?

(d) What is the marginal revenue if 150 units are sold?

(e) As the number of units sold passes through 150, what happens to revenue?

46. *Marginal revenue* Suppose the total revenue function for a blender is

$$R(x) = 36x - 0.01x^2 \text{ dollars}$$

where x is the number of units sold.

(a) What function gives the marginal revenue?

(b) What is the marginal revenue when 600 units are sold, and what does it mean?

(c) What is the marginal revenue when 2000 units are sold, and what does it mean?

(d) What is the marginal revenue when 1800 units are sold, and what does it mean?

47. *Labor force and output* The monthly output at the Olek Carpet Mill is

$$Q(x) = 15{,}000 + 2x^2 \text{ units}, \quad (40 \le x \le 60)$$

where x is the number of workers employed at the mill. If there are currently 50 workers, find the instantaneous rate of change of monthly output with respect to the number of workers. That is, find $Q'(50)$.

48. *Consumer expenditure* Suppose that the demand for x units of a product is

$$x = 10{,}000 - 100p$$

where p dollars is the price per unit. Then the consumer expenditure for the product is

$$E(p) = px = p(10{,}000 - 100p) = 10{,}000p - 100p^2$$

What is the instantaneous rate of change of consumer expenditure with respect to price at

(a) any price p?   (b) $p = 5$?   (c) $p = 20$?

In Problems 49–52, find derivatives with the numerical derivative feature of a graphing calculator.

49. *Profit* Suppose that the profit function for the monthly sales of a car by a dealership is

$$P(x) = 500x - x^2 - 100$$

where x is the number of cars sold. What is the instantaneous rate of change of profit when

(a) 200 cars are sold? Explain its meaning.

(b) 300 cars are sold? Explain its meaning.

50. *Profit* If the total revenue function and the total cost function for a toy are

$$R(x) = 2x \quad \text{and} \quad C(x) = 100 + 0.2x^2 + x$$

what is the instantaneous rate of change of profit if 10 units are produced and sold? Explain its meaning.

51. *Heat index* The highest recorded temperature in the state of Alaska was 100°F and occurred on June 27, 1915, at Fort Yukon. The *heat index* is the apparent temperature of the air at a given temperature and humidity level. If x denotes the relative humidity (in percent), then the heat index (in degrees Fahrenheit) for an air temperature of 100°F can be approximated by the function

$$f(x) = 0.009x^2 + 0.139x + 91.875$$

(a) At what rate is the heat index changing when the humidity is 50%?

(b) Write a sentence that explains the meaning of your answer in part (a).

52. *Receptivity* In learning theory, receptivity is defined as the ability of students to understand a complex concept. Receptivity is highest when the topic is introduced and tends to decrease as time passes in a lecture. Suppose that the receptivity of a group of students in a mathematics class is given by

$$g(t) = -0.2t^2 + 3.1t + 32$$

where t is minutes after the lecture begins.

(a) At what rate is receptivity changing 10 minutes after the lecture begins?

(b) Write a sentence that explains the meaning of your answer in part (a).

53. *Marginal revenue* Suppose the graph shows a manufacturer's total revenue, in thousands of dollars, from the sale of x cellular telephones to dealers.

(a) Is the marginal revenue greater at 300 cell phones or at 700? Explain.

(b) Use part (a) to decide whether the sale of the 301st cell phone or the 701st brings in more revenue. Explain.

54. *Social Security beneficiaries* The graph shows a model for the number of millions of Social Security beneficiaries projected to 2030. The model was developed with data from the Social Security Trustees Report.

(a) Was the instantaneous rate of change of the number of beneficiaries with respect to the year greater in 1960 or in 1980? Justify your answer.

(b) Is the instantaneous rate of change of the number of beneficiaries projected to be greater in 2000 or in 2030? Justify your answer.

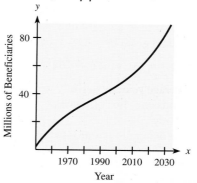

Derivative Formulas

| APPLICATION PREVIEW |

For more than 50 years, U.S. total personal income has experienced steady growth. With Bureau of Economic Analysis, U.S. Department of Commerce data for selected years from 1960 and projected to 2018, U.S. total personal income I, in billions of current dollars, can be modeled by

$$I = I(t) = 6.29t^2 - 51.7t + 601$$

where t is the number of years past 1960. We can find the rate of growth of total U.S. personal income in 2015 by using the derivative $I'(t)$ of the total personal income function. (See Example 8.)

As we discussed in the previous section, the derivative of a function can be used to find the rate of change of the function. In this section we will develop formulas that will make it easier to find certain derivatives.

Derivative of $f(x) = x^n$

We can use the definition of derivative to show the following:

$$\text{If } f(x) = x^2, \text{ then } f'(x) = 2x.$$
$$\text{If } f(x) = x^3, \text{ then } f'(x) = 3x^2.$$
$$\text{If } f(x) = x^4, \text{ then } f'(x) = 4x^3.$$
$$\text{If } f(x) = x^5, \text{ then } f'(x) = 5x^4.$$

Do you recognize a pattern here? We can use the definition of derivative and the binomial formula to verify the pattern and find a formula for the derivative of $f(x) = x^n$. If n is a positive integer, then

$$f'(x) = \lim_{h \to 0} \frac{f(x + h) - f(x)}{h} = \lim_{h \to 0} \frac{(x + h)^n - x^n}{h}$$

Because we are assuming that n is a positive integer, we can use the binomial formula, developed in Section 8.3, to expand $(x + h)^n$. This formula can be stated as follows:

$$(x + h)^n = x^n + nx^{n-1}h + \frac{n(n - 1)}{1 \cdot 2} x^{n-2} h^2 + \cdots + h^n$$

Thus the derivative formula yields

$$f'(x) = \lim_{h \to 0} \frac{\left[x^n + nx^{n-1}h + \dfrac{n(n - 1)}{1 \cdot 2} x^{n-2}h^2 + \cdots + h^n \right] - x^n}{h}$$

$$= \lim_{h \to 0} \left[nx^{n-1} + \frac{n(n - 1)}{1 \cdot 2} x^{n-2}h + \cdots + h^{n-1} \right]$$

Note that each term after nx^{n-1} contains h as a factor, so all terms except nx^{n-1} will approach 0 as $h \to 0$. Thus

$$f'(x) = nx^{n-1}$$

Even though we proved this derivative rule only for the case when n is a positive integer, the rule applies for any real number n.

Powers of x Rule

If $f(x) = x^n$, where n is a real number, then $f'(x) = nx^{n-1}$.

EXAMPLE 1   **Powers of x Rule**

Find the derivatives of the following functions.

(a) $y = x^{14}$ (b) $f(x) = x^{-2}$ (c) $y = x$ (d) $g(x) = x^{1/3}$

Solution

(a) If $y = x^{14}$, then $dy/dx = 14x^{14-1} = 14x^{13}$.

(b) The Powers of x Rule applies for all real values. Thus for $f(x) = x^{-2}$, we have

$$f'(x) = -2x^{-2-1} = -2x^{-3} = \frac{-2}{x^3}$$

(c) If $y = x$, then $dy/dx = 1x^{1-1} = x^0 = 1$. (Note that $y = x$ is a line with slope 1.)

(d) The Powers of x Rule applies to $y = x^{1/3}$.

$$g'(x) = \frac{1}{3}x^{1/3-1} = \frac{1}{3}x^{-2/3} = \frac{1}{3x^{2/3}}$$

In Example 1 we took the derivative with respect to x of *both sides* of each equation. We denote the operation "take the derivative with respect to x" by $\dfrac{d}{dx}$. Thus for $y = x^{14}$, in part (a), we can use this notation on both sides of the equation.

$$\frac{d}{dx}(y) = \frac{d}{dx}(x^{14}) \quad \text{gives} \quad \frac{dy}{dx} = 14x^{13}$$

Similarly, we can use this notation to indicate the derivative of an expression.

$$\frac{d}{dx}(x^{-2}) = -2x^{-3}$$

The differentiation rules are stated and proved for the independent variable x, but they also apply to other independent variables. The following examples illustrate differentiation involving variables other than x and y.

EXAMPLE 2   **Derivatives**

Find the derivatives of the following functions.

(a) $u(s) = s^8$ (b) $p = q^{2/3}$ (c) $C(t) = \sqrt{t}$ (d) $s = \dfrac{1}{\sqrt{t}}$

Solution

(a) If $u(s) = s^8$, then $u'(s) = 8s^{8-1} = 8s^7$.

(b) If $p = q^{2/3}$, then

$$\frac{dp}{dq} = \frac{2}{3}q^{2/3-1} = \frac{2}{3}q^{-1/3} = \frac{2}{3q^{1/3}}$$

(c) Writing $\sqrt{t}$ in its equivalent form, $t^{1/2}$, using the derivative formula, and writing the derivative in radical form gives $C'(t) = \dfrac{1}{2}t^{1/2-1} = \dfrac{1}{2}t^{-1/2} = \dfrac{1}{2}\cdot\dfrac{1}{t^{1/2}} = \dfrac{1}{2\sqrt{t}}$

(d) Writing $1/\sqrt{t}$ as $\dfrac{1}{t^{1/2}} = t^{-1/2}$, taking the derivative, and writing the derivative in a form similar to that of the original function gives

$$\frac{ds}{dt} = -\frac{1}{2}t^{-1/2-1} = -\frac{1}{2}t^{-3/2} = -\frac{1}{2}\cdot\frac{1}{t^{3/2}} = -\frac{1}{2\sqrt{t^3}}$$

EXAMPLE 3   **Tangent Line**

Write the equation of the tangent line to the graph of $y = x^3$ at $x = 1$.

Figure 9.28

Solution

Writing the equation of the tangent line to $y = x^3$ at $x = 1$ involves three steps.

1. Evaluate the function to find the point of tangency.
   At $x = 1$: $y = (1)^3 = 1$, so the point is $(1, 1)$

2. Evaluate the derivative to find the slope of the tangent.
   At any point: $m_{\text{tan}} = y' = 3x^2$
   At $x = 1$: $m_{\text{tan}} = y'|_{x=1} = 3(1^2) = 3$

3. Use $y - y_1 = m(x - x_1)$ with the point $(1, 1)$ and slope $m = 3$.
   $$y - 1 = 3(x - 1) \Rightarrow y = 3x - 3 + 1 \Rightarrow y = 3x - 2$$

   Figure 9.28 shows the graph of $y = x^3$ and the tangent line at $x = 1$.

Derivative of a Constant

A function of the form $y = f(x) = c$, where c is a constant, is called a **constant function**. We can show that the derivative of a constant function is 0, as follows.

$$f'(x) = \lim_{h \to 0} \frac{f(x + h) - f(x)}{h} = \lim_{h \to 0} \frac{c - c}{h} = \lim_{h \to 0} 0 = 0$$

We can state this rule formally.

Constant Function Rule   If $f(x) = c$, where c is a constant, then $f'(x) = 0$.

EXAMPLE 4   **Derivative of a Constant**

Find the derivative of the function defined by $y = 4$.

Solution

Because 4 is a constant, $\dfrac{dy}{dx} = 0$.

Recall that the function defined by $y = 4$ has a horizontal line as its graph. Thus the slope of the line (and the derivative of the function) is 0.

Derivative of $y = c \cdot u(x)$

We now can take derivatives of constant functions and powers of x. But we do not yet have a rule for taking derivatives of functions of the form $f(x) = 4x^5$ or $g(t) = \frac{1}{2}t^2$. The following rule provides a method for handling functions of this type.

Coefficient Rule   If $f(x) = c \cdot u(x)$, where c is a constant and $u(x)$ is a differentiable function of x, then $f'(x) = c \cdot u'(x)$.

The Coefficient Rule says that the derivative of a constant times a function is the constant times the derivative of the function.

Using Properties of Limits II and IV (from Section 9.1, "Limits"), we can show

$$\lim_{h \to 0} c \cdot g(h) = c \cdot \lim_{h \to 0} g(h)$$

We can use this result to verify the Coefficient Rule. If $f(x) = c \cdot u(x)$, then

$$f'(x) = \lim_{h \to 0} \frac{f(x+h) - f(x)}{h} = \lim_{h \to 0} \frac{c \cdot u(x+h) - c \cdot u(x)}{h}$$

$$= \lim_{h \to 0} c \cdot \left[\frac{u(x+h) - u(x)}{h} \right] = c \cdot \lim_{h \to 0} \frac{u(x+h) - u(x)}{h}$$

so $f'(x) = c \cdot u'(x)$.

EXAMPLE 5   Coefficient Rule for Derivatives

Find the derivatives of the following functions.

(a) $f(x) = 4x^5$ (b) $g(t) = \dfrac{1}{2}t^2$ (c) $p = \dfrac{5}{\sqrt{q}}$

Solution

(a) $f'(x) = 4(5x^4) = 20x^4$

(b) $g'(t) = \frac{1}{2}(2t) = t$

(c) $p = \dfrac{5}{\sqrt{q}} = 5q^{-1/2}$,   so $\dfrac{dp}{dq} = 5\left(-\dfrac{1}{2} q^{-3/2} \right) = -\dfrac{5}{2\sqrt{q^3}}$

EXAMPLE 6   World Tourism

Over the past 20 years, world tourism has grown into one of the world's major industries. Since 1990 the receipts from world tourism y, in billions of dollars, can be modeled by the function

$$y = 113.54x^{0.52584}$$

where x is the number of years past 1985 (*Source:* World Tourism Organization).

(a) Name the function that models the rate of change of the receipts from world tourism.

(b) Find the function from part (a).

(c) Find the rate of change in world tourism in 2012.

Solution

(a) The rate of change of world tourism receipts is modeled by the derivative.

(b) $\dfrac{dy}{dx} = 113.54(0.52584x^{0.52584-1}) \approx 59.704x^{-0.47416}$

(c) $\dfrac{dy}{dx}\bigg|_{x=27} = 59.704(27^{-0.47416}) \approx 12.511$

Thus, the model estimates that world tourism changed by about \$12.511 billion per year in 2012.

Derivatives of Sums and Differences   In Example 6 of Section 9.3, "Rates of Change and Derivatives," we found the derivative of $f(x) = 3x^2 + 2x + 11$ to be $f'(x) = 6x + 2$. This result, along with the results of several of the derivatives calculated in the exercises for that section, suggest that we can find the derivative of a function by finding the derivatives of its terms and combining them. The following rules state this formally.

Sum Rule   If $f(x) = u(x) + v(x)$, where u and v are differentiable functions of x, then $f'(x) = u'(x) + v'(x)$.

We can prove this rule as follows. If $f(x) = u(x) + v(x)$, then

$$f'(x) = \lim_{h \to 0} \frac{f(x+h) - f(x)}{h} = \lim_{h \to 0} \frac{[u(x+h) + v(x+h)] - [u(x) + v(x)]}{h}$$

$$= \lim_{h \to 0} \left[\frac{u(x+h) - u(x)}{h} + \frac{v(x+h) - v(x)}{h} \right]$$

$$= \lim_{h \to 0} \frac{u(x+h) - u(x)}{h} + \lim_{h \to 0} \frac{v(x+h) - v(x)}{h}$$

$$= u'(x) + v'(x)$$

A similar rule applies to the difference of functions.

Difference Rule

If $f(x) = u(x) - v(x)$, where u and v are differentiable functions of x, then $f'(x) = u'(x) - v'(x)$.

EXAMPLE 7 Sum and Difference Rules

Find the derivatives of the following functions.

(a) $y = 3x + 5$ (b) $f(x) = 4x^3 - 2x^2 + 5x - 3$

(c) $p = \frac{1}{3}q^3 + 2q^2 - 3$ (d) $u(x) = 5x^4 + x^{1/3}$

(e) $y = 4x^3 + \sqrt{x}$ (f) $s = 5t^6 - \dfrac{1}{t^2}$

Solution

(a) $y' = 3 \cdot 1 + 0 = 3$

(b) The rules regarding the derivatives of sums and differences of two functions also apply if more than two functions are involved. We may think of the functions that are added and subtracted as terms of the function f. Then it would be correct to say that we may take the derivative of a function term by term. Thus,

$$f'(x) = 4(3x^2) - 2(2x) + 5(1) - 0 = 12x^2 - 4x + 5$$

(c) $\dfrac{dp}{dq} = \frac{1}{3}(3q^2) + 2(2q) - 0 = q^2 + 4q$

(d) $u'(x) = 5(4x^3) + \frac{1}{3}x^{-2/3} = 20x^3 + \dfrac{1}{3x^{2/3}}$

(e) We may write the function as $y = 4x^3 + x^{1/2}$, so

$$y' = 4(3x^2) + \frac{1}{2}x^{-1/2} = 12x^2 + \frac{1}{2x^{1/2}} = 12x^2 + \frac{1}{2\sqrt{x}}$$

(f) We may write $s = 5t^6 - 1/t^2$ as $s = 5t^6 - t^{-2}$, so

$$\frac{ds}{dt} = 5(6t^5) - (-2t^{-3}) = 30t^5 + 2t^{-3} = 30t^5 + \frac{2}{t^3}$$

Each derivative in Example 7 has been *simplified*. This means that the final form of the derivative contains no negative exponents and the use of radicals or fractional exponents matches the original problem.

Also, in part (a) of Example 7, we saw that the derivative of $y = 3x + 5$ is 3. Because the slope of a line is the same at all points on the line, it is reasonable that the derivative of a linear equation is a constant. In particular, the slope of the graph of the equation $y = mx + b$ is m at all points on its graph because the derivative of $y = mx + b$ is $y' = f'(x) = m$.

EXAMPLE 8 Personal Income | APPLICATION PREVIEW |

Suppose that t is the number of years past 1960 and that

$$I = I(t) = 6.29t^2 - 51.7t + 601$$

models the U.S. total personal income in billions of current dollars. For 2015, find the model's prediction for

(a) the U.S. total personal income.
(b) the rate of change of U.S. total personal income.

Solution
(a) For 2015, $t = 55$ and

$$I(55) = 6.29(55^2) - 51.7(55) + 601 \approx 16{,}785 \text{ billion (current dollars)}$$

(b) The rate of change of U.S. total personal income is given by

$$I'(t) = 12.58t - 51.7$$

The predicted rate for 2015 is

$$I'(55) = \$640.2 \text{ billion (current dollars) per year}$$

This predicts that U.S. total personal income will change by about \$640.2 billion from 2015 to 2016.

CHECKPOINT

1. True or false: The derivative of a constant times a function is equal to the constant times the derivative of the function.
2. True or false: The derivative of the sum of two functions is equal to the sum of the derivatives of the two functions.
3. True or false: The derivative of the difference of two functions is equal to the difference of the derivatives of the two functions.
4. Does the Coefficient Rule apply to $f(x) = x^n/c$, where c is a constant? Explain.
5. Find the derivative of each of the following functions.

   (a) $f(x) = x^{10} - 10x + 5$ (b) $s = \dfrac{1}{t^5} - 10^7 + 1$

6. Find the slope of the line tangent to $f(x) = x^3 - 4x^2 + 1$ at $x = -1$.

EXAMPLE 9   Horizontal Tangents

Figure 9.29

Find all points on the graph of $f(x) = x^3 + 3x^2 - 45x + 4$ where the tangent line is horizontal.

Solution
A horizontal line has slope equal to 0. Thus, to find the desired points, we solve $f'(x) = 0$.

$$f'(x) = 3x^2 + 6x - 45$$

We solve $3x^2 + 6x - 45 = 0$ as follows:

$$3x^2 + 6x - 45 = 0 \Rightarrow 3(x^2 + 2x - 15) = 0 \Rightarrow 3(x + 5)(x - 3) = 0$$

Solving $3(x + 5)(x - 3) = 0$ gives $x = -5$ and $x = 3$. The y-coordinates for these x-values come from $f(x)$. The desired points are $(-5, f(-5)) = (-5, 179)$ and $(3, f(3)) = (3, -77)$. Figure 9.29 shows the graph of $y = f(x)$ with these points and the tangent lines at them indicated.

Marginal Revenue   The marginal revenue $R'(x)$ is used to estimate the change in revenue caused by the sale of one additional unit.

EXAMPLE 10   Revenue

Suppose that a manufacturer of a product knows that because of the demand for this product, his revenue is given by

$$R(x) = 1500x - 0.02x^2, \quad 0 \le x \le 1000$$

where x is the number of units sold and $R(x)$ is in dollars.

(a) Find the marginal revenue at $x = 500$.
(b) Find the change in revenue caused by the increase in sales from 500 to 501 units.

Solution

(a) The marginal revenue for any value of x is

$$R'(x) = 1500 - 0.04x$$

The marginal revenue at $x = 500$ is

$$R'(500) = 1500 - 20 = 1480 \text{ (dollars per unit)}$$

We can interpret this to mean that the approximate revenue from the sale of the 501st unit will be \$1480.

(b) The revenue at $x = 500$ is $R(500) = 745,000$, and the revenue at $x = 501$ is $R(501) = 746,479.98$, so the change in revenue is

$$R(501) - R(500) = 746,479.98 - 745,000 = 1479.98 \text{ (dollars)}$$

Notice that the marginal revenue at $x = 500$ is a good estimate of the revenue from the 501st unit.

Calculator Note We have mentioned that graphing calculators have a numerical derivative feature that can be used to estimate the derivative of a function at a specific value of x. This feature can also be used to check the derivative of a function that has been computed with a formula. See Appendix C, Section 9.4, for details. We graph both the derivative calculated with a formula and the numerical derivative. If the two graphs lie on top of one another, the computed derivative agrees with the numerical derivative. Figure 9.30 illustrates this idea for the derivative of $f(x) = \frac{1}{3}x^3 - 2x^2 + 4$. Figure 9.30(a) shows $f'(x) = x^2 - 4x$ as y_1 and the calculator's numerical derivative of $f(x)$ as y_2. Figure 9.30(b) shows the graphs of both y_1 and y_2 (the graphs are coincident).

Figure 9.30   (a)   (b)

EXAMPLE 11   Comparing $f(x)$ and $f'(x)$

(a) Graph $f(x) = x^3 - 3x + 3$ and its derivative $f'(x)$ on the same set of axes so that all values of x that make $f'(x) = 0$ are in the x-range.
(b) Investigate the graph of $y = f(x)$ near values of x where $f'(x) = 0$. Does the graph of $y = f(x)$ appear to turn at values where $f'(x) = 0$?
(c) Compare the interval of x values where $f'(x) < 0$ with the interval where the graph of $y = f(x)$ is decreasing from left to right.
(d) What is the relationship between the intervals where $f'(x) > 0$ and where the graph of $y = f(x)$ is increasing from left to right?

Solution

(a) The graphs of $f(x) = x^3 - 3x + 3$ and $f'(x) = 3x^2 - 3$ are shown in Figure 9.31.
(b) The values where $f'(x) = 0$ are the x-intercepts, $x = -1$ and $x = 1$. The graph of $y = x^3 - 3x + 3$ appears to turn at both these values.

(c) $f'(x) < 0$ where the graph of $y = f'(x)$ is below the x-axis, for $-1 < x < 1$. The graph of $y = f(x)$ appears to be decreasing on this interval.

(d) They appear to be the same intervals.

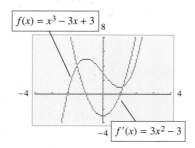

Figure 9.31

CHECKPOINT SOLUTIONS

1. True, by the Coefficient Rule.
2. True, by the Sum Rule.
3. True, by the Difference Rule.
4. Yes, $f(x) = x^n/c = (1/c)x^n$, so the coefficient is $(1/c)$.
5. (a) $f'(x) = 10x^9 - 10$
   (b) Note that $s = t^{-5} - 10^7 + 1$ and that 10^7 and 1 are constants.

$$\frac{ds}{dt} = -5t^{-6} = \frac{-5}{t^6}$$

6. The slope of the tangent at $x = -1$ is $f'(-1)$.

$$f'(x) = 3x^2 - 8x, \quad f'(-1) = 3(-1)^2 - 8(-1) = 11$$

| EXERCISES | 9.4

Find the derivatives of the functions in Problems 1–14.

1. $y = 4$
2. $f(s) = 6$
3. $f(t) = t$
4. $s = t^2$
5. $y = 6 - 8x + 2x^2$
6. $y = 12 + 2x - 7x^3$
7. $f(x) = 3x^4 - x^6$
8. $f(x) = 3x^4 - x^9$
9. $y = 10x^5 - 3x^3 + 5x - 11$
10. $y = 3x^5 - 5x^3 - 8x + 8$
11. $w = z^7 - 3z^6 + 13$
12. $u = 2t^{10} - 5t^5 - 9$
13. $g(x) = 2x^{12} - 5x^6 + 9x^4 + x - 5$
14. $h(x) = 12x^{20} + 8x^{10} - 2x^7 + 17x - 9$

In Problems 15–18, at the indicated points, find (a) the slope of the tangent to the curve, and (b) the instantaneous rate of change of the function.

15. $y = 7x^2 + 2x + 1, \quad x = 2$
16. $C(x) = 3x^2 - 5, \quad (3, 22)$
17. $P(x) = x^3 - 6x, \quad (2, -4)$
18. $R(x) = 16x + x^2, \quad x = 1$

In Problems 19–26, find the derivative of each function.

19. $y = x^{-5} + x^{-8} - 3$
20. $y = x^{-1} - x^{-2} + 13$
21. $y = 3x^{11/3} - 2x^{7/4} - x^{1/2} + 8$
22. $y = 5x^{8/5} - 3x^{5/6} + x^{1/3} + 5$
23. $f(x) = 5x^{-4/5} + 2x^{-4/3}$
24. $f(x) = 6x^{-8/3} - x^{-2/3}$
25. $g(x) = \dfrac{3}{x^5} + \dfrac{2}{x^4} + 6\sqrt[3]{x}$
26. $h(x) = \dfrac{7}{x^7} - \dfrac{3}{x^3} + 8\sqrt{x}$

In Problems 27–30, write the equation of the tangent line to each curve at the indicated point. As a check, graph both the function and the tangent line.

27. $y = x^3 - 5x^2 + 7$ at $x = 1$
28. $y = x^4 - 4x^3 - 2$ at $x = 2$
29. $f(x) = 4x^2 - \dfrac{1}{x}$ at $x = -\dfrac{1}{2}$
30. $f(x) = \dfrac{x^3}{3} - \dfrac{3}{x^3}$ at $x = -1$

In Problems 31–34, find the coordinates of points where the graph of $f(x)$ has horizontal tangents. As a check, graph $f(x)$ and see whether the points you found look as though they have horizontal tangents.

31. $f(x) = -x^3 + 9x^2 - 15x + 6$

32. $f(x) = \dfrac{1}{3}x^3 - 3x^2 - 16x + 8$

33. $f(x) = x^4 - 4x^3 + 9$

34. $f(x) = 3x^5 - 5x^3 + 2$

In Problems 35 and 36, find each derivative at the given x-value (a) with the appropriate rule and (b) with the numerical derivative feature of a graphing calculator.

35. $y = 5 - 2\sqrt{x}$ at $x = 4$

36. $y = 1 + 3x^{2/3}$ at $x = -8$

In Problems 37–40, complete the following.
(a) **Calculate the derivative of each function with the appropriate formula.**
(b) **Check your result from part (a) by graphing your calculated derivative and the numerical derivative of the given function with respect to x evaluated at x.**

37. $f(x) = 2x^3 + 5x - \pi^4 + 8$

38. $f(x) = 3x^2 - 8x + 2^5 - 20$

39. $h(x) = \dfrac{10}{x^3} - \dfrac{10}{\sqrt[5]{x^2}} + x^2 + 1$

40. $g(x) = \dfrac{5}{x^{10}} + \dfrac{4}{\sqrt[4]{x^3}} + x^5 - 4$

The tangent line to a curve at a point closely approximates the curve near the point. In fact, for x-values close enough to the point of tangency, the function and its tangent line are virtually indistinguishable. Problems 41 and 42 explore this relationship. Use each given function and the indicated point to complete the following.
(a) **Write the equation of the tangent line to the curve at the indicated point.**
(b) **Use a graphing calculator to graph both the function and its tangent line. Be sure your graph shows the point of tangency.**
(c) **Repeatedly zoom in on the point of tangency until the function and the tangent line cannot be distinguished. Identify the x- and y-ranges in this window.**

41. $f(x) = 3x^2 + 2x$ at $x = 1$

42. $f(x) = 4x - x^2$ at $x = 5$

For each function in Problems 43–46, do the following.
(a) **Find $f'(x)$.**
(b) **Graph both $f(x)$ and $f'(x)$ with a graphing utility.**
(c) **Use the graph of $f'(x)$ to identify x-values where $f'(x) = 0, f'(x) > 0$, and $f'(x) < 0$.**
(d) **Use the graph of $f(x)$ to identify x-values where $f(x)$ has a maximum or minimum point, where the graph of $f(x)$ is rising, and where the graph of $f(x)$ is falling.**

43. $f(x) = 8 - 2x - x^2$

44. $f(x) = x^2 + 4x - 12$

45. $f(x) = x^3 - 12x - 5$

46. $f(x) = 7 - 3x^2 - \dfrac{x^3}{3}$

APPLICATIONS

47. *Revenue* Suppose that a wholesaler expects that his monthly revenue, in dollars, for an electronic game will be

$$R(x) = 100x - 0.1x^2, \quad 0 \le x \le 800$$

where x is the number of units sold. Find his marginal revenue and interpret it when the quantity sold is
(a) $x = 300$.
(b) $x = 600$.

48. *Revenue* The total revenue, in dollars, for a commodity is described by the function

$$R = 300x - 0.02x^2$$

(a) What is the marginal revenue when 40 units are sold?
(b) Interpret your answer to part (a).

49. *Workers and output* The number of units of weekly output of a certain product is

$$Q(x) = 200x + 6x^2$$

where x is the number of workers on the assembly line. There are presently 60 workers on the line.
(a) Find $Q'(x)$ and estimate the change in the weekly output caused by the addition of one worker.
(b) Calculate $Q(61) - Q(60)$ to see the actual change in the weekly output.

50. *Capital investment and output* The monthly output of a certain product is

$$Q(x) = 800x^{5/2}$$

where x is the capital investment in millions of dollars. Find dQ/dx, which can be used to estimate the effect on the output if an additional capital investment of $1 million is made.

51. *Demand* The demand for q units of a product depends on the price p (in dollars) according to

$$q = \frac{1000}{\sqrt{p}} - 1, \quad \text{for } p > 0$$

Find and explain the meaning of the instantaneous rate of change of demand with respect to price when the price is
(a) $25. (b) $100.

52. *Demand* Suppose that the demand for a product depends on the price p according to

$$D(p) = \frac{50,000}{p^2} - \frac{1}{2}, \quad p > 0$$

where p is in dollars. Find and explain the meaning of the instantaneous rate of change of demand with respect to price when
(a) $p = 50$. (b) $p = 100$.

53. **Cost and average cost** Suppose that the total cost function, in dollars, for the production of x units of a product is given by

$$C(x) = 4000 + 55x + 0.1x^2$$

Then the average cost of producing x items is

$$\overline{C(x)} = \frac{\text{total cost}}{x} = \frac{4000}{x} + 55 + 0.1x$$

   (a) Find the instantaneous rate of change of average cost with respect to the number of units produced, at any level of production.
   (b) Find the level of production at which this rate of change equals zero.
   (c) At the value found in part (b), find the instantaneous rate of change of cost and find the average cost. What do you notice?

54. **Cost and average cost** Suppose that the total cost function, in dollars, for a certain commodity is given by

$$C(x) = 40,500 + 190x + 0.2x^2$$

   where x is the number of units produced.
   (a) Find the instantaneous rate of change of the average cost

$$\overline{C} = \frac{40,500}{x} + 190 + 0.2x$$

   for any level of production.
   (b) Find the level of production where this rate of change equals zero.
   (c) At the value found in part (b), find the instantaneous rate of change of cost and find the average cost. What do you notice?

55. **Cost-benefit** Suppose that for a certain city the cost C, in dollars, of obtaining drinking water that contains p percent impurities (by volume) is given by

$$C = \frac{120,000}{p} - 1200$$

   (a) Find the rate of change of cost with respect to p when impurities account for 1% (by volume).
   (b) Write a sentence that explains the meaning of your answer in part (a).

56. **Cost-benefit** Suppose that the cost C, in dollars, of processing the exhaust gases at an industrial site to ensure that only p percent of the particulate pollution escapes is given by

$$C(p) = \frac{8100(100 - p)}{p}$$

   (a) Find the rate of change of cost C with respect to the percent of particulate pollution that escapes when $p = 2$ (percent).
   (b) Write a sentence interpreting your answer to part (a).

57. **Wind chill** One form of the formula that meteorologists use to calculate wind chill temperature (WC) is

$$WC = 35.74 + 0.6215t - 35.75s^{0.16} + 0.4275t\,s^{0.16}$$

   where s is the wind speed in mph and t is the actual air temperature in degrees Fahrenheit. Suppose temperature is constant at $15°$.
   (a) Express wind chill WC as a function of wind speed s.
   (b) Find the rate of change of wind chill with respect to wind speed when the wind speed is 25 mph.
   (c) Interpret your answer to part (b).

58. **Allometric relationships—crabs** For fiddler crabs, data gathered by Thompson[*] show that the allometric relationship between the weight C of the claw and the weight W of the body is given by

$$C = 0.11W^{1.54}$$

   Find the function that gives the rate of change of claw weight with respect to body weight.

Recall that for all modeling problems, use the unrounded model for any calculations.

59. **Modeling** *U.S. cellular subscriberships* The table shows the number of U.S. cellular subscriberships (in millions) from 1995 to 2008.

Year	Subscriberships	Year	Subscriberships
1995	33.786	2002	140.767
1996	44.043	2003	158.722
1997	55.312	2004	182.140
1998	69.209	2005	207.896
1999	86.047	2006	233.041
2000	109.478	2007	255.396
2001	128.375	2008	270.334

Source: The CTIA Semi-Annual Wireless Industry Survey

   (a) Model these data with a power function $S(x)$, where S is the number of U.S. cellular subscriberships (in millions) and x is the number of years past 1985.
   (b) For the period from 1998 to 2008, use the data to find the average rate of change of U.S. cellular subscriberships.
   (c) Find and interpret the instantaneous rate of change of the modeling function $S(x)$ for the year 2008.

60. **Modeling** *U.S. poverty threshold* The table shows the yearly poverty threshold income for a single person for selected years from 1990 to 2008.

[*]d'Arcy Thompson, *On Growth and Form* (Cambridge, England: Cambridge University Press, 1961).

Year	Income	Year	Income
1990	$6652	2003	9573
1995	7763	2005	10,160
1998	8316	2008	10,991
2000	8959		

Source: U.S. Bureau of the Census

(a) Model these data with a power function $p(t)$, where p is the poverty threshold income for a single person and t is the number of years past 1980.
(b) Find the function that models the rate of change of the poverty threshold income for a single person.
(c) Use the model in part (b) to find and interpret the rate of change of the poverty threshold income in 2010.

61. **Modeling** *U.S. population* The table gives the U.S. population to the nearest million (actual or projected) for selected years.

Year	Population (in millions)	Year	Population (in millions)
1960	181	1995	263
1965	194	1998	271
1970	205	2000	281
1975	216	2003	291
1980	228	2005	296
1985	238	2025	348
1990	250	2050	420

Source: U.S. Bureau of the Census

(a) Find a cubic function $P(t)$ that models these data, where P is the U.S. population in millions and t is the number of years past 1960.
(b) Find the function that models the instantaneous rate of change of the U.S. population.
(c) Find and interpret the instantaneous rates of change in 2000 and 2025.

62. **Modeling** *Gross domestic product* The table shows U.S. gross domestic product (GDP) in billions of dollars for selected years from 2000 to 2070 (actual and projected).

Year	GDP	Year	GDP
2000	9143	2040	79,680
2005	12,145	2045	103,444
2010	16,174	2050	133,925
2015	21,270	2055	173,175
2020	27,683	2060	224,044
2025	35,919	2065	290,042
2030	46,765	2070	375,219
2035	61,100		

Source: Social Security Administration Trustees Report

(a) Model these data with a cubic function $g = g(t)$, where g is in billions of dollars and t represents the number of years past 2000.
(b) Use the model to find the predicted instantaneous rate of change of the GDP in 2015.
(c) Interpret your answer to part (b).

OBJECTIVES

- To use the Product Rule to find the derivatives of certain functions
- To use the Quotient Rule to find the derivatives of certain functions

9.5

The Product Rule and the Quotient Rule

▮ | APPLICATION PREVIEW | ▮

When medicine is administered, reaction (measured in change of blood pressure or temperature) can be modeled by

$$R = m^2 \left(\frac{c}{2} - \frac{m}{3} \right)$$

where c is a positive constant and m is the amount of medicine absorbed into the blood.* The rate of change of R with respect to m is the sensitivity of the body to medicine. To find an expression for sensitivity as a function of m, we calculate dR/dm. We can find this derivative with the Product Rule for derivatives. See Example 5.

*Source: R. M. Thrall et al., *Some Mathematical Models in Biology,* U.S. Department of Commerce, 1967.

Product Rule　We have simple formulas for finding the derivatives of the sums and differences of functions. But we are not so lucky with products. The derivative of a product is *not* the product of the derivatives. To see this, we consider the function $f(x) = x \cdot x$. Because this function is $f(x) = x^2$, its derivative is $f'(x) = 2x$. But the product of the derivatives of x and x would give $1 \cdot 1 = 1 \neq 2x$. Thus we need a different formula to find the derivative of a product. This formula is given by the **Product Rule.**

Product Rule | If $f(x) = u(x) \cdot v(x)$, where u and v are differentiable functions of x, then

$$f'(x) = u(x) \cdot v'(x) + v(x) \cdot u'(x)$$

Thus the derivative of a product of two functions is the first function times the derivative of the second plus the second function times the derivative of the first.

We can prove the Product Rule as follows. If $f(x) = u(x) \cdot v(x)$, then

$$\lim_{h \to 0} \frac{f(x + h) - f(x)}{h} = \lim_{h \to 0} \frac{u(x + h) \cdot v(x + h) - u(x) \cdot v(x)}{h}$$

Subtracting and adding $u(x + h) \cdot v(x)$ in the numerator gives

$$f'(x) = \lim_{h \to 0} \frac{u(x + h) \cdot v(x + h) - u(x + h) \cdot v(x) + u(x + h) \cdot v(x) - u(x) \cdot v(x)}{h}$$

$$= \lim_{h \to 0} \left\{ u(x + h) \left[\frac{v(x + h) - v(x)}{h} \right] + v(x) \left[\frac{u(x + h) - u(x)}{h} \right] \right\}$$

Properties III and IV of limits (from Section 9.1, "Limits") give

$$f'(x) = \lim_{h \to 0} u(x + h) \cdot \lim_{h \to 0} \frac{v(x + h) - v(x)}{h} + \lim_{h \to 0} v(x) \cdot \lim_{h \to 0} \frac{u(x + h) - u(x)}{h}$$

Because u is differentiable and hence continuous, it follows that $\lim_{h \to 0} u(x + h) = u(x)$, so we have the formula we seek:

$$f'(x) = u(x) \cdot v'(x) + v(x) \cdot u'(x)$$

EXAMPLE　1　Product Rule

(a)　Find dy/dx if $y = (2x^3 + 3x + 1)(x^2 + 4)$.
(b)　Find the slope of the tangent to the graph of
　　$y = f(x) = (4x^3 + 5x^2 - 6x + 5)(x^3 - 4x^2 + 1)$ at $x = 1$.

Solution

(a)　Using the Product Rule with $u(x) = 2x^3 + 3x + 1$ and $v(x) = x^2 + 4$, we have

$$\frac{dy}{dx} = (2x^3 + 3x + 1)(2x) + (x^2 + 4)(6x^2 + 3)$$

$$= 4x^4 + 6x^2 + 2x + 6x^4 + 3x^2 + 24x^2 + 12$$

$$= 10x^4 + 33x^2 + 2x + 12$$

(b)　$f'(x) = (4x^3 + 5x^2 - 6x + 5)(3x^2 - 8x) + (x^3 - 4x^2 + 1)(12x^2 + 10x - 6)$
　　If we substitute $x = 1$ into $f'(x)$, we find that the slope of the curve at $x = 1$ is $f'(1) = 8(-5) + (-2)(16) = -72$.　◼

　　We could, of course, avoid using the Product Rule by multiplying the two factors before taking the derivative. But multiplying the factors first might involve more work than using the Product Rule.

Quotient Rule   For a quotient of two functions, we might be tempted to take the derivative of the numerator divided by the derivative of the denominator; but this is incorrect. With the example $f(x) = x^3/x$ (which equals x^2 if $x \neq 0$), this approach would give $3x^2/1 = 3x^2$ as the derivative, rather than $2x$. Thus, finding the derivative of a function that is the quotient of two functions requires the **Quotient Rule.**

Quotient Rule

If $f(x) = \dfrac{u(x)}{v(x)}$, where u and v are differentiable functions of x, with $v(x) \neq 0$, then

$$f'(x) = \frac{v(x) \cdot u'(x) - u(x) \cdot v'(x)}{[v(x)]^2}$$

The preceding formula says that the derivative of a quotient is the denominator times the derivative of the numerator minus the numerator times the derivative of the denominator, all divided by the square of the denominator.

To see that this rule is reasonable, again consider the function $f(x) = x^3/x, x \neq 0$. Using the Quotient Rule, with $u(x) = x^3$ and $v(x) = x$, we get

$$f'(x) = \frac{x(3x^2) - x^3(1)}{x^2} = \frac{3x^3 - x^3}{x^2} = \frac{2x^3}{x^2} = 2x$$

We see that $f'(x) = 2x$ is the correct derivative. The proof of the Quotient Rule is left for the student in Problem 37 of the exercises in this section.

EXAMPLE 2   Quotient Rule

(a) If $f(x) = \dfrac{x^2 - 4x}{x + 5}$, find $f'(x)$.

(b) If $f(x) = \dfrac{x^3 - 3x^2 + 2}{x^2 - 4}$, find the instantaneous rate of change of $f(x)$ at $x = 3$.

Solution

(a) Using the Quotient Rule with $u(x) = x^2 - 4x$ and $v(x) = x + 5$, we get

$$f'(x) = \frac{(x + 5)(2x - 4) - (x^2 - 4x)(1)}{(x + 5)^2}$$

$$= \frac{2x^2 + 6x - 20 - x^2 + 4x}{(x + 5)^2} = \frac{x^2 + 10x - 20}{(x + 5)^2}$$

(b) We evaluate $f'(x)$ at $x = 3$ to find the desired rate of change. Using the Quotient Rule with $u(x) = x^3 - 3x^2 + 2$ and $v(x) = x^2 - 4$, we get

$$f'(x) = \frac{(x^2 - 4)(3x^2 - 6x) - (x^3 - 3x^2 + 2)(2x)}{(x^2 - 4)^2}$$

$$= \frac{(3x^4 - 6x^3 - 12x^2 + 24x) - (2x^4 - 6x^3 + 4x)}{(x^2 - 4)^2} = \frac{x^4 - 12x^2 + 20x}{(x^2 - 4)^2}$$

Thus, the instantaneous rate of change at $x = 3$ is $f'(3) = 33/25 = 1.32$

EXAMPLE 3   Quotient Rule

Use the Quotient Rule to find the derivative of $y = 1/x^3$.

Solution

Letting $u(x) = 1$ and $v(x) = x^3$, we get

$$y' = \frac{x^3(0) - 1(3x^2)}{(x^3)^2} = -\frac{3x^2}{x^6} = -\frac{3}{x^4}$$

Note that we could have found the derivative more easily by rewriting y.

$$y = 1/x^3 = x^{-3} \quad \text{gives} \quad y' = -3x^{-4} = -\frac{3}{x^4}$$

Recall that we proved the Powers of x Rule for positive integer powers and assumed that it was true for all real number powers. In Problem 38 of the exercises in this section, you will be asked to use the Quotient Rule to show that the Powers of x Rule applies to negative integers.

It is not necessary to use the Quotient Rule when the denominator of the function in question contains only a constant. For example, the function $y = (x^3 - 3x)/3$ can be written $y = \frac{1}{3}(x^3 - 3x)$, so the derivative is $y' = \frac{1}{3}(3x^2 - 3) = x^2 - 1$.

CHECKPOINT

1. True or false: The derivative of the product of two functions is equal to the product of the derivatives of the two functions.
2. True or false: The derivative of the quotient of two functions is equal to the quotient of the derivatives of the two functions.
3. Find $f'(x)$ for each of the following.
   (a) $f(x) = (x^{12} + 8x^5 - 7)(10x^7 - 4x + 19)$ Do not simplify.
   (b) $f(x) = \dfrac{2x^4 + 3}{3x^4 + 2}$ Simplify.
4. If $y = \frac{4}{3}(x^2 + 3x - 4)$, does finding y' require the Product Rule? Explain.
5. If $y = f(x)/c$, where c is a constant, does finding y' require the Quotient Rule? Explain.

EXAMPLE 4   Marginal Revenue

Suppose that the revenue function for a flash drive is given by

$$R(x) = 10x + \frac{100x}{3x + 5}$$

where x is the number of flash drives sold and R is in dollars.

(a) Find the marginal revenue function.
(b) Find the marginal revenue when $x = 15$.

Solution

(a) We must use the Quotient Rule to find the marginal revenue (the derivative).

$$\overline{MR} = R'(x) = 10 + \frac{(3x + 5)(100) - 100x(3)}{(3x + 5)^2}$$

$$= 10 + \frac{300x + 500 - 300x}{(3x + 5)^2} = 10 + \frac{500}{(3x + 5)^2}$$

$$= 10 + \frac{500}{(3x + 5)^2}$$

(b) The marginal revenue when $x = 15$ is $R'(15)$.

$$R'(15) = 10 + \frac{500}{[(3)(15) + 5]^2} = 10 + \frac{500}{(50)^2} = 10.20 \text{ (dollars per unit)}$$

Recall that $R'(15)$ estimates the revenue from the sale of the 16th flash drive.

R'(15) = $10.20

EXAMPLE 5   Sensitivity to a Drug | APPLICATION PREVIEW |

When medicine is administered, reaction (measured in change of blood pressure or temperature) can be modeled by

$$R = m^2 \left(\frac{c}{2} - \frac{m}{3} \right)$$

where c is a positive constant and m is the amount of medicine absorbed into the blood. The rate of change of R with respect to m is the sensitivity of the body to medicine. Find an expression for sensitivity s as a function of m.

Solution
The sensitivity is the rate of change of R with respect to m, or the derivative. Thus

$$s = \frac{dR}{dm} = m^2 \left(0 - \frac{1}{3} \right) + \left(\frac{c}{2} - \frac{1}{3}m \right)(2m)$$

$$= -\frac{1}{3}m^2 + mc - \frac{2}{3}m^2 = mc - m^2$$

CHECKPOINT SOLUTIONS

1. False. The derivative of a product is equal to the first function times the derivative of the second plus the second function times the derivative of the first. That is,

$$\frac{d}{dx}(fg) = f \cdot \frac{dg}{dx} + g \cdot \frac{df}{dx}$$

2. False. The derivative of a quotient is equal to the denominator times the derivative of the numerator minus the numerator times the derivative of the denominator, all divided by the square of the denominator. That is,

$$\frac{d}{dx}\left(\frac{f}{g} \right) = \frac{g \cdot f' - f \cdot g'}{g^2}$$

3. (a) $f'(x) = (x^{12} + 8x^5 - 7)(70x^6 - 4) + (10x^7 - 4x + 19)(12x^{11} + 40x^4)$

    (b) $f'(x) = \dfrac{(3x^4 + 2)(8x^3) - (2x^4 + 3)(12x^3)}{(3x^4 + 2)^2}$

    $= \dfrac{24x^7 + 16x^3 - 24x^7 - 36x^3}{(3x^4 + 2)^2} = \dfrac{-20x^3}{(3x^4 + 2)^2}$

4. No; y' can be found with the Coefficient Rule:

$$y' = \frac{4}{3}(2x + 3)$$

5. No; y' can be found with the Coefficient Rule:

$$y' = \left(\frac{1}{c} \right) f'(x)$$

| EXERCISES | 9.5

In Problems 1–4, find the derivative and simplify.

1. $y = (5x + 3)(x^2 - 2x)$
2. $s = (t^4 + 1)(t^3 - 1)$
3. $f(x) = (x^{12} + 3x^4 + 4)(2x^3 - 1)$
4. $y = (3x^7 + 4)(8x^6 - 6x^4 - 9)$

In Problems 5–8, find the derivative, but do not simplify your answer.

5. $y = (7x^6 - 5x^4 + 2x^2 - 1)(4x^9 + 3x^7 - 5x^2 + 3x)$
6. $y = (9x^9 - 7x^7 - 6x)(3x^5 - 4x^4 + 3x^3 - 8)$
7. $y = (x^2 + x + 1)(\sqrt[3]{x} - 2\sqrt{x} + 5)$
8. $y = (\sqrt[5]{x} - 2\sqrt[4]{x} + 1)(x^3 - 5x - 7)$

In Problems 9 and 10, at each indicated point find
(a) the slope of the tangent line, and
(b) the instantaneous rate of change of the function.

9. $y = (x^2 + 1)(x^3 - 4x)$ at $(-2, 0)$
10. $y = (x^3 - 3)(x^2 - 4x + 1)$ at $(2, -15)$

In Problems 11–20, find the indicated derivatives and simplify.

11. $\dfrac{dp}{dq}$ for $p = \dfrac{q^2 + 3}{2q - 1}$ 12. $C'(x)$ for $C(x) = \dfrac{2x^3}{3x^4 + 2}$

13. $\dfrac{dy}{dx}$ for $y = \dfrac{1 - 2x^2}{x^4 - 2x^2 + 5}$

14. $\dfrac{ds}{dt}$ for $s = \dfrac{t^3 - 4}{t^3 - 2t^2 - t - 5}$

15. $\dfrac{dz}{dx}$ for $z = x^2 + \dfrac{x^2}{1 - x - 2x^2}$

16. $\dfrac{dy}{dx}$ for $y = 200x - \dfrac{100x}{3x + 1}$

17. $\dfrac{dp}{dq}$ for $p = \dfrac{3\sqrt[3]{q}}{1 - q}$ 18. $\dfrac{dy}{dx}$ for $y = \dfrac{2\sqrt{x} - 1}{1 - 4\sqrt{x^3}}$

19. y' for $y = \dfrac{x(x^2 + 4)}{x - 2}$

20. $f'(x)$ for $f(x) = \dfrac{(x + 1)(x - 2)}{x^2 + 1}$

In Problems 21 and 22, at the indicated point for each function, find
(a) the slope of the tangent line, and
(b) the instantaneous rate of change of the function.

21. $y = \dfrac{x^2 + 1}{x + 3}$ at $(2, 1)$

22. $y = \dfrac{x^2 - 4x}{x^2 + 2x}$ at $\left(2, -\dfrac{1}{2}\right)$

In Problems 23–26, write the equation of the tangent line to the graph of the function at the indicated point. Check the reasonableness of your answer by graphing both the function and the tangent line.

23. $y = (9x^2 - 6x + 1)(1 + 2x)$ at $x = 1$
24. $y = (4x^2 + 4x + 1)(7 - 2x)$ at $x = 0$
25. $y = \dfrac{3x^4 - 2x - 1}{4 - x^2}$ at $x = 1$
26. $y = \dfrac{x^2 - 4x}{2x - x^3}$ at $x = 2$

In Problems 27–30, use the numerical derivative feature of a graphing calculator to find the derivative of each function at the given x-value.

27. $y = \left(4\sqrt{x} + \dfrac{3}{x}\right)\left(3\sqrt[3]{x} - \dfrac{5}{x^2} - 25\right)$ at $x = 1$

28. $y = (3\sqrt[4]{x^5} + \sqrt[5]{x^4} - 1)\left(\dfrac{2}{x^3} - \dfrac{1}{\sqrt{x}}\right)$ at $x = 1$

29. $f(x) = \dfrac{4x - 4}{3x^{2/3}}$ at $x = 1$

30. $f(x) = \dfrac{3\sqrt[3]{x} + 1}{x + 2}$ at $x = -1$

In Problems 31–34, complete the following.
(a) Find the derivative of each function, and check your work by graphing both your calculated derivative and the numerical derivative of the function.
(b) Use your graph of the derivative to find points where the original function has horizontal tangent lines.
(c) Use a graphing calculator to graph the function and indicate the points found in part (b) on the graph.

31. $f(x) = (x^2 + 4x + 4)(x - 7)$
32. $f(x) = (x^2 - 14x + 49)(2x + 1)$
33. $y = \dfrac{x^2}{x - 2}$ 34. $y = \dfrac{x^2 - 7}{4 - x}$

In Problems 35 and 36,
(a) find $f'(x)$.
(b) graph both $f(x)$ and $f'(x)$ with a graphing utility.
(c) identify the x-values where $f'(x) = 0$, $f'(x) > 0$, and $f'(x) < 0$.
(d) identify x-values where $f(x)$ has a maximum point or a minimum point, where $f(x)$ is increasing, and where $f(x)$ is decreasing.

35. $f(x) = \dfrac{10x^2}{x^2 + 1}$ 36. $f(x) = \dfrac{8 - x^2}{x^2 + 4}$

37. Prove the Quotient Rule for differentiation. (*Hint:* Add $[-u(x) \cdot v(x) + u(x) \cdot v(x)]$ to the expanded numerator and use steps similar to those used to prove the Product Rule.)

38. Use the Quotient Rule to show that the Powers of x Rule applies to negative integer powers. That is, show that $(d/dx)x^n = nx^{n-1}$ when $n = -k$, $k > 0$, by finding the derivative of $f(x) = 1/(x^k)$.

APPLICATIONS

39. *Cost-benefit* If the cost C (in dollars) of removing p percent of the particulate pollution from the exhaust gases at an industrial site is given by

$$C(p) = \frac{8100p}{100 - p}$$

find the rate of change of C with respect to p.

40. *Cost-benefit* If the cost C (in dollars) of removing p percent of the impurities from the waste water in a manufacturing process is given by

$$C(p) = \frac{9800p}{101 - p}$$

find the rate of change of C with respect to p.

41. *Revenue* Suppose the revenue (in dollars) from the sale of x units of a product is given by

$$R(x) = \frac{60x^2 + 74x}{2x + 2}$$

Find the marginal revenue when 49 units are sold. Interpret your result.

42. *Revenue* The revenue (in dollars) from the sale of x units of a product is given by

$$R(x) = \frac{3000}{2x + 2} + 80x - 1500$$

Find the marginal revenue when 149 units are sold. Interpret your result.

43. *Revenue* A travel agency will plan a group tour for groups of size 25 or larger. If the group contains exactly 25 people, the cost is $300 per person. If each person's cost is reduced by $10 for each additional person above the 25, then the revenue is given by

$$R(x) = (25 + x)(300 - 10x)$$

where x is the number of additional people above 25. Find the marginal revenue if the group contains 30 people. Interpret your result.

44. *Revenue* McRobert's Electronics sells 200 TVs per month at a price of $400 per unit. Market research indicates that the store can sell one additional TV for each $1 it reduces the price. In this case the total revenue is

$$R(x) = (200 + x)(400 - x)$$

where x is the number of additional TVs beyond the 200. If the store sells a total of 250 TVs, find the marginal revenue. Interpret your result.

45. *Response to a drug* The reaction R to an injection of a drug is related to the dosage x (in milligrams) according to

$$R(x) = x^2 \left(500 - \frac{x}{3} \right)$$

where 1000 mg is the maximum dosage. If the rate of reaction with respect to the dosage defines the sensitivity to the drug, find the sensitivity.

46. *Nerve response* The number of action potentials produced by a nerve, t seconds after a stimulus, is given by

$$N(t) = 25t + \frac{4}{t^2 + 2} - 2$$

Find the rate at which the action potentials are produced by the nerve.

47. *Test reliability* If a test having reliability r is lengthened by a factor n, the reliability of the new test is given by

$$R = \frac{nr}{1 + (n - 1)r}, \quad 0 < r \le 1$$

Find the rate at which R changes with respect to n.

48. *Advertising and sales* The sales of a product s (in thousands of dollars) are related to advertising expenses (in thousands of dollars) by

$$s = \frac{200x}{x + 10}$$

Find and interpret the meaning of the rate of change of sales with respect to advertising expenses when
(a) $x = 10$.   (b) $x = 20$.

49. *Candidate recognition* Suppose that the proportion P of voters who recognize a candidate's name t months after the start of the campaign is given by

$$P(t) = \frac{13t}{t^2 + 100} + 0.18$$

(a) Find the rate of change of P when $t = 6$, and explain its meaning.
(b) Find the rate of change of P when $t = 12$, and explain its meaning.
(c) One month prior to the election, is it better for $P'(t)$ to be positive or negative? Explain.

50. *Endangered species population* It is determined that a wildlife refuge can support a group of up to 120 of a certain endangered species. If 75 are introduced onto the refuge and their population after t years is given by

$$p(t) = 75\left(1 + \frac{4t}{t^2 + 16} \right)$$

find the rate of population growth after t years. Find the rate after each of the first 7 years.

51. *Wind chill* According to the National Climatic Data Center, during 1991, the lowest temperature recorded in Indianapolis, Indiana, was 0°F. If x is the wind speed in miles per hour and $x \ge 5$, then the wind chill (in degrees Fahrenheit) for an air temperature of 0°F can be approximated by the function

$$f(x) = \frac{289.173 - 58.5731x}{x + 1}$$

(a) At what rate is the wind chill changing when the wind speed is 20 mph?

(b) Explain the meaning of your answer to part (a).

52. **Response to injected adrenalin** Experimental evidence has shown that the response y of a muscle is related to the concentration of injected adrenaline x according to the equation

$$y = \frac{x}{a + bx}$$

where a and b are constants. Find the rate of change of response with respect to the concentration.

53. **Social Security beneficiaries** The table gives the number of millions of Social Security beneficiaries (actual and projected) for selected years from 1950 through 2030.

Year	Number of Beneficiaries (millions)	Year	Number of Beneficiaries (millions)
1950	2.9	2000	44.8
1960	14.3	2010	53.3
1970	25.2	2020	68.8
1980	35.1	2030	82.7
1990	39.5		

Source: Social Security Trustees Report

With $B(t)$ representing the number of beneficiaries (in millions) t years past 1950, these data can be modeled by the function

$$B(t) = (0.01t + 3)(0.02383t^2 - 9.79t + 3097.19)$$
$$- 9289.371$$

(a) Find the function that gives the instantaneous rate of change of the number of beneficiaries.

(b) Find and interpret the instantaneous rate of change in 2010.

(c) Use the data to determine which of the average rates of change (from 2000 to 2010, from 2010 to 2020, or from 2000 to 2020) best approximates the instantaneous rate from part (b).

54. **Emissions** The table shows data for sulfur dioxide emissions from electricity generation (in millions of short tons) for selected years from 2000 and projected to 2035. These data can be modeled by the function

$$E(x) = (0.001x - 0.062)(-0.18x^2 + 8.2x - 200)$$

where x is the number of years past 2000.

(a) Find the function that models the rate of change of these emissions.

(b) Find and interpret $E'(20)$.

Year	Short Tons (in millions)
2000	11.4
2005	10.2
2008	7.6
2015	4.7
2020	4.2
2025	3.8
2030	3.7
2035	3.8

Source: U.S. Department of Energy

55. **Females in the work force** For selected years from 1950 and with projections to 2050, the table shows the percent of total U.S. workers who were female.

Year	% Female	Year	% Female
1950	29.6	2010	47.9
1960	33.4	2015	48.3
1970	38.1	2020	48.1
1980	42.5	2030	48.0
1990	45.2	2040	47.9
2000	46.6	2050	47.7

Source: U.S. Bureau of the Census

Assume these data can be modeled with the function

$$p(t) = \frac{78.6t + 2090}{1.38t + 64.1}$$

where $p(t)$ is the percent of the U.S. work force that is female and t is the number of years past 1950.

(a) Find the function that models the instantaneous rate of change of the percent of U.S. workers who were female.

(b) Use the function from part (a) to find the instantaneous rates of change in 2005 and in 2020.

(c) Interpret each of the rates of change in part (b).

56. **Paved roads** For selected years from 1960 to 2008, the table shows the percent of public roads that were paved.

Year	% Paved	Year	% Paved
1960	34.7	1995	60.8
1965	39.4	2000	63.4
1970	44.5	2002	64.8
1975	48.3	2004	64.5
1980	53.7	2006	65.2
1985	54.7	2008	67.4
1990	58.3		

Source: U.S. Bureau of Transportation Statistics

Assume these data can be modeled with the function

$$P(t) = \frac{2900t + 106{,}200}{8.52t + 3550}$$

where $P(t)$ is the percent of paved roads and t is the number of years past 1960.

(a) Find the function that gives the instantaneous rate of change of this model.

(b) Find and interpret the instantaneous rate of change of the percent of paved roads in 2008.

(c) Use the data in the table to find the average rate of change of the percent of paved roads from 2006 to 2008. How well does this approximate the instantaneous rate found in part (b)?

OBJECTIVES

9.6

- To use the Chain Rule to differentiate functions
- To use the Power Rule to differentiate functions

The Chain Rule and the Power Rule

| APPLICATION PREVIEW |

The demand x for a product is given by

$$x = \frac{98}{\sqrt{2p + 1}} - 1$$

where p is the price per unit. To find how fast demand is changing when price is $24, we take the derivative of x with respect to p. If we write this function with a power rather than a radical, it has the form

$$x = 98(2p + 1)^{-1/2} - 1$$

The formulas learned so far cannot be used to find this derivative. We use a new formula, the Power Rule, to find this derivative. (See Example 6.) In this section we will discuss the Chain Rule and the Power Rule, which is one of the results of the Chain Rule, and we will use these formulas to solve applied problems.

Composite Functions   Recall from Section 1.2, "Functions," that if f and g are functions, then the composite functions g of f (denoted $g \circ f$) and f of g (denoted $f \circ g$) are defined as follows:

$$(g \circ f)(x) = g(f(x)) \quad \text{and} \quad (f \circ g)(x) = f(g(x))$$

EXAMPLE   1   **Composite Function**

If $f(x) = 3x^2$ and $g(x) = 2x - 1$, find $F(x) = f(g(x))$.

Solution
Substituting $g(x) = 2x - 1$ for x in $f(x)$ gives

$$f(g(x)) = f(2x - 1) = 3(2x - 1)^2 \quad \text{or} \quad F(x) = 3(2x - 1)^2 \qquad ■$$

Chain Rule   We could find the derivative of the function $F(x) = 3(2x - 1)^2$ by expanding the expression $3(2x - 1)^2$. Then

$$F(x) = 3(4x^2 - 4x + 1) = 12x^2 - 12x + 3$$

so $F'(x) = 24x - 12$. But we can also use a very powerful rule, called the **Chain Rule,** to find derivatives of composite functions. If we write the composite function $y = f(g(x))$ in the form $y = f(u)$, where $u = g(x)$, we state the Chain Rule as follows.

Chain Rule

If f and g are differentiable functions with $y = f(u)$, and $u = g(x)$, then y is a differentiable function of x, and

$$\frac{dy}{dx} = f'(u) \cdot g'(x)$$

or, equivalently,

$$\frac{dy}{dx} = \frac{dy}{du} \cdot \frac{du}{dx}$$

Note that dy/du represents the derivative of $y = f(u)$ *with respect to u* and du/dx represents the derivative of $u = g(x)$ *with respect to x*. For example, if $y = 3(2x - 1)^2$, then the outside function, f, is the squaring function, and the inside function, g, is $2x - 1$, so we may write $y = f(u) = 3u^2$, where $u = g(x) = 2x - 1$. Then the derivative is

$$\frac{dy}{dx} = \frac{dy}{du} \cdot \frac{du}{dx} = 6u \cdot 2 = 12u$$

To write this derivative in terms of x, we substitute $2x - 1$ for u. Thus

$$\frac{dy}{dx} = 12(2x - 1) = 24x - 12$$

Note that we get the same result by using the Chain Rule as we did by expanding $f(x) = 3(2x - 1)^2$. The Chain Rule is important because it is not always possible to rewrite the function as a polynomial. Consider the following example.

EXAMPLE **2** **Chain Rule**

If $y = \sqrt{x^2 - 1}$, find $\dfrac{dy}{dx}$.

Solution

If we write this function as $y = f(u) = \sqrt{u} = u^{1/2}$, with $u = x^2 - 1$, we can find the derivative.

$$\frac{dy}{dx} = \frac{dy}{du} \cdot \frac{du}{dx} = \frac{1}{2} \cdot u^{-1/2} \cdot 2x = u^{-1/2} \cdot x = \frac{1}{\sqrt{u}} \cdot x = \frac{x}{\sqrt{u}}$$

To write this derivative in terms of x alone, we substitute $x^2 - 1$ for u. Then

$$\frac{dy}{dx} = \frac{x}{\sqrt{x^2 - 1}}$$

Note that we could not find the derivative of a function like that of Example 2 by the methods learned previously. However, if

$$y = \frac{1}{x^2 + 3x + 1}$$

then we can find the derivative with the Chain Rule (using $u = x^2 + 3x + 1$ and $y = u^{-1}$) or with the Quotient Rule.

EXAMPLE 3   Allometric Relationships

The relationship between the length L (in meters) and weight W (in kilograms) of a species of fish in the Pacific Ocean is given by $W = 10.375L^3$. The rate of growth in length is given by $\dfrac{dL}{dt} = 0.36 - 0.18L$, where t is measured in years.

(a) Determine a formula for the rate of growth in weight $\dfrac{dW}{dt}$ in terms of L.

(b) If a fish weighs 30 kilograms, approximate its rate of growth in weight using the formula found in part (a).

Solution

(a) The rate of change uses the Chain Rule, as follows:

$$\frac{dW}{dt} = \frac{dW}{dL} \cdot \frac{dL}{dt} = 31.125L^2 (0.36 - 0.18L) = 11.205L^2 - 5.6025L^3$$

(b) From $W = 10.375L^3$ and $W = 30$ kg, we can find L by solving

$$30 = 10.375L^3$$

$$\frac{30}{10.375} = L^3 \quad \text{so} \quad L = \sqrt[3]{\frac{30}{10.375}} \approx 1.4247 \text{ m}$$

Hence, the rate of growth in weight is

$$\frac{dW}{dt} = 11.205(1.4247)^2 - 5.6025(1.4247)^3 \approx 6.542 \text{ kilograms/year}$$

Power Rule   The Chain Rule is very useful and will be extremely important with functions that we will study later. A special case of the Chain Rule, called the **Power Rule,** is useful for the algebraic functions we have studied so far, composite functions where the outside function is a power.

Power Rule

If $y = u^n$, where u is a differentiable function of x, then

$$\frac{dy}{dx} = nu^{n-1} \cdot \frac{du}{dx}$$

EXAMPLE 4   Power Rule

(a) If $y = (x^2 - 4x)^6$, find $\dfrac{dy}{dx}$.   (b) If $p = \dfrac{4}{3q^2 + 1}$, find $\dfrac{dp}{dq}$.

Solution

(a) This has the form $y = u^n = u^6$, with $u = x^2 - 4x$. Thus, by the Power Rule,

$$\frac{dy}{dx} = nu^{n-1} \cdot \frac{du}{dx} = 6u^5 (2x - 4)$$

Substituting $x^2 - 4x$ for u gives

$$\frac{dy}{dx} = 6(x^2 - 4x)^5 (2x - 4) = (12x - 24)(x^2 - 4x)^5$$

(b) We can use the Power Rule to find dp/dq if we write the equation in the form

$$p = 4(3q^2 + 1)^{-1}$$

Then

$$\frac{dp}{dq} = 4[-1(3q^2 + 1)^{-2}(6q)] = \frac{-24q}{(3q^2 + 1)^2} .$$

The derivative of the function in Example 4(b) can also be found by using the Quotient Rule, but the Power Rule provides a more efficient method.

EXAMPLE 5   **Power Rule with Radicals**

Find the derivatives of (a) $y = 3\sqrt[3]{x^2 - 3x + 1}$ and (b) $g(x) = \dfrac{1}{\sqrt{(x^2 + 1)^3}} .$

Solution

(a) Because $y = 3(x^2 - 3x + 1)^{1/3}$, we can make use of the Power Rule with $u = x^2 - 3x + 1$.

$$y' = 3\left(nu^{n-1}\frac{du}{dx}\right) = 3\left[\frac{1}{3}u^{-2/3}(2x - 3)\right]$$

$$= (x^2 - 3x + 1)^{-2/3}(2x - 3) = \frac{2x - 3}{(x^2 - 3x + 1)^{2/3}}$$

(b) Writing $g(x)$ as a power gives $g(x) = (x^2 + 1)^{-3/2}$. Then

$$g'(x) = -\frac{3}{2}(x^2 + 1)^{-5/2}(2x) = -3x \cdot \frac{1}{(x^2 + 1)^{5/2}} = \frac{-3x}{\sqrt{(x^2 + 1)^5}}$$

CHECKPOINT

1. (a) If $f(x) = (3x^4 + 1)^{10}$, does $f'(x) = 10(3x^4 + 1)^9$?
   (b) If $f(x) = (2x + 1)^5$, does $f'(x) = 10(2x + 1)^4$?
   (c) If $f(x) = \dfrac{[u(x)]^n}{c}$, where c is a constant, does $f'(x) = \dfrac{n[u(x)]^{n-1} \cdot u'(x)}{c}$?

2. (a) If $f(x) = \dfrac{12}{2x^2 - 1}$, find $f'(x)$ by using the Power Rule (not the Quotient Rule).

   (b) If $f(x) = \dfrac{\sqrt{x^3 - 1}}{3}$, find $f'(x)$ by using the Power Rule (not the Quotient Rule).

EXAMPLE 6   **Demand | APPLICATION PREVIEW |**

The demand for x hundred units of a product is given by

$$x = 98(2p + 1)^{-1/2} - 1$$

where p is the price per unit in dollars. Find the rate of change of the demand with respect to price when $p = 24$.

Solution

The rate of change of demand with respect to price is

$$\frac{dx}{dp} = 98\left[-\frac{1}{2}(2p + 1)^{-3/2}(2)\right] = -98(2p + 1)^{-3/2}$$

When $p = 24$, the rate of change is

$$\frac{dx}{dp}\bigg|_{p=24} = -98(48 + 1)^{-3/2} = -98 \cdot \frac{1}{49^{3/2}} = -\frac{2}{7}$$

This means that when the price is $24, demand is changing at the rate of $-2/7$ hundred units per dollar, or if the price changes by $1, demand will change by about $-200/7$ units.

CHECKPOINT SOLUTIONS

1. (a) No, $f'(x) = 10(3x^4 + 1)^9 (12x^3)$.   (b) Yes   (c) Yes

2. (a) $f(x) = 12(2x^2 - 1)^{-1}$

$$f'(x) = -12(2x^2 - 1)^{-2}(4x) = \frac{-48x}{(2x^2 - 1)^2}$$

(b) $f(x) = \frac{1}{3}(x^3 - 1)^{1/2}$

$$f'(x) = \frac{1}{6}(x^3 - 1)^{-1/2}(3x^2) = \frac{x^2}{2\sqrt{x^3 - 1}}$$

| EXERCISES | 9.6

In Problems 1–4, find $\dfrac{dy}{du}, \dfrac{du}{dx}$, and $\dfrac{dy}{dx}$.

1. $y = u^3$ and $u = x^2 + 1$
2. $y = u^4$ and $u = x^2 + 4x$
3. $y = u^4$ and $u = 4x^2 - x + 8$
4. $y = u^{10}$ and $u = x^2 + 5x$

Differentiate the functions in Problems 5–22.

5. $f(x) = (3x^5 - 2)^{20}$ 6. $g(x) = (3 - 2x)^{10}$
7. $h(x) = \frac{3}{4}(x^5 - 2x^3 + 5)^8$
8. $k(x) = \frac{5}{7}(2x^3 - x + 6)^{14}$
9. $s(t) = 5t - 3(2t^4 + 7)^3$
10. $p(q) = 4(3q^2 - 1)^4 - 13q$
11. $g(x) = (x^4 - 5x)^{-2}$ 12. $p = (q^3 + 1)^{-5}$

13. $f(x) = \dfrac{3}{(2x^5 + 1)^4}$ 14. $g(x) = \dfrac{1}{4x^3 + 1}$

15. $g(x) = \dfrac{1}{(2x^3 + 3x + 5)^{3/4}}$

16. $y = \dfrac{1}{(3x^3 + 4x + 1)^{3/2}}$

17. $y = \sqrt{3x^2 + 4x + 9}$ 18. $y = \sqrt{x^2 + 3x}$

19. $y = \dfrac{11(x^3 - 7)^6}{9}$ 20. $y = \dfrac{5\sqrt{1 - x^3}}{6}$

21. $y = \dfrac{(3x + 1)^5 - 3x}{7}$

22. $y = \dfrac{\sqrt{2x - 1} - \sqrt{x}}{2}$

At the indicated point, for each function in Problems 23–26, find
(a) the slope of the tangent line, and
(b) the instantaneous rate of change of the function.
You may use the numerical derivative feature on a graphing calculator to check your work.

23. $y = (x^3 + 2x)^4$ at $x = 2$
24. $y = \sqrt{5x^2 + 2x}$ at $x = 1$
25. $y = \sqrt{x^3 + 1}$ at $(2, 3)$
26. $y = (4x^3 - 5x + 1)^3$ at $(1, 0)$

In Problems 27–30, write the equation of the line tangent to the graph of each function at the indicated point. As a check, graph both the function and the tangent line you found to see whether it looks correct.

27. $y = (x^2 - 3x + 3)^3$ at $(2, 1)$
28. $y = (x^2 + 1)^3$ at $(2, 125)$
29. $y = \sqrt{3x^2 - 2}$ at $x = 3$
30. $y = \left(\dfrac{1}{x^3 - x}\right)^3$ at $x = 2$

 In Problems 31 and 32, complete the following for each function.
(a) Find $f'(x)$.
(b) Check your result in part (a) by graphing both it and the numerical derivative of the function.
(c) Find x-values for which the slope of the tangent is 0.
(d) Find points (x, y) where the slope of the tangent is 0.
(e) Use a graphing utility to graph the function and locate the points found in part (d).

31. $f(x) = (x^2 - 4)^3 + 12$
32. $f(x) = 10 - (x^2 - 2x - 8)^2$

 In Problems 33 and 34, do the following for each function $f(x)$.
(a) Find $f'(x)$.
(b) Graph both $f(x)$ and $f'(x)$ with a graphing utility.
(c) Determine x-values where $f'(x) = 0$, $f'(x) > 0$, $f'(x) < 0$.
(d) Determine x-values for which $f(x)$ has a maximum or minimum point, where the graph is increasing, and where it is decreasing.

33. $f(x) = 12 - 3(1 - x^2)^{4/3}$
34. $f(x) = 3 + \dfrac{1}{16}(x^2 - 4x)^4$

In Problems 35 and 36, find the derivative of each function.

35. (a) $y = \dfrac{2x^3}{3}$ (b) $y = \dfrac{2}{3x^3}$

(c) $y = \dfrac{(2x)^3}{3}$ (d) $y = \dfrac{2}{(3x)^3}$

36. (a) $y = \dfrac{3}{(5x)^5}$ (b) $y = \dfrac{3x^5}{5}$

(c) $y = \dfrac{3}{5x^5}$ (d) $y = \dfrac{(3x)^5}{5}$

APPLICATIONS

37. *Ballistics* Ballistics experts are able to identify the weapon that fired a certain bullet by studying the markings on the bullet. Tests are conducted by firing into a bale of paper. If the distance s, in inches, that the bullet travels into the paper is given by

$$s = 27 - (3 - 10t)^3$$

for $0 \leq t \leq 0.3$ second, find the velocity of the bullet one-tenth of a second after it hits the paper.

38. *Population of microorganisms* Suppose that the population of a certain microorganism at time t (in minutes) is given by

$$P = 1000 - 1000(t + 10)^{-1}$$

Find the rate of change of population.

39. *Revenue* The revenue from the sale of a product is

$$R = 1500x + 3000(2x + 3)^{-1} - 1000 \quad \text{dollars}$$

where x is the number of units sold. Find the marginal revenue when 100 units are sold. Interpret your result.

40. *Revenue* The revenue from the sale of x units of a product is

$$R = 15(3x + 1)^{-1} + 50x - 15 \quad \text{dollars}$$

Find the marginal revenue when 40 units are sold. Interpret your result.

41. *Pricing and sales* Suppose that the weekly sales volume y (in thousands of units sold) depends on the price per unit (in dollars) of the product according to

$$y = 32(3p + 1)^{-2/5}, \quad p > 0$$

(a) What is the rate of change in sales volume when the price is $21?

(b) Interpret your answer to part (a).

42. *Pricing and sales* A chain of auto service stations has found that its monthly sales volume y (in thousands of dollars) is related to the price p (in dollars) of an oil change according to

$$y = \frac{90}{\sqrt{p + 5}}, \quad p > 10$$

(a) What is the rate of change of sales volume when the price is $20?

(b) Interpret your answer to part (a).

43. *Demand* Suppose that the demand for q units of a product priced at p per unit is described by

$$p = \frac{200,000}{(q + 1)^2}$$

(a) What is the rate of change of price with respect to the quantity demanded when $q = 49$?

(b) Interpret your answer to part (a).

Stimulus-response **The relation between the magnitude of a sensation y and the magnitude of the stimulus x is given by**

$$y = k(x - x_0)^n$$

where k is a constant, x_0 is the threshold of effective stimulus, and n depends on the type of stimulus. Find the rate of change of sensation with respect to the amount of stimulus for each of Problems 44–46.

44. For the stimulus of visual brightness $y = k(x - x_0)^{1/3}$

45. For the stimulus of warmth $y = k(x - x_0)^{8/5}$

46. For the stimulus of electrical stimulation $y = k(x - x_0)^{7/2}$

47. *Demand* If the demand for q units of a product priced at p per unit is described by the equation

$$p = \frac{100}{\sqrt{2q + 1}}$$

find the rate of change of p with respect to q.

48. *Advertising and sales* The daily sales S (in thousands of dollars) attributed to an advertising campaign are given by

$$S = 1 + \frac{3}{t + 3} - \frac{18}{(t + 3)^2}$$

where t is the number of weeks the campaign runs. What is the rate of change of sales at

(a) $t = 8$?   (b) $t = 10$?

(c) Should the campaign be continued after the 10th week? Explain.

49. *Body-heat loss* The description of body-heat loss due to convection involves a coefficient of convection, K_c, which depends on wind velocity according to the following equation.

$$K_c = 4\sqrt{4v + 1}$$

Find the rate of change of the coefficient with respect to the wind velocity.

50. *Data entry speed* The data entry speed (in entries per minute) of a data clerk trainee is

$$S = 10\sqrt{0.8x + 4}, \quad 0 \leq x \leq 100$$

where x is the number of hours of training he has had. What is the rate at which his speed is changing and what does this rate mean when he has had

(a) 15 hours of training?

(b) 40 hours of training?

51. *Investments* If an IRA is a variable-rate investment for 20 years at rate r percent per year, compounded monthly, then the future value S that accumulates from an initial investment of $1000 is

$$S = 1000 \left[1 + \frac{0.01r}{12} \right]^{240}$$

What is the rate of change of S with respect to r and what does it tell us if the interest rate is (a) 6%? (b) 12%?

52. *Concentration of body substances* The concentration C of a substance in the body depends on the quantity of the substance Q and the volume V through which it is distributed. For a static substance, this is given by

$$C = \frac{Q}{V}$$

For a situation like that in the kidneys, where the fluids are moving, the concentration is the ratio of the rate of change of quantity with respect to time and the rate of change of volume with respect to time.
(a) Formulate the equation for concentration of a moving substance.
(b) Show that this is equal to the rate of change of quantity with respect to volume.

53. *National health expenditures* The table shows the total national expenditures for health (both actual and projected, in billions of dollars) for the years from 2001 to 2018. (These data include expenditures for medical research and medical facilities construction.)

Year	Amount	Year	Amount
2001	$1469	2010	$2624
2002	1602	2011	2770
2003	1735	2012	2931
2004	1855	2013	3111
2005	1981	2014	3313
2006	2113	2015	3541
2007	2241	2016	3790
2008	2379	2017	4062
2009	2509	2018	4353

Source: U.S. Centers for Medicare and Medicaid Services

Assume these data can be modeled with the function

$$A(t) = 445(0.1t + 1)^3 - 2120(0.1t + 1)^2 + 4570(0.1t + 1) - 1600$$

where $A(t)$ is in billions of dollars and t is the number of years past 2000.
(a) Use this model to determine and interpret the instantaneous rates of change of the total national health expenditures in 2008 and 2015.
(b) Use the data to find an average rate of change that approximates the 2015 instantaneous rate.

54. *Weekly earnings* The table gives the average weekly earnings for U.S. production workers for selected years from 1970 to 2009.

Year	Earnings	Year	Earnings
1970	$125.80	1997	$431.25
1975	170.28	2000	480.41
1980	240.77	2003	517.30
1985	304.68	2005	544.33
1990	349.29	2007	590.04
1994	390.73	2009	617.11

Source: Bureau of Labor Statistics

Assume these data can be modeled with the function

$$E(t) = 0.00033(2t + 5)^3 - 0.0305(2t + 5)^2 + 6.509(2t + 5) + 89.5$$

where $E(t)$ is average weekly earnings in dollars and t is the number of years past 1970. Use this model to find and interpret the instantaneous rates of change in weekly earnings in 2005 and 2015.

55. *Gross domestic product* The table shows U.S. gross domestic product (GDP) in billions of dollars for selected years from 2000 to 2070 (actual and projected).

Year	GDP	Year	GDP
2000	9143	2040	79,680
2005	12,145	2045	103,444
2010	16,174	2050	133,925
2015	21,270	2055	173,175
2020	27,683	2060	224,044
2025	35,919	2065	290,042
2030	46,765	2070	375,219
2035	61,100		

Source: Social Security Administration Trustees Report

Assume the GDP can be modeled with the function

$$G(t) = 212.9(0.2t + 5)^3 - 5016(0.2t + 5)^2 + 8810.4t + 104,072$$

where $G(t)$ is in billions of dollars and t is the number of years past 2000.
(a) Use the model to find and interpret the instantaneous rates of change of the GDP in 2005 and 2015.
(b) Use the data in the table to find the average rate of change of the GDP from 2005 to 2015.
(c) How well does your answer from part (b) approximate the instantaneous rate of change of GDP in 2010?

56. *Diabetes* The figure shows the percent of the U.S. population with diabetes (diagnosed and undiagnosed) for selected years from 2010 and projections to 2050. Assume this percent can be modeled by

$$y = 6.97(0.5x + 5)^{0.495}$$

where y is the percent and x is the number of years past 2010.

PERCENT WITH DIABETES*

*Estimated

Source: Newsweek, 11/8/2010, Centers for Disease Control and Prevention

(a) Use the figure to find the average rate of change from 2010 to 2050.

(b) Use the model to find the instantaneous rate of change of the U.S. population with diabetes in 2020. Is the average rate found in part (a) a good approximation of the 2020 instantaneous rate?

(c) Use the model to find and interpret the instantaneous rate of change of the percent of the U.S. population with diabetes in 2050.

OBJECTIVE   9.7

- To use derivative formulas separately and in combination with each other

Using Derivative Formulas

| APPLICATION PREVIEW |

Suppose the weekly revenue function for a product is given by

$$R(x) = \frac{36{,}000{,}000x}{(2x + 500)^2}$$

where $R(x)$ is the dollars of revenue from the sale of x units. We can find marginal revenue by finding the derivative of the revenue function. This revenue function contains both a quotient and a power, so its derivative is found by using both the Quotient Rule and the Power Rule. But first we must decide the order in which to apply these formulas. (See Example 4.)

We have used the Power Rule to find the derivatives of functions like

$$y = (x^3 - 3x^2 + x + 1)^5$$

but we have not found the derivatives of functions like

$$y = [(x^2 + 1)(x^3 + x + 1)]^5$$

This function is different because the function u (which is raised to the fifth power) is the product of two functions, $(x^2 + 1)$ and $(x^3 + x + 1)$. The equation is of the form $y = u^5$, where $u = (x^2 + 1)(x^3 + x + 1)$. This means that the Product Rule should be used to find du/dx. Then

$$\frac{dy}{dx} = 5u^4 \cdot \frac{du}{dx}$$

$$= 5[(x^2 + 1)(x^3 + x + 1)]^4 [(x^2 + 1)(3x^2 + 1) + (x^3 + x + 1)(2x)]$$

$$= 5[(x^2 + 1)(x^3 + x + 1)]^4 (5x^4 + 6x^2 + 2x + 1)$$

$$= (25x^4 + 30x^2 + 10x + 5)[(x^2 + 1)(x^3 + x + 1)]^4$$

A different type of problem involving the Power Rule and the Product Rule is finding the derivative of $y = (x^2 + 1)^5 (x^3 + x + 1)$. We may think of y as the *product* of two functions, one of which is a power. Thus the fundamental formula we should use is the Product Rule. The two functions are $u(x) = (x^2 + 1)^5$ and $v(x) = x^3 + x + 1$. The Product Rule gives

$$\frac{dy}{dx} = u(x) \cdot v'(x) + v(x) \cdot u'(x)$$

$$= (x^2 + 1)^5 (3x^2 + 1) + (x^3 + x + 1)[5(x^2 + 1)^4(2x)]$$

Note that the Power Rule was used to find $u'(x)$, since $u(x) = (x^2 + 1)^5$.

We can simplify dy/dx by factoring $(x^2 + 1)^4$ from both terms:

$$\frac{dy}{dx} = (x^2 + 1)^4[(x^2 + 1)(3x^2 + 1) + (x^3 + x + 1) \cdot 5 \cdot 2x]$$

$$= (x^2 + 1)^4(13x^4 + 14x^2 + 10x + 1)$$

EXAMPLE 1   Power of a Quotient

If $y = \left(\dfrac{x^2}{x - 1}\right)^5$, find y'.

Solution

We again have an equation of the form $y = u^n$, but this time u is a quotient. Thus we will need the Quotient Rule to find du/dx.

$$y' = nu^{n-1} \cdot \frac{du}{dx} = 5u^4 \frac{(x - 1) \cdot 2x - x^2 \cdot 1}{(x - 1)^2}$$

Substituting for u and simplifying give

$$y' = 5\left(\frac{x^2}{x - 1}\right)^4 \cdot \frac{2x^2 - 2x - x^2}{(x - 1)^2} = \frac{5x^8(x^2 - 2x)}{(x - 1)^6} = \frac{5x^{10} - 10x^9}{(x - 1)^6}$$

EXAMPLE 2   Quotient of Two Powers

Find $f'(x)$ if $f(x) = \dfrac{(x - 1)^2}{(x^4 + 3)^3}$.

Solution

This function is the quotient of two functions, $(x - 1)^2$ and $(x^4 + 3)^3$, so we must use the Quotient Rule to find the derivative of $f(x)$, but taking the derivatives of $(x - 1)^2$ and $(x^4 + 3)^3$ will require the Power Rule.

$$f'(x) = \frac{[v(x) \cdot u'(x) - u(x) \cdot v'(x)]}{[v(x)]^2}$$

$$= \frac{(x^4 + 3)^3[2(x - 1)(1)] - (x - 1)^2[3(x^4 + 3)^2 \, 4x^3]}{[(x^4 + 3)^3]^2}$$

$$= \frac{2(x^4 + 3)^3(x - 1) - 12x^3(x - 1)^2(x^4 + 3)^2}{(x^4 + 3)^6}$$

We see that 2, $(x^4 + 3)^2$, and $(x - 1)$ are all factors in both terms of the numerator, so we can factor them from both terms and reduce the fraction.

$$f'(x) = \frac{2(x^4 + 3)^2(x - 1)[(x^4 + 3) - 6x^3(x - 1)]}{(x^4 + 3)^6}$$

$$= \frac{2(x - 1)(-5x^4 + 6x^3 + 3)}{(x^4 + 3)^4}$$

EXAMPLE 3   Product with a Power

Find $f'(x)$ if $f(x) = (x^2 - 1)\sqrt{3 - x^2}$.

Solution

The function is the product of two functions, $x^2 - 1$ and $\sqrt{3 - x^2}$. Therefore, we will use the Product Rule to find the derivative of $f(x)$, but the derivative of $\sqrt{3 - x^2} = (3 - x^2)^{1/2}$ will require the Power Rule.

$$f'(x) = u(x) \cdot v'(x) + v(x) \cdot u'(x)$$

$$= (x^2 - 1)\left[\frac{1}{2}(3 - x^2)^{-1/2}(-2x)\right] + (3 - x^2)^{1/2}(2x)$$

$$= (x^2 - 1)[-x(3 - x^2)^{-1/2}] + (3 - x^2)^{1/2}(2x)$$

$$= \frac{-x^3 + x}{(3 - x^2)^{1/2}} + 2x(3 - x^2)^{1/2}$$

We can combine these terms over the common denominator $(3 - x^2)^{1/2}$ as follows:

$$f'(x) = \frac{-x^3 + x}{(3 - x^2)^{1/2}} + \frac{2x(3 - x^2)^1}{(3 - x^2)^{1/2}} = \frac{-x^3 + x + 6x - 2x^3}{(3 - x^2)^{1/2}} = \frac{-3x^3 + 7x}{(3 - x^2)^{1/2}}$$

We should note that in Example 3 we could have written $f'(x)$ in the form

$$f'(x) = (-x^3 + x)(3 - x^2)^{-1/2} + 2x(3 - x^2)^{1/2}$$

Now the factor $(3 - x^2)$, to different powers, is contained in both terms of the expression. Thus we can factor $(3 - x^2)^{-1/2}$ from both terms. (We choose the $-1/2$ power because it is the smaller of the two powers.) Dividing $(3 - x^2)^{-1/2}$ into the first term gives $(-x^3 + x)$, and dividing it into the second term gives $2x(3 - x^2)^1$. (Why?) Thus we have

$$f'(x) = (3 - x^2)^{-1/2}[(-x^3 + x) + 2x(3 - x^2)] = \frac{-3x^3 + 7x}{(3 - x^2)^{1/2}}$$

which agrees with our previous answer.

CHECKPOINT

1. If a function has the form $y = [u(x)]^n \cdot v(x)$, where n is a constant, we begin to find the derivative by using the _____ Rule and then use the _____ Rule to find the derivative of $[u(x)]^n$.
2. If a function has the form $y = [u(x)/v(x)]^n$, where n is a constant, we begin to find the derivative by using the _____ Rule and then use the _____ Rule.
3. Find the derivative of each of the following and simplify.

   (a) $f(x) = 3x^4(2x^4 + 7)^5$ (b) $g(x) = \dfrac{(4x + 3)^7}{2x - 9}$

EXAMPLE 4   Revenue | APPLICATION PREVIEW |

Suppose that the weekly revenue function for a product is given by

$$R(x) = \frac{36{,}000{,}000x}{(2x + 500)^2}$$

where $R(x)$ is the dollars of revenue from the sale of x units.

(a) Find the marginal revenue function.
(b) Find the marginal revenue when 50 units are sold.

Solution

(a) $\overline{MR} = R'(x)$

$$= \frac{(2x + 500)^2(36,000,000) - 36,000,000x[2(2x + 500)^1(2)]}{(2x + 500)^4}$$

$$= \frac{36,000,000(2x + 500)(2x + 500 - 4x)}{(2x + 500)^4} = \frac{36,000,000(500 - 2x)}{(2x + 500)^3}$$

(b) $\overline{MR}(50) = R'(50) = \dfrac{36,000,000(500 - 100)}{(100 + 500)^3} = \dfrac{36,000,000(400)}{(600)^3} = \dfrac{200}{3} \approx 66.67$

The marginal revenue is $66.67 when 50 units are sold. That is, the predicted revenue from the sale of the 51st unit is approximately $66.67.

It may be helpful to review the formulas needed to find the derivatives of various types of functions. Table 9.5 presents examples of different types of functions and the formulas needed to find their derivatives.

| TABLE 9.5 |

SUMMARY OF DERIVATIVE FORMULAS

Examples	Formulas
$f(x) = 14$	If $f(x) = c$, then $f'(x) = 0$.
$y = x^4$	If $f(x) = x^n$, then $f'(x) = nx^{n-1}$.
$g(x) = 5x^3$	If $g(x) = cf(x)$, then $g'(x) = cf'(x)$.
$y = 3x^2 + 4x$	If $f(x) = u(x) + v(x)$, then $f'(x) = u'(x) + v'(x)$.
$y = (x^2 - 2)(x + 4)$	If $f(x) = u(x) \cdot v(x)$, then $f'(x) = u(x) \cdot v'(x) + v(x) \cdot u'(x)$.
$f(x) = \dfrac{x^3}{x^2 + 1}$	If $f(x) = \dfrac{u(x)}{v(x)}$ then $f'(x) = \dfrac{v(x) \cdot u'(x) - u(x) \cdot v'(x)}{[v(x)]^2}$.
$y = (x^3 - 4x)^{10}$	If $y = u^n$ and $u = g(x)$, then $\dfrac{dy}{dx} = nu^{n-1} \cdot \dfrac{du}{dx}$.
$y = \left(\dfrac{x-1}{x^2+3}\right)^3$	Power Rule, then Quotient Rule to find $\dfrac{du}{dx}$, where $u = \dfrac{x-1}{x^2+3}$.
$y = (x+1)\sqrt{x^3 + 1}$	Product Rule, then Power Rule to find $v'(x)$, where $v(x) = \sqrt{x^3 + 1}$.
$y = \dfrac{(x^2 - 3)^4}{x + 1}$	Quotient Rule, then Power Rule to find the derivative of the numerator.

CHECKPOINT SOLUTIONS

1. Product, Power
2. Power, Quotient
3. (a) $f'(x) = 3x^4[5(2x^4 + 7)^4(8x^3)] + (2x^4 + 7)^5(12x^3)$
   $= 120x^7(2x^4 + 7)^4 + 12x^3(2x^4 + 7)^5$
   $= 12x^3(2x^4 + 7)^4[10x^4 + (2x^4 + 7)] = 12x^3(12x^4 + 7)(2x^4 + 7)^4$

   (b) $g'(x) = \dfrac{(2x - 9)[7(4x + 3)^6(4)] - (4x + 3)^7(2)}{(2x - 9)^2}$
   $= \dfrac{2(4x + 3)^6[14(2x - 9) - (4x + 3)]}{(2x - 9)^2} = \dfrac{2(24x - 129)(4x + 3)^6}{(2x - 9)^2}$

| EXERCISES | 9.7

Find the derivatives of the functions in Problems 1–32. Simplify and express the answer using positive exponents only.

1. $f(x) = \pi^4$

2. $f(x) = \dfrac{1}{4}$

3. $g(x) = \dfrac{4}{x^4}$

4. $y = \dfrac{x^4}{4}$

5. $g(x) = 5x^3 + \dfrac{4}{x}$

6. $y = 3x^2 + 4\sqrt{x}$

7. $y = (x^2 - 2)(x + 4)$

8. $y = (x^3 - 5x^2 + 1)(x^3 - 3)$

9. $f(x) = \dfrac{x^3 + 1}{x^2}$

10. $y = \dfrac{1 + x^2 - x^4}{1 + x^4}$

11. $y = \dfrac{(x^3 - 4x)^{10}}{10}$

12. $y = \dfrac{5}{2}(3x^4 - 6x^2 + 2)^5$

13. $y = \dfrac{5}{3}x^3(4x^5 - 5)^3$

14. $y = 3x^4(2x^5 + 1)^7$

15. $y = (x - 1)^2(x^2 + 1)$

16. $f(x) = (5x^3 + 1)(x^4 + 5x)^2$

17. $y = \dfrac{(x^2 - 4)^3}{x^2 + 1}$

18. $y = \dfrac{(x^2 - 3)^4}{x}$

19. $p = [(q + 1)(q^3 - 3)]^3$

20. $y = [(4 - x^2)(x^2 + 5x)]^4$

21. $R(x) = [x^2(x^2 + 3x)]^4$

22. $c(x) = [x^3(x^2 + 1)]^{-3}$

23. $y = \left(\dfrac{2x - 1}{x^2 + x}\right)^4$

24. $y = \left(\dfrac{5 - x^2}{x^4}\right)^3$

25. $g(x) = (8x^4 + 3)^2(x^3 - 4x)^3$

26. $y = (3x^3 - 4x)^3(4x^2 - 8)^2$

27. $f(x) = \dfrac{\sqrt[3]{x^2 + 5}}{4 - x^2}$

28. $g(x) = \dfrac{\sqrt[3]{2x - 1}}{2x + 1}$

29. $y = x^2\sqrt[3]{4x - 3}$

30. $y = 3x\sqrt[4]{4x^4 + 3}$

31. $c(x) = 2x\sqrt{x^3 + 1}$

32. $R(x) = x\sqrt[3]{3x^3 + 2}$

In Problems 33 and 34, find the derivative of each function.

33. (a) $F_1(x) = \dfrac{3(x^4 + 1)^5}{5}$

(b) $F_2(x) = \dfrac{3}{5(x^4 + 1)^5}$

(c) $F_3(x) = \dfrac{(3x^4 + 1)^5}{5}$

(d) $F_4(x) = \dfrac{3}{(5x^4 + 1)^5}$

34. (a) $G_1(x) = \dfrac{2(x^3 - 5)^3}{3}$

(b) $G_2(x) = \dfrac{(2x^3 - 5)^3}{3}$

(c) $G_3(x) = \dfrac{2}{3(x^3 - 5)^3}$

(d) $G_4(x) = \dfrac{2}{(3x^3 - 5)^3}$

APPLICATIONS

35. *Physical output* The total physical output P of workers is a function of the number of workers, x. The function $P = f(x)$ is called the physical productivity function. Suppose that the physical productivity of x construction workers is given by

$$P = 10(3x + 1)^3 - 10$$

Find the marginal physical productivity, dP/dx.

36. *Revenue* Suppose that the revenue function for a certain product is given by

$$R(x) = 15(2x + 1)^{-1} + 30x - 15$$

where x is in thousands of units and R is in thousands of dollars.

(a) Find the marginal revenue when 2000 units are sold.

(b) How is revenue changing when 2000 units are sold?

37. *Revenue* Suppose that the revenue in dollars from the sale of x campers is given by

$$R(x) = 60,000x + 40,000(10 + x)^{-1} - 4000$$

(a) Find the marginal revenue when 10 units are sold.

(b) How is revenue changing when 10 units are sold?

38. *Production* Suppose that the production of x items of a new line of products is given by

$$x = 200[(t + 10) - 400(t + 40)^{-1}]$$

where t is the number of weeks the line has been in production. Find the rate of production, dx/dt.

39. *National consumption* If the national consumption function is given by

$$C(y) = 2(y + 1)^{1/2} + 0.4y + 4$$

find the marginal propensity to consume, dC/dy.

40. *Demand* Suppose that the demand function for q units of an appliance priced at $\$p$ per unit is given by

$$p = \dfrac{400(q + 1)}{(q + 2)^2}$$

Find the rate of change of price with respect to the number of appliances.

41. *Volume* When squares of side x inches are cut from the corners of a 12-inch-square piece of cardboard, an open-top box can be formed by folding up the sides. The volume of this box is given by

$$V = x(12 - 2x)^2$$

Find the rate of change of volume with respect to the size of the squares.

42. *Advertising and sales* Suppose that sales (in thousands of dollars) are directly related to an advertising campaign according to

$$S = 1 + \frac{3t - 9}{(t + 3)^2}$$

where t is the number of weeks of the campaign.
(a) Find the rate of change of sales after 3 weeks.
(b) Interpret the result in part (a).

43. *Advertising and sales* An inferior product with an extensive advertising campaign does well when it is released, but sales decline as people discontinue use of the product. If the sales S (in thousands of dollars) after t weeks are given by

$$S(t) = \frac{200t}{(t + 1)^2}, \quad t \geq 0$$

what is the rate of change of sales when $t = 9$? Interpret your result.

44. *Advertising and sales* An excellent film with a very small advertising budget must depend largely on word-of-mouth advertising. If attendance at the film after t weeks is given by

$$A = \frac{100t}{(t + 10)^2}$$

what is the rate of change in attendance and what does it mean when (a) $t = 10$? (b) $t = 20$?

45. *Per capita expenditures for U.S. health care* The dollars spent per person per year for health care is shown in the table.

Year	$ per Person	Year	$ per Person
2000	4789	2010	8465
2002	5563	2012	9275
2004	6331	2014	10,289
2006	7091	2016	11,520
2008	7826	2018	12,994

Source: U.S. Medicare and Medicaid Services

These data can be modeled by

$$y = \frac{4.38(x - 10)^2 + 78(x - 10) + 1430}{0.0029x + 0.25}$$

where x is the number of years past 1990 and y is the per capita expenditures for health care.
(a) Find the instantaneous rate of change of per capita health care expenditures in 2005 and 2015.
(b) Interpret the rate of change for 2015 found in part (a).
(c) Use the data to find the average rate of change of per capita health care expenditures from 2004 to 2006. How well does this approximate the instantaneous rate of change in 2005?

OBJECTIVE

9.8

- To find second derivatives and higher-order derivatives of certain functions

Higher-Order Derivatives

| APPLICATION PREVIEW |

Since cell phones were introduced, their popularity has increased enormously. Figure 9.32(a) shows a graph of the millions of worldwide cellular subscribers (actual and projected) as a function of the number of years past 1995 (*Source:* International Telecommunications Union). Note that the number of subscribers is always increasing and that the rate of change of that number (as seen from tangent lines to the graph) is always positive. However, the tangent lines shown in Figure 9.32(b) indicate that the rate of change of the number of subscribers is greater at *B* than at either *A* or *C*.

Figure 9.32

(a) (b)

Furthermore, the rate of change of the number of subscribers (the slopes of tangents) increases from A to B and then decreases from B to C. To learn how the rate of change of the number of subscribers is changing, we are interested in finding the derivative of the rate of change of the number of subscribers—that is, the derivative of the derivative of the number of subscribers. (See Example 4.) This is called the second derivative. In this section we will discuss second and higher-order derivatives.

Second Derivatives Because the derivative of a function is itself a function, we can take a derivative of the derivative. The derivative of a first derivative is called a **second derivative.** We can find the second derivative of a function f by differentiating it twice. If f' represents the first derivative of a function, then f'' represents the second derivative of that function.

EXAMPLE 1 **Second Derivative**

(a) Find the second derivative of $y = x^4 - 3x^2 + x^{-2}$.
(b) If $f(x) = 3x^3 - 4x^2 + 5$, find $f''(x)$.

Solution
(a) The first derivative is $y' = 4x^3 - 6x - 2x^{-3}$.
    The second derivative, which we may denote by y'', is

$$y'' = 12x^2 - 6 + 6x^{-4}$$

(b) The first derivative is $f'(x) = 9x^2 - 8x$.
    The second derivative is $f''(x) = 18x - 8$.

It is also common to use $\dfrac{d^2y}{dx^2}$ and $\dfrac{d^2f(x)}{dx^2}$ to denote the second derivative of a function.

EXAMPLE 2 **Second Derivative**

If $y = \sqrt{2x - 1}$, find d^2y/dx^2.

Solution
The first derivative is

$$\frac{dy}{dx} = \frac{1}{2}(2x - 1)^{-1/2}(2) = (2x - 1)^{-1/2}$$

The second derivative is

$$\frac{d^2y}{dx^2} = -\frac{1}{2}(2x - 1)^{-3/2}(2) = -(2x - 1)^{-3/2}$$

$$= \frac{-1}{(2x - 1)^{3/2}} = \frac{-1}{\sqrt{(2x - 1)^3}}$$

Higher-Order Derivatives

We can also find third, fourth, fifth, and higher derivatives, continuing indefinitely. The third, fourth, and fifth derivatives of a function f are denoted by f''', $f^{(4)}$, and $f^{(5)}$, respectively. Other notations for the third and fourth derivatives include

$$y''' = \frac{d^3y}{dx^3} = \frac{d^3f(x)}{dx^3}, \qquad y^{(4)} = \frac{d^4y}{dx^4} = \frac{d^4f(x)}{dx^4}$$

EXAMPLE 3   Higher-Order Derivatives

Find the first four derivatives of $f(x) = 4x^3 + 5x^2 + 3$.

Solution

$$f'(x) = 12x^2 + 10x, \quad f''(x) = 24x + 10, \quad f'''(x) = 24, \quad f^{(4)}(x) = 0$$

Just as the first derivative, $f'(x)$, can be used to determine the rate of change of a function $f(x)$, the second derivative, $f''(x)$, can be used to determine the rate of change of $f'(x)$.

EXAMPLE 4   Worldwide Cellular Subscriberships | APPLICATION PREVIEW |

By using the International Telecommunications Union data, the millions of worldwide cellular subscribers (both actual and projected) can be modeled by

$$C(t) = -0.895t^3 + 30.6t^2 + 2.99t + 55.6$$

where t is the number of years past 1995.

(a) Find the instantaneous rate of change of the worldwide cellular subscribers function.
(b) Find the instantaneous rate of change of the function found in part (a).
(c) Find where the function in part (b) equals zero. Then explain how the rate of change of the number of cellular subscribers is changing for one t-value before and one after this value.

Solution
(a) The instantaneous rate of change of $C(t)$ is

$$C'(t) = -2.685t^2 + 61.2t + 2.99$$

(b) The instantaneous rate of change of $C'(t)$ is

$$C''(t) = -5.37t + 61.2$$

(c) $0 = -5.37t + 61.2 \implies 5.37t = 61.2 \quad \text{so} \quad t = \frac{61.2}{5.37} \approx 11.4$

For $t = 11$, which is less than 11.4,

$$C''(11) = -5.37(11) + 61.2 = 2.13$$

This means that for $t = 11$, the rate of change of the number of cellular subscribers is changing at the rate of 2.13 million subscribers per year, per year. Thus the number of cellular subscribers is increasing at an increasing rate. See Figure 9.32(a) earlier in this section. For $t = 12$,

$$C''(12) = -5.37(12) + 61.2 = -3.24$$

This means that the rate of change of the number of cellular subscribers is changing at the rate of -3.24 million subscribers per year, per year. Thus the number of cellular subscribers is (still) increasing but at a decreasing (slower) rate. See Figure 9.32(a).

EXAMPLE 5   Rate of Change of a Derivative

Let $f(x) = 3x^4 + 6x^3 - 3x^2 + 4$.

(a) How fast is $f(x)$ changing at $(1, 10)$?
(b) How fast is $f'(x)$ changing at $(1, 10)$?
(c) Is $f'(x)$ increasing or decreasing at $(1, 10)$?

Solution

(a) Because $f'(x) = 12x^3 + 18x^2 - 6x$, we have

$$f'(1) = 12 + 18 - 6 = 24$$

Thus the rate of change of $f(x)$ at $(1, 10)$ is 24 (y units per x unit).

(b) Because $f''(x) = 36x^2 + 36x - 6$, we have

$$f''(1) = 66$$

Thus the rate of change of $f'(x)$ at $(1, 10)$ is 66 (y units per x unit per x unit).

(c) Because $f''(1) = 66 > 0$, $f'(x)$ is increasing at $(1, 10)$. ∎

EXAMPLE 6   Acceleration

Suppose that a particle travels according to the equation

$$s = 100t - 16t^2 + 200$$

where s is the distance in feet and t is the time in seconds. Then ds/dt is the velocity, and $d^2s/dt^2 = dv/dt$ is the acceleration of the particle. Find the acceleration.

Solution

The velocity is $v = ds/dt = 100 - 32t$ feet per second, and the acceleration is

$$\frac{dv}{dt} = \frac{d^2s}{dt^2} = -32 \text{ (feet/second)/second} = -32 \text{ feet/second}^2$$ ∎

CHECKPOINT   Suppose that the distance a particle travels is given by

$$s = 4x^3 - 12x^2 + 6$$

where s is in feet and x is in seconds.

1. Find the function that describes the velocity of this particle.
2. Find the function that describes the acceleration of this particle.
3. Is the acceleration always positive?
4. When does the *velocity* of this particle increase?

Calculator Note   We can use the numerical derivative feature of a graphing calculator to find the second derivative of a function at a point. Figure 9.33 shows how the numerical derivative feature of a graphing calculator can be used to find $f''(2)$ if $f(x) = \sqrt{x^3 - 1}$. See Appendix C, Section 9.8, for details.

```
nDeriv(nDeriv(√(
X^3-1),X,X),X,2)

           .323969225
```

Figure 9.33

The figure shows that $f''(2) = 0.323969225 \approx 0.32397$. We can check this result by calculating $f''(x)$ with formulas.

$$f'(x) = \frac{1}{2}(x^3 - 1)^{-\frac{1}{2}}(3x^2)$$

$$f''(x) = \frac{1}{2}(x^3 - 1)^{-\frac{1}{2}}(6x) + (3x^2)\left[-\frac{1}{4}(x^3 - 1)^{-\frac{3}{2}}(3x^2)\right]$$

$$f''(2) = 0.3239695483 \approx 0.32397$$

Thus we see that the numerical derivative approximation is quite accurate.

CHECKPOINT SOLUTIONS

1. The velocity is described by $s'(x) = 12x^2 - 24x$.
2. The acceleration is described by $s''(x) = 24x - 24$.
3. No; the acceleration is positive when $s''(x) > 0$—that is, when $24x - 24 > 0$. It is zero when $24x - 24 = 0$ and negative when $24x - 24 < 0$. Thus acceleration is negative when $x < 1$ second, zero when $x = 1$ second, and positive when $x > 1$ second.
4. The velocity increases when the acceleration is positive. Thus the velocity is increasing after 1 second.

| EXERCISES | 9.8

In Problems 1–6, find the second derivative.

1. $f(x) = 2x^{10} - 18x^5 - 12x^3 + 4$
2. $y = 6x^5 - 3x^4 + 12x^2$
3. $g(x) = x^3 - \dfrac{1}{x}$
4. $h(x) = x^2 - \dfrac{1}{x^2}$
5. $y = x^3 - \sqrt{x}$
6. $y = 3x^2 - \sqrt[3]{x^2}$

In Problems 7–12, find the third derivative.

7. $y = x^5 - 16x^3 + 12$
8. $y = 6x^3 - 12x^2 + 6x$
9. $f(x) = 2x^9 - 6x^6$
10. $f(x) = 3x^5 - x^6$
11. $y = 1/x$
12. $y = 1/x^2$

In Problems 13–24, find the indicated derivative.

13. If $y = x^5 - x^{1/2}$, find $\dfrac{d^2y}{dx^2}$.

14. If $y = x^4 + x^{1/3}$, find $\dfrac{d^2y}{dx^2}$.

15. If $f(x) = \sqrt{x + 1}$, find $f'''(x)$.

16. If $f(x) = \sqrt{x - 5}$, find $f'''(x)$.

17. Find $\dfrac{d^4y}{dx^4}$ if $y = 4x^3 - 16x$.

18. Find $y^{(4)}$ if $y = x^6 - 15x^3$.

19. Find $f^{(4)}(x)$ if $f(x) = \sqrt{x}$.

20. Find $f^{(4)}(x)$ if $f(x) = 1/x$.

21. Find $y^{(4)}$ if $y' = \sqrt{4x - 1}$.

22. Find $y^{(5)}$ if $\dfrac{d^2y}{dx^2} = \sqrt[3]{3x + 2}$.

23. Find $f^{(6)}(x)$ if $f^{(4)}(x) = x(x + 1)^{-1}$.

24. Find $f^{(3)}(x)$ if $f'(x) = \dfrac{x^2}{x^2 + 1}$.

25. If $f(x) = 16x^2 - x^3$, what is the rate of change of $f'(x)$ at $(1, 15)$?

26. If $y = 36x^2 - 6x^3 + x$, what is the rate of change of y' at $(1, 31)$?

 In Problems 27–30, use the numerical derivative feature of a graphing calculator to approximate the given second derivatives.

27. $f''(3)$ for $f(x) = x^3 - \dfrac{27}{x}$

28. $f''(-1)$ for $f(x) = \dfrac{x^2}{4} - \dfrac{4}{x^2}$

29. $f''(21)$ for $f(x) = \sqrt{x^2 + 4}$

30. $f''(3)$ for $f(x) = \dfrac{1}{\sqrt{x^2 + 7}}$

 In Problems 31 and 32, do the following for each function $f(x)$.

(a) Find $f'(x)$ and $f''(x)$.
(b) Graph $f(x)$, $f'(x)$, and $f''(x)$ with a graphing utility.
(c) Identify x-values where $f''(x) = 0$, $f''(x) > 0$, and $f''(x) < 0$.
(d) Identify x-values where $f'(x)$ has a maximum point or a minimum point, where $f'(x)$ is increasing, and where $f'(x)$ is decreasing.

(e) When $f(x)$ has a maximum point, is $f''(x) > 0$ or $f''(x) < 0$?

(f) When $f(x)$ has a minimum point, is $f''(x) > 0$ or $f''(x) < 0$?

31. $f(x) = x^3 - 3x^2 + 5$ 32. $f(x) = 2 + 3x - x^3$

APPLICATIONS

33. *Acceleration* A particle travels as a function of time according to the formula

$$s = 100 + 10t + 0.01t^3$$

where s is in meters and t is in seconds. Find the acceleration of the particle when $t = 2$.

34. *Acceleration* If the formula describing the distance s (in feet) an object travels as a function of time (in seconds) is

$$s = 100 + 160t - 16t^2$$

what is the acceleration of the object when $t = 4$?

35. *Revenue* The revenue (in dollars) from the sale of x units of a certain product can be described by

$$R(x) = 100x - 0.01x^2$$

Find the instantaneous rate of change of the marginal revenue.

36. *Revenue* Suppose that the revenue (in dollars) from the sale of a product is given by

$$R = 70x + 0.5x^2 - 0.001x^3$$

where x is the number of units sold. How fast is the marginal revenue $\overline{MR}$ changing when $x = 100$?

37. *Sensitivity* When medicine is administered, reaction (measured in change of blood pressure or temperature) can be modeled by

$$R = m^2 \left(\frac{c}{2} - \frac{m}{3} \right)$$

where c is a positive constant and m is the amount of medicine absorbed into the blood (*Source:* R. M. Thrall et al., *Some Mathematical Models in Biology*, U.S. Department of Commerce, 1967). The sensitivity to the medication is defined to be the rate of change of reaction R with respect to the amount of medicine m absorbed in the blood.

(a) Find the sensitivity.

(b) Find the instantaneous rate of change of sensitivity with respect to the amount of medicine absorbed in the blood.

(c) Which order derivative of reaction gives the rate of change of sensitivity?

38. *Photosynthesis* The amount of photosynthesis that takes place in a certain plant depends on the intensity of light x according to the equation

$$f(x) = 145x^2 - 30x^3$$

(a) Find the rate of change of photosynthesis with respect to the intensity.

(b) What is the rate of change when $x = 1$? When $x = 3$?

(c) How fast is the rate found in part (a) changing when $x = 1$? When $x = 3$?

39. *Revenue* The revenue (in thousands of dollars) from the sale of a product is

$$R = 15x + 30(4x + 1)^{-1} - 30$$

where x is the number of units sold.

(a) At what rate is the marginal revenue $\overline{MR}$ changing when the number of units being sold is 25?

(b) Interpret your result in part (a).

40. *Advertising and sales* The sales of a product S (in thousands of dollars) are given by

$$S = \frac{600x}{x + 40}$$

where x is the advertising expenditure (in thousands of dollars).

(a) Find the rate of change of sales with respect to advertising expenditure.

(b) Use the second derivative to find how this rate is changing at $x = 20$.

(c) Interpret your result in part (b).

41. *Advertising and sales* The daily sales S (in thousands of dollars) that are attributed to an advertising campaign are given by

$$S = 1 + \frac{3}{t + 3} - \frac{18}{(t + 3)^2}$$

where t is the number of weeks the campaign runs.

(a) Find the rate of change of sales at any time t.

(b) Use the second derivative to find how this rate is changing at $t = 15$.

(c) Interpret your result in part (b).

42. *Advertising and sales* A product with a large advertising budget has its sales S (in millions of dollars) given by

$$S = \frac{500}{t + 2} - \frac{1000}{(t + 2)^2}$$

where t is the number of months the product has been on the market.

(a) Find the rate of change of sales at any time t.

(b) What is the rate of change of sales at $t = 2$?

(c) Use the second derivative to find how this rate is changing at $t = 2$.

(d) Interpret your results from parts (b) and (c).

43. *Starbucks stores* The table gives the total number of Starbucks stores and the total number of U.S. Starbucks stores for selected years since 1992.

Year	Total Stores	Total U.S. Stores
1992	127	113
1994	300	264
1996	746	663
1998	1568	1321
2000	2674	2119
2002	5104	3756
2004	7567	5452
2005	10,241	7353
2006	12,440	8896
2007	15,011	10,684
2008	16,680	11,567
2009	16,635	11,128

Source: Starbucks.com

Assume the total number of U.S. stores, y, can be modeled as a function of the total number of stores, x, with the function

$$y = 1.25x^{0.94}$$

(a) Use this model to find a function that models the instantaneous rate of change of y.

(b) Find a function that models the rate at which the instantaneous rate from part (a) is changing.

(c) Use the results from parts (a) and (b) to find and interpret $y'(18,000)$ and $y''(18,000)$.

44. *U.S. cellular subscriberships* The table shows the numbers of U.S. cellular subscriberships (in millions) from 1995 to 2008.

Year	Subscriberships	Year	Subscriberships
1995	33.786	2002	140.767
1996	44.043	2003	158.722
1997	55.312	2004	182.140
1998	69.209	2005	207.896
1999	86.047	2006	233.041
2000	109.478	2007	255.396
2001	128.375	2008	270.334

Source: The CTIA Semi-Annual Wireless Industry Survey

Assume that the number of U.S. cellular subscriberships, in millions, can be modeled by the function

$$S(t) = 0.105t^{2.531}$$

where t is the number of years past 1985.

(a) Find the function that models the instantaneous rate of change of the U.S. cellular subscriberships.

(b) Use the second derivative to determine how fast the rate found in part (a) was changing in 1995 and 2008.

(c) Write sentences that explain the meanings of $S'(28)$ and $S''(28)$.

45. **Modeling** *Economic Dependency Ratio* The economic dependency ratio is defined as the number of persons in the total population who are not in the work force per 100 in the work force. Since 1960, Baby Boomers in the work force coupled with a decrease in the birth rate have caused a significant decrease in the economic dependency ratio.

The table shows the economic dependency ratio for selected years from 1960 and projected to 2050.

Year	Ratio	Year	Ratio
1960	150.4	2015	91.9
1970	140.4	2020	97.4
1980	108.9	2030	106.4
1990	98.3	2040	109.0
2000	93.9	2050	111.4
2010	90.3		

Source: U.S. Bureau of Labor Statistics

(a) Model these data with a cubic function, $R(x)$, where $R(x)$ is the economic dependency ratio and x is the number of years past 1950.

(b) Use the result from part (a) to find the function that models the rate of change of $R(x)$.

(c) Find the function that gives the rate of change of $R'(x)$.

(d) Find and interpret $R'(90)$ and $R''(90)$.

46. **Modeling** *U.S. Population* The table gives the U.S. population to the nearest million (actual or projected) for selected years.

Year	Population (in millions)	Year	Population (in millions)
1960	181	1995	263
1965	194	1998	271
1970	205	2000	281
1975	216	2003	291
1980	228	2005	296
1985	238	2025	348
1990	250	2050	420

Source: U.S. Bureau of the Census

(a) Find a cubic function $P(t)$ that models these data, where P is the U.S. population in millions and t is the number of years past 1960.

(b) Find the function that models the instantaneous rate of change of the U.S. population.

(c) Use the second derivative to determine how fast this rate was changing in 2000 and 2020.

(d) Write sentences that explain the meanings of $P'(60)$ and $P''(60)$.

OBJECTIVES

9.9

- To find the marginal cost and marginal revenue at different levels of production
- To find the marginal profit function, given information about cost and revenue

Applications: Marginals and Derivatives

| APPLICATION PREVIEW |

If the total cost in dollars to produce x kitchen blenders is given by

$$C(x) = 0.001x^3 - 0.3x^2 + 32x + 2500$$

what is the marginal cost function and what does it tell us about how costs are changing when $x = 80$ and $x = 200$ blenders are produced? See Example 3.

In Section 1.6, "Applications of Functions in Business and Economics," we defined the marginals for linear total cost, total revenue, and profit functions as the rate of change or slope of the respective function. In Section 9.3, we extended the notion of marginal revenue to nonlinear total revenue functions by defining marginal revenue as the derivative of total revenue. In this section, we extend the notion of marginal to nonlinear functions for any total cost or profit function.

Marginal Revenue   As we saw earlier, the instantaneous rate of change (the derivative) of the revenue function gives the **marginal revenue function.**

Marginal Revenue   If $R = R(x)$ is the total revenue function for a commodity, then the **marginal revenue function** is $\overline{MR} = R'(x)$.

Recall that if the demand function for a product in a monopoly market is $p = f(x)$, then the total revenue from the sale of x units is

$$R(x) = px = f(x) \cdot x$$

EXAMPLE   1   **Revenue and Marginal Revenue**

If the demand for a product in a monopoly market is given by

$$p = 16 - 0.02x$$

where x is the number of units and p is the price per unit, (a) find the total revenue function, and (b) find the marginal revenue for this product at $x = 40$.

Solution

(a) The total revenue function is

$$R(x) = px = (16 - 0.02x)x = 16x - 0.02x^2$$

(b) The marginal revenue function is

$$\overline{MR} = R'(x) = 16 - 0.04x$$

At $x = 40$, $R'(40) = 16 - 1.6 = 14.40$ dollars per unit. Thus the 41st item sold will increase the total revenue by approximately $14.40.

The marginal revenue is an approximation or estimate of the revenue gained from the sale of 1 additional unit. We have used marginal revenue in Example 1 to find that the revenue from the sale of the 41st item will be approximately $14.40. The actual increase in revenue from the sale of the 41st item is

$$R(41) - R(40) = 622.38 - 608 = \$14.38$$

Marginal revenue (and other marginals) can be used to predict for more than one additional unit. For instance, in Example 1, $\overline{MR}\,(40) = \$14.40$ per unit means that the expected or approximate revenue for the 41st through the 45th items sold would be $5(\$14.40) = \$72.00$. The actual revenue for these 5 items is $R(45) - R(40) = \$679.50 - \$608 = \$71.50$.

EXAMPLE 2   Maximum Revenue

Use the graphs in Figure 9.34 to determine the x-value where the revenue function has its maximum. What is happening to the marginal revenue at and near this x-value?

Solution

Figure 9.34(a) shows that the total revenue function has a maximum value at $x = 400$. After that, the total revenue function decreases. This means that the total revenue will be reduced each time a unit is sold if more than 400 are produced and sold. The graph of the marginal revenue function in Figure 9.34(b) shows that the marginal revenue is positive to the left of 400. This indicates that the rate at which the total revenue is changing is positive until 400 units are sold; thus the total revenue is increasing. Then, at 400 units, the rate of change is 0. After 400 units are sold, the marginal revenue is negative, which indicates that the total revenue is now decreasing. It is clear from looking at either graph that 400 units should be produced and sold to maximize the total revenue function $R(x)$. That is, the *total revenue function* has its maximum at $x = 400$.

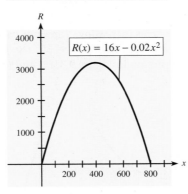

Figure 9.34   (a) Total revenue function   (b) Marginal revenue function

Marginal Cost   As with marginal revenue, the derivative of a total cost function gives the **marginal cost function.**

Marginal Cost

If $C = C(x)$ is a total cost function for a commodity, then its derivative, $\overline{MC} = C'(x)$, is the **marginal cost function.**

Notice that the linear total cost function with equation

$$C(x) = 300 + 6x \qquad \text{(in dollars)}$$

has marginal cost \$6 per unit because its slope is 6. Taking the derivative of $C(x)$ also gives

$$\overline{MC} = C'(x) = 6$$

which verifies that the marginal cost is \$6 per unit at all levels of production.

EXAMPLE 3   Marginal Cost | APPLICATION PREVIEW |

Suppose the daily total cost in dollars for a certain factory to produce x kitchen blenders is

$$C(x) = 0.001x^3 - 0.3x^2 + 32x + 2500$$

(a) Find the marginal cost function for these blenders.

(b) Find and interpret the marginal cost when $x = 80$ and $x = 200$.

Solution

(a) The marginal cost function is the derivative of $C(x)$.

$$\overline{MC} = C'(x) = 0.003x^2 - 0.6x + 32$$

(b) $C'(80) = 0.003(80)^2 - 0.6(80) + 32 = 3.2$ dollars per unit

$C'(200) = 0.003(200)^2 - 0.6(200) + 32 = 32$ dollars per unit

These values for the marginal cost can be used to *estimate* the amount that total cost would change if production were increased by one blender. Thus,

$$C'(80) = 3.2$$

means total cost would increase by *about* $3.20 if an 81st blender were produced. Note that

$$C(81) - C(80) = 3.141 \approx \$3.14$$

is the actual increase in total cost for an 81st blender.

Also, $C'(200) = 32$ means that total cost would increase by *about* $32 if a 201st blender were produced.

Whenever $C'(x)$ is positive it means that an additional unit produced adds to or increases the total cost. In addition, the value of the derivative (or marginal cost) measures how fast $C(x)$ is increasing. Thus, our calculations above indicate that $C(x)$ is increasing faster at $x = 200$ than at $x = 80$. The graphs of the total cost function and the marginal cost function in Figure 9.35(a) and (b) also illustrate these facts. ■

Figure 9.35   (a) Total cost   (b) Marginal cost

The graphs of many marginal cost functions tend to be U-shaped; they eventually will rise, even though there may be an initial interval where they decrease. Looking at the marginal cost graph in Figure 9.35(b), we see that marginal cost reaches its minimum near $x = 100$. We can also see this in Figure 9.35(a) by noting that tangent lines drawn to the total cost graph would have slopes that decrease until about $x = 100$ and then would increase.

Because producing more units can never reduce the total cost of production, the following properties are valid for total cost functions.

1. The total cost can never be negative. If there are fixed costs, the cost of producing 0 units is positive; otherwise, the cost of producing 0 units is 0.
2. The total cost function is always increasing; the more units produced, the higher the total cost. Thus the marginal cost is always positive.
3. There may be limitations on the units produced, such as those imposed by plant space.

EXAMPLE 4 Total and Marginal Cost

Suppose the graph in Figure 9.36 shows the monthly total cost for producing a product.

(a) Estimate the total cost of producing 400 items.
(b) Estimate the cost of producing the 401st item.
(c) Will producing the 151st item cost more or less than producing the 401st item?

Figure 9.36

Solution

(a) The total cost of producing 400 items is the height of the total cost graph when $x = 400$, or about \$50,000.
(b) The approximate cost of the 401st item is the marginal cost when $x = 400$, or the slope of the tangent line drawn to the graph at $x = 400$. Figure 9.37 shows the total cost graph with a tangent line at $x = 400$.

Note that the tangent line passes through the point $(0, 40{,}000)$, so we can find the slope by using the points $(0, 40{,}000)$ and $(400, 50{,}000)$.

$$m = \frac{y_2 - y_1}{x_2 - x_1} = \frac{50{,}000 - 40{,}000}{400 - 0} = \frac{10{,}000}{400} = 25$$

Thus the marginal cost at $x = 400$ is 25 dollars per item, so the approximate cost of the 401st item is \$25.

(c) From Figure 9.37 we can see that if a tangent line to the graph were drawn where $x = 150$, it would be steeper than the one at $x = 400$. Because the slope of the tangent is the marginal cost and the marginal cost predicts the cost of the next item, this means that it would cost more to produce the 151st item than to produce the 401st. ∎

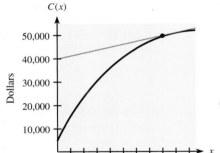

Figure 9.37

CHECKPOINT

Suppose the total cost function for a commodity is $C(x) = 0.01x^3 - 0.9x^2 + 33x + 3000$.
1. Find the marginal cost function.
2. What is the marginal cost if $x = 50$ units are produced?
3. Use marginal cost to estimate the cost of producing the 51st unit.
4. Calculate $C(51) - C(50)$ to find the actual cost of producing the 51st unit.
5. True or false: For products that have linear cost functions, the actual cost of producing the $(x + 1)$st unit is equal to the marginal cost at x.

Marginal Profit

As with marginal cost and marginal revenue, the derivative of a profit function for a commodity will give us the **marginal profit function** for the commodity.

Marginal Profit

> If $P = P(x)$ is the profit function for a commodity, then the **marginal profit function** is $\overline{MP} = P'(x)$.

EXAMPLE 5 Marginal Profit

If the total profit, in thousands of dollars, for a product is given by $P(x) = 20\sqrt{x + 1} - 2x - 22$, what is the marginal profit at a production level of 15 units?

Solution

The marginal profit function is

$$\overline{MP} = P'(x) = 20 \cdot \frac{1}{2}(x + 1)^{-1/2} - 2 = \frac{10}{\sqrt{x + 1}} - 2$$

If 15 units are produced, the marginal profit is

$$P'(15) = \frac{10}{\sqrt{15 + 1}} - 2 = \frac{1}{2}$$

This means that the profit from the sale of the 16th unit is approximately $\frac{1}{2}$ (thousand dollars), or $500.

In a **competitive market,** each firm is so small that its actions in the market cannot affect the price of the product. The price of the product is determined in the market by the intersection of the market demand curve (from all consumers) and the market supply curve (from all firms that supply this product). The firm can sell as little or as much as it desires at the given market price, which it cannot change.

Therefore, a firm in a competitive market has a total revenue function given by $R(x) = px$, where p is the market equilibrium price for the product and x is the quantity sold.

EXAMPLE 6 Profit in a Competitive Market

A firm in a competitive market must sell its product for $200 per unit. The cost per unit (per month) is $80 + x$, where x represents the number of units sold per month. Find the marginal profit function.

Solution

If the cost per unit is $80 + x$, then the total cost of x units is given by the equation $C(x) = (80 + x)x = 80x + x^2$. The revenue per unit is $200, so the total revenue is given by $R(x) = 200x$. Thus the profit function is

$$P(x) = R(x) - C(x) = 200x - (80x + x^2), \quad \text{or} \quad P(x) = 120x - x^2$$

The marginal profit is $P'(x) = 120 - 2x$.

The marginal profit in Example 6 is not always positive, so producing and selling a certain number of items will maximize profit. Note that the marginal profit will be negative (that is, profit will decrease) if more than 60 items per month are produced. We will discuss methods of maximizing total revenue and profit, and of minimizing average cost, in the next chapter.

CHECKPOINT

If the total profit function for a product is $P(x) = 20\sqrt{x + 1} - 2x - 22$, then the marginal profit is

$$P'(x) = \frac{10}{\sqrt{x + 1}} - 2 \quad \text{and} \quad P''(x) = \frac{-5}{\sqrt{(x + 1)^3}}$$

6. Is $P''(x) < 0$ for all values of $x \geq 0$?
7. Is the marginal profit decreasing for all $x \geq 0$?

EXAMPLE 7 Marginal Profit

Figure 9.38 shows graphs of a company's total revenue and total cost functions.

Figure 9.38

(a) If 100 units are being produced and sold, will producing the 101st item increase or decrease the profit?

(b) If 300 units are being produced and sold, will producing the 301st item increase or decrease the profit?

(c) If 1000 units are being produced and sold, will producing the 1001st item increase or decrease the profit?

Solution

At a given x-value, the slope of the tangent line to each function gives the marginal at that x-value.

(a) At $x = 100$, we can see that the graph of $R(x)$ is steeper than the graph of $C(x)$. Thus, the tangent line to $R(x)$ will be steeper than the tangent line to $C(x)$. Hence $\overline{MR}(100) > \overline{MC}(100)$, which means that the revenue from the 101st item will exceed the cost. Therefore, profit will increase when the 101st item is produced. Note that at $x = 100$, total costs are greater than total revenue, so the company is losing money but should still sell the 101st item because it will reduce the amount of loss.

(b) At $x = 300$, we can see that the tangent line to $R(x)$ again will be steeper than the tangent line to $C(x)$. Hence $\overline{MR}(300) > \overline{MC}(300)$, which means that the revenue from the 301st item will exceed the cost. Therefore, profit will increase when the 301st item is produced.

(c) At $x = 1000$, we can see that the tangent line to $C(x)$ will be steeper than the tangent line to $R(x)$. Hence $\overline{MC}(1000) > \overline{MR}(1000)$, which means that the cost of the 1001st item will exceed the revenue. Therefore, profit will decrease when the 1001st item is produced.

 EXAMPLE 8   Profit and Marginal Profit

In Example 5, we found that the profit (in thousands of dollars) for a company's products is given by $P(x) = 20\sqrt{x + 1} - 2x - 22$ and its marginal profit is given by $P'(x) = \dfrac{10}{\sqrt{x + 1}} - 2$.

(a) Use the graphs of $P(x)$ and $P'(x)$ to determine the relationship between the two functions.

(b) When is the marginal profit 0? What is happening to profit at this level of production?

Solution

(a) By comparing the graphs of the two functions (shown in Figure 9.39 on the next page), we see that for $x > 0$, profit $P(x)$ is increasing over the interval where the marginal profit $P'(x)$ is positive, and profit is decreasing over the interval where the marginal profit $P'(x)$ is negative.

(b) By using ZERO or SOLVER, or by using algebra, we see that $P'(x) = 0$ when $x = 24$. This level of production ($x = 24$) is where profit is maximized, at 30 (thousand dollars). ∎

Figure 9.39

CHECKPOINT SOLUTIONS

1. $\overline{MC} = C'(x) = 0.03x^2 - 1.8x + 33$
2. $C'(50) = 18$
3. $C'(50) = 18$, so it will cost approximately $18 to produce the 51st unit.
4. $C(51) - C(50) = 3668.61 - 3650 = 18.61$
5. True   6. Yes   7. Yes, because $P''(x) < 0$ for $x \geq 0$.

| EXERCISES | 9.9

MARGINAL REVENUE, COST, AND PROFIT

In Problems 1–8, total revenue is in dollars and x is the number of units.

1. (a) If the total revenue function for a product is $R(x) = 4x$, what is the marginal revenue function for that product?
   (b) What does this marginal revenue function tell us?

2. If the total revenue function for a product is $R(x) = 32x$, what is the marginal revenue for the product? What does this mean?

3. Suppose that the total revenue function for a commodity is $R = 36x - 0.01x^2$.
   (a) Find $R(100)$ and tell what it represents.
   (b) Find the marginal revenue function.
   (c) Find the marginal revenue at $x = 100$, and tell what it predicts about the sale of the next unit and the next 3 units.
   (d) Find $R(101) - R(100)$ and explain what this value represents.

4. Suppose that the total revenue function for a commodity is $R(x) = 25x - 0.05x^2$.
   (a) Find $R(50)$ and tell what it represents.
   (b) Find the marginal revenue function.
   (c) Find the marginal revenue at $x = 50$, and tell what it predicts about the sale of the next unit and the next 2 units.
   (d) Find $R(51) - R(50)$ and explain what this value represents.

5. Suppose that demand for local cable TV service is given by

$$p = 80 - 0.4x$$

where p is the monthly price in dollars and x is the number of subscribers (in hundreds).
   (a) Find the total revenue as a function of the number of subscribers.
   (b) Find the number of subscribers when the company charges $50 per month for cable service. Then find the total revenue for $p = \$50$.
   (c) How could the company attract more subscribers?
   (d) Find and interpret the marginal revenue when the price is $50 per month. What does this suggest about the monthly charge to subscribers?

6. Suppose that in a monopoly market, the demand function for a product is given by

$$p = 160 - 0.1x$$

where x is the number of units and p is the price in dollars.
   (a) Find the total revenue from the sale of 500 units.
   (b) Find and interpret the marginal revenue at 500 units.
   (c) Is more revenue expected from the 501st unit sold or from the 701st? Explain.

7. (a) Graph the marginal revenue function from Problem 3.
   (b) At what value of x will total revenue be maximized for Problem 3.
   (c) What is the maximum revenue?

8. (a) Graph the marginal revenue function from Problem 4.
   (b) Determine the number of units that must be sold to maximize total revenue.
   (c) What is the maximum revenue?

In Problems 9–16, cost is in dollars and x is the number of units. Find the marginal cost functions for the given cost functions.

9. $C(x) = 40 + 8x$ 10. $C(x) = 200 + 16x$

11. $C(x) = 500 + 13x + x^2$

12. $C(x) = 300 + 10x + \frac{1}{100}x^2$

13. $C = x^3 - 6x^2 + 24x + 10$

14. $C = 0.1x^3 - 1.5x^2 + 9x + 15$

15. $C = 400 + 27x + x^3$ 16. $C(x) = 50 + 48x + x^3$

17. Suppose that the cost function for a commodity is

$$C(x) = 40 + x^2 \quad \text{dollars}$$

  (a) Find the marginal cost at $x = 5$ units and tell what this predicts about the cost of producing 1 additional unit.

  (b) Calculate $C(6) - C(5)$ to find the actual cost of producing 1 additional unit.

18. Suppose that the cost function for a commodity is

$$C(x) = 300 + 6x + \tfrac{1}{20}x^2 \quad \text{dollars}$$

  (a) Find the marginal cost at $x = 8$ units and tell what this predicts about the cost of producing 1 additional unit.

  (b) Calculate $C(9) - C(8)$ to find the actual cost of producing 1 additional unit.

19. If the cost function for a commodity is

$$C(x) = x^3 - 4x^2 + 30x + 20 \quad \text{dollars}$$

find the marginal cost at $x = 4$ units and tell what this predicts about the cost of producing 1 additional unit and 3 additional units.

20. If the cost function for a commodity is

$$C(x) = \tfrac{1}{90}x^3 + 4x^2 + 4x + 10 \quad \text{dollars}$$

find the marginal cost at $x = 3$ units and tell what this predicts about the cost of producing 1 additional unit and 2 additional units.

21. If the cost function for a commodity is

$$C(x) = 300 + 4x + x^2$$

graph the marginal cost function.

22. If the cost function for a commodity is

$$C(x) = x^3 - 12x^2 + 63x + 15$$

graph the marginal cost function.

In each of Problems 23 and 24, the graph of a company's total cost function is shown. For each problem, use the graph to answer the following questions.

(a) **Will the 101st item or the 501st item cost more to produce? Explain.**

(b) **Does this total cost function represent a manufacturing process that is getting more efficient or less efficient? Explain.**

23.

24.

In Problems 25–28, cost, revenue, and profit are in dollars and x is the number of units.

25. If the total profit function is $P(x) = 5x - 25$, find the marginal profit. What does this mean?

26. If the total profit function is $P(x) = 16x - 32$, find the marginal profit. What does this mean?

27. Suppose that the total revenue function for a product is $R(x) = 50x$ and that the total cost function is $C(x) = 1900 + 30x + 0.01x^2$.

  (a) Find the profit from the production and sale of 500 units.

  (b) Find the marginal profit function.

  (c) Find $\overline{MP}$ at $x = 500$ and explain what it predicts.

  (d) Find $P(501) - P(500)$ and explain what this value represents.

28. Suppose that the total revenue function is given by

$$R(x) = 46x$$

and that the total cost function is given by

$$C(x) = 100 + 30x + \tfrac{1}{10}x^2$$

  (a) Find $P(100)$.

  (b) Find the marginal profit function.

  (c) Find $\overline{MP}$ at $x = 100$ and explain what it predicts.

  (d) Find $P(101) - P(100)$ and explain what this value represents.

In each of Problems 29 and 30, the graphs of a company's total revenue function and total cost function are shown. For each problem, use the graph to answer the following questions.

(a) From the sale of 100 items, 400 items, and 700 items, rank from smallest to largest the amount of profit received. Explain your choices and note whether any of these scenarios results in a loss.

(b) From the sale of the 101st item, the 401st item, and the 701st item, rank from smallest to largest the amount of profit received. Explain your choices, and note whether any of these scenarios results in a loss.

29.

30.

In each of Problems 31 and 32, the graph of a company's profit function is shown. For each problem, use the graph to answer the following questions about points *A*, *B*, and *C*.

(a) Rank from smallest to largest the amounts of profit received at these points. Explain your choices, and note whether any point results in a loss.

(b) Rank from smallest to largest the marginal profit at these points. Explain your choices, and note whether any marginal is negative and what this means.

31.

32.

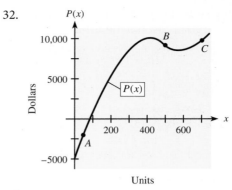

33. (a) Graph the marginal profit function for the profit function $P(x) = 30x - x^2 - 200$, where $P(x)$ is in thousands of dollars and x is hundreds of units.
    (b) What level of production and sales will give a 0 marginal profit?
    (c) At what level of production and sales will profit be at a maximum?
    (d) What is the maximum profit?

34. (a) Graph the marginal profit function for the profit function $P(x) = 16x - 0.1x^2 - 100$, where $P(x)$ is in hundreds of dollars and x is hundreds of units.
    (b) What level of production and sales will give a 0 marginal profit?
    (c) At what level of production and sales will profit be at a maximum?
    (d) What is the maximum profit?

35. The price of a product in a competitive market is $300. If the cost per unit of producing the product is $160 + 0.1x$ dollars, where x is the number of units produced per month, how many units should the firm produce and sell to maximize its profit?

36. The cost per unit of producing a product is $60 + 0.2x$ dollars, where x represents the number of units produced per week. If the equilibrium price determined by a competitive market is $220, how many units should the firm produce and sell each week to maximize its profit?

37. If the daily cost per unit of producing a product by the Ace Company is $10 + 0.1x$ dollars, and if the price on the competitive market is $70, what is the maximum daily profit the Ace Company can expect on this product?

38. The Mary Ellen Candy Company produces chocolate Easter bunnies at a cost per unit of $0.40 + 0.005x$ dollars, where x is the number produced. If the price on the competitive market for a bunny this size is $10.00, how many should the company produce to maximize its profit?

KEY TERMS AND FORMULAS

Section	Key Terms	Formulas
9.1	Limit One-sided limits Properties of limits 0/0 indeterminate form	
9.2	Continuous function Vertical asymptote Horizontal asymptote Limit at infinity	
9.3	Average rate of change of f over $[a, b]$	$\dfrac{f(b) - f(a)}{b - a}$
	Average velocity Velocity Instantaneous rate of change	
	Derivative	$f'(x) = \lim\limits_{h \to 0} \dfrac{f(x + h) - f(x)}{h}$
	Marginal revenue	$\overline{MR} = R'(x)$
	Tangent line Secant line Slope of a curve Differentiability and continuity	
9.4	Powers of x Rule	$\dfrac{d(x^n)}{dx} = nx^{n-1}$
	Constant Function Rule	$\dfrac{d(c)}{dx} = 0$ for constant c
	Coefficient Rule	$\dfrac{d}{dx}[c \cdot f(x)] = c \cdot f'(x)$
	Sum Rule	$\dfrac{d}{dx}(u + v) = \dfrac{du}{dx} + \dfrac{dv}{dx}$
	Difference Rule	$\dfrac{d}{dx}(u - v) = \dfrac{du}{dx} - \dfrac{dv}{dx}$
9.5	Product Rule	$\dfrac{d}{dx}(uv) = uv' + vu'$
	Quotient Rule	$\dfrac{d}{dx}\left(\dfrac{u}{v}\right) = \dfrac{vu' - uv'}{v^2}$
9.6	Chain Rule	$\dfrac{dy}{dx} = \dfrac{dy}{du} \cdot \dfrac{du}{dx}$
	Power Rule	$\dfrac{d}{dx}(u^n) = nu^{n-1}\dfrac{du}{dx}$
9.8	Second derivative; third derivative; higher-order derivatives	
9.9	Marginal revenue function Marginal cost function Marginal profit function	$\overline{MR} = R'(x)$ $\overline{MC} = C'(x)$ $\overline{MP} = P'(x)$

REVIEW EXERCISES

In Problems 1–6, use the graph of $y = f(x)$ in Figure 9.40 to find the functional values and limits, if they exist.

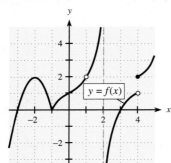

Figure 9.40

1. (a) $f(-2)$ (b) $\lim_{x \to -2} f(x)$
2. (a) $f(-1)$ (b) $\lim_{x \to -1} f(x)$
3. (a) $f(4)$ (b) $\lim_{x \to 4} f(x)$
4. (a) $\lim_{x \to 4^+} f(x)$ (b) $\lim_{x \to 4} f(x)$
5. (a) $f(1)$ (b) $\lim_{x \to 1} f(x)$
6. (a) $f(2)$ (b) $\lim_{x \to 2} f(x)$

In Problems 7–20, find each limit, if it exists.

7. $\lim_{x \to 4} (3x^2 + x + 3)$
8. $\lim_{x \to 4} \dfrac{x^2 - 16}{x + 4}$
9. $\lim_{x \to -1} \dfrac{x^2 - 1}{x + 1}$
10. $\lim_{x \to 5} \dfrac{x^2 - 6x + 5}{x^2 - 5x}$
11. $\lim_{x \to 2} \dfrac{4x^3 - 8x^2}{4x^3 - 16x}$
12. $\lim_{x \to -\frac{1}{2}} \dfrac{x^2 - \frac{1}{4}}{6x^2 + x - 1}$
13. $\lim_{x \to 3} \dfrac{x^2 - 16}{x - 3}$
14. $\lim_{x \to -3} \dfrac{x^2 - x - 12}{2x - 6}$
15. $\lim_{x \to 1} \dfrac{x^2 - 9}{x - 3}$
16. $\lim_{x \to 2} \dfrac{x^2 - 8}{x - 2}$

17. $\lim_{x \to 1} f(x)$ where $f(x) = \begin{cases} 4 - x^2 & \text{if } x < 1 \\ 4 & \text{if } x = 1 \\ 2x + 1 & \text{if } x > 1 \end{cases}$

18. $\lim_{x \to -2} f(x)$ where $f(x) = \begin{cases} x^3 - x & \text{if } x < -2 \\ 2 - x^2 & \text{if } x \geq -2 \end{cases}$

19. $\lim_{h \to 0} \dfrac{3(x + h)^2 - 3x^2}{h}$

20. $\lim_{h \to 0} \dfrac{[(x + h) - 2(x + h)^2] - (x - 2x^2)}{h}$

In Problems 21 and 22, use tables to investigate each limit. Check your result analytically or graphically.

21. $\lim_{x \to 2} \dfrac{x^2 + 10x - 24}{x^2 - 5x + 6}$
22. $\lim_{x \to -\frac{1}{2}} \dfrac{x^2 + \frac{1}{6}x - \frac{1}{6}}{x^2 + \frac{5}{6}x + \frac{1}{6}}$

Use the graph of $y = f(x)$ in Figure 9.40 to answer the questions in Problems 23 and 24.

23. Is $f(x)$ continuous at
    (a) $x = -1$?   (b) $x = 1$?
24. Is $f(x)$ continuous at
    (a) $x = -2$?   (b) $x = 2$?

In Problems 25–30, suppose that

$$f(x) = \begin{cases} x^2 + 1 & \text{if } x \leq 0 \\ x & \text{if } 0 < x < 1 \\ 2x^2 - 1 & \text{if } x \geq 1 \end{cases}$$

25. What is $\lim_{x \to -1} f(x)$?
26. What is $\lim_{x \to 0} f(x)$, if it exists?
27. What is $\lim_{x \to 1} f(x)$, if it exists?
28. Is $f(x)$ continuous at $x = 0$?
29. Is $f(x)$ continuous at $x = 1$?
30. Is $f(x)$ continuous at $x = -1$?

For the functions in Problems 31–34, determine which are continuous. Identify discontinuities for those that are not continuous.

31. $y = \dfrac{x^2 + 25}{x - 5}$
32. $y = \dfrac{x^2 - 3x + 2}{x - 2}$
33. $f(x) = \begin{cases} x + 2 & \text{if } x \leq 2 \\ 5x - 6 & \text{if } x > 2 \end{cases}$
34. $y = \begin{cases} x^4 - 3 & \text{if } x \leq 1 \\ 2x - 3 & \text{if } x > 1 \end{cases}$

In Problems 35 and 36, use the graphs to find (a) the points of discontinuity, (b) $\lim_{x \to +\infty} f(x)$, and (c) $\lim_{x \to -\infty} f(x)$.

35.

36.

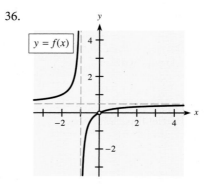

In Problems 37 and 38, evaluate the limits, if they exist. Then state what each limit tells about any horizontal asymptotes.

37. $\lim\limits_{x \to -\infty} \dfrac{2x^2}{1 - x^2}$

38. $\lim\limits_{x \to +\infty} \dfrac{3x^{2/3}}{x + 1}$

39. Find the average rate of change of

$$f(x) = 2x^4 - 3x + 7 \text{ over } [-1, 2]$$

In Problems 40 and 41, decide whether the statements are true or false.

40. $\lim\limits_{h \to 0} \dfrac{f(x + h) - f(x)}{h}$ gives the formula for the slope of the tangent and the instantaneous rate of change of $f(x)$ at any value of x.

41. $\lim\limits_{h \to 0} \dfrac{f(c + h) - f(c)}{h}$ gives the equation of the tangent line to $f(x)$ at $x = c$.

42. Use the definition of derivative to find $f'(x)$ for $f(x) = 3x^2 + 2x - 1$.

43. Use the definition of derivative to find $f'(x)$ if $f(x) = x - x^2$.

Use the graph of $y = f(x)$ in Figure 9.40 to answer the questions in Problems 44–46.

44. Explain which is greater: the average rate of change of f over $[-3, 0]$ or over $[-1, 0]$.

45. Is $f(x)$ differentiable at
    (a) $x = -1$?   (b) $x = 1$?

46. Is $f(x)$ differentiable at
    (a) $x = -2$?   (b) $x = 2$?

47. Let $f(x) = \dfrac{\sqrt[3]{4x}}{(3x^2 - 10)^2}$. Approximate $f'(2)$
    (a) by using the numerical derivative feature of a graphing calculator, and
    (b) by evaluating $\dfrac{f(2 + h) - f(2)}{h}$ with $h = 0.0001$.

48. Use the given table of values for $g(x)$ to
    (a) find the average rate of change of $g(x)$ over $[2, 5]$.
    (b) approximate $g'(4)$ as accurately as possible.

x	2	2.3	3.1	4	4.3	5
g(x)	13.2	12.1	9.7	12.2	14.3	18.1

Use the following graph of $f(x)$ to complete Problems 49 and 50.

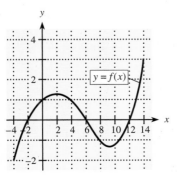

49. Estimate $f'(4)$.

50. Rank the following from smallest to largest and explain.
    $A: f'(2)$ $B: f'(6)$
    C: the average rate of change of $f(x)$ over $[2, 10]$

51. If $c = 4x^5 - 6x^3$, find c'.

52. If $f(x) = 10x^9 - 5x^6 + 4x - 2^7 + 19$, find $f'(x)$.

53. If $p = q + \sqrt{7}$, find dp/dq.

54. If $y = \sqrt{x}$, find y'.

55. If $f(z) = \sqrt[3]{2^4}$, find $f'(z)$.

56. If $v(x) = 4/\sqrt[3]{x}$, find $v'(x)$.

57. If $y = \dfrac{1}{x} - \dfrac{1}{\sqrt{x}}$, find y'.

58. If $f(x) = \dfrac{3}{2x^2} - \sqrt[3]{x} + 4^5$, find $f'(x)$.

59. Write the equation of the line tangent to the graph of $y = 3x^5 - 6$ at $x = 1$.

60. Write the equation of the line tangent to the curve $y = 3x^3 - 2x$ at the point where $x = 2$.

In Problems 61 and 62, (a) find all x-values where the slope of the tangent equals zero, (b) find points (x, y) where the slope of the tangent equals zero, and (c) use a graphing utility to graph the function and label the points found in part (b).

61. $f(x) = x^3 - 3x^2 + 1$ 62. $f(x) = x^6 - 6x^4 + 8$

63. If $f(x) = (3x - 1)(x^2 - 4x)$, find $f'(x)$.

64. Find y' if $y = (x^4 + 3)(3x^3 + 1)$.

65. If $p = \dfrac{5q^3}{2q^3 + 1}$, find $\dfrac{dp}{dq}$.

66. Find $\dfrac{ds}{dt}$ if $s = \dfrac{\sqrt{t}}{(3t + 1)}$.

67. Find $\dfrac{dy}{dx}$ for $y = \sqrt{x}\,(3x + 2)$.

68. Find $\dfrac{dC}{dx}$ for $C = \dfrac{5x^4 - 2x^2 + 1}{x^3 + 1}$.

69. If $y = (x^3 - 4x^2)^3$, find y'.

70. If $y = (5x^6 + 6x^4 + 5)^6$, find y'.

71. If $y = (2x^4 - 9)^9$, find $\dfrac{dy}{dx}$.

72. Find $g'(x)$ if $g(x) = \dfrac{1}{\sqrt{x^3 - 4x}}$.

73. Find $f'(x)$ if $f(x) = x^2(2x^4 + 5)^8$.

74. Find S' if $S = \dfrac{(3x + 1)^2}{x^2 - 4}$.

75. Find $\dfrac{dy}{dx}$ if $y = [(3x + 1)(2x^3 - 1)]^{12}$.

76. Find y' if $y = \left(\dfrac{x + 1}{1 - x^2}\right)^3$.

77. Find y' if $y = x\sqrt{x^2 - 4}$.

78. Find $\dfrac{dy}{dx}$ if $y = \dfrac{x}{\sqrt[3]{3x - 1}}$.

In Problems 79 and 80, find the second derivatives.

79. $y = \sqrt{x} - x^2$ 80. $y = x^4 - \dfrac{1}{x}$

In Problems 81 and 82, find the fifth derivatives.

81. $y = (2x + 1)^4$

82. $y = \dfrac{(1 - x)^6}{24}$

83. If $\dfrac{dy}{dx} = \sqrt{x^2 - 4}$, find $\dfrac{d^3y}{dx^3}$.

84. If $\dfrac{d^2y}{dx^2} = \dfrac{x}{x^2 + 1}$, find $\dfrac{d^4y}{dx^4}$.

APPLICATIONS

Cost, revenue, and profit **In Problems 85–88, assume that a company's monthly total revenue and total cost (both in dollars) are given by**

$$R(x) = 140x - 0.01x^2 \quad \text{and} \quad C(x) = 60x + 70,000$$

where x is the number of units. (Let $P(x)$ denote the profit function.)

85. Find (a) $\lim\limits_{x \to 4000} R(x)$, (b) $\lim\limits_{x \to 4000} C(x)$, and (c) $\lim\limits_{x \to 4000} P(x)$.

86. Find and interpret (a) $\lim\limits_{x \to 0^+} C(x)$ and (b) $\lim\limits_{x \to 1000} P(x)$.

87. If $\overline{R}(x) = \dfrac{R(x)}{x}$ and $\overline{C}(x) = \dfrac{C(x)}{x}$ are, respectively, the company's average revenue per unit and average cost per unit, find

    (a) $\lim\limits_{x \to 0^+} \overline{R}(x)$.   (b) $\lim\limits_{x \to 0^+} \overline{C}(x)$.

88. Evaluate and explain the meanings of

    (a) $\lim\limits_{x \to \infty} C(x)$.   (b) $\lim\limits_{x \to \infty} \overline{C}(x) = \lim\limits_{x \to \infty} \dfrac{C(x)}{x}$.

Elderly in the work force **The graph shows the percent of elderly men and women in the work force for selected years from 1950 to 2008. Use this graph in Problems 89 and 90.**

89. For the period from 1990 to 2008, find and interpret the annual average rate of change of
    (a) elderly men in the work force and
    (b) elderly women in the work force.

90. (a) Find the annual average rate of change of the percent of elderly men in the work force from 1950 to 1960 and from 2000 to 2008.
    (b) Find the annual average rate of change of the percent of elderly women in the work force from 1950 to 1960 and from 2000 to 2008.

Elderly in the Labor Force, 1950–2008

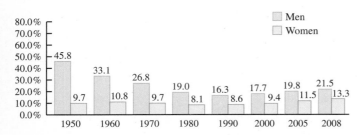

Source: Bureau of the Census, U.S. Department of Commerce

91. *Demand* Suppose that the demand for x units of a product is given by $x = (100/p) - 1$, where p is the price per unit of the product. Find and interpret the rate of change of demand with respect to price if the price is
    (a) $10.   (b) $20.

92. *Severe weather ice makers* Thunderstorms severe enough to produce hail develop when an upper-level low (a pool of cold air high in the atmosphere) moves through a region where there is warm, moist air at the surface. These storms create an updraft that draws the moist air into subfreezing air above 10,000 feet. Data from the National Weather Service indicates that the strength of the updraft, as measured by its speed s in mph, affects the size of the hail according to

$$h = 0.000595s^{1.922}$$

where h is the diameter of the hail (in inches). Find and interpret $h(100)$ and $h'(100)$.

93. *Revenue* The graph shows the revenue function for a commodity. Will the $(A + 1)$st item sold or the $(B + 1)$st item sold produce more revenue? Explain.

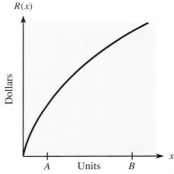

94. *Revenue* In a 100-unit apartment building, when the price charged per apartment rental is $(830 + 30x)$ dollars, then the number of apartments rented is $100 - x$ and the total revenue for the building is

$$R(x) = (830 + 30x)(100 - x)$$

where x is the number of $30 rent increases (and also the resulting number of unrented apartments). Find the marginal revenue when $x = 10$. Does this tell you that the rent should be raised (causing more vacancies) or lowered? Explain.

95. *Productivity* Suppose the productivity of a worker (in units per hour) after x hours of training and time on the job is given by

$$P(x) = 3 + \dfrac{70x^2}{x^2 + 1000}$$

    (a) Find and interpret $P(20)$.
    (b) Find and interpret $P'(20)$.

96. *Demand* The demand q for a product at price p is given by

$$q = 10,000 - 50\sqrt{0.02p^2 + 500}$$

Find the rate of change of demand with respect to price.

97. *Supply* The number of units x of a product that is supplied at price p is given by

$$x = \sqrt{p - 1}, \quad p \geq 1$$

If the price p is \$10, what is the rate of change of the supply with respect to the price, and what does it tell us?

98. *Acceleration* Suppose an object moves so that its distance to a sensor, in feet, is given by

$$s(t) = 16 + 140t + 8\sqrt{t}$$

where t is the time in seconds. Find the acceleration at time $t = 4$ seconds.

99. *Profit* Suppose a company's profit (in dollars) is given by

$$P(x) = 70x - 0.1x^2 - 5500$$

where x is the number of units. Find and interpret $P'(300)$ and $P''(300)$.

In Problems 100–107, cost, revenue, and profit are in dollars and x is the number of units.

100. *Cost* If the cost function for a particular good is $C(x) = 3x^2 + 6x + 600$, what is the
 (a) marginal cost function?
 (b) marginal cost if 30 units are produced?
 (c) interpretation of your answer in part (b)?

101. *Cost* If the total cost function for a commodity is $C(x) = 400 + 5x + x^3$, what is the marginal cost when 4 units are produced, and what does it mean?

102. *Revenue* The total revenue function for a commodity is $R = 40x - 0.02x^2$, with x representing the number of units.
 (a) Find the marginal revenue function.
 (b) At what level of production will marginal revenue be 0?

103. *Profit* If the total revenue function for a product is given by $R(x) = 60x$ and the total cost function is given by $C = 200 + 10x + 0.1x^2$, what is the marginal profit at $x = 10$? What does the marginal profit at $x = 10$ predict?

104. *Revenue* The total revenue function for a commodity is given by $R = 80x - 0.04x^2$.
 (a) Find the marginal revenue function.
 (b) What is the marginal revenue at $x = 100$?
 (c) Interpret your answer in part (b).

105. *Revenue* If the revenue function for a product is

$$R(x) = \frac{60x^2}{2x + 1}$$

find the marginal revenue.

106. *Profit* A firm has monthly costs given by

$$C = 45{,}000 + 100x + x^3$$

where x is the number of units produced per month. The firm can sell its product in a competitive market for \$4600 per unit. Find the marginal profit.

107. *Profit* A small business has weekly costs of

$$C = 100 + 30x + \frac{x^2}{10}$$

where x is the number of units produced each week. The competitive market price for this business's product is \$46 per unit. Find the marginal profit.

108. *Cost, revenue, and profit* The graph shows the total revenue and total cost functions for a company. Use the graph to decide (and justify) at which of points A, B, and C
 (a) the revenue from the next item will be least.
 (b) the profit will be greatest.
 (c) the profit from the sale of the next item will be greatest.
 (d) the next item sold will reduce the profit.

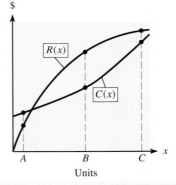

9   **CHAPTER TEST**

1. Evaluate the following limits, if they exist. Use algebraic methods.
 (a) $\displaystyle\lim_{x \to -2} \frac{4x - x^2}{4x - 8}$
 (b) $\displaystyle\lim_{x \to \infty} \frac{8x^2 - 4x + 1}{2 + x - 5x^2}$
 (c) $\displaystyle\lim_{x \to 7} \frac{x^2 - 5x - 14}{x^2 - 6x - 7}$
 (d) $\displaystyle\lim_{x \to -5} \frac{5x - 25}{x + 5}$

2. (a) Write the limit definition for $f'(x)$.
 (b) Use the definition from (a) to find $f'(x)$ for $f(x) = 3x^2 - x + 9$.

3. Let $f(x) = \dfrac{4x}{x^2 - 8x}$. Identify all x-values where $f(x)$ is *not* continuous.

4. Use derivative formulas to find the derivative of each of the following. Simplify, except for part (d).
 (a) $B = 0.523W - 5176$
 (b) $p = 9t^{10} - 6t^7 - 17t + 23$

(c) $y = \dfrac{3x^3}{2x^7 + 11}$

(d) $f(x) = (3x^5 - 2x + 3)(4x^{10} + 10x^4 - 17)$

(e) $g(x) = \frac{3}{4}(2x^5 + 7x^3 - 5)^{12}$

(f) $y = (x^2 + 3)(2x + 5)^6$

(g) $f(x) = 12\sqrt{x} - \dfrac{10}{x^2} + 17$

5. Find $\dfrac{d^3y}{dx^3}$ for $y = x^3 - x^{-3}$.

6. Let $f(x) = x^3 - 3x^2 - 24x - 10$.
   (a) Write the equation of the line tangent to the graph of $y = f(x)$ at $x = -1$.
   (b) Find all points (both x- and y-coordinates) where $f'(x) = 0$.

7. Find the average rate of change of $f(x) = 4 - x - 2x^2$ over $[1, 6]$.

8. Use the given tables to evaluate the following limits, if they exist.
   (a) $\lim\limits_{x \to 5} f(x)$ (b) $\lim\limits_{x \to 5} g(x)$ (c) $\lim\limits_{x \to 5^-} g(x)$

x	4.99	4.999	→ 5 ←	5.001	5.01
$f(x)$	2.01	2.001	→ ? ←	1.999	1.99

x	4.99	4.999	→ 5 ←	5.001	5.01
$g(x)$	−3.99	−3.999	→ ? ←	6.999	6.99

9. Use the definition of continuity to investigate whether $g(x)$ is continuous at $x = -2$. Show your work.

$$g(x) = \begin{cases} 6 - x & \text{if } x \le -2 \\ x^3 & \text{if } x > -2 \end{cases}$$

In Problems 10 and 11, suppose a company has its total cost for a product given by $C(x) = 200x + 10{,}000$ dollars and its total revenue given by $R(x) = 250x - 0.01x^2$ dollars, where x is the number of units produced and sold.

10. (a) Find the marginal revenue function.
    (b) Find $R(72)$ and $R'(72)$ and tell what each represents or predicts.

11. (a) Form the profit function for this product.
    (b) Find the marginal profit function.
    (c) Find the marginal profit when $x = 1000$, and then write a sentence that interprets this result.

12. Suppose that $f(x)$ is a differentiable function. Use the table of values to approximate $f'(3)$ as accurately as possible.

x	2	2.5	2.999	3	3.01	3.1
$f(x)$	0	18.4	44.896	45	46.05	56.18

13. Use the graph to perform the evaluations (a)–(f) and to answer (g)–(i). If no value exists, so indicate.
    (a) $f(1)$
    (b) $\lim\limits_{x \to 6} f(x)$
    (c) $\lim\limits_{x \to 3^-} f(x)$
    (d) $\lim\limits_{x \to -4} f(x)$
    (e) $\lim\limits_{x \to -\infty} f(x)$
    (f) Estimate $f'(4)$.
    (g) Find all x-values where $f'(x)$ does not exist.
    (h) Find all x-values where $f(x)$ is not continuous.
    (i) Rank from smallest to largest: $f'(-2), f'(2)$, and the average rate of change of $f(x)$ over $[-2, 2]$.

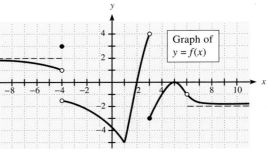

14. Given that the line $y = \frac{2}{3}x - 8$ is tangent to the graph of $y = f(x)$ at $x = 6$, find
    (a) $f'(6)$.
    (b) $f(6)$.
    (c) the instantaneous rate of change of $f(x)$ with respect to x at $x = 6$.

15. The graph shows the total revenue and total cost functions for a company. Use the graph to decide (and justify) at which of points A, B, and C
    (a) profit is the greatest.
    (b) there is a loss.
    (c) producing and selling another item will increase profit.
    (d) the next item sold will decrease profit.

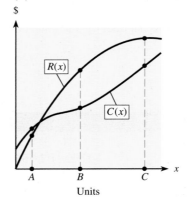

I. Marginal Return to Sales

A tire manufacturer studying the effectiveness of television advertising and other promotions on sales of its GRIPPER-brand tires attempted to fit data it had gathered to the equation

$$S = a_0 + a_1 x + a_2 x^2 + b_1 y$$

where S is sales revenue in millions of dollars, x is millions of dollars spent on television advertising, y is millions of dollars spent on other promotions, and a_0, a_1, a_2, and b_1 are constants. The data, gathered in two different regions of the country where expenditures for other promotions were kept constant (at B_1 and B_2), resulted in the following quadratic equations relating TV advertising and sales.

$$\text{Region 1: } S_1 = 30 + 20x - 0.4x^2 + B_1$$
$$\text{Region 2: } S_2 = 20 + 36x - 1.3x^2 + B_2$$

The company wants to know how to make the best use of its advertising dollars in the regions and whether the current allocation could be improved. Advise management about current advertising effectiveness, allocation of additional expenditures, and reallocation of current advertising expenditures by answering the following questions.

1. In the analysis of sales and advertising, **marginal return to sales** is usually used, and it is given by dS_1/dx for Region 1 and dS_2/dx for Region 2.
   (a) Find $\dfrac{dS_1}{dx}$ and $\dfrac{dS_2}{dx}$.
   (b) If \$10 million is being spent on TV advertising in each region, what is the marginal return to sales in each region?
2. Which region would benefit more from additional advertising expenditure, if \$10 million is currently being spent in each region?
3. If any additional money is made available for advertising, in which region should it be spent?
4. How could money already being spent be reallocated to produce more sales revenue?

II. Tangent Lines and Optimization in Business and Economics

In business and economics, common questions of interest include how to maximize profit or revenue, how to minimize average costs, and how to maximize average productivity. For questions such as these, the description of how to obtain the desired maximum or minimum represents an optimal (or best possible) solution to the problem. And the process of finding an optimal solution is called optimization. Answering these questions often involves tangent lines. In this project, we examine how tangent lines can be used to minimize average costs.

Suppose that Wittage, Inc. manufactures paper shredders for home and office use and that its weekly total costs (in dollars) for x shredders are given by

$$C(x) = 0.03x^2 + 12.75x + 6075$$

The average cost per unit for x units (denoted by $\overline{C}(x)$) is the total cost divided by the number of units. Thus, the average cost function for Wittage, Inc. is

$$\overline{C}(x) = \frac{C(x)}{x} = \frac{0.03x^2 + 12.75x + 6075}{x} = \frac{0.03x^2}{x} + \frac{12.75x}{x} + \frac{6075}{x}$$

$$\overline{C}(x) = 0.03x + 12.75 + \frac{6075}{x}$$

Wittage, Inc. would like to know how the company can use marginal costs to gain information about minimizing average costs. To investigate this relationship, answer the following questions.

1. Find Wittage's marginal cost function, then complete the following table.

x	100	200	300	400	500	600
$\overline{C}(x)$						
$\overline{MC}(x)$						

2. (a) For what x-values in the table is $\overline{C}$ getting smaller?
   (b) For these x-values, is $\overline{MC} < \overline{C}, \overline{MC} > \overline{C}$, or $\overline{MC} = \overline{C}$?
3. (a) For what x-values in the table is $\overline{C}$ getting larger?
   (b) For these x-values, is $\overline{MC} < \overline{C}, \overline{MC} > \overline{C}$, or $\overline{MC} = \overline{C}$?
4. Between what pair of consecutive x-values in the table will $\overline{C}$ reach its minimum?
5. Interpret (a) $\overline{C}(200)$ and $\overline{MC}(200)$ and (b) $\overline{C}(400)$ and $\overline{MC}(400)$.
6. On the basis of what $\overline{C}$ and $\overline{MC}$ tell us, and the work so far, complete the following statements by filling the blank with *increase, decrease,* or *stay the same.* Explain your reasoning.
   (a) $\overline{MC} < \overline{C}$ means that if Wittage makes one more unit, then $\overline{C}$ will _____ .
   (b) $\overline{MC} > \overline{C}$ means that if Wittage makes one more unit, then $\overline{C}$ will _____ .
7. (a) On the basis of your answers to Question 6, how will $\overline{C}$ and $\overline{MC}$ be related when $\overline{C}$ is minimized? Write a careful statement.
   (b) Use your idea from part (a) to find x where $\overline{C}$ is minimized. Then check your calculations by graphing $\overline{C}$ and locating the minimum from the graph.

Next, let's examine graphically the relationship that emerged in Question 7 to see whether it is true in general. Figure 9.41 shows a typical total cost function (Wittage's total cost function has a similar shape) and an arbitrary point on the graph.

Figure 9.41

8. (a) Measure the slope of the line joining the point $(x, C(x))$ and the origin.
   (b) How is this slope related to the function $\overline{C}$ at $(x, C(x))$?
9. Figure 9.42(a) shows a typical total cost function with several points labeled.
   (a) Explain how you can tell at a glance that $\overline{C}(x)$ is decreasing as the level of production moves from A to B to C to D.
   (b) Explain how you can tell at a glance that $\overline{C}(x)$ is increasing as the level of production moves from Q to R to S to T.

Figure 9.42   (a)   (b)

10. In Figure 9.42(b), a line from (0, 0) is drawn tangent to $C(x)$ and the point of tangency is labeled P. At point P in Figure 9.42(b), what represents
    (a) the average cost, $\overline{C}(x)$?
    (b) the marginal cost, $\overline{MC}(x)$?
    (c) Explain how Figure 9.42 confirms that $\overline{C}(x)$ is minimized when $\overline{MC}(x) = \overline{C}(x)$.

On the basis of the numerical approach for Wittage's total cost function and the general graphical approach, what recommendation would you give Wittage about determining the number of units that will minimize average costs (even if the total cost function changes)?

Tischenko Irina/Shutterstock.com

10 CHAPTER

Applications of Derivatives

The derivative can be used to determine where a function has a "turning point" on its graph, so that we can determine where the graph reaches its highest or lowest point within a particular interval. These points are called the relative maxima and relative minima, respectively, and are useful in sketching the graph of the function. The techniques for finding these points are also useful in solving applied problems, such as finding the maximum profit, the minimum average cost, and the maximum productivity. The second derivative can be used to find points of inflection of the graph of a function and to find the point of diminishing returns in certain applications.

The topics and applications discussed in this chapter include the following.

SECTIONS	APPLICATIONS
10.1 Relative Maxima and Minima: Curve Sketching	Advertising, marijuana use
10.2 Concavity: Points of Inflection Second derivative test	Water purity, profit
10.3 Optimization in Business and Economics Maximizing revenue Minimizing average cost Maximizing profit	Maximizing revenue, minimizing average cost, maximizing profit
10.4 Applications of Maxima and Minima	Company growth, minimizing cost, postal restriction, production costs, property development
10.5 Rational Functions: More Curve Sketching Asymptotes More curve sketching	Production costs

Prerequisite Problem Type	For Section	Answer	Section for Review
Write $\frac{1}{3}(x^2 - 1)^{-2/3}(2x)$ with positive exponents.	**10.2**	$\dfrac{2x}{3(x^2 - 1)^{2/3}}$	0.3, 0.4 Exponents and radicals
Factor: (a) $x^3 - x^2 - 6x$ (b) $8000 - 80x - 3x^2$	**10.1** **10.2** **10.3**	(a) $x(x - 3)(x + 2)$ (b) $(40 - x)(200 + 3x)$	0.6 Factoring
(a) For what values of x is $\dfrac{2}{3\sqrt[3]{x + 2}}$ undefined? (b) For what values of x is $\frac{1}{3}(x^2 - 1)^{-2/3}(2x)$ undefined?	**10.1** **10.2** **10.5**	(a) $x = -2$ (b) $x = -1, x = 1$	1.2 Domains of functions
If $f(x) = \frac{1}{3}x^3 - x^2 - 3x + 2$, and $f'(x) = x^2 - 2x - 3$, (a) find $f(-1)$. (b) find $f'(-2)$.	**10.1**	(a) $\dfrac{11}{3}$ (b) 5	1.2 Function notation
(a) Solve $0 = x^2 - 2x - 3$. (b) If $f'(x) = 3x^2 - 3$, what values of x make $f'(x) = 0$?	**10.1–10.5**	(a) $x = -1, x = 3$ (b) $x = -1, x = 1$	2.1 Solving quadratic equations
Does $\lim\limits_{x \to -2} \dfrac{2x - 4}{3x + 6}$ exist?	**10.5**	No; unbounded	9.1 Limits
(a) Find $f''(x)$ if $f(x) = x^3 - 4x^2 + 3$. (b) Find $P''(x)$ if $P(x) = 48x - 1.2x^2$.	**10.2**	(a) $f''(x) = 6x - 8$ (b) $P''(x) = -2.4$	9.8 Higher-order derivatives
Find the derivatives: (a) $y = \dfrac{1}{3}x^3 - x^2 - 3x + 2$ (b) $f = x + 2\left(\dfrac{80{,}000}{x}\right)$ (c) $p(t) = 1 + \dfrac{4t}{t^2 + 16}$ (d) $y = (x + 2)^{2/3}$ (e) $y = \sqrt[3]{x^2 - 1}$	**10.1** **10.2** **10.3** **10.4**	(a) $y' = x^2 - 2x - 3$ (b) $f' = 1 - \dfrac{160{,}000}{x^2}$ (c) $p'(t) = \dfrac{64 - 4t^2}{(t^2 + 16)^2}$ (d) $y' = \dfrac{2}{3(x + 2)^{1/3}}$ (e) $y' = \dfrac{2x}{3(x^2 - 1)^{2/3}}$	9.4, 9.5, 9.6 Derivatives

10.1

- To find relative maxima and minima and horizontal points of inflection of functions
- To sketch graphs of functions by using information about maxima, minima, and horizontal points of inflection

Relative Maxima and Minima: Curve Sketching

▮ | APPLICATION PREVIEW | ▮

When a company initiates an advertising campaign, there is typically a surge in weekly sales. As the effect of the campaign lessens, sales attributable to it usually decrease. For example, suppose a company models its weekly sales revenue during an advertising campaign by

$$S = \frac{100t}{t^2 + 100}$$

where t is the number of weeks since the beginning of the campaign. The company would like to determine accurately when the revenue function is increasing, when it is decreasing, and when sales revenue is maximized. (See Example 4.)

In this section we will use the derivative of a function to decide whether the function is increasing or decreasing on an interval and to find where the function has relative maximum points and relative minimum points. We will use the information about derivatives of functions to graph the functions and to solve applied problems.

Recall that we can find the maximum value or the minimum value of a quadratic function by finding the vertex of its graph. But for functions of higher degree, the special features of their graphs may be harder to find accurately, even when a graphing utility is used. In addition to intercepts and asymptotes, we can use the first derivative as an aid in graphing. The first derivative identifies the "turning points" of the graph, which help us determine the general shape of the graph and choose a viewing window that includes the interesting points of the graph. Note that for a quadratic function $f(x) = ax^2 + bx + c$, the solution to $f'(x) = 2ax + b = 0$ is $x = -b/2a$. This solution is the x-coordinate of the vertex (turning point) of $f(x)$, found in Section 2.2.

In Figure 10.1(a) we see that the graph of $y = \frac{1}{3}x^3 - x^2 - 3x + 2$ has two "turning points," at $\left(-1, \frac{11}{3}\right)$ and $(3, -7)$. The curve has a relative maximum at $\left(-1, \frac{11}{3}\right)$ because this point is higher than any other point "near" it on the curve; the curve has a relative minimum at $(3, -7)$ because this point is lower than any other point "near" it on the curve. A formal definition follows.

Relative Maxima and Minima

The point $(x_1, f(x_1))$ is a **relative maximum point** of the function f if there is an interval around x_1 on which $f(x_1) \geq f(x)$ for all x in the interval. In this case, we say the relative maximum *occurs* at $x = x_1$ and the relative maximum is $f(x_1)$.

The point $(x_2, f(x_2))$ is a **relative minimum point** of the function f if there is an interval around x_2 on which $f(x_2) \leq f(x)$ for all x in the interval. In this case, we say the relative minimum *occurs* at $x = x_2$ and the relative minimum is $f(x_2)$.

In order to determine whether a turning point of a function is a maximum point or a minimum point, it is frequently helpful to know what the graph of the function does in intervals on either side of the turning point. We say a function is **increasing** on an interval if the values of the function increase as the x-values increase (that is, if the graph rises as we move from left to right on the interval). Similarly, a function is **decreasing** on an interval if the values of the function decrease as the x-values increase (that is, if the graph falls as we move from left to right on the interval).

We have seen that if the slope of a line is positive, then the linear function is increasing and its graph is rising. Similarly, if $f(x)$ is differentiable over an interval and if each tangent line to the curve over that interval has positive slope, then the curve is rising over the interval and the function is increasing. Because the derivative of the function gives the slope of the tangent to the curve, we see that if $f'(x) > 0$ on an interval, then $f(x)$ is increasing on that interval. A similar conclusion can be reached when the derivative is negative on the interval.

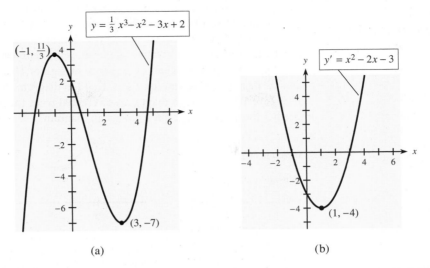

| | (a) | | (b) |

Figure 10.1

Increasing and Decreasing Functions

If f is a function that is differentiable on an interval (a, b), then

if $f'(x) > 0$ for all x in (a, b), f is increasing on (a, b).
if $f'(x) < 0$ for all x in (a, b), f is decreasing on (a, b).

Figure 10.1(a) shows the graph of a function, and Figure 10.1(b) shows the graph of its derivative. The figures show that the graph of $y = f(x)$ is increasing for the same x-values for which the graph of $y' = f'(x)$ is above the x-axis (when $f'(x) > 0$). Similarly, the graph of $y = f(x)$ is decreasing for the same x-values $(-1 < x < 3)$ for which the graph of $y' = f'(x)$ is below the x-axis (when $f'(x) < 0$).

The derivative $f'(x)$ can change signs only at values of x at which $f'(x) = 0$ or $f'(x)$ is undefined. We call these values of x **critical values.** The point corresponding to a critical value for x is a **critical point.**[*] Because a curve changes from increasing to decreasing at a relative maximum and from decreasing to increasing at a relative minimum (see Figure 10.1(a)), we have the following.

Relative Maximum and Minimum

If f has a relative maximum or a relative minimum at $x = x_0$, then $f'(x_0) = 0$ or $f'(x_0)$ is undefined.

Figure 10.2 shows a function with two relative maxima, one at $x = x_1$ and the second at $x = x_3$, and one relative minimum at $x = x_2$. At $x = x_1$ and $x = x_2$, we see that $f'(x) = 0$, and at $x = x_3$ the derivative does not exist.

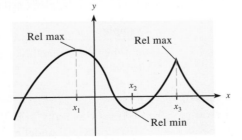

Figure 10.2

Thus we can find relative maxima and minima for a curve by finding values of x for which the function has critical points. The behavior of the derivative to the left and right

---

[*]There may be some critical values at which both $f'(x)$ and $f(x)$ are undefined. Critical points do not occur at these values, but studying the derivative on either side of such values may be of interest.

of (and near) these points will tell us whether they are relative maxima, relative minima, or neither.

Because the critical values are the only values at which the graph can have turning points, the derivative cannot change sign anywhere except at a critical value. Thus, in an interval between two critical values, the sign of the derivative at any value in the interval will be the sign of the derivative at all values in the interval.

Using the critical values of $f(x)$ and the sign of $f'(x)$ between those critical values, we can create a **sign diagram for $f'(x)$**. The sign diagram for the graph in Figure 10.2 is shown in Figure 10.3. This sign diagram was created from the graph of f, but it is also possible to predict the shape of a graph from a sign diagram.

Direction of graph of $f(x)$:

Signs and values of $f'(x)$:

x-axis with critical values:

Figure 10.3   *means $f'(x_3)$ is undefined

Figure 10.4 shows the two ways that a function can have a relative maximum at a critical point, and Figure 10.5 shows the two ways for a relative minimum.

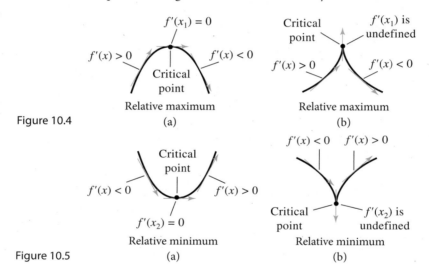

Figure 10.4

Figure 10.5

The preceding discussion suggests the following procedure for finding relative maxima and minima of a function.

First-Derivative Test

Procedure	**Example**
To find relative maxima and minima of a function:	Find the relative maxima and minima of $f(x) = \frac{1}{3}x^3 - x^2 - 3x + 2$.
1. Find the first derivative of the function.	1. $f'(x) = x^2 - 2x - 3$
2. Set the derivative equal to 0, and solve for values of x that satisfy $f'(x) = 0$. These are called **critical values**. Values that make $f'(x)$ undefined are also critical values.	2. $0 = x^2 - 2x - 3 = (x + 1)(x - 3)$ has solutions $x = -1$, $x = 3$. No values of x make $f'(x) = x^2 - 2x - 3$ undefined. Critical values are -1 and 3.
3. Substitute the critical values into the *original function* to find the **critical points**.	3. $f(-1) = \frac{11}{3}$ $f(3) = -7$ The critical points are $\left(-1, \frac{11}{3}\right)$ and $(3, -7)$.

First-Derivative Test (continued)

Procedure	Example

Procedure

4. Evaluate $f'(x)$ at a value of x to the left and one to the right of each critical point to develop a sign diagram.
   (a) If $f'(x) > 0$ to the left and $f'(x) < 0$ to the right of the critical value, the critical point is a relative maximum point.
   (b) If $f'(x) < 0$ to the left and $f'(x) > 0$ to the right of the critical value, the critical point is a relative minimum point.

Example

4. $f'(-2) = 5 > 0$ and $f'(0) = -3 < 0$
   Thus $(-1, 11/3)$ is a relative maximum point.
   $f'(2) = -3 < 0$ and $f'(4) = 5 > 0$
   Thus $(3, -7)$ is a relative minimum point. The sign diagram for $f'(x)$ is

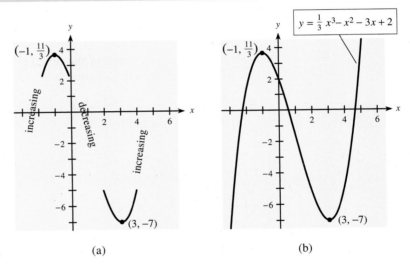

5. Use the information from the sign diagram and selected points to sketch the graph.

5. The information from this sign diagram is shown in Figure 10.6(a). Plotting additional points gives the graph of the function, which is shown in Figure 10.6(b).

Figure 10.6   (a)   (b)

Because the critical values are the only x-values at which the graph can have turning points, we can test to the left and right of each critical value by testing to the left of the smallest critical value, then testing a value *between* each two successive critical values, and then testing to the right of the largest critical value. The following example illustrates this procedure.

EXAMPLE 1   Maxima and Minima

Find the relative maxima and minima of $f(x) = \frac{1}{4}x^4 - \frac{1}{3}x^3 - 3x^2 + 8$, and sketch its graph.

Solution

1. $f'(x) = x^3 - x^2 - 6x$
2. Setting $f'(x) = 0$ gives $0 = x^3 - x^2 - 6x$. Solving for x gives

$$0 = x(x - 3)(x + 2)$$

$x = 0$	$x - 3 = 0$	$x + 2 = 0$
	$x = 3$	$x = -2$

Thus the critical values are $x = 0$, $x = 3$, and $x = -2$.

3. Substituting the critical values into the original function gives the critical points:

$$f(-2) = \tfrac{8}{3}, \quad \text{so } \left(-2, \tfrac{8}{3}\right) \text{ is a critical point.}$$
$$f(0) = 8, \quad \text{so } (0, 8) \text{ is a critical point.}$$
$$f(3) = -\tfrac{31}{4}, \quad \text{so } \left(3, -\tfrac{31}{4}\right) \text{ is a critical point.}$$

4. Testing $f'(x)$ to the left of the smallest critical value, then between the critical values, and finally to the right of the largest critical value will give the sign diagram. Evaluating $f'(x)$ at the test values $x = -3$, $x = -1$, $x = 1$, and $x = 4$ gives the signs to determine relative maxima and minima.

The sign diagram for $f'(x)$ is

Thus we have

$\left(-2, \tfrac{8}{3}\right)$ is a relative minimum.

$(0, 8)$ is a relative maximum.

$\left(3, -\tfrac{31}{4}\right)$ is a relative minimum.

5. Figure 10.7(a) shows the graph of the function near the critical points, and Figure 10.7(b) shows the graph of the function. ■

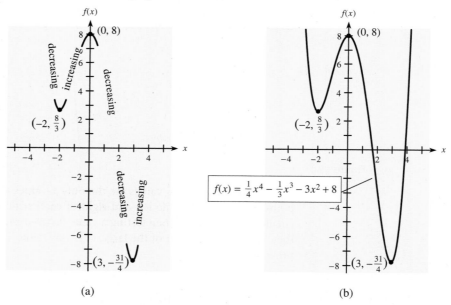

Figure 10.7   (a)   (b)

Note that we substitute the critical values into the *original function* $f(x)$ to find the y-values of the critical points, but we test for relative maxima and minima by substituting values near the critical values into the *derivative of the function*, $f'(x)$.

Only four values were needed to test three critical points in Example 1. This method will work *only if* the critical values are tested in order from smallest to largest.

If the first derivative of f is 0 at x_0 but does not change from positive to negative or from negative to positive as x passes through x_0, then the critical point at x_0 is neither a relative maximum nor a relative minimum. In this case we say that f has a **horizontal point of inflection** (abbreviated HPI) at x_0.

EXAMPLE 2 Maxima, Minima, and Horizontal Points of Inflection

Find the relative maxima, relative minima, and horizontal points of inflection of $h(x) = \frac{1}{4}x^4 - \frac{2}{3}x^3 - 2x^2 + 8x + 4$, and sketch its graph.

Solution

1. $h'(x) = x^3 - 2x^2 - 4x + 8$
2. $0 = x^3 - 2x^2 - 4x + 8$ or $0 = x^2(x - 2) - 4(x - 2)$. Therefore, we have $0 = (x - 2)(x^2 - 4)$. Thus $x = -2$ and $x = 2$ are solutions.
3. The critical points are $\left(-2, -\frac{32}{3}\right)$ and $\left(2, \frac{32}{3}\right)$.
4. Using test values, such as $x = -3$, $x = 0$, and $x = 3$, gives the sign diagram for $h'(x)$.

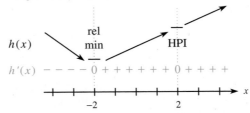

5. Figure 10.8(a) shows the graph of the function near the critical points, and Figure 10.8(b) shows the graph of the function.

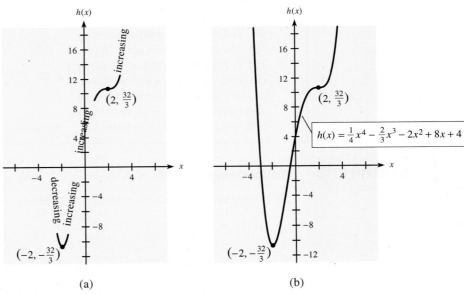

Figure 10.8   (a)   (b)

Technology Note See Appendices C and D, Section 10.1, for details on using a graphing calculator and Excel to find critical values and to determine maxima and minima. See also the Online Excel Guide.

EXAMPLE 3 Undefined Derivatives

Find the relative maxima and minima (if any) of the graph of $y = (x + 2)^{2/3}$.

Solution

1. $y' = f'(x) = \frac{2}{3}(x + 2)^{-1/3} = \frac{2}{3\sqrt[3]{x + 2}}$
2. $0 = \frac{2}{3\sqrt[3]{x + 2}}$ has no solutions; $f'(x)$ is undefined at $x = -2$.
3. $f(-2) = 0$, so the critical point is $(-2, 0)$.
4. The sign diagram for $f'(x)$ is

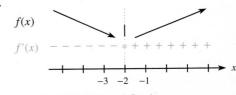

Thus a relative minimum occurs at $(-2, 0)$.

*means $f'(-2)$ is undefined.

5. Figure 10.9(a) shows the graph of the function near the critical point, and Figure 10.9(b) shows the graph. ■

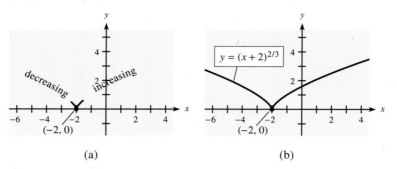

Figure 10.9   (a)   (b)

CHECKPOINT

1. The x-values of critical points are found where $f'(x)$ is _____ or _____.
2. Decide whether the following are true or false.
   (a) If $f'(1) = 7$, then $f(x)$ is increasing at $x = 1$.
   (b) If $f'(-2) = 0$, then a relative maximum or a relative minimum occurs at $x = -2$.
   (c) If $f'(-3) = 0$ and $f'(x)$ changes from positive on the left to negative on the right of $x = -3$, then a relative minimum occurs at $x = -3$.
3. If $f(x) = 7 + 3x - x^3$, then $f'(x) = 3 - 3x^2$. Use these functions to decide whether the following statements are true or false.
   (a) The only critical value is $x = 1$.
   (b) The critical points are $(1, 0)$ and $(-1, 0)$.
4. If $f'(x)$ has the following partial sign diagram, make a "stick-figure" sketch of $f(x)$ and label where any maxima and minima occur. Assume that $f(x)$ is defined for all real numbers.

*means $f'(0)$ is undefined.

EXAMPLE 4   **Advertising** | APPLICATION PREVIEW |

The weekly sales S of a product during an advertising campaign are given by

$$S = \frac{100t}{t^2 + 100}, \qquad 0 \le t \le 20$$

where t is the number of weeks since the beginning of the campaign and S is in thousands of dollars.

(a) Over what interval are sales increasing? Decreasing?
(b) What are the maximum weekly sales?
(c) Sketch the graph for $0 \le t \le 20$.

Solution

(a) To find where S is increasing, we first find $S'(t)$

$$S'(t) = \frac{(t^2 + 100)100 - (100t)2t}{(t^2 + 100)^2}$$
$$= \frac{10{,}000 - 100t^2}{(t^2 + 100)^2}$$

We see that $S'(t) = 0$ when $10{,}000 - 100t^2 = 0$, or

$$100(100 - t^2) = 0$$
$$100(10 + t)(10 - t) = 0$$
$$t = -10 \quad \text{or} \quad t = 10$$

Because $S'(t)$ is never undefined ($t^2 + 100 \ne 0$ for any real t) and because $0 \le t \le 20$, our only critical value is $t = 10$. Testing $S'(t)$ to the left and right of $t = 10$ gives the sign diagram.

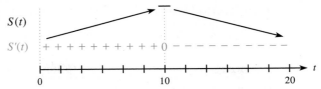

Hence, S is increasing on the interval $[0, 10)$ and decreasing on the interval $(10, 20]$.

(b) Because S is increasing to the left of $t = 10$ and S is decreasing to the right of $t = 10$, the maximum value of S occurs at $t = 10$ and is

$$S = S(10) = \frac{100(10)}{10^2 + 100} = \frac{1000}{200} = 5\,(\text{thousand dollars})$$

(c) Plotting some additional points gives the graph; see Figure 10.10.

Figure 10.10

Calculator Note   With a graphing calculator, choosing an appropriate viewing window is the key to understanding the graph of a function. See Appendix C, Section 10.1, for details.

EXAMPLE 5   Critical Points and Viewing Windows

Find the critical values of $f(x) = 0.0001x^3 + 0.003x^2 - 3.6x + 5$. Use them to determine an appropriate viewing window. Then sketch the graph.

Solution

The critical points are helpful in graphing the function. We begin by finding $f'(x)$.

$$f'(x) = 0.0003x^2 + 0.006x - 3.6$$

Now we solve $f'(x) = 0$ to find the critical values.

$$0 = 0.0003x^2 + 0.006x - 3.6$$
$$0 = 0.0003(x^2 + 20x - 12{,}000)$$
$$0 = 0.0003(x + 120)(x - 100)$$
$$x = -120 \quad \text{or} \quad x = 100$$

We choose a window that includes $x = -120$ and $x = 100$, and use VALUE to find $f(-120) = 307.4$ and $f(100) = -225$. We then graph $y = f(x)$ in a window that includes $y = -225$ and $y = 307.4$ (see Figure 10.11). On this graph we can see that $(-120, 307.4)$ is a relative maximum and that $(100, -225)$ is a relative minimum.

Figure 10.11

MODELING EXAMPLE 6   Marijuana Use

The table gives the percents of high school seniors who claimed to have tried marijuana for selected years from 1990 to 2006.

(a) With x as the number of years past 1990, find a function that models these data.
(b) During what years does the model indicate that the maximum and minimum use occurred?

Year	Percent	Year	Percent
1990	40.7	2000	48.8
1991	36.7	2001	49.8
1993	35.3	2002	47.8
1995	41.7	2003	46.7
1997	49.6	2004	45.7
1998	49.1	2005	44.8
1999	47.7	2006	42.3

Source: National Institute on Drug Abuse

Figure 10.12

Solution

(a) A model for the data is $y = f(x) = -0.0187x^3 + 0.3329x^2 - 0.3667x + 38.10$. (See Figure 10.12.)

(b) We use $f'(x) = -0.0561x^2 + 0.6658x - 0.3667$ and solve $f'(x) = 0$ to find the critical values. We can solve

$$-0.0561x^2 + 0.6658x - 0.3667 = 0$$

with the quadratic formula or with a graphing calculator. The two solutions are approximately

$$x = 0.58 \quad \text{and} \quad x = 11.29.$$

The sign diagram shows that $x = 0.58$ gives a relative minimum (during 1991) and that $x = 11.29$ gives a relative maximum (during 2002).

Spreadsheet Note   The Solver feature of Excel can be used to solve optimization problems from calculus. Details are given in Appendix D, Section 10.1, and the Online Excel Guide.

CHECKPOINT SOLUTIONS

1. $f'(x) = 0$ or $f'(x)$ is undefined.
2. (a) True. $f(x)$ is increasing when $f'(x) > 0$.
   (b) False. There may be a horizontal point of inflection at $x = -2$. (See Figure 10.8 earlier in this section.)
   (c) False. A relative maximum occurs at $x = -3$.
3. (a) False. Critical values are solutions to $3 - 3x^2 = 0$, or $x = 1$ and $x = -1$.
   (b) False. y-coordinates of critical points come from $f(x) = 7 + 3x - x^3$. Thus critical points are $(1, 9)$ and $(-1, 5)$.

4.

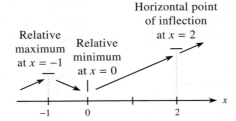

Horizontal point
of inflection
at $x = 2$

Relative
maximum
at $x = -1$

Relative
minimum
at $x = 0$

| EXERCISES | 10.1

In Problems 1 and 2, use the indicated points on the graph of $y = f(x)$ to identify points at which $f(x)$ has (a) a relative maximum, (b) a relative minimum, and (c) a horizontal point of inflection.

1.

2.
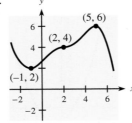

3. Use the graph of $y = f(x)$ in Problem 1 to identify at which of the indicated points the derivative $f'(x)$ (a) changes from positive to negative, (b) changes from negative to positive, and (c) does not change sign.

4. Use the graph of $y = f(x)$ in Problem 2 to identify at which of the indicated points the derivative $f'(x)$ (a) changes from positive to negative, (b) changes from negative to positive, and (c) does not change sign.

In Problems 5 and 6, use the sign diagram for $f'(x)$ to determine (a) the critical values of $f(x)$, (b) intervals on which $f(x)$ increases, (c) intervals on which $f(x)$ decreases, (d) x-values at which relative maxima occur, and (e) x-values at which relative minima occur.

5. $f'(x)$ $- - - \; 0 + + + + + \; 0 - - -$
 $3 7$

6. $f'(x)$ $+ + + + 0 + + + + + + + 0 - - - -$
 $-5 8$

In Problems 7–10, (a) find the critical values of the function, and (b) make a sign diagram and determine the relative maxima and minima.

7. $y = 2x^3 - 12x^2 + 6$
8. $y = x^3 - 3x^2 + 6x + 1$
9. $y = 2x^5 + 5x^4 - 11$
10. $y = 3x^5 - 5x^3 + 3$

For each function and graph in Problems 11–14:
(a) **Estimate the coordinates of the relative maxima, relative minima, or horizontal points of inflection by observing the graph.**
(b) **Use $y' = f'(x)$ to find the critical values.**
(c) **Find the critical points.**
(d) **Do the results in part (c) confirm your estimates in part (a)?**

11. $y = x^3 - 3x + 4$ 12. $y = x - \frac{1}{3}x^3$

      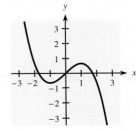

13. $y = x^3 + 3x^2 + 3x - 2$ 14. $y = x^3 - 6x^2 + 12x + 1$

For each function in Problems 15–20:
(a) **Find $y' = f'(x)$.**
(b) **Find the critical values.**
(c) **Find the critical points.**
(d) **Find intervals of x-values where the function is increasing and where it is decreasing.**
(e) **Classify the critical points as relative maxima, relative minima, or horizontal points of inflection. In each case, you may check your conclusions with a graphing utility.**

15. $y = \frac{1}{2}x^2 - x$ 16. $y = x^2 + 4x$

17. $y = \frac{x^3}{3} + \frac{x^2}{2} - 2x + 1$ 18. $y = \frac{x^4}{4} - \frac{x^3}{3} - 2$

19. $y = x^{2/3}$ 20. $y = -(x - 3)^{2/3}$

For each function and graph in Problems 21–24:
(a) Use the graph to identify x-values for which
    $y' > 0$, $y' < 0$, $y' = 0$, and y' does not exist.
(b) Use the derivative to check your conclusions.

21. $y = 6 - x - x^2$

22. $y = \frac{1}{2}x^2 - 4x + 1$

23. $y = 6 + x^3 - \frac{1}{15}x^5$

24. $y = x^4 - 2x^2 - 1$

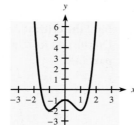

For each function in Problems 25–30, find the relative maxima, relative minima, horizontal points of inflection, and sketch the graph. You may check your graph with a graphing utility.

25. $y = \frac{1}{3}x^3 - x^2 + x + 1$

26. $y = \frac{1}{4}x^4 - \frac{2}{3}x^3 + \frac{1}{2}x^2 - 2$

27. $y = \frac{1}{3}x^3 + x^2 - 24x + 20$

28. $C(x) = x^3 - \frac{3}{2}x^2 - 18x + 5$

29. $y = 3x^5 - 5x^3 + 1$

30. $y = \frac{1}{6}x^6 - x^4 + 7$

In Problems 31–36, both a function and its derivative are given. Use them to find critical values, critical points, intervals on which the function is increasing and decreasing, relative maxima, relative minima, and horizontal points of inflection; sketch the graph of each function.

31. $y = (x^2 - 2x)^2$ $\dfrac{dy}{dx} = 4x(x - 1)(x - 2)$

32. $f(x) = (x^2 - 4)^2$ $f'(x) = 4x(x + 2)(x - 2)$

33. $y = \dfrac{x^3(x - 5)^2}{27}$ $\dfrac{dy}{dx} = \dfrac{5x^2(x - 3)(x - 5)}{27}$

34. $y = \dfrac{x^2(x - 5)^3}{27}$ $\dfrac{dy}{dx} = \dfrac{5x(x - 2)(x - 5)^2}{27}$

35. $f(x) = x^{2/3}(x - 5)$ $f'(x) = \dfrac{5(x - 2)}{3x^{1/3}}$

36. $f(x) = x - 3x^{2/3}$ $f'(x) = \dfrac{x^{1/3} - 2}{x^{1/3}}$

In Problems 37–42, use the derivative to locate critical points and determine a viewing window that shows all features of the graph. Use a graphing utility to sketch a complete graph.

37. $f(x) = x^3 - 225x^2 + 15{,}000x - 12{,}000$

38. $f(x) = x^3 - 15x^2 - 16{,}800x + 80{,}000$

39. $f(x) = x^4 - 160x^3 + 7200x^2 - 40{,}000$

40. $f(x) = x^4 - 240x^3 + 16{,}200x^2 - 60{,}000$

41. $y = 7.5x^4 - x^3 + 2$ 42. $y = 2 - x^3 - 7.5x^4$

In each of Problems 43–46, a graph of $f'(x)$ is given. Use the graph to determine the critical values of $f(x)$, where $f(x)$ is increasing, where it is decreasing, and where it has relative maxima, relative minima, and horizontal points of inflection. In each case sketch a possible graph for $f(x)$ that passes through $(0, 0)$.

43. $f'(x) = x^2 - x - 2$

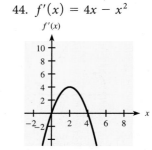

44. $f'(x) = 4x - x^2$

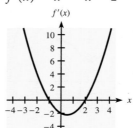

45. $f'(x) = x^3 - 3x^2$

46. $f'(x) = x(x - 2)^2$

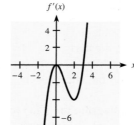

In Problems 47 and 48, two graphs are given. One is the graph of f and the other is the graph of f'. Decide which is which and explain your reasoning.

47.

48.

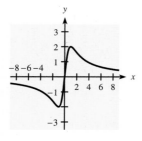

APPLICATIONS

49. *Advertising and sales* Suppose that the daily sales (in dollars) t days after the end of an advertising campaign are given by

$$S = 1000 + \frac{400}{t + 1}, \quad t \geq 0$$

Does S increase for all $t \geq 0$, decrease for all $t \geq 0$, or change direction at some point?

50. *Pricing and sales* Suppose that a chain of auto service stations, Quick-Oil, Inc., has found that its monthly sales volume y (in thousands of dollars) is related to the price p (in dollars) of an oil change by

$$y = \frac{90}{\sqrt{p + 5}}, \quad p > 10$$

Is y increasing or decreasing for all values of $p > 10$?

51. *Productivity* A time study showed that, on average, the productivity of a worker after t hours on the job can be modeled by

$$P(t) = 27t + 6t^2 - t^3, \quad 0 \leq t \leq 8$$

where P is the number of units produced per hour.
   (a) Find the critical values of this function.
   (b) Which critical value makes sense in this model?
   (c) For what values of t is P increasing?
   (d) Graph the function for $0 \leq t \leq 8$.

52. *Production* Analysis of daily output of a factory shows that, on average, the number of units per hour y produced after t hours of production is

$$y = 70t + \frac{1}{2}t^2 - t^3, \quad 0 \leq t \leq 8$$

   (a) Find the critical values of this function.
   (b) Which critical values make sense in this particular problem?
   (c) For which values of t, for $0 \leq t \leq 8$, is y increasing?
   (d) Graph this function.

53. *Production costs* Suppose that the average cost, in dollars, of producing a shipment of a certain product is

$$\overline{C} = 5000x + \frac{125,000}{x}, \quad x > 0$$

where x is the number of machines used in the production process.
   (a) Find the critical values of this function.
   (b) Over what interval does the average cost decrease?
   (c) Over what interval does the average cost increase?

54. *Average costs* Suppose the average costs of a mining operation depend on the number of machines used, and average costs, in dollars, are given by

$$\overline{C}(x) = 2900x + \frac{1,278,900}{x}, \quad x > 0$$

where x is the number of machines used.

   (a) Find the critical values of $\overline{C}(x)$ that lie in the domain of the problem.
   (b) Over what interval in the domain do average costs decrease?
   (c) Over what interval in the domain do average costs increase?
   (d) How many machines give minimum average costs?
   (e) What is the minimum average cost?

55. *Marginal revenue* Suppose the weekly marginal revenue function for selling x units of a product is given by the graph in the figure.

$$\overline{MR} = \frac{36,000,000(500 - 2x)}{(2x + 500)^3}$$

   (a) At each of $x = 150$, $x = 250$, and $x = 350$, what is happening to revenue?
   (b) Over what interval is revenue increasing?
   (c) How many units must be sold to maximize revenue?

56. *Earnings* Suppose that the rate of change $f'(x)$ of the average annual earnings of new car salespersons is shown in the figure.

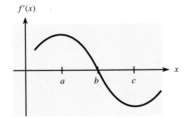

   (a) If a, b, and c represent certain years, what is happening to $f(x)$, the average annual earnings of the salespersons, at a, b, and c?
   (b) Over what interval (involving a, b, or c) is there an increase in $f(x)$, the average annual earnings of the salespersons?

57. *Revenue* The weekly revenue of a certain recently released film is given by

$$R(t) = \frac{50t}{t^2 + 36}, \quad t \geq 0$$

where R is in millions of dollars and t is in weeks.
   (a) Find the critical values.
   (b) For how many weeks will weekly revenue increase?

58. *Medication* Suppose that the concentration C of a medication in the bloodstream t hours after an injection is given by

$$C(t) = \frac{0.2t}{t^2 + 1}$$

(a) Determine the number of hours before C attains its maximum.

(b) Find the maximum concentration.

59. *Candidate recognition* Suppose that the proportion P of voters who recognize a candidate's name t months after the start of the campaign is given by

$$P(t) = \frac{13t}{t^2 + 100} + 0.18$$

(a) How many months after the start of the campaign is recognition at its maximum?

(b) To have greatest recognition on November 1, when should a campaign be launched?

60. *Medication* The number of milligrams x of a medication in the bloodstream t hours after a dose is taken can be modeled by

$$x(t) = \frac{2000t}{t^2 + 16}$$

(a) For what t-values is x increasing?

(b) Find the t-value at which x is maximum.

(c) Find the maximum value of x.

61. *U.S. railroad miles* The graph shows the number of miles of U.S. railroads for selected years from 1850 to 2006. Suppose that data can be modeled with the function

$$R(t) = 0.000062t^3 - 0.046t^2 + 6.55t - 25.6$$

where $R(t)$ is thousands of miles of railroads and t is the number of years past 1850.

(a) Find the year in which the model indicates the number of railroad miles is maximum. Does this agree with the data?

(b) The data seem to be leveling off beyond 2000. For the year 2010, does $R'(t)$ indicate that this is true for the model?

U.S. Railroad Miles, 1850–2006

Note: Figures show aggregate length of U.S.-owned operating roadway, excluding yard tracks, sidings, and parallel tracks.

Source: Association of American Railroads

62. *Economic dependency ratio* The economic dependency ratio is defined as the number of persons in the total population who are not in the work force per 100 in the work force. Since 1960, Baby Boomers in the work

force and a decrease in the birth rate have caused a significant decrease in the economic dependency ratio. With data for selected years from 1960 and projected to 2050, the economic dependency ratio R can be modeled by the function

$$R(x) = -0.0002x^3 + 0.052x^2 - 4.06x + 192$$

where x is the number of years past 1950 (*Source*: U.S. Department of Labor). Use this model to find the year in which the economic dependency ratio reached its minimum. What was happening in the United States around this time that helps explain why the minimum occurred in this year?

63. **Modeling** *Homicide rate* The numbers of homicides per 100,000 people for selected years from 1960 to 2008 are given in the table.

Year	Homicides per 100,000	Year	Homicides per 100,000
1960	5.1	1990	9.4
1965	5.1	1995	8.2
1970	7.9	2000	5.6
1975	9.6	2005	5.6
1980	10.2	2008	5.4
1985	7.9		

Source: FBI, Uniform Crime Statistics

(a) Find a cubic model for these data. Use $x = 0$ to represent 1950.

(b) Find the year in which the maximum number of homicides per 100,000 people occurs, according to the model.

64. **Modeling** *U.S. executions* The table shows the numbers of executions in the U.S. for selected years from 1990 to 2007.

Year	Number	Year	Number
1990	23	2000	85
1992	31	2001	66
1994	31	2003	65
1996	45	2005	60
1998	68	2007	42

Source: www.cuadp.org

(a) With x as the number of years past 1990, find a cubic model for these data.

(b) Find the year when the number of executions was maximum, according to the model.

65. **Modeling** *Union membership* The table gives the thousands of U.S. workers who were union members for selected years from 1930 to 2009.

Year	Members	Year	Members
1930	3401	1975	19,611
1935	3584	1980	19,843
1940	8717	1985	16,996
1945	14,322	1990	16,740
1950	14,267	1995	16,360
1955	16,802	2000	16,258
1960	17,049	2005	15,685
1965	17,299	2009	16,904
1970	19,381		

Source: U.S. Department of Labor

(a) With $t = 0$ representing 1900, find a cubic function that models these data.
(b) Find the critical values for the model and classify them.
(c) How well does the relative maximum from the model agree with the data?
(d) Do you think that union membership will reach a minimum and then increase as the model predicts? Explain.

OBJECTIVES

10.2

- To find points of inflection of graphs of functions
- To use the second-derivative test to graph functions

Concavity; Points of Inflection

| APPLICATION PREVIEW |

Suppose that a retailer wishes to sell his store and uses the graph in Figure 10.13 to show how profits have increased since he opened the store and the potential for profit in the future. Can we conclude that profits will continue to grow, or should we be concerned about future earnings?

Note that although profits are still increasing in 2013, they seem to be increasing more slowly than in previous years. Indeed, they appear to have been growing at a decreasing rate since about 2011. We can analyze this situation more carefully by identifying the point at which profit begins to grow more slowly, that is, the *point of diminishing returns.* (See Example 3.)

Figure 10.13

Just as we used the first derivative to determine whether a curve was increasing or decreasing on a given interval, we can use the second derivative to determine whether the curve is concave up or concave down on an interval.

Concavity   A curve is said to be **concave up** on an interval (a, b) if at each point on the interval the curve is above its tangent at the point (see Figure 10.14(a) on the next page). If the curve is below all its tangents on a given interval, it is **concave down** on the interval (Figure 10.14(b)).

Looking at Figure 10.14(a), we see that the *slopes* of the tangent lines increase over the interval where the graph is concave up. Because $f'(x)$ gives the slopes of those tangents, it follows that $f'(x)$ is increasing over the interval where $f(x)$ is concave up. However, we know that $f'(x)$ is increasing when its derivative, $f''(x)$, is positive. That is, if the second derivative is positive, the curve is concave up.

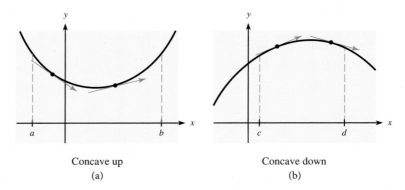

Figure 10.14

Concave up
(a)

Concave down
(b)

Similarly, if the second derivative of a function is negative over an interval, the slopes of the tangents to the graph decrease over that interval. This happens when the tangent lines are above the graph, as in Figure 10.14(b), so the graph must be concave down on this interval.

Thus we see that the second derivative can be used to determine the concavity of a curve.

Concave Up and Concave Down	Assume that the first and second derivatives of function f exist. The function f is **concave up** on an interval I, if $f''(x) > 0$ on I, and **concave up** at the point $(a, f(a))$, if $f''(a) > 0$. The function f is **concave down** on an interval I, if $f''(x) < 0$ on I, and **concave down** at the point $(a, f(a))$, if $f''(a) < 0$.

EXAMPLE 1   Concavity at a Point

Is the graph of $f(x) = x^3 - 4x^2 + 3$ concave up or down at the point
(a) $(1, 0)$?   (b) $(2, -5)$?

Solution
(a) We must find $f''(x)$ before we can answer this question.

$$f'(x) = 3x^2 - 8x \quad f''(x) = 6x - 8$$

Then $f''(1) = 6(1) - 8 = -2$, so the graph is concave down at $(1, 0)$.
(b) Because $f''(2) = 6(2) - 8 = 4$, the graph is concave up at $(2, -5)$. The graph of $f(x) = x^3 - 4x^2 + 3$ is shown in Figure 10.15(a). ∎

Points of Inflection   Looking at the graph of $y = x^3 - 4x^2 + 3$ [Figure 10.15(a)], we see that the curve is concave down on the left and concave up on the right. Thus it has changed from concave down to concave up, and from Example 1 we would expect the concavity to change somewhere between $x = 1$ and $x = 2$. Figure 10.15(b) shows the graph of $y'' = f''(x) = 6x - 8$, and we can see that $y'' = 0$ when $x = \frac{4}{3}$ and that $y'' < 0$ for $x < \frac{4}{3}$ and $y'' > 0$ for $x > \frac{4}{3}$. Thus the second derivative changes sign at $x = \frac{4}{3}$, so the concavity of the graph of $y = f(x)$ changes at $x = \frac{4}{3}, y = -\frac{47}{27}$. The point where concavity changes is called a **point of inflection**.

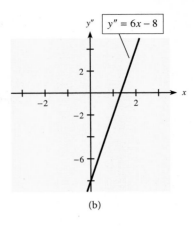

Figure 10.15 (a) (b)

| **Point of Inflection** | A point (x_0, y_0) on the graph of a function f is called a **point of inflection** if the curve is concave up on one side of the point and concave down on the other side. The second derivative at this point, $f''(x_0)$, will be 0 or undefined. |

In general, we can find points of inflection and information about concavity as follows.

Finding Points of Inflection and Concavity

Procedure	**Example**
To find the point(s) of inflection of a curve and intervals where it is concave up and where it is concave down:	Find the points of inflection and concavity of the graph of $$y = \frac{x^4}{2} - x^3 + 5.$$
1. Find the second derivative of the function.	1. $y' = f'(x) = 2x^3 - 3x^2$ $y'' = f''(x) = 6x^2 - 6x$
2. Set the second derivative equal to 0, and solve for x. Potential points of inflection occur at these values of x or at values of x where $f(x)$ is defined and $f''(x)$ is undefined.	2. $0 = 6x^2 - 6x = 6x(x - 1)$ has solutions $x = 0, x = 1$. $f''(x)$ is defined everywhere.
3. Find the potential points of inflection.	3. $(0, 5)$ and $\left(1, \frac{9}{2}\right)$ are potential points of inflection.
4. If the second derivative has opposite signs on the two sides of one of these values of x, a point of inflection occurs. The curve is concave up where $f''(x) > 0$ and concave down where $f''(x) < 0$. The changes in the sign of $f''(x)$ correspond to changes in concavity and occur at points of inflection.	4. A **sign diagram for $f''(x)$** is $(0, 5)$ and $\left(1, \frac{9}{2}\right)$ are points of inflection. See the graph in Figure 10.16 on the next page.

The graph of $y = \frac{1}{2}x^4 - x^3 + 5$ is shown in Figure 10.16. Note the points of inflection at $(0, 5)$ and $\left(1, \frac{9}{2}\right)$. The point of inflection at $(0, 5)$ is a horizontal point of inflection because $f'(x)$ is also 0 at $x = 0$.

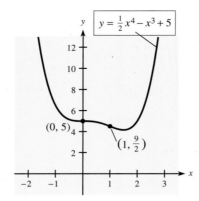

Figure 10.16

EXAMPLE 2 Water Purity

Suppose that a real estate developer wishes to remove pollution from a small lake so that she can sell lakefront homes on a "crystal clear" lake. The graph in Figure 10.17 shows the relation between dollars spent on cleaning the lake and the purity of the water. The point of inflection on the graph is called the **point of diminishing returns** on her investment because it is where the *rate* of return on her investment changes from increasing to decreasing. Show that the rate of change in the purity of the lake, $f'(x)$, is maximized at this point, $x = c$. Assume that $f(c)$, $f'(c)$, and $f''(c)$ are defined.

Figure 10.17

Solution

Because $x = c$ is a point of inflection for $f(x)$, we know that the concavity must change at $x = c$. From the figure we see the following.

$$x < c: \quad f(x) \text{ is concave up, so } f''(x) > 0.$$
$$f''(x) > 0 \text{ means that } f'(x) \text{ is increasing.}$$
$$x > c: \quad f(x) \text{ is concave down, so } f''(x) < 0.$$
$$f''(x) < 0 \text{ means that } f'(x) \text{ is decreasing.}$$

Thus $f'(x)$ has $f'(c)$ as its relative maximum.

EXAMPLE 3 Diminishing Returns | APPLICATION PREVIEW |

Suppose the annual profit for a store (in thousands of dollars) is given by

$$P(x) = -0.2x^3 + 3x^2 + 6$$

where x is the number of years past 2006. If this model is accurate, find the point of diminishing returns for the profit.

Solution

The point of diminishing returns occurs at the point of inflection. Thus we seek the point where the graph of this function changes from concave up to concave down, if such a point exists.

$$P'(x) = -0.6x^2 + 6x$$
$$P''(x) = -1.2x + 6$$
$$P''(x) = 0 \quad \text{when} \quad 0 = -1.2x + 6 \quad \text{or} \quad \text{when } x = 5$$

Thus $x = 5$ is a possible point of inflection. We test $P''(x)$ to the left and the right of $x = 5$.

$$P''(4) = 1.2 > 0 \Rightarrow \text{concave up to the left of } x = 5$$
$$P''(6) = -1.2 < 0 \Rightarrow \text{concave down to the right of } x = 5$$

Thus $(5, 56)$ is the point of inflection for the graph, and the point of diminishing returns for the profit is when $x = 5$ (in the year 2011) and is $P(5) = 56$ thousand dollars. Figure 10.18 shows the graphs of $P(x)$, $P'(x)$, and $P''(x)$. At $x = 5$, we see that the point of diminishing returns on the graph of $P(x)$ corresponds to the maximum point of the graph of $P'(x)$ and the zero (or x-intercept) of the graph of $P''(x)$. ∎

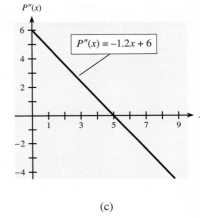

Figure 10.18   (a)   (b)   (c)

CHECKPOINT

1. If $f''(x) > 0$, then $f(x)$ is concave _____.
2. At what value of x does the graph $y = \frac{1}{3}x^3 - 2x^2 + 2x$ have a point of inflection?
3. On the graph below, locate any points of inflection (approximately) and label where the curve satisfies $f''(x) > 0$ and $f''(x) < 0$.

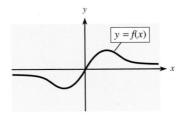

4. Determine whether the following is true or false. If $f''(0) = 0$, then $f(x)$ has a point of inflection at $x = 0$.

Second-Derivative Test

We can use information about points of inflection and concavity to help sketch graphs. For example, if we know that the curve is concave up at a critical point where $f'(x) = 0$, then the point must be a relative minimum because the tangent to the curve is horizontal at the critical point, and only a point at the bottom of a "concave up" curve could have a horizontal tangent (see Figure 10.19(a)).

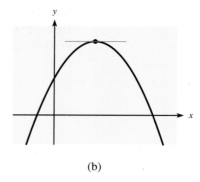

Figure 10.19   (a)   (b)

On the other hand, if the curve is concave down at a critical point where $f'(x) = 0$, then the point is a relative maximum (see Figure 10.19(b)).

Thus we can use the **second-derivative test** to determine whether a critical point where $f'(x) = 0$ is a relative maximum or minimum.

Second-Derivative Test

Procedure	Example
To find relative maxima and minima of a function:	Find the relative maxima and minima of $y = f(x) = \frac{1}{3}x^3 - x^2 - 3x + 2$.
1. Find the critical values of the function.	1. $f'(x) = x^2 - 2x - 3$ $0 = (x - 3)(x + 1)$ has solutions $x = -1$ and $x = 3$. No values of x make $f'(x)$ undefined.
2. Substitute the critical values into $f(x)$ to find the critical points.	2. $f(-1) = \frac{11}{3}$ $f(3) = -7$ The critical points are $\left(-1, \frac{11}{3}\right)$ and $(3, -7)$.
3. Evaluate $f''(x)$ at each critical value for which $f'(x) = 0$. (a) If $f''(x_0) < 0$, a relative maximum occurs at x_0. (b) If $f''(x_0) > 0$, a relative minimum occurs at x_0. (c) If $f''(x_0) = 0$, or $f''(x_0)$ is undefined, the second-derivative test fails; use the first-derivative test.	3. $f''(x) = 2x - 2$ $f''(-1) = 2(-1) - 2 = -4 < 0$, so $\left(-1, \frac{11}{3}\right)$ is a relative maximum point. $f''(3) = 2(3) - 2 = 4 > 0$, so $(3, -7)$ is a relative minimum point. (The graph is shown in Figure 10.20.)

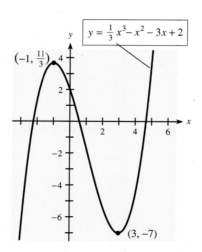

Figure 10.20

Because the second-derivative test (just shown) and the first-derivative test (in Section 10.1) are both methods for classifying critical values, let's compare the advantages and disadvantages of the second derivative test.

Advantage of the Second-Derivative Test	Disadvantages of the Second-Derivative Test
It is quick and easy for many functions.	The second derivative is difficult to find for some functions. The second-derivative test sometimes fails to give results.

EXAMPLE 4   Maxima, Minima, and Points of Inflection

Find the relative maxima and minima and points of inflection of $y = 3x^4 - 4x^3 - 2$.

Solution

$$y' = f'(x) = 12x^3 - 12x^2$$

Solving $0 = 12x^3 - 12x^2 = 12x^2(x - 1)$ gives $x = 1$ and $x = 0$. Thus the critical points are $(1, -3)$ and $(0, -2)$.

$$y'' = f''(x) = 36x^2 - 24x$$
$$f''(1) = 12 > 0 \Rightarrow (1, -3) \text{ is a relative minimum point.}$$
$$f''(0) = 0 \Rightarrow \text{the second-derivative test fails.}$$

Because the second-derivative test fails, we must use the first-derivative test at the critical point $(0, -2)$. A sign diagram for $f'(x)$ shows that $(0, -2)$ is a horizontal point of inflection.

We look for points of inflection by setting $f''(x) = 0$ and solving for x. We find that $0 = 36x^2 - 24x$ has solutions $x = 0$ and $x = \frac{2}{3}$. The sign diagram for $f''(x)$ shows points of inflection at both of these x-values, that is at the points $(0, -2)$ and $\left(\frac{2}{3}, -\frac{70}{27}\right)$. The point $(0, -2)$ is a special point, where the curve changes concavity *and* has a horizontal tangent (see Figure 10.21).

Figure 10.21

Calculator Note We can use a graphing calculator to explore the relationships among f, f', and f'', as we did in the previous section for f and f'. See Appendix C, Section 10.2, for details.

EXAMPLE 5

Concavity from the Graph of $y = f(x)$

Figure 10.22 shows the graph of $f(x) = \frac{1}{6}(2x^3 - 3x^2 - 12x + 12)$.

(a) From the graph, identify points where $f''(x) = 0$.
(b) From the graph, observe intervals where $f''(x) > 0$ and where $f''(x) < 0$.
(c) Check the conclusions from parts (a) and (b) by calculating $f''(x)$ and graphing it.

Figure 10.22

Solution

(a) From Figure 10.22, the point of inflection appears to be near $x = \frac{1}{2}$, so we expect $f''(x) = 0$ at (or very near) $x = \frac{1}{2}$.
(b) We see that the graph is concave down (so $f''(x) < 0$) to the left of the point of inflection. That is, $f''(x) < 0$ when $x < \frac{1}{2}$. Similarly, $f''(x) > 0$ when $x = \frac{1}{2}$.
(c) $f(x) = \frac{1}{6}(2x^3 - 3x^2 - 12x + 12)$
   $f'(x) = \frac{1}{6}(6x^2 - 6x - 12) = x^2 - x - 2$
   $f''(x) = 2x - 1$
   Thus $f''(x) = 0$ when $x = \frac{1}{2}$.
   Figure 10.23 shows the graph of $f''(x) = 2x - 1$. We see that the graph crosses the x-axis ($f''(x) = 0$) when $x = \frac{1}{2}$, is below the x-axis ($f''(x) < 0$) when $x < \frac{1}{2}$, and is above the x-axis ($f''(x) > 0$) when $x > \frac{1}{2}$. This verifies our conclusions from parts (a) and (b).

Figure 10.23

Spreadsheet Note We can investigate the function in Example 5 by using Excel to find the outputs of $f(x) = \frac{1}{6}(2x^3 - 3x^2 - 12x + 12)$, $f'(x)$, and $f''(x)$ for values of x at and near the critical points. See Appendix D, Section 10.2, and the Online Excel Guide for details.

	A	B	C	D
1	x	$f(x)$	$f'(x)$	$f''(x)$
2	-2	1.3333	4	-5
3	-1	3.1667	0	-3
4	0	2	-2	-1
5	1/2	0.9167	-2.25	0
6	1	-0.1667	-2	1
7	2	-1.3333	0	3
8	3	0.5	4	5

By looking at column C, we see that $f'(x)$ changes from positive to negative as x passes through the value $x = -1$ and that the derivative changes from negative to positive as x passes through the value $x = 2$. Thus the graph has a relative maximum at $x = -1$ and a relative minimum at $x = 2$. By looking at column D, we can also see that $f''(x)$ changes from negative to positive as x passes through the value $x = 1/2$, so the graph has a point of inflection at $x = 1/2$.

EXAMPLE   6

Concavity from the Graph of $y = f'(x)$

Figure 10.24 shows the graph of $f'(x) = -x^2 - 2x$. Use the graph of $f'(x)$ to do the following.

(a) Find intervals on which $f(x)$ is concave down and concave up.
(b) Find x-values at which $f(x)$ has a point of inflection.
(c) Check the conclusions from parts (a) and (b) by finding $f''(x)$ and graphing it.
(d) For $f(x) = \frac{1}{3}(9 - x^3 - 3x^2)$, calculate $f'(x)$ to verify that this could be $f(x)$.

Figure 10.24

Solution

(a) Concavity for $f(x)$ can be found from the sign of $f''(x)$. Because $f''(x)$ is the first derivative of $f'(x)$, wherever the graph of $f'(x)$ is increasing, it follows that $f''(x) > 0$. Thus $f''(x) > 0$ and $f(x)$ is concave up when $x < -1$. Similarly, $f''(x) < 0$, and $f(x)$ is concave down, when $f'(x)$ is decreasing—that is, when $x > -1$.

(b) From (a) we know that $f''(x)$ changes sign at $x = -1$, so $f(x)$ has a point of inflection at $x = -1$. Note that $f'(x)$ has its maximum at the x-value where $f(x)$ has a point of inflection. In fact, points of inflection for $f(x)$ will correspond to relative extrema for $f'(x)$.

(c) For $f'(x) = -x^2 - 2x$, we have $f''(x) = -2x - 2$. Figure 10.25 shows the graph of $y = f''(x)$ and verifies our conclusions from (a) and (b).

(d) If $f(x) = \frac{1}{3}(9 - x^3 - 3x^2)$, then $f'(x) = \frac{1}{3}(-3x^2 - 6x) = -x^2 - 2x$. Figure 10.26 shows the graph of $f(x) = \frac{1}{3}(9 - x^3 - 3x^2)$. Note that the point of inflection and the concavity correspond to what we discovered in parts (a) and (b). ∎

Figure 10.25

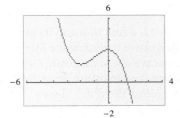

Figure 10.26

The relationships among $f(x)$, $f'(x)$, and $f''(x)$ that we explored in Example 6 can be summarized as follows.

$f(x)$	Concave Up	Concave Down	Point of Inflection	
$f'(x)$	increasing	decreasing	maximum	minimum
$f''(x)$	positive $(+)$	negative $(-)$	$(+)$ to $(-)$	$(-)$ to $(+)$

CHECKPOINT SOLUTIONS

1. Up

2. The second derivative of $y = \frac{1}{3}x^3 - 2x^2 + 2x$ is $y'' = 2x - 4$, so $y'' = 0$ at $x = 2$. Because $y'' < 0$ for $x < 2$ and $y'' > 0$ for $x > 2$, a point of inflection occurs at $x = 2$.

3. Points of inflection at A, B, and C
   $f''(x) < 0$ to the left of A and between B and C
   $f''(x) > 0$ between A and B and to the right of C

4. (a) False. For example, if $f(x) = x^4$, then $f'(x) = 4x^3$ and $f''(x) = 12x^2$. Note that $f''(0) = 0$, but $f''(x)$ does not change sign from $x < 0$ to $x > 0$.

| EXERCISES | 10.2

In Problems 1 and 2, determine whether each function is concave up or concave down at the indicated points.

1. $f(x) = x^3 - 3x^2 + 1$ at (a) $x = -2$ (b) $x = 3$
2. $f(x) = x^3 + 6x - 4$ at (a) $x = -5$ (b) $x = 7$

In Problems 3–8, use the indicated x-values on the graph of $y = f(x)$ to find the following.

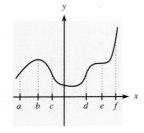

3. Find intervals over which the graph is concave down.
4. Find intervals over which the graph is concave up.
5. Find intervals where $f''(x) > 0$.
6. Find intervals where $f''(x) < 0$.
7. Find the x-coordinates of three points of inflection.
8. Find the x-coordinate of a horizontal point of inflection.

In Problems 9–12, a function and its graph are given. Use the second derivative to determine intervals on which the function is concave up, to determine intervals on which it is concave down, and to locate points of inflection. Check these results against the graph shown.

9. $f(x) = x^3 - 6x^2 + 5x + 6$

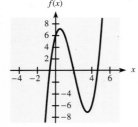

10. $y = x^3 - 9x^2$

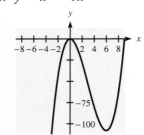

11. $f(x) = \frac{1}{4}x^4 + \frac{1}{2}x^3 - 3x^2 + 3$

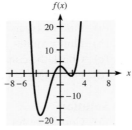

12. $y = 2x^4 - 6x^2 + 4$

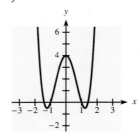

Find the relative maxima, relative minima, and points of inflection, and sketch the graphs of the functions, in Problems 13–18.

13. $y = x^2 - 4x + 2$ 14. $y = x^3 - x^2$
15. $y = \frac{1}{3}x^3 - 2x^2 + 3x + 2$
16. $y = x^3 - 3x^2 + 6$
17. $y = x^4 - 16x^2$ 18. $y = x^4 - 8x^3 + 16x^2$

In Problems 19–22, a function and its first and second derivatives are given. Use these to find critical values, relative maxima, relative minima, and points of inflection; sketch the graph of each function.

19. $f(x) = 3x^5 - 20x^3$
   $f'(x) = 15x^2(x - 2)(x + 2)$
   $f''(x) = 60x(x^2 - 2)$
20. $f(x) = x^5 - 5x^4$
   $f'(x) = 5x^3(x - 4)$
   $f''(x) = 20x^2(x - 3)$
21. $y = x^{1/3}(x - 4)$ 22. $y = x^{4/3}(x - 7)$

   $y' = \dfrac{4(x - 1)}{3x^{2/3}}$ $y' = \dfrac{7x^{1/3}(x - 4)}{3}$

   $y'' = \dfrac{4(x + 2)}{9x^{5/3}}$ $y'' = \dfrac{28(x - 1)}{9x^{2/3}}$

 In Problems 23 and 24, a function and its graph are given.
(a) **From the graph, estimate where $f''(x) > 0$, where $f''(x) < 0$, and where $f''(x) = 0$.**
(b) **Use (a) to decide where $f'(x)$ has its relative maxima and relative minima.**
(c) **Verify your results in parts (a) and (b) by finding $f'(x)$ and $f''(x)$ and then graphing each with a graphing utility.**

23. $f(x) = -\frac{1}{3}x^3 + x^2 + 8x - 12$

24. $f(x) = \frac{1}{3}x^3 + 2x^2 - 12x - 20$

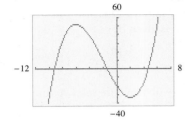

In Problems 25 and 26, $f'(x)$ and its graph are given. Use the graph of $f'(x)$ to determine the following.
(a) **Where is the graph of $f(x)$ concave up and where is it concave down?**
(b) **Where does $f(x)$ have any points of inflection?**
(c) **Find $f''(x)$ and graph it. Then use that graph to check your conclusions from parts (a) and (b).**
(d) **Sketch a possible graph of $f(x)$.**

25. $f'(x) = 4x - x^2$

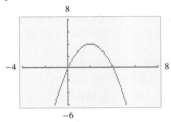

26. $f'(x) = x^2 - x - 2$

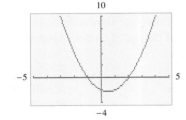

In Problems 27 and 28, use the graph shown in Figure 10.27 and identify points from A through I that satisfy the given conditions.

27. (a) $f'(x) > 0$ and $f''(x) > 0$
    (b) $f'(x) < 0$ and $f''(x) < 0$
    (c) $f'(x) = 0$ and $f''(x) > 0$
    (d) $f'(x) > 0$ and $f''(x) = 0$
    (e) $f'(x) = 0$ and $f''(x) = 0$

28. (a) $f'(x) > 0$ and $f''(x) < 0$
    (b) $f'(x) < 0$ and $f''(x) > 0$
    (c) $f'(x) = 0$ and $f''(x) < 0$
    (d) $f'(x) < 0$ and $f''(x) = 0$

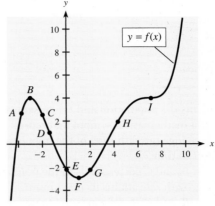

Figure 10.27

In Problems 29 and 30, a graph is given. Tell where $f(x)$ is concave up, where it is concave down, and where it has points of inflection on the interval $-2 < x < 2$, if the given graph is the graph of
(a) $f(x)$.   (b) $f'(x)$.   (c) $f''(x)$.

29.

30.

APPLICATIONS

31. *Productivity—diminishing returns* The figure is a typical graph of worker productivity as a function of time on the job.

(a) If P represents the productivity and t represents the time, write a mathematical symbol that represents the rate of change of productivity with respect to time.
(b) Which of A, B, and C is the critical point for the rate of change found in part (a)? This point actually corresponds to the point at which the rate of production is maximized, or the point for maximum worker efficiency. In economics, this is called the point of diminishing returns.

(c) Which of A, B, and C corresponds to the upper limit of worker productivity?

32. **Population growth** The figure shows the growth of a population as a function of time.

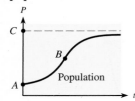

(a) If P represents the population and t represents the time, write a mathematical symbol that represents the rate of change (growth *rate*) of the population with respect to time.
(b) Which of A, B, and C corresponds to the point at which the growth *rate* attains its maximum?
(c) Which of A, B, and C corresponds to the upper limit of population?

33. **Advertising and sales** The figure shows the daily sales volume S as a function of time t since an ad campaign began.

(a) Which of A, B, and C is the point of inflection for the graph?
(b) On which side of C is $d^2S/dt^2 > 0$?
(c) Does the *rate of change* of sales volume attain its minimum at C?

34. **Oxygen purity** The figure shows the oxygen level P (for purity) in a lake t months after an oil spill.

(a) Which of A, B, and C is the point of inflection for the graph?
(b) On which side of C is $d^2P/dt^2 < 0$?
(c) Does the *rate of change* of purity attain its maximum at C?

35. **Production** Suppose that the total number of units produced by a worker in t hours of an 8-hour shift can be modeled by the production function $P(t)$:

$$P(t) = 27t + 12t^2 - t^3$$

(a) Find the number of hours before production is maximized.

(b) Find the number of hours before the rate of production is maximized. That is, find the point of diminishing returns.

36. **Poiseuille's law—velocity of blood** According to Poiseuille's law, the speed S of blood through an artery of radius r at a distance x from the artery wall is given by

$$S = k[r^2 - (r - x)^2]$$

where k is a constant. Find the distance x that maximizes the speed.

37. **Advertising and sales—diminishing returns** Suppose that a company's daily sales volume attributed to an advertising campaign is given by

$$S(t) = \frac{3}{t + 3} - \frac{18}{(t + 3)^2} + 1$$

(a) Find how long it will be before sales volume is maximized.
(b) Find how long it will be before the rate of change of sales volume is minimized. That is, find the point of diminishing returns.

38. **Oxygen purity—diminishing returns** Suppose that the oxygen level P (for purity) in a body of water t months after an oil spill is given by

$$P(t) = 500\left[1 - \frac{4}{t + 4} + \frac{16}{(t + 4)^2}\right]$$

(a) Find how long it will be before the oxygen level reaches its minimum.
(b) Find how long it will be before the rate of change of P is maximized. That is, find the point of diminishing returns.

39. **Civilian labor force** The table gives the size of the civilian labor force (in millions) for selected years from 1950 and projected to 2050. These data can be modeled by

$$y = -0.0001x^3 + 0.0088x^2 + 1.43x + 57.9$$

where x is the number of years past 1950. Use the model to find the year when the second derivative predicts that the rate of change of civilian labor force begins to decrease.

Year	Civilian Labor Force (in millions)	Year	Civilian Labor Force (in millions)
1950	62.2	2010	157.7
1960	69.6	2015	162.8
1970	82.8	2020	164.7
1980	106.9	2030	170.1
1990	125.8	2040	180.5
2000	140.9	2050	191.8

Source: U.S. Bureau of Labor Statistics

40. *Consumer prices* The data in the table can be modeled by the function

$$c(x) = -0.000783x^3 + 0.124x^2 - 1.74x + 25.2$$

where $x = 0$ represents 1945 and $c(x)$ is the consumer price index (CPI) in year $1945 + x$. During what year does the model predict that the rate of change of the CPI reached its maximum?

Year	CPI	Year	CPI
1945	18.0	1980	82.4
1950	24.1	1985	107.6
1955	26.8	1990	130.7
1960	29.6	1995	152.4
1965	31.5	2000	172.2
1970	38.8	2005	195.3
1975	53.8	2009	214.5

Source: U.S. Bureau of Labor Statistics

41. **Modeling** *Foreign-born population* The figure gives the percent of the U.S. population that was foreign-born for selected years from 1900 to 2007.
    (a) Find the cubic function that is the best fit for the data. Use $x = 0$ to represent 1900.
    (b) Find the critical point of the graph of the cubic model for $x > 50$.
    (c) Interpret this point in terms of the percent of foreign-born people in the U.S. population.

**Percent of Population That Was
Foreign-Born, 1900–2007**

Source: Bureau of the Census, U.S. Department of Commerce

42. **Modeling** *Elderly men in the work force* The table gives the percent of men 65 years or older in the work force for selected years from 1920 and projected to 2030.
    (a) With $x = 0$ representing 1900, find the cubic function that models these data.

(b) Use the model to determine when the rate of change of the percent of elderly men in the work force reached its minimum.
(c) On the graph of this model, to what does the result in part (b) correspond?

Year	Percent	Year	Percent
1920	55.6	1980	19.0
1930	54.0	1990	16.3
1940	41.8	2000	17.7
1950	45.8	2010	22.6
1960	33.1	2020	27.2
1970	21.8	2030	27.6

Source: U.S. Bureau of the Census

43. **Modeling** *Gross national product* The table gives the U.S. gross national product (GNP) for the years 1913–1922.
    (a) Using $x = 0$ to represent 1912, find the cubic function that models the data.
    (b) During what year in this time interval does the model predict a minimum GNP?
    (c) During what year in this time interval does the model predict a maximum GNP?

Year	Gross National Product (GNP)
1913	39.6
1914	38.6
1915	40.0
1916	48.3
1917	60.4
1918	76.4
1919	84.0
1920	91.5
1921	69.6
1922	74.1

Source: *National Debt in Perspective*, Oscar Falconi, Wholesale Nutrition (Internet)

Optimization in Business and Economics

■ | APPLICATION PREVIEW | ■

Suppose a travel agency charges $300 per person for a certain tour when the tour group has 25 people, but will reduce the price by $10 per person for each additional person above the 25. In order to determine the group size that will maximize the revenue, the agency must create a model for the revenue. With such a model, the techniques of calculus can be useful in determining the maximum revenue. (See Example 2.)

Most companies (such as the travel agency) are interested in obtaining the greatest possible revenue or profit. Similarly, manufacturers of products are concerned about producing their products for the lowest possible average cost per unit. Therefore, rather than just finding the relative maxima or relative minima of a function, we will consider where the absolute maximum or absolute minimum of a function occurs in a given interval.

In this section we will discuss how to find the absolute extrema of a function and then use these techniques to solve applications involving revenue, cost, and profit.

As their name implies, **absolute extrema** are the functional values that are the largest or smallest values over the entire domain of the function (or over the interval of interest).

Absolute Extrema

The value $f(a)$ is the **absolute maximum** of f if $f(a) \geq f(x)$ for all x in the domain of f (or over the interval of interest).

The value $f(b)$ is the **absolute minimum** of f if $f(b) \leq f(x)$ for all x in the domain of f (or over the interval of interest).

Let us begin by considering the graph of $y = (x - 1)^2$, shown in Figure 10.28(a). This graph has a relative minimum at $(1, 0)$. Note that the relative minimum is the lowest point on the graph. In this case, the point $(1, 0)$ is an **absolute minimum point**, and 0 is the absolute minimum for the function. Similarly, when there is a point that is the highest point on the graph over the domain of the function, we call the point an **absolute maximum point** of the graph of the function.

In Figure 10.28(a), we see that there is no relative maximum. However, if the domain of the function is restricted to the interval $\left[\frac{1}{2}, 2\right]$, then we get the graph shown in Figure 10.28(b). In this case, there is an absolute maximum of 1 at the point $(2, 1)$ and the absolute minimum of 0 is still at $(1, 0)$.

If the domain of $y = (x - 1)^2$ is restricted to the interval $[2, 3]$, the resulting graph is that shown in Figure 10.28(c). In this case, the absolute minimum is 1 and occurs at the point $(2, 1)$, and the absolute maximum is 4 and occurs at $(3, 4)$.

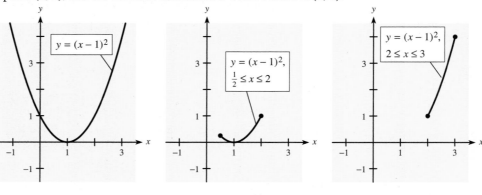

Figure 10.28   (a)   (b)   (c)

As the preceding discussion indicates, if the domain of a continuous function is limited to a closed interval, the absolute maximum or minimum may occur at an endpoint of the domain. In testing functions with limited domains for absolute maxima and minima, we must compare the function values at the endpoints of the domain with the function values at the critical values found by taking derivatives. In the management, life, and social sciences, a limited domain occurs very often, because many quantities are required to be positive, or at least nonnegative.

Maximizing Revenue

Because the marginal revenue is the first derivative of the total revenue, it should be obvious that the total revenue function will have a critical point at the point where the marginal revenue equals 0. With the total revenue function $R(x) = 16x - 0.02x^2$, the point where $R'(x) = 0$ is clearly a maximum because $R(x)$ is a parabola that opens downward. But the domain may be limited, the revenue function may not always be a parabola, or the critical point may not always be a maximum, so it is important to verify where the maximum value occurs.

EXAMPLE 1   Revenue

The total revenue in dollars for a firm is given by

$$R(x) = 8000x - 40x^2 - x^3$$

where x is the number of units sold per day. If only 50 units can be sold per day, find the number of units that must be sold to maximize revenue. Find the maximum revenue.

Solution
This revenue function is limited to x in the interval $[0, 50]$. Thus, the maximum revenue will occur at a critical value in this interval or at an endpoint. $R'(x) = 8000 - 80x - 3x^2$, so we must solve $8000 - 80x - 3x^2 = 0$ for x:

$$(40 - x)(200 + 3x) = 0 \quad \text{means} \quad 40 - x = 0 \quad \text{or} \quad 200 + 3x = 0$$

Thus

$$x = 40 \quad \text{or} \quad x = -\frac{200}{3}$$

We reject the negative value of x and then use either the second-derivative test or the first-derivative test with a sign diagram.

Second-Derivative Test	First-Derivative Test
$R''(x) = -80 - 6x$, $R''(40) = -320 < 0$, so 40 is a relative maximum.	

These tests show that a relative maximum occurs at $x = 40$, giving revenue $R(40) = \$192,000$. Checking the endpoints $x = 0$ and $x = 50$ gives $R(0) = \$0$ and $R(50) = \$175,000$. Thus $R = \$192,000$ at $x = 40$ is the (absolute) maximum revenue.

CHECKPOINT

1. True or false: If $R(x)$ is the revenue function, we find all possible points where $R(x)$ could be maximized by solving $\overline{MR} = 0$ for x.

EXAMPLE 2   Revenue | APPLICATION PREVIEW |

A travel agency will plan tours for groups of 25 or larger. If the group contains exactly 25 people, the price is $300 per person. However, the price per person is reduced by $10 for each additional person above the 25. What size group will produce the largest revenue for the agency?

Solution

The total revenue is

$$R = (\text{number of people})(\text{price per person})$$

The table shows how the revenue is changed by increases in the size of the group.

Number in Group	Price per Person	Revenue
25	300	7500
25 + 1	300 − 10	7540
25 + 2	300 − 20	7560
⋮	⋮	⋮
25 + x	300 − 10x	(25 + x)(300 − 10x)

Thus when x is the number of people added to the 25, the total revenue will be

$$R = R(x) = (25 + x)(300 - 10x) \qquad \text{or} \qquad R(x) = 7500 + 50x - 10x^2$$

This is a quadratic function, so its graph is a parabola that is concave down. A maximum will occur at its vertex, where $R'(x) = 0$.

$R'(x) = 50 - 20x$, and the solution to $0 = 50 - 20x$ is $x = 2.5$. Thus adding 2.5 people to the group should maximize the total revenue. But we cannot add half a person, so we will test the total revenue function for 27 people and 28 people. This will determine the optimal group size because $R(x)$ is concave down for all x.

For $x = 2$ (giving 27 people) we get $R(2) = 7500 + 50(2) - 10(2)^2 = 7560$. For $x = 3$ (giving 28 people) we get $R(3) = 7500 + 50(3) - 10(3)^2 = 7560$. Note that both 27 and 28 people give the same total revenue and that this revenue is greater than the revenue for 25 people. Thus the revenue is maximized at either 27 or 28 people in the group. (See Figure 10.29.)

Figure 10.29

Minimizing Average Cost   Because the total cost function is always increasing for $x \geq 0$, the number of units that will make the total cost a minimum is always $x = 0$ units, which gives an absolute minimum. However, it is more useful to find the number of units that will make the **average cost** per unit a minimum.

Average Cost

If the total cost function is $C = C(x)$, then the per unit **average cost function** is

$$\overline{C} = \frac{C(x)}{x}$$

Note that the average cost per unit is undefined if no units are produced.

We can use derivatives to find the minimum of the average cost function, as the next example shows.

EXAMPLE   3   Average Cost

If the total cost function for a commodity is given by $C = \frac{1}{4}x^2 + 4x + 100$ dollars, where x represents the number of units produced, producing how many units will result in a minimum *average cost* per unit? Find the minimum average cost.

Solution

Begin by finding the average cost function and its derivative:

$$\overline{C} = \frac{\frac{1}{4}x^2 + 4x + 100}{x} = \frac{1}{4}x + 4 + \frac{100}{x}$$

$$\overline{C}' = \overline{C}'(x) = \frac{1}{4} - \frac{100}{x^2}$$

Setting $\overline{C}' = 0$ gives

$$0 = \frac{1}{4} - \frac{100}{x^2} \qquad \text{so} \qquad 0 = x^2 - 400 \quad \text{and} \quad x = \pm 20$$

Because the quantity produced must be positive, 20 units should minimize the average cost per unit. We show that it is an absolute minimum by using the second derivative.

$$\overline{C}''(x) = \frac{200}{x^3} \quad \text{so} \quad \overline{C}''(x) > 0 \quad \text{when } x > 0$$

Thus the minimum average cost per unit occurs if 20 units are produced. The graph of the average cost per unit is shown in Figure 10.30. The minimum average cost per unit is $\overline{C}(20) = \$14$.

Figure 10.30

CHECKPOINT   2. If $C(x) = 0.01x^2 + 20x + 2500$, form $\overline{C}(x)$, the average cost function, and find the minimum average cost.

The graph of the cost function for the commodity in Example 3 is shown in Figure 10.31, along with several lines that join $(0, 0)$ to a point of the form $(x, C(x))$ on the total cost graph. Note that the slope of each of these lines has the form

$$\frac{C(x) - 0}{x - 0} = \frac{C(x)}{x}$$

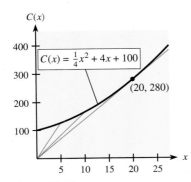

Figure 10.31

so the slope of each line is the *average cost* for the given number of units at the point on $C(x)$. Note that the line from the origin to the point on the curve where $x = 20$ is tangent to the total cost curve. Hence, when $x = 20$, the slope of this line represents both the derivative of the cost function (the *marginal cost*) and the *average cost*. All lines from the origin to points with x-values larger than 20 or smaller than 20 are steeper (and therefore have greater slopes) than the line to the point where $x = 20$. Thus the minimum average cost occurs where the average cost equals the marginal cost. You will be asked to show this analytically in Problems 21 and 22 of the 10.3 Exercises.

Maximizing Profit   We have defined the marginal profit function as the derivative of the profit function. That is,

$$\overline{MP} = P'(x)$$

In this chapter we have seen how to use the derivative to find maxima and minima for various functions. Now we can apply those same techniques in the context of **profit maximization.** We can use marginal profit to maximize profit functions.

If there is a physical limitation on the number of units that can be produced in a given period of time, then the endpoints of the interval caused by these limitations should also be checked.

EXAMPLE 4   Profit

Suppose that the production capacity for a certain commodity cannot exceed 30. If the total profit for this commodity is

$$P(x) = 4x^3 - 210x^2 + 3600x - 200 \quad \text{dollars}$$

where x is the number of units sold, find the number of items that will maximize profit.

Solution
The restrictions on capacity mean that $P(x)$ is restricted by $0 \leq x \leq 30$. The marginal profit function is

$$P'(x) = 12x^2 - 420x + 3600$$

Setting $P'(x)$ equal to 0, we get

$$0 = 12(x - 15)(x - 20)$$

so $P'(x) = 0$ at $x = 15$ *and* $x = 20$. A sign diagram for $P'(x)$ tests these critical values.

Thus, at (15, 20,050) the total profit function has a *relative* maximum, but we must check the endpoints (0 and 30) before deciding whether it is the absolute maximum.

$$P(0) = -200 \quad \text{and} \quad P(30) = 26,800$$

Thus the absolute maximum profit is $26,800, and it occurs at the endpoint, $x = 30$. Figure 10.32 shows the graph of the profit function.

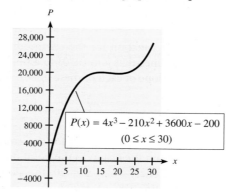

Figure 10.32

In a **monopolistic market,** the seller who has a monopoly controls the supply of a product and can force the price higher by limiting supply.

If the demand function for the product is $p = f(x)$, total revenue for the sale of x units is $R(x) = px = f(x) \cdot x$. Note that the price p is fixed by the market in a competitive market but varies with output for the monopolist.

If $\overline{C} = \overline{C}(x)$ represents the average cost per unit sold, then the total cost for the x units sold is $C = \overline{C} \cdot x = \overline{C}x$. Because we have both total cost and total revenue as a function of the quantity, x, we can maximize the profit function, $P(x) = px - \overline{C}x$, where p represents the demand function $p = f(x)$ and $\overline{C}$ represents the average cost function $\overline{C} = \overline{C}(x)$.

| EXAMPLE 5 | **Profit in a Monopoly Market** |

MONOPOLY

One big player controls supply and dictates pricing.

The price of a product in dollars is related to the number of units x demanded daily by

$$p = 168 - 0.2x$$

A monopolist finds that the daily average cost for this product is

$$\overline{C} = 120 + x \quad \text{dollars}$$

(a) How many units must be sold daily to maximize profit?
(b) What is the selling price at this "optimal" level of production?
(c) What is the maximum possible daily profit?

Solution

(a) The total revenue function for the product is

$$R(x) = px = (168 - 0.2x)x = 168x - 0.2x^2$$

and the total cost function is

$$C(x) = \overline{C} \cdot x = (120 + x)x = 120x + x^2$$

Thus the profit function is

$$P(x) = R(x) - C(x) = 168x - 0.2x^2 - (120x + x^2) = 48x - 1.2x^2$$

Then $P'(x) = 48 - 2.4x$, so $P'(x) = 0$ when $x = 20$. We see that $P''(20) = -2.4$, so by the second-derivative test, $P(x)$ has a maximum at $x = 20$. That is, selling 20 units will maximize profit.

COMPETITION

(b) The selling price is determined by $p = 168 - 0.2x$, so the price that will result from supplying 20 units per day is $p = 168 - 0.2(20) = 164$. That is, the "optimal" selling price is $164 per unit.

(c) The profit at $x = 20$ is $P(20) = 48(20) - 1.2(20)^2 = 960 - 480 = 480$. Thus the maximum possible profit is $480 per day.

Several players are so small that individual actions cannot affect product

In a **competitive market,** each firm is so small that its actions in the market cannot affect the price of the product. The price of the product is determined in the market by the intersection of the market demand curve (from all consumers) and market supply curve (from all firms that supply this product). The firm can sell as little or as much as it desires at the market equilibrium price.

Therefore, a firm in a competitive market has a total revenue function given by $R(x) = px$, where p is the market equilibrium price for the product and x is the quantity sold.

| EXAMPLE 6 | **Profit in a Competitive Market** |

A firm in a competitive market must sell its product for $200 per unit. The average cost per unit (per month) is $\overline{C} = 80 + x$, where x is the number of units sold per month. How many units should be sold to maximize profit?

Solution

If the average cost per unit is $\overline{C} = 80 + x$, then the total cost of x units is given by $C(x) = (80 + x)x = 80x + x^2$. The revenue per unit is \$200, so the total revenue is given by $R(x) = 200x$. Thus the profit function is

$$P(x) = R(x) - C(x) = 200x - (80x + x^2), \quad \text{or} \quad P(x) = 120x - x^2$$

Then $P'(x) = 120 - 2x$. Setting $P'(x) = 0$ and solving for x gives $x = 60$. Because $P''(60) = -2$, the profit is maximized when the firm sells 60 units per month. ∎

CHECKPOINT

3. (a) If $p = 5000 - x$ gives the demand function in a monopoly market, find $R(x)$, if it is possible with this information.
   (b) If $p = 5000 - x$ gives the demand function in a competitive market, find $R(x)$, if it is possible with this information.

4. If $R(x) = 400x - 0.25x^2$ and $C(x) = 150x + 0.25x^2 + 8500$ are the total revenue and total cost (both in dollars) for x units of a product, find the number of units that gives maximum profit and find the maximum profit.

Calculator Note

As we have seen, graphing calculators can be used to locate maximum values. In addition, if it is difficult to determine critical values algebraically, we may be able to approximate them graphically. For example, if

$$P(x) = 2500 - \frac{3000}{x + 1} - 12x - x^2 \quad \text{then} \quad P'(x) = \frac{3000}{(x + 1)^2} - 12 - 2x$$

Finding the critical values by solving $P'(x) = 0$ is difficult unless we use a graphing approach. Figure 10.33(a) shows the graph of $P(x)$, and Figure 10.33(b) shows the graph of $P'(x)$. These figures indicate that the maximum occurs near $x = 10$.

By adjusting the viewing window for $P'(x)$, we obtain the graph in Figure 10.34. This shows that $P'(x) = 0$ when $x = 9$. The maximum is $P(9) = 2500 - 300 - 108 - 81 = 2011$. See Appendix C, Section 10.3, for additional details. ∎

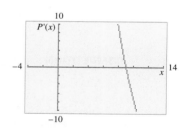

Figure 10.33   (a)   (b)   Figure 10.34

CHECKPOINT SOLUTIONS

1. False. $\overline{MR} = R'(x)$, but there may also be critical points where $R'(x)$ is undefined, or $R(x)$ may be maximized at endpoints of a restricted domain.

2. $$\overline{C}(x) = \frac{C(x)}{x} = \frac{0.01x^2 + 20x + 2500}{x} = 0.01x + 20 + \frac{2500}{x}$$

$$\overline{C}'(x) = 0.01 - \frac{2500}{x^2}$$

Solving $\overline{C}'(x) = 0$ gives

$$0.01 - \frac{2500}{x^2} = 0 \quad \text{so} \quad x^2 = 250{,}000 \quad \text{and} \quad x = \pm 500$$

Using $\overline{C}''(x) = 5000/x^3$ we see that $\overline{C}''(500) > 0$ so $x = 500$ gives the minimum average cost per unit of $\overline{C}(500) = 5 + 20 + 5 = 30$ dollars per unit.

3. (a) $R(x) = p \cdot x = (5000 - x)x = 5000x - x^2$

(b) In a competitive market, $R(x) = p \cdot x$, where p is the constant equilibrium price. Thus we need to know the supply function and find the equilibrium price before we can form $R(x)$.

4. $P(x) = R(x) - C(x) = 250x - 0.5x^2 - 8500$ and $P'(x) = 250 - x$. $P'(x) = 0$ when $x = 250$ and $P''(x) = -1$ for all x. Hence the second-derivative test shows that the (absolute) maximum profit occurs when $x = 250$ and is $P(250) = \$22{,}750$.

| EXERCISES | 10.3

In Problems 1–4, find the absolute maxima and minima for $f(x)$ on the interval $[a, b]$.

1. $f(x) = x^3 - 2x^2 - 4x + 2, [-1, 3]$
2. $f(x) = x^3 - 3x + 3, [-3, 1.5]$
3. $f(x) = x^3 + x^2 - x + 1, [-2, 0]$
4. $f(x) = x^3 - x^2 - x, [-0.5, 2]$

MAXIMIZING REVENUE

5. (a) If the total revenue function for a hammer is $R = 36x - 0.01x^2$, then sale of how many hammers, x, will maximize the total revenue in dollars? Find the maximum revenue.

(b) Find the maximum revenue if production is limited to at most 1500 hammers.

6. (a) If the total revenue function for a blender is $R(x) = 25x - 0.05x^2$, sale of how many units, x, will provide the maximum total revenue in dollars? Find the maximum revenue.

(b) Find the maximum revenue if production is limited to at most 200 blenders.

7. If the total revenue function for a computer is $R(x) = 2000x - 20x^2 - x^3$, find the level of sales, x, that maximizes revenue and find the maximum revenue in dollars.

8. A firm has total revenues given by

$$R(x) = 2800x - 8x^2 - x^3 \text{ dollars}$$

for x units of a product. Find the maximum revenue from sales of that product.

9. An agency charges $100 per person for a trip to a concert if 70 people travel in a group. But for each person above the 70, the charge will be reduced by $1.00. How many people will maximize the total revenue for the agency if the trip is limited to at most 90 people?

10. A company handles an apartment building with 70 units. Experience has shown that if the rent for each of the units is $540 per month, all the units will be filled, but 1 unit will become vacant for each $10 increase in the monthly rate. What rent should be charged to maximize the total revenue from the building if the upper limit on the rent is $650 per month?

11. A cable TV company has 4000 customers paying $55 each month. If each $1 reduction in price attracts 100 new customers, find the price that yields maximum revenue. Find the maximum revenue.

12. If club members charge $5 admission to a classic car show, 1000 people will attend, and for each $1 increase in price, 100 fewer people will attend. What price will give the maximum revenue for the show? Find the maximum revenue.

13. The function $\overline{R}(x) = R(x)/x$ defines the average revenue for selling x units. For

$$R(x) = 2000x + 20x^2 - x^3$$

(a) find the maximum average revenue.

(b) show that $\overline{R}(x)$ attains its maximum at an x-value where $\overline{R}(x) = \overline{MR}$.

14. For the revenue function given by

$$R(x) = 2800x + 8x^2 - x^3$$

(a) find the maximum average revenue.

(b) show that $\overline{R}(x)$ attains its maximum at an x-value where $\overline{R}(x) = \overline{MR}$.

MINIMIZING AVERAGE COST

15. If the total cost function for a lamp is $C(x) = 250 + 33x + 0.1x^2$ dollars, producing how many units, x, will result in a minimum average cost per unit? Find the minimum average cost.

16. If the total cost function for a product is $C(x) = 300 + 10x + 0.03x^2$ dollars, producing how many units, x, will result in a minimum average cost per unit? Find the minimum average cost.

17. If the total cost function for a product is $C(x) = 810 + 0.1x^2$ dollars, producing how many units, x, will result in a minimum average cost per unit? Find the minimum average cost.

18. If the total cost function for a product is $C(x) = 250 + 6x + 0.1x^2$ dollars, producing how many units, x, will minimize the average cost? Find the minimum average cost.

19. If the total cost function for a product is $C(x) = 100(0.02x + 4)^3$ dollars, where x represents the number of hundreds of units produced, producing how many units will minimize average cost? Find the minimum average cost.

20. If the total cost function for a product is $C(x) = (x + 5)^3$ dollars, where x represents the number of hundreds of units produced, producing how many units will minimize average cost? Find the minimum average cost.

21. For the cost function $C(x) = 25 + 13x + x^2$, show that average costs are minimized at the x-value where

$$\overline{C}(x) = \overline{MC}$$

22. For the cost function $C(x) = 300 + 10x + 0.03x^2$, show that average costs are minimized at the x-value where

$$\overline{C}(x) = \overline{MC}$$

The graphs in Problems 23 and 24 show total cost functions. For each problem:
(a) Explain how to use the total cost graph to determine the level of production at which average cost is minimized.
(b) Determine that level of production.

23.

24.

MAXIMIZING PROFIT

25. If the profit function for a product is $P(x) = 5600x + 85x^2 - x^3 - 200{,}000$ dollars, selling how many items, x, will produce a maximum profit? Find the maximum profit.

26. If the profit function for a commodity is $P = 6400x - 18x^2 - \frac{1}{3}x^3 - 40{,}000$ dollars, selling how many units, x, will result in a maximum profit? Find the maximum profit.

27. A manufacturer estimates that its product can be produced at a total cost of $C(x) = 45{,}000 + 100x + x^3$ dollars. If the manufacturer's total revenue from the sale of x units is $R(x) = 4600x$ dollars, determine the level of production x that will maximize the profit. Find the maximum profit.

28. A product can be produced at a total cost $C(x) = 800 + 100x^2 + x^3$ dollars, where x is the number produced. If the total revenue is given by $R(x) = 60{,}000x - 50x^2$ dollars, determine the level of production, x, that will maximize the profit. Find the maximum profit.

29. A firm can produce only 1000 units per month. The monthly total cost is given by $C(x) = 300 + 200x$ dollars, where x is the number produced. If the total revenue is given by $R(x) = 250x - \frac{1}{100}x^2$ dollars, how many items, x, should the firm produce for maximum profit? Find the maximum profit.

30. A firm can produce 100 units per week. If its total cost function is $C = 500 + 1500x$ dollars and its total revenue function is $R = 1600x - x^2$ dollars, how many units, x, should it produce to maximize its profit? Find the maximum profit.

31. *Marginal revenue and marginal cost* The figure shows the graph of a quadratic revenue function and a linear cost function.
(a) At which of the four x-values shown is the distance between the revenue and the cost greatest?
(b) At which of the four x-values shown is the profit largest?
(c) At which of the four x-values shown is the slope of the tangent to the revenue curve equal to the slope of the cost line?
(d) What is the relationship between marginal cost and marginal revenue when profit is at its maximum value?

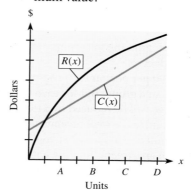

32. *Marginal revenue and marginal cost* The figure shows the graph of revenue function $y = R(x)$ and cost function $y = C(x)$.
(a) At which of the four x-values shown is the profit largest?
(b) At which of the four x-values shown is the slope of the tangent to the revenue curve equal to the slope of the tangent to the cost curve?

(c) What is the relationship between marginal cost and marginal revenue when profit is at its maximum value?

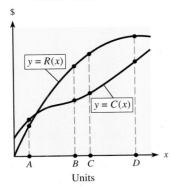

33. A company handles an apartment building with 50 units. Experience has shown that if the rent for each of the units is $720 per month, all of the units will be filled, but 1 unit will become vacant for each $20 increase in this monthly rate. If the monthly cost of maintaining the apartment building is $12 per rented unit, what rent should be charged per month to maximize the profit?

34. A travel agency will plan a tour for groups of size 25 or larger. If the group contains exactly 25 people, the cost is $500 per person. However, each person's cost is reduced by $10 for each additional person above the 25. If the travel agency incurs a cost of $125 per person for the tour, what size group will give the agency the maximum profit?

35. A firm has monthly average costs, in dollars, given by

$$\overline{C} = \frac{45{,}000}{x} + 100 + x$$

where x is the number of units produced per month. The firm can sell its product in a competitive market for $1600 per unit. If production is limited to 600 units per month, find the number of units that gives maximum profit, and find the maximum profit.

36. A small business has weekly average costs, in dollars, of

$$\overline{C} = \frac{100}{x} + 30 + \frac{x}{10}$$

where x is the number of units produced each week. The competitive market price for this business's product is $46 per unit. If production is limited to 150 units per week, find the level of production that yields maximum profit, and find the maximum profit.

37. The weekly demand function for x units of a product sold by only one firm is $p = 600 - \frac{1}{2}x$ dollars, and the average cost of production and sale is $\overline{C} = 300 + 2x$ dollars.
    (a) Find the quantity that will maximize profit.
    (b) Find the selling price at this optimal quantity.
    (c) What is the maximum profit?

38. The monthly demand function for x units of a product sold by a monopoly is $p = 8000 - x$ dollars, and its average cost is $\overline{C} = 4000 + 5x$ dollars.
    (a) Determine the quantity that will maximize profit.
    (b) Determine the selling price at the optimal quantity.
    (c) Determine the maximum profit.

39. The monthly demand function for a product sold by a monopoly is $p = 1960 - \frac{1}{3}x^2$ dollars, and the average cost is $\overline{C} = 1000 + 2x + x^2$ dollars. Production is limited to 1000 units and x is in hundreds of units.
    (a) Find the quantity that will give maximum profit.
    (b) Find the maximum profit.

40. The monthly demand function for x units of a product sold by a monopoly is $p = 5900 - \frac{1}{2}x^2$ dollars, and its average cost is $\overline{C} = 3020 + 2x$ dollars. If production is limited to 100 units, find the number of units that maximizes profit. Will the maximum profit result in a profit or loss?

41. An industry with a monopoly on a product has its average weekly costs, in dollars, given by

$$\overline{C} = \frac{10{,}000}{x} + 60 - 0.03x + 0.00001x^2$$

The weekly demand for x units of the product is given by $p = 120 - 0.015x$ dollars. Find the price the industry should set and the number of units it should produce to obtain maximum profit. Find the maximum profit.

42. A large corporation with monopolistic control in the marketplace has its average daily costs, in dollars, given by

$$\overline{C} = \frac{800}{x} + 100x + x^2$$

The daily demand for x units of its product is given by $p = 60{,}000 - 50x$ dollars. Find the quantity that gives maximum profit, and find the maximum profit. What selling price should the corporation set for its product?

43. Coastal Soda Sales has been granted exclusive market rights to the upcoming Beaufort Seafood Festival. This means that during the festival Coastal will have a monopoly, and it is anxious to take advantage of this position in its pricing strategy. The daily demand function is

$$p = 2 - 0.0004x$$

and the daily total cost function is

$$C(x) = 800 + 0.2x + 0.0001x^2$$

where x is the number of units.
    (a) Determine Coastal's total revenue and profit functions.
    (b) What profit-maximizing price per soda should Coastal charge, how many sodas per day would it expect to sell at this price, and what would be the daily profits?

(c) If the festival organizers wanted to set an economically efficient price of $1.25 per soda, how would this change the results from part (b)? Would Coastal be willing to provide sodas for the festival at this regulated price? Why or why not?

44. A retiree from a large Atlanta financial services firm decides to keep busy and supplement her retirement income by opening a small upscale folk art company near Charleston, South Carolina. The company, Sand Dollar Art, manufactures and sells in a purely competitive market, and the following monthly market information for x units at $$p$ per unit applies:

Demand: $p = 2000 - 4.5x$
Supply: $p = 100 + 0.25x$

(a) Find the market equilibrium quantity and price for this market.
(b) If Sand Dollar Art's monthly cost function is

$$C(x) = 400 + 100x + x^2$$

find the profit-maximizing monthly quantity. What are the total monthly revenues and total monthly costs? What monthly profit does Sand Dollar Art earn?
(c) Assuming that Sand Dollar Art is representative of firms in this competitive market, what is its market share?

MISCELLANEOUS APPLICATIONS

45. **Modeling** *Social Security beneficiaries* The numbers of millions of Social Security beneficiaries for selected years and projected into the future are given in the table.
(a) Find the cubic function that models these data, with x equal to the number of years past 1950.
(b) Find the point of inflection of the graph of this function for $x > 0$.
(c) Graph this function and discuss what the point of inflection indicates.

Year	Number of Beneficiaries (millions)	Year	Number of Beneficiaries (millions)
1950	2.9	2002	44.8
1960	14.3	2010	53.3
1970	25.2	2020	68.8
1980	35.1	2030	82.7
1990	39.5		

Source: 2000 Social Security Trustees Report

46. **Modeling** *Poverty level* The table gives the millions of people in the United States below the poverty level for selected years from 1990 to 2009.

Year	Number	Year	Number
1990	35.6	2002	34.6
1992	38.0	2004	37.0
1994	38.1	2006	36.5
1996	36.5	2008	39.8
1998	34.5	2009	43.6
2000	31.6		

Source: U.S. Bureau of the Census

(a) With $t = 0$ representing 1990, find a cubic function that models these data.
(b) For the years from 1990 to 2009, use the model to determine the absolute maximum and absolute minimum points. Interpret the coordinates of each point.
(c) Find the absolute maximum and absolute minimum for the data.

47. *Dow Jones Industrial Average* The figure shows the Dow Jones Industrial Average for all of 2001, the year of the terrorist attacks on New York City and Washington, D.C.
(a) Approximate when during 2001 the Dow reached its absolute maximum for that year.
(b) When do you think the Dow reached its absolute minimum for this period? What happened to trigger this?

Dow Jones Industrial Average

J A S O N D J F M A M J J A S O N D J
  2000   2001

Source: From *The Wall Street Journal,* January 17, 2002. Copyright © 2002 by Dow Jones & Co. Reprinted by permission of Dow Jones & Co. via Copyright Clearance Center.

48. *Dow Jones averages* The figure shows the daily Dow Jones Industrial Average (DJIA) and its 30-day moving average from late July to early November. Use the figure to complete the following.
(a) Approximate the absolute maximum point and absolute minimum point for the daily DJIA.
(b) Approximate the absolute maximum point and absolute minimum point for the DJIA 30-day moving average.

$INDU (Dow Jones Industrial Average) INDX

Close 12987.55 **Volume** 680.1M **Chg** −55.19(−0.42%) ▼

— $INDU (daily) 12987.55
— MA (30) 13753.53

14,000
13,800
13,600
13,400
13,200
13,000
12,800

Aug 6 13 20 27 **Sep**10 17 24 **Oct** 8 15 22 29 **Nov** 12

Source: StockCharts.com

49. *Social Security support* The graph shows the number of workers, $W = f(t)$, still in the work force per Social Security beneficiary (historically and projected into the future) as a function of time t, in calendar years with $1950 \leq t \leq 2050$. Use the graph to answer the following.

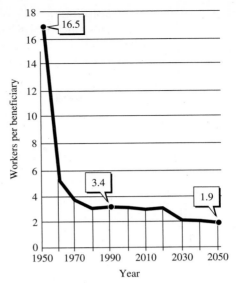

Source: Social Security Administration

(a) What is the absolute maximum of $f(t)$?
(b) What is the absolute minimum of $f(t)$?
(c) Does this graph suggest that Social Security taxes will rise or will fall in the early 21st century? Explain.

10.4

- To apply the procedures for finding maxima and minima to solve problems from the management, life, and social sciences

Applications of Maxima and Minima

▌| APPLICATION PREVIEW |▌

Suppose that a company needs 1,000,000 items during a year and that preparation costs are $800 for each production run. Suppose further that it costs the company $6 to produce each item and $1 to store each item for up to a year. Find the number of units that should be produced in each production run so that the total costs of production and storage are minimized. This question is answered using an inventory cost model (see Example 4).

This inventory-cost determination is a typical example of the kinds of questions and important business applications that require the use of the derivative for finding maxima and minima. As managers, workers, or consumers, we may be interested in such things as maximum revenue, maximum profit, minimum cost, maximum medical dosage, maximum utilization of resources, and so on.

If we have functions that model cost, revenue, or population growth, we can apply the methods of this chapter to find the maxima and minima of those functions.

EXAMPLE 1 **Company Growth**

Suppose that a new company begins production in 2010 with eight employees and the growth of the company over the next 10 years is predicted by

$$N = N(t) = 8\left(1 + \frac{160t}{t^2 + 16}\right), \quad 0 \leq t \leq 10$$

where N is the number of employees t years after 2010.

Determine in what year the number of employees will be maximized and the maximum number of employees.

Solution

This function will have a relative maximum when $N'(t) = 0$.

$$N'(t) = 8\left[\frac{(t^2 + 16)(160) - (160t)(2t)}{(t^2 + 16)^2}\right]$$

$$= 8\left[\frac{160t^2 + 2560 - 320t^2}{(t^2 + 16)^2}\right]$$

$$= 8\left[\frac{2560 - 160t^2}{(t^2 + 16)^2}\right]$$

Because $N'(t) = 0$ when its numerator is 0 (note that this denominator is never 0), we must solve

$$2560 - 160t^2 = 0$$
$$160(4 + t)(4 - t) = 0$$

so
$$t = -4 \quad \text{or} \quad t = 4$$

We are interested only in positive t-values, so we test $t = 4$.

$$\left.\begin{array}{l} N'(0) = 8\left[\dfrac{2560}{256}\right] > 0 \\[2em] N'(10) = 8\left[\dfrac{-13{,}440}{(116)^2}\right] < 0 \end{array}\right\} \Rightarrow \textit{relative maximum}$$

The relative maximum is

$$N(4) = 8\left(1 + \frac{640}{32}\right) = 168$$

Figure 10.35

At $t = 0$, the number of employees is $N(0) = 8$, and it increases to $N(4) = 168$. After $t = 4$ (in 2014), $N(t)$ decreases to $N(10) = 118$ (approximately), so $N(4) = 168$ is the maximum number of employees. Figure 10.35 verifies these conclusions.

Sometimes we must develop the function we need from the statement of the problem. In this case, it is important to understand what is to be maximized or minimized and to express that quantity as a function of *one* variable.

EXAMPLE 2 Minimizing Cost

A farmer needs to enclose a rectangular pasture containing 1,600,000 square feet. Suppose that along the road adjoining his property he wants to use a more expensive fence and that he needs no fence on one side perpendicular to the road because a river bounds his property on that side. If the fence costs $15 per foot along the road and $10 per foot along the two remaining sides that must be fenced, what dimensions of his rectangular field will minimize his cost?

Figure 10.36

Solution

In Figure 10.36, x represents the length of the pasture along the road (and parallel to the road) and y represents the width. The cost function for the fence used is

$$C = 15x + 10y + 10x = 25x + 10y$$

We cannot use a derivative to find where C is minimized unless we write C as a function of x or y only. Because the area of the rectangular field must be 1,600,000 square feet, we have

$$A = xy = 1{,}600{,}000$$

Solving for y in terms of x and substituting give C as a function of x.

$$y = \frac{1,600,000}{x}$$

$$C = 25x + 10\left(\frac{1,600,000}{x}\right) = 25x + \frac{16,000,000}{x}$$

The derivative of C with respect to x is

$$C'(x) = 25 - \frac{16,000,000}{x^2}$$

and we find the relative minimum of C as follows:

$$0 = 25 - \frac{16,000,000}{x^2}$$
$$0 = 25x^2 - 16,000,000$$
$$25x^2 = 16,000,000$$
$$x^2 = 640,000 \Rightarrow x = \pm 800$$
We use $x = 800$ feet

Testing to see whether $x = 800$ gives the minimum cost, we find

$$C''(x) = \frac{32,000,000}{x^3}$$

$C''(x) > 0$ for $x > 0$, so $C(x)$ is concave up for all positive x. Thus $x = 800$ gives the absolute minimum, and $C(800) = 40,000$ is the minimum cost. The other dimension of the rectangular field is $y = 1,600,000/800 = 2000$ feet. Figure 10.37 verifies that $C(x)$ reaches its minimum (of 40,000) at $x = 800$. ■

$C(x)$

(thousands)

$C(x) = 25x + \dfrac{16,000,000}{x}$

(800, 40)

Figure 10.37

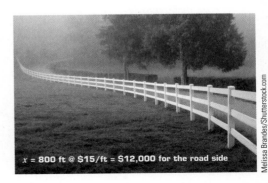

x = 800 ft @ $15/ft = $12,000 for the road side

EXAMPLE 3   Postal Restrictions

Postal restrictions limit the size of packages sent through the mail. If the restrictions are that the length plus the girth may not exceed 108 inches, find the volume of the largest box with square cross section that can be mailed.

Solution
Let l equal the length of the box, and let s equal a side of the square end. See Figure 10.38. The volume we seek to maximize is given by

$$V = s^2l$$

We can use the restriction that girth plus length equals 108,

$$4s + l = 108$$

to express V as a function of s or l. Because $l = 108 - 4s$, the equation for V becomes

$$V = s^2(108 - 4s) = 108s^2 - 4s^3$$

Girth = distance around

Figure 10.38

Figure 10.39

Thus we can use dV/ds to find the critical values.

$$\frac{dV}{ds} = 216s - 12s^2$$

$$0 = s(216 - 12s)$$

The critical values are $s = 0, s = \frac{216}{12} = 18$. The critical value $s = 0$ will not maximize the volume, for in this case, $V = 0$. Testing to the left and right of $s = 18$ gives

$$V'(17) > 0 \quad \text{and} \quad V'(19) < 0$$

Thus $s = 18$ inches and $l = 108 - 4(18) = 36$ inches yield a maximum volume of 11,664 cubic inches. Once again we can verify our results graphically. Figure 10.39 shows that $V = 108s^2 - 4s^3$ achieves its maximum when $s = 18$.

CHECKPOINT

Suppose we want to find the minimum value of $C = 5x + 2y$ and we know that x and y must be positive and that $xy = 1000$.
1. What equation do we differentiate to solve this problem?
2. Find the critical values.
3. Find the minimum value of C.

We next consider **inventory cost models,** in which x items are produced in each production run and items are removed from inventory at a fixed constant rate. Because items are removed at a constant rate, the average number stored at any time is $x/2$. Also, when $x = 0$, new items must be added to inventory from a production run. Thus the number of units in storage changes with time and is illustrated in Figure 10.40. In these models there are costs associated with both production and storage, but lowering one of these costs means increasing the other. To see how inventory cost models work, consider the following example.

Figure 10.40

EXAMPLE 4 Inventory Cost Model | APPLICATION PREVIEW |

Suppose that a company needs 1,000,000 items during a year and that preparation costs are $800 for each production run. Suppose further that it costs the company $6 to produce each item and $1 to store an item for up to a year. If each production run consists of x items, find x so that the total costs of production and storage are minimized.

Solution

The total production costs are given by

$$\binom{\text{No. of}}{\text{runs}}\binom{\text{cost}}{\text{per run}} + \binom{\text{no. of}}{\text{items}}\binom{\text{cost}}{\text{per item}} = \left(\frac{1,000,000}{x}\right)(\$800) + (1,000,000)(\$6)$$

The total storage costs are

$$\binom{\text{Average}}{\text{no. stored}}\binom{\text{storage cost}}{\text{per item}} = \left(\frac{x}{2}\right)(\$1)$$

Thus the total costs of production and storage are

$$C = \left(\frac{1{,}000{,}000}{x}\right)(800) + 6{,}000{,}000 + \frac{x}{2} = \frac{800{,}000{,}000}{x} + 6{,}000{,}000 + \frac{x}{2}$$

We wish to find x so that C is minimized.

$$C' = \frac{-800{,}000{,}000}{x^2} + \frac{1}{2}$$

If $x > 0$, critical values occur when $C' = 0$.

$$0 = \frac{-800{,}000{,}000}{x^2} + \frac{1}{2}$$

$$\frac{800{,}000{,}000}{x^2} = \frac{1}{2}$$

$$1{,}600{,}000{,}000 = x^2$$

$$x = \pm\,40{,}000$$

Because x must be positive, we test $x = 40{,}000$ with the second derivative.

$$C''(x) = \frac{1{,}600{,}000{,}000}{x^3}, \quad \text{so} \quad C''(40{,}000) > 0$$

Note that $x = 40{,}000$ yields an absolute minimum value of C, because $C'' > 0$ for all $x > 0$. That is, production runs of 40,000 items yield minimum total costs for production and storage.

Technology Note   Problems of the types we've studied in this section could also be solved (at least approximately) with a graphing calculator or Excel. With this approach, our first goal is still to express the quantity to be maximized or minimized as a function of one variable. Then that function can be graphed, and the (at least approximate) optimal value can be obtained from the graph. See Appendices C and D, Section 10.4, and the Online Excel Guide for details.

  EXAMPLE 5   **Property Development**

A developer of a campground has to pay for utility line installation to the community center from a transformer on the street at the corner of her property. Because of local restrictions, the lines must be underground on her property. Suppose that the costs are $50 per meter along the street and $100 per meter underground. How far from the transformer should the line enter the property to minimize installation costs? See Figure 10.41.

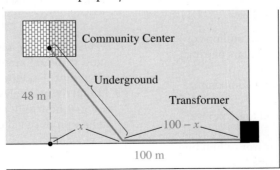

Figure 10.41

Solution

If the developer had the cable placed underground from the community center perpendicular to the street and then to the transformer, then $x = 0$ in Figure 10.41 and the cost would be

$$\$100(48) + \$50(100) = \$9800$$

Figure 10.42

It may be possible to save some money by placing the cable on a diagonal to the street, but then only $x \leq 100$ makes sense. By using the Pythagorean Theorem, we find that the length of the underground cable that meets the street x meters closer to the transformer is

$$\sqrt{48^2 + x^2} = \sqrt{2304 + x^2} \quad \text{meters}$$

Thus the cost C of installation is given by

$$C = 100\sqrt{2304 + x^2} + 50(100 - x) \quad \text{dollars}$$

Figure 10.42 shows the graph of this function over an interval for x that contains $0 \leq x \leq 100$. Because any extrema must occur in this interval, we can find the minimum by using the MIN command on a calculator or Excel. See Appendices C and D, Section 10.4, and the Online Excel Guide for the steps. The minimum cost is \$9156.92, when $x = 27.7$ meters (that is, when the cable meets the street 72.3 meters from the transformer). ∎

CHECKPOINT SOLUTIONS

1. We must differentiate C, but first C must be expressed as a function of one variable: $xy = 1000$ means that $y = 1000/x$. If we substitute $1000/x$ for y in $C = 5x + 2y$, we get

$$C(x) = 5x + 2\left(\frac{1000}{x}\right) = 5x + \frac{2000}{x}$$

   Find $C'(x)$ to solve the problem.

2. $C'(x) = 5 - 2000/x^2$, so $C'(x) = 0$ when

$$5 - \frac{2000}{x^2} = 0, \quad \text{or} \quad x = \pm 20$$

   Because x must be positive, the only critical value is $x = 20$.

3. $C''(x) = 4000/x^3$, so $C''(x) > 0$ for all $x > 0$. Thus $x = 20$ yields the minimum value. Also, when $x = 20$, we have $y = 50$, so the minimum value of C is $C = 5(20) + 2(50) = 200$.

| EXERCISES | 10.4

APPLICATIONS

1. **Return to sales** The manufacturer of GRIPPER tires modeled its return to sales from television advertising expenditures in two regions, as follows:

   Region 1: $S_1 = 30 + 20x_1 - 0.4x_1^2$
   Region 2: $S_2 = 20 + 36x_2 - 1.3x_2^2$

   where S_1 and S_2 are the sales revenue in millions of dollars and x_1 and x_2 are millions of dollars of expenditures for television advertising.
   (a) What advertising expenditures would maximize sales revenue in each district?
   (b) How much money will be needed to maximize sales revenue in both districts?

2. **Projectiles** A ball thrown into the air from a building 100 ft high travels along a path described by

$$y = \frac{-x^2}{110} + x + 100$$

   where y is its height in feet and x is the horizontal distance from the building in feet. What is the maximum height the ball will reach?

3. **Profit** The profit from a grove of orange trees is given by $x(200 - x)$ dollars, where x is the number of orange trees per acre. How many trees per acre will maximize the profit?

4. **Reaction rates** The velocity v of an autocatalytic reaction can be represented by the equation

$$v = x(a - x)$$

   where a is the amount of material originally present and x is the amount that has been decomposed at any given time. Find the maximum velocity of the reaction.

5. **Productivity** Analysis of daily output of a factory during an 8-hour shift shows that the hourly number of units y produced after t hours of production is

$$y = 70t + \tfrac{1}{2}t^2 - t^3, \quad 0 \leq t \leq 8$$

   (a) After how many hours will the hourly number of units be maximized?
   (b) What is the maximum hourly output?

6. **Productivity** A time study showed that, on average, the productivity of a worker after t hours on the job can be modeled by

$$P = 27t + 6t^2 - t^3, \quad 0 \leq t \leq 8$$

where P is the number of units produced per hour. After how many hours will productivity be maximized? What is the maximum productivity?

7. *Consumer expenditure* Suppose that the demand x (in units) for a product is $x = 10{,}000 - 100p$, where p dollars is the market price per unit. Then the consumer expenditure for the product is

$$E = px = 10{,}000p - 100p^2$$

For what market price will expenditure be greatest?

8. *Production costs* Suppose that the monthly cost in dollars of mining a certain ore is related to the number of pieces of equipment used, according to

$$C = 25{,}000x + \frac{870{,}000}{x}, \quad x > 0$$

where x is the number of pieces of equipment used. Using how many pieces of equipment will minimize the cost?

Medication **For Problems 9 and 10, consider that when medicine is administered, reaction (measured in change of blood pressure or temperature) can be modeled by**

$$R = m^2 \left(\frac{c}{2} - \frac{m}{3} \right)$$

where c is a positive constant and m is the amount of medicine absorbed into the blood (*Source:* R. M. Thrall et al., *Some Mathematical Models in Biology*, U.S. Department of Commerce, 1967).

9. Find the amount of medicine that is being absorbed into the blood when the reaction is maximum.

10. The rate of change of reaction R with respect to the amount of medicine m is defined to be the sensitivity.
    (a) Find the sensitivity, S.
    (b) Find the amount of medicine that is being absorbed into the blood when the sensitivity is maximum.

11. *Advertising and sales* An inferior product with a large advertising budget sells well when it is introduced, but sales fall as people discontinue use of the product. Suppose that the weekly sales S are given by

$$S = \frac{200t}{(t + 1)^2}, \quad t \geq 0$$

where S is in millions of dollars and t is in weeks. After how many weeks will sales be maximized?

12. *Revenue* A newly released film has its weekly revenue given by

$$R(t) = \frac{50t}{t^2 + 36}, \quad t \geq 0$$

where R is in millions of dollars and t is in weeks.
    (a) After how many weeks will the weekly revenue be maximized?
    (b) What is the maximum weekly revenue?

13. *News impact* Suppose that the percent p (as a decimal) of people who could correctly identify two of eight defendants in a drug case t days after their trial began is given by

$$p(t) = \frac{6.4t}{t^2 + 64} + 0.05$$

Find the number of days before the percent is maximized, and find the maximum percent.

14. *Candidate recognition* Suppose that in an election year the proportion p of voters who recognize a certain candidate's name t months after the campaign started is given by

$$p(t) = \frac{7.2t}{t^2 + 36} + 0.2$$

After how many months is the proportion maximized?

15. *Minimum fence* Two equal rectangular lots are enclosed by fencing the perimeter of a rectangular lot and then putting a fence across its middle. If each lot is to contain 1200 square feet, what is the minimum amount of fence needed to enclose the lots (include the fence across the middle)?

16. *Minimum fence* The running yard for a dog kennel must contain at least 900 square feet. If a 20-foot side of the kennel is used as part of one side of a rectangular yard with 900 square feet, what dimensions will require the least amount of fencing?

17. *Minimum cost* A rectangular field with one side along a river is to be fenced. Suppose that no fence is needed along the river, the fence on the side opposite the river costs $20 per foot, and the fence on the other sides costs $5 per foot. If the field must contain 45,000 square feet, what dimensions will minimize costs?

18. *Minimum cost* From a tract of land a developer plans to fence a rectangular region and then divide it into two identical rectangular lots by putting a fence down the middle. Suppose that the fence for the outside boundary costs $5 per foot and the fence for the middle costs $2 per foot. If each lot contains 13,500 square feet, find the dimensions of each lot that yield the minimum cost for the fence.

19. *Optimization at a fixed cost* A rectangular area is to be enclosed and divided into thirds. The family has $800 to spend for the fencing material. The outside fence costs $10 per running foot installed, and the dividers cost $20 per running foot installed. What are the dimensions that will maximize the area enclosed? (The answer contains a fraction.)

20. *Minimum cost* A kennel of 640 square feet is to be constructed as shown. The cost is $4 per running foot for the sides and $1 per running foot for the ends and dividers. What are the dimensions of the kennel that will minimize the cost?

21. **Minimum cost** The base of a rectangular box is to be twice as long as it is wide. The volume of the box is 256 cubic inches. The material for the top costs $0.10 per square inch and the material for the sides and bottom costs $0.05 per square inch. Find the dimensions that will make the cost a minimum.

22. **Velocity of air during a cough** According to B. F. Visser, the velocity v of air in the trachea during a cough is related to the radius r of the trachea according to

$$v = ar^2(r_0 - r)$$

where a is a constant and r_0 is the radius of the trachea in a relaxed state. Find the radius r that produces the maximum velocity of air in the trachea during a cough.

23. **Inventory cost model** Suppose that a company needs 1,500,000 items during a year and that preparation for each production run costs $600. Suppose also that it costs $15 to produce each item and $2 per year to store an item. Use the inventory cost model to find the number of items in each production run so that the total costs of production and storage are minimized.

24. **Inventory cost model** Suppose that a company needs 60,000 items during a year and that preparation for each production run costs $400. Suppose further that it costs $4 to produce each item and $0.75 to store an item for one year. Use the inventory cost model to find the number of items in each production run that will minimize the total costs of production and storage.

25. **Inventory cost model** A company needs 150,000 items per year. It costs the company $360 to prepare a production run of these items and $7 to produce each item. If it also costs the company $0.75 per year for each item stored, find the number of items that should be produced in each run so that total costs of production and storage are minimized.

26. **Inventory cost model** A company needs 450,000 items per year. Production costs are $500 to prepare for a production run and $10 for each item produced. Inventory costs are $2 per item per year. Find the number of items that should be produced in each run so that the total costs of production and storage are minimized.

27. **Volume** A rectangular box with a square base is to be formed from a square piece of metal with 12-inch sides. If a square piece with side x is cut from each corner of the metal and the sides are folded up to form an open box, the volume of the box is $V = (12 - 2x)^2 x$. What value of x will maximize the volume of the box?

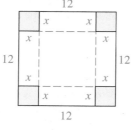

28. **Volume**
    (a) A square piece of cardboard 36 centimeters on a side is to be formed into a rectangular box by cutting squares with length x from each corner and folding up the sides. What is the maximum volume possible for the box?

    (b) Show that if the piece of cardboard is k centimeters on each side, cutting squares of size $k/6$ and folding up the sides gives the maximum volume.

29. **Revenue** The owner of an orange grove must decide when to pick one variety of oranges. She can sell them for $8 a bushel if she sells them now, with each tree yielding an average of 5 bushels. The yield increases by half a bushel per week for the next 5 weeks, but the price per bushel decreases by $0.50 per bushel each week. When should the oranges be picked for maximum return?

30. **Minimum material**
    (a) A box with an open top and a square base is to be constructed to contain 4000 cubic inches. Find the dimensions that will require the minimum amount of material to construct the box.

    (b) A box with an open top and a square base is to be constructed to contain k cubic inches. Show that the minimum amount of material is used to construct the box when each side of the base is

$$x = (2k)^{1/3} \text{ and the height is } y = \left(\frac{k}{4}\right)^{1/3}$$

31. **Minimum cost** A printer has a contract to print 100,000 posters for a political candidate. He can run the posters by using any number of plates from 1 to 30 on his press. If he uses x metal plates, they will produce x copies of the poster with each impression of the press. The metal plates cost $20.00 to prepare, and it costs $125.00 per hour to run the press. If the press can make 1000 impressions per hour, how many metal plates should the printer make to minimize costs?

32. **Shortest time** A vacationer on an island 8 miles offshore from a point that is 48 miles from town must travel to town occasionally. (See the figure.) The vacationer has a boat capable of traveling 30 mph and can go by auto along the coast at 55 mph. At what point should the car be left to minimize the time it takes to get to town?

33. **Worldwide cellular subscribers** The millions of worldwide cellular subscribers can be modeled by

$$C(t) = -0.895t^3 + 30.6t^2 + 2.99t + 55.6$$

where t is the number of years past 1995.

    (a) In what year does the model predict the number of worldwide cellular subscribers will reach a maximum?

    (b) Do you think the number of worldwide cellular subscribers will decrease after the year found in part (a)?

| OBJECTIVES | **10.5** |

- To locate horizontal asymptotes
- To locate vertical asymptotes
- To sketch graphs of functions that have vertical and/or horizontal asymptotes

Rational Functions: More Curve Sketching

■ | APPLICATION PREVIEW |

Suppose that the total cost of producing a shipment of a product is

$$C(x) = 5000x + \frac{125,000}{x}, \quad x > 0$$

where x is the number of machines used in the production process. To find the number of machines that will minimize the total cost, we find the minimum value of this rational function. (See Example 3.) The graph of this function contains a vertical asymptote at $x = 0$. We will discuss graphs and applications involving asymptotes in this section.

The procedures for using the first-derivative test and the second-derivative test are given in previous sections, but none of the graphs discussed in those sections contains vertical asymptotes or horizontal asymptotes. In this section, we consider how to use information about asymptotes along with the first and second derivatives, and we present a unified approach to curve sketching.

Asymptotes   In Section 2.4, "Special Functions and Their Graphs," we first discussed asymptotes and saw that they are important features of the graphs that have them. Then, in our discussion of limits in Sections 9.1 and 9.2, we discovered the relationship between certain limits and asymptotes. The formal definition of **vertical asymptotes** uses limits.

Vertical Asymptote

The line $x = x_0$ is a **vertical asymptote** of the graph of $y = f(x)$ if the values of $f(x)$ approach $+\infty$ or $-\infty$ as x approaches x_0 (from the left or the right).

From our work with limits, recall that a vertical asymptote will occur on the graph of a function at an x-value at which the denominator (but not the numerator) of the function is equal to zero. These observations allow us to determine where vertical asymptotes occur.

Vertical Asymptote of a Rational Function

The graph of the rational function

$$h(x) = \frac{f(x)}{g(x)}$$

has a vertical asymptote at $x = c$ if $g(c) = 0$ and $f(c) \neq 0$.

Because a **horizontal asymptote** tells us the behavior of the values of the function (y-coordinates) when x increases or decreases without bound, we use limits at infinity to determine the existence of horizontal asymptotes.

Horizontal Asymptote

The graph of a rational function $y = f(x)$ will have a **horizontal asymptote** at $y = b$, for a constant b, if

$$\lim_{x \to +\infty} f(x) = b \quad \text{or} \quad \lim_{x \to -\infty} f(x) = b$$

Otherwise, the graph has no horizontal asymptote.

For a rational function f, $\lim_{x \to +\infty} f(x) = b$ if and only if $\lim_{x \to -\infty} f(x) = b$, so we only need to find one of these limits to locate a horizontal asymptote. In Problems 37 and 38 in the 9.2 Exercises, the following statements regarding horizontal asymptotes of the graphs of rational functions were proved.

Horizontal Asymptotes of Rational Functions

Consider the rational function $y = \dfrac{f(x)}{g(x)} = \dfrac{a_n x^n + \cdots + a_1 x + a_0}{b_m x^m + \cdots + b_1 x + b_0}$.

1. If $n < m$ (that is, if the degree of the numerator is less than that of the denominator), a horizontal asymptote occurs at $y = 0$ (the x-axis).

2. If $n = m$ (that is, if the degree of the numerator equals that of the denominator), a horizontal asymptote occurs at $y = \dfrac{a_n}{b_m}$ (the ratio of the leading coefficients).

3. If $n > m$ (that is, if the degree of the numerator is greater than that of the denominator), there is no horizontal asymptote.

EXAMPLE 1

Vertical and Horizontal Asymptotes

Find any vertical and horizontal asymptotes for

(a) $f(x) = \dfrac{2x - 1}{x + 2}$ (b) $f(x) = \dfrac{x^2 + 3}{1 - x}$

Solution

(a) The denominator of this function is 0 at $x = -2$, and because this value does not make the numerator 0, there is a vertical asymptote at $x = -2$. Because the function is rational, with the degree of the numerator equal to that of the denominator and with the ratio of the leading coefficients equal to 2, the graph of the function has a horizontal asymptote at $y = 2$. The graph is shown in Figure 10.43(a).

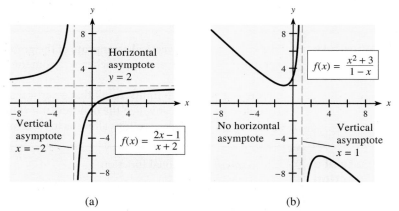

Figure 10.43   (a)   (b)

(b) At $x = 1$, the denominator of $f(x)$ is 0 and the numerator is not, so a vertical asymptote occurs at $x = 1$. The function is rational with the degree of the numerator greater than that of the denominator, so there is no horizontal asymptote. The graph is shown in Figure 10.43(b).

More Curve Sketching   We now extend our first- and second-derivative techniques of curve sketching to include functions that have asymptotes.

In general, the following steps are helpful when we sketch the graph of a function.

Graphing Guidelines

1. Determine the domain of the function. The domain may be restricted by the nature of the problem or by the equation.
2. Look for vertical asymptotes, especially if the function is a rational function.
3. Look for horizontal asymptotes, especially if the function is a rational function.
4. Find the relative maxima and minima by using the first-derivative test or the second-derivative test.
5. Use the second derivative to find the points of inflection if this derivative is easily found.
6. Use other information (intercepts, for example) and plot additional points to complete the sketch of the graph.

EXAMPLE 2

Graphing with Asymptotes

Sketch the graph of the function $f(x) = \dfrac{x^2}{(x+1)^2}$.

Solution

1. The domain is the set of all real numbers except $x = -1$.
2. Because $x = -1$ makes the denominator 0 and does not make the numerator 0, there is a vertical asymptote at $x = -1$.
3. Because $\dfrac{x^2}{(x+1)^2} = \dfrac{x^2}{x^2 + 2x + 1}$

   the function is rational with the degree of the numerator equal to that of the denominator and with the ratio of the leading coefficients equal to 1. Hence, the graph of the function has a horizontal asymptote at $y = 1$.
4. To find any maxima and minima, we first find $f'(x)$.

$$f'(x) = \frac{(x+1)^2\,(2x) - x^2\,[2(x+1)]}{(x+1)^4} = \frac{2x(x+1)[(x+1)-x]}{(x+1)^4} = \frac{2x}{(x+1)^3}$$

Thus $f'(x) = 0$ when $x = 0$ (and $y = 0$), and $f'(x)$ is undefined at $x = -1$ (where the vertical asymptote occurs). Using $x = 0$ and $x = -1$ gives the following sign diagram for $f'(x)$. The sign diagram shows that the critical point $(0, 0)$ is a relative minimum and shows how the graph approaches the vertical asymptote at $x = -1$.

*$x = -1$ is a vertical asymptote.

5. The second derivative is

$$f''(x) = \frac{(x+1)^3\,(2) - 2x[3(x+1)^2]}{(x+1)^6}$$

Factoring $(x+1)^2$ from the numerator and simplifying give

$$f''(x) = \frac{2 - 4x}{(x+1)^4}$$

We can see that $f''(0) = 2 > 0$, so the second-derivative test also shows that $(0, 0)$ is a relative minimum. We see that $f''(x) = 0$ when $x = \frac{1}{2}$. Checking $f''(x)$ between $x = -1$ (where it is undefined) and $x = \frac{1}{2}$ shows that the graph is concave up on this

(a)

(b)

Figure 10.44

interval. Note also that $f''(x) < 0$ for $x > \frac{1}{2}$, so the point $(\frac{1}{2}, \frac{1}{9})$ is a point of inflection. Also see the sign diagram for $f''(x)$.

*$x = -1$ is a vertical asymptote.

6. To see how the graph approaches the horizontal asymptote, we check $f(x)$ for large values of $|x|$.

$$f(-100) = \frac{(-100)^2}{(-99)^2} = \frac{10{,}000}{9{,}801} > 1, \quad f(100) = \frac{100^2}{101^2} = \frac{10{,}000}{10{,}201} < 1$$

Thus the graph has the characteristics shown in Figure 10.44(a). The graph is shown in Figure 10.44(b). ∎

When we wish to learn about a function $f(x)$ or sketch its graph, it is important to understand what information we obtain from $f(x)$, from $f'(x)$, and from $f''(x)$. The following summary may be helpful.

■ | DERIVATIVES AND GRAPHS |

Source	Information Provided
$f(x)$	y-coordinates; horizontal asymptotes, vertical asymptotes; domain restrictions
$f'(x)$	Increasing $[f'(x) > 0]$; decreasing $[f'(x) < 0]$; critical points $[f'(x) = 0$ or $f'(x)$ undefined$]$; sign-diagram tests for maxima and minima
$f''(x)$	Concave up $[f''(x) > 0]$; concave down $[f''(x) < 0]$; possible points of inflection $[f''(x) = 0$ or $f''(x)$ undefined$]$; sign-diagram tests for points of inflection; second-derivative test for maxima and minima

CHECKPOINT

1. Let $f(x) = \dfrac{2x + 10}{x - 1}$ and decide whether the following are true or false.
   (a) $f(x)$ has a vertical asymptote at $x = 1$.
   (b) $f(x)$ has $y = 2$ as its horizontal asymptote.

2. Let $f(x) = \dfrac{x^3 - 16}{x} + 1$; then $f'(x) = \dfrac{2x^3 + 16}{x^2}$ and $f''(x) = \dfrac{2x^3 - 32}{x^3}$.

   Use these to determine whether the following are true or false.
   (a) There are no asymptotes.
   (b) $f'(x) = 0$ when $x = -2$
   (c) A partial sign diagram for $f'(x)$ is

   $f'(x)$ $- - - - 0 + + + + * + + + +$

   ```
         |       |
        -2       0
   ```

   *means $f'(0)$ is undefined.
   (d) There is a relative minimum at $x = -2$.
   (e) A partial sign diagram for $f''(x)$ is

   $f''(x)$ $+ + + + * - - - - 0 + + + +$

   ```
         |       |
         0     ∛16
   ```

   *means $f''(0)$ is undefined.
   (f) There are points of inflection at $x = 0$ and $x = \sqrt[3]{16}$.

EXAMPLE 3   Production Costs | APPLICATION PREVIEW |

Suppose that the total cost of producing a shipment of a certain product is

$$C(x) = 5000x + \frac{125,000}{x}, \quad x > 0$$

where x is the number of machines used in the production process.

(a) Determine any asymptotes for $C(x)$.
(b) How many machines should be used to minimize the total cost?
(c) Graph this total cost function.

Solution
(a) Writing this function with all terms over a common denominator gives

$$C(x) = 5000x + \frac{125,000}{x} = \frac{5000x^2 + 125,000}{x}$$

The domain of $C(x)$ does not include 0, and $C \to +\infty$ as $x \to 0^+$, so there is a vertical asymptote at $x = 0$. Thus the cost increases without bound as the number of machines used in the process approaches zero. Because the numerator has a higher degree than the denominator, there is no horizontal asymptote.

(b) Finding the derivative of $C(x)$ gives

$$C'(x) = 5000 - \frac{125,000}{x^2} = \frac{5000x^2 - 125,000}{x^2}$$

Setting $C'(x) = 0$ and solving for x gives the critical values of x.

$$0 = \frac{5000(x + 5)(x - 5)}{x^2}$$

$$x = 5 \quad \text{or} \quad x = -5$$

Because $C''(x) = 250,000x^{-3} = \frac{250,000}{x^3}$ is positive for all $x > 0$, using 5 machines minimizes the cost at $C(5) = 50,000$.

(c) The graph is shown in Figure 10.45.

$C(x) = 5000x + \dfrac{125,000}{x}$

Figure 10.45

Calculator Note

The procedures previously outlined in this section are necessary to generate a complete and accurate graph. With a graphing calculator, the graph of a function is easily generated as long as the viewing window dimensions are appropriate. We frequently need information provided by derivatives to obtain a window that shows all features of a graph. See Appendix C, Section 10.5, for details.

Figure 10.46

EXAMPLE 4 Horizontal and Vertical Asymptotes

Figure 10.46 shows the graph of $f(x) = \dfrac{71x^2}{28(3 - 2x^2)}$.

(a) Determine whether the function has horizontal or vertical asymptotes, and estimate where they occur.

(b) Check your conclusions to part (a) analytically.

Solution

(a) The graph appears to have a horizontal asymptote somewhere between $y = -1$ and $y = -2$, perhaps near $y = -1.5$. Also, there are two vertical asymptotes located approximately at $x = 1.25$ and $x = -1.25$.

(b) The function

$$f(x) = \frac{71x^2}{28(3 - 2x^2)} = \frac{71x^2}{84 - 56x^2}$$

is a rational function with the degree of the numerator equal to that of the denominator and with the ratio of the leading coefficients equal to $-71/56$. Thus the graph of the function has a horizontal asymptote at $y = -71/56 \approx -1.27$.

Vertical asymptotes occur at x-values where $28(3 - 2x^2) = 0$. Solving gives

$$3 - 2x^2 = 0 \quad \text{or} \quad 3 = 2x^2 \quad \text{so} \quad \frac{3}{2} = x^2$$

$$\text{Thus} \quad \pm\sqrt{\frac{3}{2}} = x \quad \text{or} \quad x \approx \pm 1.225$$

An accurate graph shows all features, but not necessarily the details of any feature. Even with a graphing calculator, sometimes analytic methods are needed to determine an appropriate viewing window.

EXAMPLE 5 Graphing with Technology

The standard viewing window of the graph of $f(x) = \dfrac{x + 10}{x^2 + 300}$ appears blank (check and see). Find any asymptotes, maxima, and minima, and determine an appropriate viewing window. Sketch the graph.

Solution

Because $x^2 + 300 = 0$ has no real solution, there are no vertical asymptotes. The function is rational with the degree of the numerator less than that of the denominator, so the horizontal asymptote is $y = 0$, which is the x-axis.

We then find an appropriate viewing window by locating the critical points.

$$f'(x) = \frac{(x^2 + 300)(1) - (x + 10)(2x)}{(x^2 + 300)^2}$$

$$= \frac{x^2 + 300 - 2x^2 - 20x}{(x^2 + 300)^2} = \frac{300 - 20x - x^2}{(x^2 + 300)^2}$$

$f'(x) = 0$ when the numerator is zero. Thus

$$300 - 20x - x^2 = 0$$
$$0 = x^2 + 20x - 300$$
$$0 = (x + 30)(x - 10)$$
$$x + 30 = 0 \qquad x - 10 = 0$$

$$x = -30 \qquad x = 10$$

$f(x)$

$f'(x)$ $- - - \; 0 + + + \; 0 \; - - -$

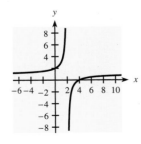

The critical points are $x = -30$, $y = -\frac{1}{60} \approx -0.01666667$ and $x = 10$, $y = \frac{1}{20} = 0.05$. A sign diagram for $f'(x)$ is shown above.

Without using the information above, a graphing calculator may not give a useful graph. An x-range that includes -30 and 10 is needed. Because $y = 0$ is a horizontal asymptote, these relative extrema are absolute, and the y-range must be quite small for the shape of the graph to be seen clearly. Figure 10.47 shows the graph.

Figure 10.47

CHECKPOINT SOLUTIONS

1. (a) True, $x = 1$ makes the denominator of $f(x)$ equal to zero, whereas the numerator is nonzero.
   (b) True, the function is rational with the degree of the numerator equal to that of the denominator and with the ratio of the leading coefficients equal to 2.
2. (a) False. There are no horizontal asymptotes, but $x = 0$ is a vertical asymptote.
   (b) True
   (c) True
   (d) True. The relative minimum point is $(-2, f(-2)) = (-2, 13)$.
   (e) True
   (f) False. There is a point of inflection only at $(\sqrt[3]{16}, 1)$. At $x = 0$ the vertical asymptote occurs, so there is no point on the graph and hence no point of inflection.

| EXERCISES | 10.5

In Problems 1–4, a function and its graph are given. Use the graph to find each of the following, if they exist. Then confirm your results analytically.

(a) vertical asymptotes

(b) $\lim_{x \to \infty} f(x)$

(c) $\lim_{x \to -\infty} f(x)$

(d) horizontal asymptotes

1. $f(x) = \dfrac{x - 4}{x - 2}$

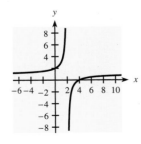

2. $f(x) = \dfrac{8}{x + 2}$

3. $f(x) = \dfrac{3(x^4 + 2x^3 + 6x^2 + 2x + 5)}{(x^2 - 4)^2}$

4. $f(x) = \dfrac{x^2}{(x - 2)^2}$

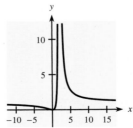

In Problems 5–10, find any horizontal and vertical asymptotes for each function.

5. $y = \dfrac{2x}{x - 3}$

6. $y = \dfrac{3x - 1}{x + 5}$

7. $y = \dfrac{x + 1}{x^2 - 4}$

8. $y = \dfrac{4x}{9 - x^2}$

9. $y = \dfrac{3x^3 - 6}{x^2 + 4}$

10. $y = \dfrac{6x^3}{4x^2 + 9}$

For each function in Problems 11–18, find any horizontal and vertical asymptotes, and use information from the first derivative to sketch the graph.

11. $f(x) = \dfrac{2x + 2}{x - 3}$

12. $f(x) = \dfrac{5x - 15}{x + 2}$

13. $y = \dfrac{x^2 + 4}{x}$

14. $y = \dfrac{x^2 + 4}{x^2}$

15. $y = \dfrac{27x^2}{(x + 1)^3}$

16. $y = \left(\dfrac{x + 2}{x - 3}\right)^2$

17. $f(x) = \dfrac{16x}{x^2 + 1}$

18. $f(x) = \dfrac{4x^2}{x^4 + 1}$

In Problems 19–24, a function and its first and second derivatives are given. Use these to find any horizontal and vertical asymptotes, critical points, relative maxima, relative minima, and points of inflection. Then sketch the graph of each function.

19. $y = \dfrac{x}{(x - 1)^2}$

$y' = -\dfrac{x + 1}{(x - 1)^3}$

$y'' = \dfrac{2x + 4}{(x - 1)^4}$

20. $y = \dfrac{(x - 1)^2}{x^2}$

$y' = \dfrac{2(x - 1)}{x^3}$

$y'' = \dfrac{6 - 4x}{x^4}$

21. $y = x + \dfrac{3}{\sqrt[3]{x - 3}}$

$y' = 1 - \dfrac{1}{(x - 3)^{4/3}}$

$y'' = \dfrac{4}{3(x - 3)^{7/3}}$

22. $y = 3\sqrt[3]{x} + \dfrac{1}{x}$

$y' = \dfrac{x^{4/3} - 1}{x^2}$

$y'' = \dfrac{6 - 2x^{4/3}}{3x^3}$

23. $f(x) = \dfrac{9(x - 2)^{2/3}}{x^2}$

$f'(x) = \dfrac{12(3 - x)}{x^3(x - 2)^{1/3}}$

$f''(x) = \dfrac{4(7x^2 - 42x + 54)}{x^4(x - 2)^{4/3}}$

24. $f(x) = \dfrac{3x^{2/3}}{x + 1}$

$f'(x) = \dfrac{2 - x}{x^{1/3}(x + 1)^2}$

$f''(x) = \dfrac{2(2x^2 - 8x - 1)}{3x^{4/3}(x + 1)^3}$

In Problems 25–28, a function and its graph are given.
(a) Use the graph to estimate the locations of any horizontal or vertical asymptotes.
(b) Use the function to determine precisely the locations of any asymptotes.

25. $f(x) = \dfrac{9x}{17 - 4x}$

26. $f(x) = \dfrac{5 - 13x}{3x + 20}$

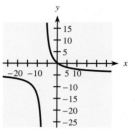

27. $f(x) = \dfrac{20x^2 + 98}{9x^2 - 49}$

28. $f(x) = \dfrac{15x^2 - x}{7x^2 - 35}$

 For each function in Problems 29–34, complete the following steps.
(a) Use a graphing calculator to graph the function in the standard viewing window.
(b) Analytically determine the location of any asymptotes and extrema.
(c) Graph the function in a viewing window that shows all features of the graph. State the ranges for x-values and y-values for your viewing window.

29. $f(x) = \dfrac{x + 25}{x^2 + 1400}$

30. $f(x) = \dfrac{x - 50}{x^2 + 1100}$

31. $f(x) = \dfrac{100(9 - x^2)}{x^2 + 100}$

32. $f(x) = \dfrac{200x^2}{x^2 + 100}$

33. $f(x) = \dfrac{1000x - 4000}{x^2 - 10x - 2000}$

34. $f(x) = \dfrac{900x + 5400}{x^2 - 30x - 1800}$

APPLICATIONS

35. *Cost-benefit* The percent p of particulate pollution that can be removed from the smokestacks of an industrial plant by spending C dollars is given by

$$p = \frac{100C}{7300 + C}$$

(a) Find any C-values at which the rate of change of p with respect to C does not exist. Make sure that these make sense in the problem.
(b) Find C-values for which p is increasing.
(c) If there is a horizontal asymptote, find it.
(d) Can 100% of the pollution be removed?

36. *Cost-benefit* The percent p of impurities that can be removed from the waste water of a manufacturing process at a cost of C dollars is given by

$$p = \frac{100C}{8100 + C}$$

(a) Find any C-values at which the rate of change of p with respect to C does not exist. Make sure that these make sense in the problem.
(b) Find C-values for which p is increasing.
(c) Find any horizontal asymptotes.
(d) Can 100% of the pollution be removed?

37. *Revenue* A recently released film has its weekly revenue given by

$$R(t) = \frac{50t}{t^2 + 36}, \quad t \geq 0$$

where $R(t)$ is in millions of dollars and t is in weeks.
(a) Graph $R(t)$.
(b) When will revenue be maximized?
(c) Suppose that if revenue decreases for 4 consecutive weeks, the film will be removed from theaters and will be released as a video 12 weeks later. When will the video come out?

38. *Minimizing average cost* If the total daily cost, in dollars, of producing plastic rafts for swimming pools is given by

$$C(x) = 500 + 8x + 0.05x^2$$

where x is the number of rafts produced per day, then the average cost per raft produced is given by $\overline{C}(x) = C(x)/x$, for $x > 0$.
(a) Graph this function.
(b) Discuss what happens to the average cost as the number of rafts decreases, approaching 0.
(c) Find the level of production that minimizes average cost.

39. *Wind chill* If x is the wind speed in miles per hour and is greater than or equal to 5, then the wind chill (in degrees Fahrenheit) for an air temperature of 0°F can be approximated by the function

$$f(x) = \frac{289.173 - 58.5731x}{x + 1}, \quad x \geq 5$$

(a) Ignoring the restriction $x \geq 5$, does $f(x)$ have a vertical asymptote? If so, what is it?
(b) Does $f(x)$ have a vertical asymptote within its domain?
(c) Does $f(x)$ have a horizontal asymptote? If so, what is it?
(d) In the context of wind chill, does $\lim\limits_{x \to \infty} f(x)$ have a physical interpretation? If so, what is it, and is it meaningful?

40. *Profit* An entrepreneur starts new companies and sells them when their growth is maximized. Suppose that the annual profit for a new company is given by

$$P(x) = 22 - \frac{1}{2}x - \frac{18}{x + 1}$$

where P is in thousands of dollars and x is the number of years after the company is formed. If she wants to sell the company before profits begin to decline, after how many years should she sell it?

41. *Productivity* The figure is a typical graph of worker productivity per hour P as a function of time t on the job.
(a) What is the horizontal asymptote?
(b) What is $\lim\limits_{x \to \infty} P(t)$?
(c) What is the horizontal asymptote for $P'(t)$?
(d) What is $\lim\limits_{x \to \infty} P'(t)$?

Worker productivity

42. *Sales volume* The figure shows a typical curve that gives the volume of sales S as a function of time t after an ad campaign.
(a) What is the horizontal asymptote?
(b) What is $\lim\limits_{t \to \infty} S(t)$?
(c) What is the horizontal asymptote for $S'(t)$?
(d) What is $\lim\limits_{t \to \infty} S'(t)$?

Sales volume

43. *Females in the work force* For selected years from 1950 and projected to 2050, the table shows the percent of total U.S. workers who were female.

Year	% Female	Year	% Female
1950	29.6	2010	47.9
1960	33.4	2015	48.3
1970	38.1	2020	48.1
1980	42.5	2030	48.0
1990	45.2	2040	47.9
2000	46.6	2050	47.7

Source: U.S. Bureau of Labor Statistics

Assume these data can be modeled with the function

$$p(t) = \frac{0.786t + 20.9}{1.38t + 64.1}$$

where $p(t)$ is the percent of the U.S. work force that is female and t is the number of years past 1950.

(a) Find $\lim\limits_{t\to\infty} p(t)$.

(b) Interpret your answer to part (a).

(c) Does $p(t)$ have any vertical asymptotes within its domain $t \geq 0$?

(d) Whenever $p(t) < 0$ or $p(t) > 100$, the model would be inappropriate. Determine whether the model is ever inappropriate for $t \geq 0$.

44. *Paved roads* For selected years from 1960 to 2008, the table shows the percent of public roads that were paved.

Year	% Paved	Year	% Paved
1960	34.7	1995	60.8
1965	39.4	2000	63.4
1970	44.5	2002	64.8
1975	48.3	2004	64.5
1980	53.7	2006	65.2
1985	54.7	2008	67.4
1990	58.3		

Source: U.S. Bureau of Transportation Statistics

Assume these data can be modeled with the function

$$P(t) = \frac{0.944t^3 - 94.7t^2 + 5490t + 122{,}000}{0.013t^3 - 1.00t^2 + 30.0t + 3550}$$

where $P(t)$ is the percent of paved roads and t is the number of years past 1960.

(a) Find $\lim\limits_{t\to\infty} p(t)$.

(b) Interpret your answer to part (a).

(c) Find the vertical asymptote for $P(t)$. Is this in the domain of the model?

45. *Barometric pressure* The figure shows a barograph readout of the barometric pressure as recorded by Georgia Southern University's meteorological equipment. The figure shows a tremendous drop in barometric pressure on Saturday morning, March 13, 1993.

(a) If $B(t)$ is barometric pressure expressed as a function of time, as shown in the figure, does $B(t)$ have a vertical asymptote sometime after 8 A.M. on Saturday, March 13, 1993? Explain why or why not.

(b) Consult your library or some other resource to find out what happened in Georgia (and in the eastern United States) on March 13, 1993, to cause such a dramatic drop in barometric pressure.

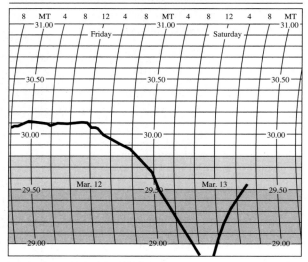

SOURCE: *Statesboro Herald*, March 14, 1993.

KEY TERMS AND FORMULAS

Section	Key Terms	Formulas
10.1	Relative maxima and minima Increasing Decreasing Critical points Sign diagram for $f'(x)$ First-derivative test Horizontal point of inflection	$f'(x) > 0$ $f'(x) < 0$ $f'(x) = 0$ or $f'(x)$ undefined
10.2	Concave up Concave down Point of inflection Sign diagram for $f''(x)$ Second-derivative test	$f''(x) > 0$ $f''(x) < 0$ May occur where $f''(x) = 0$ or $f''(x)$ undefined
10.3	Absolute extrema Average cost	$\overline{C}(x) = C(x)/x$

Section	Key Terms	Formulas
	Profit maximization	
	Competitive market	$R(x) = p \cdot x$ where $p =$ equilibrium price
	Monopolistic market	$R(x) = p \cdot x$ where $p = f(x)$ is the demand function
10.4	Inventory cost models	
10.5	Asymptotes	
	Horizontal: $y = b$	$f(x) \to b$ as $x \to \infty$ or $x \to -\infty$
	Vertical: $x = c$	y unbounded near $x = c$
	For rational function	Vertical: $x = c$ if $g(c) = 0$ and $f(c) \neq 0$
	$y = f(x)/g(x)$	Horizontal: Key on highest-power terms of $f(x)$ and $g(x)$

REVIEW EXERCISES

In Problems 1–4, find all critical points and determine whether they are relative maxima, relative minima, or horizontal points of inflection.

1. $y = -x^2$
2. $p = q^2 - 4q - 5$
3. $f(x) = 1 - 3x + 3x^2 - x^3$
4. $f(x) = \dfrac{3x}{x^2 + 1}$

In Problems 5–10:

(a) **Find all critical values, including those at which $f'(x)$ is undefined.**
(b) **Find the relative maxima and minima, if any exist.**
(c) **Find the horizontal points of inflection, if any exist.**
(d) **Sketch the graph.**

5. $y = x^3 + x^2 - x - 1$
6. $f(x) = 4x^3 - x^4$
7. $f(x) = x^3 - \dfrac{15}{2}x^2 - 18x + \dfrac{3}{2}$
8. $y = 5x^7 - 7x^5 - 1$
9. $y = x^{2/3} - 1$
10. $y = x^{2/3}(x - 4)^2$

11. Is the graph of $y = x^4 - 3x^3 + 2x - 1$ concave up or concave down at $x = 2$?
12. Find intervals on which the graph of $y = x^4 - 2x^3 - 12x^2 + 6$ is concave up and intervals on which it is concave down, and find points of inflection.
13. Find the relative maxima, relative minima, and points of inflection of the graph of $y = x^3 - 3x^2 - 9x + 10$.

In Problems 14 and 15, find any relative maxima, relative minima, and points of inflection, and sketch each graph.

14. $y = x^3 - 12x$
15. $y = 2 + 5x^3 - 3x^5$
16. Given $R = 280x - x^2$, find the absolute maximum and minimum for R when (a) $0 \le x \le 200$ and (b) $0 \le x \le 100$.

17. Given $y = 6400x - 18x^2 - \dfrac{x^3}{3}$, find the absolute maximum and minimum for y when (a) $0 \le x \le 50$ and (b) $0 \le x \le 100$.

In Problems 18 and 19, use the graphs to find the following items.

(a) **vertical asymptotes**
(b) **horizontal asymptotes**
(c) $\displaystyle \lim_{x \to +\infty} f(x)$
(d) $\displaystyle \lim_{x \to -\infty} f(x)$

18.

19.

In Problems 20 and 21, find any horizontal asymptotes and any vertical asymptotes.

20. $y = \dfrac{3x + 2}{2x - 4}$

21. $y = \dfrac{x^2}{1 - x^2}$

In Problems 22–24:

(a) Find any horizontal and vertical asymptotes.

(b) Find any relative maxima and minima.

(c) Sketch each graph.

22. $y = \dfrac{3x}{x + 2}$

23. $y = \dfrac{8(x - 2)}{x^2}$

24. $y = \dfrac{x^2}{x - 1}$

In Problems 25 and 26, a function and its graph are given.

(a) Use the graph to determine (estimate) x-values where $f'(x) > 0$, where $f'(x) < 0$, and where $f'(x) = 0$.

(b) Use the graph to determine x-values where $f''(x) > 0$, where $f''(x) < 0$, and where $f''(x) = 0$.

(c) Check your conclusions to (a) by finding $f'(x)$ and graphing it with a graphing calculator.

(d) Check your conclusions to (b) by finding $f''(x)$ and graphing it with a graphing calculator.

25. $f(x) = x^3 - 4x^2 + 4x$

26. $f(x) = 0.0025x^4 + 0.02x^3 - 0.48x^2 + 0.08x + 4$

In Problems 27 and 28, $f'(x)$ and its graph are given.

(a) Use the graph of $f'(x)$ to determine (estimate) where the graph of $f(x)$ is increasing, where it is decreasing, and where it has relative extrema.

(b) Use the graph of $f'(x)$ to determine where $f''(x) > 0$, where $f''(x) < 0$, and where $f''(x) = 0$.

(c) Verify that the given $f(x)$ has $f'(x)$ as its derivative, and graph $f(x)$ to check your conclusions in part (a).

(d) Calculate $f''(x)$ and graph it to check your conclusions in part (b).

27. $f'(x) = x^2 + 4x - 5 \left(\text{for } f(x) = \dfrac{x^3}{3} + 2x^2 - 5x \right)$

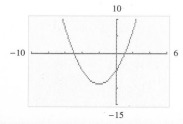

28. $f'(x) = 6x^2 - x^3 \left(\text{for } f(x) = 2x^3 - \dfrac{x^4}{4} \right)$

In Problems 29 and 30, $f''(x)$ and its graph are given.

(a) Use the graph to determine (estimate) where the graph of $f(x)$ is concave up, where it is concave down, and where it has points of inflection.

(b) Verify that the given $f(x)$ has $f''(x)$ as its second derivative, and graph $f(x)$ to check your conclusions in part (a).

29. $f''(x) = 4 - x \left(\text{for } f(x) = 2x^2 - \dfrac{x^3}{6} \right)$

30. $f''(x) = 6 - x - x^2 \left(\text{for } f(x) = 3x^2 - \dfrac{x^3}{6} - \dfrac{x^4}{12} \right)$

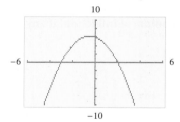

APPLICATIONS

In Problems 31–36, cost, revenue, and profit are in dollars and x is the number of units.

31. *Cost* Suppose the total cost function for a product is

$$C(x) = 3x^2 + 15x + 75$$

How many units will minimize the average cost? Find the minimum average cost.

32. *Revenue* Suppose the total revenue function for a product is given by

$$R(x) = 32x - 0.01x^2$$

(a) How many units will maximize the total revenue? Find the maximum revenue.

(b) If production is limited to 1500 units, how many units will maximize the total revenue? Find the maximum revenue.

33. *Profit* Suppose the profit function for a product is

$$P(x) = 1080x + 9.6x^2 - 0.1x^3 - 50{,}000$$

Find the maximum profit.

34. *Profit* How many units (x) will maximize profit if $R(x) = 46x - 0.01x^2$ and $C(x) = 0.05x^2 + 10x + 1100$?

35. *Profit* A product can be produced at a total cost of $C(x) = 800 + 4x$, where x is the number produced and is limited to at most 150 units. If the total revenue is given by $R(x) = 80x - \frac{1}{4}x^2$, determine the level of production that will maximize the profit.

36. *Average cost* The total cost function for a product is $C = 2x^2 + 54x + 98$. How many units must be produced to minimize average cost?

37. *Marginal profit* The figure shows the graph of a marginal profit function for a company. At what level of sales will profit be maximized? Explain.

38. *Productivity—diminishing returns* Suppose the productivity P of an individual worker (in number of items produced per hour) is a function of the number of hours of training t according to

$$P(t) = 5 + \frac{95t^2}{t^2 + 2700}$$

Find the number of hours of training at which the rate of change of productivity is maximized. (That is, find the point of diminishing returns.)

39. *Output* The figure shows a typical graph of output y (in thousands of dollars) as a function of capital investment I (also in thousands of dollars).
    (a) Is the point of diminishing returns closest to the point at which $I = 20$, $I = 60$, or $I = 120$? Explain.
    (b) The average output per dollar of capital investment is defined as the total output divided by the amount of capital investment; that is,

$$\text{Average output} = \frac{f(I)}{I}$$

Calculate the slope of a line from $(0, 0)$ to an arbitrary point $(I, f(I))$ on the output graph. How is this slope related to the average output?

(c) Is the maximum average output attained when the capital investment is closest to $I = 40$, to $I = 70$, or to $I = 140$? Explain.

40. *Revenue* MMR II Extreme Bike Shop sells 54 basic-style mountain bikes per month at a price of $385 each. Market research indicates that MMR II could sell 10 more of these bikes if the price were $25 lower. At what selling price will MMR II maximize the revenue from these bikes?

41. *Profit* If in Problem 40 the mountain bikes cost the shop $200 each, at what selling price will MMR II's profit be a maximum?

42. *Profit* Suppose that for a product in a competitive market, the demand function is $p = 1200 - 2x$ and the supply function is $p = 200 + 2x$, where x is the number of units and p is in dollars. A firm's average cost function for this product is

$$\overline{C}(x) = \frac{12{,}000}{x} + 50 + x$$

Find the maximum profit. (*Hint:* First find the equilibrium price.)

43. *Profit* The monthly demand function for x units of a product sold at p per unit by a monopoly is $p = 800 - x$, and its average cost is $\overline{C} = 200 + x$.
    (a) Determine the quantity that will maximize profit.
    (b) Find the selling price at the optimal quantity.

44. *Profit* Suppose that in a monopolistic market, the demand function for a commodity is

$$p = 7000 - 10x - \frac{x^2}{3}$$

where x is the number of units and p is in dollars. If a company's average cost function for this commodity is

$$\overline{C}(x) = \frac{40{,}000}{x} + 600 + 8x$$

find the maximum profit.

45. *Reaction to a drug* The reaction R to an injection of a drug is related to the dose x (in milligrams) according to

$$R(x) = x^2\left(500 - \frac{x}{3}\right)$$

Find the dose that yields the maximum reaction.

46. *Productivity* The number of parts produced per hour by a worker is given by

$$N = 4 + 3t^2 - t^3$$

where t is the number of hours on the job without a break. If the worker starts at 8 A.M., when will she be at maximum productivity during the morning?

47. *Population* Population estimates show that the equation $P = 300 + 10t - t^2$ represents the size of the graduating class of a high school, where t represents the number of years after 2010, $0 \leq t \leq 10$. What will be the largest graduating class in the next 10 years?

48. *Night brightness* Suppose that an observatory is to be built between cities A and B, which are 30 miles apart. For the best viewing, the observatory should be located where the night brightness from these cities is minimum. If the night brightness of city A is 8 times that of city B, then the night brightness b between the two cities and x miles from A is given by

$$b = \frac{8k}{x^2} + \frac{k}{(30 - x)^2}$$

where k is a constant. Find the best location for the observatory; that is, find x that minimizes b.

49. *Product design* A playpen manufacturer wants to make a rectangular enclosure with maximum play area. To remain competitive, he wants the perimeter of the base to be only 16 feet. What dimensions should the playpen have?

50. *Printing design* A printed page is to contain 56 square inches and have a $\frac{3}{4}$-inch margin at the bottom and 1-inch margins at the top and on both sides. Find the dimensions that minimize the size of the page (and hence the costs for paper).

51. *Drug sensitivity* The reaction R to an injection of a drug is related to the dose x, in milligrams, according to

$$R(x) = x^2\left(500 - \frac{x}{3}\right)$$

The sensitivity to the drug is defined by dR/dx. Find the dose that maximizes sensitivity.

52. *Per capita health care costs* For the years from 2000 and projected to 2018, the U.S. per capita out-of-pocket cost for health care C (in dollars) can be modeled by the function

$$C(t) = 0.118t^3 - 2.51t^2 + 40.2t + 677$$

where t is the number of years past 2000 (*Source:* U.S. Centers for Medicare and Medicaid Services).
(a) When does the rate of change of health care costs per capita reach its minimum?
(b) On a graph of $C(t)$, what feature occurs at the t-value found in part (a)?

53. *Inventory cost model* A company needs to produce 288,000 items per year. Production costs are $1500 to prepare for a production run and $30 for each item produced. Inventory costs are $1.50 per year for each item stored. Find the number of items that should be produced in each run so that the total costs of production and storage are minimum.

54. *Average cost* Suppose the total cost of producing x units of a product is given by

$$C(x) = 4500 + 120x + 0.05x^2 \quad \text{dollars}$$

(a) Find any asymptotes of the average cost function $\overline{C}(x) = C(x)/x$.
(b) Graph the average cost function.

55. *Market share* Suppose a company's percent share of the market (actual and projected) for a new product t quarters after its introduction is given by

$$M(t) = \frac{3.8t^2 + 3}{0.1t^2 + 1}$$

(a) Find the company's market share when the product is introduced.
(b) Find any horizontal asymptote of the graph of $M(t)$, and write a sentence that explains the meaning of this asymptote.

10   CHAPTER TEST

Find the local maxima, local minima, points of inflection, and asymptotes, if they exist, for each of the functions in Problems 1–3. Graph each function.
1. $f(x) = x^3 + 6x^2 + 9x + 3$
2. $y = 4x^3 - x^4 - 10$
3. $y = \dfrac{x^2 - 3x + 6}{x - 2}$

In Problems 4–6, use the function $y = 3x^5 - 5x^3 + 2$.
4. Over what intervals is the graph of this function concave up?
5. Find the points of inflection of this function.

6. Find the relative maxima and minima of this function.
7. Find the absolute maximum and minimum for $f(x) = 2x^3 - 15x^2 + 3$ on the interval $[-2, 8]$.
8. Find all horizontal and vertical asymptotes of the function

$$f(x) = \frac{200x - 500}{x + 300}.$$

9. Use the graph of $y = f(x)$ and the indicated points to complete the chart. Enter $+$, $-$, or 0, according to whether f, f', and f'' are positive, negative, or zero at each point.

Point	f	f'	f"
A			
B			
C			

10. Use the figure to complete the following.
    (a) $\lim\limits_{x \to -\infty} f(x) = ?$
    (b) What is the vertical asymptote?
    (c) Find the horizontal asymptote.

11. If $f(6) = 10, f'(6) = 0$, and $f''(6) = -3$, what can we conclude about the point on the graph of $y = f(x)$ where $x = 6$? Explain.

12. Using U.S. Census Bureau data since 1870, the average number of acres per U.S. farm can be modeled with the function

    $$A(t) = -0.000377t^3 + 0.1021t^2 - 4.731t + 174.3$$

    where t is the number of years past 1870.
    (a) Find the years when the model has a relative maximum and a relative minimum.
    (b) What changes in our society and in the economy during the last half of the 20th century have caused $A(t)$ to increase then?

13. The revenue function for a product is $R(x) = 164x$ dollars and the cost function for the product is

    $$C(x) = 0.01x^2 + 20x + 300 \text{ dollars}$$

    where x is the number of units produced and sold.
    (a) How many units of the product should be sold to obtain maximum profit?
    (b) What is the maximum possible profit?

14. The cost of producing x units of a product is given by

    $$C(x) = 100 + 20x + 0.01x^2 \text{ dollars}$$

    How many units should be produced to minimize average cost?

15. A firm sells 100 TV sets per month at $300 each, but market research indicates that it can sell 1 more set per month for each $2 reduction of the price. At what price will the revenue be maximized?

16. An open-top box is made by cutting squares from the corners of a piece of tin and folding up the sides. If the piece of tin was originally 20 centimeters on a side, how long should the sides of the removed squares be to maximize the resulting volume?

17. A company estimates that it will need 784,000 items during the coming year. It costs $420 to manufacture each item, $2500 to prepare for each production run, and $5 per year for each item stored. How many units should be in each production run so that the total costs of production and storage are minimized?

18. **Modeling** The table gives the number of women age 16 years and older (in millions) in the U.S. civilian work force for selected years from 1950 and projected to 2050.
    (a) Use x as the number of years past 1950 to create a cubic model using these data.
    (b) During what year does the model indicate that the rate of change of the number of women in the work force reached its maximum?
    (c) What feature of the graph of the function found in part (a) is the result found in part (b)?

Year	Women in the Work Force (in millions)
1950	18.4
1960	23.2
1970	31.5
1980	45.5
1990	56.8
2000	65.6
2010	75.5
2015	78.6
2020	79.2
2030	81.6
2040	86.5
2050	91.5

Source: U.S. Bureau of Labor Statistics

I. Production Management

Metal Containers, Inc. is reviewing the way it submits bids on U.S. Army contracts. The army often requests open-top boxes, with square bases and of specified volumes. The army also specifies the materials for the boxes, and the base is usually made of a different material than the sides. The box is assembled by riveting a bracket at each of the eight corners. For Metal Containers, the total cost of producing a box is the sum of the cost of the materials for the box and the labor costs associated with affixing each bracket.

Instead of estimating each job separately, the company wants to develop an overall approach that will allow it to cost out proposals more easily. To accomplish this, company managers need you to devise a formula for the total cost of producing each box and determine the dimensions that allow a box of specified volume to be produced at minimum cost. Use the following notation to help you solve this problem.

Cost of the material for the
 base $= A$ per square unit
Cost of each bracket $= C$
Length of the sides of the base $= x$
Volume specified by the army $= V$

Cost of the material for the
 sides $= B$ per square unit
Cost to affix each bracket $= D$
Height of the box $= h$

1. Write an expression for the company's total cost in terms of these quantities.
2. At the time an order is received for boxes of a specified volume, the costs of the materials and labor will be fixed and only the dimensions will vary. Find a formula for each dimension of the box so that the total cost is a minimum.
3. The army requests bids on boxes of 48 cubic feet with base material costing the container company $12 per square foot and side material costing $8 per square foot. Each bracket costs $5, and the associated labor cost is $1 per bracket. Use your formulas to find the dimensions of the box that meet the army's requirements at a minimum cost. What is this cost?

Metal Containers asks you to determine how best to order the brackets it uses on its boxes. You are able to obtain the following information: The company uses approximately 100,000 brackets a year, and the purchase price of each is $5. It buys the same number of brackets (say, n) each time it places an order with the supplier, and it costs $60 to process each order. Metal Containers also has additional costs associated with storing, insuring, and financing its inventory of brackets. These carrying costs amount to 15% of the average value of inventory annually. The brackets are used steadily and deliveries are made just as inventory reaches zero, so that inventory fluctuates between zero and n brackets.

4. If the total annual cost associated with the bracket supply is the sum of the annual purchasing cost and the annual carrying costs, what order size n would minimize the total cost?
5. In the general case of the bracket-ordering problem, the order size n that minimizes the total cost of the bracket supply is called the economic order quantity, or EOQ. Use the following notations to determine a general formula for the EOQ.

Fixed cost per order $= F$
Quantity purchased per year $= P$

Unit cost $= C$
Carrying cost (as a decimal rate) $= r$

II. Room Pricing in the Off-Season (Modeling)

The data in the table, from a survey of resort hotels with comparable rates on Hilton Head Island, show that room occupancy during the off-season (November through February) is related to the price charged for a basic room.

Price per Day	Occupancy Rate, %
$104	53
134	47
143	46
149	45
164	40
194	32

The goal is to use these data to help answer the following questions.

A. What price per day will maximize the daily off-season revenue for a typical hotel in this group if it has 200 rooms available?
B. Suppose that for this typical hotel the daily cost is $5510 plus $30 per occupied room. What price will maximize the profit for this hotel in the off-season?

The price per day that will maximize the off-season profit for this typical hotel applies to this group of hotels. To find the room price per day that will maximize the daily revenue and the room price per day that will maximize the profit for this hotel (and thus the group of hotels) in the off-season, complete the following.

1. Multiply each occupancy rate by 200 to get the hypothetical room occupancy. Create the revenue data points that compare the price with the revenue, R, which is equal to price times the room occupancy.
2. Use technology to create an equation that models the revenue, R, as a function of the price per day, x.
3. Use maximization techniques to find the price that these hotels should charge to maximize the daily revenue.
4. Use technology to get the occupancy as a function of the price, and use the occupancy function to create a daily cost function.
5. Form the profit function.
6. Use maximization techniques to find the price that will maximize the profit.

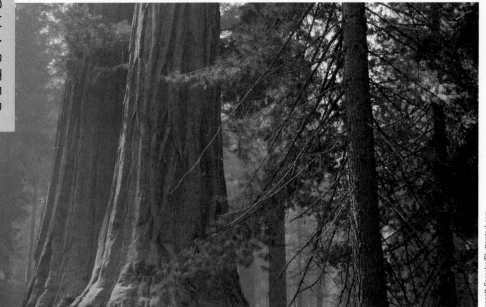
Kenneth Sponsler/Shutterstock.com

11 CHAPTER

Derivatives Continued

In this chapter we will develop derivative formulas for logarithmic and exponential functions, focusing primarily on base *e* exponentials and logarithms. We will apply logarithmic and exponential functions and use their derivatives to solve maximization and minimization problems in the management and life sciences.

We will also develop methods for finding the derivative of one variable with respect to another even when the first variable is not a function of the other. This method is called implicit differentiation. We will use implicit differentiation with respect to time to solve problems involving rates of change of two or more variables. These problems are called related-rates problems.

The topics and applications discussed in this chapter include the following.

SECTIONS	APPLICATIONS
11.1 Derivatives of Logarithmic Functions	Life span, cost
11.2 Derivatives of Exponential Functions	Future value, revenue
11.3 Implicit Differentiation	Production, demand
11.4 Related Rates	Allometric relationships, blood flow, flight, oil slicks
11.5 Applications in Business and Economics **Elasticity of demand** **Taxation in a competitive market**	Elasticity and revenue, maximizing tax revenue

Prerequisite Problem Type	For Section	Answer	Section for Review
(a) Simplify: $\dfrac{1}{(3x)^{1/2}} \cdot \dfrac{1}{2}(3x)^{-1/2} \cdot 3$ (b) Write with a positive exponent: $\sqrt{x^2 - 1}$	**11.1**	(a) $\dfrac{1}{2x}$ (b) $(x^2 - 1)^{1/2}$	0.4 Rational exponents
(a) Vertical lines have _____ slopes. (b) Horizontal lines have _____ slopes.	**11.3**	(a) Undefined (b) 0	1.3 Slopes
Write the equation of the line passing through $(-2, -2)$ with slope 5.	**11.3**	$y = 5x + 8$	1.3 Equations of lines
Solve: $x^2 + y^2 - 9 = 0$, for y.	**11.3**	$y = \pm\sqrt{9 - x^2}$	2.1 Quadratic equations
(a) Write $\log_a (x + h) - \log_a x$ as an expression involving one logarithm. (b) Does $\ln x^4 = 4 \ln x$? (c) Does $\dfrac{x}{h} \log_a \left(\dfrac{x + h}{x} \right) = \log_a \left(1 + \dfrac{h}{x} \right)^{x/h}$? (d) Expand $\ln (xy)$ to separate x and y. (e) If $y = a^x$, then $x =$ _____. (f) Simplify $\ln e^x$.	**11.1** **11.2**	(a) $\log_a \left(\dfrac{x + h}{x} \right)$ (b) Yes (c) Yes (d) $\ln x + \ln y$ (e) $\log_a y$ (f) x	5.2 Logarithms
Find the derivative of (a) $y = x^2 - 2x - 2$ (b) $T(q) = 400q - \dfrac{4}{3}q^2$ (c) $y = \sqrt{9 - x^2}$	**11.1–11.5**	(a) $y' = 2x - 2$ (b) $T'(q) = 400 - \dfrac{8}{3}q$ (c) $y' = -x(9 - x^2)^{-1/2}$	9.4–9.6 Derivatives
If $\dfrac{dy}{dx} = \dfrac{-1}{2\sqrt{x}}$, find the slope of the tangent to $y = f(x)$ at $x = 4$.	**11.3**	Slope $= -\dfrac{1}{4}$	9.3–9.7 Derivatives

OBJECTIVE

11.1

- To find derivatives of logarithmic functions

Derivatives of Logarithmic Functions

| APPLICATION PREVIEW |

The table shows the expected life spans at birth for people born in certain years in the United States, with projections to 2020. These data can be modeled by the function $l(x) = 11.249 + 14.244 \ln x$, where x is the number of years past 1900. The graph of this function is shown in Figure 11.1. If we wanted to use this model to find the rate of change of life span with respect to the number of years past 1900, we would need the derivative of this function and hence the derivative of the logarithmic function $\ln x$. (See Example 4.)

Year	Life Span (years)	Year	Life Span (years)
1920	54.1	1985	74.7
1930	59.7	1990	75.4
1940	62.9	1995	75.8
1950	68.2	2000	77.0
1960	69.7	2005	77.9
1970	70.8	2010	78.1
1975	72.6	2015	78.9
1980	73.7	2020	79.5

Source: National Center for Health Statistics

$l(x) = 11.249 + 14.244 \ln x$

Figure 11.1

Logarithmic Functions   Recall that we define the **logarithmic function** $y = \log_a x$ as follows.

Logarithmic Function

For $a > 0$ and $a \neq 1$, the **logarithmic function**

$$y = \log_a x \quad \text{(logarithmic form)}$$

has domain $x > 0$, base a, and is defined by

$$a^y = x \quad \text{(exponential form)}$$

The a is called the **base** in both $\log_a x = y$ and $a^y = x$, and y is the *logarithm* in $\log_a x = y$ and the *exponent* in $a^y = x$. Thus **a logarithm is an exponent.** Although logarithmic functions can have any base a, where $a > 0$ and $a \neq 1$, most problems in calculus and many of the applications to the management, life, and social sciences involve logarithms with base e, called **natural logarithms.** In this section we'll see why this base is so important. Recall that the natural logarithmic function $(y = \log_e(x))$ is written $y = \ln x$; see Figure 11.2 for the graph.

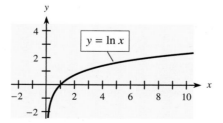

Figure 11.2

Derivative of $y = \ln x$

From Figure 11.2 we see that for $x > 0$, the graph of $y = \ln x$ is always increasing, so the slope of the tangent line to any point must be positive. This means that the derivative of $y = \ln x$ is always positive. Figure 11.3 shows the graph of $y = \ln x$ with tangent lines drawn at several points and with their slopes indicated.

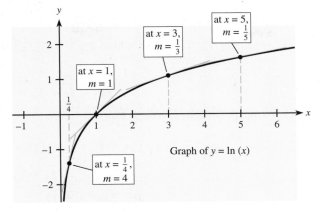

Figure 11.3

Note in Figure 11.3 that at each point where a tangent line is drawn, the slope of the tangent line is the reciprocal of the x-coordinate. In fact, this is true for every point on $y = \ln x$, so the slope of the tangent at any point is given by $1/x$. Thus we have the following:

Derivative of $y = \ln x$

If $y = \ln x$, then $\dfrac{dy}{dx} = \dfrac{1}{x}$.

This formula for the derivative of $y = \ln x$ is proved at the end of this section.

EXAMPLE 1 Derivatives Involving ln x

(a) If $y = x^3 + 3 \ln x$, find dy/dx.   (b) If $y = x^2 \ln x$, find y'.

Solution

(a) $\dfrac{dy}{dx} = 3x^2 + 3\left(\dfrac{1}{x}\right) = 3x^2 + \dfrac{3}{x}$

(b) By the Product Rule,

$$y' = x^2 \cdot \dfrac{1}{x} + (\ln x)(2x) = x + 2x \ln x$$

We can use the Chain Rule to find the formula for the derivative of $y = \ln u$, where $u = f(x)$.

Derivatives of Natural Logarithmic Functions

If $y = \ln u$, where u is a differentiable function of x, then

$$\dfrac{dy}{dx} = \dfrac{1}{u} \cdot \dfrac{du}{dx}$$

EXAMPLE 2 Derivatives of $y = \ln (u)$

Find the derivative for each of the following.

(a) $f(x) = \ln (x^4 - 3x + 7)$ (b) $f(x) = \frac{1}{3}\ln (2x^6 - 3x + 2)$

(c) $g(x) = \dfrac{\ln (2x + 1)}{2x + 1}$

Solution

(a) $f'(x) = \dfrac{1}{x^4 - 3x + 7}(4x^3 - 3) = \dfrac{4x^3 - 3}{x^4 - 3x + 7}$

(b) $f'(x)$ is $\frac{1}{3}$ of the derivative of $\ln(2x^6 - 3x + 2)$.

$$f'(x) = \frac{1}{3} \cdot \frac{1}{2x^6 - 3x + 2}(12x^5 - 3)$$

$$= \frac{4x^5 - 1}{2x^6 - 3x + 2}$$

(c) We begin with the Quotient Rule.

$$g'(x) = \frac{(2x + 1)\dfrac{1}{2x + 1}(2) - [\ln(2x + 1)]2}{(2x + 1)^2}$$

$$= \frac{2 - 2\ln(2x + 1)}{(2x + 1)^2}$$

CHECKPOINT

1. If $y = \ln(3x^2 + 2)$, find y'.
2. If $y = \ln x^6$, find y'.

Using Properties of Logarithms A logarithmic function of products, quotients, or powers, such as $y = \ln[x(x^5 - 2)^{10}]$, can be rewritten with properties of logarithms so that finding the derivative is much easier. The properties of logarithms, which were introduced in Section 5.2, are stated here for logarithms with an arbitrary base a (with $a > 0$ and $a \neq 1$) and for natural logarithms.

Properties of Logarithms

Let M, N, p, and a be real numbers with $M > 0$, $N > 0$, $a > 0$, and $a \neq 1$.

Base a Logarithms

I. $\log_a(a^x) = x$ (for any real x)

II. $a^{\log_a(x)} = x$ (for $x > 0$)

III. $\log_a(MN) = \log_a M + \log_a N$

IV. $\log_a\left(\dfrac{M}{N}\right) = \log_a M - \log_a N$

V. $\log_a(M^p) = p \log_a M$

Natural Logarithms

I. $\ln(e^x) = x$

II. $e^{\ln x} = x$

III. $\ln(MN) = \ln M + \ln N$

IV. $\ln\left(\dfrac{M}{N}\right) = \ln M - \ln N$

V. $\ln(M^p) = p \ln M$

For example, to find the derivative of $f(x) = \ln\sqrt[3]{2x^6 - 3x + 2}$, it is easier to rewrite this as follows:

$$f(x) = \ln[(2x^6 - 3x + 2)^{1/3}] = \tfrac{1}{3}\ln(2x^6 - 3x + 2)$$

Then take the derivative, as in Example 2(b).

EXAMPLE 3 Logarithm Properties and Derivatives

Use logarithm properties to find the derivatives for

(a) $y = \ln[x(x^5 - 2)^{10}]$.   (b) $f(x) = \ln\left(\dfrac{\sqrt[3]{3x + 5}}{x^2 + 11}\right)^4$.

Solution

(a) We use logarithm Properties III and V to rewrite the function.

$$y = \ln x + \ln \left(x^5 - 2\right)^{10} \qquad \text{Property III}$$
$$y = \ln x + 10 \ln \left(x^5 - 2\right) \qquad \text{Property V}$$

We now take the derivative.

$$\frac{dy}{dx} = \frac{1}{x} + 10 \cdot \frac{1}{x^5 - 2} \cdot 5x^4$$

$$= \frac{1}{x} + \frac{50x^4}{x^5 - 2}$$

(b) Again we begin by using logarithm properties.

$$f(x) = \ln \left(\frac{\sqrt[3]{3x + 5}}{x^2 + 11}\right)^4 = 4 \ln \left(\frac{\sqrt[3]{3x + 5}}{x^2 + 11}\right) \qquad \text{Property V}$$

$$f(x) = 4\left[\tfrac{1}{3} \ln \left(3x + 5\right) - \ln \left(x^2 + 11\right)\right] \qquad \text{Properties IV and V}$$

We now take the derivative.

$$f'(x) = 4\left(\frac{1}{3} \cdot \frac{1}{3x + 5} \cdot 3 - \frac{1}{x^2 + 11} \cdot 2x\right)$$

$$= 4\left(\frac{1}{3x + 5} - \frac{2x}{x^2 + 11}\right) = \frac{4}{3x + 5} - \frac{8x}{x^2 + 11}$$

CHECKPOINT

3. If $y = \ln \sqrt[3]{x^2 + 1}$, find y'.

4. Find $f'(x)$ for $f(x) = \ln \left[\dfrac{2x^4}{(5x + 7)^5}\right]$.

EXAMPLE 4   Life Span | APPLICATION PREVIEW |

Assume that the average life span (in years) for people born from 1920 and projected to 2020 can be modeled by

$$l(x) = 11.249 + 14.244 \ln x$$

where x is the number of years past 1900.

(a) Find the function that models the rate of change of life span.

(b) Does $l(x)$ have a maximum value for $x > 0$?

(c) Evaluate $\lim\limits_{x \to \infty} l'(x)$.

(d) What do the results of parts (b) and (c) tell us about the average life span?

Solution

(a) The rate of change of life span is given by the derivative.

$$l'(x) = 0 + 14.244\left(\frac{1}{x}\right) = \frac{14.244}{x}$$

(b) For $x > 0$, we see that $l'(x) > 0$. Hence $l(x)$ is increasing for all values of $x > 0$, so $l(x)$ never achieves a maximum value. That is, there is no maximum life span.

(c) $\lim\limits_{x \to \infty} l'(x) = \lim\limits_{x \to \infty} \dfrac{14.244}{x} = 0$

(d) If this model is accurate, life span will continue to increase, but at an ever slower rate.

EXAMPLE 5   Cost

Suppose the cost function for x skateboards is given by

$$C(x) = 18{,}250 + 615 \ln \left(4x + 10\right)$$

where $C(x)$ is in dollars. Find the marginal cost when 100 units are produced, and explain what it means.

Solution

Marginal cost is given by $C'(x)$.

$$\overline{MC} = C'(x) = 615\left(\frac{1}{4x + 10}\right)(4) = \frac{2460}{4x + 10}$$

$$\overline{MC}(100) = \frac{2460}{4(100) + 10} = \frac{2460}{410} = 6$$

When 100 units are produced, the marginal cost is 6. This means that the approximate cost of producing the 101st skateboard is $6.

Derivative of
$y = \log_a (x)$

So far we have found derivatives of natural logarithmic functions. If we have a logarithmic function with a base other than e, then we can use the **change-of-base formula.**

Change-of-Base Formula	To express a logarithm base a as a natural logarithm, use

$$\log_a x = \frac{\ln x}{\ln a}$$

We can apply this change-of-base formula to find the derivative of a logarithm with any base, as the following example illustrates.

EXAMPLE 6   **Derivative of** $y = \log_a (u)$

If $y = \log_4 (x^3 + 1)$, find dy/dx.

Solution

By using the change-of-base formula, we have

$$y = \log_4 (x^3 + 1) = \frac{\ln (x^3 + 1)}{\ln 4} = \frac{1}{\ln 4} \cdot \ln (x^3 + 1)$$

Thus

$$\frac{dy}{dx} = \frac{1}{\ln 4} \cdot \frac{1}{x^3 + 1} \cdot 3x^2 = \frac{3x^2}{(x^3 + 1) \ln 4}$$

Note that this formula means that logarithms with bases other than e will have the *constant* $1/\ln a$ as a factor in their derivatives (as Example 6 had $1/\ln 4$ as a factor). This means that derivatives involving natural logarithms have a simpler form, and we see why base e logarithms are used more frequently in calculus.

EXAMPLE 7   **Critical Values**

Let $f(x) = x \ln x - x$. Use the graph of the derivative of $f(x)$ for $x > 0$ to answer the following questions.

(a)   At what value a does the graph of $f'(x)$ cross the x-axis (that is, where is $f'(x) = 0$)?
(b)   What value a is a critical value for $y = f(x)$?
(c)   Does $f(x)$ have a relative maximum or a relative minimum at $x = a$?

Solution

$f'(x) = x \cdot \dfrac{1}{x} + \ln x - 1 = \ln x$. The graph of $f'(x) = \ln x$ is shown in Figure 11.4.

(a) The graph crosses the x-axis at $x = 1$, so $f'(a) = 0$ if $a = 1$.

(b) $a = 1$ is a critical value of $f(x)$.

(c) Because $f'(x)$ is negative for $x < 1$, $f(x)$ is decreasing for $x < 1$.
Because $f'(x)$ is positive for $x > 1$, $f(x)$ is increasing for $x > 1$.
Therefore, $f(x)$ has a relative minimum at $x = 1$.
The graph of $f(x) = x \ln x - x$ is shown in Figure 11.5. It has a relative minimum at the point $(1, -1)$.

Figure 11.4

Figure 11.5

Calculator Note

Critical values can also be found by using the SOLVER feature of a graphing calculator. See Appendix C, Section 11.1, for details.

Proof That $\dfrac{d}{dx}(\ln x) = \dfrac{1}{x}$

For completeness, we now include the formal proof that if $y = \ln x$, then $dy/dx = 1/x$.

$$\frac{dy}{dx} = \lim_{h \to 0} \frac{f(x + h) - f(x)}{h}$$

$$= \lim_{h \to 0} \frac{\ln(x + h) - \ln x}{h}$$

$$= \lim_{h \to 0} \frac{\ln\left(\dfrac{x + h}{x}\right)}{h} \qquad \text{Property IV}$$

$$= \lim_{h \to 0} \frac{x}{x} \cdot \frac{1}{h} \ln\left(\frac{x + h}{x}\right) \qquad \text{Introduce } \frac{x}{x}$$

$$= \lim_{h \to 0} \frac{1}{x} \cdot \frac{x}{h} \ln\left(1 + \frac{h}{x}\right)$$

$$= \lim_{h \to 0} \frac{1}{x} \ln\left(1 + \frac{h}{x}\right)^{x/h} \qquad \text{Property V}$$

$$= \frac{1}{x} \lim_{h \to 0} \left[\ln\left(1 + \frac{h}{x}\right)^{x/h}\right]^{*}$$

$$= \frac{1}{x} \ln\left[\lim_{h \to 0}\left(1 + \frac{h}{x}\right)^{x/h}\right]$$

If we let $a = \dfrac{h}{x}$, then $h \to 0$ means $a \to 0$, and we have

$$\frac{dy}{dx} = \frac{1}{x} \ln\left[\lim_{a \to 0}(1 + a)^{1/a}\right]$$

In Problem 47 in the 9.1 Exercises, we saw that $\lim_{a \to 0}(1 + a)^{1/a} = e$. Hence,

$$\frac{dy}{dx} = \frac{1}{x} \ln e = \frac{1}{x}$$

---

*The next step uses a new limit property for continuous composite functions. In particular,
$\lim_{x \to c} \ln(f(x)) = \ln\left[\lim_{x \to c} f(x)\right]$ when $\lim_{x \to c} f(x)$ exists and is positive.

CHECKPOINT SOLUTIONS

1. $y' = \dfrac{6x}{3x^2 + 2}$ 2. $y' = \dfrac{1}{x^6} \cdot 6x^5 = \dfrac{6}{x}$

3. By first using logarithm Property V, we get $y = \ln (x^2 + 1)^{1/3} = \frac{1}{3} \ln (x^2 + 1)$. Then

$$y' = \frac{1}{3} \cdot \frac{2x}{x^2 + 1} = \frac{2x}{3(x^2 + 1)}$$

4. By using logarithm Properties IV and V, we get

$$f(x) = \ln (2x^4) - \ln [(5x + 7)^5] = \ln (2x^4) - 5 \ln (5x + 7)$$

Thus

$$f'(x) = \frac{1}{2x^4} \cdot 8x^3 - 5 \cdot \frac{1}{5x + 7} \cdot 5 = \frac{4}{x} - \frac{25}{5x + 7}$$

| EXERCISES | 11.1

Find the derivatives of the functions in Problems 1–10.

1. $f(x) = 4 \ln x$
2. $y = 3 \ln x$
3. $y = \ln 8x$
4. $y = \ln 5x$
5. $y = \ln x^4$
6. $f(x) = \ln x^3$
7. $f(x) = \ln (4x + 9)$
8. $y = \ln (6x + 1)$
9. $y = \ln (2x^2 - x) + 3x$
10. $y = \ln (8x^3 - 2x) - 2x$
11. Find dp/dq if $p = \ln (q^2 + 1)$.
12. Find $\dfrac{ds}{dq}$ if $s = \ln \left(\dfrac{q^2}{4} + 1 \right)$.

In each of Problems 13–18, find the derivative of the function in part (a). Then find the derivative of the function in part (b) or show that the function in part (b) is the same function as that in part (a).

13. (a) $y = \ln x - \ln (x - 1)$
    (b) $y = \ln \dfrac{x}{x - 1}$
14. (a) $y = \ln (x - 1) + \ln (2x + 1)$
    (b) $y = \ln [(x - 1)(2x + 1)]$
15. (a) $y = \frac{1}{3} \ln (x^2 - 1)$ 16. (a) $y = 3 \ln (x^4 - 1)$
    (b) $y = \ln \sqrt[3]{x^2 - 1}$ (b) $y = \ln (x^4 - 1)^3$
17. (a) $y = \ln (4x - 1) - 3 \ln x$
    (b) $y = \ln \left(\dfrac{4x - 1}{x^3} \right)$
18. (a) $y = 3 \ln x - \ln (x + 1)$

    (b) $y = \ln \left(\dfrac{x^3}{x + 1} \right)$
19. Find $\dfrac{dp}{dq}$ if $p = \ln \left(\dfrac{q^2 - 1}{q} \right)$.

20. Find $\dfrac{ds}{dt}$ if $s = \ln [t^3(t^2 - 1)]$.

21. Find $\dfrac{dy}{dt}$ if $y = \ln \left(\dfrac{t^2 + 3}{\sqrt{1 - t}} \right)$.

22. Find $\dfrac{dy}{dx}$ if $y = \ln \left(\dfrac{3x + 2}{x^2 - 5} \right)^{1/4}$.

23. Find $\dfrac{dy}{dx}$ if $y = \ln (x^3 \sqrt{x + 1})$.

24. Find $\dfrac{dy}{dx}$ if $y = \ln [x^2(x^4 - x + 1)]$.

In Problems 25–38, find y'.

25. $y = x - \ln x$
26. $y = x^2 \ln (2x + 3)$
27. $y = \dfrac{\ln x}{x}$
28. $y = \dfrac{1 + \ln x}{x^2}$
29. $y = \ln (x^4 + 3)^2$
30. $y = \ln (3x + 1)^{1/2}$
31. $y = (\ln x)^4$
32. $y = (\ln x)^{-1}$
33. $y = [\ln (x^4 + 3)]^2$
34. $y = \sqrt{\ln (3x + 1)}$
35. $y = \log_4 x$
36. $y = \log_5 x$
37. $y = \log_6 (x^4 - 4x^3 + 1)$
38. $y = \log_2 (1 - x - x^2)$

In Problems 39–42, find the relative maxima and relative minima, and sketch the graph with a graphing utility to check your results.

39. $y = x \ln x$
40. $y = x^2 \ln x$
41. $y = x^2 - 8 \ln x$
42. $y = \ln x - x$

APPLICATIONS

43. *Marginal cost* Suppose that the total cost (in dollars) for a product is given by

$$C(x) = 1500 + 200 \ln (2x + 1)$$

    where x is the number of units produced.
    (a) Find the marginal cost function.
    (b) Find the marginal cost when 200 units are produced, and interpret your result.
    (c) Total cost functions always increase because producing more items costs more. What then must be true of the marginal cost function? Does it apply in this problem?

44. *Investment* If money is invested at the constant rate r, the time to increase the investment by a factor x is

$$t = \frac{\ln x}{r}$$

(a) At what rate $\dfrac{dt}{dx}$ is the time changing at $x = 2$?

(b) What happens to $\dfrac{dt}{dx}$ as x gets very large? Interpret this result.

45. *Marginal revenue* The total revenue, in dollars, from the sale of x units of a product is given by

$$R(x) = \frac{2500x}{\ln (10x + 10)}$$

(a) Find the marginal revenue function.
(b) Find the marginal revenue when 100 units are sold, and interpret your result.

46. *Supply* Suppose that the supply of x units of a product at price p dollars per unit is given by

$$p = 10 + 50 \ln (3x + 1)$$

(a) Find the rate of change of supply price with respect to the number of units supplied.
(b) Find the rate of change of supply price when the number of units is 33.
(c) Approximate the price increase associated with the number of units supplied changing from 33 to 34.

47. *Demand* The demand function for a product is given by $p = 4000/\ln (x + 10)$, where p is the price per unit in dollars when x units are demanded.
(a) Find the rate of change of price with respect to the number of units sold when 40 units are sold.
(b) Find the rate of change of price with respect to the number of units sold when 90 units are sold.
(c) Find the second derivative to see whether the rate at which the price is changing at 40 units is increasing or decreasing.

48. *pH level* The pH of a solution is given by

$$pH = -\log [H^+]$$

where $[H^+]$ is the concentration of hydrogen ions (in gram atoms per liter). What is the rate of change of pH with respect to $[H^+]$?

49. *Drug concentration* Concentration (in mg/ml) in the bloodstream of a certain drug is related to the time t (in minutes) after an injection and can be calculated using y in the equation

$$y = A \ln (t) - Bt + C$$

where A, B, and C are positive constants. In terms of A and B, find t at which y (and hence the drug concentration) reaches its maximum.

50. *Decibels* The loudness of sound (L, measured in decibels) perceived by the human ear depends on intensity levels (I) according to

$$L = 10 \log (I/I_0)$$

where I_0 is the standard threshold of audibility. If $x = I/I_0$, then using the change-of-base formula, we get

$$L = \frac{10 \ln (x)}{\ln 10}$$

At what rate is the loudness changing with respect to x when the intensity is 100 times the standard threshold of audibility (that is, when $x = 100$)?

51. *Richter scale* The Richter scale reading, R, used for measuring the magnitude of an earthquake with intensity I is determined by

$$R = \frac{\ln (I/I_0)}{\ln 10}$$

where I_0 is a standard minimum threshold of intensity. If $I_0 = 1$, what is the rate of change of the Richter scale reading with respect to intensity?

52. *Women in the work force* From 1950 and projected to 2050, the percent of women in the work force can be modeled by

$$w(x) = 9.42 + 8.70 \ln x$$

where x is the number of years past 1940 (*Source:* U.S. Bureau of Labor Statistics). If this model is accurate, at what rate will the percent be changing in 2020?

53. *Modeling* *Poverty threshold* The table gives the average poverty thresholds for individuals for selected years from 1990 to 2008.
(a) Use a logarithmic equation to model these data, with x equal to the number of years past 1980.
(b) Use this model to predict the rate at which the poverty threshold will be growing in 2015.

Year	Poverty Threshold Income	Year	Poverty Threshold Income
1990	$6652	2000	$8794
1992	7143	2002	9182
1995	7763	2005	10,160
1998	8316	2008	10,991

Source: U.S. Bureau of the Census

54. *Modeling* *U.S. households with cable/satellite TV* The table gives the percent of U.S. households with cable or satellite TV for selected years from 1980 to 2009.
(a) Let $x = 0$ represent 1970 and find a logarithmic function $C(x)$ that models these data.
(b) Find the function that models the rate of change of the percent of households with cable/satellite TV.
(c) Find $C(45)$ and $C'(45)$.
(d) Interpret the results of (c).

Year	Percent	Year	Percent
1980	22.6	2005	85.7
1985	45.3	2006	86.2
1990	58.6	2007	83.8
1995	65.1	2008	88.2
2000	68.0	2009	89.7

Source: Nielson Media Research

OBJECTIVE
11.2

* To find derivatives of
  exponential functions

Derivatives of Exponential Functions

■ | APPLICATION PREVIEW | ■

We saw in Chapter 6, "Mathematics of Finance," that the amount that accrues when $100 is invested at 8%, compounded continuously, is

$$S(t) = 100e^{0.08t}$$

where t is the number of years. If we want to find the rate at which the money in this account is growing at the end of 1 year, then we need to find the derivative of this exponential function. (See Example 4.)

Derivative of $y = e^x$ Just as base e logarithms are most convenient, we begin by focusing on base e exponentials. Figure 11.6(a) shows the graph of $f(x) = e^x$, and Figure 11.6(b) shows the same graph with tangent lines drawn to several points.

Figure 11.6

(a)   (b)

Note in Figure 11.6(b) that when $x < 0$, tangent lines have slopes near 0, much like the y-coordinates of $f(x) = e^x$. Furthermore, as x increases to $x = 0$ and for $x > 0$, the slopes of the tangents increase just as the values of the function do. This suggests that the function that gives the slope of the tangent to the graph of $f(x) = e^x$ (that is, the derivative) is similar to the function itself. In fact, the derivative of $f(x) = e^x$ is exactly the function itself, which we prove as follows:

From logarithms Property I, we know that

$$\ln e^x = x$$

Taking the derivative, with respect to x, of both sides of this equation, we have

$$\frac{d}{dx}(\ln e^x) = \frac{d}{dx}(x)$$

Using the Chain Rule for logarithms gives

$$\frac{1}{e^x} \cdot \frac{d}{dx}(e^x) = 1$$

and solving for $\frac{d}{dx}(e^x)$ yields

$$\frac{d}{dx}(e^x) = e^x$$

Thus we can conclude the following.

Derivative of $y = e^x$ If $y = e^x$, then $\dfrac{dy}{dx} = e^x$.

EXAMPLE 1 Derivative of an Exponential Function

If $y = 3e^x + 4x - 11$, find $\dfrac{dy}{dx}$.

Solution

$$\frac{dy}{dx} = 3e^x + 4$$

Derivative of $y = e^u$ As with logarithmic functions, the Chain Rule permits us to expand our derivative formulas.

Derivatives of Exponential Functions

If $y = e^u$, where u is a differentiable function of x, then

$$\frac{dy}{dx} = e^u \cdot \frac{du}{dx}$$

EXAMPLE 2 Derivatives of $y = e^u$

(a) If $f(x) = e^{4x^3}$, find $f'(x)$.
(b) If $s = 3te^{3t^2 + 5t}$, find ds/dt.
(c) If $u = w/e^{3w}$, find u'.

Solution
(a) $f'(x) = e^{4x^3} \cdot (12x^2) = 12x^2\, e^{4x^3}$
(b) We begin with the Product Rule.

$$\frac{ds}{dt} = 3t \cdot e^{3t^2 + 5t}(6t + 5) + e^{3t^2 + 5t} \cdot 3$$

$$= (18t^2 + 15t)e^{3t^2 + 5t} + 3e^{3t^2 + 5t}$$

$$= 3e^{3t^2 + 5t}(6t^2 + 5t + 1)$$

(c) The function is a quotient. Using the Quotient Rule gives

$$u' = \frac{(e^{3w})(1) - (w)(e^{3w} \cdot 3)}{(e^{3w})^2} = \frac{e^{3w} - 3we^{3w}}{e^{6w}} = \frac{1 - 3w}{e^{3w}}$$

EXAMPLE 3 Derivatives and Logarithmic Properties

If $y = e^{\ln x^2}$, find y'.

Solution

$$y' = e^{\ln x^2} \cdot \frac{1}{x^2} \cdot 2x = \frac{2}{x} e^{\ln x^2}$$

By logarithm Property II (see the previous section), $e^{\ln u} = u$, and we can simplify the derivative to

$$y' = \frac{2}{x} \cdot x^2 = 2x$$

Note that if we had used this property *before* taking the derivative, we would have had

$$y = e^{\ln x^2} = x^2$$

Then the derivative is $y' = 2x$.

CHECKPOINT

1. If $y = 2e^{4x}$, find y'.   2. If $y = e^{x^2 + 6x}$, find y'.   3. If $s = te^{t^2}$, find ds/dt.

EXAMPLE 4 Future Value | APPLICATION PREVIEW |

When \$100 is invested at 8% compounded continuously, the amount that accrues after t years, which is called the future value, is $S(t) = 100e^{0.08t}$. At what rate is the money in this account growing

(a) at the end of 1 year?   (b) at the end of 10 years?

Solution

The rate of growth of the money is given by

$$S'(t) = 100e^{0.08t}(0.08) = 8e^{0.08t}$$

(a) The rate of growth of the money at the end of 1 year is

$$S'(1) = 8e^{0.08} \approx 8.666$$

Thus the future value will change by about \$8.67 during the next year.

(b) The rate of growth of the money at the end of 10 years is

$$S'(10) = 8e^{0.08(10)} \approx 17.804$$

Thus the future value will change by about \$17.80 during the next year.

EXAMPLE 5 Revenue

Lilyana Vynogradova/Shutterstock.com

North Forty, Inc. is a manufacturer of wilderness camping equipment. The revenue function for its best-selling tent, the Sierra, can be modeled by the function

$$R(x) = 250xe^{(1 - 0.01x)}$$

where $R(x)$ is the revenue in thousands of dollars from the sale of x thousand Sierra tents. Find the marginal revenue when 75,000 tents are sold, and explain what it means.

Solution

The marginal revenue function is given by $R'(x)$, and to find this derivative we use the Product Rule.

$$R'(x) = \overline{MR} = 250x[e^{(1 - 0.01x)} \cdot (-0.01)] + e^{(1 - 0.01x)}(250)$$
$$\overline{MR} = 250e^{(1 - 0.01x)}(1 - 0.01x)$$

To find the marginal revenue when 75,000 tents are sold, we use $x = 75$.

$$\overline{MR}(75) = 250e^{(1 - 0.75)}(1 - 0.75) \approx 80.25$$

This means that the sale of one (thousand) more Sierra tents will yield approximately \$80.25 (thousand) in additional revenue.

CHECKPOINT

4. If the sales of a product are given by $S = 1000e^{-0.2x}$, where x is the number of days after the end of an advertising campaign, what is the rate of decline in sales 20 days after the end of the campaign?

Derivative of $y = a^u$ In a manner similar to that used to find the derivative of $y = e^x$, we can develop a formula for the derivative of $y = a^x$ for any base $a > 0$ and $a \neq 1$.

Derivative of $y = a^u$

If $y = a^x$, with $a > 0$, $a \neq 1$, then

$$\frac{dy}{dx} = a^x \ln a$$

If $y = a^u$, with $a > 0$, $a \neq 1$, where u is a differentiable function of x, then

$$\frac{dy}{dx} = a^u \frac{du}{dx} \ln a$$

EXAMPLE   6   Derivatives of $y = a^u$

(a) If $y = 4^x$, find dy/dx.   (b) If $y = 5^{x^2 + x}$, find y'.

Solution

(a) $\dfrac{dy}{dx} = 4^x \ln 4$

(b) $y' = 5^{x^2 + x}(2x + 1) \ln 5$

Calculator Note   We can make use of a graphing calculator to find maxima and minima of functions involving enponentials. See Appendix C, Section 11.2, for details.

 EXAMPLE   7   Technology and Critical Values

For the function $y = e^x - 3x^2$, complete the following.

(a) Approximate the critical values of the function to four decimal places.
(b) Determine whether relative maxima or relative minima occur at the critical values.

Solution

(a) The derivative is $y' = e^x - 6x$. Using the ZERO feature of a graphing calculator, we find that $y' = 0$ at $x \approx 0.2045$ (see Figure 11.7(a)) and at $x \approx 2.8331$.

(b) From the graph of $y' = e^x - 6x$ in Figure 11.7(a), we can observe where $y' > 0$ and where $y' < 0$. From this we can make a sign diagram to determine relative maxima and relative minima.

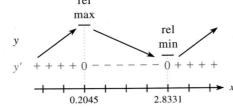

The graph of $y = e^x - 3x^2$ in Figure 11.7(b) shows that the relative maximum point is $(0.2045, 1.1015)$ and that the relative minimum point is $(2.8331, -7.0813)$.

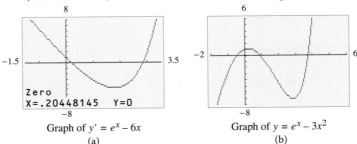

Graph of $y' = e^x - 6x$ Graph of $y = e^x - 3x^2$
(a)   (b)

 Figure 11.7

Calculator Note   The SOLVER and TABLE features of a graphing calculator can also be used to find maxima and minima of the function in Example 7. See Appendix C, Section 11.2, for details.

CHECKPOINT SOLUTIONS

1. $y' = 2e^{4x}(4) = 8e^{4x}$

2. $y' = (2x + 6)e^{x^2 + 6x}$

3. By the Product Rule, $\dfrac{ds}{dt} = e^{t^2}(1) + t[e^{t^2}(2t)] = e^{t^2} + 2t^2 e^{t^2}$.

4. The rate of decline is given by dS/dx.

$$\frac{dS}{dx} = 1000e^{-0.2x}(-0.2) = -200e^{-0.2x}$$

$$\frac{dS}{dx}\bigg|_{x=20} = -200e^{(-0.2)(20)}$$

$$= -200e^{-4}$$

$$\approx -3.663 \text{ sales/day}$$

| EXERCISES | 11.2

Find the derivatives of the functions in Problems 1–34.

1. $y = 5e^x - x$

2. $y = x^2 - 3e^x$

3. $f(x) = e^x - x^e$

4. $f(x) = 4e^x - \ln x$

5. $g(x) = 500(1 - e^{-0.1x})$

6. $h(x) = 750e^{0.04x}$

7. $y = e^{x^3}$

8. $y = e^{x^2 - 1}$

9. $y = 6e^{3x^2}$

10. $y = 1 - 2e^{-x^3}$

11. $y = 2e^{(x^2 + 1)^3}$

12. $y = e^{\sqrt{x^2 - 9}}$

13. $y = e^{\ln x^3}$

14. $y = e^3 + e^{\ln x}$

15. $y = e^{-1/x}$

16. $y = 2e^{\sqrt{x}}$

17. $y = e^{-1/x^2} + e^{-x^2}$

18. $y = \dfrac{2}{e^{2x}} + \dfrac{e^{2x}}{2}$

19. $s = t^2 e^t$

20. $p = 4qe^{q^3}$

21. $y = e^{x^4} - (e^x)^4$

22. $y = 4(e^x)^3 - 4e^{x^3}$

23. $y = \ln(e^{4x} + 2)$

24. $y = \ln(e^{2x} + 1)$

25. $y = e^{-3x} \ln(2x)$

26. $y = e^{2x^2} \ln(4x)$

27. $y = \dfrac{1 + e^{5x}}{e^{3x}}$

28. $y = \dfrac{x}{1 + e^{2x}}$

29. $y = (e^{3x} + 4)^{10}$

30. $y = \dfrac{e^x - e^{-x}}{e^x + e^{-x}}$

31. $y = 6^x$

32. $y = 3^x$

33. $y = 4^{x^2}$

34. $y = 5^{2x - 1}$

35. (a) What is the slope of the line tangent to $y = xe^{-x}$ at $x = 1$?

   (b) Write the equation of the line tangent to the graph of $y = xe^{-x}$ at $x = 1$.

36. (a) What is the slope of the line tangent to $y = e^{-x}/(1 + e^{-x})$ at $x = 0$?

   (b) Write the equation of the line tangent to the graph of $y = e^{-x}/(1 + e^{-x})$ at $x = 0$.

37. The equation for the standard normal probability distribution is

$$y = \frac{1}{\sqrt{2\pi}} e^{-z^2/2}$$

(a) At what value of z will the curve be at its highest point?

(b) Graph this function with a graphing utility to verify your answer.

38. (a) Find the mode of the normal distribution* given by

$$y = \frac{1}{\sqrt{2\pi}} e^{-(x-10)^2/2}$$

(b) What is the mean of this normal distribution?

(c) Use a graphing utility to verify your answer.

In Problems 39–42, find any relative maxima and minima. Use a graphing utility to check your results.

39. $y = \dfrac{e^x}{x}$

40. $y = \dfrac{x}{e^x}$

41. $y = x - e^x$

42. $y = \dfrac{x^2}{e^x}$

APPLICATIONS

43. *Future value* If P is invested for n years at 10% compounded continuously, the future value that results after n years is given by the function

$$S = Pe^{0.1n}$$

(a) At what rate is the future value growing at any time (for any nonnegative n)?

(b) At what rate is the future value growing after 1 year $(n = 1)$?

(c) Is the rate of growth of the future value after 1 year greater than 10%? Why?

44. *Future value* The future value that accrues when $700 is invested at 9%, compounded continuously, is

$$S(t) = 700e^{0.09t}$$

where t is the number of years.

---

* The mode occurs at the highest point on normal curves and equals the mean.

(a) At what rate is the money in this account growing when $t = 4$?

(b) At what rate is it growing when $t = 10$?

45. *Sales decay* After the end of an advertising campaign, the sales of a product are given by

$$S = 100,000e^{-0.5t}$$

where S is weekly sales in dollars and t is the number of weeks since the end of the campaign.

(a) Find the rate of change of S (that is, the rate of *sales decay*).

(b) Give a reason from looking at the function and another reason from looking at the derivative that explain how you know sales are decreasing.

46. *Sales decay* The sales decay for a product is given by

$$S = 50,000e^{-0.8t}$$

where S is the daily sales in dollars and t is the number of days since the end of a promotional campaign. Find the rate of sales decay.

47. *Marginal cost* Suppose that the total cost in dollars of producing x units of a product is given by

$$C(x) = 10,000 + 20xe^{x/600}$$

Find the marginal cost when 600 units are produced.

48. *Marginal revenue* Suppose that the revenue in dollars from the sale of x units of a product is given by

$$R(x) = 1000xe^{-x/50}$$

Find the marginal revenue function.

49. *Drugs in a bloodstream* The percent concentration y of a certain drug in the bloodstream at any time t (in hours) is given by

$$y = 100(1 - e^{-0.462t})$$

(a) What function gives the instantaneous rate of change of the concentration of the drug in the bloodstream?

(b) Find the rate of change of the concentration after 1 hour. Give your answer to three decimal places.

50. *Radioactive decay* The amount of the radioactive isotope thorium-234 present at time t in years is given by

$$Q(t) = 100e^{-0.02828t}$$

(a) What function describes how rapidly the isotope is decaying?

(b) Find the rate of radioactive decay of the isotope.

51. *Pollution* Pollution levels in Lake Sagamore have been modeled by the equation

$$x = 0.05 + 0.18e^{-0.38t}$$

where x is the volume of pollutants (in cubic kilometers) and t is the time (in years). What is the rate of change of x with respect to time?

52. *Drug concentration* Suppose the concentration $C(t)$, in mg/ml, of a drug in the bloodstream t minutes after an injection is given by

$$C(t) = 20te^{-0.04t}$$

(a) Find the instantaneous rate of change of the concentration after 10 minutes.

(b) Find the maximum concentration and when it occurs.

53. *National health care* With U.S. Department of Health and Human Services data from 2000 and projected to 2018, the total public expenditures for health care H can be modeled by

$$H = 624e^{0.07t}$$

where t is the number of years past 2000 and H is in billions of dollars. If this model is accurate, at what rate will health care expenditures change in 2020?

54. *Personal consumption* By using U.S. Bureau of Labor Statistics data for selected years from 1988 and projected to 2018, the billions of dollars spent for personal consumption in the United States can be modeled by

$$P = 2969e^{0.051t}$$

where t is the number of years past 1985. If this model is accurate, find and interpret the rate of change of personal consumption in 2015.

55. *Richter scale* The intensity of an earthquake is related to the Richter scale reading R by

$$\frac{I}{I_0} = 10^R$$

where I_0 is a standard minimum intensity. If $I_0 = 1$, what is the rate of change of the intensity I with respect to the Richter scale reading?

56. *Decibel readings* The intensity level of sound, I, is given by

$$\frac{I}{I_0} = 10^{L/10}$$

where L is the decibel reading and I_0 is the standard threshold of audibility. If $I/I_0 = y$, at what rate is y changing with respect to L when $L = 20$?

57. *U.S. debt* For selected years from 1900 to 2009, the national debt d, in billions of dollars, can be modeled by

$$d = 1.67e^{0.0825t}$$

where t is the number of years past 1900 (*Source*: Bureau of Public Debt, U.S. Treasury).

(a) What function describes how fast the national debt is changing?

(b) Find the instantaneous rate of change of the national debt model $d(t)$ in 1950 and 2015.

58. *Blood pressure* Medical research has shown that between heartbeats, the pressure in the aorta of a normal adult is a function of time in seconds and can be modeled by the equation

$$P = 95e^{-0.491t}$$

(a) Use the derivative to find the rate at which the pressure is changing at any time t.

(b) Use the derivative to find the rate at which the pressure is changing after 0.1 second.

(c) Is the pressure increasing or decreasing?

59. *Spread of disease* Suppose that the spread of a disease through the student body at an isolated college campus can be modeled by

$$y = \frac{10,000}{1 + 9999e^{-0.99t}}$$

where y is the total number affected at time t (in days). Find the rate of change of y.

60. *Spread of a rumor* The number of people $N(t)$ in a community who are reached by a particular rumor at time t (in days) is given by

$$N(t) = \frac{50,500}{1 + 100e^{-0.7t}}$$

Find the rate of change of $N(t)$.

61. *World population* Using figures from the U.S. Bureau of the Census, International Data Base, world population can be considered to be growing according to

$$P(t) = \frac{10.94}{1 + 3.97e^{-0.029t}}$$

where $t = 0$ represents 1945 and $P(t)$ is in billions.

(a) Find the rate of change of $P(t)$.

(b) Find and interpret $P'(100)$.

(c) Use the numerical derivative feature of a graphing calculator to find whether the rate of change of population growth is predicted to be increasing or decreasing in 2040.

62. *Internet usage* The percent of the U.S. population that used the Internet during selected years from 2000 can be modeled by the function

$$y = \frac{80.8}{1 + 0.20e^{-0.324x}}$$

where x is the number of years past 2000.

(a) Find and interpret $y'(20)$.

(b) What does this tell us about the future percent of the U.S. population that uses the Internet after 2020?

63. *Purchasing power* The table gives the purchasing power of a 1983 dollar based on consumer prices for selected years from 1968 to 2008. Using these data with $x = 0$ representing 1960, the dollar's purchasing power, P, can be modeled by

$$P = 3.41e^{-0.044x}$$

(a) Use the model to find the rate of decay of the purchasing power of $1 in 2008.

(b) Interpret the result in part (a).

(c) Use the data to find the average rate of change from 2007 to 2008, which approximates the rate of change in 2008.

Year	Purchasing Power of $1	Year	Purchasing Power of $1
1968	2.873	1992	0.713
1972	2.391	1996	0.637
1976	1.757	2000	0.581
1980	1.215	2004	0.529
1984	0.961	2007	0.482
1988	0.846	2008	0.464

Source: U.S. Bureau of Labor Statistics

64. *Personal income* Total personal income in the United States (in billions of dollars) for selected years from 1960 and projected to 2018 is given in the table.

Year	1960	1970	1980	1990	2000	2008	2018
Personal Income	411.5	838.8	2307.9	4878.6	8429.7	12,100.7	19,129.6

Source: Bureau of Economic Analysis, U.S. Department of Commerce

These data can be modeled by

$$I = 492.4e^{0.067x}$$

where x is the number of years past 1960.

(a) If this model is accurate, find the rate of change of the total U.S. personal income in 2008 and 2015.

(b) Use the data to find the average rate of change from 2000 to 2008.

65. *World tourism* The receipts (in billions of dollars) for world tourism can be modeled by the function

$$y = 165.550(1.055^x)$$

where x is the number of years past 1980.

(a) Write the function that models the rate of change in the tourism receipts.

(b) Predict the rate of change of tourism receipts in 2015.

66. *Students per computer* The average number of students per computer in public schools for the school years ending after 1985 can be modeled by

$$y = 98.221(1.149^{-x})$$

where x is the number of years past 1980.

(a) What function describes how rapidly the number of students per computer is changing?

(b) Find and interpret $y'(35)$.

67. **Modeling** *Consumer price index* The consumer price index (CPI) is calculated by finding the total price of various items that have been averaged according to a prescribed formula. The table gives the consumer price index of all urban consumers (CPI-U) for selected years from 1940 to 2008.

(a) With x representing years past 1900, find an exponential equation that models these data.

(b) Use your model to predict the rate of growth in this price index in 2018.

(c) For these data, name and find the model for another type of function that involves exponential functions.

(d) With the model from (c), use the numerical derivative feature of your calculator to find the rate of change in 2018.

Year	Consumer Price Index	Year	Consumer Price Index
1940	14.0	1990	130.7
1950	24.1	2000	172.2
1960	29.6	2005	195.3
1970	38.8	2008	215.3
1980	82.4		

Source: U.S. Bureau of the Census

OBJECTIVES   11.3

- To find derivatives by using implicit differentiation
- To find slopes of tangents by using implicit differentiation

Implicit Differentiation

| APPLICATION PREVIEW |

In the retail electronics industry, suppose the monthly demand for Precision, Inc. headphones is given by

$$p = \frac{10,000}{(x + 1)^2}$$

where p is the price in dollars per set of headphones and x is demand in hundreds of sets of headphones. If we want to find the rate of change of the quantity demanded with respect to the price, then we need to find dx/dp. (See Example 8.) Although we can solve this equation for x so that dx/dp can be found, the resulting equation does not define x as a function of p. In this case, and in other cases where we cannot solve equations for the variables we need, we can find derivatives with a technique called implicit differentiation.

Up to this point, functions involving x and y have been written in the form $y = f(x)$, defining y as an *explicit function* of x. However, not all equations involving x and y can be written in the form $y = f(x)$, and we need a new technique for taking their derivatives. For example, solving $y^2 = x$ for y gives $y = \pm\sqrt{x}$ so that y is not a function of x. We can write $y = \sqrt{x}$ and $y = -\sqrt{x}$, but then finding the derivative $\frac{dy}{dx}$ at a point on the graph of $y^2 = x$ would require determining which of these functions applies before taking the derivative. Alternatively, we can *imply* that y is a function of x and use a technique called **implicit differentiation.** When y is an implied function of x, we find $\frac{dy}{dx}$ by differentiating both sides of the equation with respect to x and then algebraically solving for $\frac{dy}{dx}$.

EXAMPLE   1   Implicit Differentiation

(a) Use implicit differentiation to find $\frac{dy}{dx}$ for $y^2 = x$.

(b) Find the slopes of the tangents to the graph of $y^2 = x$ at the points $(4, 2)$ and $(4, -2)$.

Solution

(a) First take the derivative of both sides of the equation with respect to x.

$$\frac{d}{dx}(y^2) = \frac{d}{dx}(x)$$

Because y is an implied, or implicit, function of x, we can think of $y^2 = x$ as meaning $[u(x)]^2 = x$ for some function u. We use the Chain Rule to take the derivative of y^2 in the same way we would for $[u(x)]^2$. Thus

$$\frac{d}{dx}(y^2) = \frac{d}{dx}(x) \quad \text{gives} \quad 2y\frac{dy}{dx} = 1$$

Solving for $\dfrac{dy}{dx}$ gives $\dfrac{dy}{dx} = \dfrac{1}{2y}$.

(b) To find the slopes of the tangents at the points $(4, 2)$ and $(4, -2)$, we use the coordinates of the points to evaluate $\dfrac{dy}{dx}$ at those points.

$$\frac{dy}{dx}\bigg|_{(4,\,2)} = \frac{1}{2(2)} = \frac{1}{4} \quad \text{and} \quad \frac{dy}{dx}\bigg|_{(4,\,-2)} = \frac{1}{2(-2)} = \frac{-1}{4}$$

Figure 11.8 shows the graph of $y^2 = x$ with tangent lines drawn at $(4, 2)$ and $(4, -2)$.

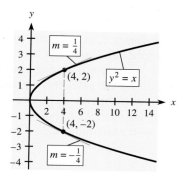

Figure 11.8

As noted previously, solving $y^2 = x$ for y gives the two functions $y = \sqrt{x} = x^{1/2}$ and $y = -\sqrt{x} = -x^{1/2}$; see Figures 11.9(a) and (b).

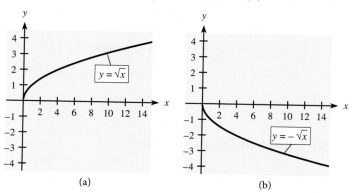

Figure 11.9   (a)   (b)

Let us now compare the results obtained in Example 1 with the results from the derivatives of the two functions $y = \sqrt{x}$ and $y = -\sqrt{x}$. The derivatives of these two functions are as follows:

$$\text{For } y = x^{1/2}, \text{ then } \frac{dy}{dx} = \frac{1}{2}x^{-1/2} = \frac{1}{2\sqrt{x}}$$

For $y = -x^{1/2}$, then $\dfrac{dy}{dx} = -\dfrac{1}{2}x^{-1/2} = \dfrac{-1}{2\sqrt{x}}$

We cannot find the slope of a tangent line at $x = 4$ unless we also know the y-coordinate and hence which function and which derivative to use.

At $(4, 2)$ use $y = \sqrt{x}$ so $\dfrac{dy}{dx}\bigg|_{(4,\,2)} = \dfrac{1}{2\sqrt{4}} = \dfrac{1}{4}$

At $(4, -2)$ use $y = -\sqrt{x}$ so $\dfrac{dy}{dx}\bigg|_{(4,\,-2)} = \dfrac{-1}{2\sqrt{4}} = \dfrac{-1}{4}$

These are the same results that we obtained directly after implicit differentiation. In this example, we could easily solve for y in terms of x and work the problem two different ways. However, sometimes solving explicitly for y is difficult or impossible. For these functions, implicit differentiation is necessary and extends our ability to find derivatives.

EXAMPLE 2 Slope of a Tangent

Find the slope of the tangent to the graph of $x^2 + y^2 - 9 = 0$ at $(\sqrt{5}, 2)$.

Solution
We find the derivative dy/dx from $x^2 + y^2 - 9 = 0$ by taking the derivative term by term on both sides of the equation.

$$\frac{d}{dx}(x^2) + \frac{d}{dx}(y^2) + \frac{d}{dx}(-9) = \frac{d}{dx}(0)$$
$$2x + 2y \cdot \frac{dy}{dx} + 0 = 0$$

Solving for dy/dx gives

$$\frac{dy}{dx} = -\frac{2x}{2y} = -\frac{x}{y}$$

The slope of the tangent to the curve at $(\sqrt{5}, 2)$ is the value of the derivative at this point. Evaluating $dy/dx = -x/y$ at $(\sqrt{5}, 2)$ gives the slope of the tangent as $-\sqrt{5}/2$. ∎

As we have seen in Examples 1 and 2, the Chain Rule yields $\dfrac{d}{dx}(y^n) = ny^{n-1}\dfrac{dy}{dx}$. Just as we needed this result to find derivatives of powers of y, the next example discusses how to find the derivative of xy.

EXAMPLE 3 Equation of a Tangent Line

Write the equation of the tangent to the graph of $x^3 + xy + 4 = 0$ at the point $(2, -6)$.

Solution
Note that the second term is the *product* of x and y. Because we are assuming that y is a function of x, and because x is a function of x, we must use the Product Rule to find $\dfrac{d}{dx}(xy)$.

$$\frac{d}{dx}(xy) = x \cdot 1\frac{dy}{dx} + y \cdot 1 = x\frac{dy}{dx} + y$$

Thus we have

$$\frac{d}{dx}(x^3) + \frac{d}{dx}(xy) + \frac{d}{dx}(4) = \frac{d}{dx}(0)$$
$$3x^2 + \left(x\frac{dy}{dx} + y\right) + 0 = 0$$

Solving for dy/dx gives $\dfrac{dy}{dx} = \dfrac{-3x^2 - y}{x}$

The slope of the tangent to the curve at $x = 2, y = -6$ is

$$m = \frac{-3(2)^2 - (-6)}{2} = -3$$

The equation of the tangent line is

$$y - (-6) = -3[x - (2)], \quad \text{or} \quad y = -3x$$

Technology Note   A graphing utility can be used to graph the function of Example 3 and the line that is tangent to the curve at $(2, -6)$. To graph the equation, we solve the equation for y, getting

$$y = \frac{-x^3 - 4}{x}$$

The graph of the equation and the line that is tangent to the curve at $(2, -6)$ are shown in Figure 11.10.

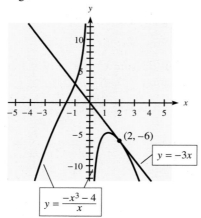

Figure 11.10

EXAMPLE 4   Implicit Differentiation

Find dy/dx if $x^4 + 5xy^4 = 2y^2 + x - 1$.

Solution

By viewing $5xy^4$ as the product $(5x)(y^4)$ and differentiating implicitly, we get

$$\frac{d}{dx}(x^4) + \frac{d}{dx}(5xy^4) = \frac{d}{dx}(2y^2) + \frac{d}{dx}(x) - \frac{d}{dx}(1)$$

$$4x^3 + 5x\left(4y^3\frac{dy}{dx}\right) + y^4(5) = 4y\frac{dy}{dx} + 1$$

To solve for $\dfrac{dy}{dx}$, we first rewrite the equation with terms containing $\dfrac{dy}{dx}$ on one side and the other terms on the other side.

$$20xy^3\frac{dy}{dx} - 4y\frac{dy}{dx} = 1 - 4x^3 - 5y^4$$

Now $\dfrac{dy}{dx}$ is a factor of one side. To complete the solution, we factor out $\dfrac{dy}{dx}$ and divide both sides by its coefficient.

$$(20xy^3 - 4y)\frac{dy}{dx} = 1 - 4x^3 - 5y^4$$

$$\frac{dy}{dx} = \frac{1 - 4x^3 - 5y^4}{20xy^3 - 4y}$$

CHECKPOINT

1. Find the following:

   (a) $\dfrac{d}{dx}(x^3)$ (b) $\dfrac{d}{dx}(y^4)$ (c) $\dfrac{d}{dx}(x^2 y^5)$

2. Find $\dfrac{dy}{dx}$ for $x^3 + y^4 = x^2 y^5$.

EXAMPLE 5   Production

Suppose that a company's weekly production output is $384,000 and that this output is related to hours of labor x and dollars of capital investment y by

$$384{,}000 = 30x^{1/3}\, y^{2/3}$$

(This relationship is an example of a Cobb-Douglas production function, studied in more detail in Chapter 14.) Find and interpret the rate of change of capital investment with respect to labor hours when labor hours are 512 and capital investment is $64,000.

Solution

The desired rate of change is given by the value of dy/dx when $x = 512$ and $y = 64{,}000$. Taking the derivative implicitly gives

$$\frac{d}{dx}(384{,}000) = \frac{d}{dx}(30x^{1/3}\, y^{2/3})$$

$$0 = 30x^{1/3}\left(\frac{2}{3}y^{-1/3}\frac{dy}{dx}\right) + y^{2/3}(10x^{-2/3})$$

$$0 = \frac{20x^{1/3}}{y^{1/3}}\cdot\frac{dy}{dx} + \frac{10y^{2/3}}{x^{2/3}}$$

$$\frac{-20x^{1/3}}{y^{1/3}}\cdot\frac{dy}{dx} = \frac{10y^{2/3}}{x^{2/3}}$$

Multiplying both sides by $\dfrac{-y^{1/3}}{20x^{1/3}}$ gives

$$\frac{dy}{dx} = \left(\frac{10y^{2/3}}{x^{2/3}}\right)\left(\frac{-y^{1/3}}{20x^{1/3}}\right) = \frac{-y}{2x}$$

When $x = 512$ and $y = 64{,}000$, we obtain

$$\frac{dy}{dx} = \frac{-64{,}000}{2(512)} = -62.5$$

This means that when labor hours are 512 and capital investment is $64,000, if labor hours change by 1 hour, then capital investment could decrease by about $62.50.

EXAMPLE 6   Horizontal and Vertical Tangents

(a) At what point(s) does $x^2 + 4y^2 - 2x + 4y - 2 = 0$ have a horizontal tangent?

(b) At what point(s) does it have a vertical tangent?

Solution

(a) First we find the derivative implicitly, with y' representing $\dfrac{dy}{dx}$.

$$2x + 8y \cdot y' - 2 + 4y' - 0 = 0$$

We isolate the y' terms, factor out y', and solve for y'.

$$8yy' + 4y' = 2 - 2x$$

$$(8y + 4)y' = 2 - 2x$$

$$y' = \frac{2 - 2x}{8y + 4} = \frac{1 - x}{4y + 2}$$

Horizontal tangents will occur where $y' = 0$; that is, where $1 - x = 0$, or $x = 1$. We can now find the corresponding y-value(s) by substituting 1 for x in the original equation and solving.

$$1 + 4y^2 - 2 + 4y - 2 = 0$$
$$4y^2 + 4y - 3 = 0$$
$$(2y - 1)(2y + 3) = 0$$
$$y = \frac{1}{2} \quad \text{or} \quad y = -\frac{3}{2}$$

Thus horizontal tangents occur at $\left(1, \frac{1}{2}\right)$ and $\left(1, -\frac{3}{2}\right)$; see Figure 11.11.

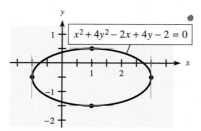

Figure 11.11

(b) Vertical tangents will occur where the derivative is undefined—that is, where $4y + 2 = 0$, or $y = -\frac{1}{2}$. To find the corresponding x-value(s), we substitute $-\frac{1}{2}$ in the equation for y and solve for x.

$$x^2 + 4\left(-\frac{1}{2}\right)^2 - 2x + 4\left(-\frac{1}{2}\right) - 2 = 0$$

$$x^2 - 2x - 3 = 0$$

$$(x - 3)(x + 1) = 0$$

$$x = 3 \quad \text{or} \quad x = -1$$

Thus vertical tangents occur at $\left(3, -\frac{1}{2}\right)$ and $\left(-1, -\frac{1}{2}\right)$; see Figure 11.11.

EXAMPLE 7   Implicit Derivatives with Logarithms and Exponentials

Find dy/dx for each of the following.
(a) $\ln xy = 6$ (b) $4x^2 + e^{xy} = 6y$

Solution
(a) Using the properties of logarithms, we have

$$\ln x + \ln y = 6$$

which leads to the implicit derivative

$$\frac{1}{x} + \frac{1}{y}\frac{dy}{dx} = 0$$

Solving gives $\quad \dfrac{1}{y}\dfrac{dy}{dx} = -\dfrac{1}{x} \quad$ so $\quad \dfrac{dy}{dx} = -\dfrac{y}{x}$

(b) We take the derivative of both sides of $4x^2 + e^{xy} = 6y$ and obtain

$$8x + e^{xy}\left(x\frac{dy}{dx} + y\right) = 6\frac{dy}{dx}$$

$$8x + xe^{xy}\frac{dy}{dx} + ye^{xy} = 6\frac{dy}{dx}$$

$$8x + ye^{xy} = 6\frac{dy}{dx} - xe^{xy}\frac{dy}{dx}$$

$$8x + ye^{xy} = (6 - xe^{xy})\frac{dy}{dx} \qquad \text{so} \qquad \frac{8x + ye^{xy}}{6 - xe^{xy}} = \frac{dy}{dx}$$

EXAMPLE 8 Demand | APPLICATION PREVIEW |

Suppose the demand for Precision, Inc. headphones is given by

$$p = \frac{10{,}000}{(x + 1)^2}$$

where p is the price per set in dollars and x is in hundreds of headphone sets demanded. Find the rate of change of demand with respect to price when 19 (hundred) sets are demanded.

Solution
The rate of change of demand with respect to price is dx/dp. Using implicit differentiation, we get

$$\frac{d}{dp}(p) = \frac{d}{dp}\left[\frac{10{,}000}{(x+1)^2}\right] = \frac{d}{dp}[10{,}000(x+1)^{-2}]$$

$$1 = 10{,}000\left[-2(x+1)^{-3}\frac{dx}{dp}\right]$$

$$1 = \frac{-20{,}000}{(x+1)^3} \cdot \frac{dx}{dp}$$

$$\frac{(x+1)^3}{-20{,}000} = \frac{dx}{dp}$$

When 19 (hundred) headphone sets are demanded we use $x = 19$, and the rate of change of demand with respect to price is

$$\frac{dx}{dp}\bigg|_{x=19} = \frac{(19+1)^3}{-20{,}000} = \frac{8000}{-20{,}000} = -0.4$$

This result means that when 19 (hundred) headphone sets are demanded, if the price per set is increased by \$1, then the expected change in demand is a decrease of 0.4 hundred, or 40, headphone sets.

Calculator Note To graph a function with a graphing calculator, we need to write y as an *explicit* function of x (such as $y = \sqrt{4 - x^2}$). If an equation defines y as an *implicit* function of x, we have to solve for y in terms of x before we can use the graphing calculator. Sometimes we cannot solve for y, and other times, such as for

$$x^{2/3} + y^{2/3} = 8^{2/3}$$

y cannot be written as a single function of x. If this equation is solved for y as a single function and a graphing calculator is used to graph that function, the resulting graph usually shows only the portion of the graph that lies in Quadrants I and II. The complete graph is shown in Figure 11.12. In general, for the graph of an implicitly defined function, a graphing calculator must be used carefully (and sometimes cannot be used at all). ∎

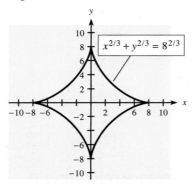

Figure 11.12

CHECKPOINT SOLUTIONS

1. (a) $\dfrac{d}{dx}(x^3) = 3x^2$ (b) $\dfrac{d}{dx}(y^4) = 4y^3\dfrac{dy}{dx}$

   (c) $\dfrac{d}{dx}(x^2y^5) = x^2\left(5y^4\dfrac{dy}{dx}\right) + y^5(2x)$ (by the Product Rule)

2. For $x^3 + y^4 = x^2y^5$, we can use the answers to Question 1 to obtain

$$3x^2 + 4y^3\dfrac{dy}{dx} = x^2\left(5y^4\dfrac{dy}{dx}\right) + y^5(2x)$$

$$3x^2 + 4y^3\dfrac{dy}{dx} = 5x^2y^4\dfrac{dy}{dx} + 2xy^5$$

$$3x^2 - 2xy^5 = (5x^2y^4 - 4y^3)\dfrac{dy}{dx}$$

$$\dfrac{3x^2 - 2xy^5}{5x^2y^4 - 4y^3} = \dfrac{dy}{dx}$$

| EXERCISES | 11.3

In Problems 1–6, find dy/dx at the given point without first solving for y.

1. $x^2 - 4y - 17 = 0$ at $(1, -4)$
2. $3x^2 - 10y + 400 = 0$ at $(10, 70)$
3. $xy^2 = 8$ at $(2, 2)$
4. $e^y = x$ at $(1, 0)$
5. $x^2 + 3xy - 4 = 0$ at $(1, 1)$
6. $x^2 + 5xy + 4 = 0$ at $(1, -1)$

Find dy/dx for the functions in Problems 7–10.

7. $x^2 + 2y^2 - 4 = 0$
8. $x + y^2 - 4y + 6 = 0$
9. $x^2 + 4x + y^2 - 3y + 1 = 0$
10. $x^2 - 5x + y^3 - 3y - 3 = 0$
11. If $x^2 + y^2 = 4$, find y'.
12. If $p^2 + 4p - q = 4$, find dp/dq.
13. If $xy^2 - y^3 = 1$, find y'.
14. If $p^2 - q = 4$, find dp/dq.
15. If $p^2q = 4p - 2$, find dp/dq.
16. If $x^2 - 3y^4 = 2x^5 + 7y^3 - 5$, find dy/dx.
17. If $3x^5 - 5y^3 = 5x^2 + 3y^5$, find dy/dx.
18. If $x^2 + 3x^2y^4 = y + 8$, find dy/dx.
19. If $x^4 + 2x^3y^2 = x - y^3$, find dy/dx.

20. If $(x + y)^2 = 5x^4y^3$, find dy/dx.
21. Find dy/dx for $x^4 + 3x^3y^2 - 2y^5 = (2x + 3y)^2$.
22. Find y' for $2x + 2y = \sqrt{x^2 + y^2}$.

For Problems 23–26, find the slope of the tangent to the curve.

23. $x^2 + 4x + y^2 + 2y - 4 = 0$ at $(1, -1)$
24. $x^2 - 4x + 2y^2 - 4 = 0$ at $(2, 2)$
25. $x^2 + 2xy + 3 = 0$ at $(-1, 2)$
26. $y + x^2 + xy = 13$ at $(2, 3)$
27. Write the equation of the line tangent to the curve $x^2 - 2y^2 + 4 = 0$ at $(2, 2)$.
28. Write the equation of the line tangent to the curve $x^2 + y^2 + 2x - 3 = 0$ at $(-1, 2)$.
29. Write the equation of the line tangent to the curve $4x^2 + 3y^2 - 4y - 3 = 0$ at $(-1, 1)$.
30. Write the equation of the line tangent to the curve $xy + y^2 = 0$ at $(3, 0)$.
31. If $\ln x = y^2$, find dy/dx.
32. If $\ln (x + y) = y^2$, find dy/dx.
33. If $y^2 \ln x = 4$, find dy/dx.
34. If $\ln (xy - 1) = x + 2$, find dy/dx.

35. Find the slope of the tangent to the curve $y^2 \ln x + x^2 y = 3$ at the point $(1, 3)$.

36. Write the equation of the line tangent to the curve $x \ln y + 2xy = 2$ at the point $(1, 1)$.

37. If $xe^y = 6$, find dy/dx.

38. If $x + e^{xy} = 10$, find dy/dx.

39. If $xe^{xy} = 4$, find dy/dx.

40. If $x - xe^y = 3$, find dy/dx.

41. If $ye^x - y = 3$, find dy/dx.

42. If $x^2 y = e^{x+y}$, find dy/dx.

43. Find the slope of the line tangent to the graph of $ye^x = y^2 + x - 2$ at $(0, 2)$.

44. Find the slope of the line tangent to the curve $xe^y = 3x^2 + y - 24$ at $(3, 0)$.

45. Write the equation of the line tangent to the curve $xe^y = 2y + 3$ at $(3, 0)$.

46. Write the equation of the line tangent to the curve $ye^x = 2y + 1$ at $(0, -1)$.

47. At what points does the curve defined by $x^2 + 4y^2 - 4x - 4 = 0$ have
    (a) horizontal tangents?
    (b) vertical tangents?

48. At what points does the curve defined by $x^2 + 4y^2 - 4 = 0$ have
    (a) horizontal tangents?
    (b) vertical tangents?

49. In Problem 11, the derivative y' was found to be

$$y' = \frac{-x}{y}$$

when $x^2 + y^2 = 4$.
    (a) Take the implicit derivative of the equation for y' to show that

$$y'' = \frac{-y + xy'}{y^2}$$

    (b) Substitute $-x/y$ for y' in the expression for y'' in part (a) and simplify to show that

$$y'' = -\frac{(x^2 + y^2)}{y^3}$$

    (c) Does $y'' = -4/y^3$? Why or why not?

50. (a) Find y' implicitly for $x^3 - y^3 = 8$.
    (b) Then, by taking derivatives implicitly, use part (a) to show that

$$y'' = \frac{2x(y - xy')}{y^3}$$

    (c) Substitute x^2/y^2 for y' in the expression for y'' and simplify to show that

$$y'' = \frac{2x(y^3 - x^3)}{y^5}$$

    (d) Does $y'' = -16x/y^5$? Why or why not?

51. Find y'' for $\sqrt{x} + \sqrt{y} = 1$ and simplify.

52. Find y'' for $\dfrac{1}{x} - \dfrac{1}{y} = 1$.

In Problems 53 and 54, find the maximum and minimum values of y. Use a graphing utility to verify your conclusion.

53. $x^2 + y^2 - 9 = 0$

54. $4x^2 + y^2 - 8x = 0$

APPLICATIONS

55. *Advertising and sales* Suppose that a company's sales volume y (in thousands of units) is related to its advertising expenditures x (in thousands of dollars) according to

$$xy - 20x + 10y = 0$$

Find the rate of change of sales volume with respect to advertising expenditures when $x = 10$ (thousand dollars).

56. *Insect control* Suppose that the number of mosquitoes N (in thousands) in a certain swampy area near a community is related to the number of pounds of insecticide x sprayed on the nesting areas according to

$$Nx - 10x + N = 300$$

Find the rate of change of N with respect to x when 49 pounds of insecticide is used.

57. *Production* Suppose that a company can produce 12,000 units when the number of hours of skilled labor y and unskilled labor x satisfy

$$384 = (x + 1)^{3/4}(y + 2)^{1/3}$$

Find the rate of change of skilled-labor hours with respect to unskilled-labor hours when $x = 255$ and $y = 214$. This can be used to approximate the change in skilled-labor hours required to maintain the same production level when unskilled-labor hours are increased by 1 hour.

58. *Production* Suppose that production of 10,000 units of a certain agricultural crop is related to the number of hours of labor x and the number of acres of the crop y according to

$$300x + 30,000y = 11xy - 0.0002x^2 - 5y$$

Find the rate of change of the number of hours with respect to the number of acres.

59. *Demand* If the demand function for q units of a product at \$$p$ per unit is given by

$$p(q + 1)^2 = 200,000$$

find the rate of change of quantity with respect to price when $p = \$80$. Interpret this result.

60. *Demand* If the demand function for q units of a commodity at \$$p$ per unit is given by

$$p^2(2q + 1) = 100,000$$

find the rate of change of quantity with respect to price when $p = \$50$. Interpret this result.

61. ***Radioactive decay*** The number of grams of radium, y, that will remain after t years if 100 grams existed originally can be found by using the equation

$$-0.000436t = \ln\left(\frac{y}{100}\right)$$

Use implicit differentiation to find the rate of change of y with respect to t—that is, the rate at which the radium will decay.

62. ***Disease control*** Suppose the proportion P of people affected by a certain disease is described by

$$\ln\left(\frac{P}{1 - P}\right) = 0.5t$$

where t is the time in months. Find dP/dt, the rate at which P grows.

63. ***Temperature-humidity index*** The temperature-humidity index (THI) is given by

$$\text{THI} = t - 0.55(1 - h)(t - 58)$$

where t is the air temperature in degrees Fahrenheit and h is the relative humidity. If the THI remains constant, find the rate of change of humidity with respect to temperature if the temperature is 70°F (*Source:* "Temperature-Humidity Indices," *UMAP Journal*, Fall 1989).

OBJECTIVE 11.4

- To use implicit differentiation to solve problems that involve related rates

Related Rates

▮ | APPLICATION PREVIEW |

According to Poiseuille's law, the flow of blood F is related to the radius r of the vessel according to

$$F = kr^4$$

where k is a constant. When the radius of a blood vessel is reduced, such as by cholesterol deposits, the flow of blood is also restricted. Drugs can be administered that increase the radius of the blood vessel and, hence, the flow of blood. The rate of change of the blood flow and the rate of change of the radius of the blood vessel are time rates of change that are related to each other, so they are called related rates. We can use these related rates to find the percent rate of change in the blood flow that corresponds to the percent rate of change in the radius of the blood vessel caused by the drug. (See Example 2.)

Related Rates   We have seen that the derivative represents the instantaneous rate of change of one variable with respect to another. When the derivative is taken with respect to time, it represents the rate at which that variable is changing with respect to time (or the velocity). For example, if distance x is measured in miles and time t in hours, then dx/dt is measured in miles per hour and indicates how fast x is changing. Similarly, if V represents the volume (in cubic feet) of water in a swimming pool and t is time (in minutes), then dV/dt is measured in cubic feet per minute (ft^3/min) and might measure the rate at which the pool is being filled with water or being emptied.

Sometimes, two (or more) quantities that depend on time are also related to each other. For example, the height of a tree h (in feet) is related to the radius r (in inches) of its trunk, and this relationship can be modeled by

$$h = kr^{2/3}$$

where k is a constant.* Of course, both h and r are also related to time, so the rates of change dh/dt and dr/dt are related to each other. Thus they are called **related rates.**

The specific relationship between dh/dt and dr/dt can be found by differentiating $h = kr^{2/3}$ implicitly with respect to time t.

---

*T. McMahon, "Size and Shape in Biology," *Science* 179 (1979): 1201.

EXAMPLE 1   Tree Height and Trunk Radius

Suppose that for a certain type of tree, the height of the tree (in feet) is related to the radius of its trunk (in inches) by

$$h = 15r^{2/3}$$

Suppose that the rate of change of r is $\frac{3}{4}$ inch per year. Find how fast the height is changing when the radius is 8 inches.

Solution

To find how the rates dh/dt and dr/dt are related, we differentiate $h = 15r^{2/3}$ implicitly with respect to time t.

$$\frac{dh}{dt} = 10r^{-1/3}\frac{dr}{dt}$$

Using $r = 8$ inches and $dr/dt = \frac{3}{4}$ inch per year gives

$$\frac{dh}{dt} = 10(8)^{-1/3}(3/4) = \frac{15}{4} = 3\tfrac{3}{4} \text{ feet per year}$$

Percent Rates of Change   The work in Example 1 shows how to obtain related rates, but the different units (feet per year and inches per year) may be somewhat difficult to interpret. For this reason, many applications in the life sciences deal with **percent rates of change**. The percent rate of change of a quantity is the rate of change of the quantity divided by the quantity.

EXAMPLE 2   Blood Flow | APPLICATION PREVIEW |

Poiseuille's law expresses the flow of blood F as a function of the radius r of the vessel according to

$$F = kr^4$$

where k is a constant. When the radius of a blood vessel is restricted, such as by cholesterol deposits, drugs can be administered that will increase the radius of the blood vessel (and hence the blood flow). Find the percent rate of change of the flow of blood that corresponds to the percent rate of change of the radius of a blood vessel caused by the drug.

Solution

We seek the percent rate of change of flow, $(dF/dt)/F$, that results from a given percent rate of change of the radius $(dr/dt)/r$. We first find the related rates of change by differentiating

$$F = kr^4$$

implicitly with respect to time.

$$\frac{dF}{dt} = k\left(4r^3\frac{dr}{dt}\right)$$

Then the percent rate of change of flow can be found by dividing both sides of the equation by F.

$$\frac{\dfrac{dF}{dt}}{F} = \frac{4kr^3\dfrac{dr}{dt}}{F}$$

If we replace F on the right side of the equation with kr^4 and reduce, we get

$$\frac{\dfrac{dF}{dt}}{F} = \frac{4kr^3\dfrac{dr}{dt}}{kr^4} = 4\left(\frac{\dfrac{dr}{dt}}{r}\right)$$

Thus we see that the percent rate of change of the flow of blood is 4 times the corresponding percent rate of change of the radius of the blood vessel. This means that a drug that would cause a 12% increase in the radius of a blood vessel at a certain time would produce a corresponding 48% increase in blood flow through that vessel at that time. ▪

Solving Related-Rates Problems   In the examples above, the equation relating the time-dependent variables has been given. For some problems, the original equation relating the variables must first be developed from the statement of the problem. These problems can be solved with the aid of the following procedure.

Solving a Related-Rates Problem

Procedure	Example
To solve a related-rates problem:	Sand falls at a rate of 5 ft³/min on a conical pile, with the diameter always equal to the height of the pile. At what rate is the height increasing when the pile is 10 ft high?
1. Use geometric and/or physical conditions to write an equation that relates the time-dependent variables.	1. The conical pile has its volume given by $$V = \frac{1}{3}\pi r^2 h$$
2. Substitute into the equation values or relationships that are true at *all times*.	2. The radius $r = \frac{1}{2}h$ at all times, so $$V = \frac{1}{3}\pi\left(\frac{1}{4}h^2\right)h = \frac{\pi}{12}h^3$$
3. Differentiate both sides of the equation implicitly with respect to time. This equation is valid for all times.	3. $\dfrac{dV}{dt} = \dfrac{\pi}{12}\left(3h^2\dfrac{dh}{dt}\right) = \dfrac{\pi}{4}h^2\dfrac{dh}{dt}$
4. Substitute the values that are known at the instant specified, and solve the equation.	4. $\dfrac{dV}{dt} = 5$ at all times, so when $h = 10$, $$5 = \frac{\pi}{4}(10^2)\frac{dh}{dt}$$
5. Solve for the specified quantity at the given time.	5. $\dfrac{dh}{dt} = \dfrac{20}{100\pi} = \dfrac{1}{5\pi}$ (feet/minute)

Note that you should *not* substitute numerical values for any quantity that varies with time until after the derivative is taken. If values are substituted before the derivative is taken, that quantity will have the constant value resulting from the substitution and hence will have a derivative equal to zero.

EXAMPLE 3   Hot Air Balloon

A hot air balloon has a velocity of 50 feet per minute and is flying at a constant height of 500 feet. An observer on the ground is watching the balloon approach. How fast is the distance between the balloon and the observer changing when the balloon is 1000 feet from the observer?

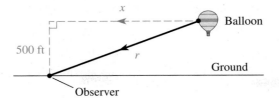

Figure 11.13

Solution

If we let r be the distance between the balloon and the observer and let x be the horizontal distance from the balloon to a point directly above the observer, then we see that these quantities are related by the equation

$$x^2 + 500^2 = r^2 \quad \text{(See Figure 11.13)}$$

Because the distance x is decreasing, we know that dx/dt must be negative. Thus we are given that $dx/dt = -50$ at all times, and we need to find dr/dt when $r = 1000$. Taking the derivative with respect to t of both sides of the equation $x^2 + 500^2 = r^2$ gives

$$2x\frac{dx}{dt} + 0 = 2r\frac{dr}{dt}$$

Using $dx/dt = -50$ and $r = 1000$, we get

$$2x(-50) = 2000\frac{dr}{dt}$$

$$\frac{dr}{dt} = \frac{-100x}{2000} = \frac{-x}{20}$$

Using $r = 1000$ in $x^2 + 500^2 = r^2$ gives $x^2 = 750{,}000$. Thus $x = 500\sqrt{3}$, and

$$\frac{dr}{dt} = \frac{-500\sqrt{3}}{20} = -25\sqrt{3} \approx -43.3$$

The distance is decreasing at 43.3 feet per minute.

CHECKPOINT

1. If V represents volume, write a mathematical symbol that represents "the rate of change of volume with respect to time."
2. (a) Differentiate $x^2 + 64 = y^2$ implicitly with respect to time.
   (b) Suppose that we know that y is increasing at 2 units per minute. Use part (a) to find the rate of change of x at the instant when $x = 6$ and $y = 10$.
3. True or false: In solving a related-rates problem, we substitute all numerical values into the equation before we take derivatives.

EXAMPLE 4   Spread of an Oil Slick

Suppose that oil is spreading in a circular pattern from a leak at an offshore rig. If the rate at which the radius of the oil slick is growing is 1 foot per minute at what rate is the area of the oil slick growing when the radius is 600 feet?

Solution

The area of the circular oil slick is given by

$$A = \pi r^2$$

where r is the radius. The rate at which the area is changing is

$$\frac{dA}{dt} = 2\pi r \frac{dr}{dt}$$

Using $r = 600$ feet and $dr/dt = 1$ foot per minute gives

$$\frac{dA}{dt} = 2\pi \,(600 \text{ ft})\,(1 \text{ ft/min}) = 1200\pi \text{ ft}^2/\text{min}$$

Thus when the radius of the oil slick is 600 feet, the area is growing at the rate of 1200π square feet per minute, or approximately 3770 square feet per minute. ∎

CHECKPOINT SOLUTIONS

1. dV/dt

2. (a) $2x\dfrac{dx}{dt} + 0 = 2y\dfrac{dy}{dt}$

   $x\dfrac{dx}{dt} = y\dfrac{dy}{dt}$

   (b) Use $\dfrac{dy}{dt} = 2$, $x = 6$, and $y = 10$ in part (a) to obtain

   $6\dfrac{dx}{dt} = 10(2)$ or $\dfrac{dx}{dt} = \dfrac{20}{6} = \dfrac{10}{3}$

3. False. The numerical values for any quantity that is varying with time should not be substituted until after the derivative is taken.

| EXERCISES | 11.4

In Problems 1–4, find dy/dt using the given values.
1. $y = x^3 - 3x$ for $x = 2$, $dx/dt = 4$
2. $y = 3x^3 + 5x^2 - x$ for $x = 4$, $dx/dt = 3$
3. $xy = 4$ for $x = 8$, $dx/dt = -2$
4. $xy = x + 3$ for $x = 3$, $dx/dt = -1$

In Problems 5–8, assume that x and y are differentiable functions of t. In each case, find dx/dt given that $x = 5$, $y = 12$, and $dy/dt = 2$.
5. $x^2 + y^2 = 169$ 6. $y^2 - x^2 = 119$
7. $y^2 = 2xy + 24$ 8. $x^2(y - 6) = 12y + 6$
9. If $x^2 + y^2 = z^2$, find dy/dt when $x = 3$, $y = 4$, $dx/dt = 10$, and $dz/dt = 2$.
10. If $s = 2\pi r(r + h)$, find dr/dt when $r = 2$, $h = 8$, $dh/dt = 3$, and $ds/dt = 10\pi$.
11. A point is moving along the graph of the equation $y = -4x^2$. At what rate is y changing when $x = 5$ and is changing at a rate of 2 units/sec?
12. A point is moving along the graph of the equation $y = 5x^3 - 2x$. At what rate is y changing when $x = 4$ and is changing at a rate of 3 units/sec?
13. The radius of a circle is increasing at a rate of 2 ft/min. At what rate is its area changing when the radius is 3 ft? (Recall that for a circle, $A = \pi r^2$.)

14. The area of a circle is changing at a rate of 1 in²/sec. At what rate is its radius changing when the radius is 2 in.?
15. The volume of a cube is increasing at a rate of 64 in³/sec. At what rate is the length of each edge of the cube changing when the edges are 6 in. long? (Recall that for a cube, $V = x^3$.)
16. The lengths of the edges of a cube are increasing at a rate of 8 ft/min. At what rate is the surface area changing when the edges are 24 ft long? (Recall that for a cube, $S = 6x^2$.)

APPLICATIONS

17. *Profit* Suppose that the daily profit (in dollars) from the production and sale of x units of a product is given by

$$P = 180x - \frac{x^2}{1000} - 2000$$

At what rate per day is the profit changing when the number of units produced and sold is 100 and is increasing at a rate of 10 units per day?

18. *Profit* Suppose that the monthly revenue and cost (in dollars) for x units of a product are

$$R = 400x - \frac{x^2}{20} \quad \text{and} \quad C = 5000 + 70x$$

At what rate per month is the profit changing if the number of units produced and sold is 200 and is increasing at a rate of 5 units per month?

19. *Demand* Suppose that the price p (in dollars) of a product is given by the demand function

$$p = \frac{1000 - 10x}{400 - x}$$

where x represents the quantity demanded. If the daily demand is *decreasing* at a rate of 20 units per day, at what rate is the price changing when the demand is 20 units?

20. *Supply* The supply function for a product is given by $p = 40 + 100\sqrt{2x + 9}$, where x is the number of units supplied and p is the price in dollars. If the price is increasing at a rate of $1 per month, at what rate is the supply changing when $x = 20$?

21. *Capital investment and production* Suppose that for a particular product, the number of units x produced per month depends on the number of thousands of dollars y invested, with $x = 30y + 20y^2$. At what rate will production increase if $10,000 is invested and if the investment capital is increasing at a rate of $1000 per month?

22. *Boyle's law* Boyle's law for enclosed gases states that at a constant temperature, the pressure is related to the volume by the equation

$$P = \frac{k}{V}$$

where k is a constant. If the volume is increasing at a rate of 5 cubic inches per hour, at what rate is the pressure changing when the volume is 30 cubic inches and $k = 2$ inch-pounds?

Tumor growth **For Problems 23 and 24, suppose that a tumor in a person's body has a spherical shape and that treatment is causing the radius of the tumor to decrease at a rate of 1 millimeter per month.**

23. At what rate is the volume decreasing when the radius is 3 mm? (Recall that $V = \frac{4}{3}\pi r^3$.)

24. At what rate is the surface area of the tumor decreasing when the radius is 3 mm? (Recall that for a sphere, $S = 4\pi r^2$.)

25. *Allometric relationships—fish* For many species of fish, the allometric relationship between the weight W and the length L is approximately $W = kL^3$, where k is a constant. Find the percent rate of change of the weight as a corresponding percent rate of change of the length.

26. *Blood flow* The resistance R of a blood vessel to the flow of blood is a function of the radius r of the blood vessel and is given by

$$R = \frac{k}{r^4}$$

where k is a constant. Find the percent rate of change of the resistance of a blood vessel in terms of the percent rate of change in the radius of the blood vessel.

27. *Allometric relationships—crabs* For fiddler crabs, data gathered by Thompson[*] show that the allometric relationship between the weight C of the claw and the weight W of the body is given by

$$C = 0.11W^{1.54}$$

Find the percent rate of change of the claw weight in terms of the percent rate of change of the body weight for fiddler crabs.

28. *Body weight and surface area* For human beings, the surface area S of the body is related to the body's weight W according to

$$S = kW^{2/3}$$

where k is a constant. Find the percent rate of change of the body's surface area in terms of the percent rate of change of the body's weight.

29. *Cell growth* A bacterial cell has a spherical shape. If the volume of the cell is increasing at a rate of 4 cubic micrometers per day, at what rate is the radius of the cell increasing when it is 2 micrometers? (Recall that for a sphere, $V = \frac{4}{3}\pi r^3$.)

30. *Water purification* Assume that water is being purified by causing it to flow through a conical filter that has a height of 15 inches and a radius of 5 inches. If the depth of the water is decreasing at a rate of 1 inch per minute when the depth is 6 inches, at what rate is the volume of water flowing out of the filter at this instant?

31. *Volume and radius* Suppose that air is being pumped into a spherical balloon at a rate of 5 in³/min. At what rate is the radius of the balloon increasing when the radius is 5 in.?

32. *Boat docking* Suppose that a boat is being pulled toward a dock by a winch that is 5 ft above the level of the boat deck, as shown in the figure. If the winch is pulling the cable at a rate of 3 ft/min, at what rate is the boat approaching the dock when it is 12 ft from the dock?

33. *Ladder safety* A 30-ft ladder is leaning against a wall. If the bottom is pulled away from the wall at a rate of 1 ft/sec, at what rate is the top of the ladder sliding down the wall when the bottom is 18 ft from the wall?

[*]d'Arcy Thompson, *On Growth and Form* (Cambridge, England: Cambridge University Press, 1961).

34. *Flight* A kite is 30 ft high and is moving horizontally at a rate of 10 ft/min. If the kite string is taut, at what rate is the string being played out when 50 ft of string is out?

35. *Flight* A plane is flying at a constant altitude of 1 mile and a speed of 300 mph. If it is flying toward an observer on the ground, how fast is the plane approaching the observer when it is 5 miles from the observer?

36. *Distance* Two boats leave the same port at the same time, with boat A traveling north at 15 knots (nautical miles per hour) and boat B traveling east at 20 knots. How fast is the distance between them changing when boat A is 30 nautical miles from port?

37. *Distance* Two cars are approaching an intersection on roads that are perpendicular to each other. Car A is north of the intersection and traveling south at 40 mph. Car B is east of the intersection and traveling west at 55 mph. How fast is the distance between the cars changing when car A is 15 miles from the intersection and car B is 8 miles from the intersection?

38. *Water depth* Water is flowing into a barrel in the shape of a right circular cylinder at the rate of 200 in^3/min. If the radius of the barrel is 18 in., at what rate is the depth of the water changing when the water is 30 in. deep?

39. *Water depth* Suppose that water is being pumped into a rectangular swimming pool of uniform depth at 10 ft^3/hr. If the pool is 10 ft wide and 25 ft long, at what rate is the water rising when it is 4 ft deep?

OBJECTIVES

11.5

- To find the elasticity of demand
- To find the tax per unit that will maximize tax revenue

Applications in Business and Economics

■ | **APPLICATION PREVIEW** |

Suppose that the demand for a product is given by

$$p = \frac{1000}{(q + 1)^2}$$

We can measure how sensitive the demand for this product is to price changes by finding the elasticity of demand. (See Example 2.) This elasticity can be used to measure the effects that price changes have on total revenue. We also consider taxation in a competitive market, which examines how a tax levied on goods shifts market equilibrium. We will find the tax per unit that, despite changes in market equilibrium, maximizes tax revenue.

Elasticity of Demand   We know from the law of demand that consumers will respond to changes in prices; if prices increase, the quantities demanded will decrease. But the degree of responsiveness of the consumers to price changes will vary widely for different products. For example, a price increase in insulin will not greatly decrease the demand for it by diabetics, but a price increase in clothes may cause consumers to buy less and wear their old clothes longer. When the response to price changes is considerable, we say the demand is *elastic*. When price changes cause relatively small changes in demand for a product, the demand is said to be *inelastic* for that product.

Economists measure the **elasticity of demand** as follows.

Elasticity   The **elasticity of demand** at the point (q_A, p_A) is

$$\eta = -\frac{p}{q} \cdot \frac{dq}{dp}\bigg|_{(q_A, p_A)}$$

EXAMPLE 1   Elasticity

Find the elasticity of the demand function $p + 5q = 100$ when

(a) the price is \$40.   (b) the price is \$60.   (c) the price is \$50.

Solution

Solving the demand function for q gives $q = 20 - \frac{1}{5}p$. Then $dq/dp = -\frac{1}{5}$ and

$$\eta = -\frac{p}{q}\left(-\frac{1}{5}\right)$$

(a) When $p = 40$, $q = 12$ and $\eta = -\frac{p}{q}\left(-\frac{1}{5}\right)\Big|_{(12,\,40)} = -\frac{40}{12}\left(-\frac{1}{5}\right) = \frac{2}{3}$.

(b) When $p = 60$, $q = 8$ and $\eta = -\frac{p}{q}\left(-\frac{1}{5}\right)\Big|_{(8,\,60)} = -\frac{60}{8}\left(-\frac{1}{5}\right) = \frac{3}{2}$.

(c) When $p = 50$, $q = 10$ and $\eta = -\frac{p}{q}\left(-\frac{1}{5}\right)\Big|_{(10,\,50)} = -\frac{50}{10}\left(-\frac{1}{5}\right) = 1$.

Note that in Example 1 the demand equation was $p + 5q = 100$, so the demand "curve" is a straight line, with slope $m = -5$. But the elasticity was $\eta = \frac{2}{3}$ at (12, 40), $\eta = \frac{3}{2}$ at (8, 60), and $\eta = 1$ at (10, 50). This illustrates that the elasticity of demand may be different at different points on the demand curve, even though the slope of the demand "curve" is constant. (See Figure 11.14.)

Figure 11.14

This example shows that the elasticity of demand is more than just the slope of the demand curve, which is the rate at which the demand is changing. Recall that the elasticity measures the consumers' degree of responsiveness to a price change.

Economists use η to measure how responsive demand is to price at different points on the demand curve for a product.

Elasticity of Demand

- If $\eta > 1$, the demand is **elastic,** and the percent decrease in demand is greater than the corresponding percent increase in price.
- If $\eta < 1$, the demand is **inelastic,** and the percent decrease in demand is less than the corresponding percent increase in price.
- If $\eta = 1$, the demand is **unitary elastic,** and the percent decrease in demand is approximately equal to the corresponding percent increase in price.

We can also use implicit differentiation to find dq/dp in evaluating the point elasticity of demand.

EXAMPLE 2   Elasticity | APPLICATION PREVIEW |

The demand for a certain product is given by

$$p = \frac{1000}{(q + 1)^2}$$

where p is the price per unit in dollars and q is demand in units of the product. Find the elasticity of demand with respect to price when $q = 19$.

Solution

To find the elasticity, we need to find dq/dp. Using implicit differentiation, we get the following:

$$\frac{d}{dp}(p) = \frac{d}{dp}\left[1000(q+1)^{-2}\right]$$

$$1 = 1000\left[-2(q+1)^{-3}\frac{dq}{dp}\right]$$

$$1 = \frac{-2000}{(q+1)^3}\frac{dq}{dp}$$

$$\frac{(q+1)^3}{-2000} = \frac{dq}{dp}$$

When $q = 19$, we have $p = 1000/(19+1)^2 = 1000/400 = 5/2$ and

$$\left.\frac{dq}{dp}\right|_{(q=19)} = \frac{(19+1)^3}{-2000} = \frac{8000}{-2000} = -4$$

The elasticity of demand when $q = 19$ is

$$\eta = \frac{-p}{q}\cdot\frac{dq}{dp} = -\frac{(5/2)}{19}\cdot(-4) = \frac{10}{19} < 1$$

Thus the demand for this product is inelastic.

Elasticity and Revenue

Elasticity is related to revenue in a special way. We can see how by computing the derivative with respect to p of the revenue function

$$R = pq$$

$$\frac{dR}{dp} = p\cdot\frac{dq}{dp} + q\cdot 1$$

$$= \frac{q}{q}\cdot p\cdot\frac{dq}{dp} + q = q\cdot\frac{p}{q}\cdot\frac{dq}{dp} + q$$

$$= q(-\eta) + q$$

$$= q(1 - \eta)$$

From this we can summarize the relationship of elasticity and revenue.

Elasticity and Revenue

The rate of change of revenue R with respect to price p is related to elasticity in the following way.

- Elastic $(\eta > 1)$ means $\dfrac{dR}{dp} < 0.$ $\begin{cases}\text{Hence if price increases, revenue decreases,}\\ \text{and if price decreases, revenue increases.}\end{cases}$

- Inelastic $(\eta < 1)$ means $\dfrac{dR}{dp} > 0.$ $\begin{cases}\text{Hence if price increases, revenue increases,}\\ \text{and if price decreases, revenue decreases.}\end{cases}$

- Unitary elastic $(\eta = 1)$ means $\dfrac{dR}{dp} = 0.$ Hence an increase or decrease in price will not change revenue. Revenue is optimized at this point.

EXAMPLE 3   **Elasticity and Revenue**

The demand for a product is given by

$$p = 10\sqrt{100 - q}, \quad 0 \le q \le 100$$

(a) Find the point at which demand is of unitary elasticity, and find intervals in which the demand is inelastic and in which it is elastic.
(b) Find q where revenue is increasing, where it is decreasing, and where it is maximized.
(c) Use a graphing utility to show the graph of the revenue function $R = pq$, with $0 \le q \le 100$, and confirm the results from part (b).

Solution

The elasticity is

$$\eta = \frac{-p}{q} \cdot \frac{dq}{dp} = -\frac{10\sqrt{100 - q}}{q} \cdot \frac{dq}{dp}$$

Finding dq/dp implicitly, we have

$$1 = 10\left[\frac{1}{2}(100 - q)^{-1/2}\left(-\frac{dq}{dp}\right)\right] = \frac{-5}{\sqrt{100 - q}} \cdot \frac{dq}{dp}$$

so

$$\frac{dq}{dp} = \frac{-\sqrt{100 - q}}{5}$$

Thus

$$\eta = \left(-\frac{10\sqrt{100 - q}}{q}\right)\left(\frac{-\sqrt{100 - q}}{5}\right) = \frac{200 - 2q}{q}$$

(a) Unitary elasticity occurs where $\eta = 1$.

$$1 = \frac{200 - 2q}{q}$$
$$q = 200 - 2q$$
$$3q = 200$$
$$q = 66\tfrac{2}{3}$$

so unitary elasticity occurs when $66\tfrac{2}{3}$ units are sold, at a price of $57.74. For values of q between 0 and $66\tfrac{2}{3}$, $\eta > 1$ and demand is elastic. For values of q between $66\tfrac{2}{3}$ and 100, $\eta < 1$ and demand is inelastic.

(b) When q increases over $0 < q < 66\tfrac{2}{3}$, p decreases, so $\eta > 1$ means R increases. Similarly, when q increases over $66\tfrac{2}{3} < q < 100$, p decreases, so $\eta < 1$ means R decreases. Revenue is maximized where $\eta = 1$, at $q = 66\tfrac{2}{3}$ and $p = 57.74$.

(c) The graph of this revenue function,

$$R = 10q\sqrt{100 - q}$$

is shown in Figure 11.15. The maximum revenue is $3849 at $q = 66\tfrac{2}{3}$. ∎

Figure 11.15

CHECKPOINT

1. Write the formula for point elasticity, η.
2. (a) If $\eta > 1$, the demand is called _____.
   (b) If $\eta < 1$, the demand is called _____.
   (c) If $\eta = 1$, the demand is called _____.
3. Find the elasticity of demand for $q = \dfrac{100}{p} - 1$ when $p = 10$ and $q = 9$.

Taxation in a Competitive Market

Many taxes imposed by governments are "hidden." That is, the tax is levied on goods produced, and the producers must pay the tax. Of course, the tax becomes a cost to the producers, and they pass that cost on to the consumer in the form of higher prices for goods.

Suppose the government imposes a tax of t dollars on each unit produced and sold by producers. If we are in pure competition in which the consumers' demand depends only on price, the *demand function* will not change. The tax will change the supply function, of course, because at each level of output q, the firm will want to charge a price $p + t$ per unit, where p is the original price per unit and t is the tax per unit.

The graphs of the market demand function, the original market supply function, and the market supply function after taxes are shown in Figure 11.16. Because the tax added to each item is constant, the graph of the new supply function is t units above the original supply function. If $p = f(q)$ defines the original supply function, then $p = f(q) + t$ defines the supply function after taxation.

Figure 11.16

Note in this case that after the taxes are imposed, *no* items are supplied at the price that was the equilibrium price before taxation. After the taxes are imposed, the consumers simply have to pay more for the product. Because taxation does not change the demand curve, the quantity purchased at market equilibrium will be less than it was before taxation. Thus governments planning taxes should recognize that they will not collect taxes on the original equilibrium quantity. They will collect on the *new* equilibrium quantity, a quantity reduced by their taxation. Thus a large tax on each item may reduce the quantity demanded at the new market equilibrium so much that very little revenue results from the tax!

If the tax revenue is represented by $T = tq$, where t is the tax per unit and q is the equilibrium quantity of the supply and demand functions after taxation, we can use the following procedure for maximizing the total tax revenue in a competitive market.

Maximizing Total Tax Revenue

Procedure	Example
To find the tax per item (under pure competition) that will maximize total tax revenue:	Suppose the demand and supply functions are given by $p = 600 - q$ and $p = 200 + \frac{1}{3}q$, respectively, where $\$p$ is the price per unit and q is the number of units. Find the tax t that will maximize the total tax revenue T.
1. Write the supply function after taxation.	1. $p = 200 + \frac{1}{3}q + t$
2. Set the demand function and the new supply function equal, and solve for t in terms of q.	2. $600 - q = 200 + \frac{1}{3}q + t$ $400 - \frac{4}{3}q = t$
3. Form the total tax revenue function, $T = tq$, by multiplying the expression for t by q, and then take its derivative with respect to q.	3. $T = tq = 400q - \frac{4}{3}q^2$ $T'(q) = \frac{dT}{dq} = 400 - \frac{8}{3}q$
4. Set $T' = 0$, and solve for q. This is the q that should maximize T. Use the second-derivative test to verify it.	4. $0 = 400 - \frac{8}{3}q$ $q = 150$ $T''(q) = -\frac{8}{3}$. Thus T is maximized at $q = 150$.
5. Substitute the value of q in the equation for t (in Step 2). This is the value of t that will maximize T.	5. $t = 400 - \frac{4}{3}(150) = 200$ A tax of $200 per item will maximize the total tax revenue. The total tax revenue for the period would be $\$200 \cdot (150) = \$30{,}000$.

Note that in the example just given, if a tax of $300 were imposed, market equilibrium would occur at $q = 75$, and the total tax revenue the government would receive would be

$$(\$300)(75) = \$22{,}500$$

Thus, with a tax of $300 per unit rather than $200, the government's tax revenue would be $22,500 rather than $30,000. In addition, with a $300 tax, suppliers would sell only 75 units rather than 150, and consumers would pay $p = 200 + 25 + 300 = \$525$ per item, which is $75 more than the price with a $200 tax. Thus everyone would suffer if the tax rate were raised to $300.

CHECKPOINT 4. For problems involving taxation in a competitive market, if supply is $p = f(q)$ and demand is $p = g(q)$, is the tax t added to $f(q)$ or to $g(q)$?

EXAMPLE 4 Maximizing Tax Revenue

The demand and supply functions for a product are $p = 900 - 20q - \frac{1}{3}q^2$ and $p = 200 + 10q$, respectively, where p is in dollars and q is the number of units. Find the tax per unit that will maximize the tax revenue T.

Solution

After taxation, the supply function is $p = 200 + 10q + t$, where t is the tax per unit. The demand function will meet the new supply function where

$$900 - 20q - \frac{1}{3}q^2 = 200 + 10q + t$$

so

$$t = 700 - 30q - \frac{1}{3}q^2$$

Then the total tax T is $T = tq = 700q - 30q^2 - \frac{1}{3}q^3$, and we maximize T as follows:

$$T'(q) = 700 - 60q - q^2$$

$$0 = -(q + 70)(q - 10)$$

$$q = 10 \quad \text{or} \quad q = -70$$

$$T''(q) = -60 - 2q, \text{ so } T''(q) < 0 \text{ for } q \geq 0$$

Thus the curve is concave down for $q \geq 0$, and $q = 10$ gives an absolute maximum for the tax revenue T. The maximum possible tax revenue is

$$T(10) \approx \$3666.67$$

The tax per unit that maximizes T is

$$t = 700 - 30(10) - \frac{1}{3}(10)^2 \approx \$366.67$$

An infamous example of a tax increase that resulted in decreased tax revenue and economic disaster is the "luxury tax" enacted in 1991. This was a 10% excise tax on the sale of expensive jewelry, furs, airplanes, certain expensive boats, and luxury automobiles. The Congressional Joint Tax Committee had estimated that the luxury tax would raise $6 million from airplanes alone, but it raised only $53,000 while it destroyed the small-airplane market (one company lost $130 million and 480 jobs in a single year). It also capsized the boat market. The luxury tax was repealed at the end of 1993 (except for automobiles).*

CHECKPOINT SOLUTIONS

1. $\eta = \dfrac{-p}{q} \cdot \dfrac{dq}{dp}$

2. (a) elastic (b) inelastic (c) unitary elastic

3. $\dfrac{dq}{dp} = \dfrac{-100}{p^2}$ and $\dfrac{dq}{dp} = -1$ when $p = 10, q = 9$

   $\eta = \dfrac{-10}{9}(-1) = \dfrac{10}{9}$ (elastic)

4. Tax t is added to supply: $p = f(q) + t$.

*Fortune, Sept. 6, 1993; Motor Trend, December 1993.

| EXERCISES | 11.5

ELASTICITY OF DEMAND

In Problems 1–8, p is in dollars and q is the number of units.

1. (a) Find the elasticity of the demand function $p + 4q = 80$ at $(10, 40)$.
   (b) How will a price increase affect total revenue?

2. (a) Find the elasticity of the demand function $2p + 3q = 150$ at the price $p = 15$.
   (b) How will a price increase affect total revenue?

3. (a) Find the elasticity of the demand function $p^2 + 2p + q = 49$ at $p = 6$.
   (b) How will a price increase affect total revenue?

4. (a) Find the elasticity of the demand function $pq = 81$ at $p = 3$.
   (b) How will a price increase affect total revenue?

5. Suppose that the demand for a product is given by $pq + p = 5000$.

(a) Find the elasticity when $p = \$50$ and $q = 99$.
(b) Tell what type of elasticity this is: unitary, elastic, or inelastic.
(c) How would revenue be affected by a price increase?

6. Suppose that the demand for a product is given by $2p^2q = 10,000 + 9000p^2$.
   (a) Find the elasticity when $p = \$50$ and $q = 4502$.
   (b) Tell what type of elasticity this is: unitary, elastic, or inelastic.
   (c) How would revenue be affected by a price increase?

7. Suppose that the demand for a product is given by $pq + p + 100q = 50,000$.
   (a) Find the elasticity when $p = \$401$.
   (b) Tell what type of elasticity this is.
   (c) How would a price increase affect revenue?

8. Suppose that the demand for a product is given by

$$(p + 1)\sqrt{q + 1} = 1000$$

   (a) Find the elasticity when $p = \$39$.
   (b) Tell what type of elasticity this is.
   (c) How would a price increase affect revenue?

9. Suppose the demand function for a product is given by

$$p = \frac{1}{2}\ln\left(\frac{5000 - q}{q + 1}\right)$$

   where p is in hundreds of dollars and q is the number of tons.
   (a) What is the elasticity of demand when the quantity demanded is 2 tons and the price is $371?
   (b) Is the demand elastic or inelastic?

10. Suppose the weekly demand function for a product is

$$q = \frac{5000}{1 + e^{2p}} - 1$$

   where p is the price in thousands of dollars and q is the number of units demanded. What is the elasticity of demand when the price is $1000 and the quantity demanded is 595?

In Problems 11 and 12, the demand functions for specialty steel products are given, where p is in dollars and q is the number of units. For both problems:
(a) **Find the elasticity of demand as a function of the quantity demanded, q.**
(b) **Find the point at which the demand is of unitary elasticity and find intervals in which the demand is inelastic and in which it is elastic.**
(c) **Use information about elasticity in part (b) to decide where the revenue is increasing, where it is decreasing, and where it is maximized.**
(d) **Graph the revenue function $R = pq$, and use it to find where revenue is maximized. Is it at the same quantity as that determined in part (c)?**

11. $p = 120\sqrt[3]{125 - q}$
12. $p = 30\sqrt{49 - q}$
13. South West Electronics Corporation (SWEC) designs high-tech business and residential security systems.

The company's marketing analyst has been assigned to analyze market demand for SWEC's top-selling system, The Terminator. Monthly demand for The Terminator has been estimated as follows:

$$q = 445 - 8p + 25A + 4.5C + 6Y$$

where $q =$ Expected number of system sales per month
   $p =$ Selling price for The Terminator (in dollars)
   $A =$ Advertising (in thousands of dollars)
   $C =$ SWEC's only competitor's average price (in dollars)
   $Y =$ Disposable annual per capita income (in thousands of dollars)

   A recent survey of the potential customer market indicates that monthly advertising is $25,000, per capita disposable income is $80,000 per year, and the average price of the only competitor is $100.
   (a) Based on this information, what is the monthly demand function $p = f(q)$ for The Terminator?
   (b) Find the elasticity of demand for The Terminator.
   (c) If SWEC's current price for The Terminator is $175, is demand elastic, inelastic, or unitary elastic? Is SWEC's revenue for The Terminator maximized at the current price?
   (d) Use the elasticity of demand found in part (b) to determine the price for The Terminator that would maximize SWEC's revenue. Find the maximum revenue.

14. The owner and manager of Pleasantville Deli is considering the expansion of current menu offerings to include a new line of take-out sandwiches. The deli serves primarily the Pleasantville business districts and students from a nearby college, yet it is unclear exactly what level of demand to anticipate for this new product offering and how to price the product in order to maximize sales.
   Over the past few months the information shown in the table was collected from existing customers and from mailings to businesses in the area.

Sandwich Price	$12	10	8	6	4	2
Weekly Demand	0	400	800	1200	1600	2000

   (a) Develop a function $p = f(q)$ that represents this demand schedule.
   (b) Compute the elasticity of demand for the new sandwich.
   (c) Find the elasticity at the possible prices of $4 and $10. Classify these prices as elastic, inelastic, or unitary elastic.
   (d) Determine the price and quantity that would maximize weekly revenues for the new sandwich. Find the maximum weekly revenue.

TAXATION IN A COMPETITIVE MARKET

In Problems 15–24, p is the price per unit in dollars and q is the number of units.
15. If the weekly demand function is $p = 30 - q$ and the supply function before taxation is $p = 6 + 2q$, what tax per item will maximize the total tax revenue?

16. If the demand function for a fixed period of time is given by $p = 38 - 2q$ and the supply function before taxation is $p = 8 + 3q$, what tax per item will maximize the total tax revenue?

17. If the demand and supply functions for a product are $p = 800 - 2q$ and $p = 100 + 0.5q$, respectively, find the tax per unit t that will maximize the tax revenue T.

18. If the demand and supply functions for a product are $p = 2100 - 3q$ and $p = 300 + 1.5q$, respectively, find the tax per unit t that will maximize the tax revenue T.

19. If the weekly demand function is $p = 200 - 2q^2$ and the supply function before taxation is $p = 20 + 3q$, what tax per item will maximize the total tax revenue?

20. If the monthly demand function is $p = 7230 - 5q^2$ and the supply function before taxation is $p = 30 + 30q^2$, what tax per item will maximize the total revenue?

21. Suppose the weekly demand for a product is given by $p + 2q = 840$ and the weekly supply before taxation is given by $p = 0.02q^2 + 0.55q + 7.4$. Find the tax per item that produces maximum tax revenue. Find the tax revenue.

22. If the daily demand for a product is given by the function $p + q = 1000$ and the daily supply before taxation is $p = q^2/30 + 2.5q + 920$, find the tax per item that maximizes tax revenue. Find the tax revenue.

23. If the demand and supply functions for a product are $p = 2100 - 10q - 0.5q^2$ and $p = 300 + 5q + 0.5q^2$, respectively, find the tax per unit t that will maximize the tax revenue T.

24. If the demand and supply functions for a product are $p = 5000 - 20q - 0.7q^2$ and $p = 500 + 10q + 0.3q^2$, respectively, find the tax per unit t that will maximize the tax revenue T.

KEY TERMS AND FORMULAS

Section	Key Terms	Formulas
11.1	Logarithmic function	$y = \log_a x$, defined by $x = a^y$
	Natural logarithm	$\ln x = \log_e x$; $y = \ln(x)$ means $e^y = x$
	Logarithmic Properties I–V for natural logarithms	$\ln e^x = x$; $e^{\ln x} = x$
		$\ln(MN) = \ln M + \ln N$
		$\ln(M/N) = \ln M - \ln N$
		$\ln(M^p) = p(\ln M)$
	Change-of-base formula	$\log_a x = \dfrac{\ln x}{\ln a}$
	Derivatives of logarithmic functions	$\dfrac{d}{dx}(\ln x) = \dfrac{1}{x}$
		$\dfrac{d}{dx}(\ln u) = \dfrac{1}{u} \cdot \dfrac{du}{dx}$
11.2	Derivatives of exponential functions	$\dfrac{d}{dx}(e^x) = e^x$
		$\dfrac{d}{dx}e^u = e^u \dfrac{du}{dx}$
		$\dfrac{d}{dx}a^u = a^u \dfrac{du}{dx} \ln a$
11.3	Implicit differentiation	$\dfrac{d}{dx}(y^n) = ny^{n-1}\dfrac{dy}{dx}$
11.4	Related rates	Differentiate implicitly with respect to time, t
	Percent rates of change	
11.5	Elasticity of demand	$\eta = \dfrac{-p}{q} \cdot \dfrac{dq}{dp}$
	Elastic	$\eta > 1$
	Inelastic	$\eta < 1$
	Unitary elastic	$\eta = 1$
	Taxation in competitive market	
	Supply function after taxation	$p = f(q) + t$

REVIEW EXERCISES

In Problems 1–12, find the indicated derivative.

1. If $y = e^{3x^2 - x}$, find dy/dx.
2. If $y = \ln e^{x^2}$, find y'.
3. If $p = \ln\left(\dfrac{q}{q^2 - 1}\right)$, find $\dfrac{dp}{dq}$.
4. If $y = xe^{x^2}$, find dy/dx.
5. If $f(x) = 5e^{2x} - 40e^{-0.1x} + 11$, find $f'(x)$.
6. If $g(x) = (2e^{3x+1} - 5)^3$, find $g'(x)$.
7. If $y = \ln(3x^4 + 7x^2 - 12)$, find dy/dx.
8. If $s = \dfrac{3}{4}\ln(x^{12} - 2x^4 + 5)$, find ds/dx.
9. If $y = 3^{3x-4}$, find dy/dx.
10. If $y = 1 + \log_8(x^{10})$, find dy/dx.
11. If $y = \dfrac{\ln x}{x}$, find $\dfrac{dy}{dx}$.
12. If $y = \dfrac{1 + e^{-x}}{1 - e^{-x}}$, find $\dfrac{dy}{dx}$.
13. Write the equation of the line tangent to $y = 4e^{x^3}$ at $x = 1$.
14. Write the equation of the line tangent to $y = x\ln x$ at $x = 1$.

In Problems 15–20, find the indicated derivative.

15. If $y\ln x = 5y^2 + 11$, find dy/dx.
16. Find dy/dx for $e^{xy} = y$.
17. Find dy/dx for $y^2 = 4x - 1$.
18. Find dy/dx for $x^2 + 3y^2 + 2x - 3y + 2 = 0$.
19. Find dy/dx for $3x^2 + 2x^3y^2 - y^5 = 7$.
20. Find the second derivative y'' if $x^2 + y^2 = 1$.
21. Find the slope of the tangent to the curve $x^2 + 4x - 3y^2 + 6 = 0$ at $(3, 3)$.
22. Find the points where tangents to the graph of the equation in Problem 21 are horizontal.
23. Suppose $3x^2 - 2y^3 = 10y$, where x and y are differentiable functions of t. If $dx/dt = 2$, find dy/dt when $x = 10$ and $y = 5$.
24. A right triangle with legs of lengths x and y has its area given by

$$A = \frac{1}{2}xy$$

If the rate of change of x is 2 units per minute and the rate of change of y is 5 units per minute, find the rate of change of the area when $x = 4$ and $y = 1$.

APPLICATIONS

25. *Deforestation* One of the major causes of rain forest deforestation is agricultural and residential development. The number of hectares destroyed in a particular year t can be modeled by

$$y = -3.91435 + 2.62196\ln t$$

where $t = 0$ represents 1950.

   (a) Find $y'(t)$.
   (b) Find and interpret $y(50)$ and $y'(50)$.
26. *Nonmarital childbearing* The percent of live births to unmarried mothers for the years 1970–2007 can be modeled by the function

$$y = -33.410 + 18.035\ln x$$

   where x is the number of years past 1960.
   (a) What does the model predict the rate of change of this percent to be in 2015?
   (b) Is the percent of live births to unmarried mothers predicted to increase or decrease after 2015?
27. *Compound interest* If the future value of $1000 invested for n years at 12%, compounded continuously, is given by

$$S = 1000e^{0.12n} \text{ dollars}$$

   find the rate at which the future value is growing after 1 year.
28. *Compound interest*
   (a) In Problem 27, find the rate of growth of the future value after 2 years.
   (b) How much faster is the future value growing at the end of 2 years than after 1 year?
29. *Radioactive decay* A breeder reactor converts stable uranium-238 into the isotope plutonium-239. The decay of this isotope is given by

$$A(t) = A_0 e^{-0.00002876t}$$

   where $A(t)$ is the amount of isotope at time t, in years, and A_0 is the original amount. This isotope has a half-life of 24,101 years (that is, half of it will decay away in 24,101 years).
   (a) At what rate is $A(t)$ decaying at this point in time?
   (b) At what rate is $A(t)$ decaying after 1 year?
   (c) Is the rate of decay at its half-life greater or less than after 1 year?
30. *Marginal cost* The average cost of producing x units of a product is $\overline{C} = 600e^{x/600}$ dollars per unit. What is the marginal cost when 600 units are produced?
31. *Inflation* The impact of inflation on a $20,000 pension can be measured by the purchasing power P of $20,000 after t years. For an inflation rate of 5% per year, compounded annually, P is given by

$$P = 20{,}000e^{-0.0495t}$$

   At what rate is purchasing power changing when $t = 10$? (*Source: Viewpoints, VALIC*)
32. *Evaporation* A spherical droplet of water evaporates at a rate of 1 mm^3/min. Find the rate of change of the radius when the droplet has a radius of 2.5 mm.
33. *Worker safety* A sign is being lowered over the side of a building at the rate of 2 ft/min. A worker handling

a guide line is 7 ft away from a spot directly below the sign. How fast is the worker taking in the guide line at the instant the sign is 25 ft from the worker's hands? See the figure.

Guide line

7 ft

34. *Environment* Suppose that in a study of water birds, the relationship between the area A of wetlands (in square miles) and the number of different species S of birds found in the area was determined to be

$$S = kA^{1/3}$$

where k is constant. Find the percent rate of change of the number of species in terms of the percent rate of change of the area.

35. *Taxes* Can increasing the tax per unit sold actually lead to a decrease in tax revenues?

36. *Taxes* Suppose the demand and supply functions for a product are

$$p = 2800 - 8q - \frac{q^2}{3} \text{ and } p = 400 + 2q$$

respectively, where p is in dollars and q is the number of units. Find the tax per unit t that will maximize the tax revenue T, and find the maximum tax revenue.

37. *Taxes* Suppose the supply and demand functions for a product are

$$p = 40 + 20q \text{ and } p = \frac{5000}{q + 1}$$

respectively, where p is in dollars and q is the number of units. Find the tax t that maximizes the tax revenue T, and find the maximum tax revenue.

38. *Elasticity* A demand function is given by

$$pq = 27$$

where p is in dollars and q is the number of units.
(a) Find the elasticity of demand at $(9, 3)$.
(b) How will a price increase affect total revenue?

39. *Elasticity* Suppose the demand for a product is given by

$$p^2(2q + 1) = 10{,}000$$

where p is in dollars and q is the number of units.
(a) Find the elasticity of demand when $p = \$20$.
(b) How will a price increase affect total revenue?

40. *Elasticity* Suppose the weekly demand function for a product is given by

$$p = 100e^{-0.1q}$$

where p is the price in dollars and q is the number of tons demanded.
(a) What is the elasticity of demand when the price is $\$36.79$ and the quantity demanded is 10?
(b) How will a price increase affect total revenue?

41. *Revenue* A product has the demand function

$$p = 100 - 0.5q$$

where p is in dollars and q is the number of units.
(a) Find the elasticity $\eta(q)$ as a function of q, and graph the function

$$f(q) = \eta(q)$$

(b) Find where $f(q) = 1$, which gives the quantity for which the product has unitary elasticity.
(c) The revenue function for this product is

$$R(q) = pq = (100 - 0.5q)q$$

Graph $R(q)$ and find the q-value for which the maximum revenue occurs.
(d) What is the relationship between elasticity and maximum revenue?

---

11   CHAPTER TEST

In Problems 1–8, find the derivative of each function.
1. $y = 5e^{x^3} + x^2$
2. $y = 4 \ln (x^3 + 1)$
3. $y = \ln (x^4 + 1)^3$
4. $f(x) = 10(3^{2x})$
5. $S = te^{t^4}$
6. $y = \dfrac{e^{x^3 + 1}}{x}$
7. $y = \dfrac{\ln x}{x}$
8. $g(x) = 2 \log_5 (4x + 7)$
9. Find y' if $3x^4 + 2y^2 + 10 = 0$.

10. Let $x^2 + y^2 = 100$.
If $\dfrac{dx}{dt} = 2$, find $\dfrac{dy}{dt}$ when $x = 6$ and $y = 8$.

11. Find y' if $xe^y = 10y$.

12. Suppose the weekly revenue and weekly cost (both in dollars) for a product are given by $R(x) = 300x - 0.001x^2$ and $C(x) = 4000 + 30x$, respectively, where x is the number of units produced

and sold. Find the rate at which profit is changing with respect to time when the number of units produced and sold is 50 and is increasing at a rate of 5 units per week.

13. Suppose the demand for a product is $p^2 + 3p + q = 1500$, where p is in dollars and q is the number of units. Find the elasticity of demand at $p = 30$. If the price is raised to $31, does revenue increase or decrease?

14. Suppose the demand function for a product is given by $(p + 1)q^2 = 10{,}000$, where p is the price and q is the quantity. Find the rate of change of quantity with respect to price when $p = \$99$.

15. The sales of a product are given by $S = 80{,}000e^{-0.4t}$, where S is the daily sales and t is the number of days after the end of an advertising campaign. Find the rate of sales decay 10 days after the end of the ad campaign.

16. The table gives the total U.S. expenditures (in billions of dollars) for health services and supplies for selected years from 2000 and projected to 2018. Given that the model for these data is

$$y = 1319e^{0.062t}$$

where $t = 0$ in 2000.
(a) Find the function that models the rate of change.
(b) Find the model's value for the rate of change of U.S. expenditures for health services and supplies in 2005 and in 2020.

Year	Health Expenditures	Year	Health Expenditures
2000	1264	2010	2458
2002	1498	2012	2746
2004	1733	2014	3107
2006	1976	2016	3556
2008	2227	2018	4086

Source: U.S. Centers for Medicare and Medicaid Services

17. Suppose the demand and supply functions for a product are $p = 1100 - 5q$ and $p = 20 + 0.4q$, respectively, where p is in dollars and q is the number of units. Find the tax per unit t that will maximize the tax revenue $T = tq$.

18. *Modeling* Projections indicate that the percent of U.S. adults with diabetes could dramatically increase, and already in 2007 this disease had cost the country almost $175 billion. The table gives the percent of U.S. adults with diabetes for selected years from 2010 and projected to 2050.
(a) Find a logarithmic model, $y = f(x)$, for these data. Use $x = 0$ to represent 2000.
(b) Find the function that models the rate of change of the percent of U.S. adults with diabetes.
(c) Find and interpret $f(25)$ and $f'(25)$.

Year	Percent	Year	Percent
2010	15.7	2035	29.0
2015	18.9	2040	31.4
2020	21.1	2045	32.1
2025	24.2	2050	34.3
2030	27.2		

Source: Centers for Disease Control and Prevention

19. By using data from the U.S. Bureau of Labor Statistics for the years 1968–2008, the purchasing power P of a 1983 dollar can be modeled by the function

$$P(t) = 3.443(1.046)^{-t}$$

where t is the number of years past 1960.

Use the model to find the function that models the rate of change of the purchasing power of the 1983 dollar and use that function to predict the rate of change in the year 2015.

I. Inflation

Hollingsworth Pharmaceuticals specializes in manufacturing generic medicines. Recently it developed an antibiotic with outstanding profit potential. The new antibiotic's total costs, sales, and sales growth, as well as projected inflation, are described as follows.

Total monthly costs, in dollars, to produce x units (1 unit is 100 capsules):

$$C(x) = \begin{cases} 15,000 + 10x & 0 \le x \le 11,000 \\ 15,000 + 10x + 0.001(x - 11,000)^2 & x \ge 11,000 \end{cases}$$

Sales: 10,000 units per month and growing at 1.25% per month, compounded continuously
Selling price: $34 per unit
Inflation: Approximately 0.25% per month, compounded continuously, affecting both total costs and selling price

Company owners are pleased with the sales growth but are concerned about the projected increase in variable costs when production levels exceed 11,000 units per month. The consensus is that improvements eventually can be made that will reduce costs at higher production levels, thus altering the current cost function model. To plan properly for these changes, Hollingsworth Pharmaceuticals would like you to determine when the company's profits will begin to decrease. To help you determine this, answer the following.

1. If inflation is assumed to be compounded continuously, the selling price and total costs must be multiplied by the factor $e^{0.0025t}$. In addition, if sales growth is assumed to be compounded continuously, then sales must be multiplied by a factor of the form e^{rt}, where r is the monthly sales growth rate (expressed as a decimal) and t is time in months. Use these factors to write each of the following as a function of time t:
   (a) selling price p per unit (including inflation).
   (b) number of units x sold per month (including sales growth).
   (c) total revenue. (Recall that $R = px$.)
2. Determine how many months it will be before monthly sales exceed 11,000 units.
3. If you restrict your attention to total costs when $x \ge 11,000$, then, after expanding and collecting like terms, $C(x)$ can be written as follows:

   $$C(x) = 136,000 - 12x + 0.001x^2 \text{ for } x \ge 11,000$$

   Use this form for $C(x)$ with your result from Question 1(b) and with the inflationary factor $e^{0.0025t}$ to express these total costs as a function of time.
4. Form the profit function that would be used when monthly sales exceed 11,000 units by using the total revenue function from Question 1(c) and the total cost function from Question 3. This profit function should be a function of time t.
5. Find how long it will be before the profit is maximized. You may have to solve $P'(t) = 0$ by using a graphing calculator or computer to find the t-intercept of the graph of $P'(t)$. In addition, because $P'(t)$ has large numerical coefficients, you may want to divide both sides of $P'(t) = 0$ by 1000 before solving or graphing.

II. Knowledge Workers (Modeling)

The representation of women in leadership positions in our economy has changed dramatically in the past 20 years. In this application we'll investigate whether some predictions made in 1997 are still valid.

In January 1997, *Working Woman* made the following points about the U.S. economy and the place of women in the economy.

- The telecommunications industry employs more people than the auto and auto parts industries combined.
- More Americans make semiconductors than make construction equipment.
- Almost twice as many Americans make surgical and medical instruments as make plumbing and heating products.
- The ratio of male to female knowledge workers (engineers, scientists, technicians, professionals, and senior managers) was 3 to 2 in 1983. The table, which gives the numbers (in millions) of male and female knowledge workers from 1983 to 1997, shows how that ratio is changing.

Year	Female Knowledge Workers (millions)	Male Knowledge Workers (millions)	Year	Female Knowledge Workers (millions)	Male Knowledge Workers (millions)
1983	11.0	15.4	1991	16.1	18.4
1984	11.6	15.9	1992	16.7	18.66
1985	12.3	16.3	1993	17.3	18.7
1986	12.9	16.7	1994	18.0	19.0
1987	13.6	16.8	1995	18.5	19.8
1988	14.3	17.6	1996	19.0	19.6
1989	15.3	18.1	1997	19.5	19.8
1990	15.9	18.6			

Source: Working Woman, January 1997

To compare how the growth in the number of female knowledge workers compares with that of male knowledge workers, do the following:

1. Find a logarithmic equation (with $x = 0$ representing 1980) that models the number of females, and find a logarithmic equation (with $x = 0$ representing 1980) that models the number of males.
2. Use the models found in (1) to find the rate of growth with respect to time of (a) the number of female knowledge workers and (b) the number of male knowledge workers.
3. Compare the two rates of growth in the year 2000 and determine which rate is larger.
4. If these models indicate that it is possible for the number of females to equal the number of males, during what year do they indicate that this will occur?
5. Research this topic on the Internet to determine whether the trends of your models are supported by current data. Be sure to cite your sources and include recent data.

Indefinite Integrals

Vasily Smirnov/Shutterstock.com

When we know the derivative of a function, it is often useful to determine the function itself. For example, accountants can use linear regression to translate information about marginal cost into a linear equation defining (approximately) the marginal cost function and then use the process of antidifferentiation (or integration) as part of finding the (approximate) total cost function. We can also use integration to find total revenue functions from marginal revenue functions, to optimize profit from information about marginal cost and marginal revenue, and to find national consumption from information about marginal propensity to consume.

Integration can also be used in the social and life sciences to predict growth or decay from expressions giving rates of change. For example, we can find equations for population size from the rate of change of growth, we can write equations for the number of radioactive atoms remaining in a substance if we know the rate of the decay of the substance, and we can determine the volume of blood flow from information about rate of flow.

The topics and applications discussed in this chapter include the following.

Prerequisite Problem Type	For Section	Answer	Section for Review
Write as a power: (a) $\sqrt{x}$ (b) $\sqrt{x^2 - 9}$	**12.1.–12.4**	(a) $x^{1/2}$ (b) $(x^2 - 9)^{1/2}$	0.4 Radicals
Expand $(x^2 + 4)^2$.	**12.2**	$x^4 + 8x^2 + 16$	0.5 Special powers
Divide $x^4 - 2x^3 + 4x^2 - 7x - 1$ by $x^2 - 2x$.	**12.3**	$x^2 + 4 + \dfrac{x - 1}{x^2 - 2x}$	0.5 Division
Find the derivative of (a) $f(x) = 2x^{1/2}$ (b) $u = x^3 - 3x$	**12.1** **12.2** **12.3**	(a) $f'(x) = x^{-1/2}$ (b) $u' = 3x^2 - 3$	9.4 Derivatives
If $y = \dfrac{(x^2 + 4)^6}{6}$, what is y'?	**12.2**	$y' = (x^2 + 4)^5 2x$	9.6 Derivatives
(a) If $y = \ln u$, what is y'? (b) If $y = e^u$, what is y'?	**12.3**	(a) $y' = \dfrac{1}{u} \cdot u'$ (b) $y' = e^u \cdot u'$	11.1, 11.2 Derivatives
Solve for y: $\ln y = kt + C$	**12.5**	$y = e^{kt + C}$	5.2 Logarithmic functions
Solve for k: $0.5 = e^{5730k}$	**12.5**	$k \approx -0.00012097$	5.3 Exponential equations

OBJECTIVE

12.1

- To find certain indefinite integrals

Indefinite Integrals

| APPLICATION PREVIEW |

In our study of the theory of the firm, we have worked with total cost, total revenue, and profit functions and have found their marginal functions. In practice, it is often easier for a company to measure marginal cost, revenue, and profit and use these data to form marginal functions from which it can find total cost, revenue, and profit functions. For example, Jarus Technologies manufactures computer motherboards, and the company's sales records show that the marginal revenue (in dollars per unit) for its motherboards is given by

$$\overline{MR} = 300 - 0.2x$$

where x is the number of units sold. If we want to use this function to find the total revenue function for Jarus Technologies' motherboards, we need to find $R(x)$ from $\overline{MR} = R'(x)$. (See Example 7.) In this situation, we need to be able to reverse the process of differentiation. This reverse process is called antidifferentiation, or integration.

Indefinite Integrals   We have studied procedures for and applications of finding derivatives of a given function. We now turn our attention to reversing this process of differentiation. When we know the derivative of a function, the process of finding the function itself is called **antidifferentiation.** For example, if the derivative of a function is $2x$, we know that the function could be $f(x) = x^2$ because $\dfrac{d}{dx}(x^2) = 2x$. But the function could also be $f(x) = x^2 + 4$ because $\dfrac{d}{dx}(x^2 + 4) = 2x$. It is clear that any function of the form $f(x) = x^2 + C$, where C is an arbitrary constant, will have $f'(x) = 2x$ as its derivative. Thus we say that the **general antiderivative** of $f'(x) = 2x$ is $f(x) = x^2 + C$, where C is an arbitrary constant.

The process of finding an antiderivative is also called **integration.** The function that results when integration takes place is called an **indefinite integral** or, more simply, an **integral.** We can denote the indefinite integral (that is, the general antiderivative) of a function $f(x)$ by $\int f(x)\,dx$. Thus we can write $\int 2x\,dx$ to indicate the general antiderivative of the function $f(x) = 2x$. The expression is read as "the integral of $2x$ with respect to x." In this case, $2x$ is called the **integrand.** The **integral sign,** $\int$, indicates the process of integration, and the dx indicates that the integral is to be taken with respect to x. Because the antiderivative of $2x$ is $x^2 + C$, we can write

$$\int 2x\,dx = x^2 + C$$

EXAMPLE   1   Antidifferentiation

If $f'(x) = 3x^2$, what is $f(x)$?

Solution

The derivative of the function $f(x) = x^3$ is $f'(x) = 3x^2$. But other functions also have this derivative. They will all be of the form $f(x) = x^3 + C$, where C is a constant. Thus we write

$$\int 3x^2\,dx = x^3 + C$$

EXAMPLE 2   Integration

If $f'(x) = x^3$, what is $f(x)$?

Solution

We know that $\dfrac{d}{dx}(x^4) = 4x^3$, so the derivative of $f(x) = \frac{1}{4}x^4$ is $f'(x) = x^3$. Thus

$$f(x) = \int f'(x)\,dx = \int x^3\,dx = \tfrac{1}{4}x^4 + C$$

Powers of x Formula   It is easily seen that

$$\int x^4\,dx = \frac{x^5}{5} + C \quad \text{because} \quad \frac{d}{dx}\left(\frac{x^5}{5} + C\right) = x^4$$

$$\int x^5\,dx = \frac{x^6}{6} + C \quad \text{because} \quad \frac{d}{dx}\left(\frac{x^6}{6} + C\right) = x^5$$

In general, we have the following.

Powers of x Formula

$$\int x^n\,dx = \frac{x^{n+1}}{n+1} + C \qquad (\text{for } n \neq -1)$$

In the Powers of x Formula, we see that $n \neq -1$ is essential, because if $n = -1$, then the denominator $n + 1 = 0$. We will discuss the case when $n = -1$ later. (Can you think what function has $1/x$ as its derivative?)

In addition, we can see that this Powers of x Formula applies for any $n \neq -1$ by noting that

$$\frac{d}{dx}\left(\frac{x^{n+1}}{n+1} + C\right) = \frac{d}{dx}\left(\frac{1}{n+1}x^{n+1} + C\right) = \frac{n+1}{n+1}x^n = x^n$$

EXAMPLE 3   Powers of x Formula

Evaluate $\int x^{-1/2}\,dx$.

Solution

Using the formula, we get

$$\int x^{-1/2}\,dx = \frac{x^{-1/2+1}}{-1/2+1} + C = \frac{x^{1/2}}{1/2} + C = 2x^{1/2} + C$$

We can check by noting that the derivative of $2x^{1/2} + C$ is $x^{-1/2}$. ✔

Note that the indefinite integral in Example 3 is a function (actually a number of functions, one for each value of C). Graphs of several members of this family of functions are shown in Figure 12.1. Note that at any given x-value, the tangent line to each curve has the same slope, indicating that all family members have the same derivative.

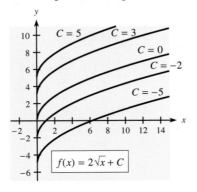

Figure 12.1

EXAMPLE 4 Powers of x Formula

Find (a) $\int \sqrt[3]{x}\,dx$ and   (b) $\int \dfrac{1}{x^2}\,dx$.

Solution

(a) $\displaystyle \int \sqrt[3]{x}\,dx = \int x^{1/3}\,dx = \dfrac{x^{4/3}}{4/3} + C$

$\qquad\qquad = \dfrac{3}{4}x^{4/3} + C = \dfrac{3}{4}\sqrt[3]{x^4} + C$

(b) We write the power of x in the numerator so that the integral has the form in the formula above.

$$\int \frac{1}{x^2}\,dx = \int x^{-2}\,dx = \frac{x^{-2+1}}{-2+1} + C = \frac{x^{-1}}{-1} + C = \frac{-1}{x} + C$$

Other Formulas and Properties

Other formulas will be useful in evaluating integrals. The following table shows how some new integration formulas result from differentiation formulas.

Integration Formulas

Derivative	Resulting Integral
$\dfrac{d}{dx}(x) = 1$	$\displaystyle \int 1\,dx = \int dx = x + C$
$\dfrac{d}{dx}[c \cdot u(x)] = c \cdot \dfrac{d}{dx}u(x)$	$\displaystyle \int c\,u(x)\,dx = c\int u(x)\,dx$
$\dfrac{d}{dx}[u(x) \pm v(x)] = \dfrac{d}{dx}u(x) \pm \dfrac{d}{dx}v(x)$	$\displaystyle \int [u(x) \pm v(x)]\,dx = \int u(x)\,dx \pm \int v(x)\,dx$

These formulas indicate that we can integrate functions term by term just as we were able to take derivatives term by term.

EXAMPLE 5 Using Integration Formulas

Evaluate: (a) $\int 4\,dx$ (b) $\int 8x^5\,dx$ (c) $\int (x^3 + 4x)\,dx$

Solution

(a) $\int 4\,dx = 4\int dx = 4(x + C_1) = 4x + C$

(Because C_1 is an unknown constant, we can write $4C_1$ as the unknown constant C.)

(b) $\displaystyle \int 8x^5\,dx = 8\int x^5\,dx = 8\left(\frac{x^6}{6} + C_1\right) = \frac{4x^6}{3} + C$

(c) $\displaystyle \int (x^3 + 4x)\,dx = \int x^3\,dx + \int 4x\,dx$

$\qquad\qquad = \left(\dfrac{x^4}{4} + C_1\right) + \left(4 \cdot \dfrac{x^2}{2} + C_2\right)$

$\qquad\qquad = \dfrac{x^4}{4} + 2x^2 + C_1 + C_2$

$\qquad\qquad = \dfrac{x^4}{4} + 2x^2 + C$

Note that we need only one constant because the sum of C_1 and C_2 is just a new constant.

EXAMPLE   6   **Integral of a Polynomial**

Evaluate $\int (x^2 - 4)^2\, dx$.

Solution

We expand $(x^2 - 4)^2$ so that the integrand is in a form that fits the basic integration formulas.

$$\int (x^2 - 4)^2\, dx = \int (x^4 - 8x^2 + 16)\, dx = \frac{x^5}{5} - \frac{8x^3}{3} + 16x + C$$

CHECKPOINT

1. True or false:

   (a) $\int (4x^3 - 2x)\, dx = \int 4x^3\, dx - \int 2x\, dx$
   $$= (x^4 + C) - (x^2 + C) = x^4 - x^2$$

   (b) $\int \dfrac{1}{3x^2}\, dx = \dfrac{1}{3(x^3/3)} + C = \dfrac{1}{x^3} + C$

2. Evaluate $\int (2x^3 + x^{-1/2} - 4x^{-5})\, dx$.

EXAMPLE   7   **Revenue | APPLICATION PREVIEW |**

Max Bukovski/Shutterstock.com

Sales records at Jarus Technologies show that the rate of change of the revenue (that is, the marginal revenue) in dollars per unit for a motherboard is $\overline{MR} = 300 - 0.2x$, where x represents the quantity sold. Find the total revenue function for the product. Then find the total revenue from the sale of 1000 motherboards.

Solution

We know that the marginal revenue can be found by differentiating the total revenue function. That is,

$$R'(x) = 300 - 0.2x$$

Thus integrating the marginal revenue function gives the total revenue function.

$$R(x) = \int (300 - 0.2x)\, dx = 300x - 0.1x^2 + K^*$$

We can use the fact that there is no revenue when no units are sold to evaluate K. Setting $x = 0$ and $R = 0$ gives $0 = 300(0) - 0.1(0)^2 + K$, so $K = 0$. Thus the total revenue function is

$$R(x) = 300x - 0.1x^2$$

The total revenue from the sale of 1000 motherboards is

$$R(1000) = 300(1000) - 0.1(1000^2) = \$200{,}000$$

We can check that the $R(x)$ we found in Example 7 is correct by verifying that $R'(x) = 300 - 0.2x$ and $R(0) = 0$. Also, graphs can help us check the reasonableness of our result. Figure 12.2 shows the graphs of $\overline{MR} = 300 - 0.2x$ and of the $R(x)$ we found. Note that $R(x)$ passes through the origin, indicating $R(0) = 0$. Also, reading both graphs from left to right, we see that $R(x)$ increases when $\overline{MR} > 0$, attains its maximum when $\overline{MR} = 0$, and decreases when $\overline{MR} < 0$.

*Here we are using K rather than C to represent the constant of integration to avoid confusion between the constant C and the cost function $C = C(x)$.

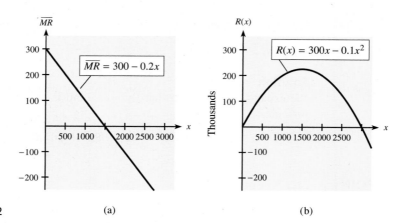

Figure 12.2   (a)   (b)

Calculator Note   We mentioned in Chapter 9, "Derivatives," that graphing calculators have a numerical derivative feature that can be used to check graphically the derivative of a function that has been calculated with a formula. We can also use the numerical integration feature on graphing calculators to check our integration (if we assume temporarily that the constant of integration is 0). We do this by graphing the integral calculated with a formula and the numerical integral from the graphing calculator on the same set of axes. If the graphs lie on top of one another, the integrals agree. See Appendix C, Section 12.1, for details. Figure 12.3 illustrates this for the function $f(x) = 3x^2 - 2x + 1$. Its integral, with the constant of integration set equal to 0, is shown as $y_1 = x^3 - x^2 + x$ in Figure 12.3(a), and the graphs of the two integrals are shown in Figure 12.3(b). Of course, it is often easier to use the derivative to check integration.

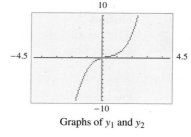

Graphs of y_1 and y_2

Figure 12.3   (a)   (b)

CHECKPOINT SOLUTIONS

1. (a) False, $\int (4x^3 - 2x)\, dx = \int 4x^3 dx - \int 2x\, dx = (x^4 + C_1) - (x^2 + C_2)$
$$= x^4 - x^2 + C$$

(b) False, $\displaystyle\int \frac{1}{3x^2}\, dx = \int \frac{1}{3} \cdot \frac{1}{x^2}\, dx = \frac{1}{3}\int x^{-2}\, dx$
$$= \frac{1}{3} \cdot \frac{x^{-1}}{-1} + C = \frac{-1}{3x} + C$$

2. $\displaystyle\int (2x^3 + x^{-1/2} - 4x^{-5})\, dx = \frac{2x^4}{4} + \frac{x^{1/2}}{1/2} - \frac{4x^{-4}}{-4} + C$
$$= \frac{x^4}{2} + 2x^{1/2} + x^{-4} + C$$

| EXERCISES | 12.1

1. If $f'(x) = 4x^3$, what is $f(x)$?
2. If $f'(x) = 5x^4$, what is $f(x)$?
3. If $f'(x) = x^6$, what is $f(x)$?
4. If $g'(x) = x^4$, what is $g(x)$?

Evaluate the integrals in Problems 5–26. Check your answers by differentiating.

5. $\int x^7 dx$

6. $\int x^5 dx$

7. $\int 8x^3 dx$

8. $\int 16x^9 dx$

9. $\int (3^3 + x^{13}) dx$

10. $\int (5^2 + x^{10}) dx$

11. $\int (3 - x^{3/2}) dx$

12. $\int (8 + x^{2/3}) dx$

13. $\int (x^4 - 9x^2 + 3) dx$

14. $\int (3x^2 - 4x - 4) dx$

15. $\int (13 - 6x + 21x^6) dx$

16. $\int (12x^5 + 12x^3 - 7) dx$

17. $\int (2 + 2\sqrt{x}) dx$

18. $\int (17 + \sqrt{x^3}) dx$

19. $\int 6\sqrt[4]{x} \, dx$

20. $\int 3\sqrt[3]{x^2} \, dx$

21. $\int \dfrac{5}{x^4} dx$

22. $\int \dfrac{6}{x^5} dx$

23. $\int \dfrac{dx}{2\sqrt[3]{x^2}}$

24. $\int \dfrac{2 \, dx}{5\sqrt{x^3}}$

25. $\int \left(x^3 - 4 + \dfrac{5}{x^6} \right) dx$

26. $\int \left(x^3 - 7 - \dfrac{3}{x^4} \right) dx$

27. $\int \left(x^9 - \dfrac{1}{x^3} + \dfrac{2}{\sqrt[3]{x}} \right) dx$

28. $\int \left(3x^8 + \dfrac{4}{x^8} - \dfrac{5}{\sqrt[5]{x}} \right) dx$

In Problems 29–32, use algebra to rewrite the integrands; then integrate and simplify.

29. $\int (4x^2 - 1)^2 x^3 \, dx$

30. $\int (x^3 + 1)^2 x \, dx$

31. $\int \dfrac{x + 1}{x^3} dx$

32. $\int \dfrac{x - 3}{\sqrt{x}} dx$

In Problems 33 and 34, find the antiderivatives and graph the resulting family members that correspond to $C = 0$, $C = 4$, $C = -4$, $C = 8$, and $C = -8$.

33. $\int (2x + 3) \, dx$

34. $\int (4 - x) \, dx$

35. If $\int f(x) \, dx = 2x^9 - 7x^5 + C$, find $f(x)$.

36. If $\int g(x) \, dx = 11x^{10} - 4x^3 + C$, find $g(x)$.

In each of Problems 37–40, a family of functions is given and graphs of some members of the family are shown. Write the indefinite integral that gives the family.

37. $F(x) = 5x - \dfrac{x^2}{4} + C$

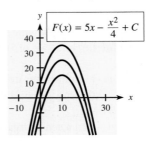

38. $F(x) = \dfrac{x^2}{2} + 3x + C$

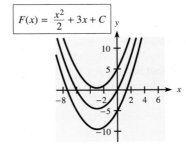

39. $F(x) = x^3 - 3x^2 + C$

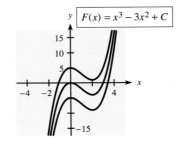

40. $F(x) = 12x - x^3 + C$

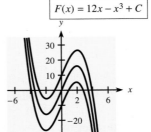

APPLICATIONS

41. **Revenue** If the marginal revenue (in dollars per unit) for a month for a commodity is $\overline{MR} = -0.4x + 30$, find the total revenue function.

42. **Revenue** If the marginal revenue (in dollars per unit) for a month for a commodity is $\overline{MR} = -0.05x + 25$, find the total revenue function.

43. **Revenue** If the marginal revenue (in dollars per unit) for a month is given by $\overline{MR} = -0.3x + 450$, what is the total revenue from the production and sale of 50 units?

44. **Revenue** If the marginal revenue (in dollars per unit) for a month is given by $\overline{MR} = -0.006x + 36$, find the total revenue from the sale of 75 units.

45. **Stimulus-response** Suppose that when a sense organ receives a stimulus at time t, the total number of action potentials is $P(t)$. If the rate at which action potentials are produced is $t^3 + 4t^2 + 6$, and if there are 0 action potentials when $t = 0$, find the formula for $P(t)$.

46. **Projectiles** Suppose that a particle has been shot into the air in such a way that the rate at which its height is changing is $v = 320 - 32t$, in feet per second, and suppose that it is 1600 feet high when $t = 10$ seconds. Write the equation that describes the height of the particle at any time t.

47. **Pollution** A factory is dumping pollutants into a river at a rate given by $dx/dt = t^{3/4}/600$ tons per week, where t is the time in weeks since the dumping began and x is the number of tons of pollutants.
    (a) Find the equation for total tons of pollutants dumped.
    (b) How many tons were dumped during the first year?

48. **Population growth** The rate of growth of the population of a city is predicted to be

$$\frac{dp}{dt} = 1000t^{1.08}$$

where p is the population at time t, and t is measured in years from the present. Suppose that the current population is 100,000. What is the predicted
    (a) rate of growth 5 years from the present?
    (b) population 5 years from the present?

49. **Average cost** The DeWitt Company has found that the rate of change of its average cost for a product is

$$\overline{C}'(x) = \frac{1}{4} - \frac{100}{x^2}$$

where x is the number of units and cost is in dollars. The average cost of producing 20 units is $40.00.
    (a) Find the average cost function for the product.
    (b) Find the average cost of 100 units of the product.

50. **Oil leakage** An oil tanker hits a reef and begins to leak. The efforts of the workers repairing the leak cause the rate at which the oil is leaking to decrease. The oil was leaking at a rate of 31 barrels per hour at the end of the first hour after the accident, and the rate is decreasing at a rate of one barrel per hour.
    (a) What function describes the rate of loss?
    (b) How many barrels of oil will leak in the first 6 hours?
    (c) When will the oil leak be stopped? How much will have leaked altogether?

51. **National health care** National expenditures for health care H (in billions of dollars) have risen dramatically in the past 20 years. By using U.S. Department of Health and Human Services, Center for Medicare and Medicaid Services data from 2000 and projected to 2015, the rate of change of expenditures can be modeled by

$$\frac{dH}{dt} = 10.066t + 100.5$$

billions of dollars per year, where $t = 0$ represents 2000.
    (a) Find the function that models the national expenditures for health care if expenditures in 2009 were $2689 billion.
    (b) Use the model from part (a) to predict the national health care expenditures for 2015.

52. **Total personal income** With U.S. Department of Commerce data for selected years from 1960 and projected to 2018, the rate of change of U.S. total personal income can be modeled by

$$\frac{dI}{dt} = 12.59t - 51.74$$

billions of current dollars per year, where $t = 0$ represents 1960.
    (a) If U.S. total personal income was $8429.7 billion in 2000, find the function that models $I(t)$.
    (b) What does $I(t)$ predict for the U.S. total personal income in 2015?

53. **Wind chill** When the air temperature is 20° F, the rate of change of the wind chill temperature t (°F) is given by

$$\frac{dt}{dw} = -4.352w^{-0.84}$$

where w is wind speed in miles per hour.
    (a) Will both the rate of change of wind chill temperature and wind chill temperature decrease as the windspeed increases? Explain.
    (b) If the wind chill temperature is 1°F when the wind speed is 31 mph and the air temperature is 20°F, find the function that models the wind chill temperature.

54. **Severe weather ice makers** Hail is produced in severe thunderstorms when an updraft draws moist surface air into subfreezing air above 10,000 feet. The speed of the updraft s, in mph, affects the diameter of hail (in inches). According to National Weather Service data, the rate of change of hail size with respect to updraft speed is

$$\frac{dh}{ds} = 0.001144s^{0.922}$$

inches of diameter per mph of updraft.

(a) When updraft speeds approach 60 mph, hail is golf-ball-sized. Use $h = 1.5$ and $s = 60$ to find a model for $h(s)$.

(b) Use the model to find the hail size for an updraft speed of 100 mph.

 55. *U.S. population* With U.S. Census Bureau data (actual and projected) for selected years from 1960 to 2050, the rate of change of U.S. population P can be modeled by

$$\frac{dP}{dt} = -0.0002187t^2 + 0.0276t + 1.98$$

million people per year, where $t = 0$ represents 1960.

(a) In what year does this rate of change reach its maximum?

(b) In 1960, the U.S. population was 181 million. Use this to find a model for $P(t)$.

(c) For 2025, the Census Bureau's predicted U.S. population is 348 million. What does the model predict?

 56. *Consumer prices* The consumer price index (CPI) measures how prices have changed for consumers. With 1995 as a reference of 100, a year with CPI = 150 indicates that consumer costs in that year were 1.5 times the 1995 costs. With U.S. Department of Labor data for selected years from 1995 and projected to 2050, the rate of change of the CPI can be modeled by

$$\frac{dC}{dt} = 0.009t^2 - 0.096t + 4.85$$

dollars per year, where $t = 0$ represents 1990.

(a) Find the function that models $C(t)$, if the CPI was 175 in 2010.

(b) What does the model from part (a) predict for the consumer costs in 2030? How does this compare to 2010?

OBJECTIVE

12.2

- To evaluate integrals of the form $\int u^n \cdot u' \, dx = \int u^n \, du$ if $n \neq -1$

The Power Rule

| APPLICATION PREVIEW |

In the previous section, we saw that total revenue could be found by integrating marginal revenue. That is,

$$R(x) = \int \overline{MR} \, dx$$

For example, if the marginal revenue for a product is given by

$$\overline{MR} = \frac{600}{\sqrt{3x + 1}} + 2$$

then

$$R(x) = \int \left[\frac{600}{\sqrt{3x + 1}} + 2 \right] dx$$

To evaluate this integral, however, we need a more general formula than the Powers of x Formula. (See Example 8.)

In this section, we will extend the Powers of x Formula to a rule for powers of a function of x.

Differentials   Our goal in this section is to extend the Powers of x Formula,

$$\int x^n dx = \frac{x^{n+1}}{n+1} + C, \quad n \neq -1$$

to powers of a function of x. In order to do this, we must understand the symbol dx.

Recall from Section 9.3, "Rates of Change and Derivatives," that the derivative of $y = f(x)$ with respect to x can be denoted by dy/dx. As we will see, there are advantages to using dy and dx as separate quantities whose ratio dy/dx equals $f'(x)$.

| Differentials | If $y = f(x)$ is a differentiable function with derivative $dy/dx = f'(x)$, then the **differential of x is dx**, and the **differential of y is dy**, where $$dy = f'(x)\,dx$$ |

Although differentials are useful in certain approximation problems, we are interested in the differential notation at this time.

EXAMPLE 1 Differentials

Find (a) dy if $y = x^3 - 4x^2 + 5$ and (b) du if $u = 5x^4 + 11$.

Solution

(a) $dy = f'(x)\,dx = (3x^2 - 8x)\,dx$

(b) If the dependent variable in a function is u, then $du = u'(x)\,dx$.

$$du = u'(x)\,dx = 20x^3\,dx$$

The Power Rule In terms of our goal of extending the Powers of x Formula, we would suspect that if x is replaced by a function of x, then dx should be replaced by the differential of that function. Let's see whether this is true.

Recall that if $y = [u(x)]^n$, the derivative of y is

$$\frac{dy}{dx} = n[u(x)]^{n-1} \cdot u'(x)$$

Using this formula for derivatives, we can see that

$$\int n[u(x)]^{n-1} \cdot u'(x)\,dx = [u(x)]^n + C$$

It is easy to see that this formula is equivalent to the following formula, which is called the **Power Rule for Integration.**

| Power Rule for Integration | $$\int [u(x)]^n \cdot u'(x)\,dx = \frac{[u(x)]^{n+1}}{n+1} + C, \quad n \neq -1$$ |

Using the fact that

$$du = u'(x)\,dx \quad \text{or} \quad du = u'\,dx$$

we can write the Power Rule in the following alternative form.

| Power Rule (Alternative Form) | If $u = u(x)$, then $$\int u^n\,du = \frac{u^{n+1}}{n+1} + C, \quad n \neq -1$$ |

Note that this formula has the same form as the formula

$$\int x^n\,dx = \frac{x^{n+1}}{n+1} + C, \quad n \neq -1$$

with the *function u substituted for x and du substituted for dx.*

EXAMPLE 2 Power Rule

Evaluate $\int (3x^2 + 4)^5 \cdot 6x\,dx$.

Solution

To use the Power Rule, we must be sure that we have the function $u(x)$, its derivative $u'(x)$, and n.

$$u = 3x^2 + 4, \quad n = 5$$
$$u' = 6x$$

All required parts are present, so the integral is of the form

$$\int (3x^2 + 4)^5 \, 6x \, dx = \int u^5 \cdot u' \, dx = \int u^5 \, du$$
$$= \frac{u^6}{6} + C = \frac{(3x^2 + 4)^6}{6} + C$$

We can check the integration by noting that the derivative of

$$\frac{(3x^2 + 4)^6}{6} + C \quad \text{is} \quad (3x^2 + 4)^5 \cdot 6x$$

EXAMPLE **3**   **Power Rule**

Evaluate $\int \sqrt{2x + 3} \cdot 2 \, dx$.

Solution

If we let $u = 2x + 3$, then $u' = 2$, and so we have

$$\int \sqrt{2x + 3} \cdot 2 \, dx = \int \sqrt{u} \, u' \, dx = \int \sqrt{u} \, du$$
$$= \int u^{1/2} \, du = \frac{u^{3/2}}{3/2} + C$$

Because $u = 2x + 3$, we have

$$\int \sqrt{2x + 3} \cdot 2 \, dx = \frac{2}{3}(2x + 3)^{3/2} + C$$

Check: The derivative of $\frac{2}{3}(2x + 3)^{3/2} + C$ is $(2x + 3)^{1/2} \cdot 2$. ✔

Some members of the family of functions given by

$$\int \sqrt{2x + 3} \cdot 2 \, dx = \frac{2}{3}(2x + 3)^{3/2} + C$$

are shown in Figure 12.4. Note from the graphs that the domain of each function is $x \geq -3/2$. This is because $2x + 3$ must be nonnegative so that $(2x + 3)^{3/2} = (\sqrt{2x + 3})^3$ is a real number.

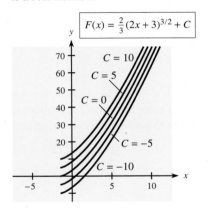

Figure 12.4

EXAMPLE 4   Power Rule

Evaluate $\int x^3(5x^4 + 11)^9\, dx$.

Solution

If we let $u = 5x^4 + 11$, then $u' = 20x^3$. Thus we do not have an integral of the form $\int u^n \cdot u'\, dx$, as we had in Example 2 and Example 3; the factor 20 is not in the integrand. To get the integrand in the correct form, we can multiply by 20 and divide it out as follows:

$$\int x^3(5x^4 + 11)^9\, dx = \int (5x^4 + 11)^9 \cdot x^3\, dx = \int (5x^4 + 11)^9\left(\frac{1}{20}\right)(20x^3)\, dx$$

Because $\frac{1}{20}$ is a constant factor, we can factor it outside the integral sign, getting

$$\int (5x^4 + 11)^9 \cdot x^3\, dx = \frac{1}{20}\int (5x^4 + 11)^9(20x^3)\, dx$$

$$= \frac{1}{20}\int u^9 \cdot u'\, dx = \frac{1}{20} \cdot \frac{u^{10}}{10} + C$$

$$= \frac{1}{200}(5x^4 + 11)^{10} + C$$

EXAMPLE 5   Power Rule

Evaluate $\int 5x^2\sqrt{x^3 - 4}\, dx$.

Solution

If we let $u = x^3 - 4$, then $u' = 3x^2$. Thus we need the factor 3, rather than 5, in the integrand. If we first reorder the factors and then multiply by the constant factor 3 (and divide it out), we have

$$\int \sqrt{x^3 - 4} \cdot 5x^2\, dx = \int \sqrt{x^3 - 4} \cdot \frac{5}{3}(3x^2)\, dx$$

$$= \frac{5}{3}\int (x^3 - 4)^{1/2} \cdot 3x^2\, dx$$

This integral is of the form $\frac{5}{3}\int u^{1/2} \cdot u'\, dx$, resulting in

$$\frac{5}{3} \cdot \frac{u^{3/2}}{3/2} + C = \frac{5}{3} \cdot \frac{(x^3 - 4)^{3/2}}{3/2} + C = \frac{10}{9}(x^3 - 4)^{3/2} + C$$

Note that we can factor a constant outside the integral sign to obtain the integrand in the form we seek. But if the integral requires the introduction of a variable to obtain the form $u^n \cdot u'\, dx$, we *cannot* use this form and must try something else.

EXAMPLE 6   Power Rule Fails

Evaluate $\int (x^2 + 4)^2\, dx$.

Solution

If we let $u = x^2 + 4$, then $u' = 2x$. Because we would have to introduce a variable to get u' in the integral, we cannot solve this problem by using the Power Rule. We must find another method. We can evaluate this integral by squaring and then integrating term by term.

$$\int (x^2 + 4)^2\, dx = \int (x^4 + 8x^2 + 16)\, dx$$

$$= \frac{x^5}{5} + \frac{8x^3}{3} + 16x + C$$

Note that if we tried to introduce the factor $2x$ into the integral in Example 6, we would get

$$\int (x^2 + 4)^2 \, dx = \int (x^2 + 4)^2 \cdot \frac{1}{2x}(2x) \, dx$$

Although it is tempting to factor $1/2x$ outside the integral and use the Power Rule, this leads to an "answer" that does not check. That is, the derivative of the "answer" is not the integrand. (Try it and see.) To emphasize again, we can introduce only *a constant factor* to get an integral in the proper form.

EXAMPLE 7   Power Rule

Evaluate:

(a) $\displaystyle\int (2x^2 - 4x)^2(x - 1) \, dx$ (b) $\displaystyle\int \frac{x^2 - 1}{(x^3 - 3x)^3} \, dx$

Solution

(a) If we want to treat this as an integral of the form $\int u^n u' \, dx$, we will have to let $u = 2x^2 - 4x$. Then $u' = 4x - 4$. Multiplying and dividing by 4 will give us this form.

$$\int (2x^2 - 4x)^2(x - 1) \, dx = \int (2x^2 - 4x)^2 \cdot \frac{1}{4} \cdot 4(x - 1) \, dx$$

$$= \frac{1}{4}\int (2x^2 - 4x)^2(4x - 4) \, dx$$

$$= \frac{1}{4}\int u^2 u' \, dx = \frac{1}{4} \cdot \frac{u^3}{3} + C$$

$$= \frac{1}{4}\frac{(2x^2 - 4x)^3}{3} + C$$

$$= \frac{1}{12}(2x^2 - 4x)^3 + C$$

(b) This integral can be treated as $\int u^{-3} u' \, dx$ if we let $u = x^3 - 3x$.

$$\int \frac{x^2 - 1}{(x^3 - 3x)^3} \, dx = \int (x^3 - 3x)^{-3}(x^2 - 1) \, dx$$

Then $u' = 3x^2 - 3$ and we can multiply and divide by 3 to get the form we need.

$$= \int (x^3 - 3x)^{-3} \cdot \frac{1}{3} \cdot 3(x^2 - 1) \, dx$$

$$= \frac{1}{3}\int (x^3 - 3x)^{-3}(3x^2 - 3) \, dx$$

$$= \frac{1}{3}\left[\frac{(x^3 - 3x)^{-2}}{-2}\right] + C$$

$$= \frac{-1}{6(x^3 - 3x)^2} + C$$

CHECKPOINT

1. Which of the following can be evaluated with the Power Rule?
    (a) $\int (4x^2 + 1)^{10}(8x \, dx)$
    (b) $\int (4x^2 + 1)^{10}(x \, dx)$
    (c) $\int (4x^2 + 1)^{10}(8 \, dx)$
    (d) $\int (4x^2 + 1)^{10} \, dx$

2. Which of the following is equal to $\int (2x^3 + 5)^{-2}(6x^2\, dx)$?

(a) $\dfrac{[(2x^4)/4 + 5x]^{-1}}{-1} \cdot \dfrac{6x^3}{3} + C$

(b) $\dfrac{(2x^3 + 5)^{-1}}{-1} \cdot \dfrac{6x^3}{3} + C$

(c) $\dfrac{(2x^3 + 5)^{-1}}{-1} + C$

3. True or false: Constants can be factored outside the integral sign.
4. Evaluate the following.

(a) $\int (x^3 + 9)^5(3x^2\, dx)$

(b) $\int (x^3 + 9)^{15}(x^2\, dx)$

(c) $\int (x^3 + 9)^2(x\, dx)$

EXAMPLE 8   Revenue | APPLICATION PREVIEW |

Suppose that the marginal revenue for a product is given by

$$\overline{MR} = \frac{600}{\sqrt{3x + 1}} + 2$$

Find the total revenue function.

Solution

$$R(x) = \int \overline{MR}\, dx = \int \left[\frac{600}{(3x + 1)^{1/2}} + 2 \right] dx$$

$$= \int 600(3x + 1)^{-1/2}\, dx + \int 2\, dx$$

$$= 600 \left(\frac{1}{3} \right) \int (3x + 1)^{-1/2}(3\, dx) + 2 \int dx$$

$$= 200 \frac{(3x + 1)^{1/2}}{1/2} + 2x + K$$

$$= 400\sqrt{3x + 1} + 2x + K$$

We know that $R(0) = 0$, so we have

$$0 = 400\sqrt{1} + 0 + K \quad \text{or} \quad K = -400$$

Thus the total revenue function is

$$R(x) = 400\sqrt{3x + 1} + 2x - 400$$

Note in Example 8 that even though $R(0) = 0$, the constant of integration K was *not* 0. This is because $x = 0$ does not necessarily mean that $u(x)$ will also be 0.

The formulas we have stated and used in this and the previous section are all the result of "reversing" derivative formulas. We summarize in the following box.

Integration Formula		Derivative Formula
$\displaystyle\int dx = x + C$	because	$\dfrac{d}{dx}(x + C) = 1$
$\displaystyle\int x^n\, dx = \dfrac{x^{n+1}}{n+1} + C \ \ (n \neq -1)$	because	$\dfrac{d}{dx}\left(\dfrac{x^{n+1}}{n+1} + C\right) = x^n$
$\displaystyle\int [u(x) + v(x)]\, dx = \int u(x)\, dx + \int v(x)\, dx$	because	$\dfrac{d}{dx}[u(x) + v(x)] = \dfrac{du}{dx} + \dfrac{dv}{dx}$
$\displaystyle\int [u(x) - v(x)]\, dx = \int u(x)\, dx - \int v(x)\, dx$	because	$\dfrac{d}{dx}[u(x) - v(x)] = \dfrac{du}{dx} - \dfrac{dv}{dx}$
$\displaystyle\int cf(x)\, dx = c\int f(x)\, dx$	because	$\dfrac{d}{dx}[cf(x)] = c\left(\dfrac{df}{dx}\right)$
$\displaystyle\int u^n u'\, dx = \dfrac{u^{n+1}}{n+1} + C \ \ (n \neq -1)$	because	$\dfrac{d}{dx}\left(\dfrac{u^{n+1}}{n+1} + C\right) = u^n \cdot u'$

Note that there are no integration formulas that correspond to "reversing" the derivative formulas for a product or for a quotient. This means that functions that may be easy to differentiate can be quite difficult (or even impossible) to integrate. Hence, in general, integration is a more difficult process than differentiation. In fact, some functions whose derivatives can be readily found cannot be integrated, such as

$$f(x) = \sqrt{x^3 + 1} \ \text{ and } \ g(x) = \frac{2x^2}{x^4 + 1}$$

In the next section, we will add to this list of basic integration formulas by "reversing" the derivative formulas for exponential and logarithmic functions.

CHECKPOINT SOLUTIONS

1. Expressions (a) and (b) can be evaluated with the Power Rule. For expression (a), if we let $u = 4x^2 + 1$, then $u' = 8x$ so that the integral becomes

$$\int u^{10} u'\, dx = \int u^{10}\, du$$

For expression (b), we let $u = 4x^2 + 1$ again. Then $u' = 8x$ and the integral becomes

$$\int (4x^2 + 1)^{10} \cdot x\, dx = \int (4x^2 + 1)^{10} \cdot \frac{1}{8}(8x)\, dx = \frac{1}{8}\int u^{10} u'\, dx = \frac{1}{8}\int u^{10}\, du$$

Expressions (c) and (d) do not fit the format of the Power Rule, because neither integral has an x with the dx outside the power (so they need to be multiplied out before integrating).

2. $u = 2x^3 + 5$, so $u' = 6x^2$

$$\int (2x^3 + 5)^{-2}(6x^2)\, dx = \int u^{-2} u'\, dx = \int u^{-2}\, du = u^{-1}/(-1) + C$$

$$= -u^{-1} + C = -(2x^3 + 5)^{-1} + C$$

Thus expression (c) is the correct choice.

3. True

4. (a) $\int (x^3 + 9)^5(3x^2\ dx) = \int u^5u'\ dx = \dfrac{u^6}{6} + C = \dfrac{(x^3 + 9)^6}{6} + C$

   (b) $\int (x^3 + 9)^{15}(x^2\ dx) = \dfrac{1}{3}\int (x^3 + 9)^{15}(3x^2\ dx)$

         $= \dfrac{1}{3}\cdot\dfrac{(x^3 + 9)^{16}}{16} + C = \dfrac{(x^3 + 9)^{16}}{48} + C$

   (c) The Power Rule does not fit, so we expand the integrand.

$$\int (x^3 + 9)^2(x\ dx) = \int (x^6 + 18x^3 + 81)x\ dx$$

$$= \int (x^7 + 18x^4 + 81x)\ dx$$

$$= \dfrac{x^8}{8} + \dfrac{18x^5}{5} + \dfrac{81x^2}{2} + C$$

| EXERCISES | 12.2

In Problems 1 and 2, find du**.**

1. $u = 2x^5 + 9$ 2. $u = 3x^4 - 4x^3$

Evaluate the integrals in Problems 3–32. Check your results by differentiation.

3. $\int (x^2 + 3)^3 2x\ dx$ 4. $\int (3x^3 + 1)^4 9x^2\ dx$

5. $\int (5x^3 + 11)^4\ 15x^2\ dx$ 6. $\int (8x^4 + 5)^3(32x^3)\ dx$

7. $\int (3x - x^3)^2(3 - 3x^2)\ dx$

8. $\int (4x^2 - 3x)^4(8x - 3)\ dx$

9. $\int 4x^3(7x^4 + 12)^3\ dx$ 10. $\int 9x^5(3x^6 - 4)^6\ dx$

11. $\int 7(4x - 1)^6\ dx$ 12. $\int 3(5 - x)^{-3}\ dx$

13. $\int 8x^5(4x^6 + 15)^{-3}\ dx$ 14. $\int 5x^3(3x^4 + 7)^{-4}\ dx$

15. $\int (x - 1)(x^2 - 2x + 5)^4\ dx$

16. $\int (2x^3 - x)(x^4 - x^2)^6\ dx$

17. $\int 2(x^3 - 1)(x^4 - 4x + 3)^{-5}\ dx$

18. $\int 3(x^5 - 2x)(x^6 - 6x^2 + 7)^{-2}\ dx$

19. $\int 7x^3\sqrt{x^4 + 6}\ dx$ 20. $\int 3x\sqrt{5 - x^2}\ dx$

21. $\int (x^3 + 1)^2(3x\ dx)$ 22. $\int (x^2 - 5)^2(2x^2\ dx)$

23. $\int (3x^4 - 1)^2\ 12x\ dx$ 24. $\int (2x^4 + 3)^2(8x\ dx)$

25. $\int \sqrt{x^3 - 3x}\ (x^2 - 1)\ dx$

26. $\int \sqrt[3]{x^2 + 2x}\ (x + 1)\ dx$

27. $\displaystyle\int \dfrac{3x^4\ dx}{(2x^5 - 5)^4}$ 28. $\displaystyle\int \dfrac{5x^3\ dx}{(x^4 - 8)^3}$

29. $\displaystyle\int \dfrac{x^3 - 1}{(x^4 - 4x)^3}\ dx$ 30. $\displaystyle\int \dfrac{3x^5 - 2x^3}{(x^6 - x^4)^5}\ dx$

31. $\displaystyle\int \dfrac{x^2 - 4x}{\sqrt{x^3 - 6x^2 + 2}}\ dx$ 32. $\displaystyle\int \dfrac{x^2 + 1}{\sqrt{x^3 + 3x + 10}}\ dx$

33. If $\int f(x)\ dx = (7x - 13)^{10} + C$, find $f(x)$.

34. If $\int g(x)\ dx = (5x^2 + 2)^6 + C$, find $g(x)$.

 In Problems 35 and 36, (a) evaluate each integral and (b) graph the members of the solution family for $C = -5$**,** $C = 0$**, and** $C = 5$**.**

35. $\int x(x^2 - 1)^3\ dx$ 36. $\int (3x - 11)^{1/3}\ dx$

 Each of Problems 37 and 38 has the form $\int f(x)\ dx$**.**

(a) **Evaluate each integral to obtain a family of functions.**

(b) **Find and graph the family member that passes through the point** $(0, 2)$**. Call that function** $F(x)$**.**

(c) **Find any** x**-values where** $f(x)$ **is not defined but** $F(x)$ **is.**

(d) **At the** x**-values found in part (c), what kind of tangent line does** $F(x)$ **have?**

37. $\displaystyle\int \dfrac{3\ dx}{(2x - 1)^{3/5}}$ 38. $\displaystyle\int \dfrac{x^2\ dx}{(x^3 - 1)^{1/3}}$

In each of Problems 39 and 40, a family of functions is given, together with the graphs of some functions in the family. Write the indefinite integral that gives the family.

39. $F(x) = (x^2 - 1)^{4/3} + C$

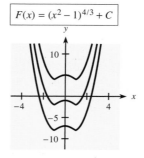

40. $F(x) = 54(4x^2 + 9)^{-1} + C$

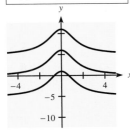

In parts (a)–(c) of Problems 41 and 42, three integrals are given. Integrate those that can be done by the methods studied so far. Additionally, as part (d), give your own example of an integral that looks as though it might use the Power Rule but that cannot be integrated by using methods studied so far.

41. (a) $\displaystyle\int \frac{7x^3 \, dx}{(x^3 + 4)^2}$ (b) $\displaystyle\int \frac{7x^2 \, dx}{(x^3 + 4)^2}$

   (c) $\displaystyle\int \frac{\sqrt{x^2 + 4}}{x} \, dx$

42. (a) $\displaystyle\int \frac{(2x^5 + 1)^{7/2}}{3x^4} \, dx$ (b) $\displaystyle\int 10x(2x^5 + 1)^{7/2} \, dx$

   (c) $\displaystyle\int \frac{5x^3}{(2x^4 + 1)^{7/2}} \, dx$

APPLICATIONS

43. *Revenue* Suppose that the marginal revenue for a product is given by
$$\overline{MR} = \frac{-30}{(2x + 1)^2} + 30$$
where x is the number of units and revenue is in dollars. Find the total revenue.

44. *Revenue* The marginal revenue for a new calculator is given by
$$\overline{MR} = 60{,}000 - \frac{40{,}000}{(10 + x)^2}$$
where x represents hundreds of calculators and revenue is in dollars. Find the total revenue function for these calculators.

45. *Physical productivity* The total physical output of a number of machines or workers is called *physical productivity* and is a function of the number of machines or workers. If $P = f(x)$ is the productivity, dP/dx is the marginal physical productivity. If the marginal physical productivity for bricklayers is $dP/dx = 90(x + 1)^2$, where P is the number of bricks laid per day and x is the number of bricklayers, find the physical productivity of 4 bricklayers. (*Note:* $P = 0$ when $x = 0$.)

46. *Production* The rate of production of a new line of products is given by
$$\frac{dx}{dt} = 200\left[1 + \frac{400}{(t + 40)^2}\right]$$

where x is the number of items and t is the number of weeks the product has been in production.
   (a) Assuming that $x = 0$ when $t = 0$, find the total number of items produced as a function of time t.
   (b) How many items were produced in the fifth week?

47. *Data entry speed* The rate of change in data entry speed of the average student is $ds/dx = 5(x + 1)^{-1/2}$, where x is the number of lessons the student has had and s is in entries per minute.
   (a) Find the data entry speed as a function of the number of lessons if the average student can complete 10 entries per minute with no lessons ($x = 0$).
   (b) How many entries per minute can the average student complete after 24 lessons?

48. *Productivity* Because a new employee must learn an assigned task, production will increase with time. Suppose that for the average new employee, the rate of performance is given by
$$\frac{dN}{dt} = \frac{1}{2\sqrt{t + 1}}$$
where N is the number of units completed t hours after beginning a new task. If 2 units are completed after 3 hours, how many units are completed after 8 hours?

49. *Film attendance* An excellent film with a very small advertising budget must depend largely on word-of-mouth advertising. In this case, the rate at which weekly attendance might grow can be given by
$$\frac{dA}{dt} = \frac{-100}{(t + 10)^2} + \frac{2000}{(t + 10)^3}$$
where t is the time in weeks since release and A is attendance in millions.
   (a) Find the function that describes weekly attendance at this film.
   (b) Find the attendance at this film in the tenth week.

50. *Product quality and advertising* An inferior product with a large advertising budget does well when it is introduced, but sales decline as people discontinue use of the product. Suppose that the rate of weekly sales revenue is given by
$$S'(t) = \frac{400}{(t + 1)^3} - \frac{200}{(t + 1)^2}$$
where S is sales in thousands of dollars and t is time in weeks.
   (a) Find the function that describes the weekly sales.
   (b) Find the sales for the first week and the ninth week.

51. *Demographics* Because of job outsourcing, a western Pennsylvania town predicts that its public school population will decrease at the rate
$$\frac{dN}{dx} = \frac{-300}{\sqrt{x + 9}}$$
where x is the number of years and N is the total school population. If the present population ($x = 0$) is 8000, what population size is expected in 7 years?

52. *Franchise growth* A new fast-food firm predicts that the number of franchises for its products will grow at the rate

$$\frac{dn}{dt} = 9\sqrt{t + 1}$$

where t is the number of years, $0 \le t \le 10$. If there is one franchise ($n = 1$) at present ($t = 0$), how many franchises are predicted for 8 years from now?

53. *Poverty line* Suppose the rate of change of the number of people (in millions) in the United States who lived below the poverty level can be modeled by

$$\frac{dp}{dt} = -0.0005728(2t + 3)^3 + 0.04452(2t + 3)^2$$
$$- 0.9744(2t + 3) + 5.572$$

where t is the number of years past 1990.

Year	Persons below the Poverty Level (millions)	Year	Persons below the Poverty Level (millions)
1991	35.7	2000	31.1
1992	38.0	2002	34.6
1993	39.3	2003	35.9
1994	38.1	2004	37.0
1995	36.4	2005	37.0
1996	36.5	2006	36.5
1997	35.6	2007	37.2
1998	34.5	2008	39.8
1999	32.3	2009	43.6

Source: U.S. Bureau of the Census

(a) Use integration and the data point for 2008 to find the function that models the number of people, in millions, in the United States who lived below the poverty level.

(b) The data in the table show the numbers of people, in millions, in the United States who lived below the poverty level for selected years. Graph the function from part (a) with the data in the table with $t = 0$ representing 1990.

(c) How well does the model fit the data?

54. *Social Security beneficiaries* Suppose the rate of change of the number of Social Security beneficiaries (in millions per year) can be modeled by

$$\frac{dB}{dt} = 0.07149(0.1t + 1)^2 - 0.67114(0.1t + 1) + 2.2016$$

where t is the number of years past 1950.

Year	Number of Beneficiaries (millions)	Year	Number of Beneficiaries (millions)
1950	2.9	2000	44.8
1960	14.3	2010	53.3
1970	25.2	2020	68.8
1980	35.1	2030	82.7
1990	39.5		

Source: Social Security Administration

(a) Use integration and the data point for 2000 to find the function $B(t)$ that models the millions of Social Security beneficiaries.

(b) The data in the table give the millions of Social Security beneficiaries for selected years from 1950 and projected to 2030. Graph $B(t)$ from part (a) with the data in the table; let $t = 0$ represent 1950.

(c) How well does the model fit the data?

55. *Females in the work force* Suppose the rate of change of the percent p of total U.S. workers who are female can be modeled by

$$\frac{dp}{dt} = \frac{2154.18}{(1.38t + 64.1)^2}$$

percentage points per year, where t is the number of years past 1950.

Year	% Female	Year	% Female
1950	29.6	2010	47.9
1960	33.4	2015	48.3
1970	38.1	2020	48.1
1980	42.5	2030	48.0
1990	45.2	2040	47.9
2000	46.6	2050	47.9

Source: U.S. Census Bureau

(a) Use integration and the data point for 2040 to find the function $p(t)$ that models the percent of the work force that is female.

(b) For selected years from 1950 and projected to 2050, the data in the table show the percent of total U.S. workers who are female. With t as the number of years past 1950, graph these data with the model found in part (a).

(c) Comment on the model's fit to the data.

56. *Paved roads* Suppose the rate of change of the percent P of U.S. public roads that are paved can be modeled by

$$\frac{dP}{dt} = \frac{938.9}{(0.0852t + 35.5)^2}$$

percentage points per year, where t is the number of years past 1960.

Year	% Paved	Year	% Paved
1960	34.7	1995	60.8
1965	39.4	2000	63.4
1970	44.5	2002	64.8
1975	48.3	2004	64.5
1980	53.7	2006	65.2
1985	54.7	2008	67.4
1990	58.3		

Source: U.S. Bureau of Transportation Statistics

(a) Use integration and the data point for 2000 to find the function $P(t)$ that models the percent of public roads that are paved.

(b) For selected years from 1960 to 2008, the data in the table show the percent of U.S. public roads that are paved. With $t = 0$ representing 1960, graph these data and the model found in part (a).

(c) Find the model's predicted percent for 2015.

OBJECTIVES   12.3

- To evaluate integrals of the form $\int e^u u'\, dx$ or, equivalently, $\int e^u\, du$
- To evaluate integrals of the form $\int \dfrac{u'}{u}\, dx$ or, equivalently, $\int \dfrac{1}{u}\, du$

Integrals Involving Exponential and Logarithmic Functions

| APPLICATION PREVIEW |

The rate of growth of the market value of a home has typically exceeded the inflation rate. Suppose, for example, that the real estate market has an average annual inflation rate of 8%. Then the rate of change of the value of a house that cost $200,000 can be modeled by

$$\frac{dV}{dt} = 15.4e^{0.077t}$$

where V is the value of the home in thousands of dollars and t is the time in years since the home was purchased. To find the market value of such a home 10 years after it was purchased, we would first have to integrate dV/dt. That is, we must be able to integrate an exponential. (See Example 3.)

In this section, we consider integration formulas that result in natural logarithms and formulas for integrating exponentials.

Integrals Involving Exponential Functions

We know that

$$\frac{d}{dx}(e^x) = e^x \qquad \text{and} \qquad \frac{d}{dx}(e^u) = e^u \cdot u'$$

The corresponding integrals are given by the following.

Exponential Formula

If u is a function of x,

$$\int e^u \cdot u'\, dx = \int e^u\, du = e^u + C$$

In particular, $\int e^x\, dx = e^x + C$.

EXAMPLE 1   Integral of an Exponential

Evaluate $\int 5e^x \, dx$.

Solution

$\int 5e^x \, dx = 5\int e^x \, dx = 5e^x + C$

EXAMPLE 2   Integral of $e^u \, du$

Evaluate: (a) $\int 2xe^{x^2} \, dx$ (b) $\int \dfrac{x^2 \, dx}{e^{x^3}}$

Solution

(a) Letting $u = x^2$ implies that $u' = 2x$, and the integral is of the form $\int e^u \cdot u' \, dx$. Thus

$$\int 2xe^{x^2} \, dx = \int e^{x^2}(2x) \, dx = \int e^u \cdot u' \, dx = e^u + C = e^{x^2} + C$$

(b) In order to use $\int e^u \cdot u' \, dx$, we write the exponential in the numerator. Thus

$$\int \frac{x^2 \, dx}{e^{x^3}} = \int e^{-x^3}(x^2 \, dx)$$

This is *almost* of the form $\int e^u \cdot u' \, dx$. Letting $u = -x^3$ gives $u' = -3x^2$. Thus

$$\int e^{-x^3}(x^2 \, dx) = -\frac{1}{3}\int e^{-x^3}(-3x^2 \, dx) = -\frac{1}{3}e^{-x^3} + C = \frac{-1}{3e^{x^3}} + C$$

CHECKPOINT

1. True or false:

(a) $\int e^{x^2}(2x \, dx) = e^{x^2} \cdot x^2 + C$ (b) $\int e^{-3x} \, dx = -\frac{1}{3}e^{-3x} + C$

(c) $\int \dfrac{dx}{e^{3x}} = \dfrac{1}{3}\left(\dfrac{1}{e^{3x}}\right) + C$ (d) $\int e^{3x+1}(3 \, dx) = \dfrac{e^{3x+2}}{3x+2} + C$

EXAMPLE 3   Real Estate Inflation | APPLICATION PREVIEW |

As the housing market emerges from the collapse of 2008, suppose the rate of change of the value of a house that cost $200,000 in 2011 can be modeled by

$$\frac{dV}{dt} = 15.4e^{0.077t}$$

where V is the market value of the home in thousands of dollars and t is the time in years since 2011.

(a) Find the function that expresses the value V in terms of t.
(b) Find the predicted value in 2021 (after 10 years).

Solution

(a) $V = \displaystyle\int \frac{dV}{dt} \, dt = \int 15.4e^{0.077t} \, dt$

$$V = 15.4\int e^{0.077t}\left(\frac{1}{0.077}\right)(0.077 \, dt)$$

$$V = 15.4\left(\frac{1}{0.077}\right)\int e^{0.077t}(0.077 \, dt)$$

$$V = 200e^{0.077t} + C$$

Using $V = 200$ (thousand) when $t = 0$, we have

$$200 = 200 + C$$
$$0 = C$$

Thus we have the value as a function of time given by

$$V = 200e^{0.077t}$$

(b) The value after 10 years is found by using $t = 10$.

$$V = 200e^{0.077(10)} = 200e^{0.77} \approx 431.95$$

Thus, in 2021, the predicted value of the home is $431,950.

EXAMPLE 4   Graphs of Functions and Integrals

Figure 12.5 shows the graphs of $g(x) = 5e^{-x^2}$ and $h(x) = -10xe^{-x^2}$. One of these functions is $f(x)$ and the other is $\int f(x)\, dx$ with $C = 0$.

(a) Decide which of $g(x)$ and $h(x)$ is $f(x)$ and which is $\int f(x)\, dx$.
(b) How can the graph of $f(x)$ be used to locate and classify the extrema of $\int f(x)\, dx$?
(c) What feature of the graph of $f(x)$ occurs at the same x-values as the inflection points of the graph of $\int f(x)\, dx$?

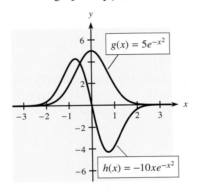

Figure 12.5

Solution

(a) The graph of $h(x)$ looks like the graph of $g'(x)$ because $h(x) > 0$ where $g(x)$ is increasing, $h(x) < 0$ where $g(x)$ is decreasing, and $h(x) = 0$ where $g(x)$ has its maximum. However, if $h(x) = g'(x)$, then, equivalently,

$$\int h(x)\, dx = \int g'(x)\, dx$$
$$= g(x) + C$$

so $h(x) = f(x)$ and $g(x) = \int f(x)\, dx$. We can verify this by noting that

$$\int -10xe^{-x^2}\, dx = 5\int e^{-x^2}(-2x\, dx)$$
$$= 5e^{-x^2} + C$$

(b) We know that $f(x)$ is the derivative of $\int f(x)\, dx$, so, as we saw in part (a), the x-intercepts of $f(x)$ locate the critical values and extrema of $\int f(x)\, dx$.
(c) The first derivative of $\int f(x)\, dx$ is $f(x)$, and its second derivative is $f'(x)$. Hence the inflection points of $\int f(x)\, dx$ occur where $f'(x) = 0$. But $f(x)$ has its extrema where $f'(x) = 0$. Thus the extrema of $f(x)$ occur at the same x-values as the inflection points of $\int f(x)\, dx$.

Integrals Involving Logarithmic Functions

Recall that the Power Rule for integrals applies only if $n \neq -1$. That is,

$$\int u^n u' \, dx = \frac{u^{n+1}}{n+1} + C \quad \text{if } n \neq -1$$

The following formula applies when $n = -1$.

Logarithmic Formula

If u is a function of x, then

$$\int u^{-1} u' \, dx = \int \frac{u'}{u} \, dx = \int \frac{1}{u} \, du = \ln |u| + C$$

In particular, $\int \frac{1}{x} \, dx = \ln |x| + C.$

We use the absolute value of u in the integral because the logarithm is defined only when the quantity is positive. This logarithmic formula is a direct result of the fact that

$$\frac{d}{dx} \left(\ln |u| \right) = \frac{1}{u} \cdot u'$$

We can see this result by considering the following.

For $u > 0$: $\quad \dfrac{d}{dx} \left(\ln |u| \right) = \dfrac{d}{dx} \left(\ln u \right) = \dfrac{1}{u} \cdot u'$

For $u < 0$: $\quad \dfrac{d}{dx} \left(\ln |u| \right) = \dfrac{d}{dx} \left[\ln (-u) \right] = \dfrac{1}{(-u)} \cdot (-u') = \dfrac{1}{u} \cdot u'$

In addition to this verification, we can graphically illustrate the need for the absolute value sign. Figure 12.6(a) shows that $f(x) = 1/x$ is defined for $x \neq 0$, and from Figures 12.6(b) and 12.6(c), we see that $F(x) = \int 1/x \, dx = \ln |x|$ is also defined for $x \neq 0$, but $y = \ln x$ is defined only for $x > 0$.

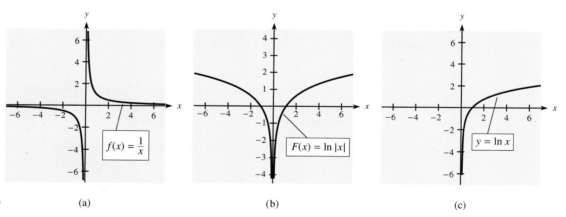

Figure 12.6   (a)   (b)   (c)

EXAMPLE 5   Integral Resulting in a Logarithmic Function

Evaluate $\int \dfrac{4}{4x + 8} \, dx$.

Solution

This integral is of the form

$$\int \frac{u'}{u} \, dx = \ln |u| + C$$

with $u = 4x + 8$ and $u' = 4$. Thus

$$\int \frac{4}{4x + 8}\, dx = \ln|4x + 8| + C$$

Figure 12.7 shows several members of the family

$$F(x) = \int \frac{4\, dx}{4x + 8} = \ln|4x + 8| + C$$

We can choose different values for C and use a graphing utility to graph families of curves such as those in Figure 12.7.

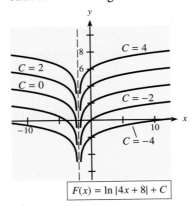

$$\boxed{F(x) = \ln|4x + 8| + C}$$

Figure 12.7

EXAMPLE 6   **Integral of *du/u***

Evaluate $\displaystyle\int \frac{x - 3}{x^2 - 6x + 1}\, dx$.

Solution

This integral is of the form $\int (u'/u)\, dx$, *almost*. If we let $u = x^2 - 6x + 1$, then $u' = 2x - 6$. If we multiply (and divide) the numerator by 2, we get

$$\int \frac{x - 3}{x^2 - 6x + 1}\, dx = \frac{1}{2}\int \frac{2(x - 3)}{x^2 - 6x + 1}\, dx$$

$$= \frac{1}{2}\int \frac{2x - 6}{x^2 - 6x + 1}\, dx$$

$$= \frac{1}{2}\int \frac{u'}{u}\, dx = \frac{1}{2}\ln|u| + C$$

$$= \frac{1}{2}\ln|x^2 - 6x + 1| + C$$

EXAMPLE 7   **Population Growth**

Because the world contains only about 10 billion acres of arable land, world population is limited. Suppose that world population is limited to 40 billion people and that the rate of population growth per year is given by

$$\frac{dP}{dt} = k(40 - P)$$

where P is the population in billions at time t and k is a positive constant. Then the relationship between the year and the population during that year is given by the integral

$$t = \frac{1}{k}\int \frac{1}{40 - P}\, dP$$

where $40 - P > 0$ because 40 billion is the population's upper limit.

(a) Evaluate this integral to find the relationship.

(b) Use properties of logarithms and exponential functions to write P as a function of t.

Solution

(a) $t = \dfrac{1}{k} \displaystyle\int \dfrac{1}{40 - P}\, dP = -\dfrac{1}{k} \displaystyle\int \dfrac{-dP}{40 - P} = -\dfrac{1}{k} \ln |40 - P| + C_1$

(b) $t = -\dfrac{1}{k} \ln (40 - P) + C_1$ because $40 - P > 0$ means $|40 - P| = 40 - P$.

Solving this equation for P requires converting to exponential form.

$$-k(t - C_1) = \ln (40 - P)$$
$$e^{C_1 k - kt} = 40 - P$$
$$e^{C_1 k} \cdot e^{-kt} = 40 - P$$

Because $e^{C_1 k}$ is an unknown constant, we replace it with C and solve for P.

$$P = 40 - Ce^{-kt}$$

If an integral contains a fraction in which the degree of the numerator is equal to or greater than that of the denominator, we should divide the denominator into the numerator as a first step.

EXAMPLE 8   Integral Requiring Division

Evaluate $\displaystyle\int \dfrac{x^4 - 2x^3 + 4x^2 - 7x - 1}{x^2 - 2x}\, dx$.

Solution

Because the numerator is of higher degree than the denominator, we begin by dividing $x^2 - 2x$ into the numerator.

$$
\begin{array}{r}
x^2 \qquad\quad + 4 \\
x^2 - 2x \overline{\smash{\big)}\, x^4 - 2x^3 + 4x^2 - 7x - 1} \\
\underline{x^4 - 2x^3} \qquad\qquad\qquad \\
4x^2 - 7x - 1 \\
\underline{4x^2 - 8x} \\
x - 1
\end{array}
$$

Thus

$$\int \dfrac{x^4 - 2x^3 + 4x^2 - 7x - 1}{x^2 - 2x}\, dx = \int \left(x^2 + 4 + \dfrac{x - 1}{x^2 - 2x} \right) dx$$

$$= \int (x^2 + 4)\, dx + \dfrac{1}{2} \int \dfrac{2(x - 1)\, dx}{x^2 - 2x}$$

$$= \dfrac{x^3}{3} + 4x + \dfrac{1}{2} \ln |x^2 - 2x| + C$$

CHECKPOINT

2. True or false:

(a) $\displaystyle\int \dfrac{3x^2\, dx}{x^3 + 4} = \ln |x^3 + 4| + C$ (b) $\displaystyle\int \dfrac{2x\, dx}{\sqrt{x^2 + 1}} = \ln |\sqrt{x^2 + 1}| + C$

(c) $\displaystyle\int \dfrac{2}{x}\, dx = 2 \ln |x| + C$ (d) $\displaystyle\int \dfrac{x}{x + 1}\, dx = x \int \dfrac{1}{x + 1}\, dx = x \ln |x + 1| + C$

(e) To evaluate $\displaystyle\int \dfrac{4x}{4x + 1}\, dx$, our first step is to divide $4x + 1$ into $4x$.

3. (a) Divide $4x + 1$ into $4x$.   (b) Evaluate $\displaystyle\int \dfrac{4x}{4x + 1}\, dx$.

CHECKPOINT SOLUTIONS

1. (a) False. The correct solution is $e^{x^2} + C$ (see Example 2a).

(b) True

(c) False; $\displaystyle\int \frac{dx}{e^{3x}} = \int e^{-3x}\,dx = -\frac{1}{3}e^{-3x} + C = \frac{-1}{3e^{3x}} + C$

(d) False; $\displaystyle\int e^{3x+1}(3\,dx) = e^{3x+1} + C$

2. (a) True

(b) False; $\displaystyle\int \frac{2x\,dx}{\sqrt{x^2+1}} = \int (x^2+1)^{-1/2}(2x\,dx)$

$$= \frac{(x^2+1)^{1/2}}{1/2} + C = 2(x^2+1)^{1/2} + C$$

(c) True

(d) False. We cannot factor the variable x outside the integral sign.

(e) True

3. (a)
$$4x + 1\overline{)\begin{array}{c}1\\ 4x\\ \underline{4x+1}\\ -1\end{array}}$$
so $\dfrac{4x}{4x+1} = 1 - \dfrac{1}{4x+1}$

(b) $\displaystyle\int \frac{4x\,dx}{4x+1} = \int\left(1 - \frac{1}{4x+1}\right)dx = x - \frac{1}{4}\ln|4x+1| + C$

| EXERCISES | 12.3

Evaluate the integrals in Problems 1–32.

1. $\displaystyle\int 3e^{3x}\,dx$

2. $\displaystyle\int 4e^{4x}\,dx$

3. $\displaystyle\int e^{-x}\,dx$

4. $\displaystyle\int e^{2x}\,dx$

5. $\displaystyle\int 1000e^{0.1x}\,dx$

6. $\displaystyle\int 1600e^{0.4x}\,dx$

7. $\displaystyle\int 840e^{-0.7x}\,dx$

8. $\displaystyle\int 250e^{-0.5x}\,dx$

9. $\displaystyle\int x^3 e^{3x^4}\,dx$

10. $\displaystyle\int xe^{2x^2}\,dx$

11. $\displaystyle\int \frac{3}{e^{2x}}\,dx$

12. $\displaystyle\int \frac{4}{e^{1-2x}}\,dx$

13. $\displaystyle\int \frac{x^5}{e^{2-3x^6}}\,dx$

14. $\displaystyle\int \frac{x^3}{e^{4x^4}}\,dx$

15. $\displaystyle\int \left(e^{4x} - \frac{3}{e^{x/2}}\right)dx$

16. $\displaystyle\int \left(xe^{3x^2} - \frac{5}{e^{x/3}}\right)dx$

17. $\displaystyle\int \frac{3x^2}{x^3+4}\,dx$

18. $\displaystyle\int \frac{8x^7}{x^8-1}\,dx$

19. $\displaystyle\int \frac{dz}{4z+1}$

20. $\displaystyle\int \frac{y}{y^2+1}\,dy$

21. $\displaystyle\int \frac{6x^3}{2x^4+1}\,dx$

22. $\displaystyle\int \frac{7x^2}{4x^3-9}\,dx$

23. $\displaystyle\int \frac{4x}{5x^2-4}\,dx$

24. $\displaystyle\int \frac{5x^2}{3x^3-8}\,dx$

25. $\displaystyle\int \frac{3x^2-2}{x^3-2x}\,dx$

26. $\displaystyle\int \frac{4x^3+2x}{x^4+x^2}\,dx$

27. $\displaystyle\int \frac{z^2+1}{z^3+3z+17}\,dz$

28. $\displaystyle\int \frac{(x+2)\,dx}{x^2+4x-9}$

29. $\displaystyle\int \frac{x^3-x^2+1}{x-1}\,dx.$

30. $\displaystyle\int \frac{2x^3+x^2+2x+3}{2x+1}\,dx$

31. $\displaystyle\int \frac{x^2+x+3}{x^2+3}\,dx$

32. $\displaystyle\int \frac{x^4-2x^2+x}{x^2-2}\,dx$

In Problems 33 and 34, graphs of two functions labeled $g(x)$ and $h(x)$ are given. Decide which is the graph of $f(x)$ and which is one member of the family $\int f(x)\,dx$. Check your conclusions by evaluating the integral.

33.

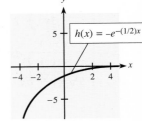
$g(x) = 2e^{-(1/2)x}$

$h(x) = -e^{-(1/2)x}$

34.

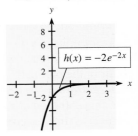
$g(x) = e^{-2x}$

$h(x) = -2e^{-2x}$

In Problems 35 and 36, a function $f(x)$ and its graph are given. Find the family $F(x) = \int f(x)\,dx$ and graph the member that satisfies $F(0) = 0$.

35.

$f(x) = \dfrac{1}{3-x}$

36.

$f(x) = \dfrac{1}{x+2}$

In Problems 37–40, a family of functions is given and graphs of some members are shown. Find the function $f(x)$ such that the family is given by $\int f(x)\, dx$.

37. $F(x) = x + \ln|x| + C$ 38. $F(x) = -\ln(x^2 + 4) + C$

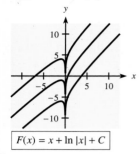

$$\boxed{F(x) = x + \ln|x| + C}$$

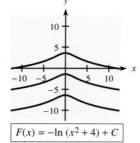

$$\boxed{F(x) = -\ln(x^2 + 4) + C}$$

39. $F(x) = 5xe^{-x} + C$ 40. $F(x) = e^{0.4x} + e^{-0.4x} + C$

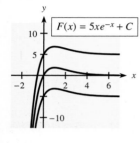

$$\boxed{F(x) = 5xe^{-x} + C}$$

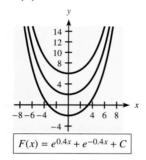

$$\boxed{F(x) = e^{0.4x} + e^{-0.4x} + C}$$

In parts (a)–(d) of Problems 41 and 42, integrate those that can be done by the methods studied so far.

41. (a) $\int xe^{x^3}\, dx$ (b) $\int \dfrac{x+2}{x^2 + 2x + 7}\, dx$

   (c) $\int \dfrac{x^2 + 2x}{x^3 + 3x^2 + 7}\, dx$ (d) $\int 5x^3 e^{2x^4}\, dx$

42. (a) $\int \dfrac{3x-1}{x^3 - x + 2}\, dx$ (b) $\int \dfrac{3x-1}{6x^2 - 4x + 9}\, dx$

   (c) $\int 5\sqrt{x}\, e^{\sqrt{x}}\, dx$ (d) $\int 6xe^{-x^2/8}\, dx$

APPLICATIONS

43. *Revenue* Suppose that the marginal revenue from the sale of x units of a product is $\overline{MR} = R'(x) = 6e^{0.01x}$. What is the revenue in dollars from the sale of 100 units of the product?

44. *Concentration of a drug* Suppose that the rate at which the concentration of a drug in the blood changes with respect to time t is given by

$$C'(t) = \frac{c}{b-a}(be^{-bt} - ae^{-at}), \quad t \geq 0$$

   where a, b, and c are constants depending on the drug administered, with $b > a$. Assuming that $C(t) = 0$ when $t = 0$, find the formula for the concentration of the drug in the blood at any time t.

45. *Radioactive decay* The rate of disintegration of a radioactive substance can be described by

$$\frac{dn}{dt} = n_0(-K)e^{-Kt}$$

where n_0 is the number of radioactive atoms present when time t is 0, and K is a positive constant that depends on the substance involved. Using the fact that the constant of integration is 0, integrate dn/dt to find the number of atoms n that are still radioactive after time t.

46. *Radioactive decay* Radioactive substances decay at a rate that is proportional to the amount present. Thus, if the amount present is x, the decay rate is

$$\frac{dx}{dt} = kx \quad (t \text{ in hours})$$

   This means that the relationship between the time and the amount of substance present can be found by evaluating the integral

$$t = \int \frac{dx}{kx}$$

   (a) Evaluate the integral to find the relationship.
   (b) Use properties of logarithms and exponential functions to write x as a function of t.

47. *Memorization* The rate of vocabulary memorization of the average student in a foreign language course is given by

$$\frac{dv}{dt} = \frac{40}{t+1}$$

   where t is the number of continuous hours of study, $0 < t \leq 4$, and v is the number of words. How many words would the average student memorize in 3 hours?

48. *Population growth* The rate of growth of world population can be modeled by

$$\frac{dN}{dt} = N_0 re^{rt}, \quad r < 1$$

   where t is the time in years from the present and N_0 and r are constants. What function describes world population if the present population is N_0?

49. *Compound interest* If $\$P$ is invested for n years at 10% compounded continuously, the rate at which the future value is growing is

$$\frac{dS}{dn} = 0.1Pe^{0.1n}$$

   (a) What function describes the future value at the end of n years?
   (b) In how many years will the future value double?

50. *Temperature changes* When an object is moved from one environment to another, its temperature T changes at a rate given by

$$\frac{dT}{dt} = kCe^{kt}$$

   where t is the time in the new environment (in hours), C is the temperature difference (old – new) between the two environments, and k is a constant. If the temperature of the object (and the old environment) is 70°F, and $C = -10°F$, what function describes the temperature T of the object t hours after it is moved?

51. **Blood pressure in the aorta** The rate at which blood pressure decreases in the aorta of a normal adult after a heartbeat is

$$\frac{dp}{dt} = -46.645e^{-0.491t}$$

where t is time in seconds.
(a) What function describes the blood pressure in the aorta if $p = 95$ when $t = 0$?
(b) What is the blood pressure 0.1 second after a heartbeat?

52. **Sales and advertising** A store finds that its sales decline after the end of an advertising campaign, with its daily sales for the period declining at the rate $S'(t) = -1477.8e^{-0.2t}$, $0 \le t \le 35$, where t is the number of days since the end of the campaign. Suppose that $S = 7389$ units when $t = 0$.
(a) Find the function that describes the number of daily sales t days after the end of the campaign.
(b) Find the total number of sales 10 days after the end of the advertising campaign.

53. **Life expectancy** Suppose the rate of change of the expected life span l at birth of people born in the United States can be modeled by

$$\frac{dl}{dt} = \frac{14.304}{t + 20}$$

where t is the number of years past 1920.

Year	Life Span (years)	Year	Life Span (years)
1920	54.1	1994	75.7
1930	59.7	1996	76.1
1940	62.9	1998	76.7
1950	68.2	2000	76.9
1960	69.7	2001	77.2
1970	70.8	2003	77.5
1975	72.6	2005	77.9
1980	73.7	2010	78.1
1985	74.7	2015	78.9
1990	75.4	2020	79.5
1992	75.5		

Source: National Center for Health Statistics

(a) Use integration and the data point for 2000 to find the function that models the life span.
(b) The data in the table give the expected life spans for people born in various years. Graph the function from part (a) with the data, with $t = 0$ representing 1920.
(c) How well does the model fit the data?

54. **U.S. households with cable/satellite TV** Suppose the rate of change of the percent P of U.S. households with cable/satellite TV can be modeled by

$$\frac{dP}{dt} = \frac{46.20}{t + 5}$$

where t is the number of years past 1975.
(a) Use integration and the data point for 2007 to find the function $P(t)$ that models the percent of U.S. households with cable/satellite TV.
(b) How well does the model from part (a) fit the data in the table? Explain.
(c) If the model remains valid, use it to predict the percent of U.S. households with cable/satellite TV in 2020.

Year	Percent	Year	Percent
1980	22.6	2000	67.8
1985	46.2	2005	85.7
1990	59.0	2007	83.8
1995	65.7	2009	89.7

Source: Nielsen Media Research

55. **Consumer price index** The Social Security Administration makes projections about the consumer price index (CPI) in order to understand the effects of inflation on Social Security benefits and to plan for cost-of-living increases. Suppose the rate of change of the CPI can be modeled with the function

$$\frac{dC}{dt} = 3.087e^{0.0384t}$$

dollars per year, where C is the consumer price index and t is the number of years past 1990.
(a) Does the model for the rate reflect the fact that the Social Security Administration's data (actual and projected for selected years from 1995 to 2070) in the table show that the CPI is increasing? Explain.
(b) Use integration and the table's data point for 2005 to find the function that models the Social Security Administration's CPI figures.
(c) Find and interpret $C(35)$ and $C'(35)$.

Year	CPI	Year	CPI
1995	100.00	2035	465.98
2000	118.21	2040	566.94
2005	143.67	2045	689.77
2010	174.80	2050	839.21
2015	212.67	2055	1021.02
2020	258.74	2060	1242.23
2025	314.80	2065	1511.36
2030	383.00	2070	1838.81

Source: Social Security Administration

56. *Personal income* Suppose the rate of change of total personal income I in the United States (in billions of dollars) can be modeled by

$$\frac{dI}{dt} = 33.68e^{0.0676t}$$

where t is the number of years past 1960.
(a) Is the average rate of change of total personal income from 2005 to 2008 found from the data in the table a better estimate for the instantaneous rate for 2005 or for 2008?
(b) Use the data point for 1970 to find the function that models $I(t)$.

(c) Find and interpret $I(55)$ and $I'(55)$.

Year	Personal Income	Year	Personal Income
1960	411.5	2000	8422.1
1970	838.8	2005	10,284.4
1980	2307.9	2008	12,100.7
1990	4861.9	2018	19,129.6
1995	6144.7		

Source: Bureau of Economic Analysis, U.S. Department of Commerce

---

OBJECTIVES

12.4

- To use integration to find total cost functions from information involving marginal cost
- To optimize profit, given information regarding marginal cost and marginal revenue
- To use integration to find national consumption functions from information about marginal propensity to consume and marginal propensity to save

Applications of the Indefinite Integral in Business and Economics

▌ APPLICATION PREVIEW ▌

If we know that the consumption of a nation is $9 billion when income is $0 and the marginal propensity to save is 0.25, we can easily find the marginal propensity to consume and use integration to find the national consumption function. (See Example 6.)

In this section, we also use integration to derive total cost and profit functions from the marginal cost and marginal revenue functions. One of the reasons for the marginal approach in economics is that firms can observe marginal changes in real life. If they know the marginal cost and the total cost when a given quantity is sold, they can develop their total cost function.

Total Cost and Profit   We know that the marginal cost for a commodity is the derivative of the total cost function—that is, $\overline{MC} = C'(x)$, where $C(x)$ is the total cost function. Thus if we have the marginal cost function, we can integrate (or "reverse" the process of differentiation) to find the total cost. That is, $C(x) = \int \overline{MC}\, dx$.

If, for example, the marginal cost is $\overline{MC} = 4x + 3$, the total cost is given by

$$C(x) = \int \overline{MC}\, dx$$
$$= \int (4x + 3)\, dx$$
$$= 2x^2 + 3x + K$$

where K represents the constant of integration. We know that the total revenue is 0 if no items are produced, but the total cost may not be 0 if nothing is produced. The fixed costs accrue whether goods are produced or not. Thus the value of the constant of integration depends on the fixed costs FC of production.

Thus we cannot determine the total cost function from the marginal cost unless additional information is available to help us determine the fixed costs.

EXAMPLE   1   **Total Cost**

Suppose the marginal cost function for a month for a certain product is $\overline{MC} = 3x + 50$, where x is the number of units and cost is in dollars. If the fixed costs related to the product amount to $10,000 per month, find the total cost function for the month.

Solution
The total cost function is

$$C(x) = \int (3x + 50)\, dx$$

$$= \frac{3x^2}{2} + 50x + K$$

The constant of integration K is found by using the fact that $C(0) = FC = 10,000$. Thus

$$3(0)^2 + 50(0) + K = 10,000, \quad \text{so } K = 10,000$$

and the total cost for the month is given by

$$C(x) = \frac{3x^2}{2} + 50x + 10,000$$

EXAMPLE   2   **Cost**

Suppose monthly records show that the rate of change of the cost (that is, the marginal cost) for a product is $\overline{MC} = 3(2x + 25)^{1/2}$, where x is the number of units and cost is in dollars. If the fixed costs for the month are $11,125, what would be the total cost of producing 300 items per month?

Solution
We can integrate the marginal cost to find the total cost function.

$$C(x) = \int \overline{MC}\, dx = \int 3(2x + 25)^{1/2}\, dx$$

$$= 3 \cdot \left(\frac{1}{2}\right) \int (2x + 25)^{1/2}(2\, dx)$$

$$= \left(\frac{3}{2}\right) \frac{(2x + 25)^{3/2}}{3/2} + K$$

$$= (2x + 25)^{3/2} + K$$

We can find K by using the fact that fixed costs are $11,125.

$$C(0) = 11,125 = (25)^{3/2} + K$$
$$11,125 = 125 + K, \quad \text{or} \quad K = 11,000$$

Thus the total cost function is

$$C(x) = (2x + 25)^{3/2} + 11,000$$

and the cost of producing 300 items per month is

$$C(300) = (625)^{3/2} + 11,000$$
$$= 26,625 \quad \text{(dollars)}$$

It can be shown that the profit is usually maximized when $\overline{MR} = \overline{MC}$. To see that this does not always give us a maximum *positive* profit, consider the following facts concerning the manufacture of widgets over the period of a month.

1. The marginal revenue is $\overline{MR} = 400 - 30x$.
2. The marginal cost is $\overline{MC} = 20x + 50$.
3. When 5 widgets are produced and sold, the total cost is $1750. The profit *should* be maximized when $\overline{MR} = \overline{MC}$, or when $400 - 30x = 20x + 50$. Solving for x gives $x = 7$. To see whether our profit is maximized when 7 units are produced and sold, let us examine the profit function.

The profit function is given by $P(x) = R(x) - C(x)$, where
$$R(x) = \int \overline{MR}\, dx \quad \text{and} \quad C(x) = \int \overline{MC}\, dx$$

Integrating, we get
$$R(x) = \int (400 - 30x)\, dx = 400x - 15x^2 + K$$

but $R(0) = 0$ gives $K = 0$ for this total revenue function, so
$$R(x) = 400x - 15x^2$$

The total cost function is
$$C(x) = \int (20x + 50)\, dx = 10x^2 + 50x + K$$

The value of fixed cost can be determined by using the fact that 5 widgets cost $1750. This tells us that $C(5) = 1750 = 250 + 250 + K$, so $K = 1250$.

Thus the total cost is $C(x) = 10x^2 + 50x + 1250$. Thus, the profit is
$$P(x) = R(x) - C(x) = (400x - 15x^2) - (10x^2 + 50x + 1250)$$

Simplifying gives
$$P(x) = 350x - 25x^2 - 1250$$

We have found that $\overline{MR} = \overline{MC}$ if $x = 7$, and the graph of $P(x)$ is a parabola that opens downward, so profit is maximized at $x = 7$. But if $x = 7$, profit is
$$P(7) = 2450 - 1225 - 1250 = -25$$

That is, the production and sale of 7 items result in a loss of $25.

The preceding discussion indicates that even though setting $\overline{MR} = \overline{MC}$ may optimize profit, it does not indicate the level of profit or loss, as forming the profit function does.

If the widget firm is in a competitive market, and its optimal level of production results in a loss, it has two options. It can continue to produce at the optimal level in the short run until it can lower or eliminate its fixed costs, even though it is losing money; or it can take a larger loss (its fixed cost) by stopping production. Producing 7 units causes a loss of $25 per month, and ceasing production results in a loss of $1250 (the fixed cost) per month. If this firm and many others like it cease production, the supply will be reduced, causing an eventual increase in price. The firm can resume production when the price increase indicates that it can make a profit.

EXAMPLE 3   Maximum Profit

Given that $\overline{MR} = 200 - 4x$, $\overline{MC} = 50 + 2x$, and the total cost of producing 10 Wagbats is $700, at what level should the Wagbat firm hold production in order to maximize the profits?

Solution

Setting $\overline{MR} = \overline{MC}$, we can solve for the production level that maximizes profit.

$$200 - 4x = 50 + 2x$$
$$150 = 6x$$
$$25 = x$$

The level of production that should optimize profit is 25 units. To see whether 25 units maximizes profits or minimizes the losses (in the short run), we must find the total revenue and total cost functions.

$$R(x) = \int (200 - 4x)\, dx = 200x - 2x^2 + K$$
$$= 200x - 2x^2, \quad \text{because } K = 0$$
$$C(x) = \int (50 + 2x)\, dx = 50x + x^2 + K$$

We find K by noting that $C(x) = 700$ when $x = 10$.

$$700 = 50(10) + (10)^2 + K$$

so $K = 100$.

Thus the cost is given by $C = C(x) = 50x + x^2 + 100$. At $x = 25$, $R = R(25) = 200(25) - 2(25)^2 = \$3750$ and $C = C(25) = 50(25) + (25)^2 + 100 = \$1975$.

We see that the total revenue is greater than the total cost, so production should be held at 25 units, which results in a maximum profit. ▨

Calculator Note   If it is difficult to solve $\overline{MC} = \overline{MR}$ analytically, we can use a graphing calculator to solve this equation by finding the point of intersection of the graphs of $\overline{MC}$ and $\overline{MR}$. We may also be able to integrate $\overline{MC}$ and $\overline{MR}$ to find the functions $C(x)$ and $R(x)$ and then use a graphing calculator to graph them. From the graphs of $C(x)$ and $R(x)$ we can learn about these functions—and hence about profit. ▨

    EXAMPLE 4   Cost, Revenue, and Profit

Suppose that $\overline{MC} = 1.01(x + 190)^{0.01}$ and $\overline{MR} = (1/\sqrt{2x + 1}) + 2$, where x is the number of thousands of units and both revenue and cost are in thousands of dollars. Suppose further that fixed costs are $100,236 and that production is limited to at most 180 thousand units.

(a) Determine $C(x)$ and $R(x)$ and graph them to determine whether a profit can be made.
(b) Estimate the level of production that yields maximum profit, and find the maximum profit.

Solution

(a) $C(x) = \int \overline{MC}\, dx = \int 1.01(x + 190)^{0.01}\, dx$

$$= 1.01 \frac{(x + 190)^{1.01}}{1.01} + K$$

When we say that fixed costs equal $100,236, we mean $C(0) = 100.236$.

$$100.236 = C(0) = (190)^{1.01} + K$$
$$100.236 = 200.236 + K$$
$$-100 = K$$

Thus $C(x) = (x + 190)^{1.01} - 100$.

$$R(x) = \int \overline{MR}\, dx = \int [(2x + 1)^{-1/2} + 2]dx$$

$$= \frac{1}{2}\int (2x + 1)^{-1/2}(2\, dx) + \int 2\, dx$$

$$= \frac{\frac{1}{2}(2x + 1)^{1/2}}{1/2} + 2x + K$$

$R(0) = 0$ means

$$0 = R(0) = (1)^{1/2} + 0 + K, \quad \text{or} \quad K = -1$$

Thus $R(x) = (2x + 1)^{1/2} + 2x - 1$.

The graphs of $C(x)$ and $R(x)$ are shown in Figure 12.8. (The x-range is chosen to include the production range from 0 to 180 (thousand) units. The y-range is chosen to extend beyond fixed costs of about 100 thousand dollars.)

From the figure we see that a profit can be made as long as the number of units sold exceeds about 95 (thousand). We could locate this break even value more precisely by using INTERSECT.

(b) From the graph we also see that $R(x) - C(x) = P(x)$ is at its maximum at the right edge of the graph. Because production is limited to at most 180 thousand units, profit will be maximized when $x = 180$ and the maximum profit is

$$P(180) = R(180) - C(180)$$
$$= [(361)^{1/2} + 360 - 1] - [(370)^{1.01} - 100]$$
$$\approx 85.46 \quad \text{(thousand dollars)}$$

Figure 12.8

CHECKPOINT

1. True or false:
    (a) If $C(x) = \int \overline{MC}\, dx$, then the constant of integration equals the fixed costs.
    (b) If $R(x) = \int \overline{MR}\, dx$, then the constant of integration equals 0.
2. Find $C(x)$ if $\overline{MC} = \dfrac{100}{\sqrt{x + 1}}$ and fixed costs are \$8000.

National Consumption and Savings

The consumption function is one of the basic ingredients in a larger discussion of how an economy can have persistent high unemployment or persistent high inflation. This study is often called **Keynesian analysis,** after its founder John Maynard Keynes (pronounced "canes").

If C represents national consumption (in billions of dollars), then a **national consumption function** has the form $C = f(y)$, where y is disposable national income (also in billions of dollars). The **marginal propensity to consume** is the derivative of the national consumption function with respect to y, or $dC/dy = f'(y)$. For example, suppose that

$$C = f(y) = 0.8y + 6$$

is a national consumption function; then the marginal propensity to consume is $f'(y) = 0.8$.

If we know the marginal propensity to consume, we can integrate with respect to y to find national consumption:

$$C = \int f'(y)\, dy = f(y) + K$$

We can find the unique national consumption function if we have additional information to help us determine the value of K, the constant of integration.

EXAMPLE 5   National Consumption

If consumption is \$6 billion when disposable income is \$0, and if the marginal propensity to consume is $dC/dy = 0.3 + 0.4/\sqrt{y}$ (in billions of dollars), find the national consumption function.

Solution
If

$$\frac{dC}{dy} = 0.3 + \frac{0.4}{\sqrt{y}}$$

then

$$C = \int \left(0.3 + \frac{0.4}{\sqrt{y}} \right) dy$$

$$= \int (0.3 + 0.4y^{-1/2}) \, dy$$

$$= 0.3y + 0.4\frac{y^{1/2}}{1/2} + K = 0.3y + 0.8y^{1/2} + K$$

Now, if $C = 6$ when $y = 0$, then $6 = 0.3(0) + 0.8\sqrt{0} + K$. Thus the constant of integration is $K = 6$, and the consumption function is

$$C = 0.3y + 0.8\sqrt{y} + 6 \quad \text{(billions of dollars)}$$

If S represents national savings, we can assume that the disposable national income is given by $y = C + S$, or $S = y - C$. Then the **marginal propensity to save** is $dS/dy = 1 - dC/dy$.

EXAMPLE 6   Consumption and Savings | APPLICATION PREVIEW |

If the consumption is \$9 billion when income is \$0, and if the marginal propensity to save is 0.25, find the consumption function.

Solution
If $dS/dy = 0.25$, then $0.25 = 1 - dC/dy$, or $dC/dy = 0.75$. Thus

$$C = \int 0.75 \, dy = 0.75y + K$$

If $C = 9$ when $y = 0$, then $9 = 0.75(0) + K$, or $K = 9$. Then the consumption function is $C = 0.75y + 9$ (billions of dollars).

CHECKPOINT

3. If the marginal propensity to save is

$$\frac{dS}{dy} = 0.7 - \frac{0.4}{\sqrt{y}}$$

find the marginal propensity to consume.

4. Find the national consumption function if the marginal propensity to consume is

$$\frac{dC}{dy} = \frac{1}{\sqrt{y + 4}} + 0.2$$

and national consumption is \$6.8 billion when disposable income is \$0.

1. (a) False. $C(0)$ equals the fixed costs. It may or may not be the constant of integration. (See Examples 1 and 2.)

   (b) False. We use $R(0) = 0$ to determine the constant of integration, but it may be nonzero. See Example 4.

2. $C(x) = 100 \int (x + 1)^{-1/2} \, dx = 100 \left[\dfrac{(x + 1)^{1/2}}{1/2} \right] + K$

   $C(x) = 200\sqrt{x + 1} + K$

   When $x = 0$, $C(x) = 8000$, so

   $$8000 = 200\sqrt{1} + K$$
   $$7800 = K$$
   $$C(x) = 200\sqrt{x + 1} + 7800$$

3. $\dfrac{dC}{dy} = 1 - \dfrac{dS}{dy} = 1 - \left(0.7 - \dfrac{0.4}{\sqrt{y}} \right) = 0.3 + \dfrac{0.4}{\sqrt{y}}$

4. $C(y) = \int \left(\dfrac{1}{\sqrt{y + 4}} + 0.2 \right) dy$

   $= \int [(y + 4)^{-1/2} + 0.2] \, dy$

   $= \dfrac{(y + 4)^{1/2}}{1/2} + 0.2y + K$

   $C(y) = 2\sqrt{y + 4} + 0.2y + K$

   Using $C(0) = 6.8$ gives $6.8 = 2\sqrt{4} + 0 + K$, or $K = 2.8$.

   Thus $C(y) = 2\sqrt{y + 4} + 0.2y + 2.8$.

| EXERCISES | 12.4

TOTAL COST AND PROFIT

In Problems 1–12, cost, revenue, and profit are in dollars and x is the number of units.

1. If the monthly marginal cost for a product is $\overline{MC} = 2x + 100$, with fixed costs amounting to $200, find the total cost function for the month.

2. If the monthly marginal cost for a product is $\overline{MC} = x + 30$, and the related fixed costs are $50, find the total cost function for the month.

3. If the marginal cost for a product is $\overline{MC} = 4x + 2$, and the production of 10 units results in a total cost of $300, find the total cost function.

4. If the marginal cost for a product is $\overline{MC} = 3x + 50$, and the total cost of producing 20 units is $2000, find the total cost function.

5. If the marginal cost for a product is $\overline{MC} = 4x + 40$, and the total cost of producing 25 units is $3000, find the cost of producing 30 units.

6. If the marginal cost for producing a product is $\overline{MC} = 5x + 10$, with a fixed cost of $800, find the cost of producing 20 units.

7. A firm knows that its marginal cost for a product is $\overline{MC} = 3x + 20$, that its marginal revenue is $\overline{MR} = 44 - 5x$, and that the cost of production and sale of 80 units is $11,400.

   (a) Find the optimal level of production.

   (b) Find the profit function.

   (c) Find the profit or loss at the optimal level.

8. A certain firm's marginal cost for a product is $\overline{MC} = 6x + 60$, its marginal revenue is $\overline{MR} = 180 - 2x$, and its total cost of production of 10 items is $1000.

   (a) Find the optimal level of production.

   (b) Find the profit function.

   (c) Find the profit or loss at the optimal level of production.

   (d) Should production be continued for the short run?

   (e) Should production be continued for the long run?

9. Suppose that the marginal revenue for a product is $\overline{MR} = 900$ and the marginal cost is $\overline{MC} = 30\sqrt{x + 4}$, with a fixed cost of $1000.

   (a) Find the profit or loss from the production and sale of 5 units.

   (b) How many units will result in a maximum profit?

10. Suppose that the marginal cost for a product is $\overline{MC} = 60\sqrt{x + 1}$ and its fixed cost is $340.00. If the marginal revenue for the product is $\overline{MR} = 80x$, find the profit or loss from production and sale of

    (a) 3 units.   (b) 8 units.

11. The average cost of a product changes at the rate

$$\overline{C}'(x) = -6x^{-2} + 1/6$$

and the average cost of 6 units is $10.00.
(a) Find the average cost function.
(b) Find the average cost of 12 units.

12. The average cost of a product changes at the rate

$$\overline{C}'(x) = \frac{-10}{x^2} + \frac{1}{10}$$

and the average cost of 10 units is $20.00.
(a) Find the average cost function.
(b) Find the average cost of 20 units.

13. Suppose that marginal cost for a certain product is given by $\overline{MC} = 1.05(x + 180)^{0.05}$ and marginal revenue is given by $\overline{MR} = (1/\sqrt{0.5x + 4}) + 2.8$, where x is in thousands of units and both revenue and cost are in thousands of dollars. Fixed costs are $200,000 and production is limited to at most 200 thousand units.
(a) Find $C(x)$ and $R(x)$.
(b) Graph $C(x)$ and $R(x)$ to determine whether a profit can be made.
(c) Determine the level of production that yields maximum profit, and find the maximum profit (or minimum loss).

14. Suppose that the marginal cost for a certain product is given by $\overline{MC} = 1.02(x + 200)^{0.02}$ and marginal revenue is given by $\overline{MR} = (2/\sqrt{4x + 1}) + 1.75$, where x is in thousands of units and revenue and cost are in thousands of dollars. Suppose further that fixed costs are $150,000 and production is limited to at most 200 thousand units.
(a) Find $C(x)$ and $R(x)$.
(b) Graph $C(x)$ and $R(x)$ to determine whether a profit can be made.
(c) Determine what level of production yields maximum profit, and find the maximum profit (or minimum loss).

NATIONAL CONSUMPTION AND SAVINGS

15. If consumption is $7 billion when disposable income is $0, and if the marginal propensity to consume is 0.80, find the national consumption function (in billions of dollars).

16. If national consumption is $9 billion when income is $0, and if the marginal propensity to consume is 0.30, what is consumption when disposable income is $20 billion?

17. If consumption is $8 billion when income is $0, and if the marginal propensity to consume is

$$\frac{dC}{dy} = 0.3 + \frac{0.2}{\sqrt{y}} \quad \text{(in billions of dollars)}$$

find the national consumption function.

18. If consumption is $5 billion when disposable income is $0, and if the marginal propensity to consume is

$$\frac{dC}{dy} = 0.4 + \frac{0.3}{\sqrt{y}} \quad \text{(in billions of dollars)}$$

find the national consumption function.

19. If consumption is $6 billion when disposable income is $0, and if the marginal propensity to consume is

$$\frac{dC}{dy} = \frac{1}{\sqrt{y + 1}} + 0.4 \quad \text{(in billions of dollars)}$$

find the national consumption function.

20. If consumption is $5.8 billion when disposable income is $0, and if the marginal propensity to consume is

$$\frac{dC}{dy} = \frac{1}{\sqrt{2y + 9}} + 0.8 \quad \text{(in billions of dollars)}$$

find the national consumption function.

21. Suppose that the marginal propensity to consume is

$$\frac{dC}{dy} = 0.7 - e^{-2y} \quad \text{(in billions of dollars)}$$

and that consumption is $5.65 billion when disposable income is $0. Find the national consumption function.

22. Suppose that the marginal propensity to consume is

$$\frac{dC}{dy} = 0.04 + \frac{\ln (y + 1)}{y + 1} \quad \text{(in billions of dollars)}$$

and that consumption is $6.04 billion when disposable income is $0. Find the national consumption function.

23. Suppose that the marginal propensity to save is

$$\frac{dS}{dy} = 0.15 \quad \text{(in billions of dollars)}$$

and that consumption is $5.15 billion when disposable income is $0. Find the national consumption function.

24. Suppose that the marginal propensity to save is

$$\frac{dS}{dy} = 0.22 \quad \text{(in billions of dollars)}$$

and that consumption is $8.6 billion when disposable income is $0. Find the national consumption function.

25. Suppose that the marginal propensity to save is

$$\frac{dS}{dy} = 0.2 - \frac{1}{\sqrt{3y + 7}} \quad \text{(in billions of dollars)}$$

and that consumption is $6 billion when disposable income is $0. Find the national consumption function.

26. If consumption is $3 billion when disposable income is $0, and if the marginal propensity to save is

$$\frac{dS}{dy} = 0.2 + e^{-1.5y} \quad \text{(in billions of dollars)}$$

find the national consumption function.

12.5

Differential Equations

| APPLICATION PREVIEW |

Carbon-14 dating, used to determine the age of fossils, is based on three facts. First, the half-life of carbon-14 is 5730 years. Second, the amount of carbon-14 in any living organism is essentially constant. Third, when an organism dies, the rate of change of carbon-14 in the organism is proportional to the amount present. If y represents the amount of carbon-14 present in the organism, then we can express the rate of change of carbon-14 by the differential equation

$$\frac{dy}{dt} = ky$$

where k is a constant and t is time in years. In this section, we study methods that allow us to find a function y that satisfies this differential equation, and then we use that function to date a fossil. (See Example 6.)

Recall that we introduced the derivative as an instantaneous rate of change and denoted the instantaneous rate of change of y with respect to time as dy/dt. For many growth or decay processes, such as carbon-14 decay, the rate of change of the amount of a substance with respect to time is proportional to the amount present. As we noted above, this can be represented by the equation

$$\frac{dy}{dt} = ky \quad (k = \text{constant})$$

An equation of this type, where y is an unknown function of x or t, is called a **differential equation** because it contains derivatives (or differentials). In this section, we restrict ourselves to differential equations where the highest derivative present in the equation is the first derivative. These differential equations are called **first-order differential equations**. Examples are

$$f'(x) = \frac{1}{x + 1}, \quad \frac{dy}{dt} = 2t, \quad \text{and} \quad x \, dy = (y + 1) \, dx$$

Solution of Differential Equations   The solution to a differential equation is a function [say $y = f(x)$] that, when used in the differential equation, results in an identity.

EXAMPLE 1   Differential Equation

Show that $y = 4e^{-5t}$ is a solution to $dy/dt + 5y = 0$.

Solution
We must show that substituting $y = 4e^{-5t}$ into the equation $dy/dt + 5y = 0$ results in an identity:

$$\frac{d}{dt}(4e^{-5t}) + 5(4e^{-5t}) = 0$$
$$-20e^{-5t} + 20e^{-5t} = 0$$
$$0 = 0$$

Thus $y = 4e^{-5t}$ is a solution.

Now that we know what it means for a function to be a solution to a differential equation, let us consider how to find solutions.

The most elementary differential equations are of the form

$$\frac{dy}{dx} = f(x)$$

where $f(x)$ is a continuous function. These equations are elementary to solve because the solutions are found by integration:

$$y = \int f(x)\, dx$$

EXAMPLE 2   **Solving a Differential Equation**

Find the solution of

$$f'(x) = \frac{1}{x + 1}$$

Solution

The solution is

$$f(x) = \int f'(x)\, dx = \int \frac{1}{x + 1}\, dx = \ln |x + 1| + C \qquad \blacksquare$$

The solution in Example 2, $f(x) = \ln |x + 1| + C$, is called the **general solution** because every solution to the equation has this form, and different values of C give different **particular solutions.** Figure 12.9 shows the graphs of several members of the family of solutions to this differential equation. (We cannot, of course, show all of them.)

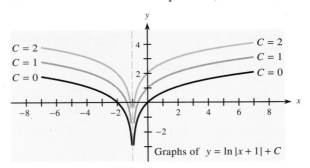

Figure 12.9

Graphs of $y = \ln |x + 1| + C$

We can find a particular solution to a differential equation when we know that the solution must satisfy additional conditions, such as **initial conditions** or **boundary conditions.** For instance, to find the particular solution to

$$f'(x) = \frac{1}{x + 1} \qquad \text{with the condition that} \quad f(-2) = 2$$

we use $f(-2) = 2$ in the general solution, $f(x) = \ln |x + 1| + C$.

$$2 = f(-2) = \ln |-2 + 1| + C$$
$$2 = \ln |-1| + C \quad \text{so} \quad C = 2$$

Thus the particular solution is

$$f(x) = \ln |x + 1| + 2$$

and is shown in Figure 12.9 with $C = 2$.

We frequently denote the value of the solution function $y = f(t)$ at the initial time $t = 0$ as $y(0)$ instead of $f(0)$.

Calculator Note   We can use a graphing calculator to solve differential equations with boundary conditions. Details can be found in Appendix C, Section 12.5. $\blacksquare$

CHECKPOINT

1. Given $f'(x) = 2x - [1/(x + 1)], f(0) = 4$,
   (a) find the general solution to the differential equation.
   (b) find the particular solution that satisfies $f(0) = 4$.

Just as we can find the differential of both sides of an equation, we can find the solution to a differential equation of the form

$$G(y)\, dy = f(x)\, dx$$

by integrating both sides.

EXAMPLE 3   Differential Equation with a Boundary Condition

Solve $3y^2\, dy = 2x\, dx$, if $y(1) = 2$.

Solution
We find the general solution by integrating both sides.

$$\int 3y^2\, dy = \int 2x\, dx$$
$$y^3 + C_1 = x^2 + C_2$$
$$y^3 = x^2 + C, \qquad \text{where } C = C_2 - C_1$$

By using $y(1) = 2$, we can find C.

$$2^3 = 1^2 + C$$
$$7 = C$$

Thus the particular solution is given implicitly by

$$y^3 = x^2 + 7$$

Separable Differential Equations

It is frequently necessary to change the form of a differential equation before it can be solved by integrating both sides.

For example, the equation

$$\frac{dy}{dx} = y^2$$

cannot be solved by simply integrating both sides of the equation with respect to x because we cannot evaluate $\int y^2\, dx$.

However, we can multiply both sides of $dy/dx = y^2$ by dx/y^2 to obtain an equation that has all terms containing y on one side of the equation and all terms containing x on the other side. That is, we obtain

$$\frac{dy}{y^2} = dx$$

Separable Differential Equations

When a differential equation can be equivalently expressed in the form

$$g(y)\, dy = f(x)\, dx$$

we say that the equation is **separable.**

The solution of a separable differential equation is obtained by integrating both sides of the equation after the variables have been separated.

EXAMPLE 4   Separable Differential Equation

Solve the differential equation

$$(x^2y + x^2)\, dy = x^3\, dx$$

Solution

To write the equation in separable form, we first factor x^2 from the left side and divide both sides by it.

$$x^2(y + 1)\,dy = x^3\,dx$$

$$(y + 1)\,dy = \frac{x^3}{x^2}\,dx$$

The equation is now separated, so we integrate both sides.

$$\int (y + 1)\,dy = \int x\,dx$$

$$\frac{y^2}{2} + y + C_1 = \frac{x^2}{2} + C_2$$

This equation, as well as the equation

$$y^2 + 2y - x^2 = C, \quad \text{where} \quad C = 2(C_2 - C_1)$$

gives the solution implicitly.

Note that we need not write both C_1 and C_2 when we integrate, because it is always possible to combine the two constants into one. ◼

EXAMPLE 5   Separable Differential Equation

Solve the differential equation

$$\frac{dy}{dt} = ky \quad (k = \text{constant})$$

Solution

To solve the equation, we write it in separated form and integrate both sides:

$$\frac{dy}{y} = k\,dt \quad \Rightarrow \quad \int \frac{dy}{y} = \int k\,dt \quad \Rightarrow \quad \ln |y| = kt + C_1$$

Assuming that $y > 0$ and writing this equation in exponential form gives

$$y = e^{kt + C_1}$$

$$y = e^{kt} \cdot e^{C_1} = Ce^{kt}, \quad \text{where } C = e^{C_1}$$

This solution,

$$y = Ce^{kt}$$

is the general solution to the differential equation $dy/dt = ky$ because all solutions have this form, with different values of C giving different particular solutions. The case of $y < 0$ is covered by values of $C < 0$. ◼

CHECKPOINT

2. True or false:
   (a) The general solution to $dy = (x/y)\,dx$ can be found from
   $$\int y\,dy = \int x\,dx$$
   (b) The first step in solving $dy/dx = -2xy^2$ is to separate it.
   (c) The equation $dy/dx = -2xy^2$ separates as $y^2\,dy = -2x\,dx$.
3. Suppose that $(xy + x)(dy/dx) = x^2y + y$.
   (a) Separate this equation.   (b) Find the general solution.

In many applied problems that can be modeled with differential equations, we know conditions that allow us to obtain a particular solution.

Applications of Differential Equations

We now consider two applications that can be modeled by differential equations. These are radioactive decay and one-container mixture problems (as a model for drugs in an organ).

EXAMPLE 6   Carbon-14 Dating | APPLICATION PREVIEW |

When an organism dies, the rate of change of the amount of carbon-14 present is proportional to the amount present and is represented by the differential equation

$$\frac{dy}{dt} = ky$$

where y is the amount present, k is a constant, and t is time in years. If we denote the initial amount of carbon-14 in an organism as y_0, then $y = y_0$ represents the amount present at time $t = 0$ (when the organism dies). Suppose that anthropologists discover a fossil that contains 1% of the initial amount of carbon-14. Find the age of the fossil. (Recall that the half-life of carbon-14 is 5730 years.)

Solution

We must find a particular solution to

$$\frac{dy}{dt} = ky$$

subject to the fact that when $t = 0$, $y = y_0$, and we must determine the value of k on the basis of the half-life of carbon-14 ($t = 5730$ years, $y = \frac{1}{2}y_0$ units.) From Example 5, we know that the general solution to the differential equation $dy/dt = ky$ is $y = Ce^{kt}$. Using $y = y_0$ when $t = 0$, we obtain $y_0 = C$, so the equation becomes $y = y_0 e^{kt}$. Using $t = 5730$ and $y = \frac{1}{2}y_0$ in this equation gives

$$\frac{1}{2}y_0 = y_0 e^{5730k} \quad \text{or} \quad 0.5 = e^{5730k}$$

Rewriting this equation in logarithmic form and then solving for k, we get

$$\ln(0.5) = 5730k$$
$$-0.69315 = 5730k$$
$$-0.00012097 = k$$

Thus the equation we seek is

$$y = y_0 e^{-0.00012097t}$$

Using the fact that $y = 0.01y_0$ when the fossil was discovered, we can find its age t by solving

$$0.01y_0 = y_0 e^{-0.00012097t} \quad \text{or} \quad 0.01 = e^{-0.00012097t}$$

Rewriting this in logarithmic form and then solving give

$$\ln(0.01) = -0.00012097t$$
$$-4.6051702 = -0.00012097t$$
$$38,069 \approx t$$

Thus the fossil is approximately 38,069 years old.

The differential equation $dy/dt = ky$, which describes the decay of radioactive substances in Example 6, also models the rate of growth of an investment that is compounded continuously and the rate of decay of purchasing power due to inflation.

Another application of differential equations comes from a group of applications called *one-container mixture problems*. In problems of this type, there is a substance whose amount in a container is changing with time, and the goal is to determine the amount of the substance at any time t. The differential equations that model these problems are of the following form:

$$\begin{bmatrix} \text{Rate of change} \\ \text{of the amount} \\ \text{of the substance} \end{bmatrix} = \begin{bmatrix} \text{Rate at which} \\ \text{the substance} \\ \text{enters the container} \end{bmatrix} - \begin{bmatrix} \text{Rate at which} \\ \text{the substance} \\ \text{leaves the container} \end{bmatrix}$$

We consider this application as it applies to the amount of a drug in an organ.

EXAMPLE 7   **Drug in an Organ**

A liquid carries a drug into an organ of volume 300 cubic centimeters at a rate of 5 cubic centimeters per second, and the liquid leaves the organ at the same rate. If the concentration of the drug in the entering liquid is 0.1 grams per cubic centimeter, and if x represents the amount of drug in the organ at any time t, then using the fact that the rate of change of the amount of the drug in the organ, dx/dt, equals the rate at which the drug enters minus the rate at which it leaves, we have

$$\frac{dx}{dt} = \left(\frac{5\ \text{cc}}{\text{s}}\right)\left(\frac{0.1\ \text{g}}{\text{cc}}\right) - \left(\frac{5\ \text{cc}}{\text{s}}\right)\left(\frac{x\ \text{g}}{300\ \text{cc}}\right)$$

or

$$\frac{dx}{dt} = 0.5 - \frac{x}{60} = \frac{30}{60} - \frac{x}{60} = \frac{30 - x}{60}, \quad \text{in grams per second}$$

Find the amount of the drug in the organ as a function of time t.

Solution

Multiplying both sides of the equation $\dfrac{dx}{dt} = \dfrac{30 - x}{60}$ by $\dfrac{dt}{(30 - x)}$ gives

$$\frac{dx}{30 - x} = \frac{1}{60}\,dt$$

The equation is now separated, so we can integrate both sides.

$$\int \frac{dx}{30 - x} = \int \frac{1}{60}\,dt$$

$$-\ln(30 - x) = \frac{1}{60}t + C_1 \quad (30 - x > 0)$$

$$\ln(30 - x) = -\frac{1}{60}t - C_1$$

Rewriting this in exponential form gives

$$30 - x = e^{-t/60 - C_1} = e^{-t/60} \cdot e^{-C_1}$$

Letting $C = e^{-C_1}$ yields

$$30 - x = Ce^{-t/60}$$

so

$$x = 30 - Ce^{-t/60}$$

and we have the desired function.

CHECKPOINT SOLUTIONS

1. (a) $f(x) = \displaystyle\int\left(2x - \frac{1}{x + 1}\right)dx = x^2 - \ln|x + 1| + C$

    (b) If $f(0) = 4$, then $4 = 0^2 - \ln|1| + C$, so $C = 4$.
    Thus $f(x) = x^2 - \ln|x + 1| + 4$ is the particular solution.

2. (a) True, and the solution is

$$\int y\,dy = \int x\,dx \quad \Rightarrow \quad \frac{y^2}{2} = \frac{x^2}{2} + C$$

    (b) True

    (c) False. It separates as $dy/y^2 = -2x\,dx$, and the solution is

$$\int \frac{-dy}{y^2} = \int 2x\,dx \quad \Rightarrow \quad y^{-1} = x^2 + C$$

$$\frac{1}{y} = x^2 + C$$

$$y = \frac{1}{x^2 + C}$$

3. (a) $x(y + 1)\dfrac{dy}{dx} = (x^2 + 1)y$

$\dfrac{y + 1}{y}\,dy = \dfrac{x^2 + 1}{x}\,dx$

$\left(1 + \dfrac{1}{y}\right)dy = \left(x + \dfrac{1}{x}\right)dx$

(b) $\displaystyle\int\left(1 + \dfrac{1}{y}\right)dy = \int\left(x + \dfrac{1}{x}\right)dx$

$y + \ln|y| = \dfrac{x^2}{2} + \ln|x| + C$

This is the general solution.

| EXERCISES | 12.5

In Problems 1–4, show that the given function is a solution to the differential equation.

1. $y = x^2$;　　　　$4y - 2xy' = 0$
2. $y = x^3$;　　　　$3y - xy' = 0$
3. $y = 3x^2 + 1$;　$2y\,dx - x\,dy = 2\,dx$
4. $y = 4x^3 + 2$;　$3y\,dx - x\,dy = 6\,dx$

In Problems 5–10, use integration to find the general solution to each differential equation.

5. $dy = xe^{x^2+1}\,dx$
6. $dy = x^2 e^{x^3-1}\,dx$
7. $2y\,dy = 4x\,dx$
8. $4y\,dy = 4x^3\,dx$
9. $3y^2\,dy = (2x - 1)\,dx$
10. $4y^3\,dy = (3x^2 + 2x)\,dx$

In Problems 11–14, find the particular solution.

11. $y' = e^{x-3}$;　　　　　　$y(0) = 2$
12. $y' = e^{2x+1}$;　　　　　$y(0) = e$
13. $dy = \left(\dfrac{1}{x} - x\right)dx$;　　$y(1) = 0$
14. $dy = \left(x^2 - \dfrac{1}{x + 1}\right)dx$;　$y(0) = \dfrac{1}{3}$

In Problems 15–28, find the general solution to the given differential equation.

15. $\dfrac{dy}{dx} = \dfrac{x^2}{y}$
16. $y^3\,dx = \dfrac{dy}{x^3}$
17. $dx = x^3 y\,dy$
18. $dy = x^2 y^3\,dx$
19. $dx = (x^2 y^2 + x^2)\,dy$
20. $dy = (x^2 y^3 + xy^3)\,dx$
21. $y^2\,dx = x\,dy$
22. $y\,dx = x\,dy$
23. $\dfrac{dy}{dx} = \dfrac{x}{y}$
24. $\dfrac{dy}{dx} = \dfrac{x^2 + x}{y + 1}$
25. $(x + 1)\dfrac{dy}{dx} = y$
26. $x^2 y\dfrac{dy}{dx} = y^2 + 1$
27. $(x^2 + 2)e^y\,dx = xy\,dy$
28. $e^{4x}(y + 1)\,dx + e^{2x}y\,dy = 0$

In Problems 29–36, find the particular solution to each differential equation.

29. $\dfrac{dy}{dx} = \dfrac{x^2}{y^3}$　when $x = 1$, $y = 1$

30. $\dfrac{dy}{dx} = \dfrac{x + 1}{xy}$　when $x = 1$, $y = 3$
31. $2y^2\,dx = 3x^2\,dy$　when $x = 2$, $y = -1$
32. $(x + 1)\,dy = y^2\,dx$　when $x = 0$, $y = 2$
33. $x^2 e^{2y}\,dy = (x^3 + 1)\,dx$　when $x = 1$, $y = 0$
34. $y' = \dfrac{1}{xy}$　when $x = 1$, $y = 3$
35. $2xy\dfrac{dy}{dx} = y^2 + 1$　when $x = 1$, $y = 2$
36. $xe^y\,dx = (x + 1)\,dy$　when $x = 0$, $y = 0$

APPLICATIONS

37. ***Allometric growth*** If x and y are measurements of certain parts of an organism, then the rate of change of y with respect to x is proportional to the ratio of y to x. That is, these measurements satisfy

$$\dfrac{dy}{dx} = k\dfrac{y}{x}$$

which is referred to as an allometric law of growth. Solve this differential equation.

38. ***Bimolecular chemical reactions*** A bimolecular chemical reaction is one in which two chemicals react to form another substance. Suppose that one molecule of each of the two chemicals reacts to form two molecules of a new substance. If x represents the number of molecules of the new substance at time t, then the rate of change of x is proportional to the product of the numbers of molecules of the original chemicals available to be converted. That is, if each of the chemicals initially contained A molecules, then

$$\dfrac{dx}{dt} = k(A - x)^2$$

If 40% of the initial amount A is converted after 1 hour, how long will it be before 90% is converted?

Compound interest **In Problems 39 and 40, use the following information.**

When interest is compounded continuously, the rate of change of the amount x of the investment is proportional to the amount present. In this case, the proportionality constant is the annual interest rate r (as a decimal); that is,

$$\frac{dx}{dt} = rx$$

39. (a) If $10,000 is invested at 6%, compounded continuously, find an equation for the future value of the investment as a function of time t in years.
    (b) What is the future value of the investment after 1 year? After 5 years?
    (c) How long will it take for the investment to double?

40. (a) If $2000 is invested at 8%, compounded continuously, find an equation for the future value of the investment as a function of time t, in years.
    (b) How long will it take for the investment to double?
    (c) What will be the future value of this investment after 35 years?

41. *Investing* When the interest on an investment is compounded continuously, the investment grows at a rate that is proportional to the amount in the account, so that if the amount present is P, then

$$\frac{dP}{dt} = kP$$

where P is in dollars, t is in years, and k is a constant. If $100,000 is invested (when $t = 0$) and the amount in the account after 15 years is $211,700, find the function that gives the value of the investment as a function of t. What is the interest rate on this investment?

42. *Investing* When the interest on an investment is compounded continuously, the investment grows at a rate that is proportional to the amount in the account. If $20,000 is invested (when $t = 0$) and the amount in the account after 22 years is $280,264, find the function that gives the value of the investment as a function of t. What is the interest rate on this investment?

43. *Bacterial growth* Suppose that the growth of a certain population of bacteria satisfies

$$\frac{dy}{dt} = ky$$

where y is the number of organisms and t is the number of hours. If initially there are 10,000 organisms and the number triples after 2 hours, how long will it be before the population reaches 100 times the original population?

44. *Bacterial growth* Suppose that, for a certain population of bacteria, growth occurs according to

$$\frac{dy}{dt} = ky \quad (t \text{ in hours})$$

If the doubling rate depends on temperature, find how long it takes for the number of bacteria to reach 50 times the original number at each given temperature in parts (a) and (b).

(a) At 90°F, the number doubles after 30 minutes ($\frac{1}{2}$ hour).
(b) At 40°F, the number doubles after 3 hours.

45. *Sales and pricing* Suppose that in a certain company, the relationship between the price per unit p of its product and the weekly sales volume y, in thousands of dollars, is given by

$$\frac{dy}{dp} = -\frac{2}{5}\left(\frac{y}{p + 8}\right)$$

Solve this differential equation if $y = 8$ when $p = 24.

46. *Sales and pricing* Suppose that a chain of auto service stations, Quick-Oil, Inc., has found that the relationship between its price p for an oil change and its monthly sales volume y, in thousands of dollars, is

$$\frac{dy}{dp} = -\frac{1}{2}\left(\frac{y}{p + 5}\right)$$

Solve this differential equation if $y = 18$ when $p = 20.

47. *Half-life* A breeder reactor converts uranium-238 into an isotope of plutonium-239 at a rate proportional to the amount present at any time. After 10 years, 0.03% of the radioactivity has dissipated (that is, 0.9997 of the initial amount remains). Suppose that initially there is 100 pounds of this substance. Find the half-life.

48. *Radioactive decay* A certain radioactive substance has a half-life of 50 hours. Find how long it will take for 90% of the radioactivity to be dissipated if the amount of material x satisfies

$$\frac{dx}{dt} = kx \quad (t \text{ in hours})$$

49. *Drug in an organ* Suppose that a liquid carries a drug into a 100-cc organ at a rate of 5 cc/s and leaves the organ at the same rate. Suppose that the concentration of the drug entering is 0.06 g/cc. If initially there is no drug in the organ, find the amount of drug in the organ as a function of time t.

50. *Drug in an organ* Suppose that a liquid carries a drug into a 250-cc organ at a rate of 10 cc/s and leaves the organ at the same rate. Suppose that the concentration of the drug entering is 0.15 g/cc. Find the amount of drug in the organ as a function of time t if initially there is none in the organ.

51. *Drug in an organ* Suppose that a liquid carries a drug with concentration 0.1 g/cc into a 200-cc organ at a rate of 5 cc/s and leaves the organ at the same rate. If initially there is 10 g of the drug in the organ, find the amount of drug in the organ as a function of time t.

52. *Drug in an organ* Suppose that a liquid carries a drug with concentration 0.05 g/cc into a 150-cc organ at a rate of 6 cc/s and leaves at the same rate. If initially there is 1.5 g of drug in the organ, find the amount of drug in the organ as a function of time t.

53. **Tumor volume** Let V denote the volume of a tumor, and suppose that the growth rate of the tumor satisfies

$$\frac{dV}{dt} = 0.2Ve^{-0.1t}$$

If the initial volume of the tumor is 1.86 units, find an equation for V as a function of t.

54. **Gompertz curves** The differential equation

$$\frac{dx}{dt} = x(a - b \ln x)$$

where x represents the number of objects at time t, and a and b are constants, is the model for Gompertz curves. Recall from Section 5.3, "Solutions of Exponential Equations," that Gompertz curves can be used to study growth or decline of populations, organizations, and revenue from sales of a product, as well as forecast equipment maintenance costs. Solve the differential equation to obtain the Gompertz curve formula

$$x = e^{a/b}e^{-ce^{-bt}}$$

55. **Cell growth** If V is the volume of a spherical cell, then in certain cell growth and for some fetal growth models, the rate of change of V is given by

$$\frac{dV}{dt} = kV^{2/3}$$

where k is a constant depending on the organism. If $V = 0$ when $t = 0$, find V as a function of t.

56. **Atmospheric pressure** The rate of change of atmospheric pressure P with respect to the altitude above sea level h is proportional to the pressure. That is,

$$\frac{dP}{dh} = kP$$

Suppose that the pressure at sea level is denoted by P_0, and at 18,000 ft the pressure is half what it is at sea level. Find the pressure, as a percent of P_0, at 25,000 ft.

57. **Newton's law of cooling** Newton's law of cooling (and warming) states that the rate of change of temperature $u = u(t)$ of an object is proportional to the temperature difference between the object and its surroundings, where T is the constant temperature of the surroundings. That is,

$$\frac{du}{dt} = k(u - T)$$

Suppose an object at $0°C$ is placed in a room where the temperature is $20°C$. If the temperature of the object is $8°C$ after 1 hour, how long will it take for the object to reach $18°C$?

58. **Newton's law of cooling** Newton's law of cooling can be used to estimate time of death. (Actually the estimate may be quite rough, because cooling does not begin until metabolic processes have ceased.) Suppose a corpse is discovered at noon in a $70°F$ room, and at that time the body temperature is $96.1°F$. If at 1:00 P.M. the body temperature is $94.6°F$, use Newton's law of cooling to estimate the time of death.

59. **Fossil-fuel emissions** The amount of carbon in the atmosphere has been estimated to have increased at a rate of about 3.09% per year since 1850. This increase is due to carbon emissions from fossil-fuel burning and can be modeled by the differential equation

$$\frac{dE}{dt} = 0.0309E$$

where t is the number of years since 1850 and E is fossil-fuel emissions in millions of metric tons per year.

(a) Solve this differential equation, and find a particular solution that satisfies $E(0) = 85.53$.

(b) The graph shows actual CO_2 emissions since 1815. Graph your solution and compare it with the graph below for the years since 1850.

Source: New York Times, September 14, 2004. Copyright © 2004 The New York Times Co. Reprinted with permission.

60. **Gross domestic product** With Social Security Administration data from 1995 and projected to 2070, the billions of dollars G of gross domestic product (GDP) can be modeled by

$$\frac{dG}{dt} = 0.05317G, \quad G(15) = 12{,}145$$

where t is the number of years past 1990 (and thus $G(15)$ is the GDP in 2005).

(a) Find the particular solution to this differential equation.

(b) The Social Security Administration's forecast for the 2020 GDP is $27,683 billion. What does the model predict for the 2020 GDP?

61. **Impact of inflation** The impact of a 5% inflation rate on an $80,000-per-year pension can be severe. If P represents the purchasing power (in dollars) of an $80,000 pension, then the effect of a 5% inflation rate can be modeled by the differential equation

$$\frac{dP}{dt} = -0.05P, \quad P(0) = 80{,}000$$

where t is in years.

(a) Find the particular solution to this differential equation.

(b) Find the purchasing power after 15 years.

62. ***Students per computer*** The table shows the average number of students per computer in public schools for selected school years from 1985–1986 to 2005–2006. If S represents the students per computer, then the rate of change of these data can be modeled by the differential equation

$$\frac{dS}{dt} = -0.12935S, \quad S(7) = 18$$

where t is the number of school years past the 1984–1985 school year.

(a) Find the particular solution to this differential equation.

(b) Check the model you found in part (a) against the data in the table. Is the model more accurate for the school data near 1985–1986 or near 2001–2002?

Year	Students per Computer
'85–'86	50
'87–'88	32
'89–'90	22
'91–'92	18
'93–'94	14
'95–'96	10
'97–'98	6.1
'99–'00	5.4
'01–'02	4.9
'03–'04	4.4
'05–'06	3.9

Source: Quality Education Data, Inc., Denver, CO. Reprinted by permission.

KEY TERMS AND FORMULAS

Section	Key Terms	Formulas
12.1	General antiderivative of $f'(x)$	$f(x) + C$
	Integral	$\int f(x)\, dx$
	Powers of x Formula	$\int x^n\, dx = \dfrac{x^{n+1}}{n+1} + C \ (n \neq -1)$
	Integration Formulas	$\int dx = x + C$
		$\int cu(x)\, dx = c\int u(x)\, dx \ (c = \text{a constant})$
		$\int [u(x) \pm v(x)]\, dx = \int u(x)\, dx \pm \int v(x)\, dx$
12.2	Power Rule	$\int [u(x)]^n\, u'(x)\, dx = \dfrac{[u(x)]^{n+1}}{n+1} + C \ (n \neq -1)$
12.3	Exponential Formula	$\int e^u u'\, dx = \int e^u\, du = e^u + C$
	Logarithmic Formula	$\int \dfrac{u'}{u}\, dx = \int \dfrac{1}{u}\, du = \ln |u| + C$

Section	Key Terms	Formulas
12.4	Total cost	$C(x) = \int \overline{MC} \, dx$
	Total revenue	$R(x) = \int \overline{MR} \, dx$
	Profit	
	Marginal propensity to consume	$\dfrac{dC}{dy}$
	Marginal propensity to save	$\dfrac{dS}{dy} = 1 - \dfrac{dC}{dy}$
	National consumption	$C = \int f'(y) \, dy = \int \dfrac{dC}{dy} \, dy$

12.5	Differential equations
	    Solutions
	        General
	        Particular	

	First order	$\dfrac{dy}{dx} = f(x) \Rightarrow y = \int f(x) \, dx$
	Separable	$g(y) \, dy = f(x) \, dx \Rightarrow \int g(y) \, dy = \int f(x) \, dx$
	Radioactive decay	$\dfrac{dy}{dt} = ky$
	Drug in an organ	Rate = (rate in) − (rate out)

REVIEW EXERCISES

Evaluate the integrals in Problems 1–26.

1. $\int x^6 \, dx$

2. $\int x^{1/2} \, dx$

3. $\int (12x^3 - 3x^2 + 4x + 5) \, dx$

4. $\int 7(x^2 - 1)^2 \, dx$

5. $\int 7x(x^2 - 1)^2 \, dx$

6. $\int (x^3 - 3x^2)^5 (x^2 - 2x) \, dx$

7. $\int (x^3 + 4)^2 3x \, dx$

8. $\int 5x^2(3x^3 + 7)^6 \, dx$

9. $\int \dfrac{x^2}{x^3 + 1} \, dx$

10. $\int \dfrac{x^2}{(x^3 + 1)^2} \, dx$

11. $\int \dfrac{x^2 \, dx}{\sqrt[3]{x^3 - 4}}$

12. $\int \dfrac{x^2 \, dx}{x^3 - 4}$

13. $\int \dfrac{x^3 + 1}{x^2} \, dx$

14. $\int \dfrac{x^3 - 3x + 1}{x - 1} \, dx$

15. $\int y^2 e^{y^3} \, dy$

16. $\int (3x - 1)^{12} \, dx$

17. $\int \dfrac{3x^2}{2x^3 - 7} \, dx$

18. $\int \dfrac{5 \, dx}{e^{4x}}$

19. $\int (x^3 - e^{3x}) \, dx$

20. $\int xe^{1 + x^2} \, dx$

21. $\int \dfrac{6x^7}{(5x^8 + 7)^3} \, dx$

22. $\int \dfrac{7x^3}{\sqrt{1 - x^4}} \, dx$

23. $\int \left(\dfrac{e^{2x}}{2} + \dfrac{2}{e^{2x}} \right) dx$

24. $\int \left[x - \dfrac{1}{(x + 1)^2} \right] dx$

25. (a) $\int (x^2 - 1)^4 x \, dx$ (b) $\int (x^2 - 1)^{10} x \, dx$

    (c) $\int (x^2 - 1)^7 3x \, dx$ (d) $\int (x^2 - 1)^{-2/3} x \, dx$

26. (a) $\int \dfrac{2x \, dx}{x^2 - 1}$ (b) $\int \dfrac{2x \, dx}{(x^2 - 1)^2}$

    (c) $\int \dfrac{3x \, dx}{\sqrt{x^2 - 1}}$ (d) $\int \dfrac{3x \, dx}{x^2 - 1}$

In Problems 27–32, find the general solution to each differential equation.

27. $\dfrac{dy}{dt} = 4.6e^{-0.05t}$

28. $dy = (64 + 76x - 36x^2) \, dx$

29. $\dfrac{dy}{dx} = \dfrac{4x}{y - 3}$

30. $t \, dy = \dfrac{dt}{y + 1}$

31. $\dfrac{dy}{dx} = \dfrac{x}{e^y}$

32. $\dfrac{dy}{dt} = \dfrac{4y}{t}$

In Problems 33 and 34, find the particular solution to each differential equation.

33. $y' = \dfrac{x^2}{y + 1}, \quad y(0) = 4$

34. $y' = \dfrac{2x}{1 + 2y}, \quad y(2) = 0$

APPLICATIONS

35. *Revenue* If the marginal revenue for a month for a product is $\overline{MR} = 0.06x + 12$ dollars per unit, find the total revenue from the sale of $x = 800$ units of the product.

36. *Productivity* Suppose that the rate of change of production of the average worker at a factory is given by

$$\frac{dp}{dt} = 27 + 24t - 3t^2, \quad 0 \le t \le 8$$

where p is the number of units the worker produces in t hours. How many units will the average worker produce in an 8-hour shift? (Assume that $p = 0$ when $t = 0$.)

37. *Oxygen levels in water* The rate of change of the oxygen level (in mmol/l) per month in a body of water after an oil spill is given by

$$P'(t) = 400 \left[\frac{5}{(t+5)^2} - \frac{50}{(t+5)^3} \right]$$

where t is the number of months after the spill. What function gives the oxygen level P at any time t if $P = 400$ mmol/l when $t = 0$?

38. *Bacterial growth* A population of bacteria grows at the rate

$$\frac{dp}{dt} = \frac{100{,}000}{(t+100)^2}$$

where p is the population and t is time. If the population is 1000 when $t = 1$, write the equation that gives the size of the population at any time t.

39. *Market share* The rate of change of the market share (as a percent) a firm expects for a new product is

$$\frac{dy}{dt} = 2.4e^{-0.04t}$$

where t is the number of months after the product is introduced.
   (a) Write the equation that gives the expected market share y at any time t. (Note that $y = 0$ when $t = 0$.)
   (b) What market share does the firm expect after 1 year?

40. *Revenue* If the marginal revenue for a product is

$$\overline{MR} = \frac{800}{x+2},$$ find the total revenue function.

41. *Cost* The marginal cost for a product is $\overline{MC} = 6x + 4$ dollars per unit, and the cost of producing 100 items is $31,400.
   (a) Find the fixed costs.
   (b) Find the total cost function.

42. *Profit* Suppose a product has a daily marginal revenue $\overline{MR} = 46$ and a daily marginal cost $\overline{MC} = 30 + \frac{1}{5}x$, both in dollars per unit. If the daily fixed cost is $200, how many units will give maximum profit and what is the maximum profit?

43. *National consumption* If consumption is $8.5 billion when disposable income is $0, and if the marginal propensity to consume is

$$\frac{dC}{dy} = \frac{1}{\sqrt{2y+16}} + 0.6 \quad \text{(in billions of dollars)}$$

find the national consumption function.

44. *National consumption* Suppose that the marginal propensity to save is

$$\frac{dS}{dy} = 0.2 - 0.1e^{-2y} \quad \text{(in billions of dollars)}$$

and consumption is $7.8 billion when disposable income is $0. Find the national consumption function.

45. *Allometric growth* For many species of fish, the length L and weight W of a fish are related by

$$\frac{dW}{dL} = \frac{3W}{L}$$

The general solution to this differential equation expresses the allometric relationship between the length and weight of a fish. Find the general solution.

46. *Investment* When the interest on an investment is compounded continuously, the investment grows at a rate that is proportional to the amount in the account, so that if the amount present is P, then

$$\frac{dP}{dt} = kP$$

where P is in dollars, t is in years, and k is a constant.
   (a) Solve this differential equation to find the relationship.
   (b) Use properties of logarithms and exponential functions to write P as a function of t.
   (c) If $50,000 is invested (when $t = 0$) and the amount in the account after 10 years is $135,914, find the function that gives the value of the investment as a function of t.
   (d) In part (c), what does the value of k represent?

47. *Fossil dating* Radioactive beryllium is sometimes used to date fossils found in deep-sea sediment. The amount of radioactive material x satisfies

$$\frac{dx}{dt} = kx$$

Suppose that 10 units of beryllium are present in a living organism and that the half-life of beryllium is 4.6 million years. Find the age of a fossil if 20% of the original radioactivity is present when the fossil is discovered.

48. *Drug in an organ* Suppose that a liquid carries a drug into a 120-cc organ at a rate of 4 cc/s and leaves the organ at the same rate. If initially there is no drug in the organ and if the concentration of drug in the liquid is 3 g/cc, find the amount of drug in the organ as a function of time.

49. *Chemical mixture* A 300-gal tank initially contains a solution with 100 lb of a chemical. A mixture containing 2 lb/gal of the chemical enters the tank at 3 gal/min, and the well-stirred mixture leaves at the same rate. Find an equation that gives the amount of the chemical in the tank as a function of time. How long will it be before there is 500 lb of chemical in the tank?

12 CHAPTER TEST

Evaluate the integrals in Problems 1–8.

1. $\int (6x^2 + 8x - 7)\, dx$

2. $\int \left(4 + \sqrt{x} - \dfrac{1}{x^2}\right) dx$

3. $\int 5x^2(4x^3 - 7)^9\, dx$

4. $\int (3x^2 - 6x + 1)^{-3}(2x - 2)\, dx$

5. $\int \dfrac{s^3}{2s^4 - 5}\, ds$

6. $\int 100e^{-0.01x}\, dx$

7. $\int 5y^3 e^{2y^4 - 1}\, dy$

8. $\int \left(e^x + \dfrac{5}{x} - 1\right) dx$

9. Evaluate $\int \dfrac{x^2}{x + 1}\, dx$. Use long division.

10. If $\int f(x)\, dx = 2x^3 - x + 5e^x + C$, find $f(x)$.

In Problems 11 and 12, find the particular solution to each differential equation.

11. $y' = 4x^3 + 3x^2$, if $y(0) = 4$

12. $\dfrac{dy}{dx} = e^{4x}$, if $y(0) = 2$

13. Find the general solution of the separable differential equation $\dfrac{dy}{dx} = x^3 y^2$.

14. Suppose the rate of growth of the population of a city is predicted to be

$$\frac{dp}{dt} = 2000t^{1.04}$$

where p is the population and t is the number of years past 2010. If the population in the year 2010 is 50,000, what is the predicted population in the year 2020?

15. Suppose that the marginal cost for x units of a product is $\overline{MC} = 4x + 50$, the marginal revenue is $\overline{MR} = 500$, and the cost of the production and sale of 10 units is $1000. What is the profit function for this product?

16. Suppose the marginal propensity to save is given by

$$\frac{dS}{dy} = 0.22 - \frac{0.25}{\sqrt{0.5y + 1}} \quad \text{(in billions of dollars)}$$

and national consumption is $6.6 billion when disposable income is $0. Find the national consumption function.

17. A certain radioactive material has a half-life of 100 days. If the amount of material present, x, satisfies $\dfrac{dx}{dt} = kx$, where t is in days, how long will it take for 90% of the radioactivity to dissipate?

18. Suppose that a liquid carries a drug with concentration 0.1 g/cc into a 160-cc organ at the rate of 4 cc/sec, and leaves at the same rate. Find the amount of drug in the organ as a function of time t, if initially there is none in the organ.

I. Employee Production Rate

The manager of a plant has been instructed to hire and train additional employees to manufacture a new product. She must hire a sufficient number of new employees so that within 30 days they will be producing 2500 units of the product each day.

Because a new employee must learn an assigned task, production will increase with training. Suppose that research on similar projects indicates that production increases with training according to the learning curve, so that for the average employee, the rate of production per day is given by

$$\frac{dN}{dt} = be^{-at}$$

where N is the number of units produced per day after t days of training and a and b are constants that depend on the project. Because of experience with a similar project, the manager expects the rate for this project to be

$$\frac{dN}{dt} = 2.5e^{-0.05t}$$

The manager tested her training program with 5 employees and learned that the average employee could produce 11 units per day after 5 days of training. On the basis of this information, she must decide how many employees to hire and begin to train so that a month from now they will be producing 2500 units of the product per day. She estimates that it will take her 10 days to hire the employees, and thus she will have 15 days remaining to train them. She also expects a 10% attrition rate during this period.

How many employees would you advise the plant manager to hire? Check your advice by answering the following questions.

1. Use the expected rate of production and the results of the manager's test to find the function relating N and t—that is, $N = N(t)$.
2. Find the number of units the average employee can produce after 15 days of training. How many such employees would be needed to maintain a production rate of 2500 units per day?
3. Explain how you would revise this last result to account for the expected 10% attrition rate. How many new employees should the manager hire?

II. Supply and Demand

If p is the price in dollars of a given commodity at time t, then we can think of price as a function of time. Similarly, the number of units demanded by consumers q_d at any time, and the number of units supplied by producers q_s at any time, may also be considered as functions of time as well as functions of price.

Both the quantity demanded and the quantity supplied depend not only on the price at the time, but also on the direction and rate of change that consumers and producers ascribe to prices. For example, even when prices are high, if consumers feel that prices are rising, the demand may rise. Similarly, if prices are low but producers feel they may go lower, the supply may rise.

If we assume that prices are determined in the marketplace by supply and demand, then the equilibrium price is the one we seek.

Suppose the supply and demand functions for a certain commodity in a competitive market are given, in hundreds of units, by

$$q_s = 30 + p + 5\frac{dp}{dt}$$
$$q_d = 51 - 2p + 4\frac{dp}{dt}$$

where dp/dt denotes the rate of change of the price with respect to time. If, at $t = 0$, the market equilibrium price is \$12, we can express the market equilibrium price as a function of time.

Our goals are as follows.

A. To express the market equilibrium price as a function of time.
B. To determine whether there is price stability in the marketplace for this item (that is, to determine whether the equilibrium price approaches a constant over time).

To achieve these goals, do the following.

1. Set the expressions for q_s and q_d equal to each other.
2. Solve this equation for $\dfrac{dp}{dt}$.
3. Write this equation in the form $f(p)\, dp = g(t)\, dt$.
4. Integrate both sides of this separated differential equation.
5. Solve the resulting equation for p in terms of t.
6. Use the fact that $p = 12$ when $t = 0$ to find C, the constant of integration, and write the market equilibrium price p as a function of time t.
7. Find $\lim\limits_{t \to \infty} p$, which gives the price we can expect this product to approach. If this limit is finite, then for this item there is price stability in the marketplace. If $p \to +\infty$ as $t \to +\infty$, then price will continue to increase until economic conditions change.

13 CHAPTER

Gerald Bernard/Shutterstock.com

Definite Integrals: Techniques of Integration

We saw some applications of the indefinite integral in Chapter 12. In this chapter we define the definite integral and discuss a theorem and techniques that are useful in evaluating or approximating it. We will also see how it can be used in many interesting applications, such as consumer's and producer's surplus and total value, present value, and future value of continuous income streams. Improper integrals can be used to find the capital value of a continuous income stream.

The topics and applications discussed in this chapter include the following.

SECTIONS	APPLICATIONS
13.1 Area Under a Curve	Ore production, healthcare expenses
13.2 The Definite Integral: The Fundamental Theorem of Calculus	Income streams, product life
13.3 Area Between Two Curves	Gini coefficient of income, average cost
13.4 Applications of Definite Integrals in Business and Economics	Continuous income streams, consumer's surplus, producer's surplus
13.5 Using Tables of Integrals	Telecommunications revenue, cost
13.6 Integration by Parts	Equipment present value, world tourism
13.7 Improper Integrals and Their Applications	Capital value, probability density functions
13.8 Numerical Integration Methods: The Trapezoidal Rule and Simpson's Rule	Pharmaceutical testing, income distributions

Prerequisite Problem Type	For Section	Answer	Section for Review
Simplify: $\dfrac{1}{n^3}\left[\dfrac{n(n+1)(2n+1)}{6} - \dfrac{2n(n+1)}{2} + n\right]$	**13.1**	$\dfrac{2n^2 - 3n + 1}{6n^2}$	0.7 Fractions
(a) If $F(x) = \dfrac{x^4}{4} + 4x + C$, what is $F(4) - F(2)$? (b) If $F(x) = -\dfrac{1}{9}\ln\left(\dfrac{9 + \sqrt{81 - 9x^2}}{3x}\right)$ what is $F(3) - F(2)$?	**13.2** **13.5**	(a) 68 (b) $\dfrac{1}{9}\ln\left(\dfrac{3 + \sqrt{5}}{2}\right)$	1.2 Function notation
Find the limit: (a) $\lim\limits_{n \to +\infty} \dfrac{n^2 + n}{2n^2}$ (b) $\lim\limits_{n \to +\infty} \dfrac{2n^2 - 3n + 1}{6n^2}$ (c) $\lim\limits_{b \to \infty} \left(1 - \dfrac{1}{b}\right)$ (d) $\lim\limits_{b \to \infty} \left(\dfrac{-100{,}000}{e^{0.10b}} + 100{,}000\right)$	**13.1** **13.7**	(a) $\frac{1}{2}$ (b) $\frac{1}{3}$ (c) 1 (d) 100,000	9.2 Limits at infinity
Find the derivative of $y = \ln x$.	**13.6**	$\dfrac{1}{x}$	11.1 Derivatives of logarithmic functions
Integrate: (a) $\int (x^3 + 4)\,dx$ (b) $\int x\sqrt{x^2 - 9}\,dx$ (c) $\int e^{2x}\,dx$	**13.2–13.7**	(a) $\dfrac{x^4}{4} + 4x + C$ (b) $\frac{1}{3}(x^2 - 9)^{3/2} + C$ (c) $\frac{1}{2}e^{2x} + C$	12.1, 12.2, 12.3 Integration

OBJECTIVES

13.1

- To use the sum of areas of rectangles to approximate the area under a curve
- To use Σ notation to denote sums
- To find the exact area under a curve

Area Under a Curve

■ | APPLICATION PREVIEW |

One way to find the accumulated production (such as the production of ore from a mine) over a period of time is to graph the rate of production as a function of time and find the area under the resulting curve over a specified time interval. For example, if a coal mine produces at a rate of 30 tons per day, the production over 10 days $(30 \cdot 10 = 300)$ could be represented by the area under the line $y = 30$ between $x = 0$ and $x = 10$ (see Figure 13.1).

Using area to determine the accumulated production is very useful when the rate-of-production function varies at different points in time. For example, if the rate of production (in tons per day) is represented by

$$y = 100e^{-0.1x}$$

where x represents the number of days, then the area under the curve (and above the x-axis) from $x = 0$ to $x = 10$ represents the total production over the 10-day period (see Figure 13.2(a) and Example 1). In order to determine the accumulated production and to solve other types of problems, we need a method for finding areas under curves. That is the goal of this section.

Figure 13.1

Area Under a Curve To estimate the accumulated production for the example in the Application Preview, we approximate the area under the graph of the production rate function. We can find a rough approximation of the area under this curve by fitting two rectangles to the curve as shown in Figure 13.2(b). The area of the first rectangle is $5 \cdot 100 = 500$ square units, and the area of the second rectangle is $(10 - 5)[100e^{-0.1(5)}] \approx 5(60.65) = 303.25$ square units, so this rough approximation is 803.25 square units or 803.25 tons of ore. This approximation is clearly larger than the exact area under the curve. Why?

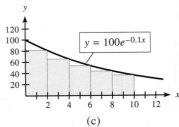

Figure 13.2   (a)   (b)   (c)

EXAMPLE   1   Ore Production | Application Preview |

Find another, more accurate approximation of the tons of ore produced by approximating the area under the curve in Figure 13.2(a). Fit five rectangles with equal bases inside the area under the curve $y = 100e^{-0.1x}$, and use them to approximate the area under the curve from $x = 0$ to $x = 10$ (see Figure 13.2(c)).

Solution

Each of the five rectangles has base 2, and the height of each rectangle is the value of the function at the right-hand endpoint of the interval forming its base. Thus the areas of the rectangles are as follows.

Rectangle	Base	Height	Area = Base × Height
1	2	$100e^{-0.1(2)} \approx 81.87$	$2(81.87) = 163.74$
2	2	$100e^{-0.1(4)} \approx 67.03$	$2(67.03) = 134.06$
3	2	$100e^{-0.1(6)} \approx 54.88$	$2(54.88) = 109.76$
4	2	$100e^{-0.1(8)} \approx 44.93$	$2(44.93) = 89.86$
5	2	$100e^{-0.1(10)} \approx 36.79$	$2(36.79) = 73.58$

The area under the curve is approximately equal to

$$163.74 + 134.06 + 109.76 + 89.86 + 73.58 = 571$$

so approximately 571 tons of ore are produced in the 10-day period. The area is actually 632.12, to 2 decimal places (or 632.12 tons of ore), so the approximation 571 is smaller than the actual area but is much better than the one we obtained with just two rectangles. In general, if we use bases of equal width, the approximation of the area under a curve improves when more rectangles are used.

Suppose that we wish to find the area between the curve $y = 2x$ and the x-axis from $x = 0$ to $x = 1$ (see Figure 13.3). As we saw in Example 1, one way to approximate this area is to use the areas of rectangles whose bases are on the x-axis and whose heights are the vertical distances from points on their bases to the curve. We can divide the interval $[0, 1]$ into n equal subintervals and use them as the bases of n rectangles whose heights are determined by the curve (see Figure 13.4). The width of each of these rectangles is $1/n$. Using the function value at the right-hand endpoint of each subinterval as the height of the rectangle, we get n rectangles as shown in Figure 13.4. Because part of each rectangle lies above the curve, the sum of the areas of the rectangles will overestimate the area.

Figure 13.3

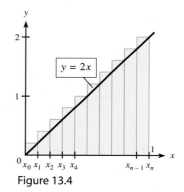

Figure 13.4

Then, with $y = f(x) = 2x$ and subinterval width $1/n$, the areas of the rectangles are as shown in the following table.

Rectangle	Base	Right Endpoint	Height	Area = Base × Height
1	$\dfrac{1}{n}$	$x_1 = \dfrac{1}{n}$	$f(x_1) = 2\left(\dfrac{1}{n}\right)$	$\dfrac{1}{n} \cdot \dfrac{2}{n} = \dfrac{2}{n^2}$
2	$\dfrac{1}{n}$	$x_2 = \dfrac{2}{n}$	$f(x_2) = 2\left(\dfrac{2}{n}\right)$	$\dfrac{1}{n} \cdot \dfrac{4}{n} = \dfrac{4}{n^2}$
3	$\dfrac{1}{n}$	$x_3 = \dfrac{3}{n}$	$f(x_3) = 2\left(\dfrac{3}{n}\right)$	$\dfrac{1}{n} \cdot \dfrac{6}{n} = \dfrac{6}{n^2}$
⋮				
i	$\dfrac{1}{n}$	$x_i = \dfrac{i}{n}$	$f(x_i) = 2\left(\dfrac{i}{n}\right)$	$\dfrac{1}{n} \cdot \dfrac{2i}{n} = \dfrac{2i}{n^2}$
⋮				
n	$\dfrac{1}{n}$	$x_n = \dfrac{n}{n}$	$f(x_n) = 2\left(\dfrac{n}{n}\right)$	$\dfrac{1}{n} \cdot \dfrac{2n}{n} = \dfrac{2n}{n^2}$

Note that $2i/n^2$ gives the area of the ith rectangle for *any* value of i. Thus for any value of n, this area can be approximated by the sum

$$A \approx \frac{2}{n^2} + \frac{4}{n^2} + \frac{6}{n^2} + \cdots + \frac{2i}{n^2} + \cdots + \frac{2n}{n^2}$$

In particular, we have the following approximations of this area for specific values of n (the number of rectangles).

$$n = 5: \qquad A \approx \frac{2}{25} + \frac{4}{25} + \frac{6}{25} + \frac{8}{25} + \frac{10}{25} = \frac{30}{25} = 1.20$$

$$n = 10: \qquad A \approx \frac{2}{100} + \frac{4}{100} + \frac{6}{100} + \cdots + \frac{20}{100} = \frac{110}{100} = 1.10$$

$$n = 100: \qquad A \approx \frac{2}{10,000} + \frac{4}{10,000} + \frac{6}{10,000} + \cdots + \frac{200}{10,000}$$

$$= \frac{10,100}{10,000} = 1.01$$

Figure 13.5 shows the rectangles associated with each of these approximations ($n = 5, 10,$ and 100) to the area under $y = 2x$ from $x = 0$ to $x = 1$. For larger n, the rectangles closely approximate the area under the curve.

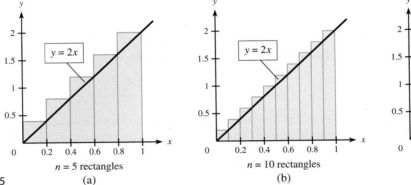

Figure 13.5   (a)   (b)   (c)

n = 5 rectangles   *n* = 10 rectangles   *n* = 100 rectangles

We can find this sum for any n more easily if we observe that the common denominator is n^2 and that the numerator is twice the sum of the first n terms of an arithmetic sequence with first term 1 and last term n. As you may recall from Section 6.1, "Simple Interest; Sequences," the first n terms of this arithmetic sequence add to $n(n + 1)/2$. Thus the area is approximated by

$$A \approx \frac{2(1 + 2 + 3 + \cdots + n)}{n^2} = \frac{2[n(n + 1)/2]}{n^2} = \frac{n + 1}{n}$$

Using this formula, we see the following.

$$n = 5: \qquad A \approx \frac{5 + 1}{5} = \frac{6}{5} = 1.20$$

$$n = 10: \qquad A \approx \frac{10 + 1}{10} = \frac{11}{10} = 1.10$$

$$n = 100: \qquad A \approx \frac{100 + 1}{100} = \frac{101}{100} = 1.01$$

As Figure 13.5 indicated, as n gets larger, the number of rectangles increases, the area of each rectangle decreases, and the approximation becomes more accurate. If we let n increase without bound, the approximation approaches the exact area.

$$A = \lim_{n \to +\infty} \frac{n + 1}{n} = \lim_{n \to +\infty} \left(1 + \frac{1}{n}\right) = 1$$

We can see that this area is correct, for we are computing the area of a triangle with base 1 and height 2. The formula for the area of a triangle gives

$$A = \frac{1}{2} bh = \frac{1}{2} \cdot 1 \cdot 2 = 1$$

Summation Notation   A special notation exists that uses the Greek letter Σ (capital sigma) to express the sum of numbers or expressions. (We used sigma notation informally in Chapter 8, "Further Topics in Probability; Data Description.") We may indicate the sum of the n numbers $a_1, a_2, a_3, a_4, \ldots, a_n$ by

$$\sum_{i=1}^{n} a_i = a_1 + a_2 + a_3 + \cdots + a_n$$

This may be read as "The sum of a_i as i goes from 1 to n." The subscript i in a_i is replaced first by 1, then by 2, then by 3, $\ldots$, until it reaches the value above the sigma. The i is called the **index of summation,** and it starts with the lower limit, 1, and ends with the upper limit, n. For example, if $x_1 = 2, x_2 = 3, x_3 = -1$, and $x_4 = -2$, then

$$\sum_{i=1}^{4} x_i = x_1 + x_2 + x_3 + x_4 = 2 + 3 + (-1) + (-2) = 2$$

The area of the triangle under $y = 2x$ that we discussed above was approximated by

$$A \approx \frac{2}{n^2} + \frac{4}{n^2} + \frac{6}{n^2} + \cdots + \frac{2i}{n^2} + \cdots + \frac{2n}{n^2}$$

Using **sigma notation,** we can write this sum as

$$A \approx \sum_{i=1}^{n} \left(\frac{2i}{n^2} \right)$$

Sigma notation allows us to represent the sums of the areas of the rectangles in an abbreviated fashion. Some formulas that simplify computations involving sums follow.

Sum Formulas

I. $\displaystyle\sum_{i=1}^{n} 1 = n$

II. $\displaystyle\sum_{i=1}^{n} cx_i = c \sum_{i=1}^{n} x_i$ $(c = \text{constant})$

III. $\displaystyle\sum_{i=1}^{n} (x_i + y_i) = \sum_{i=1}^{n} x_i + \sum_{i=1}^{n} y_i$

IV. $\displaystyle\sum_{i=1}^{n} i = \frac{n(n+1)}{2}$

V. $\displaystyle\sum_{i=1}^{n} i^2 = \frac{n(n+1)(2n+1)}{6}$

We have found that the area of the triangle discussed above was approximated by

$$A \approx \sum_{i=1}^{n} \frac{2i}{n^2}$$

We can use formulas II and IV to simplify this sum as follows.

$$\sum_{i=1}^{n} \frac{2i}{n^2} = \frac{2}{n^2} \sum_{i=1}^{n} i = \frac{2}{n^2} \left[\frac{n(n+1)}{2} \right] = \frac{n+1}{n}$$

Note that this is the same formula we obtained previously using other methods.

We can also use these sum formulas to evaluate a particular sum. For example,

$$\sum_{i=1}^{100}(2i^2 - 3) = \sum_{i=1}^{100}2i^2 - \sum_{i=1}^{100}3(1) \qquad \text{Formula III}$$

$$= 2\sum_{i=1}^{100}i^2 - 3\sum_{i=1}^{100}1 \qquad \text{Formula II}$$

$$= 2\left[\frac{100(101)(201)}{6}\right] - 3(100) \qquad \text{Formulas I and V with } n = 100$$

$$= 676{,}400$$

Areas and Summation Notation

The following example shows that we can find the area by evaluating the function at the left-hand endpoints of the subintervals.

EXAMPLE 2 Area Under a Curve

Use rectangles to find the area under $y = x^2$ (and above the x-axis) from $x = 0$ to $x = 1$.

Solution

We again divide the interval $[0, 1]$ into n equal subintervals of length $1/n$. If we evaluate the function at the left-hand endpoints of these subintervals to determine the heights of the rectangles, the sum of the areas of the rectangles will underestimate the area (see Figure 13.6). Thus we have the information shown in the following table.

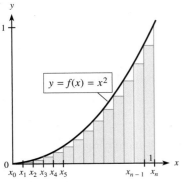

Figure 13.6

Rectangle	Base	Left Endpoint	Height	Area = Base × Height
1	$\dfrac{1}{n}$	$x_0 = 0$	$f(x_0) = 0$	$\dfrac{1}{n}\cdot 0 = 0$
2	$\dfrac{1}{n}$	$x_1 = \dfrac{1}{n}$	$f(x_1) = \dfrac{1}{n^2}$	$\dfrac{1}{n}\cdot\dfrac{1}{n^2} = \dfrac{1}{n^3}$
3	$\dfrac{1}{n}$	$x_2 = \dfrac{2}{n}$	$f(x_2) = \dfrac{4}{n^2}$	$\dfrac{1}{n}\cdot\dfrac{4}{n^2} = \dfrac{4}{n^3}$
4	$\dfrac{1}{n}$	$x_3 = \dfrac{3}{n}$	$f(x_3) = \dfrac{9}{n^2}$	$\dfrac{1}{n}\cdot\dfrac{9}{n^2} = \dfrac{9}{n^3}$
$\vdots$				
i	$\dfrac{1}{n}$	$x_{i-1} = \dfrac{i-1}{n}$	$\dfrac{(i-1)^2}{n^2}$	$\dfrac{(i-1)^2}{n^3}$
$\vdots$				
n	$\dfrac{1}{n}$	$x_{n-1} = \dfrac{n-1}{n}$	$\dfrac{(n-1)^2}{n^2}$	$\dfrac{(n-1)^2}{n^3}$

Thus: Area $= A \approx 0 + \dfrac{1}{n^3} + \dfrac{4}{n^3} + \dfrac{9}{n^3} + \cdots + \dfrac{(i-1)^2}{n^3} + \cdots + \dfrac{(n-1)^2}{n^3}.$

Note that $(i-1)^2/n^3 = (i^2 - 2i + 1)/n^3$ gives the area of the ith rectangle for *any* value of i. The sum of these areas may be written as

$$S = \sum_{i=1}^{n}\frac{i^2 - 2i + 1}{n^3} = \frac{1}{n^3}\left(\sum_{i=1}^{n}i^2 - 2\sum_{i=1}^{n}i + \sum_{i=1}^{n}1\right) \qquad \text{Formulas II and III}$$

$$= \frac{1}{n^3}\left[\frac{n(n+1)(2n+1)}{6} - \frac{2n(n+1)}{2} + n\right] \qquad \text{Formulas V, IV, and I}$$

$$= \frac{2n^3 + 3n^2 + n}{6n^3} - \frac{n^2 + n}{n^3} + \frac{n}{n^3} = \frac{2n^2 - 3n + 1}{6n^2}$$

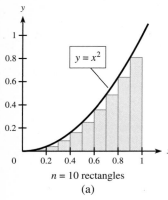

$n = 10$ rectangles
(a)

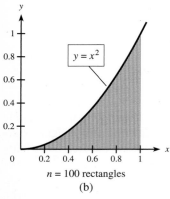

$n = 100$ rectangles
(b)

Figure 13.7

We can use this formula to find the approximate area (value of S) for different values of n.

$$\text{If } n = 10: \quad \text{Area} \approx S(10) = \frac{200 - 30 + 1}{600} = 0.285$$

$$\text{If } n = 100: \quad \text{Area} \approx S(100) = \frac{20{,}000 - 300 + 1}{60{,}000} = 0.328$$

Figure 13.7 shows the rectangles associated with each of these approximations.

As Figure 13.7 shows, the larger the value of n, the better the value of the sum approximates the exact area under the curve. If we let n increase without bound, we find the exact area.

$$A = \lim_{n \to \infty} \left(\frac{2n^2 - 3n + 1}{6n^2} \right) = \lim_{n \to \infty} \left(\frac{2 - \dfrac{3}{n} + \dfrac{1}{n^2}}{6} \right) = \frac{1}{3}$$

Note that the approximations with $n = 10$ and $n = 100$ are less than $\frac{1}{3}$. This is because all the rectangles are *under* the curve (see Figure 13.7). ■

Thus we see that we can determine the area under a curve $y = f(x)$ from $x = a$ to $x = b$ by dividing the interval $[a, b]$ into n equal subintervals of width $(b - a)/n$ and evaluating

$$A = \lim_{n \to \infty} S_R = \lim_{n \to \infty} \sum_{i=1}^{n} f(x_i)\left(\frac{b - a}{n} \right) \quad \text{(using right-hand endpoints)}$$

or

$$A = \lim_{n \to \infty} S_L = \lim_{n \to \infty} \sum_{i=1}^{n} f(x_{i-1})\left(\frac{b - a}{n} \right) \quad \text{(using left-hand endpoints)}$$

CHECKPOINT

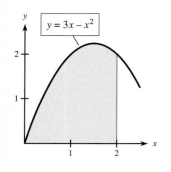

1. For the interval $[0, 2]$, determine whether the following statements are true or false.

   (a) For 4 subintervals, each subinterval has width $\dfrac{1}{2}$.

   (b) For 200 subintervals, each subinterval has width $\dfrac{1}{100}$.

   (c) For n subintervals, each subinterval has width $\dfrac{2}{n}$.

   (d) For n subintervals, $x_0 = 0$, $x_1 = \dfrac{2}{n}$, $x_2 = 2\left(\dfrac{2}{n}\right), \ldots, x_i = i\left(\dfrac{2}{n}\right), \ldots, x_n = 2$.

2. Find the area under $y = f(x) = 3x - x^2$ from $x = 0$ to $x = 2$ using right-hand endpoints (see the figure). To accomplish this, use $\dfrac{b - a}{n} = \dfrac{2}{n}$, $x_i = \dfrac{2i}{n}$, and $f(x) = 3x - x^2$; find and simplify the following.

   (a) $f(x_i)$

   (b) $f(x_i)\left(\dfrac{b - a}{n}\right)$

   (c) $S_R = \sum_{i=1}^{n} f(x_i)\left(\dfrac{b - a}{n}\right)$

   (d) $A = \lim_{n \to \infty} S_R = \lim_{n \to \infty} \sum_{i=1}^{n} f(x_i)\left(\dfrac{b - a}{n}\right)$

Technology Note

Graphing calculators and spreadsheets can be used to approximate the area under a curve. These technologies are especially useful when summations approximating the area do not simplify easily. A calculator or Excel can be used to find the sums. Steps for using graphing calculators and Excel are shown in Appendices C and D, Section 13.1, and in the Online Excel Guide that accompanies this text. ■

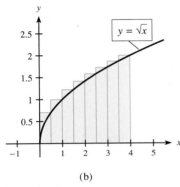

Figure 13.8

EXAMPLE 3 Estimating an Area with Technology

To approximate the area under the graph of $y = \sqrt{x}$ on the interval $[0, 4]$, do the following.

(a) Use a calculator or computer to find S_L and S_R for $n = 8$ on the interval $[0, 4]$.
(b) Predict the area under the curve in the graph by evaluating S_L and S_R for larger values of n.

Solution

Figure 13.8(a) shows the graph of $y = \sqrt{x}$ with 8 rectangles whose heights are determined by evaluating the function at the left-hand endpoint of each interval (the first of these rectangles has height 0). Figure 13.8(b) shows the same graph with 8 rectangles whose heights are determined at the right-hand endpoints.

(a) The width of the ith rectangle is $\dfrac{b - a}{n} = \dfrac{4}{n}$, and its endpoints are $x_i = \dfrac{4i}{n}$ and $x_{i-1} = \dfrac{4(i - 1)}{n}$. The formula for the sum of the areas of n rectangles over the interval $[0, 4]$, using left-hand endpoints, is

$$S_L = \sum_{i=1}^{n} \sqrt{\frac{4(i - 1)}{n}} \frac{4}{n} = \frac{8}{n^{3/2}} \sum_{i=1}^{n} \sqrt{i - 1}$$

and the formula for the sum of the areas of n rectangles over the interval $[0, 4]$, using right-hand endpoints, is

$$S_R = \sum_{i=1}^{n} \sqrt{\frac{4(i)}{n}} \frac{4}{n} = \frac{8}{n^{3/2}} \sum_{i=1}^{n} \sqrt{i}$$

We have no formulas to write either of these summations in a simpler form, but we can find the sums by hand if n is small, and we can use calculators, computer programs, or spreadsheets to find the sums for large n. For $n = 8$, the sums are

$$S_L = \frac{1}{\sqrt{8}} \sum_{i=1}^{8} \sqrt{i - 1} \quad \text{and} \quad S_R = \frac{1}{\sqrt{8}} \sum_{i=1}^{8} \sqrt{i}$$

The following Excel output shows the sum for $n = 8$ rectangles.

	A	B	C	D
1	Area for	n=8		
2		i	SL	SR
3		1	0	.35355
4		2	.35355	.5
5		3	.5	.61237
6		4	.61237	.70711
7		5	.70711	.79057
8		6	.79057	.86603
9		7	.86603	.93541
10		8	.93541	1
11	Total		4.76504	5.76504

As line 11 shows, $S_L = 4.76504$ and $S_R = 5.76504$ for $n = 8$.

(b) Larger values of n give better approximations of the area under the curve (try some). For example, $n = 1000$ gives $S_L = 5.3293$ and $S_R = 5.3373$, and because the area under the curve is between these values, the area is approximately 5.33, to two decimal places. By using values of n larger than 1000, we can get even better approximations of the area. ◼

CHECKPOINT SOLUTIONS

1. All parts are true.

2. (a) $f(x_i) = f\left(\dfrac{2i}{n}\right) = 3\left(\dfrac{2i}{n}\right) - \left(\dfrac{2i}{n}\right)^2 = \dfrac{6i}{n} - \dfrac{4i^2}{n^2}$

   (b) $f(x_i)\dfrac{b-a}{n} = \left(\dfrac{6i}{n} - \dfrac{4i^2}{n^2}\right)\left(\dfrac{2}{n}\right) = \dfrac{12i}{n^2} - \dfrac{8i^2}{n^3}$

   (c) $S_R = \displaystyle\sum_{i=1}^{n} f(x_i)\dfrac{b-a}{n} = \sum_{i=1}^{n}\left(\dfrac{12i}{n^2} - \dfrac{8i^2}{n^3}\right)$

   $\qquad = \displaystyle\sum_{i=1}^{n}\dfrac{12i}{n^2} - \sum_{i=1}^{n}\dfrac{8i^2}{n^3}$

   $\qquad = \dfrac{12}{n^2}\displaystyle\sum_{i=1}^{n} i - \dfrac{8}{n^3}\sum_{i=1}^{n} i^2$

   $\qquad = \dfrac{12}{n^2}\left[\dfrac{n(n+1)}{2}\right] - \dfrac{8}{n^3}\left[\dfrac{n(n+1)(2n+1)}{6}\right]$

   $\qquad = \dfrac{6(n+1)}{n} - \dfrac{4(n+1)(2n+1)}{3n^2}$

   (d) $A = \displaystyle\lim_{n\to\infty}\sum_{i=1}^{n} f(x_i)\dfrac{b-a}{n} = \lim_{n\to\infty}\left(\dfrac{6n+6}{n} - \dfrac{8n^2+12n+4}{3n^2}\right) = 6 - \dfrac{8}{3} = \dfrac{10}{3}$

| EXERCISES | 13.1

In Problems 1–4, approximate the area under each curve over the specified interval by using the indicated number of subintervals (or rectangles) and evaluating the function at the *right-hand* endpoints of the subintervals. (See Example 1.)

1. $f(x) = 4x - x^2$ from $x = 0$ to $x = 2$; 2 subintervals
2. $f(x) = x^3$ from $x = 0$ to $x = 3$; 3 subintervals
3. $f(x) = 9 - x^2$ from $x = 1$ to $x = 3$; 4 subintervals
4. $f(x) = x^2 + x + 1$ from $x = -1$ to $x = 1$;
   4 subintervals

In Problems 5–8, approximate the area under each curve by evaluating the function at the *left-hand* endpoints of the subintervals.

5. $f(x) = 4x - x^2$ from $x = 0$ to $x = 2$; 2 subintervals
6. $f(x) = x^3$ from $x = 0$ to $x = 3$; 3 subintervals
7. $f(x) = 9 - x^2$ from $x = 1$ to $x = 3$; 4 subintervals
8. $f(x) = x^2 + x + 1$ from $x = -1$ to $x = 1$;
   4 subintervals

When the area under $f(x) = x^2 + x$ from $x = 0$ to $x = 2$ is approximated, the formulas for the sum of n rectangles using *left-hand* endpoints and *right-hand* endpoints are

Left-hand endpoints: $S_L = \dfrac{14}{3} - \dfrac{6}{n} + \dfrac{4}{3n^2}$

Right-hand endpoints: $S_R = \dfrac{14n^2 + 18n + 4}{3n^2}$

Use these formulas to answer Problems 9–13.

9. Find $S_L(10)$ and $S_R(10)$.

10. Find $S_L(100)$ and $S_R(100)$.

11. Find $\lim\limits_{n\to\infty} S_L$ and $\lim\limits_{n\to\infty} S_R$.

12. Compare the right-hand and left-hand values by finding $S_R - S_L$ for $n = 10$, for $n = 100$, and as $n \to \infty$. (Use Problems 9–11.)

13. Because $f(x) = x^2 + x$ is increasing over the interval from $x = 0$ to $x = 2$, function values at the right-hand endpoints are maximum values for each subinterval, and function values at the left-hand endpoints are minimum values for each subinterval. How would the approximate area using $n = 10$ and *any* other point within each subinterval compare with $S_L(10)$ and $S_R(10)$? What would happen to the area result as $n \to \infty$ if any other point in each subinterval were used?

In Problems 14–19, find the value of each sum.

14. $\sum\limits_{k=1}^{3} x_k$, if $x_1 = 1, x_2 = 3, x_3 = -1, x_4 = 5$

15. $\sum\limits_{i=1}^{4} x_i$, if $x_1 = 3, x_2 = -1, x_3 = 3, x_4 = -2$

16. $\sum\limits_{i=3}^{5} (i^2 + 1)$

17. $\sum\limits_{j=2}^{5} (j^2 - 3)$

18. $\sum\limits_{i=4}^{7} \left(\dfrac{i - 3}{i^2}\right)$

19. $\sum\limits_{j=0}^{4} (j^2 - 4j + 1)$

In Problems 20–25, use the sum formulas I–V to express each of the following without the summation symbol. In Problems 20–23, find the numerical value.

20. $\sum\limits_{k=1}^{50} 1$

21. $\sum\limits_{j=1}^{60} 3$

22. $\sum\limits_{k=1}^{50} (6k^2 + 5)$

23. $\sum\limits_{k=1}^{30} (k^2 + 4k)$

24. $\sum\limits_{i=1}^{n} \left(1 - \dfrac{i^2}{n^2}\right)\left(\dfrac{2}{n}\right)$

25. $\sum\limits_{i=1}^{n} \left(1 - \dfrac{2i}{n} + \dfrac{i^2}{n^2}\right)\left(\dfrac{3}{n}\right)$

Use the function $y = 2x$ from $x = 0$ to $x = 1$ and n equal subintervals with the function evaluated at the *left-hand* endpoint of each subinterval for Problems 26 and 27.

26. What is the area of the
    (a) first rectangle?   (b) second rectangle?
    (c) ith rectangle?

27. (a) Find a formula for the sum of the areas of the n rectangles (call this S). Then find
    (b) $S(10)$.   (c) $S(100)$.
    (d) $S(1000)$.   (e) $\lim\limits_{n\to\infty} S$.

28. How do your answers to Problems 27(a)–(e) compare with the corresponding calculations in the discussion (after Example 1) of the area under $y = 2x$ using *right-hand* endpoints?

29. For parts (a)–(e), use the function $y = x^2$ from $x = 0$ to $x = 1$ with n equal subintervals and the function evaluated at the *right-hand* endpoints.
    (a) Find a formula for the sum of the areas of the n rectangles (call this S). Then find
    (b) $S(10)$.   (c) $S(100)$.
    (d) $S(1000)$.   (e) $\lim\limits_{n\to\infty} S$.

30. How do your answers to Problems 29(a)–(e) compare with the corresponding calculations in Example 2?

31. Use rectangles to find the area between $y = x^2 - 6x + 8$ and the x-axis from $x = 0$ to $x = 2$. Divide the interval $[0, 2]$ into n equal subintervals so that each subinterval has length $2/n$.

32. Use rectangles to find the area between $y = 4x - x^2$ and the x-axis from $x = 0$ to $x = 4$. Divide the interval $[0, 4]$ into n equal subintervals so that each subinterval has length $4/n$.

APPLICATIONS

33. ***Per capita health care expenses*** The annual per capita out-of-pocket expenses (in dollars) for U.S. health care for selected years from 2006 and projected to 2014 are shown in the table and figure.
    (a) Use $n = 4$ equal subdivisions and left-hand endpoints to estimate the area under the graph from 2006 to 2014.
    (b) What does this area represent in terms of per capita out-of-pocket expenses for U.S. health care?

Year	Dollars
2006	854.56
2008	917.46
2010	938.10
2012	992.73
2014	1070.20

Source: U.S. Centers for Medicare and Medicaid Services

34. ***Oil imports*** Crude oil and petroleum products are imported continuously by the United States. The table and figure on the next page show the rate of U.S. oil imports (in billions of barrels per year) (*Source:* Energy Information Administration).
    (a) Use $n = 5$ equal subdivisions and left-hand endpoints to estimate the area under the graph from 2000 to 2010.

(b) What does this area represent in terms of U.S. oil imports?

Year	Rate
2000	4.194
2002	4.209
2004	4.801
2006	5.006
2008	4.717
2010	4.357

35. **Speed trials** The figure gives the times that it takes a Porsche 911 to reach speeds from 0 mph to 100 mph, in increments of 10 mph, with a curve connecting them. The area under this curve from $t = 0$ seconds to $t = 14$ seconds represents the total amount of distance traveled over the 14-second period. Count the squares under the curve to estimate this distance. This car will travel 1/4 mile in 14 seconds, to a speed of 100.2 mph. Is your estimate close to this result? (Be careful with time units.)

Source: Motor Trend

36. **Speed trials** The figure gives the times that it takes a Mitsubishi Eclipse GSX to reach speeds from 0 mph to 100 mph, in increments of 10 mph, with a curve connecting them. The area under this curve from $t = 0$ seconds to $t = 21.1$ seconds represents the total amount of distance traveled over the 21.1-second period. Count the squares under the curve to estimate this distance. This car will travel 1/4 mile in 15.4 seconds, to a speed of 89.0 mph, so your estimate should be more than 1/4 mile. Is it? (Be careful with time units.)

Source: Road & Track

37. **Pollution monitoring** Suppose the presence of phosphates in certain waste products dumped into a lake promotes the growth of algae. Rampant growth of algae affects the oxygen supply in the water, so an environmental group wishes to estimate the area of algae growth. The group measures the length across the algae growth (see the figure) and obtains the data (in feet) in the table.

x	Length	x	Length
0	0	50	27
10	15	60	24
20	18	70	23
30	18	80	0
40	30		

Use 8 rectangles with bases of 10 feet and lengths measured at the left-hand endpoints to approximate the area of the algae growth.

38. **Drug levels in the blood** The manufacturer of a medicine wants to test how a new 300-milligram capsule is released into the bloodstream. After a volunteer is given a capsule, blood samples are drawn every half-hour, and the number of milligrams of the drug in the bloodstream is calculated. The results obtained are shown in the table.

Time t (hr)	$N(t)$ (mg)	Time t (hr)	$N(t)$ (mg)
0	0	2.0	178.3
0.5	247.3	2.5	113.9
1.0	270.0	3.0	56.2
1.5	236.4	3.5	19.3

Use 7 rectangles, each with height $N(t)$ at the left endpoint and with width 0.5 hr, to estimate the area under the graph representing these data. Divide this area by 3.5 hr to estimate the average drug level over this time period.

39. **Emissions** With U.S. Department of Energy data for selected years from 2000 and projected to 2030, sulphur dioxide emissions from electricity generation (in millions of short tons per year) can be modeled by

$$E(x) = 0.0112x^2 + 0.612x + 11.9$$

where x is the number of years past 2000. Use $n = 10$ equal subdivisions and right-hand endpoints to approximate the area under the graph of $E(x)$ between $x = 10$ and $x = 15$. What does this area represent?

40. *Per capita income* The per capita personal income (in dollars per year) in the United States for selected years from 1960 and projected to 2018 can be modeled by

$$I(t) = 13.93t^2 + 136.8t + 1971$$

where t is the number of years past 1960 (*Source*: U.S. Bureau of Labor Statistics). Use $n = 10$ equal subdivisions with right-hand endpoints to approximate the area under the graph of $I(t)$ between $t = 50$ and $t = 55$. What does this area represent?

OBJECTIVES

13.2

- To evaluate definite integrals using the Fundamental Theorem of Calculus
- To use definite integrals to find the area under a curve

The Definite Integral: The Fundamental Theorem of Calculus

▮ | APPLICATION PREVIEW |

Suppose that money flows continuously into a slot machine at a casino and grows at a rate given by $A'(t) = 100e^{0.1t}$, where t is the time in hours and $0 \leq t \leq 10$. Then the definite integral

$$\int_0^{10} 100e^{0.1t}\, dt$$

gives the total amount of money that accumulates over the 10-hour period, if no money is paid out. (See Example 6.)

In the previous section, we used the sums of areas of rectangles to approximate the areas under curves. In this section, we will see how such sums are related to the definite integral and how to evaluate definite integrals. In addition, we will see how definite integrals can be used to solve several types of applied problems.

Riemann Sums and the Definite Integral

In the previous section, we saw that we could determine the area under a curve $y = f(x)$ over a closed interval $[a, b]$ by using equal subintervals and the function values at either the left-hand endpoints or the right-hand endpoints of the subintervals. In fact, we can use subintervals that are not of equal length, and we can use any point within each subinterval, denoted by x_i^*, to determine the height of each rectangle. For the ith rectangle (for any i), if we denote the width as Δx_i then the height is $f(x_i^*)$ and the area is $f(x_i^*)\, \Delta x_i$. Then, if $[a, b]$ is divided into n subintervals, the sum of the areas of the n rectangles is

$$S = \sum_{i=1}^{n} f(x_i^*)\, \Delta x_i,$$

Such a sum is called a **Riemann sum** of f on $[a, b]$. Increasing the number of subintervals and making sure that every interval becomes smaller will in the long run improve the estimation. Thus for any subdivision of $[a, b]$ and any x_i^*, the exact area is given by

$$A = \lim_{\substack{\max \Delta x_i \to 0 \\ (n \to \infty)}} \sum_{i=1}^{n} f(x_i^*)\, \Delta x_i, \qquad \text{provided that this limit exists}$$

In addition to giving the exact area, this limit of the Riemann sum has other important applications and is called the **definite integral** of $f(x)$ over interval $[a, b]$.

Definite Integral

If f is a function on the interval $[a, b]$, then, for any subdivision of $[a, b]$ and any choice of x_i^* in the ith subinterval, the **definite integral** of f from a to b is

$$\int_a^b f(x)\,dx = \lim_{\substack{\max \Delta x_i \to 0 \\ (n \to \infty)}} \sum_{i=1}^n f(x_i^*)\,\Delta x_i$$

If f is a continuous function, and $\Delta x_i \to 0$ as $n \to \infty$, then the limit exists and we say that f is integrable on $[a, b]$.

Note that for some intervals, values of f may be negative. In this case, the product $f(x_i^*)\Delta x_i$ will be negative and can be thought of geometrically as a "signed area." (Remember that area is a positive number.) Thus a definite integral can be thought of geometrically as the sum of signed areas, just as a derivative can be thought of geometrically as the slope of a tangent line. In the case where $f(x)$ is positive for all x from a to b, the definite integral equals the area between the graph of $y = f(x)$ and the x-axis.

Fundamental Theorem of Calculus

The obvious question is how this definite integral is related to the indefinite integral (the antiderivative) discussed in Chapter 12. The connection between these two concepts is the most important result in calculus, because it connects derivatives, indefinite integrals, and definite integrals.

To help see the connection, consider the marginal revenue function

$$R'(x) = 300 - 0.2x$$

and the revenue function

$$R(x) = \int (300 - 0.2x)\,dx = 300x - 0.1x^2$$

that is the indefinite integral of the marginal revenue function. (See Figure 13.9(a).)

Using this revenue function, we can find the revenue from the sale of 1000 units to be

$$R(1000) = 300(1000) - 0.1(1000)^2 = 200{,}000 \text{ dollars}$$

and the revenue from the sale of 500 units to be

$$R(500) = 300(500) - 0.1(500)^2 = 125{,}000 \text{ dollars}$$

Thus the additional revenue received from the sale of 500 units to 1000 units is

$$200{,}000 - 125{,}000 = 75{,}000 \text{ dollars}$$

If we used the definition of the definite integral (or geometry) to find the area under the graph of the marginal revenue function from $x = 500$ to $x = 1000$, we would find that the area is 75,000 (see Figure 13.9(b)). Note in Figure 13.9(b) that the shaded area is given by

$$\text{Area} = \text{Area } (\triangle \text{ with base from 500 to 1500}) - \text{Area } (\triangle \text{ with base from 1000 to 1500})$$

Recall that the area of a triangle is $\frac{1}{2}$ (base)(height) so we have

$$\text{Area} = \tfrac{1}{2}(1000)(200) - \tfrac{1}{2}(500)(100) = 75{,}000$$

Thus we can also find this additional revenue when sales are increased from 500 to 1000 by evaluating the *definite integral*

$$\int_{500}^{1000} (300 - 0.2x)\,dx$$

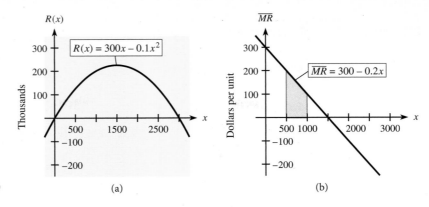

Figure 13.9   (a)   (b)

In general, the definite integral

$$\int_a^b f(x)\,dx$$

can be used to find the change in the function $F(x)$ when x changes from a to b, where $f(x)$ is the derivative of $F(x)$. This result is the **Fundamental Theorem of Calculus.**

Fundamental Theorem of Calculus	Let f be a continuous function on the closed interval $[a, b]$; then the definite integral of f exists on this interval, and $$\int_a^b f(x)\,dx = F(b) - F(a)$$ where F is any function such that $F'(x) = f(x)$ for all x in $[a, b]$.

Stated differently, this theorem says that if the function F is an indefinite integral of a function f that is continuous on the interval $[a, b]$, then

$$\int_a^b f(x)\,dx = F(b) - F(a)$$

Thus, we apply the Fundamental Theorem of Calculus by using the following two steps.

1. Integration of $f(x)$: $\displaystyle\int_a^b f(x)\,dx = F(x)\Big|_a^b$

2. Evaluation of $F(x)$: $F(x)\Big|_a^b = F(b) - F(a)$

EXAMPLE 1   Definite Integral

Evaluate $\displaystyle\int_2^4 (x^3 + 4)\,dx.$

Solution

1. $\displaystyle\int_2^4 (x^3 + 4)\,dx = \frac{x^4}{4} + 4x + C\,\Big|_2^4$

2. $\qquad\qquad\qquad = \left[\frac{(4)^4}{4} + 4(4) + C\right] - \left[\frac{(2)^4}{4} + 4(2) + C\right]$

    $\qquad\qquad\qquad = (64 + 16 + C) - (4 + 8 + C)$

    $\qquad\qquad\qquad = 68 \quad$ (Note that the C's subtract out.)

Note that the Fundamental Theorem states that F can be *any* indefinite integral of f, so we need not add the constant of integration to the integral.

EXAMPLE 2   **Fundamental Theorem**

Evaluate $\displaystyle\int_1^3 (3x^2 + 6x)\, dx$.

Solution

$$\int_1^3 (3x^2 + 6x)\, dx = x^3 + 3x^2 \Big|_1^3$$

$$= (3^3 + 3 \cdot 3^2) - (1^3 + 3 \cdot 1^2)$$

$$= 54 - 4 = 50$$

Properties   The properties of definite integrals given next follow from properties of summations.

1. $\displaystyle\int_a^b [f(x) \pm g(x)]\, dx = \int_a^b f(x)\, dx \pm \int_a^b g(x)\, dx$

2. $\displaystyle\int_a^b kf(x)\, dx = k\int_a^b f(x)\, dx$,   where k is a constant

The following example uses both of these properties.

EXAMPLE 3   **Definite Integral**

Evaluate $\displaystyle\int_3^5 (\sqrt{x^2 - 9} + 2)x\, dx$.

Solution

$$\int_3^5 (\sqrt{x^2 - 9} + 2)x\, dx = \int_3^5 \sqrt{x^2 - 9}(x\, dx) + \int_3^5 2x\, dx$$

$$= \frac{1}{2}\int_3^5 (x^2 - 9)^{1/2}(2x\, dx) + \int_3^5 2x\, dx$$

$$= \frac{1}{2}\left[\frac{2}{3}(x^2 - 9)^{3/2}\right]_3^5 + x^2 \Big|_3^5$$

$$= \frac{1}{3}[(16)^{3/2} - (0)^{3/2}] + (25 - 9)$$

$$= \frac{64}{3} + 16 = \frac{64}{3} + \frac{48}{3} = \frac{112}{3}$$

In the integral $\int_a^b f(x)\, dx$, we call a the *lower limit* and b the *upper limit* of integration. Although we developed the definite integral with the assumption that the lower limit was less than the upper limit, the following properties permit us to evaluate the definite integral even when that is not the case.

3. $\displaystyle\int_a^a f(x)\, dx = 0$

4. If f is integrable on $[a, b]$, then

$$\int_b^a f(x)\, dx = -\int_a^b f(x)\, dx$$

The following examples illustrate these properties.

EXAMPLE 4   Properties of Definite Integrals

(a) Evaluate $\displaystyle\int_4^4 x^2\, dx$.   (b) Compare $\displaystyle\int_2^4 3x^2\, dx$ and $\displaystyle\int_4^2 3x^2\, dx$.

Solution

(a) $\displaystyle\int_4^4 x^2\, dx = \left.\frac{x^3}{3}\right|_4^4 = \frac{4^3}{3} - \frac{4^3}{3} = 0$

This illustrates Property 3.

(b) $\displaystyle\int_2^4 3x^2\, dx = x^3\Big|_2^4 = 4^3 - 2^3 = 56$ and $\displaystyle\int_4^2 3x^2\, dx = x^3\Big|_4^2 = 2^3 - 4^3 = -56$

This illustrates Property 4.

Another property of definite integrals is called the additive property.

5. If f is continuous on some interval containing a, b, and c,* then

$$\int_a^c f(x)\, dx + \int_c^b f(x)\, dx = \int_a^b f(x)\, dx$$

EXAMPLE 5   Properties of Definite Integrals

Show that $\displaystyle\int_2^3 4x\, dx + \int_3^5 4x\, dx = \int_2^5 4x\, dx$.

Solution

$$\int_2^3 4x\, dx = 2x^2\Big|_2^3 = 18 - 8 = 10 \quad \text{and} \quad \int_3^5 4x\, dx = 2x^2\Big|_3^5 = 50 - 18 = 32$$

Thus $\displaystyle\int_2^5 4x\, dx = 2x^2\Big|_2^5 = 50 - 8 = 42 = \int_2^3 4x\, dx + \int_3^5 4x\, dx$

The Definite Integral and Areas

Let us now return to area problems, to see the relationship between the definite integral and the area under a curve. By the formula for the area of a triangle or by using rectangles and the limit definition of area, the area under the curve (line) $y = x$ from $x = 0$ to $x = 1$ can be shown to be $\frac{1}{2}$ (see Figure 13.10(a) on the next page). Using the definite integral to find the area gives

$$A = \int_0^1 x\, dx = \left.\frac{x^2}{2}\right|_0^1 = \frac{1}{2} - 0 = \frac{1}{2}$$

In the previous section, we used rectangles to find that the area under $y = x^2$ from $x = 0$ to $x = 1$ was $\frac{1}{3}$ (see Figure 13.10(b)). Using the definite integral, we get

$$A = \int_0^1 x^2\, dx = \left.\frac{x^3}{3}\right|_0^1 = \frac{1}{3} - 0 = \frac{1}{3}$$

which agrees with the answer obtained previously.

However, not every definite integral represents the area between the curve and the x-axis over an interval. For example,

$$\int_0^2 (x - 2)\, dx = \left.\frac{x^2}{2} - 2x\right|_0^2 = (2 - 4) - (0) = -2$$

This would indicate that the area between the curve and the x-axis is negative, but area must be positive. A look at the graph of $y = x - 2$ (see Figure 13.10(c)) shows us what is happening.

*Note that c need not be between a and b.

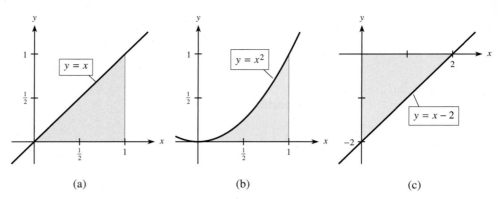

Figure 13.10   (a)   (b)   (c)

The region bounded by $y = x - 2$ and the x-axis between $x = 0$ and $x = 2$ is a triangle whose base is 2 and whose height is 2, so its area is $\frac{1}{2}bh = \frac{1}{2}(2)(2) = 2$. The integral has value -2 because $y = x - 2$ lies below the x-axis from $x = 0$ to $x = 2$, and the function values over the interval $[0, 2]$ are negative. Thus the value of the definite integral over *this* interval does not represent the area between the curve and the x-axis but, rather, represents the "signed" area as mentioned previously.

In general, the definite integral will give the **area under the curve** and above the x-axis only when $f(x) \geq 0$ for all x in $[a, b]$.

Area Under a Curve

If f is a continuous function on $[a, b]$ and $f(x) \geq 0$ on $[a, b]$, then the exact area between $y = f(x)$ and the x-axis from $x = a$ to $x = b$ is given by

$$\begin{array}{c} \text{Area} \\ (\text{shaded}) \end{array} = \int_a^b f(x)\, dx$$

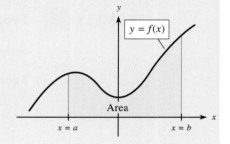

Note also that if $f(x) \leq 0$ for all x in $[a, b]$, then

$$\int_a^b f(x)\, dx = -\text{Area (between } f(x) \text{ and the } x\text{-axis)}$$

CHECKPOINT

1. True or false:

   (a) For any integral, we can omit the constant of integration (the $+C$).

   (b) $-\int_{-1}^{3} f(x)\, dx = \int_{3}^{-1} f(x)\, dx$, if f is integrable on $[-1, 3]$.

   (c) The area between $f(x)$ and the x-axis on the interval $[a, b]$ is given by $\int_a^b f(x)\, dx$.

2. Evaluate:

   (a) $\int_0^3 (x^2 + 1)\, dx$ (b) $\int_0^3 (x^2 + 1)^4 x\, dx$

If the rate of growth of some function with respect to time t is $f'(t)$, then the total growth of the function during the period from $t = 0$ to $t = k$ can be found by evaluating the definite integral

$$\int_0^k f'(t)\, dt = f(t)\Big|_0^k = f(k) - f(0)$$

For nonnegative rates of growth, this definite integral (and thus growth) is the same as the area under the graph of $f'(t)$ from $t = 0$ to $t = k$.

EXAMPLE 6 Income Stream | APPLICATION PREVIEW |

Suppose that money flows continuously into a slot machine at a casino and grows at a rate given by

$$A'(t) = 100e^{0.1t}$$

where t is time in hours and $0 \leq t \leq 10$. Find the total amount that accumulates in the machine during the 10-hour period, if no money is paid out.

Solution
The total dollar amount is given by

$$A = \int_0^{10} 100e^{0.1t}\, dt = \frac{100}{0.1}\int_0^{10} e^{0.1t}(0.1)\, dt = 1000e^{0.1t}\Big|_0^{10} = 1000e - 1000 \approx 1718.28 \quad \blacksquare$$

In Section 8.4, "Normal Probability Distribution," we stated that the total area under the normal curve is 1 and that the area under the curve from value x_1 to value x_2 represents the probability that a score chosen at random will lie between x_1 and x_2.

The normal distribution is an example of a **continuous probability distribution** because the values of the random variable are considered over intervals rather than at discrete values. The statements above relating probability and area under the graph apply to other continuous probability distributions determined by **probability density functions.** In fact, if x is a continuous random variable with probability density function $f(x)$, then the probability that x is between a and b is

$$\Pr(a \leq x \leq b) = \int_a^b f(x)\, dx$$

EXAMPLE 7 Product Life

Suppose the probability density function for the life of a computer component is $f(x) = 0.10e^{-0.10x}$, where $x \geq 0$ is the number of years the component is in use. Find the probability that the component will last between 3 and 5 years.

```
fnInt(0.10*e^(-0
.10X),X,3,5)
        .134287561
■
```

Figure 13.11

Solution
The probability that the component will last between 3 and 5 years is the area under the graph of the function between $x = 3$ and $x = 5$. The probability is given by

$$\Pr(3 \leq x \leq 5) = \int_3^5 0.10e^{-0.10x}\, dx = -e^{-0.10x}\Big|_3^5 = -e^{-0.5} + e^{-0.3}$$

$$\approx -0.6065 + 0.7408 = 0.1343 \quad \blacksquare$$

Calculator Note   Most graphing calculators have a numerical integration feature that can be used to get an accurate approximation of any definite integral. This feature can be used to evaluate definite integrals directly or to check those done with the Fundamental Theorem of Calculus. Figure 13.11 shows the numerical integration feature applied to the integral in Example 7. Note that when this answer is rounded to 4 decimal places, the results agree. Two methods of approximating definite integrals are shown in Appendix C, Section 13.1.   ■

CHECKPOINT SOLUTIONS

1. (a) False. We can omit the constant of integration $(+C)$ only for definite integrals.
    (b) True   (c) False. Only if $f(x) \geq 0$ on $[a, b]$ is this true.

2. (a) $\int_0^3 (x^2 + 1)\, dx = \frac{x^3}{3} + x\Big|_0^3 = \left(\frac{27}{3} + 3\right) - (0 + 0) = 12$

    (b) $\int_0^3 (x^2 + 1)^4 x\, dx = \frac{1}{2}\int_0^3 (x^2 + 1)^4 (2x\, dx)$

    $= \frac{1}{2} \cdot \frac{(x^2 + 1)^5}{5}\Big|_0^3$

    $= \frac{1}{10}[(3^2 + 1)^5 - (1)^5] = \frac{1}{10}(10^5 - 1) = 9999.9$

| EXERCISES | 13.2

Evaluate the definite integrals in Problems 1–30.

1. $\int_0^3 4x \, dx$

2. $\int_0^1 8x \, dx$

3. $\int_2^4 dx$

4. $\int_1^5 2 \, dy$

5. $\int_2^4 x^3 \, dx$

6. $\int_0^5 x^2 \, dx$

7. $\int_0^5 4\sqrt[3]{x^2} \, dx$

8. $\int_2^4 3\sqrt{x} \, dx$

9. $\int_1^4 (10 - 4x) \, dx$

10. $\int_{-1}^2 (6x - 9) \, dx$

11. $\int_2^4 (4x^3 - 6x^2 - 5x) \, dx$

12. $\int_0^2 (x^4 - 5x^3 + 2x) \, dx$

13. $\int_3^4 (x - 4)^9 \, dx$

14. $\int_{-1}^0 (x + 2)^{13} \, dx$

15. $\int_2^4 (x^2 + 2)^3 x \, dx$

16. $\int_0^1 5x^2 (4x^3 - 2)^4 \, dx$

17. $\int_{-1}^2 (x^3 - 3x^2)^3 (x^2 - 2x) \, dx$ 18. $\int_0^3 (2x - x^2)^4 (1 - x) \, dx$

19. $\int_{-2}^2 15x^3 (x^4 - 6)^6 \, dx$

20. $\int_0^4 (3x^2 - 2)^4 x \, dx$

21. $\int_0^4 \sqrt{4x + 9} \, dx$

22. $\int_0^2 \sqrt[3]{2x^3 - 8} \, x^2 \, dx$

23. $\int_1^3 \frac{3}{y^2} \, dy$

24. $\int_1^2 \frac{5}{z^3} \, dz$

25. $\int_0^1 e^{3x} \, dx$

26. $\int_0^2 e^{4x-3} \, dx$

27. $\int_1^e \frac{4}{z} \, dz$

28. $\int_1^{5e} 3y^{-1} \, dy$

29. $\int_0^2 8x^2 e^{-x^3} \, dx$

30. $\int_0^1 \frac{3x^3 \, dx}{4x^4 + 9}$

In Problems 31–34, evaluate each integral (a) with the Fundamental Theorem of Calculus and (b) with a graphing calculator (as a check).

31. $\int_3^6 \frac{x}{3x^2 + 4} \, dx$

32. $\int_0^2 \frac{x}{x^2 + 4} \, dx$

33. $\int_1^2 \frac{x^2 + 3}{x} \, dx$

34. $\int_1^4 \frac{4\sqrt{x} + 5}{\sqrt{x}} \, dx$

35. In the figures, which of the shaded regions (A, B, C, or D) has the area given by

(a) $\int_a^b f(x) \, dx$?   (b) $-\int_a^b f(x) \, dx$?

36. For which of the following functions $f(x)$ does

$$\int_0^2 f(x) \, dx$$

give the area between the graph of $f(x)$ and the x-axis from $x = 0$ to $x = 2$?
(a) $f(x) = x^2 + 1$ (b) $f(x) = -x^2$
(c) $f(x) = x - 1$

In Problems 37–40, (a) write the integral that describes the area of the shaded region and (b) find the area.

37.

38.

39.

40.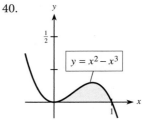

41. Find the area between the curve $y = -x^2 + 3x - 2$ and the x-axis from $x = 1$ to $x = 2$.

42. Find the area between the curve $y = x^2 + 3x + 2$ and the x-axis from $x = -1$ to $x = 3$.

43. Find the area between the curve $y = xe^{x^2}$ and the x-axis from $x = 1$ to $x = 3$.

44. Find the area between the curve $y = e^{-x}$ and the x-axis from $x = -1$ to $x = 1$.

In Problems 45 and 46, use the figures to decide which of $\int_0^a f(x) \, dx$ **or** $\int_0^a g(x) \, dx$ **is larger or if they are equal. Explain your choices.**

45.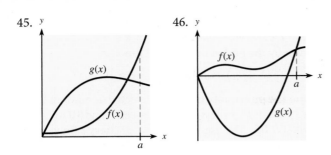

46.

In Problems 47–52, use properties of definite integrals.

47. How does $\displaystyle\int_{-1}^{-3} x\sqrt{x^2+1}\,dx$ compare with

$\displaystyle\int_{-3}^{-1} x\sqrt{x^2+1}\,dx$?

48. If $\displaystyle\int_{-1}^{0} x^3\,dx = -\frac{1}{4}$ and $\displaystyle\int_{0}^{1} x^3\,dx = \frac{1}{4}$, what does $\displaystyle\int_{-1}^{1} x^3\,dx$ equal?

49. If $\displaystyle\int_{1}^{2} (2x - x^2)\,dx = \frac{2}{3}$ and $\displaystyle\int_{2}^{4} (2x - x^2)\,dx = -\frac{20}{3}$, what does $\displaystyle\int_{1}^{4} (x^2 - 2x)\,dx$ equal?

50. If $\displaystyle\int_{1}^{2} (2x - x^2)\,dx = \frac{2}{3}$, what does $\displaystyle\int_{1}^{2} 6(2x - x^2)\,dx$ equal?

51. Evaluate $\displaystyle\int_{4}^{4} \sqrt{x^2 - 2}\,dx$.

52. Evaluate $\displaystyle\int_{2}^{2} (x^3 + 4x)^{-6}\,dx$.

APPLICATIONS

53. *Depreciation* The rate of depreciation of a building is given by $D'(t) = 3000(20 - t)$ dollars per year, $0 \le t \le 20$; see the figure.
(a) Use the graph to find the total depreciation of the building over the first 10 years ($t = 0$ to $t = 10$).
(b) Use the definite integral to find the total depreciation over the first 10 years.

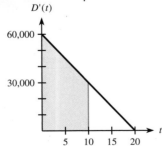

$D'(t)$

60,000

30,000

5   10   15   20 t

54. *Depreciation* The rate of depreciation of a building is given by $D'(t) = 3000(20 - t)$ dollars per year, $0 \le t \le 20$; see the figure in Problem 53.
(a) Use the graph to find the total depreciation of the building over the first 20 years.
(b) Use the definite integral to find the total depreciation over the first 20 years.

(c) Use the graph to find the total depreciation between 10 years and 20 years and check it with a definite integral.

55. *Sales and advertising* A store finds that its sales revenue changes at a rate given by

$$S'(t) = -30t^2 + 360t \quad \text{dollars per day}$$

where t is the number of days after an advertising campaign ends and $0 \le t \le 30$.
(a) Find the total sales for the first week after the campaign ends ($t = 0$ to $t = 7$).
(b) Find the total sales for the second week after the campaign ends ($t = 7$ to $t = 14$).

56. *Health care costs* The total annual health care costs in the United States (actual and projected, in billions of dollars) for selected years are given in the table. The equation

$$y = 4.447x^2 - 9.108x + 1055.4$$

models the annual health care costs, y (in billions of dollars per year), as a function of the number of years past 1990, x. Use a definite integral and this model to find the total cost of health care over the period 2005–2015.

Year	Cost	Year	Cost
2000	1353	2012	2931
2003	1735	2015	3541
2006	2113	2018	4353
2009	2509		

Source: U.S. Department of Health and Human Services

57. *Total income* The income from an oil change service chain can be considered as flowing continuously at an annual rate given by

$$f(t) = 10,000e^{0.02t} \quad \text{(dollars/year)}$$

Find the total income for this chain over the first 2 years (from $t = 0$ to $t = 2$).

58. *Total income* Suppose that a vending machine service company models its income by assuming that money flows continuously into the machines, with the annual rate of flow given by

$$f(t) = 120e^{0.01t}$$

in thousands of dollars per year. Find the total income from the machines over the first 3 years.

59. *CO_2 Emissions* Using U.S. Energy Information Administration data from 2010 and projected to 2030, the carbon dioxide emissions from biomass energy combustion (in millions of metric tons per year) can be modeled by

$$C(t) = 19.12t + 319.0$$

where t is the number of years past 2010. Evaluate $\int_{0}^{10} C(t)\,dt$ and tell what it represents.

60. *Health services and supplies expenditures* The per capita expenditures for U.S. health services and supplies (in dollars per year) for selected years from 2000 and projected to 2018 can be modeled by

$$H(t) = 4676e^{0.053t}$$

where t is the number of years past 2000 (*Source:* U.S. Centers for Medicare and Medicaid Services). Assuming the model remains valid, evaluate $\int_{10}^{20} H(t)\, dt$ and tell what it represents.

Velocity of blood In Problems 61 and 62, the velocity of blood through a vessel is given by $v = K(R^2 - r^2)$, where K is the (constant) maximum velocity of the blood, R is the (constant) radius of the vessel, and r is the distance of the particular corpuscle from the center of the vessel. The rate of flow can be found by measuring the volume of blood that flows past a point in a given time period. This volume, V, is given by

$$V = \int_0^R v(2\pi r\, dr)$$

61. If $R = 0.30$ cm and $v = (0.30 - 3.33r^2)$ cm/s, find the volume.

62. Develop a general formula for V by evaluating

$$V = \int_0^R v(2\pi r\, dr)$$

using $v = K(R^2 - r^2)$.

Production In Problems 63 and 64, the rate of production of a new line of products is given by

$$\frac{dx}{dt} = 200\left[1 + \frac{400}{(t + 40)^2}\right]$$

where x is the number of items produced and t is the number of weeks the products have been in production.

63. How many units were produced in the first 5 weeks?

64. How many units were produced in the sixth week?

65. *Testing* The time t (in minutes) needed to read an article appearing on a foreign-language placement test is given by the probability density function

$$f(t) = 0.012t^2 - 0.0012t^3, \qquad 0 \le t \le 10$$

For a test taker chosen at random, find the probability that this person takes 8 minutes or more to read the article.

66. *Response time* In a small city the response time t (in minutes) of the fire company is given by the probability density function

$$f(t) = \frac{60t^2 - 4t^3}{16,875}, \qquad 0 \le t \le 15$$

For a fire chosen at random, find the probability that the response time is 10 minutes or less.

67. *Customer service* The duration t (in minutes) of customer service calls received by a certain company is given by the probability density function

$$f(t) = 0.3e^{-0.3t}, \qquad t \ge 0$$

Find the probability that a call selected at random lasts
(a) 3 minutes or less. (b) between 5 and 10 minutes.

68. *Product life* The useful life of a car battery t (in years) is given by the probability density function

$$f(t) = 0.2e^{-0.2t}, \qquad t \ge 0$$

Find the probability that a battery chosen at random lasts
(a) 2 years or less. (b) between 4 and 6 years.

69. *Modeling* *Oil imports* Crude oil and petroleum products are imported continuously by the United States. The number of billions of barrels of oil and petroleum products imported per year for selected years from 2000 to 2010 are shown in the table.
(a) Find a cubic function $P(t)$ that models the data, with t equal to the number of years past 2000.
(b) Evaluate $\int_5^{10} P(t)\, dt$ and tell what it represents.

Year	Imports	Year	Imports
2000	4.194	2006	5.006
2002	4.209	2008	4.717
2004	4.801	2010	4.357

Source: Energy Information Administration

70. *Modeling* *Dodge Viper acceleration* Table 13.1(a) shows the time in seconds that a Dodge Viper GTS requires to reach various speeds up to 100 mph. Table 13.1(b) shows the same data, but with speeds in miles per second.
(a) Fit a power model to the data in Table 13.1(b).
(b) Use a definite integral from 0 to 9.2 of the function you found in part (a) to find the distance traveled by the Viper as it went from 0 mph to 100 mph in 9.2 seconds.

| TABLE 13.1 |

(a)		(b)	
Time (seconds)	Speed (mph)	Time (seconds)	Speed (mi/s)
1.7	30	1.7	0.00833
2.4	40	2.4	0.01111
3.2	50	3.2	0.01389
4.1	60	4.1	0.01667
5.8	70	5.8	0.01944
6.2	80	6.2	0.02222
7.8	90	7.8	0.02500
9.2	100	9.2	0.02778

Source: Motor Trend

Area Between Two Curves

■ **| APPLICATION PREVIEW |**

In economics, the **Lorenz curve** is used to represent the inequality of income distribution among different groups in the population of a country. The curve is constructed by plotting the cumulative percent of families at or below a given income level and the cumulative percent of total personal income received by these families. For example, the table shows the coordinates of some points on the Lorenz curve $y = L(x)$ that divide the income (for the United States in 2006) into 5 equal income levels (quintiles). The point (0.40, 0.120) is on the Lorenz curve because the families with incomes in the bottom 40% of the country received 12.0% of the total income in 2006. The graph of the Lorenz curve $y = L(x)$ is shown in Figure 13.12.

Figure 13.12

U.S. Income Distribution for 2006 (Points on the Lorenz Curve)

x, Cumulative Proportion of Families Below Income Level	$y = L(x)$, Cumulative Proportion of Total Income
0	0
0.20	0.034
0.40	0.120
0.60	0.265
0.80	0.498
1	1

Source: U.S. Bureau of the Census

Equality of income would result if each family received an equal proportion of the total income, so that the bottom 20% would receive 20% of the total income, the bottom 40% would receive 40%, and so on. The Lorenz curve representing this would have the equation $y = x$.

The inequality of income distribution is measured by the Gini coefficient of income, which measures how far the Lorenz curve falls below $y = x$. It is defined as

$$\frac{\text{Area between } y = x \text{ and } y = L(x)}{\text{Area below } y = x}$$

Because the area of the triangle below $y = x$ and above the x-axis from $x = 0$ to $x = 1$ is 1/2, the Gini coefficient of income is

$$\frac{\text{Area between } y = x \text{ and } y = L(x)}{1/2} = 2 \cdot [\text{area between } y = x \text{ and } y = L(x)]$$

In this section we will use the definite integral to find the area between two curves. We will use the area between two curves to find the Gini coefficient of income (see Example 4) and to find average cost, average revenue, average profit, and average inventory.

Area Between Two Curves

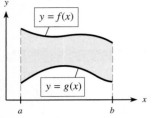

Figure 13.13

We have used the definite integral to find the area of the region between a curve and the x-axis over an interval where the curve lies above the x-axis. We can easily extend this technique to finding the area between two curves over an interval.

Suppose that the graphs of both $y = f(x)$ and $y = g(x)$ lie above the x-axis and that the graph of $y = f(x)$ lies above $y = g(x)$ throughout the interval from $x = a$ to $x = b$; that is, $f(x) \geq g(x)$ on $[a, b]$. (See Figure 13.13.)

Then Figures 13.14(a) and 13.14(b) show the areas under $y = f(x)$ and $y = g(x)$. Figure 13.14(c) shows how the difference of these two areas can be used to find the area of the region between the graphs of $y = f(x)$ and $y = g(x)$. That is,

$$\text{Area between the curves} = \int_a^b f(x)\,dx - \int_a^b g(x)\,dx$$

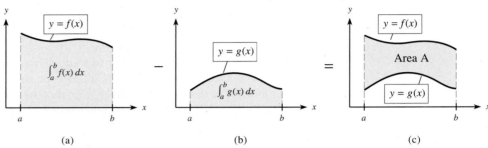

Figure 13.14   (a)   (b)   (c)

Although Figure 13.14(c) shows the graphs of both $y = f(x)$ and $y = g(x)$ lying above the x-axis, this difference of their integrals will always give the area between their graphs if both functions are continuous and if $f(x) \geq g(x)$ on the interval $[a, b]$. Using the fact that

$$\int_a^b f(x)\,dx - \int_a^b g(x)\,dx = \int_a^b [f(x) - g(x)]\,dx$$

we have the following result for the **area between two curves.**

Area Between Two Curves	If f and g are continuous functions on $[a, b]$ and if $f(x) \geq g(x)$ on $[a, b]$, then the area of the region bounded by $y = f(x)$, $y = g(x)$, $x = a$, and $x = b$ is $$A = \int_a^b [f(x) - g(x)]\,dx$$

EXAMPLE 1   Area Between Two Curves

Find the area of the region bounded by $y = x^2 + 4$, $y = x$, $x = 0$, and $x = 3$.

Solution

We first sketch the graphs of the functions on the same set of axes. The graph of the region is shown in Figure 13.15. Because $y = x^2 + 4$ lies above $y = x$ in the interval from $x = 0$ to $x = 3$, the area is

$$A = \int (\text{top curve} - \text{bottom curve})\,dx$$

$$A = \int_0^3 [(x^2 + 4) - x]\,dx = \left. \frac{x^3}{3} + 4x - \frac{x^2}{2} \right|_0^3$$

$$= \left(9 + 12 - \frac{9}{2}\right) - (0 + 0 - 0) = 16\tfrac{1}{2} \text{ square units}$$

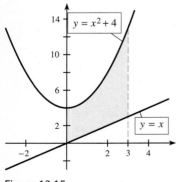

Figure 13.15

We are sometimes asked to find the area enclosed by two curves. In this case, we find the points of intersection of the curves to determine a and b.

EXAMPLE 2   Area Enclosed by Two Curves

Find the area enclosed by $y = x^2$ and $y = 2x + 3$.

Solution

We first find a and b by finding the x-coordinates of the points of intersection of the graphs. Setting the y-values equal gives

$$x^2 = 2x + 3$$
$$x^2 - 2x - 3 = 0$$
$$(x - 3)(x + 1) = 0$$
$$x = 3, \quad x = -1$$

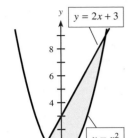

Figure 13.16

Thus with $a = -1$ and $b = 3$, we sketch the graphs of these functions on the same set of axes. Because the graphs do not intersect on the interval $(-1, 3)$, we can determine which function is larger on this interval by evaluating $2x + 3$ and x^2 at any value c where $-1 < c < 3$. Figure 13.16 shows the region between the graphs, with $2x + 3 \geq x^2$ from $x = -1$ to $x = 3$. The area of the enclosed region is

$$A = \int_{-1}^{3} [(2x + 3) - x^2] \, dx = \left. x^2 + 3x - \frac{x^3}{3} \right|_{-1}^{3}$$

$$= (9 + 9 - 9) - \left(1 - 3 + \frac{1}{3}\right) = 10\tfrac{2}{3} \text{ square units}$$

Some graphs enclose two or more regions because they have more than two points of intersection.

EXAMPLE 3   A Region with Two Sections

Find the area of the region enclosed by the graphs of
$$y = f(x) = x^3 - x^2 \quad \text{and} \quad y = g(x) = 2x.$$

Solution

To find the points of intersection of the graphs, we solve $f(x) = g(x)$, or $x^3 - x^2 = 2x$.

$$x^3 - x^2 - 2x = 0$$
$$x(x - 2)(x + 1) = 0$$
$$x = 0, \ x = 2, \ x = -1$$

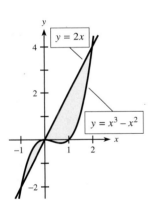

Figure 13.17

Graphing these functions between $x = -1$ and $x = 2$, we see that for any x-value in the interval $(-1, 0)$, $f(x) \geq g(x)$, so $f(x) \geq g(x)$ for the region enclosed by the curves from $x = -1$ to $x = 0$. But evaluating the functions for any x-value in the interval $(0, 2)$ shows that $f(x) \leq g(x)$ for the region enclosed by the curves from $x = 0$ to $x = 2$. See Figure 13.17.

Thus we need one integral to find the area of the region from $x = -1$ to $x = 0$ and a second integral to find the area from $x = 0$ to $x = 2$. The area is found by summing these two integrals.

$$A = \int_{-1}^{0} [(x^3 - x^2) - (2x)] \, dx + \int_{0}^{2} [(2x) - (x^3 - x^2)] \, dx$$

$$= \int_{-1}^{0} (x^3 - x^2 - 2x) \, dx + \int_{0}^{2} (2x - x^3 + x^2) \, dx$$

$$= \left. \left(\frac{x^4}{4} - \frac{x^3}{3} - x^2\right) \right|_{-1}^{0} + \left. \left(x^2 - \frac{x^4}{4} + \frac{x^3}{3}\right) \right|_{0}^{2}$$

$$= \left[(0) - \left(\frac{1}{4} - \frac{-1}{3} - 1\right)\right] + \left[\left(4 - \frac{16}{4} + \frac{8}{3}\right) - (0)\right] = \frac{37}{12}$$

The area between the curves is $\frac{37}{12}$ square units.

Calculator Note Most graphing calculators have a numerical integration feature, and some can perform both symbolic and numerical integration. Appendix C, Section 13.2, shows two methods of approximating the area between two curves with a graphing calculator. ▪

CHECKPOINT

1. True or false:
   (a) Over the interval $[a, b]$, the area between the continuous functions $f(x)$ and $g(x)$ is
   $$\int_a^b [f(x) - g(x)]\, dx$$
   (b) If $f(x) \geq g(x)$ and the area between $f(x)$ and $g(x)$ is given by
   $$\int_a^b [f(x) - g(x)]\, dx$$
   then $x = a$ and $x = b$ represent the left and right boundaries, respectively, of the region.
   (c) To find points of intersection of $f(x)$ and $g(x)$, solve $f(x) = g(x)$.

2. Consider the functions $f(x) = x^2 + 3x - 9$ and $g(x) = \dfrac{1}{4}x^2$.
   (a) Find the points of intersection of $f(x)$ and $g(x)$.
   (b) Determine which function is greater than the other between the points found in part (a).
   (c) Set up the integral used to find the area between the curves in the interval between the points found in part (a).
   (d) Find the area.

EXAMPLE | **4** | **Income Distribution** | APPLICATION PREVIEW |

The inequality of income distribution is measured by the **Gini coefficient** of income, which is defined as

$$\frac{\text{Area between } y = x \text{ and } y = L(x)}{\text{Area below } y = x} = \frac{\displaystyle\int_0^1 [x - L(x)]\, dx}{1/2}$$

$$= 2\int_0^1 [x - L(x)]\, dx$$

The function $y = L(x) = 2.266x^4 - 3.175x^3 + 2.056x^2 - 0.148x$ models the 2006 income distribution data in the Application Preview.

(a) Use this $L(x)$ to find the Gini coefficient of income for 2006.
(b) If the Census Bureau Gini coefficient of income for 1991 is 0.428, during which year is the distribution of income more nearly equal?

Solution
(a) The Gini coefficient of income for 2006 is
$$2\int_0^1 [x - L(x)]\, dx = 2\int_0^1 [x - (2.266x^4 - 3.175x^3 + 2.056x^2 - 0.148x)]\, dx$$
$$= 2[-0.453x^5 + 0.794x^4 - 0.685x^3 + 0.574x^2]_0^1 \approx 0.460$$

(b) Absolute equality of income would occur if the Gini coefficient of income were 0; and smaller coefficients indicate more nearly equal incomes. Thus the distribution of income was more nearly equal in 1991 than in 2006. ▪

Average Value   If the graph of $y = f(x)$ lies on or above the x-axis from $x = a$ to $x = b$, then the area between the graph and the x-axis is

$$A = \int_a^b f(x)\, dx \quad \text{(See Figure 13.18(a))}$$

The area A is also the area of a rectangle with base equal to $b - a$ and height equal to the **average value** (or average height) of the function $y = f(x)$ (see Figure 13.18(b)).

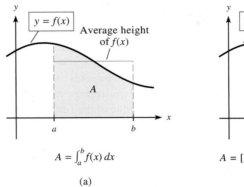

$A = \int_a^b f(x)\, dx$

(a)

$A = [\text{Average height of } f(x)](b - a)$

(b)

Figure 13.18

Thus the average value of the function in Figure 13.18 is

$$\frac{A}{b - a} = \frac{1}{b - a}\int_a^b f(x)\, dx$$

Even if $f(x) \le 0$ on all or part of the interval $[a, b]$, we can find the average value by using the integral. Thus we have the following.

Average Value

> The **average value** of a continuous function $y = f(x)$ over the interval $[a, b]$ is
>
> $$\text{Average value} = \frac{1}{b - a}\int_a^b f(x)\, dx$$

EXAMPLE 5   Average Cost

Suppose that the cost in dollars for x table lamps is given by $C(x) = 400 + x + 0.3x^2$.

(a) What is the average value of $C(x)$ for 10 to 20 units?
(b) Find the average cost per unit if 40 lamps are produced.

Solution
(a) The average value of $C(x)$ from $x = 10$ to $x = 20$ is

$$\frac{1}{20 - 10}\int_{10}^{20} (400 + x + 0.3x^2)\, dx = \frac{1}{10}\left(400x + \frac{x^2}{2} + 0.1x^3\right)\Big|_{10}^{20}$$

$$= \frac{1}{10}[(8000 + 200 + 800) - (4000 + 50 + 100)]$$

$$= 485 \quad \text{(dollars)}$$

Thus for any number of lamps between 10 and 20 the *average total cost* for that number of lamps is $485.

(b) The average cost per unit if 40 units are produced is the average cost function evaluated at $x = 40$. The average cost function is

$$\overline{C}(x) = \frac{C(x)}{x} = \frac{400}{x} + 1 + 0.3x$$

Thus the *average cost per unit* if 40 units are produced is

$$\overline{C}(40) = \frac{400}{40} + 1 + 0.3(40) = 23 \quad [\text{dollars per unit (i.e., lamp)}]$$

CHECKPOINT   3. Find the average value of $f(x) = x^2 - 4$ over $[-1, 3]$.

EXAMPLE 6   **Average Value of a Function**

Consider the functions $f(x) = x^2 - 4$ and $g(x) = x^3 - 4x$. For each function, do the following.

(a) Graph the function on the interval $[-3, 3]$.
(b) On the graph, "eyeball" the average value (height) of each function on $[-2, 2]$.
(c) Compute the average value of the function over the interval $[-2, 2]$.

Solution
For $f(x) = x^2 - 4$:

(a) The graph of $f(x) = x^2 - 4$ is shown in Figure 13.19(a).
(b) The average height of $f(x)$ over $[-2, 2]$ appears to be near -2.
(c) The average value of $f(x)$ over the interval is given by

$$\frac{1}{2 - (-2)} \int_{-2}^{2} (x^2 - 4)\, dx = \frac{1}{4}\left(\frac{x^3}{3} - 4x\right)\Big|_{-2}^{2}$$

$$= \left(\frac{8}{12} - 2\right) - \left(-\frac{8}{12} + 2\right) = \frac{4}{3} - 4 = -\frac{8}{3} = -2\tfrac{2}{3}$$

For $g(x) = x^3 - 4x$:
(a) The graph of $g(x) = x^3 - 4x$ is shown in Figure 13.19(b).
(b) The average height of $g(x)$ over $[-2, 2]$ appears to be approximately 0.
(c) The average value of $g(x)$ is given by

$$\frac{1}{2 - (-2)} \int_{-2}^{2} (x^3 - 4x)\, dx = \frac{1}{4}\left(\frac{x^4}{4} - \frac{4x^2}{2}\right)\Big|_{-2}^{2}$$

$$= \left(\frac{16}{16} - \frac{16}{8}\right) - \left(\frac{16}{16} - \frac{16}{8}\right) = 0$$

Figure 13.19   (a)   (b)

CHECKPOINT SOLUTIONS   1. (a) False. This is true only if $f(x) \geq g(x)$ over $[a, b]$.
(b) True   (c) True

2. (a) Solve $f(x) = g(x)$, or $x^2 + 3x - 9 = \frac{1}{4}x^2$.

$$\frac{3}{4}x^2 + 3x - 9 = 0$$
$$3x^2 + 12x - 36 = 0$$
$$x^2 + 4x - 12 = 0$$
$$(x + 6)(x - 2) = 0$$
$$x = -6, x = 2$$

The points of intersection are $(-6, 9)$ and $(2, 1)$.

(b) Evaluating $g(x)$ and $f(x)$ at any point in the interval $(-6, 2)$ shows that $g(x) > f(x)$, so $g(x) \geq f(x)$ on $[-6, 2]$.

(c) $A = \int_{-6}^{2} \left[\frac{1}{4}x^2 - (x^2 + 3x - 9) \right] dx$

(d) $A = \left. \frac{x^3}{12} - \frac{x^3}{3} - \frac{3x^2}{2} + 9x \right|_{-6}^{2} = 64$ square units

3. $\dfrac{1}{3 - (-1)} \displaystyle\int_{-1}^{3} (x^2 - 4)\, dx = \left. \dfrac{1}{4}\left(\dfrac{x^3}{3} - 4x \right) \right|_{-1}^{3}$

$= \dfrac{1}{4}\left[(9 - 12) - \left(-\dfrac{1}{3} + 4 \right) \right]$

$= \dfrac{1}{4}\left(\dfrac{-20}{3} \right) = -\dfrac{5}{3}$

| EXERCISES | 13.3

For each shaded region in Problems 1–6, (a) form the integral that represents the area of the shaded region and (b) find the area of the region.

For each shaded region in Problems 7–12, (a) find the points of intersection of the curves, (b) form the integral that represents the area of the shaded region, and (c) find the area of the shaded region.

1.

2.

3.

4.

5.

6.

7.

8.

9.

10.

11.

12.
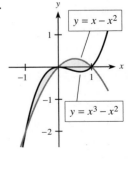

In Problems 13–26, equations are given whose graphs enclose a region. In each problem, find the area of the region.

13. $f(x) = x^2 + 2$; $g(x) = -x^2$; $x = 0$; $x = 2$
14. $f(x) = x^2$; $g(x) = -\frac{1}{10}(10 + x)$; $x = 0$; $x = 3$
15. $y = x^3 - 1$; $y = x - 1$; to the right of the y-axis
16. $y = x^2 - 2x + 1$; $y = x^2 - 5x + 4$; $x = 2$
17. $y = \frac{1}{2}x^2$; $y = x^2 - 2x$
18. $y = x^2$; $y = 4x - x^2$
19. $h(x) = x^2$; $k(x) = \sqrt{x}$
20. $g(x) = 1 - x^2$; $h(x) = x^2 + x$
21. $f(x) = x^3$; $g(x) = x^2 + 2x$
22. $f(x) = x^3$; $g(x) = 2x - x^2$
23. $f(x) = \dfrac{3}{x}$; $g(x) = 4 - x$
24. $f(x) = \dfrac{6}{x}$; $g(x) = -x - 5$
25. $y = \sqrt{x + 3}$; $x = -3$; $y = 2$
26. $y = \sqrt{4 - x}$; $x = 4$; $y = 3$

In Problems 27–32, find the average value of each function over the given interval.

27. $f(x) = 9 - x^2$ over $[0, 3]$
28. $f(x) = 2x - x^2$ over $[0, 2]$
29. $f(x) = x^3 - x$ over $[-1, 1]$
30. $f(x) = \frac{1}{2}x^3 + 1$ over $[-2, 0]$
31. $f(x) = \sqrt{x} - 2$ over $[1, 4]$
32. $f(x) = \sqrt[3]{x}$ over $[-8, -1]$

33. Use a graphing calculator or computer to find the area between the curves $y = f(x) = x^3 - 4x$ and $y = g(x) = x^2 - 4$.
34. Use a graphing calculator or computer to find the area between the curves $f(x) = \sqrt[3]{x}$ and $g(x) = x^3 - x$.

APPLICATIONS

35. *Average profit* For the product whose total cost and total revenue are shown in the figure, represent total revenue by $R(x)$ and total cost by $C(x)$ and write an integral that gives the average profit for the product over the interval from x_0 to x_1.

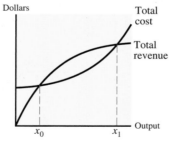

36. *Sales and advertising* The figure shows the sales growth rates under different levels of distribution and advertising from a to b. Set up an integral to determine the extra sales growth if $4 million is used in advertising rather than $2 million.

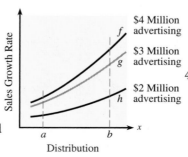

37. *Cost* The cost of producing x smart phones is $C(x) = x^2 + 400x + 2000$.
    (a) Use $C(x)$ to find the average cost of producing 1000 smart phones.
    (b) Find the average value of the cost function $C(x)$ over the interval from 0 to 1000.

38. *Inventory management* The figure shows how an inventory of a product is depleted each quarter of a given year. What is the average inventory per month for the first 3 months for this product? (Assume that the graph is a line joining (0, 1300) and (3, 100).)

Months

39. *Sales and advertising* The number of daily sales of a product was found to be given by

$$S = 100xe^{-x^2} + 100$$

x days after the start of an advertising campaign for this product.
    (a) Find the average daily sales during the first 20 days of the campaign—that is, from $x = 0$ to $x = 20$.
    (b) If no new advertising campaign is begun, what is the average number of sales per day for the next 10 days (from $x = 20$ to $x = 30$)?

40. *Demand* The demand function for a certain product is given by

$$p = 500 + \frac{1000}{q + 1}$$

where p is the price and q is the number of units demanded. Find the average price as demand ranges from 49 to 99 units.

41. *Social Security beneficiaries* With data from the Social Security Trustees Report for selected years from 1950 and projected to 2030, the number of Social Security beneficiaries (in millions) can be modeled by

$$B(t) = 0.00024t^3 - 0.026t^2 + 1.6t + 2.2$$

where t is the number of years past 1950. Use the model to find the average number of Social Security beneficiaries per year (actual and predicted) between
    (a) 1980 and 2000.   (b) 2010 and 2030.

42. *Total income* Suppose that the income from a slot machine in a casino flows continuously at a rate of

$$f(t) = 100e^{0.1t}$$

where t is the time in hours since the casino opened.

Then the total income during the first 10 hours is given by

$$\int_0^{10} 100e^{0.1t}\, dt$$

Find the average income over the first 10 hours.

43. ***Drug levels in the blood*** A drug manufacturer has developed a time-release capsule with the number of milligrams of the drug in the bloodstream given by

$$S = 30x^{18/7} - 240x^{11/7} + 480x^{4/7}$$

where x is in hours and $0 \le x \le 4$. Find the average number of milligrams of the drug in the bloodstream for the first 4 hours after a capsule is taken.

44. ***Income distribution*** The Lorenz curves for the income distribution in the United States in 1950 and in 1970 are given below. Find the Gini coefficient of income for both years and compare the distributions of income for these years.

$$1950: y = x^{2.1521}$$
$$1970: y = x^{2.2024}$$

45. ***Income distribution*** U.S. political analysts tend to believe that the tax policies of Republican administrations tend to favor the wealthy and those of Democratic administrations tend to favor the poor. The Lorenz curves for income distribution in 1988 (Reagan's final year) and 2000 (Clinton's final year) are given below. Find the Gini coefficient of income for each year and determine in which administration's final year the income distribution was more nearly equal. Does this support the conventional wisdom regarding the tax policies of Republicans versus Democrats?

$$1988: y = x^{2.3521} \qquad 2000: y = x^{2.4870}$$

46. ***Income distribution*** In an effort to make the distribution of income more nearly equal, the government of a country passes a tax law that changes the Lorenz curve from $y = 0.99x^{2.1}$ for one year to $y = 0.32x^2 + 0.68x$ for the next year. Find the Gini coefficient of income for both years and compare the distributions of income before and after the tax law was passed. Interpret the result.

47. ***Income distribution*** Data from the U.S. Bureau of the Census yields the Lorenz curves given below for income distribution among blacks and among Asians in the United States for 2003. Find the Gini coefficient of income for each group and determine in which group the income is more nearly equally distributed.

$$\text{Blacks: } y = x^{2.5938}$$
$$\text{Asians: } y = x^{2.5070}$$

48. ***Income distribution*** Suppose the Gini coefficient of income for a certain country is $2/5$. If the Lorenz curve for this country is

$$L(x) = \frac{1}{3}x + \frac{2}{3}x^p$$

find the value of p.

49. ***Gini coefficient*** If the Lorenz curve for the income distribution for a given year is $L(x) = x^p$, use integration to find a simple formula for the corresponding Gini coefficient.

50. ***Lorenz curve*** If the Lorenz curve for the income distribution for a given year has the form $L(x) = x^p$ and the Gini coefficient is G, find a formula for p.

OBJECTIVES

13.4

- To use definite integrals to find total income, present value, and future value of continuous income streams
- To use definite integrals to find the consumer's surplus
- To use definite integrals to find the producer's surplus

Applications of Definite Integrals in Business and Economics

| APPLICATION PREVIEW |

Suppose the oil pumped from a well is considered as a continuous income stream with annual rate of flow (in thousands of dollars per year) at time t years given by

$$f(t) = 600e^{-0.2(t+5)}$$

The company can use a definite integral involving $f(t)$ to estimate the well's present value over the next 10 years (see Example 2).

The definite integral can be used in a number of applications in business and economics. In addition to the present value, the definite integral can be used to find the total income over a fixed number of years from a continuous income stream.

Definite integrals also can be used to determine the savings realized in the marketplace by some consumers (called consumer's surplus) and some producers (called producer's surplus).

Continuous
Income Streams

An oil company's profits depend on the amount of oil that can be pumped from a well. Thus we can consider a pump at an oil field as producing a **continuous stream of income** for the owner. Because both the pump and the oil field "wear out" with time, the continuous stream of income is a function of time. Suppose $f(t)$ is the (annual) *rate* of flow of income from this pump; then we can find the total income from the rate of income by using integration. In particular, the total income for k years is given by

$$\text{Total income} = \int_0^k f(t) \, dt$$

EXAMPLE   1   Oil Revenue

Now ⟶ 10 Years From Now

$2,594,000 = Total Income

A small oil company considers the continuous pumping of oil from a well as a continuous income stream with its annual rate of flow at time t given by

$$f(t) = 600e^{-0.2t}$$

in thousands of dollars per year. Find an estimate of the total income from this well over the next 10 years.

Solution

$$\text{Total income} = \int_0^{10} f(t) \, dt = \int_0^{10} 600e^{-0.2t} \, dt$$

$$= \frac{600}{-0.2} e^{-0.2t} \Big|_0^{10} \approx 2594 \quad (\text{to the nearest integer})$$

Thus the total income is approximately $2,594,000. ∎

In addition to the total income from a continuous income stream, the **present value** of the stream is also important. The present value is the value today of a continuous income stream that will be providing income in the future. The present value is useful in deciding when to replace machinery or what new equipment to select.

To find the present value of a continuous stream of income with rate of flow $f(t)$, we first graph the function $f(t)$ and divide the time interval from 0 to k into n subintervals of width Δt_i, $i = 1$ to n.

The total amount of income is the area under this curve between $t = 0$ and $t = k$. We can approximate the amount of income in each subinterval by finding the area of the rectangle in that subinterval. (See Figure 13.20.)

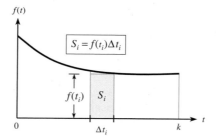

Figure 13.20

We have shown that the future value S that accrues if $P is invested for t years at an annual rate r, compounded continuously, is $S = Pe^{rt}$. Thus the present value of the investment that yields the single payment of $S after t years is

$$P = \frac{S}{e^{rt}} = Se^{-rt}$$

The contribution to S in the ith subinterval is $S_i = f(t_i) \, \Delta t_i$, and the present value of this amount is $P_i = f(t_i) \, \Delta t_i e^{-rt_i}$. Thus the total present value of S can be approximated by

$$\sum_{i=1}^{n} f(t_i) \, \Delta t_i e^{-rt_i}$$

This approximation improves as $\Delta t_i \to 0$ with the present value given by

$$\lim_{\Delta t_i \to 0} \sum_{i=1}^{n} f(t_i)\, \Delta t_i e^{-rt_i}$$

This limit gives the **present value** as a definite integral.

Present Value of a Continuous Income Stream	If $f(t)$ is the rate of continuous income flow earning interest at rate r, compounded continuously, then the **present value of the continuous income stream** is $$\text{Present value} = \int_0^k f(t)e^{-rt}\, dt$$ where $t = 0$ to $t = k$ is the time interval.

EXAMPLE 2   Present Value | APPLICATION PREVIEW |

Suppose that the oil company in Example 1 is planning to sell one of its wells because of its remote location. Suppose further that the company wants to use the present value of this well over the next 10 years to help establish its selling price. If the company determines that the annual rate of flow is

$$f(t) = 600e^{-0.2(t+5)}$$

in thousands of dollars per year, and if money is worth 10%, compounded continuously, find this present value.

Solution

$$\text{Present value} = \int_0^{10} f(t)e^{-rt}\, dt$$

$$= \int_0^{10} 600e^{-0.2(t+5)}e^{-0.1t}\, dt = \int_0^{10} 600e^{-0.3t-1}\, dt$$

If $u = -0.3t - 1$, then $u' = -0.3$ and we get

$$\frac{1}{-0.3} \int 600e^{-0.3t-1}(-0.3\, dt) = \frac{600}{-0.3} e^{-0.3t-1} \Big|_0^{10}$$

$$= -2000(e^{-4} - e^{-1}) \approx 699 \quad (\text{to the nearest integer})$$

Thus the present value is $699,000.

Recall that the future value of a continuously compounded investment at rate r after k years is Pe^{rk}, where P is the amount invested (or the present value). Thus, for a continuous income stream, the **future value** is found as follows.

Future Value of a Continuous Income Stream	If $f(t)$ is the rate of continuous income flow for k years earning interest at rate r, compounded continuously, then the **future value of the continuous income stream** is $$FV = e^{rk} \int_0^k f(t)e^{-rt}\, dt$$

EXAMPLE 3   Future Value

If the rate of flow of income from an asset is $1000e^{0.02t}$, in millions of dollars per year, and if the income is invested at 6% compounded continuously, find the future value of the asset 4 years from now.

Solution

The future value is given by

$$FV = e^{rk}\int_0^k f(t)e^{-rt}\,dt$$

$$= e^{(0.06)4}\int_0^4 1000e^{0.02t}e^{-0.06t}\,dt = e^{0.24}\int_0^4 1000e^{-0.04t}\,dt$$

$$= e^{0.24}(-25{,}000e^{-0.04t})|_0^4 = -25{,}000e^{0.24}(e^{-0.16} - 1)$$

$$\approx 4699.05 \quad \text{(millions of dollars)}$$

CHECKPOINT

1. Suppose that a continuous income stream has an annual rate of flow given by $f(t) = 5000e^{-0.01t}$, and suppose that money is worth 7% compounded continuously. Create the integral used to find
   (a) the total income for the next 5 years.
   (b) the present value for the next 5 years.
   (c) the future value 5 years from now.

Consumer's Surplus

Suppose that the demand for a product is given by $p = f(x)$ and that the supply of the product is described by $p = g(x)$. The price p_1 where the graphs of these functions intersect is the **equilibrium price** (see Figure 13.21(a)). As the demand curve shows, some consumers (but not all) would be willing to pay more than $\$p_1$ for the product.

For example, some consumers would be willing to buy x_3 units if the price were $\$p_3$. Those consumers willing to pay more than $\$p_1$ are benefiting from the lower price. The total gain for all those consumers willing to pay more than $\$p_1$ is called the **consumer's surplus**, and under proper assumptions the area of the shaded region in Figure 13.21(a) represents this consumer's surplus.

Looking at Figure 13.21(b), we see that if the demand curve has equation $p = f(x)$, the consumer's surplus is given by the area between $f(x)$ and the x-axis from 0 to x_1, *minus* the area of the rectangle denoted TR:

$$CS = \int_0^{x_1} f(x)\,dx - p_1 x_1$$

Note that with equilibrium price p_1 and equilibrium quantity x_1, the product $p_1 x_1$ is the area of the rectangle that represents the total dollars spent by consumers and received as revenue by producers (see Figure 13.21(b)).

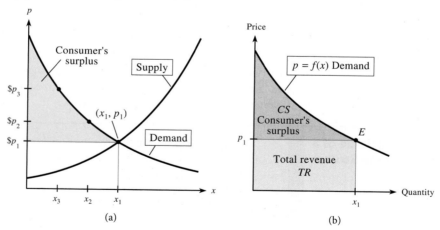

Figure 13.21   (a)   (b)

EXAMPLE 4 Consumer's Surplus

The demand function for x units of a product is $p = 1020/(x + 1)$ dollars. If the equilibrium price is $20, what is the consumer's surplus?

Solution
We must first find the quantity that will be purchased at this price. Letting $p = 20$ and solving for x, we get

$$20 = \frac{1020}{x + 1} \qquad \text{so} \qquad 20(x + 1) = 1020$$

Thus $\quad 20x + 20 = 1020 \quad$ or $\quad 20x = 1000 \quad$ so $\quad x = 50$

Thus the equilibrium point is (50, 20). The consumer's surplus is given by

$$CS = \int_0^{x_1} f(x)\, dx - p_1 x_1 = \int_0^{50} \frac{1020}{x + 1}\, dx - 20 \cdot 50$$

$$= 1020 \ln |x + 1| \Big|_0^{50} - 1000$$

$$= 1020(\ln 51 - \ln 1) - 1000$$
$$\approx 4010.46 - 1000 = 3010.46$$

The consumer's surplus is $3010.46.

EXAMPLE 5 **Consumer's Surplus**

A product's demand function is $p = \sqrt{49 - 6x}$ and its supply function is $p = x + 1$, where p is the price per unit in dollars and x is the number of units. Find the equilibrium point and the consumer's surplus there.

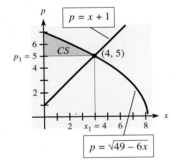

Solution
We can determine the equilibrium point by solving the two equations simultaneously.

$$\sqrt{49 - 6x} = x + 1$$
$$49 - 6x = (x + 1)^2$$
$$0 = x^2 + 8x - 48$$
$$0 = (x + 12)(x - 4)$$
$$x = 4 \quad \text{or} \quad x = -12$$

Thus the equilibrium quantity is 4 and the equilibrium price is $5 ($x = -12$ is not a solution). The graphs of the supply and demand functions are shown in Figure 13.22.
    The consumer's surplus is given by

$$CS = \int_0^4 f(x)\, dx - p_1 x_1 = \int_0^4 \sqrt{49 - 6x}\, dx - 5 \cdot 4$$

$$= -\frac{1}{6} \int_0^4 \sqrt{49 - 6x}\, (-6\, dx) - 20 = -\frac{1}{9}(49 - 6x)^{3/2} \Big|_0^4 - 20$$

$$= -\frac{1}{9}\left[(25)^{3/2} - (49)^{3/2}\right] - 20 = -\frac{1}{9}(125 - 343) - 20 \approx 4.22$$

The consumer's surplus is $4.22.

Figure 13.22

EXAMPLE 6 **Monopoly Market**

Suppose a monopoly has its total cost (in dollars) for a product given by $C(x) = 60 + 2x^2$. Suppose also that demand is given by $p = 30 - x$, where p is in dollars and x is the number of units. Find the consumer's surplus at the point where the monopoly has maximum profit.

Solution
We must first find the point where the profit function is maximized. Because the demand for x units is $p = 30 - x$, the total revenue is

$$R(x) = (30 - x)x = 30x - x^2$$

Thus the profit function is

$$P(x) = R(x) - C(x)$$
$$P(x) = 30x - x^2 - (60 + 2x^2)$$
$$P(x) = 30x - 60 - 3x^2$$

Then $P'(x) = 30 - 6x$. So $0 = 30 - 6x$ has the solution $x = 5$.

Because $P''(5) = -6 < 0$, the profit for the monopolist is maximized when $x = 5$ units are sold at price $p = 30 - x = 25$ dollars per unit.

If $f(x)$ is the demand function, the consumer's surplus at $x = 5$, $p = 25$ is given by

$$CS = \int_0^5 f(x)\, dx - 5 \cdot 25 = \int_0^5 (30 - x)\, dx - 125$$

$$= 30x - \frac{x^2}{2}\Big|_0^5 - 125 = \left(150 - \frac{25}{2}\right) - 125 = 12.50$$

The consumer's surplus is $12.50.

MONEY ON THE TABLE

Another way to understand consumer surplus is through the popular concept of "money on the table." Imagine you have $300 to spend on an iPod. When you get to the Apple store, the model you want costs only $250. You're delighted to spend only $250, but you **would** have spent all your money if the iPod had been priced at $300. In this example, Apple left money—$50 to be exact—on the table (or in your pocket). That's a consumer's surplus.

GRAVY

Now think of the iPod example in another way. Suppose Apple meets all its profit targets at a price of $200 per iPod. The fact that you pay $250 means that there is a producer surplus. Apple would sell that iPod at the $200 price point, but because you were willing to part with $250, the company receives an extra $50—or gravy—for its bottom line. That is, a producer's surplus.

Producer's Surplus

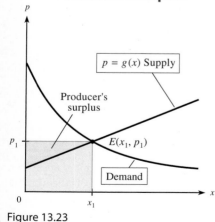

Figure 13.23

When a product is sold at the equilibrium price, some producers will also benefit, for they would have sold the product at a lower price. The area between the line $p = p_1$ and the supply curve (from $x = 0$ to $x = x_1$) gives the producer's surplus (see Figure 13.23).

If the supply function is $p = g(x)$, the **producer's surplus** is given by the area between the graph of $p = g(x)$ and the x-axis from 0 to x_1 *subtracted from $p_1 x_1$*, the area of the rectangle shown in Figure 13.23.

$$PS = p_1 x_1 - \int_0^{x_1} g(x)\, dx$$

Note that $p_1 x_1$ represents the total revenue at the equilibrium point.

EXAMPLE 7   Producer's Surplus

Suppose that the supply function for x million units of a product is $p = x^2 + x$ dollars per unit. If the equilibrium price is $20 per unit, what is the producer's surplus?

Solution

Because $p = 20$, we can find the equilibrium quantity x as follows:

$$20 = x^2 + x$$
$$0 = x^2 + x - 20$$
$$0 = (x + 5)(x - 4)$$
$$x = -5, \quad x = 4$$

The equilibrium point is $x = 4$ million units, $p = \$20$. The producer's surplus is given by

$$PS = 20 \cdot 4 - \int_0^4 (x^2 + x)\, dx$$

$$= 80 - \left(\frac{x^3}{3} + \frac{x^2}{2}\right)\Big|_0^4$$

$$= 80 - \left(\frac{64}{3} + 8\right)$$

$$\approx 50.67$$

The producer's surplus is $\$50.67$ million. See Figure 13.24.

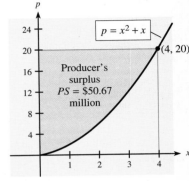

Figure 13.24

EXAMPLE 8   **Producer's Surplus**

The demand function for a product is $p = \sqrt{49 - 6x}$ and the supply function is $p = x + 1$. Find the producer's surplus.

Solution

We found the equilibrium point for these functions to be $(4, 5)$ in Example 5 (see Figure 13.22 earlier in this section). The producer's surplus is

$$PS = 5 \cdot 4 - \int_0^4 (x + 1)\, dx = 20 - \left(\frac{x^2}{2} + x\right)\Big|_0^4$$

$$= 20 - (8 + 4) = 8$$

The producer's surplus is $\$8$.

CHECKPOINT

2. Suppose that for a certain product, the supply function is $p = f(x)$, the demand function is $p = g(x)$, and the equilibrium point is (x_1, p_1). Decide whether the following are true or false.

   (a) $CS = \int_0^{x_1} f(x)\, dx - p_1 x_1$ (b) $PS = \int_0^{x_1} f(x)\, dx - p_1 x_1$

3. If demand is $p = \dfrac{100}{x + 1}$, supply is $p = x + 1$, and the market equilibrium is $(9, 10)$, create the integral used to find the
   (a) consumer's surplus.   (b) producer's surplus.

EXAMPLE 9   **Consumer's Surplus and Producer's Surplus**

Suppose that for x units of a certain product, the demand function is $p = 200e^{-0.01x}$ dollars and the supply function is $p = \sqrt{200x + 49}$ dollars.

(a) Use a graphing calculator to find the market equilibrium point.
(b) Find the consumer's surplus.
(c) Find the producer's surplus.

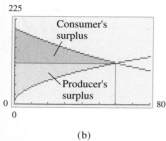

(a)

225

Consumer's surplus

Producer's surplus

0   80
0

(b)

Figure 13.25

Solution

(a) Solving $200e^{-0.01x} = \sqrt{200x + 49}$ is very difficult using algebraic techniques. Using SOLVER or INTERSECT on a graphing calculator gives $x = 60$, to the nearest unit, with a price of $109.76. (See Figure 13.25(a).)

(b) The consumer's surplus, shown in Figure 13.25(b), is

$$\int_0^{60} 200e^{-0.01x}\, dx - 109.76(60) = (-20,000e^{-0.01x})|_0^{60} - 6585.60$$
$$= -20,000e^{-0.6} + 20,000 - 6585.60$$
$$\approx 2438.17 \text{ dollars}$$

(c) The producer's surplus, shown in Figure 13.25(b), is

$$60(109.76) - \int_0^{60} \sqrt{200x + 49}\, dx = 6585.60 - \frac{1}{200}\left[\frac{(200x + 49)^{3/2}}{3/2}\right]_0^{60}$$
$$= 6585.60 - \frac{1}{300}[(12,049^{3/2} - 49^{3/2})] \approx 2178.10 \text{ dollars}$$

Note that we also could have evaluated these definite integrals with the numerical integration feature of a graphing calculator, and we would have obtained the same results. ■

CHECKPOINT SOLUTIONS

1. (a) $\displaystyle\int_0^5 5000e^{-0.01t}\, dt$

   (b) $\displaystyle\int_0^5 (5000e^{-0.01t})(e^{-0.07t})\, dt = \int_0^5 5000e^{-0.08t}\, dt$

   (c) $\displaystyle e^{(0.07)(5)}\int_0^5 (5000e^{-0.01t})(e^{-0.07t})\, dt = e^{0.35}\int_0^5 5000e^{-0.08t}\, dt$

2. (a) False. Consumer's surplus uses the demand function, so

$$CS = \int_0^{x_1} g(x)\, dx - p_1 x_1$$

   (b) False. Producer's surplus uses the supply function, but the formula is

$$PS = p_1 x_1 - \int_0^{x_1} f(x)\, dx$$

3. (a) $\displaystyle CS = \int_0^9 \frac{100}{x + 1}\, dx - 90$ (b) $\displaystyle PS = 90 - \int_0^9 (x + 1)\, dx$

| EXERCISES | 13.4

CONTINUOUS INCOME STREAMS

1. Find the total income over the next 10 years from a continuous income stream that has an annual rate of flow at time t given by $f(t) = 12,000e^{0.01t}$ (dollars per year).

2. Find the total income over the next 8 years from a continuous income stream with an annual rate of flow at time t given by $f(t) = 8500e^{-0.2t}$ (dollars per year).

3. Suppose that a steel company views the production of its continuous caster as a continuous income stream with a monthly rate of flow at time t given by

$$f(t) = 24,000e^{0.03t} \quad \text{(dollars per month)}$$

   Find the total income from this caster in the first year.

4. Suppose that the Quick-Fix Car Service franchise finds that the income generated by its stores can be modeled by assuming that the income is a continuous stream with a monthly rate of flow at time t given by

$$f(t) = 10,000e^{0.02t} \quad \text{(dollars per month)}$$

   Find the total income from a Quick-Fix store for the first 2 years of operation.

5. A small brewery considers the output of its bottling machine as a continuous income stream with an annual rate of flow at time t given by

$$f(t) = 80e^{-0.1t}$$

in thousands of dollars per year. Find the income from this stream for the next 10 years.

6. A company that services a number of vending machines considers its income as a continuous stream with an annual rate of flow at time t given by

$$f(t) = 120e^{-0.4t}$$

in thousands of dollars per year. Find the income from this stream over the next 5 years.

7. A franchise models the profit from its store as a continuous income stream with a monthly rate of flow at time t given by

$$f(t) = 3000e^{0.004t} \quad (\text{dollars per month})$$

When a new store opens, its manager is judged against the model, with special emphasis on the second half of the first year. Find the total profit for the second 6-month period ($t = 6$ to $t = 12$).

8. The Medi Spa franchise has a continuous income stream with a monthly rate of flow modeled by $f(t) = 20{,}000e^{0.03t}$ (dollars per month). Find the total income for years 2 through 5.

9. A continuous income stream has an annual rate of flow at time t given by

$$f(t) = 12{,}000e^{0.04t} \quad (\text{dollars per year})$$

If money is worth 8% compounded continuously, find the present value of this stream for the next 8 years.

10. A continuous income stream has an annual rate of flow at time t given by

$$f(t) = 9000e^{0.12t} \quad (\text{dollars per year})$$

Find the present value of this income stream for the next 10 years, if money is worth 6% compounded continuously.

11. The income from an established chain of laundromats is a continuous stream with its annual rate of flow at time t given by $f(t) = 630{,}000$ (dollars per year). If money is worth 7% compounded continuously, find the present value and future value of this chain over the next 5 years.

12. The profit from an insurance agency can be considered as a continuous income stream with an annual rate of flow at time t given by $f(t) = 840{,}000$ (dollars per year). Find the present value and future value of this agency over the next 12 years, if money is worth 8% compounded continuously.

13. Suppose that a printing firm considers its production as a continuous income stream. If the annual rate of flow at time t is given by

$$f(t) = 97.5e^{-0.2(t+3)}$$

in thousands of dollars per year, and if money is worth 6% compounded continuously, find the present value and future value of the presses over the next 10 years.

14. Suppose that a vending machine company is considering selling some of its machines. Suppose further that the income from these particular machines is a continuous stream with an annual rate of flow at time t given by

$$f(t) = 12e^{-0.4(t+3)}$$

in thousands of dollars per year. Find the present value and future value of the machines over the next 5 years if money is worth 10% compounded continuously.

15. A 58-year-old couple are considering opening a business of their own. They will either purchase an established Gift and Card Shoppe or open a new Wine Boutique. The Gift Shoppe has a continuous income stream with an annual rate of flow at time t given by

$$G(t) = 30{,}000 \quad (\text{dollars per year})$$

and the Wine Boutique has a continuous income stream with a projected annual rate of flow at time t given by

$$W(t) = 21{,}600e^{0.08t} \quad (\text{dollars per year})$$

The initial investment is the same for both businesses, and money is worth 10% compounded continuously. Find the present value of each business over the next 7 years (until the couple reach age 65) to see which is the better buy.

16. If the couple in Problem 15 plan to keep the business until age 70 (for the next 12 years), find each present value to see which business is the better buy in this case.

CONSUMER'S SURPLUS

In Problems 17–26, p and C are in dollars and x is the number of units.

17. The demand function for a product is $p = 34 - x^2$. If the equilibrium price is \$9 per unit, what is the consumer's surplus?

18. The demand function for a product is $p = 100 - 4x$. If the equilibrium price is \$40 per unit, what is the consumer's surplus?

19. The demand function for a product is $p = 200/(x + 2)$. If the equilibrium quantity is 8 units, what is the consumer's surplus?

20. The demand function for a certain product is $p = 100/(1 + 2x)$. If the equilibrium quantity is 12 units, what is the consumer's surplus?

21. The demand function for a certain product is $p = 81 - x^2$ and the supply function is $p = x^2 + 4x + 11$. Find the equilibrium point and the consumer's surplus there.

22. The demand function for a product is $p = 49 - x^2$ and the supply function is $p = 4x + 4$. Find the equilibrium point and the consumer's surplus there.

23. If the demand function for a product is $p = 12/(x + 1)$ and the supply function is $p = 1 + 0.2x$, find the consumer's surplus under pure competition.

24. If the demand function for a good is $p = 110 - x^2$ and the supply function for it is $p = 2 - \frac{6}{5}x + \frac{1}{5}x^2$, find the consumer's surplus under pure competition.

25. A monopoly has a total cost function $C = 1000 + 120x + 6x^2$ for its product, which has demand function $p = 360 - 3x - 2x^2$. Find the consumer's surplus at the point where the monopoly has maximum profit.

26. A monopoly has a total cost function $C = 500 + 2x^2 + 10x$ for its product, which has demand function $p = -\frac{1}{3}x^2 - 2x + 30$. Find the consumer's surplus at the point where the monopoly has maximum profit.

PRODUCER'S SURPLUS

In Problems 27–36, p is in dollars and x is the number of units.

27. Suppose that the supply function for a good is $p = 4x^2 + 2x + 2$. If the equilibrium price is \$422 per unit, what is the producer's surplus there?

28. Suppose that the supply function for a good is $p = 0.1x^2 + 3x + 20$. If the equilibrium price is \$36 per unit, what is the producer's surplus there?

29. If the supply function for a commodity is $p = 10e^{x/3}$, what is the producer's surplus when 15 units are sold?

30. If the supply function for a commodity is $p = 40 + 100(x + 1)^2$, what is the producer's surplus at $x = 20$?

31. Find the producer's surplus for a product if its demand function is $p = 81 - x^2$ and its supply function is $p = x^2 + 4x + 11$.

32. Find the producer's surplus for a product if its demand function is $p = 49 - x^2$ and its supply function is $p = 4x + 4$.

33. Find the producer's surplus for a product with demand function $p = 12/(x + 1)$ and supply function $p = 1 + 0.2x$.

34. Find the producer's surplus for a product with demand function $p = 110 - x^2$ and supply function $p = 2 - \frac{6}{5}x + \frac{1}{5}x^2$.

35. The demand function for a certain product is $p = 144 - 2x^2$ and the supply function is $p = x^2 + 33x + 48$. Find the producer's surplus at the equilibrium point.

36. The demand function for a product is $p = 280 - 4x - x^2$ and the supply function for it is $p = 160 + 4x + x^2$. Find the producer's surplus at the equilibrium point.

OBJECTIVE

- To use tables of integrals to evaluate certain integrals

13.5

Using Tables of Integrals

| APPLICATION PREVIEW |

With data from the International Telecommunications Union for 1990 through 2007, the rate of change of total market revenue for worldwide telecommunications (in billions of dollars per year) can be modeled by

$$\frac{dR}{dt} = 37.988(1.101^t)$$

where $t = 0$ represents 1990 and $R = \$920$ billion in 1999. Finding the function for total market revenue or the predicted revenue for 2015 (when $t = 25$) requires evaluating

$$\int 37.988(1.101^t)\, dt$$

Evaluating this integral is made easier by using a formula such as those given in Table 13.2. (See Example 4.)

The formulas in this table, and others listed in other resources, extend the number of integrals that can be evaluated. Using the formulas is not quite as easy as it may sound because finding the correct formula and using it properly may present problems. The examples in this section illustrate how some of these formulas are used.

| TABLE 13.2 |

INTEGRATION FORMULAS

1. $\displaystyle\int u^n \, du = \frac{u^{n+1}}{n+1} + C, \;\; \text{for } n \neq -1$

2. $\displaystyle\int \frac{du}{u} = \int u^{-1} \, du = \ln|u| + C$

3. $\displaystyle\int a^u \, du = a^u \log_a e + C = \frac{a^u}{\ln a} + C$

4. $\displaystyle\int e^u \, du = e^u + C$

5. $\displaystyle\int \frac{du}{a^2 - u^2} = \frac{1}{2a} \ln\left|\frac{a+u}{a-u}\right| + C$

6. $\displaystyle\int \sqrt{u^2 + a^2} \, du = \frac{1}{2}\left(u\sqrt{u^2 + a^2} + a^2 \ln|u + \sqrt{u^2 + a^2}|\right) + C$

7. $\displaystyle\int \sqrt{u^2 - a^2} \, du = \frac{1}{2}\left(u\sqrt{u^2 - a^2} - a^2 \ln|u + \sqrt{u^2 - a^2}|\right) + C$

8. $\displaystyle\int \frac{du}{\sqrt{u^2 + a^2}} = \ln|u + \sqrt{u^2 + a^2}| + C$

9. $\displaystyle\int \frac{du}{u\sqrt{a^2 - u^2}} = -\frac{1}{a} \ln\left|\frac{a + \sqrt{a^2 - u^2}}{u}\right| + C$

10. $\displaystyle\int \frac{du}{\sqrt{u^2 - a^2}} = \ln|u + \sqrt{u^2 - a^2}| + C$

11. $\displaystyle\int \frac{du}{u\sqrt{a^2 + u^2}} = -\frac{1}{a} \ln\left|\frac{a + \sqrt{a^2 + u^2}}{u}\right| + C$

12. $\displaystyle\int \frac{u \, du}{au + b} = \frac{u}{a} - \frac{b}{a^2} \ln|au + b| + C$

13. $\displaystyle\int \frac{du}{u(au + b)} = \frac{1}{b} \ln\left|\frac{u}{au + b}\right| + C$

14. $\displaystyle\int \ln u \, du = u(\ln u - 1) + C$

15. $\displaystyle\int \frac{u \, du}{(au + b)^2} = \frac{1}{a^2}\left(\ln|au + b| + \frac{b}{au + b}\right) + C$

16. $\displaystyle\int u\sqrt{au + b} \, du = \frac{2(3au - 2b)(au + b)^{3/2}}{15a^2} + C$

EXAMPLE 1   Using an Integration Formula

Evaluate $\displaystyle\int \frac{dx}{\sqrt{x^2 + 4}}$.

Solution

We must find a formula in Table 13.2 that is of the same form as this integral. We see that formula 8 has the desired form, *if* we let $u = x$ and $a = 2$. Thus

$$\int \frac{dx}{\sqrt{x^2 + 4}} = \ln|x + \sqrt{x^2 + 4}| + C$$

EXAMPLE 2   Fitting Integration Formulas

Evaluate (a) $\displaystyle\int_1^2 \frac{dx}{x^2 + 2x}$ and   (b) $\displaystyle\int \ln (2x + 1)\, dx$.

Solution

(a) There does not appear to be any formula that has exactly the same form as this integral. But if we rewrite the integral as

$$\int_1^2 \frac{dx}{x(x + 2)}$$

we see that formula 13 will work. Letting $u = x$, $a = 1$, and $b = 2$, we get

$$\int_1^2 \frac{dx}{x(x + 2)} = \frac{1}{2} \ln \left| \frac{x}{x + 2} \right| \Big|_1^2 = \frac{1}{2} \ln \left| \frac{2}{4} \right| - \frac{1}{2} \ln \left| \frac{1}{3} \right|$$

$$= \frac{1}{2} \left(\ln \frac{1}{2} - \ln \frac{1}{3} \right)$$

$$= \frac{1}{2} \ln \frac{3}{2} \approx 0.2027$$

(b) This integral has the form of formula 14, with $u = 2x + 1$. But if $u = 2x + 1$, du must be represented by the differential of $2x + 1$ (that is, $2\, dx$). Thus

$$\int \ln (2x + 1)\, dx = \frac{1}{2} \int \ln (2x + 1)(2\, dx)$$

$$= \frac{1}{2} \int \ln (u)\, du = \frac{1}{2} u[\ln (u) - 1] + C$$

$$= \frac{1}{2}(2x + 1)[\ln (2x + 1) - 1] + C$$

CHECKPOINT

1. Can both $\displaystyle\int \frac{dx}{\sqrt{x^2 - 4}}$ and $\displaystyle-\int \frac{dx}{\sqrt{4 - x^2}}$ be evaluated with formula 10 in Table 13.2?

2. Determine the formula used to evaluate $\displaystyle\int \frac{3x}{4x - 5}\, dx$, and show how the formula would be applied.

3. True or false: In order for us to use a formula, the given integral must correspond exactly to the formula, including du.

4. True or false: $\displaystyle\int \frac{dx}{x^2(3x^2 - 7)}$ can be evaluated with formula 13.

5. True or false: $\displaystyle\int \frac{dx}{(6x + 1)^2}$ can be evaluated with either formula 1 or formula 15.

6. True or false: $\displaystyle\int \sqrt{x^2 + 4}\, dx$ can be evaluated with formula 1, formula 6, or formula 16.

EXAMPLE 3   Fitting an Integration Formula

Evaluate $\displaystyle\int_1^2 \frac{dx}{x\sqrt{81 - 9x^2}}$.

Solution

This integral is similar to that of formula 9 in Table 13.2. Letting $a = 9$, letting $u = 3x$, and multiplying the numerator and denominator by 3 gives the proper form.

$$\int_1^2 \frac{dx}{x\sqrt{81 - 9x^2}} = \int_1^2 \frac{3\,dx}{3x\sqrt{81 - 9x^2}}$$

$$= -\frac{1}{9} \ln \left| \frac{9 + \sqrt{81 - 9x^2}}{3x} \right| \Bigg|_1^2$$

$$= \left[-\frac{1}{9} \ln \left(\frac{9 + \sqrt{45}}{6} \right) \right] - \left[-\frac{1}{9} \ln \left(\frac{9 + \sqrt{72}}{3} \right) \right]$$

$$\approx 0.088924836$$

Remember that the formulas given in Table 13.2 represent only a very small sample of all possible integration formulas. Additional formulas may be found in books of mathematical tables or online.

EXAMPLE 4   Worldwide Telecommunications Revenue | APPLICATION PREVIEW |

With data from 1990 through 2007, the rate of change of total market revenue for worldwide telecommunications (in billions of dollars per year) can be modeled by

$$\frac{dR}{dt} = 37.988(1.101^t)$$

where $t = 0$ represents 1990 and $R = \$920$ billion in 1999 (*Source:* International Telecommunications Union).

(a) Find the function that models the total market revenue for worldwide telecommunications.
(b) Find the predicted total market revenue for 2015.

Solution
(a) To find $R(t)$ we integrate dR/dt by using formula 3, with $a = 1.101$ and $u = t$.

$$R(t) = \int 37.988(1.101^t)\,dt = 37.988 \int (1.101^t)\,dt = 37.988\frac{(1.101^t)}{\ln(1.101)} + C.$$
$$R(t) \approx 394.808(1.101^t) + C$$

We use the fact that $R = \$920$ billion in 1999 (when $t = 9$) to find the value of C.

$$920 = 394.808(1.101^9) + C \Rightarrow 920 = 938.6 + C \Rightarrow C = -18.6$$

Thus $R(t) = 394.808(1.101^t) - 18.6$.
(b) The predicted revenue in 2015 (when $t = 25$) is

$$R(25) = 394.808(1.101^{25}) - 18.6 \approx 4357 \text{ billion dollars}$$

Calculator Note   Numerical integration with a graphing calculator is especially useful in evaluating definite integrals when the formulas for the integrals are difficult to use or are not available. For example, evaluating the definite integral in Example 3 with the numerical integration feature of a graphing calculator gives 0.08892484. The decimal approximation of the answer found in Example 3 is 0.088924836, so the numerical approximation of the answer agrees for the first 8 decimal places.

CHECKPOINT SOLUTIONS

1. No. Although $\displaystyle\int \frac{dx}{\sqrt{x^2 - 4}}$ can be evaluated with formula 10 from Table 13.2,

$$-\int \frac{dx}{\sqrt{4 - x^2}}$$ cannot, because $\sqrt{4 - x^2}$ cannot be rewritten in the form $\sqrt{u^2 - a^2}$

as is needed for this formula to be used.
2. Use formula 12 with $u = x$, $a = 4$, $b = -5$, and $du = dx$.

$$\int \frac{3x}{4x - 5}\, dx = 3\int \frac{x\, dx}{4x - 5} = 3\int \frac{u\, du}{au + b} = 3\left(\frac{u}{a} - \frac{b}{a^2} \ln |au + b| + C\right)$$

$$= \frac{3x}{4} + \frac{15}{16} \ln |4x - 5| + C$$

3. True. An exact correspondence with the formula and du is necessary.
4. False. With $u = x^2$, we must have $du = 2x\, dx$. In this problem there is no x with dx, so the problem cannot correspond to formula 13.
5. False. The integral can be evaluated with formula 1, but not with formula 15. The correspondence is $u = 6x + 1$, $du = 6\, dx$, and $n = -2$.
6. False. The integral can be evaluated only with formula 6, with $u = x$, $du = dx$, and $a = 2$, but not with formula 1 or formula 16.

| EXERCISES | 13.5

Evaluate the integrals in Problems 1–32. Identify the formula used.

1. $\displaystyle\int \frac{dx}{16 - x^2}$

2. $\displaystyle\int \frac{dx}{x(3x + 5)}$

3. $\displaystyle\int_1^4 \frac{dx}{x\sqrt{9 + x^2}}$

4. $\displaystyle\int \frac{dx}{x\sqrt{9 - x^2}}$

5. $\displaystyle\int \ln w\, dw$

6. $\displaystyle\int 4(3^x)\, dx$

7. $\displaystyle\int_0^2 \frac{q\, dq}{6q + 9}$

8. $\displaystyle\int_1^5 \frac{dq}{q\sqrt{25 + q^2}}$

9. $\displaystyle\int \frac{dv}{v(3v + 8)}$

10. $\displaystyle\int_0^3 \sqrt{x^2 + 16}\, dx$

11. $\displaystyle\int_5^7 \sqrt{x^2 - 25}\, dx$

12. $\displaystyle\int \frac{x\, dx}{(3x + 2)^2}$

13. $\displaystyle\int w\sqrt{4w + 5}\, dw$

14. $\displaystyle\int \frac{dy}{\sqrt{9 + y^2}}$

15. $\displaystyle\int x\, 5^{x^2}\, dx$

16. $\displaystyle\int \sqrt{9x^2 + 4}\, dx$

17. $\displaystyle\int_0^3 x\sqrt{x^2 + 4}\, dx$

18. $\displaystyle\int x\sqrt{x^4 - 36}\, dx$

19. $\displaystyle\int \frac{5\, dx}{x\sqrt{4 - 9x^2}}$

20. $\displaystyle\int x\, e^{x^2}\, dx$

21. $\displaystyle\int \frac{dx}{\sqrt{9x^2 - 4}}$

22. $\displaystyle\int \frac{dx}{25 - 4x^2}$

23. $\displaystyle\int \frac{3x\, dx}{(2x - 5)^2}$

24. $\displaystyle\int_0^1 \frac{x\, dx}{6 - 5x}$

25. $\displaystyle\int \frac{dx}{\sqrt{(3x + 1)^2 + 1}}$

26. $\displaystyle\int \frac{dx}{9 - (2x + 3)^2}$

27. $\displaystyle\int_0^3 x\sqrt{(x^2 + 1)^2 + 9}\, dx$

28. $\displaystyle\int_1^e x \ln x^2\, dx$

29. $\displaystyle\int \frac{x\, dx}{7 - 3x^2}$

30. $\displaystyle\int_0^1 \frac{e^x}{1 + e^x}\, dx$

31. $\displaystyle\int \frac{dx}{\sqrt{4x^2 + 7}}$

32. $\displaystyle\int e^{2x}\sqrt{3e^x + 1}\, dx$

 Use formulas or numerical integration with a graphing calculator or computer to evaluate the definite integrals in Problems 33–36.

33. $\displaystyle\int_2^3 \frac{e^{\sqrt{x-1}}}{\sqrt{x - 1}}\, dx$

34. $\displaystyle\int_2^4 \frac{3x}{\sqrt{x^4 - 9}}\, dx$

35. $\displaystyle\int_0^1 \frac{x^3\, dx}{(4x^2 + 5)^2}$

36. $\displaystyle\int_0^1 (e^x + 1)^3 e^x\, dx$

APPLICATIONS

37. **Producer's surplus** If the supply function for x units of a commodity is $p = 40 + 100 \ln (x + 1)^2$ dollars, what is the producer's surplus at $x = 20$?

38. **Consumer's surplus** If the demand function for wheat is $p = \dfrac{1500}{\sqrt{x^2 + 1}} + 4$ dollars, where x is the number of hundreds of bushels of wheat, what is the consumer's surplus at $x = 7$, $p = 216.13$?

39. **Cost** (a) If the marginal cost for x units of a good is $MC = \sqrt{x^2 + 9}$ (dollars per unit) and if the fixed cost is \$300, what is the total cost function of the good?
    (b) What is the total cost of producing 4 units of this good?

40. **Consumer's surplus** Suppose that the demand function for an appliance is

$$p = \frac{400q + 400}{(q + 2)^2}$$

where q is the number of units and p is in dollars. What is the consumer's surplus if the equilibrium price is \$19 and the equilibrium quantity is 18?

41. **Income streams** Suppose that when a new oil well is opened, its production is viewed as a continuous income stream with monthly rate of flow

$$f(t) = 10 \ln (t + 1) - 0.1t$$

where t is time in months and $f(t)$ is in thousands of dollars per month. Find the total income over the next 10 years (120 months).

42. *Spread of disease* An isolated community of 1000 people susceptible to a certain disease is exposed when one member returns carrying the disease. If x represents the number infected with the disease at time t (in days), then the rate of change of x is proportional to the product of the number infected, x, and the number still susceptible, $1000 - x$. That is,

$$\frac{dx}{dt} = kx(1000 - x) \quad \text{or} \quad \frac{dx}{x(1000 - x)} = k\,dt$$

(a) If $k = 0.001$, integrate both sides to solve this differential equation.
(b) Find how long it will be before half the population of the community is affected.
(c) Find the rate of new cases, dx/dt, every other day for the first 13 days.

OBJECTIVE 13.6

- To evaluate integrals using the method of integration by parts

Integration by Parts

| APPLICATION PREVIEW |

If the value of oil produced by a piece of oil extraction equipment is considered a continuous income stream with an annual rate of flow (in dollars per year) at time t in years given by

$$f(t) = 300{,}000 - 2500t, \quad 0 \le t \le 10$$

and if money can be invested at 8%, compounded continuously, then the present value of the piece of equipment is

$$\int_0^{10} (300{,}000 - 2500t)e^{-0.08t}\,dt$$

$$= 300{,}000 \int_0^{10} e^{-0.08t}\,dt - 2500 \int_0^{10} te^{-0.08t}\,dt$$

The first integral can be evaluated with the formula for the integral of $e^u\,du$. Evaluating the second integral can be done by using integration by parts, which is a special technique that involves rewriting an integral in a form that can be evaluated. (See Example 6.)

Integration by parts is an integration technique that uses a formula that follows from the Product Rule for derivatives (actually differentials) as follows:

$$\frac{d}{dx}(uv) = u\frac{dv}{dx} + v\frac{du}{dx} \quad \text{so} \quad d(uv) = u\,dv + v\,du$$

Rearranging the differential form and integrating both sides give the following.

$$u\,dv = d(uv) - v\,du$$
$$\int u\,dv = \int d(uv) - \int v\,du$$
$$\int u\,dv = uv - \int v\,du$$

Integration by Parts Formula

$$\int u\,dv = uv - \int v\,du$$

Integration by parts is very useful if the integral we seek to evaluate can be treated as the product of one function, u, and the differential dv of a second function, so that the two integrals $\int dv$ and $\int v\,du$ can be found. Let us consider an example using this method.

EXAMPLE 1 **Integration by Parts**

Evaluate $\int xe^x \, dx$.

Solution

We cannot evaluate this integral using methods we have learned. But we can "split" the integrand into two parts, setting one part equal to u and the other part equal to dv. This "split" must be done in such a way that $\int dv$ and $\int v \, du$ can be evaluated. Letting $u = x$ and letting $dv = e^x \, dx$ are possible choices. If we make these choices, we have

$$u = x \qquad dv = e^x \, dx$$
$$du = 1 \, dx \qquad v = \int e^x \, dx = e^x$$

Then

$$\int xe^x \, dx = uv - \int v \, du$$
$$= xe^x - \int e^x \, dx = xe^x - e^x + C$$

We see that choosing $u = x$ and $dv = e^x \, dx$ worked in evaluating $\int xe^x \, dx$ in Example 1. If we had chosen $u = e^x$ and $dv = x \, dx$, the results would not have been so successful.

How can we select u and dv to make integration by parts work? As a general guideline, we do the following.

First identify the types of functions occurring in the problem in the order

Logarithm, Polynomial (or Power of x), Radical, Exponential*

Thus, in Example 1, we had x and e^x, a polynomial and an exponential.

Second, choose u to equal the function whose type occurs first on the list; hence in Example 1 we chose $u = x$. Then dv equals the rest of the integrand (and always includes dx) so that $u \, dv$ equals the original integrand. A helpful way to remember the order of the function types that help us choose u is the sentence

"Lazy People Rarely Excel."

in which the first letters, LPRE, coordinate with the order and types of functions. Consider the following examples.

Alexander Gitlits/Shutterstock.com

EXAMPLE 2 **Integration by Parts**

Evaluate $\int x \ln x \, dx$.

Solution

The integral contains a logarithm ($\ln x$) and a polynomial (x). Thus, let $u = \ln x$ and $dv = x \, dx$. Then

$$du = \frac{1}{x} \, dx \quad \text{and} \quad v = \frac{x^2}{2}$$

so

$$\int x \ln x \, dx = u \cdot v - \int v \, du = (\ln x) \frac{x^2}{2} - \int \frac{x^2}{2} \cdot \frac{1}{x} \, dx$$
$$= \frac{x^2}{2} \ln x - \int \frac{x}{2} \, dx = \frac{x^2}{2} \ln x - \frac{x^2}{4} + C$$

Note that letting $dv = \ln x \, dx$ is contrary to our guidelines and would lead to great difficulty in evaluating $\int dv$ and $\int v \, du$.

*This order is related to the ease with which the function types can be integrated.

EXAMPLE 3 Integration by Parts

Evaluate $\int \ln x^2 \, dx$.

Solution

The only function in this problem is a logarithm, the first function type on our list for choosing u. Thus

$$u = \ln x^2 \qquad\qquad dv = dx$$
$$du = \frac{2x}{x^2} \, dx = \frac{2}{x} \, dx \qquad v = x$$

Then

$$\int \ln x^2 \, dx = x \ln x^2 - \int x \cdot \frac{2}{x} \, dx = x \ln x^2 - 2x + C$$

Note that if we write $\ln x^2$ as $2 \ln x$, we can also evaluate this integral using formula 14 in Table 13.2 in the previous section, so integration by parts would not be needed. ◼

CHECKPOINT

1. True or false: In evaluating $\int u \, dv$ by parts,
   (a) the parts u and dv are selected and the parts du and v are calculated.
   (b) the differential (often dx) is always chosen as part of dv.
   (c) the parts du and v are found from u and dv as follows:

   $$du = u' \, dx \quad \text{and} \quad v = \int dv$$

   (d) For $\int \dfrac{3x}{e^{2x}} \, dx$, we could choose $u = 3x$ and $dv = e^{2x} \, dx$.

2. For $\int \dfrac{\ln x}{x^4} \, dx$,
   (a) identify u and dv.
   (b) find du and v.
   (c) complete the evaluation of the integral.

Sometimes it is necessary to repeat integration by parts to complete the evaluation. When this occurs, at each use of integration by parts it is important to choose u and dv consistently according to our guidelines.

EXAMPLE 4 Repeated Integration by Parts

Evaluate $\int x^2 e^{2x} \, dx$.

Solution

Let $u = x^2$ and $dv = e^{2x} \, dx$, so $du = 2x \, dx$ and $v = \frac{1}{2} e^{2x}$. Then

$$\int x^2 e^{2x} \, dx = \frac{1}{2} x^2 e^{2x} - \int x e^{2x} \, dx$$

We cannot evaluate $\int x e^{2x} \, dx$ directly, but this new integral is simpler than the original, and a second integration by parts will be successful. Letting $u = x$ and $dv = e^{2x} \, dx$ gives $du = dx$ and $v = \frac{1}{2} e^{2x}$. Thus

$$\int x^2 e^{2x} \, dx = \frac{1}{2} x^2 e^{2x} - \left(\frac{1}{2} x e^{2x} - \int \frac{1}{2} e^{2x} \, dx \right)$$

$$= \frac{1}{2} x^2 e^{2x} - \frac{1}{2} x e^{2x} + \frac{1}{4} e^{2x} + C$$

$$= \frac{1}{4} e^{2x} (2x^2 - 2x + 1) + C$$

◼

The most obvious choices for u and dv are not always the correct ones, as the following example shows. Integration by parts may still involve some trial and error.

EXAMPLE 5   A Tricky Integration by Parts

Evaluate $\int x^3 \sqrt{x^2 + 1}\, dx$.

Solution

Here we have a polynomial (x^3) and a radical. However, if we choose $u = x^3$, then the resulting $dv = \sqrt{x^2 + 1}\, dx$ cannot be integrated easily. But we can use $\sqrt{x^2 + 1}$ as part of dv, and we can evaluate $\int dv$ if we let $dv = x\sqrt{x^2 + 1}\, dx$. Then

$$u = x^2 \quad dv = (x^2 + 1)^{1/2} x\, dx$$

$$du = 2x\, dx \quad v = \int (x^2 + 1)^{1/2} (x\, dx) = \frac{1}{2}\int (x^2 + 1)^{1/2} (2x\, dx)$$

$$v = \frac{1}{2}\frac{(x^2 + 1)^{3/2}}{3/2} = \frac{1}{3}(x^2 + 1)^{3/2}$$

Then $\int x^3 \sqrt{x^2 + 1}\, dx = \frac{x^2}{3}(x^2 + 1)^{3/2} - \int \frac{1}{3}(x^2 + 1)^{3/2}(2x\, dx)$

$$= \frac{x^2}{3}(x^2 + 1)^{3/2} - \frac{1}{3}\frac{(x^2 + 1)^{5/2}}{5/2} + C$$

$$= \frac{x^2}{3}(x^2 + 1)^{3/2} - \frac{2}{15}(x^2 + 1)^{5/2} + C$$

EXAMPLE 6   Income Stream | APPLICATION PREVIEW |

Suppose that the value of oil produced by a piece of oil extraction equipment is considered a continuous income stream with an annual rate of flow (in dollars per year) at time t in years given by

$$f(t) = 300{,}000 - 2500t, \quad 0 \le t \le 10$$

and that money is worth 8%, compounded continuously. Find the present value of the piece of equipment.

Solution

The present value of the piece of equipment is given by

$$\int_0^{10} (300{,}000 - 2500t)e^{-0.08t}\, dt = 300{,}000\int_0^{10} e^{-0.08t}\, dt - 2500\int_0^{10} te^{-0.08t}\, dt$$

$$= \frac{300{,}000}{-0.08} e^{-0.08t}\Big|_0^{10} - 2500\int_0^{10} te^{-0.08t}\, dt$$

The value of the first integral is

$$\frac{300{,}000}{-0.08} e^{-0.08t}\Big|_0^{10} = \frac{300{,}000}{-0.08} e^{-0.8} - \frac{300{,}000}{-0.08}$$

$$\approx -1{,}684{,}983.615 + 3{,}750{,}000 = 2{,}065{,}016.385$$

The second of these integrals can be evaluated by using integration by parts, with $u = t$ and $dv = e^{-0.08t}\,dt$. Then $du = 1\,dt$ and $v = \dfrac{e^{-0.08t}}{-0.08}$, and this integral is

$$-2500\int_0^{10} te^{-0.08t}\,dt = -2500\,\frac{te^{-0.08t}}{-0.08}\bigg|_0^{10} + 2500\int_0^{10} \frac{e^{-0.08t}}{-0.08}\,dt$$

$$= \frac{2500}{0.08}\,te^{-0.08t}\bigg|_0^{10} + \frac{2500}{0.0064}\,e^{-0.08t}\bigg|_0^{10}$$

$$= \frac{2500}{0.08}\,10e^{-0.8} + \frac{2500}{0.0064}\,e^{-0.8} - \frac{2500}{0.0064} \approx -74{,}690.572$$

Thus the sum of the integrals is

$$2{,}065{,}016.385 + (-74{,}690.572) = 1{,}990{,}325.813$$

so the present value of this piece of equipment is $1,990,325.81.

One further note about integration by parts. It can be very useful on certain types of problems, but not on all types. Don't attempt to use integration by parts when easier methods are available.

Calculator Note   Using the numerical integration feature of a graphing calculator to evaluate the integral in Example 6 gives the present value of $1,990,325.80, so this answer is the same as that found in Example 6, to the nearest dollar.

CHECKPOINT SOLUTIONS

1. (a) True   (b) True   (c) True
   (d) False. The *product* of u and dv must equal the original integrand. Rewrite as

$$\int \frac{3x}{e^{2x}}\,dx = \int 3xe^{-2x}\,dx$$

   and then choose $u = 3x$ and $dv = e^{-2x}\,dx$.

2. First we rewrite:

$$\int \frac{\ln x}{x^4}\,dx = \int \ln x\,(x^{-4}\,dx)$$

   Then the integral contains a logarithm and a power of x.

   (a) $u = \ln x$ and $dv = x^{-4}\,dx$

   (b) $du = \dfrac{1}{x}\,dx$ and $v = \displaystyle\int x^{-4}\,dx = \dfrac{x^{-3}}{-3}$

   (c) $\displaystyle\int \frac{\ln x}{x^4}\,dx = uv - \int v\,du$

$$= (\ln x)\left(\frac{x^{-3}}{-3}\right) - \int \frac{x^{-3}}{-3}\cdot\frac{1}{x}\,dx = \frac{-\ln x}{3x^3} + \frac{1}{3}\int x^{-4}\,dx$$

$$= -\frac{\ln x}{3x^3} + \frac{1}{3}\left(\frac{x^{-3}}{-3}\right) + C = -\frac{\ln x}{3x^3} - \frac{1}{9x^3} + C$$

| EXERCISES | 13.6

In Problems 1–16, use integration by parts to evaluate the integral.

1. $\displaystyle\int xe^{2x}\,dx$

2. $\displaystyle\int xe^{-x}\,dx$

3. $\displaystyle\int x^2\ln x\,dx$

4. $\displaystyle\int x^3\ln x\,dx$

5. $\displaystyle\int_4^6 q\sqrt{q-4}\,dq$

6. $\displaystyle\int_0^1 y(1-y)^{3/2}\,dy$

7. $\displaystyle\int \frac{\ln x}{x^2}\,dx$

8. $\displaystyle\int \frac{\ln(x-1)}{\sqrt{x-1}}\,dx$

9. $\displaystyle\int_1^e \ln x\,dx$

10. $\displaystyle\int \frac{x}{\sqrt{x-3}}\,dx$

11. $\displaystyle\int x\ln(2x-3)\,dx$

12. $\displaystyle\int x\ln(4x)\,dx$

13. $\displaystyle\int q^3\sqrt{q^2-3}\,dq$

14. $\displaystyle\int \frac{x^3}{\sqrt{9-x^2}}\,dx$

15. $\displaystyle\int_0^4 x^3\sqrt{x^2+9}\,dx$

16. $\displaystyle\int \sqrt{x}\,\ln x\,dx$

In Problems 17–24, use integration by parts to evaluate the integral. Note that evaluation may require integration by parts more than once.

17. $\displaystyle\int x^2 e^{-x}\,dx$

18. $\displaystyle\int_0^1 4x^2 e^x\,dx$

19. $\displaystyle\int_0^2 3x^3 e^{x^2}\,dx$

20. $\displaystyle\int x^3 e^x\,dx$

21. $\displaystyle\int x^3\ln^2 x\,dx$

22. $\displaystyle\int \frac{x^2}{\sqrt{x-3}}\,dx$

23. $\displaystyle\int e^{2x}\sqrt{e^x+1}\,dx$

24. $\displaystyle\int_1^2 (\ln x)^2\,dx$

In Problems 25–30, match each of the integrals with the formula or method (I–IV) that should be used to evaluate it. Then evaluate the integral.

I. Integration by parts

II. $\displaystyle\int e^u\,du$

III. $\displaystyle\int \frac{du}{u}$

IV. $\displaystyle\int u^n\,du$

25. $\displaystyle\int xe^{x^2}\,dx$

26. $\displaystyle\int \frac{x}{9-4x^2}\,dx$

27. $\displaystyle\int e^x\sqrt{e^x+1}\,dx$

28. $\displaystyle\int 4x^2 e^{x^3}\,dx$

29. $\displaystyle\int_0^4 \frac{t}{e^t}\,dt$

30. $\displaystyle\int x^2\sqrt{x-1}\,dx$

APPLICATIONS

31. *Producer's surplus* If the supply function for x units of a commodity is $p = 30 + 50\ln(2x+1)^2$ dollars, what is the producer's surplus at $x = 30$?

32. *Cost* If the marginal cost function for x units of a product is $\overline{MC} = 1 + 3\ln(x+1)$ dollars per unit, and if the fixed cost is \$100, find the total cost function.

33. *Present value* Suppose that a machine's production can be considered as a continuous income stream with annual rate of flow at time t given by

$$f(t) = 10{,}000 - 500t \quad \text{(dollars per year)}$$

If money is worth 10%, compounded continuously, find the present value of the machine over the next 5 years.

34. *Present value* Suppose that the production of a machine used to mine coal is considered as a continuous income stream with annual rate of flow at time t given by

$$f(t) = 280{,}000 - 14{,}000t \quad \text{(dollars per year)}$$

If money is worth 7%, compounded continuously, find the present value of this machine over the next 8 years.

35. *Income distribution* Suppose the Lorenz curve for the distribution of income of a certain country is given by

$$y = xe^{x-1}$$

Find the Gini coefficient of income.

36. *Income streams* Suppose the income from an Internet access business is a continuous income stream with annual rate of flow given by

$$f(t) = 100te^{-0.1t}$$

in thousands of dollars per year. Find the total income over the next 10 years.

37. *World tourism* With data since 1990, the total receipts for world tourism (in billions of dollars per year) can be modeled by the function

$$R(t) = -54.846 + 192.7\ln t$$

where $t = 0$ represents 1985 (*Source:* World Tourism Organization). Find the predicted total receipts for world tourism for the decade from 2005 to 2015.

38. *Life span* With data for selected years from 1920 to 2007, the life span of individuals in the United States can be modeled by

$$L(x) = 10.96 + 14.32\ln x$$

where $x = 0$ represents 1900 (*Source:* National Center for Health Statistics). Find the predicted average life span from 2000 to 2015.

- To evaluate improper integrals
- To apply improper integrals to continuous income streams and to probability density functions

Improper Integrals and Their Applications

■ | APPLICATION PREVIEW |

We saw in Section 13.4, "Applications of Definite Integrals in Business and Economics," that the present value of a continuous income stream over a fixed number of years can be found by using a definite integral. When this notion is extended to an infinite time interval, the result is called the capital value of the income stream and is given by

$$\text{Capital value} = \int_0^\infty f(t)e^{-rt}\, dt$$

where $f(t)$ is the annual rate of flow at time t, and r is the annual interest rate, compounded continuously. This is called an improper integral. For example, the capital value of a trust that provides $f(t) = \$10{,}000$ per year indefinitely (when interest is 10% compounded continuously) is found by evaluating an improper integral. (See Example 2.)

Improper Integral   Some applications of calculus to statistics or business (such as capital value) involve definite integrals over intervals of infinite length (**improper integrals**). The area of a region that extends infinitely to the left or right along the x-axis (see Figure 13.26) could be described by an improper integral.

Figure 13.26

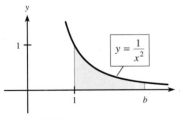

Figure 13.27

To see how to find such an area and hence evaluate an improper integral, let us consider how to find the area between the curve $y = 1/x^2$ and the x-axis to the right of $x = 1$.

To find the area under this curve from $x = 1$ to $x = b$, where b is any number greater than 1 (see Figure 13.27), we evaluate

$$A = \int_1^b \frac{1}{x^2}\, dx = \frac{-1}{x}\ \Big|_1^b = \frac{-1}{b} - \left(\frac{-1}{1}\right) = 1 - \frac{1}{b}$$

Note that the larger b is, the closer the area is to 1. If $b = 100$, $A = 0.99$; if $b = 1000$, $A = 0.999$; and if $b = 1{,}000{,}000$, $A = 0.999999$.

We can represent the area of the region under $1/x^2$ to the right of 1 using the notation

$$\lim_{b \to \infty} \int_1^b \frac{1}{x^2}\, dx = \lim_{b \to \infty} \left(1 - \frac{1}{b}\right)$$

where $\lim\limits_{b \to \infty}$ represents the limit as b gets larger without bound. Note that $\dfrac{1}{b} \to 0$ as $b \to \infty$, so

$$\lim_{b \to \infty} \left(1 - \frac{1}{b}\right) = 1 - 0 = 1$$

Thus the area under the curve $y = 1/x^2$ to the right of $x = 1$ is 1.

In general, we define the area under a curve $y = f(x)$ to the right of $x = a$, with $f(x) \geq 0$, to be

$$\text{Area} = \lim_{b \to \infty}(\text{area from } a \text{ to } b) = \lim_{b \to \infty}\int_a^b f(x)\,dx$$

This motivates the definition that follows.

Improper Integral

$$\int_a^\infty f(x)\,dx = \lim_{b \to \infty}\int_a^b f(x)\,dx$$

If the limit defining the **improper integral** is a unique finite number, we say that the integral *converges;* otherwise, we say that the integral *diverges.*

EXAMPLE 1   Improper Integrals

Evaluate the following improper integrals, if they converge.

(a) $\displaystyle\int_1^\infty \frac{1}{x^3}\,dx$ (b) $\displaystyle\int_1^\infty \frac{1}{x}\,dx$

Solution

(a) $\displaystyle\int_1^\infty \frac{1}{x^3}\,dx = \lim_{b \to \infty}\int_1^b x^{-3}\,dx = \lim_{b \to \infty}\left(\frac{x^{-2}}{-2}\right)\Bigg|_1^b$

$$= \lim_{b \to \infty}\left[\frac{-1}{2b^2} - \left(\frac{-1}{2(1)^2}\right)\right] = \lim_{b \to \infty}\left(\frac{-1}{2b^2} + \frac{1}{2}\right)$$

Notice that $1/(2b^2) \to 0$ as $b \to \infty$, so the limit converges to $0 + \frac{1}{2} = \frac{1}{2}$. That is,

$$\int_1^\infty \frac{1}{x^3}\,dx = \frac{1}{2}$$

(b) $\displaystyle\int_1^\infty \frac{1}{x}\,dx = \lim_{b \to \infty}\int_1^b \frac{1}{x}\,dx = \lim_{b \to \infty}\left(\ln|x|\right)\Bigg|_1^b = \lim_{b \to \infty}(\ln b - \ln 1)$

Here, $\ln b$ increases without bound as $b \to \infty$, so the limit diverges and we write

$$\int_1^\infty \frac{1}{x}\,dx = \infty$$

From Example 1 we can conclude that the area under the curve $y = 1/x^3$ to the right of $x = 1$ is $\frac{1}{2}$ whereas the corresponding area under the curve $y = 1/x$ is infinite. (We have already seen that the corresponding area under $y = 1/x^2$ is 1.)

As Figure 13.28 shows, the graphs of $y = 1/x^2$ and $y = 1/x$ look similar, but the graph of $y = 1/x^2$ gets "close" to the x-axis much more rapidly than the graph of $y = 1/x$. The area under $y = 1/x$ does not converge to a finite number because as $x \to \infty$ the graph of $1/x$ does not approach the x-axis rapidly enough.

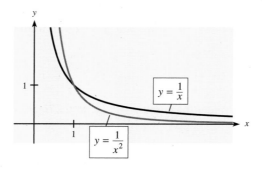

Figure 13.28

EXAMPLE 2 Capital Value | APPLICATION PREVIEW |

Suppose that an organization wants to establish a trust fund that will provide a continuous income stream with an annual rate of flow at time t given by $f(t) = 10,000$ dollars per year. If the interest rate remains at 10% compounded continuously, find the capital value of the fund.

Solution

The capital value of the fund is given by

$$\int_0^\infty f(t)e^{-rt}\, dt$$

where $f(t)$ is the annual rate of flow at time t, and r is the annual interest rate, compounded continuously.

$$\int_0^\infty 10,000e^{-0.10t}\, dt = \lim_{b\to\infty}\int_0^b 10,000e^{-0.10t}\, dt = \lim_{b\to\infty}\left(-100,000e^{-0.10t}\right)\Big|_0^b$$

$$= \lim_{b\to\infty}\left(\frac{-100,000}{e^{0.10b}} + 100,000\right) = 100,000$$

Thus the capital value of the fund is $100,000.

Another term for a fund such as the one in Example 2 is a **perpetuity.** Usually the rate of flow of a perpetuity is a constant. If the rate of flow is a constant A, it can be shown that the capital value is given by A/r (see Problem 37 in the 13.7 Exercises).

CHECKPOINT

1. True or false:

   (a) $\lim\limits_{b\to+\infty}\dfrac{1}{b^p} = 0$ if $p > 0$ (b) If $p > 0$, $b^p \to \infty$ as $b \to \infty$

   (c) $\lim\limits_{b\to+\infty} e^{-pb} = 0$ if $p > 0$

2. Evaluate the following (if they exist).

   (a) $\displaystyle\int_1^\infty \frac{1}{x^{4/3}}\, dx = \lim_{b\to\infty}\int_1^b x^{-4/3}\, dx$ (b) $\displaystyle\int_0^\infty \frac{dx}{\sqrt{x+1}}$

Two **additional improper integrals** that involve infinite limits are defined below.

Additional Improper Integrals

$$\int_{-\infty}^b f(x)\, dx = \lim_{a\to\infty}\int_{-a}^b f(x)\, dx$$

The integral converges if the limit is finite. Otherwise it diverges.

$$\int_{-\infty}^\infty f(x)\, dx = \lim_{a\to\infty}\int_{-a}^c f(x)\, dx + \lim_{b\to\infty}\int_c^b f(x)\, dx$$

for any finite constant c. (Often, c is chosen to be 0.) If both limits are finite, the improper integral converges; otherwise, it diverges.

EXAMPLE 3 Improper Integrals

Evaluate the following integrals.

(a) $\displaystyle\int_{-\infty}^4 e^{3x}\, dx$ (b) $\displaystyle\int_{-\infty}^\infty \frac{x^3}{(x^4+3)^2}\, dx$

Solution

(a) $\displaystyle\int_{-\infty}^{4} e^{3x}\, dx = \lim_{a\to\infty} \int_{-a}^{4} e^{3x}\, dx = \lim_{a\to\infty}\left[\left(\frac{1}{3}\right)e^{3x}\right]_{-a}^{4}$

$\displaystyle\qquad = \lim_{a\to\infty}\left[\left(\frac{1}{3}\right)e^{12} - \left(\frac{1}{3}\right)e^{-3a}\right] = \lim_{a\to\infty}\left[\left(\frac{1}{3}\right)e^{12} - \left(\frac{1}{3}\right)\left(\frac{1}{e^{3a}}\right)\right]$

$\displaystyle\qquad = \frac{1}{3}e^{12} \qquad \text{(because } 1/e^{3a} \to 0 \text{ as } a \to \infty)$

(b) $\displaystyle\int_{-\infty}^{\infty} \frac{x^3}{(x^4+3)^2}\, dx = \lim_{a\to\infty}\int_{-a}^{0}\frac{x^3}{(x^4+3)^2}\, dx + \lim_{b\to\infty}\int_{0}^{b}\frac{x^3}{(x^4+3)^2}\, dx$

$\displaystyle\qquad = \lim_{a\to\infty}\left[\frac{1}{4}\frac{(x^4+3)^{-1}}{-1}\right]_{-a}^{0} + \lim_{b\to\infty}\left[\frac{1}{4}\frac{(x^4+3)^{-1}}{-1}\right]_{0}^{b}$

$\displaystyle\qquad = \lim_{a\to\infty}\left[-\frac{1}{4}\left(\frac{1}{3} - \frac{1}{a^4+3}\right)\right] + \lim_{b\to\infty}\left[-\frac{1}{4}\left(\frac{1}{b^4+3} - \frac{1}{3}\right)\right]$

$\displaystyle\qquad = -\frac{1}{12} + 0 + 0 + \frac{1}{12} = 0$

$\displaystyle\qquad \left(\text{since } \lim_{a\to\infty}\frac{1}{a^4+3} = 0 \ \text{ and } \ \lim_{b\to\infty}\frac{1}{b^4+3} = 0\right)$

Probability   We noted in Chapter 8, "Further Topics in Probability; Data Description," that the sum of the probabilities for a probability distribution (a **probability density function**) equals 1. In particular, we stated that the area under the normal probability curve is 1. The normal distribution is an example of a continuous probability distribution because the values of the random variable are considered over intervals rather than at discrete values. There are many important continuous probability distributions besides the normal distribution, but all such distributions satisfy the following definition.

Probability Density Function   If $f(x) \geq 0$ for all x, then f is a **probability density function** for a continuous random variable x if and only if

$$\int_{-\infty}^{\infty} f(x)\, dx = 1$$

We have noted previously that when $f(x)$ is a continuous probability density function, then

$$Pr(a \leq x \leq b) = \int_{a}^{b} f(x)\, dx$$

EXAMPLE 4   Product Life

Suppose the probability density function for the life span of a computer component is given by

$$f(x) = \begin{cases} 0.10e^{-0.10x} & \text{if } x \geq 0 \\ 0 & \text{if } x < 0 \end{cases}$$

(a) Verify that $f(x)$ is a probability density function.
(b) Find the probability that such a component lasts more than 3 years.

Solution

(a) We can verify that $f(x)$ is a probability density function by showing that

$$\int_{-\infty}^{\infty} f(x)\, dx = 1$$

$$\int_{-\infty}^{\infty} f(x)\, dx = \int_{-\infty}^{0} f(x)\, dx + \int_{0}^{\infty} f(x)\, dx = \int_{-\infty}^{0} 0\, dx + \int_{0}^{\infty} 0.10 e^{-0.10x}\, dx$$

$$= 0 + \lim_{b \to \infty} \int_{0}^{b} 0.10 e^{-0.10x}\, dx$$

$$= \lim_{b \to \infty} (-e^{-0.10x})\big|_{0}^{b} = \lim_{b \to \infty}(-e^{-0.10b} + 1) = 1$$

(b) The probability that the component lasts more than 3 years is given by the improper integral

$$\int_{3}^{\infty} 0.10 e^{-0.10x}\, dx$$

which gives

$$\lim_{b \to \infty} \int_{3}^{b} 0.10 e^{-0.10x}\, dx = \lim_{b \to \infty} (-e^{-0.10x})\big|_{3}^{b}$$

$$= \lim_{b \to \infty} (-e^{-0.10b} + e^{-0.3}) = e^{-0.3} \approx 0.7408 \qquad ∎$$

In Section 8.3, "Discrete Probability Distributions; The Binomial Distribution," we found the expected value (mean) of a discrete probability distribution using the formula

$$E(x) = \sum x \Pr(x)$$

For continuous probability distributions, such as the normal probability distribution, the **expected value**, or **mean**, can be found by evaluating the improper integral

$$\int_{-\infty}^{\infty} x f(x)\, dx$$

Mean (Expected Value)

If x is a continuous random variable with probability density function f, then the **mean (expected value)** of the probability distribution is

$$\mu = \int_{-\infty}^{\infty} x f(x)\, dx$$

The normal distribution density function, in standard form, is

$$f(x) = \frac{1}{\sqrt{2\pi}} e^{-x^2/2}$$

so the mean of the normal probability distribution is given by

$$\mu = \int_{-\infty}^{\infty} x \left(\frac{1}{\sqrt{2\pi}} e^{-x^2/2} \right) dx$$

$$= \lim_{a \to \infty} \int_{-a}^{0} \frac{1}{\sqrt{2\pi}} x e^{-x^2/2}\, dx + \lim_{b \to \infty} \int_{0}^{b} \frac{1}{\sqrt{2\pi}} x e^{-x^2/2}\, dx$$

$$= \lim_{a \to \infty} \frac{1}{\sqrt{2\pi}} \left(-e^{-x^2/2} \right) \bigg|_{-a}^{0} + \lim_{b \to \infty} \frac{1}{\sqrt{2\pi}} \left(-e^{-x^2/2} \right) \bigg|_{0}^{b}$$

$$= \frac{1}{\sqrt{2\pi}} (-1 + 0) + \frac{1}{\sqrt{2\pi}} (0 + 1) = 0$$

This verifies the statement in Chapter 8 that the mean of the standard normal distribution is 0.

CHECKPOINT SOLUTIONS

1. (a) True   (b) True   (c) True

2. (a) $\displaystyle\lim_{b\to\infty}\int_1^b x^{-4/3}\,dx = \lim_{b\to\infty}\frac{x^{-1/3}}{-1/3}\Big|_1^b = \lim_{b\to\infty}\left(\frac{-3}{b^{1/3}} - \frac{-3}{1}\right) = 0 + 3 = 3$

   (b) $\displaystyle\lim_{b\to\infty}\int_0^b (x+1)^{-1/2}\,dx = \lim_{b\to\infty}\frac{(x+1)^{1/2}}{1/2}\Big|_0^b = \lim_{b\to\infty} 2\sqrt{x+1}\,\Big|_0^b$

   $= \displaystyle\lim_{b\to\infty}(2\sqrt{b+1} - 2)$

   The limit approaches ∞, so the integral diverges.

| EXERCISES | 13.7

In Problems 1–20, evaluate the improper integrals that converge.

1. $\displaystyle\int_1^\infty \frac{dx}{x^6}$

2. $\displaystyle\int_1^\infty \frac{1}{x^4}\,dx$

3. $\displaystyle\int_1^\infty \frac{dt}{t^{3/2}}$

4. $\displaystyle\int_5^\infty \frac{dx}{(x-1)^3}$

5. $\displaystyle\int_1^\infty e^{-x}\,dx$

6. $\displaystyle\int_0^\infty x^2 e^{-x^3}\,dx$

7. $\displaystyle\int_1^\infty \frac{dt}{t^{1/3}}$

8. $\displaystyle\int_1^\infty \frac{1}{\sqrt{x}}\,dx$

9. $\displaystyle\int_0^\infty e^{3x}\,dx$

10. $\displaystyle\int_1^\infty x e^{x^2}\,dx$

11. $\displaystyle\int_{-\infty}^{-1} \frac{10}{x^2}\,dx$

12. $\displaystyle\int_{-\infty}^{-2} \frac{x}{\sqrt{(x^2-1)^3}}\,dx$

13. $\displaystyle\int_{-\infty}^0 x^2 e^{-x^3}\,dx$

14. $\displaystyle\int_{-\infty}^0 \frac{x}{(x^2+1)^2}\,dx$

15. $\displaystyle\int_{-\infty}^{-1} \frac{6}{x}\,dx$

16. $\displaystyle\int_{-\infty}^{-2} \frac{5}{3x+5}\,dx$

17. $\displaystyle\int_{-\infty}^\infty \frac{2x}{(x^2+1)^2}\,dx$

18. $\displaystyle\int_{-\infty}^\infty \frac{9x^5}{(3x^6+7)^2}\,dx$

19. $\displaystyle\int_{-\infty}^\infty x^3 e^{-x^4}\,dx$

20. $\displaystyle\int_{-\infty}^\infty x^4 e^{-x^5}\,dx$

21. For what value of c does $\displaystyle\int_0^\infty \frac{c}{e^{0.5t}}\,dt = 1$?

22. For what value of c does $\displaystyle\int_{10}^\infty \frac{c}{x^3}\,dx = 1$?

In Problems 23–26, find the area, if it exists, of the region under the graph of $y = f(x)$ and to the right of $x = 1$.

23. $f(x) = \dfrac{x}{e^{x^2}}$

24. $f(x) = \dfrac{1}{\sqrt[5]{x^3}}$

25. $f(x) = \dfrac{1}{\sqrt[3]{x^5}}$

26. $f(x) = \dfrac{1}{x\sqrt{x}}$

27. Show that the function

$$f(x) = \begin{cases} \dfrac{200}{x^3} & \text{if } x \geq 10 \\ 0 & \text{otherwise} \end{cases}$$

is a probability density function.

28. Show that

$$f(t) = \begin{cases} 3e^{-3t} & \text{if } t \geq 0 \\ 0 & \text{if } t < 0 \end{cases}$$

is a probability density function.

29. For what value of c is the function

$$f(x) = \begin{cases} c/x^2 & \text{if } x \geq 1 \\ 0 & \text{otherwise} \end{cases}$$

a probability density function?

30. For what value of c is the function

$$f(x) = \begin{cases} c/x^3 & \text{if } x \geq 100 \\ 0 & \text{otherwise} \end{cases}$$

a probability density function?

31. If

$$f(x) = \begin{cases} ce^{-x/4} & x \geq 0 \\ 0 & x < 0 \end{cases}$$

is a probability density function, what must be the value of c?

32. If

$$f(x) = \begin{cases} ce^{-kx} & \text{if } x \geq 0 \\ 0 & \text{if } x < 0 \end{cases}$$

is a probability density function, what must be the value of c?

33. Find the mean of the probability distribution if the probability density function is

$$f(x) = \begin{cases} \dfrac{200}{x^3} & \text{if } x \geq 10 \\ 0 & \text{otherwise} \end{cases}$$

34. Find the mean of the probability distribution if the probability density function is

$$f(x) = \begin{cases} c/x^4 & \text{if } x \geq 10 \\ 0 & \text{otherwise} \end{cases}$$

35. Find the area below the graph of $y = f(x)$ and above the x-axis for $f(x) = 24xe^{-3x}$. Use the graph of $y = f(x)$ to find the interval for which $f(x) \geq 0$ and the graph of the integral of $f(x)$ over this interval to find the area.

36. Find the area below the graph of $y = f(x)$ and above the x-axis for $f(x) = x^2e^{-x}$ and $x \geq 0$. Use the graph of the integral of $f(x)$ over this interval to find the area.

APPLICATIONS

37. *Capital value* Suppose that a continuous income stream has an annual rate of flow at time t given by $f(t) = A$, where A is a constant. If the interest rate is r (as a decimal, $r > 0$), compounded continuously, show that the capital value of the stream is A/r.

38. *Capital value* Suppose that a donor wishes to provide a cash gift to a hospital that will generate a continuous income stream with an annual rate of flow at time t given by $f(t) = \$20,000$ per year. If the annual interest rate is 12% compounded continuously, find the capital value of this perpetuity.

39. *Capital value* Suppose that a business provides a continuous income stream with an annual rate of flow at time t given by $f(t) = 120e^{0.04t}$ in thousands of dollars per year. If the interest rate is 9% compounded continuously, find the capital value of the business.

40. *Capital value* Suppose that the output of the machinery in a factory can be considered as a continuous income stream with annual rate of flow at time t given by $f(t) = 450e^{-0.09t}$ (in thousands of dollars per year). If the annual interest rate is 6% compounded continuously, find the capital value of the machinery.

41. *Capital value* A business has a continuous income stream with an annual rate of flow at time t given by $f(t) = 56,000e^{0.02t}$ (dollars per year). If the interest rate is 10% compounded continuously, find the capital value of the business.

42. *Capital value* Suppose that a business provides a continuous income stream with an annual rate of flow at time t given by $f(t) = 10,800e^{0.06t}$ (dollars per year).

If money is worth 12% compounded continuously, find the capital value of the business.

43. *Repair time* In a manufacturing process involving several machines, the average down time t (in hours) for a machine that needs repair has the probability density function

$$f(t) = 0.5e^{-0.5t} \quad t \geq 0$$

Find the probability that a failed machine's down time is
(a) 2 hours or more.   (b) 8 hours or more.

44. *Customer service* The duration t (in minutes) of customer service calls received by a certain company is given by the probability density function

$$f(t) = 0.4e^{-0.4t} \quad t \geq 0$$

Find the probability that a call selected at random lasts
(a) 4 minutes or more.
(b) 10 minutes or more.

45. *Quality control* The probability density function for the life span of an electronics part is $f(t) = 0.08e^{-0.08t}$, where t is the number of months in service. Find the probability that any given part of this type lasts longer than 24 months.

46. *Warranties* A transmission repair firm that wants to offer a lifetime warranty on its repairs has determined that the probability density function for transmission failure after repair is $f(t) = 0.3e^{-0.3t}$, where t is the number of months after repair. What is the probability that a transmission chosen at random will last
(a) 3 months or less?
(b) more than 3 months?

47. *Radioactive waste* Suppose that the rate at which a nuclear power plant produces radioactive waste is proportional to the number of years it has been operating, according to $f(t) = 500t$ (in pounds per year). Suppose also that the waste decays exponentially at a rate of 3% per year. Then the amount of radioactive waste that will accumulate in b years is given by

$$\int_0^b 500te^{-0.03(b-t)} \, dt$$

(a) Evaluate this integral.
(b) How much waste will accumulate in the long run? Take the limit as $b \to \infty$ in part (a).

- To approximate definite integrals by using the Trapezoidal Rule
- To approximate definite integrals by using Simpson's Rule

Numerical Integration Methods: The Trapezoidal Rule and Simpson's Rule

| APPLICATION PREVIEW |

A pharmaceutical company tests the body's assimilation of a new drug by administering a 200-milligram dose and collecting the following data from blood samples (t is time in hours, and $R(t)$ gives the assimilation of the drug in milligrams per hour).

t	0	0.5	1.0	1.5	2.0	2.5	3.0
$R(t)$	0.0	15.3	32.3	51.0	74.8	102.0	130.9

The company would like to find the amount of drug assimilated in 3 hours, which is given by

$$\int_0^3 R(t)\,dt$$

In this section we develop straightforward and quite accurate methods for evaluating integrals such as this, even when, as with $R(t)$, only function data, rather than a formula, are given. (See Example 4.)

We have studied several techniques for integration and have even used tables to evaluate some integrals. Yet some functions that arise in practical problems cannot be integrated by using any formula. For any function $f(x) \geq 0$ on an interval $[a, b]$, however, we have seen that a definite integral can be viewed as an area and that we can usually approximate the area and hence the integral (see Figure 13.29). One such approximation method uses rectangles, as we saw when we defined the definite integral. In this section, we consider two other **numerical integration methods** to approximate a definite integral: the **Trapezoidal Rule** and **Simpson's Rule**.

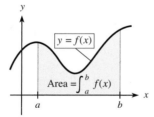

Figure 13.29

Trapezoidal Rule   To develop the Trapezoidal Rule formula, we assume that $f(x) \geq 0$ on $[a, b]$ and subdivide the interval $[a, b]$ into n equal pieces, each of length $(b - a)/n = h$. Then, within each subdivision, we can approximate the area by using a trapezoid. As shown in Figure 13.30, we can use the formula for the area of a trapezoid to approximate the area of the first subdivision. Continuing in this way for each trapezoid, we have

$$\int_a^b f(x)\,dx \approx A_1 + A_2 + A_3 + \cdots + A_{n-1} + A_n$$

$$= \left[\frac{f(x_0) + f(x_1)}{2}\right]h + \left[\frac{f(x_1) + f(x_2)}{2}\right]h +$$

$$\left[\frac{f(x_2) + f(x_3)}{2}\right]h + \cdots + \left[\frac{f(x_{n-1}) + f(x_n)}{2}\right]h$$

$$= \frac{h}{2}[f(x_0) + f(x_1) + f(x_1) + f(x_2) + f(x_2) + \cdots + f(x_{n-1}) + f(x_{n-1}) + f(x_n)]$$

This can be simplified to obtain the **Trapezoidal Rule**.

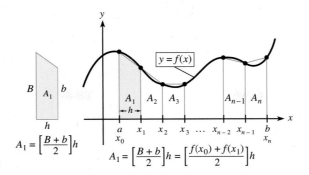

Figure 13.30

$$A_1 = \left[\frac{B+b}{2}\right]h$$

$$A_1 = \left[\frac{B+b}{2}\right]h = \left[\frac{f(x_0)+f(x_1)}{2}\right]h$$

Trapezoidal Rule

If f is continuous on $[a, b]$, then

$$\int_a^b f(x)\,dx \approx \frac{h}{2}\left[f(x_0) + 2f(x_1) + 2f(x_2) + \cdots + 2f(x_{n-1}) + f(x_n)\right]$$

where $h = \dfrac{b-a}{n}$ and n is the number of equal subdivisions of $[a, b]$.

Despite the fact that we used areas to develop the Trapezoidal Rule, we can use this rule to evaluate definite integrals even if $f(x) < 0$ on all or part of $[a, b]$.

EXAMPLE 1   Trapezoidal Rule

Use the Trapezoidal Rule to approximate $\displaystyle\int_1^3 \frac{1}{x}\,dx$ with

(a) $n = 4$.
(b) $n = 8$.

Solution

First, we note that this integral can be evaluated directly:

$$\int_1^3 \frac{1}{x}\,dx = \ln|x|\,\Big|_1^3 = \ln 3 - \ln 1 = \ln 3 \approx 1.099$$

(a) The interval $[1, 3]$ must be divided into 4 equal subintervals of width $h = \frac{3-1}{4} = \frac{2}{4} = \frac{1}{2}$ as follows:

$$
\begin{array}{ccccc}
1 & 1.5 & 2 & 2.5 & 3 \\
\hline
x_0 & x_1 & x_2 & x_3 & x_4
\end{array}
$$

Thus, from the Trapezoidal Rule, we have

$$\int_1^3 \frac{1}{x}\,dx \approx \frac{h}{2}\left[f(x_0) + 2f(x_1) + 2f(x_2) + 2f(x_3) + f(x_4)\right]$$

$$= \frac{1/2}{2}\left[f(1) + 2f(1.5) + 2f(2) + 2f(2.5) + f(3)\right]$$

$$= \frac{1}{4}\left[1 + 2\left(\frac{1}{1.5}\right) + 2\left(\frac{1}{2}\right) + 2\left(\frac{1}{2.5}\right) + \frac{1}{3}\right]$$

$$\approx 0.25(1 + 1.333 + 1 + 0.8 + 0.3333)$$

$$\approx 1.117$$

(b) In this case, the interval $[1, 3]$ is divided into 8 equal subintervals of width $h = \frac{3-1}{8} = \frac{2}{8} = \frac{1}{4}$ as follows.

Thus, from the Trapezoidal Rule, we have

$$\int_1^3 \frac{1}{x}\, dx \approx \frac{h}{2}[f(x_0) + 2f(x_1) + 2f(x_2) + 2f(x_3) + 2f(x_4) + 2f(x_5)$$
$$+ 2f(x_6) + 2f(x_7) + f(x_8)]$$

$$= \frac{1/4}{2}\left[\frac{1}{1} + 2\left(\frac{1}{1.25}\right) + 2\left(\frac{1}{1.5}\right) + 2\left(\frac{1}{1.75}\right) + 2\left(\frac{1}{2}\right) + 2\left(\frac{1}{2.25}\right)\right.$$
$$\left. + 2\left(\frac{1}{2.5}\right) + 2\left(\frac{1}{2.75}\right) + \frac{1}{3}\right]$$

$$\approx 1.103$$

In Example 1, because we know that the value of the integral is ln 3 ≈ 1.099, we can measure the accuracy of each approximation. We can see that a larger value of n (namely, $n = 8$) produced a more accurate approximation to ln 3. In general, larger values of n produce more accurate approximations, but they also make computations more difficult.

Technology Note

The TABLE feature of a graphing calculator can be used to find the values of $f(x_0)$, $f(x_1), f(x_2)$, etc. needed for the Trapezoidal Rule. Figure 13.31(a) shows the TABLE set up and Figures 13.31(b) and 13.31(c) show the TABLE values.

TABLE SETUP	
TblStart=1	
ΔTbl=.25	
Indpnt: **Auto** Ask	
Depend: **Auto** Ask	

X	Y₁
1	1
1.25	.8
1.5	.66667
1.75	.57143
2	.5
2.25	.44444
2.5	.4
X=1	

X	Y₁
1.5	.66667
1.75	.57143
2	**.5**
2.25	.44444
2.5	.4
2.75	.36364
3	.33333
Y₁=.5	

Figure 13.31

(a)   (b)   (c)

Thus for the Trapezoidal Rule, we get

$$\int_1^3 \frac{1}{x}\, dx \approx \frac{0.25}{2}\left[\begin{array}{l} 1(1) + 2(0.8) + 2(0.66667) + 2(0.57143) + 2(0.5) \\ + 2(0.44444) + 2(0.4) + 2(0.36364) + 1(0.33333) \end{array}\right] \approx 1.103$$

just as we did in Example 1.

An Excel spreadsheet also can be very useful in finding the numerical integral with the Trapezoidal Rule. A discussion of the use of Excel in finding numerical integrals is given in the Online Excel Guide that accompanies this text.

Because the exact value of an integral is rarely available when an approximation is used, it is important to have some way to judge the accuracy of an answer. The following formula, which we state without proof, can be used to bound the error that results from using the Trapezoidal Rule.

Trapezoidal Rule Error

The error E in using the Trapezoidal Rule to approximate $\int_a^b f(x)\, dx$ satisfies

$$|E| \leq \frac{(b-a)^3}{12n^2}\left[\max_{a \leq x \leq b} |f''(x)|\right]$$

where n is the number of equal subdivisions of $[a, b]$.

For a numerical method to be worthwhile, there must be some way of assessing its accuracy. Hence, this formula is important. We leave its application, however, to more advanced courses.

Simpson's Rule   The Trapezoidal Rule was developed by using a line segment to approximate the function over each subinterval and then using the areas under the line segments to approximate the area under the curve. Another numerical method, **Simpson's Rule,** uses a parabola to approximate the function over each pair of subintervals (see Figure 13.32) and then uses the areas under the parabolas to approximate the area under the curve. Because Simpson's Rule is based on pairs of subintervals, n must be even.

Simpson's Rule (n Even)

If $f(x)$ is continuous on $[a, b]$, and if $[a, b]$ is divided into an *even* number n of equal subdivisions, then

$$\int_a^b f(x)\, dx \approx \frac{h}{3}\left[f(x_0) + 4f(x_1) + 2f(x_2) + 4f(x_3) + \cdots + 2f(x_{n-2}) \right. $$
$$\left. + \, 4f(x_{n-1}) + f(x_n) \right]$$

where $h = \dfrac{b - a}{n}$.

We leave the derivation of Simpson's Rule to more advanced courses.

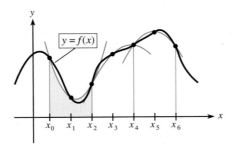

Figure 13.32

EXAMPLE   2   Simpson's Rule

Use Simpson's Rule with $n = 4$ to approximate $\displaystyle\int_1^3 \frac{1}{x}\, dx$.

Solution

Because $n = 4$ is even, Simpson's Rule can be used, and the interval is divided into four subintervals of length $h = \frac{3-1}{4} = \frac{1}{2}$ as follows:

$$\int_1^3 \frac{1}{x}\, dx \approx \frac{1/2}{3}\left[f(1) + 4f(1.5) + 2f(2) + 4f(2.5) + f(3) \right]$$

$$= \frac{1}{6}\left[\frac{1}{1} + 4\left(\frac{1}{1.5}\right) + 2\left(\frac{1}{2}\right) + 4\left(\frac{1}{2.5}\right) + \frac{1}{3} \right]$$

$$= 1.100$$

Note that the result of Example 2 is better than both the $n = 4$ and the $n = 8$ Trapezoidal Rule approximations done in Example 1. In general, Simpson's Rule is more accurate than the Trapezoidal Rule for a given number of subdivisions. We can determine the accuracy of Simpson's Rule approximations by using the following formula.

Simpson's Rule Error Formula

The error E in using Simpson's Rule to approximate $\int_a^b f(x)\, dx$ satisfies

$$|E| \leq \frac{(b - a)^5}{180 n^4}\left[\max_{a \leq x \leq b}|f^{(4)}(x)|\right]$$

where n is the number of equal subdivisions of $[a, b]$ and $f^{(4)}(x)$ is the fourth derivative of $f(x)$.

The presence of the factor $180 n^4$ in the denominator indicates that the error will often be quite small for even a modest value of n. Although Simpson's Rule often leads to more accurate results than the Trapezoidal Rule for a fixed choice of n, the Trapezoidal Rule is sometimes used because its error is more easily determined than that of Simpson's Rule or, more important, because the number of subdivisions is odd.

CHECKPOINT

1. Suppose $[1, 4]$ is divided into 6 equal subintervals.
   (a) Find the width h of each subinterval.
   (b) Find the subdivision points.
2. True or false:
   (a) When the Trapezoidal Rule is used, the number of subdivisions, n, must be even.
   (b) When Simpson's Rule is used, the number of subdivisions, n, must be even.
3. We can show that $\int_0^2 4x^3\, dx = 16$. Use $n = 4$ subdivisions to find

   (a) the Trapezoidal Rule approximation of this integral.
   (b) the Simpson's Rule approximation of this integral.

Technology Note

As mentioned previously for the Trapezoidal Rule, the TABLE feature of a graphing calculator can be used in exactly the same way with Simpson's Rule. An Excel spreadsheet also can be very useful with Simpson's Rule.

 EXAMPLE 3   Simpson's Rule

Use Simpson's Rule with $n = 10$ subdivisions to approximate

$$\int_1^6 [\ln (x)]^2\, dx$$

Solution

With $y_1 = [\ln (x)]^2$ and $h = \dfrac{b - a}{n} = \dfrac{6 - 1}{10} = 0.5$, we can use a graphing calculator with $\Delta\text{Tbl} = 0.5$ to find the following table of values.

x	y_1	x	y_1
1	0	4	1.9218
1.5	0.1644	4.5	2.2622
2	0.48045	5	2.5903
2.5	0.83959	5.5	2.9062
3	1.2069	6	3.2104
3.5	1.5694		

Thus Simpson's Rule yields

$$\int_1^6 [\ln (x)]^2 \, dx$$

$$\approx \frac{0.5}{3} \left[\begin{array}{l} 1(0) + 4(0.1644) + 2(0.48045) + 4(0.83959) + 2(1.2069) + 4(1.5694) \\ + 2(1.9218) + 4(2.2622) + 2(2.5903) + 4(2.9062) + 1(3.2104) \end{array} \right]$$

$$\approx 7.7627$$

One advantage that both the Trapezoidal Rule and Simpson's Rule offer is that they may be used when only function values at the subdivision points are known and the function formula itself is not known. This can be especially useful in applied problems.

EXAMPLE 4   **Pharmaceutical Testing** | APPLICATION PREVIEW |

A pharmaceutical company tests the body's ability to assimilate a drug. The test is done by administering a 200-milligram dose and then, every half-hour, monitoring the rate of assimilation. The following table gives the data; t is time in hours, and $R(t)$ is the rate of assimilation in milligrams per hour.

t	0	0.5	1.0	1.5	2.0	2.5	3.0
$R(t)$	0.0	15.3	32.3	51.0	74.8	102.0	130.9

To find the total amount of the drug (in milligrams) that is assimilated in the first 3 hours, the company must find

$$\int_0^3 R(t) \, dt$$

Use Simpson's Rule to approximate this definite integral.

Solution
The values of t correspond to the endpoints of the subintervals, and the values of $R(t)$ correspond to function values at those endpoints. From the table we see that $h = \frac{1}{2}$ and $n = 6$ (even); thus Simpson's Rule is applied as follows:

$$\int_0^3 R(t) \, dt \approx \frac{h}{3}[R(t_0) + 4R(t_1) + 2R(t_2) + 4R(t_3) + 2R(t_4) + 4R(t_5) + R(t_6)]$$

$$= \frac{1}{6}[0 + 4(15.3) + 2(32.3) + 4(51.0) + 2(74.8) + 4(102.0) + 130.9]$$

$$\approx 169.7 \text{ mg}$$

Thus at the end of 3 hours, the body has assimilated approximately 169.7 milligrams of the 200-milligram dose.

Note in Example 4 that the Trapezoidal Rule could also be used, because it relies only on the values of $R(t)$ at the subdivision endpoints.

In practice, these kinds of approximations are usually done with a computer, where the computations can be done quickly, even for large values of n. In addition, numerical methods (and hence computer programs) exist that approximate the errors, even in cases such as Example 4 where the function is not known. We leave any further discussion of error approximation formulas and additional numerical techniques for a more advanced course.

CHECKPOINT SOLUTIONS

1. (a) $h = \dfrac{b - a}{n} = \dfrac{4 - 1}{6} = \dfrac{1}{2} = 0.5$

   (b) $x_0 = 1, x_1 = 1.5, x_2 = 2, x_3 = 2.5, x_4 = 3, x_5 = 3.5, x_6 = 4$

2. (a) False. With the Trapezoidal Rule, n can be even or odd.

   (b) True

3. (a) $\dfrac{0.5}{2}[0 + 2(0.5) + 2(4) + 2(13.5) + 32] = 17$

   (b) $\dfrac{0.5}{3}[0 + 4(0.5) + 2(4) + 4(13.5) + 32] = 16$

| EXERCISES | 13.8

For each interval $[a, b]$ and value of n given in Problems 1–6, find h and the values of $x_0, x_1, \ldots x_n$.

1. $[0, 2]$ $n = 4$ 2. $[0, 4]$ $n = 8$
3. $[1, 4]$ $n = 6$ 4. $[2, 5]$ $n = 9$
5. $[-1, 4]$ $n = 5$ 6. $[-1, 2]$ $n = 6$

For each integral in Problems 7–12, do the following.
(a) Approximate its value by using the Trapezoidal Rule.
(b) Approximate its value by using Simpson's Rule.
(c) Find its exact value by integration.
(d) State which approximation is more accurate.
(Round each result to 2 decimal places.)

7. $\int_0^3 x^2 \, dx$; $n = 6$ 8. $\int_0^1 x^3 \, dx$; $n = 4$

9. $\int_1^2 \dfrac{1}{x^2} \, dx$; $n = 4$ 10. $\int_1^4 \dfrac{1}{x} \, dx$; $n = 6$

11. $\int_0^4 x^{1/2} \, dx$; $n = 8$ 12. $\int_0^2 x^{3/2} \, dx$; $n = 8$

In Problems 13–18, approximate each integral by
(a) the Trapezoidal Rule.
(b) Simpson's Rule.
Use $n = 4$ and round answers to 3 decimal places.

13. $\int_0^2 \sqrt{x^3 + 1} \, dx$ 14. $\int_0^2 \dfrac{dx}{\sqrt{4x^3 + 1}}$

15. $\int_0^1 e^{-x^2} \, dx$ 16. $\int_0^1 e^{x^2} \, dx$

17. $\int_1^5 \ln(x^2 - x + 1) \, dx$

18. $\int_1^5 \ln(x^2 + x + 2) \, dx$

Use the table of values given in each of Problems 19–22 to approximate $\int_a^b f(x) \, dx$. Use Simpson's Rule whenever n is even; otherwise, use the Trapezoidal Rule. Round answers to 1 decimal place.

19. Find $\int_1^4 f(x) \, dx$.

x	$f(x)$
1	1
1.6	2.2
2.2	1.8
2.8	2.9
3.4	4.6
4.0	2.1

20. Find $\int_1^2 f(x) \, dx$.

x	$f(x)$
1	1
1.2	0.5
1.4	0.3
1.6	0.1
1.8	0.8
2.0	0.1

21. Find $\int_{1.2}^{3.6} f(x) \, dx$.

x	$f(x)$
1.2	6.1
1.6	4.8
2.0	3.1
2.4	2.0
2.8	2.8
3.2	5.6
3.6	9.7

22. Find $\int_0^{1.8} f(x) \, dx$.

x	$f(x)$
0	8.8
0.3	4.6
0.6	1.5
0.9	0
1.2	0.7
1.5	2.8
1.8	7.6

APPLICATIONS

In Problems 23–30, round all calculations to 2 decimal places.

23. *Total income* Suppose that the production from an assembly line can be considered as a continuous income stream with annual rate of flow given by

$$f(t) = 100 \frac{e^{0.1t}}{t + 1} \quad \text{(in thousands of dollars per year)}$$

Use Simpson's Rule with $n = 4$ to approximate the total income over the first 2 years, given by

$$\text{Total income} = \int_0^2 \frac{100e^{0.1t}}{t + 1} \, dt$$

24. *Present value* Suppose that the rate of flow of a continuous income stream is given by $f(t) = 500t$ (in thousands of dollars per year). If money is worth 7% compounded continuously, then the present value of this stream over the next 5 years is given by

$$\text{Present value} = \int_0^5 500t \, e^{-0.07t} \, dt$$

Use the Trapezoidal Rule with $n = 5$ to approximate this present value.

25. *Cost* Suppose that a company's total cost (in dollars) of producing x items is given by $C(x) = (x^2 + 1)^{3/2} + 1000$. Use the Trapezoidal Rule with $n = 3$ to approximate the average cost for the production of $x = 30$ to $x = 33$ items.

26. *Demand* Suppose that the demand for q units of a certain product at $\$p$ per unit is given by

$$p = 850 + \frac{100}{q^2 + 1}$$

Use Simpson's Rule with $n = 6$ to approximate the average price as demand ranges from 3 to 9 items.

Supply and demand Use the supply and demand schedules in Problems 27 and 28, with p in dollars and x as the number of units.

Supply Schedule		Demand Schedule	
x	p	x	p
0	120	0	2400
10	260	10	1500
20	380	20	1200
30	450	30	950
40	540	40	800
50	630	50	730
60	680	60	680
70	720	70	640

27. Use Simpson's Rule to approximate the producer's surplus at market equilibrium. Note that market equilibrium can be found from the tables.

28. Use Simpson's Rule to approximate the consumer's surplus at market equilibrium.

29. *Production* Suppose that the rate of production of a product (in units per week) is measured at the end of each of the first 5 weeks after start-up, and the data in the table are obtained.

Weeks t	Rate R(t)	Weeks t	Rate R(t)
0	250.0	3	243.3
1	247.6	4	241.3
2	245.4	5	239.5

Approximate the total number of units produced in the first 5 weeks.

30. *Drug levels in the blood* The manufacturer of a medicine wants to test how a new 300-milligram capsule is released into the bloodstream. After a volunteer is given a capsule, blood samples are drawn every half-hour, and the number of milligrams of the drug in the bloodstream is calculated. The results obtained are as follows.

Time t (hr)	N(t) (mg)	Time t (hr)	N(t) (mg)
0	0	2.0	178.3
0.5	247.3	2.5	113.9
1.0	270	3.0	56.2
1.5	236.4	3.5	19.3

Approximate the *average* number of milligrams in the bloodstream during the first $3\frac{1}{2}$ hours.

Income distribution If the Lorenz curves for years a and b are given by $L_a(x)$ and $L_b(x)$, respectively, then from year a to year b, the change in the Gini coefficient $(G_b - G_a)$ is given by

$$2\int_0^1 [L_a(x) - L_b(x)]\, dx$$

In Problems 31 and 32, complete the following.
(a) Use the data in the table and make a new table for x and the corresponding values of $[L_a(x) - L_b(x)]$ for the given years, where year b is 2005.
(b) Use the table from part (a) in the Trapezoidal Rule to approximate

$$2\int_0^1 [L_a(x) - L_b(x)]\, dx$$

which gives $G_b - G_a$, the difference of the Gini coefficients for the two years.
(c) Is the value of the integral positive or negative? In which year was the income more equally distributed?

x	0.0	0.2	0.4	0.6	0.8	1.0
	L(x) for Blacks					
2005	0.0	0.030	0.116	0.262	0.499	1.0
1990	0.0	0.031	0.111	0.260	0.511	1.0
	L(x) for Asians					
2005	0.0	0.037	0.137	0.294	0.528	1.0
2002	0.0	0.033	0.124	0.277	0.513	1.0

Source: U.S. Bureau of the Census

31. Complete parts (a)–(c) above for Blacks in 1990 and 2005.

32. Complete parts (a)–(c) above for Asians in 2002 and 2005.

33. *Pollution monitoring* Suppose that the presence of phosphates in certain waste products dumped into a lake promotes the growth of algae. Rampant growth of algae affects the oxygen supply in the water, so an environmental group wishes to estimate the area of algae growth. Group members measure across the algae growth (see Figure 13.33 on the next page) and obtain the data (in feet) in the table.

x	Width w	x	Width w
0	0	50	27
10	15	60	24
20	18	70	23
30	18	80	0
40	30		

(a) Can either the Trapezoidal Rule or Simpson's Rule be used to calculate the area of the algae growth?
(b) When either the Trapezoidal Rule or Simpson's Rule can be used, which is usually more accurate?
(c) Use Simpson's Rule to approximate the area of the algae growth.

Figure 13.33

x	Width w(x)
0	0
100	300
200	200
300	400
400	0

Figure 13.34

34. *Development costs* A land developer is planning to dig a small lake and build a group of homes around it. To estimate the cost of the project, the area of the lake must be calculated from the proposed measurements (in feet) given in Figure 13.34 and in the data in the table. Use Simpson's Rule to approximate the area of the lake.

KEY TERMS AND FORMULAS

Section	Key Terms	Formulas
13.1	Sigma notation	$\sum_{i=1}^{n} 1 = n;\ \sum_{i=1}^{n} i = \dfrac{n(n+1)}{2}$ $\sum_{i=1}^{n} i^2 = \dfrac{n(n+1)(2n+1)}{6}$
	Area	
	Right-hand endpoints	$\lim_{n\to\infty} \sum_{i=1}^{n} f(x_i)\dfrac{b-a}{n};\ x_i = a + i\left(\dfrac{b-a}{n}\right)$
	Left-hand endpoints	$\lim_{n\to\infty} \sum_{i=1}^{n} f(x_{i-1})\dfrac{b-a}{n}$
13.2	Riemann sum	$\sum_{i=1}^{n} f(x_i^*)\Delta x_i$
	Definite integral	$\int_a^b f(x)\,dx = \lim_{\substack{\max \Delta x_i \to 0 \\ (n\to\infty)}} \sum_{i=1}^{n} f(x_i^*)\Delta x_i$
	Fundamental Theorem of Calculus	$\int_a^b f(x)\,dx = F(b) - F(a)$, where $F'(x) = f(x)$

Section	Key Terms	Formulas
13.2	Definite integral properties	$\int_a^a f(x)\,dx = 0$
		$\int_b^a f(x)\,dx = -\int_a^b f(x)\,dx$
		$\int_a^b [f(x) \pm g(x)]\,dx = \int_a^b f(x)\,dx \pm \int_a^b g(x)\,dx$
		$\int_a^b kf(x)\,dx = k\int_a^b f(x)\,dx$
		$\int_a^c f(x)\,dx + \int_c^b f(x)\,dx = \int_a^b f(x)\,dx$
	Area under $f(x)$, where $f(x) \geq 0$	$A = \int_a^b f(x)\,dx$
	$f(x)$ is a probability density function	$\Pr(a \leq x \leq b) = \int_a^b f(x)\,dx$
13.3	Area between $f(x)$ and $g(x)$, where $f(x) \geq g(x)$	$A = \int_a^b [f(x) - g(x)]\,dx$
	Average value of f over $[a, b]$	$\dfrac{1}{b-a}\int_a^b f(x)\,dx$
	Lorenz curve, $L(x)$	
	Gini coefficient	$2\int_0^1 [x - L(x)]\,dx$
13.4	Continuous income streams	
	Total income	$\int_0^k f(t)\,dt$ (for k years)
	Present value	$\int_0^k f(t)e^{-rt}\,dt$, where r is the interest rate
	Future value	$e^{rk}\int_0^k f(t)e^{-rt}\,dt$
	Consumer's surplus [demand is $f(x)$]	$CS = \int_0^{x_1} f(x)\,dx - p_1 x_1$
	Producer's surplus [supply is $g(x)$]	$PS = p_1 x_1 - \int_0^{x_1} g(x)\,dx$
13.5	Integration by formulas	See Table 13.2.
13.6	Integration by parts	$\int u\,dv = uv - \int v\,du$
13.7	Improper integrals	$\int_a^{\infty} f(x)\,dx = \lim_{b\to\infty} \int_a^b f(x)\,dx$
		$\int_{-\infty}^b f(x)\,dx = \lim_{a\to\infty} \int_{-a}^b f(x)\,dx$
		$\int_{-\infty}^{\infty} f(x)\,dx = \int_{-\infty}^c f(x)\,dx + \int_c^{\infty} f(x)\,dx$

Capital value of a continuous income stream	$\int_0^\infty f(t)e^{-rt}\,dt$
Probability density function, $f(x)$	$f(x) \geq 0$ and $\int_{-\infty}^\infty f(x)\,dx = 1$
Mean	$\mu = \int_{-\infty}^\infty xf(x)\,dx$

13.8	Trapezoidal Rule for $\int_a^b f(x)\,dx$	$\approx \dfrac{h}{2}[f(x_0) + 2f(x_1) + \cdots + 2f(x_{n-1}) + f(x_n)]$ where $h = \dfrac{b-a}{n}$
	Error formula	$\|E\| \leq \dfrac{(b-a)^3}{12n^2}\left[\max_{a\leq x\leq b}\|f''(x)\|\right]$
	Simpson's Rule for $\int_a^b f(x)\,dx$	$\approx \dfrac{h}{3}[f(x_0) + 4f(x_1) + 2f(x_2) + 4f(x_3)$ $+ \cdots + 2f(x_{n-2}) + 4f(x_{n-1}) + f(x_n)],$ where n is even and $h = \dfrac{b-a}{n}$
	Error formula	$\|E\| \leq \dfrac{(b-a)^5}{180n^4}\left[\max_{a\leq x\leq b}\|f^{(4)}(x)\|\right]$

REVIEW EXERCISES

1. Calculate $\displaystyle\sum_{k=1}^{8}(k^2 + 1)$.

2. Use formulas to simplify

$$\sum_{i=1}^{n}\frac{3i}{n^3}.$$

3. Use 6 subintervals of the same size to approximate the area under the graph of $y = 3x^2$ from $x = 0$ to $x = 1$. Use the right-hand endpoints of the subintervals to find the heights of the rectangles.

4. Use rectangles to find the area under the graph of $y = 3x^2$ from $x = 0$ to $x = 1$. Use n equal subintervals.

5. Use a definite integral to find the area under the graph of $y = 3x^2$ from $x = 0$ to $x = 1$.

6. Find the area between the graph of $y = x^3 - 4x + 5$ and the x-axis from $x = 1$ to $x = 3$.

Evaluate the integrals in Problems 7–18.

7. $\displaystyle\int_1^4 4\sqrt{x^3}\,dx$

8. $\displaystyle\int_{-3}^2 (x^3 - 3x^2 + 4x + 2)\,dx$

9. $\displaystyle\int_0^5 (x^3 + 4x)\,dx$

10. $\displaystyle\int_{-1}^3 (3x + 4)^{-2}\,dx$

11. $\displaystyle\int_{-3}^{-1} (x + 1)\,dx$

12. $\displaystyle\int_2^3 \frac{x^2}{2x^3 - 7}\,dx$

13. $\displaystyle\int_{-1}^2 (x^2 + x)\,dx$

14. $\displaystyle\int_1^4 \left(\frac{1}{x} + \sqrt{x}\right)dx$

15. $\displaystyle\int_0^2 5x^2(6x^3 + 1)^{1/2}\,dx$

16. $\displaystyle\int_0^1 \frac{x}{x^2 + 1}\,dx$

17. $\displaystyle\int_0^1 e^{-2x}\,dx$

18. $\displaystyle\int_0^1 xe^{x^2}\,dx$

Find the area between the curves in Problems 19–22.

19. $y = x^2 - 3x + 2$ and $y = x^2 + 4$ from $x = 0$ to $x = 5$

20. $y = x^2$ and $y = 4x + 5$

21. $y = x^3$ and $y = x$ from $x = -1$ to $x = 0$

22. $y = x^3 - 1$ and $y = x - 1$

Evaluate the integrals in Problems 23–26, using the formulas in Table 13.2.

23. $\displaystyle\int \sqrt{x^2 - 4}\,dx$

24. $\displaystyle\int_0^1 3^x\,dx$

25. $\displaystyle\int x \ln x^2\,dx$

26. $\displaystyle\int \frac{dx}{x(3x + 2)}$

In Problems 27–30, use integration by parts to evaluate.

27. $\displaystyle\int x^5 \ln x\,dx$

28. $\displaystyle\int x^2 e^{-2x}\,dx$

29. $\displaystyle\int \frac{x\,dx}{\sqrt{x + 5}}$

30. $\displaystyle\int_1^e \ln x\,dx$

Evaluate the improper integrals in Problems 31–34.

31. $\int_1^\infty \dfrac{1}{x+1}\, dx$

32. $\int_{-\infty}^{-1} \dfrac{200}{x^3}\, dx$

33. $\int_0^\infty 5e^{-3x}\, dx$

34. $\int_{-\infty}^0 \dfrac{x}{(x^2+1)^2}\, dx$

35. Evaluate $\int_1^3 \dfrac{2}{x^3}\, dx$
    (a) exactly.
    (b) by using the Trapezoidal Rule with $n = 4$ (to 3 decimal places).
    (c) by using Simpson's Rule with $n = 4$ (to 3 decimal places).

36. Use the Trapezoidal Rule with $n = 5$ to approximate

$$\int_0^1 \dfrac{4\, dx}{x^2+1}$$

Round your answer to 3 decimal places.

37. Use the table that follows to approximate

$$\int_1^{2.2} f(x)\, dx$$

by using Simpson's Rule. Round your answer to 1 decimal place.

x	$f(x)$
1	0
1.3	2.8
1.6	5.1
1.9	4.2
2.2	0.6

38. Suppose that a definite integral is to be approximated and it is found that to achieve a specified accuracy, n must satisfy $n \geq 4.8$. What is the smallest n that can be used, if
    (a) the Trapezoidal Rule is used?
    (b) Simpson's Rule is used?

APPLICATIONS

39. *Maintenance* Maintenance costs for buildings increase as the buildings age. If the rate of increase in maintenance costs for a building is

$$M'(t) = \dfrac{14{,}000}{\sqrt{t+16}}$$

where M is in dollars and t is time in years, $0 \leq t \leq 15$, find the total maintenance cost for the first 9 years ($t = 0$ to $t = 9$).

40. *Quality control* Suppose the probability density function for the life expectancy of a battery is

$$f(x) = \begin{cases} 1.4e^{-1.4x} & x \geq 0 \\ 0 & x < 0 \end{cases}$$

Find the probability that the battery lasts 2 years or less.

41. *Savings* The future value of $1000 invested in a savings account at 10%, compounded continuously, is $S = 1000e^{0.1t}$, where t is in years. Find the average amount in the savings account during the first 5 years.

42. *Income streams* Suppose the total income in dollars from a machine is given by

$$I = 50e^{0.2t}, \quad 0 \leq t \leq 4, t \text{ in hours}$$

Find the average income over this 4-hour period.

43. *Income distribution* In 1969, after the "Great Society" initiatives of the Johnson administration, the Lorenz curve for the U.S. income distribution was $L(x) = x^{2.1936}$. In 2000, after the stock market's historic 10-year growth, the Lorenz curve for the U.S. income distribution was $L(x) = x^{2.4870}$. Find the Gini coefficient of income for both years, and determine in which year income was more equally distributed.

44. *Consumer's surplus* The demand function for a product under pure competition is $p = \sqrt{64 - 4x}$, and the supply function is $p = x - 1$, where x is the number of units and p is in dollars.
    (a) Find the market equilibrium.
    (b) Find the consumer's surplus at market equilibrium.

45. *Producer's surplus* Find the producer's surplus at market equilibrium for Problem 44.

46. *Income streams* Find the total income over the next 10 years from a continuous income stream that has an annual flow rate at time t given by $f(t) = 125e^{0.05t}$ in thousands of dollars per year.

47. *Income streams* Suppose that a machine's production is considered a continuous income stream with an annual rate of flow at time t given by $f(t) = 150e^{-0.2t}$ in thousands of dollars per year. Money is worth 8%, compounded continuously.
    (a) Find the present value of the machine's production over the next 5 years.
    (b) Find the future value of the production 5 years from now.

48. *Average cost* Suppose the cost function for x units of a product is given by $C(x) = \sqrt{40{,}000 + x^2}$ dollars. Find the average cost over the first 150 units.

49. *Producer's surplus* Suppose the supply function for x units of a certain lamp is given by

$$p = 0.02x + 50.01 - \dfrac{10}{\sqrt{x^2+1}}$$

where p is in dollars. Find the producer's surplus if the equilibrium price is $70 and the equilibrium quantity is 1000.

50. *Income streams* Suppose the present value of a continuous income stream over the next 5 years is given by

$$P = 9000 \int_0^5 te^{-0.08t}\, dt, \quad P \text{ in dollars, } t \text{ in years}$$

Find the present value.

51. *Cost* If the marginal cost for x units of a product is $\overline{MC} = 3 + 60(x + 1) \ln (x + 1)$ dollars per unit and if the fixed cost is $2000, find the total cost function.

52. *Quality control* Find the probability that a phone lasts more than 1 year if the probability density function for its life expectancy is given by

$$f(x) = \begin{cases} 1.4e^{-1.4x} & x \geq 0 \\ 0 & x < 0 \end{cases}$$

53. *Capital value* Find the capital value of a business if its income is considered a continuous income stream with annual rate of flow given by

$$f(t) = 120e^{0.03t}$$

in thousands of dollars per year, and the current interest rate is 6% compounded continuously.

54. *Total income* Suppose that a continuous income stream has an annual rate of flow $f(t) = 100e^{-0.01t^2}$ (in thousands of dollars per year). Use Simpson's Rule with $n = 4$ to approximate the total income from this stream over the next 2 years.

55. *Revenue* A company has the data shown in the table from the sale of its product.

x	$\overline{MR}$
0	0
2	480
4	720
6	720
8	480
10	0

If x represents hundreds of units and revenue R is in hundreds of dollars, approximate the total revenue from the sale of 1000 units by approximating

$$\int_0^{10} \overline{MR} \, dx$$

with the Trapezoidal Rule.

---

13   CHAPTER TEST

1. Use left-hand endpoints and $n = 4$ subdivisions to approximate the area under $f(x) = \sqrt{4 - x^2}$ on the interval $[0, 2]$.

2. Consider $f(x) = 5 - 2x$ from $x = 0$ to $x = 1$ with n equal subdivisions.
   (a) If $f(x)$ is evaluated at right-hand endpoints, find a formula for the sum, S, of the areas of the n rectangles.
   (b) Find $\lim_{n \to \infty} S$.

3. Express the area in Quadrant I under $y = 12 + 4x - x^2$ (shaded in the figure) as an integral. Then evaluate the integral to find the area.

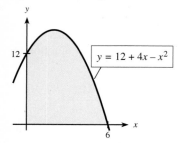

4. Evaluate the following definite integrals. (Do not approximate with technology.)
   (a) $\displaystyle\int_0^4 (9 - 4x) \, dx$ (b) $\displaystyle\int_0^3 x(8x^2 + 9)^{-1/2} \, dx$
   (c) $\displaystyle\int_1^4 \frac{5}{4x - 1} \, dx$ (d) $\displaystyle\int_1^\infty \frac{7}{x^2} \, dx$

   (e) $\displaystyle\int_{-4}^4 \sqrt{x^3 + 10} \, dx$ (f) $\displaystyle\int_0^1 5x^2e^{2x^3} \, dx$

5. Use integration by parts to evaluate the following.
   (a) $\displaystyle\int 3xe^x \, dx$ (b) $\displaystyle\int x \ln (2x) \, dx$

6. If $\displaystyle\int_1^4 f(x) \, dx = 3$ and $\displaystyle\int_3^4 f(x) \, dx = 7$, find $\displaystyle\int_1^3 2f(x) \, dx$.

7. Use Table 13.2 in Section 13.5 to evaluate each of the following.
   (a) $\displaystyle\int \ln (2x) \, dx$ (b) $\displaystyle\int x\sqrt{3x - 7} \, dx$

8. Use the numerical integration feature of a graphing calculator to approximate $\displaystyle\int_1^4 \sqrt{x^3 + 10} \, dx$.

9. Suppose the supply function for a product is $p = 40 + 0.001x^2$ and the demand function is $p = 120 - 0.2x$, where x is the number of units and p is the price in dollars. If the market equilibrium price is $80, find (a) the consumer's surplus and (b) the producer's surplus.

10. Suppose a continuous income stream has an annual rate of flow $f(t) = 85e^{-0.01t}$, in thousands of dollars per year, and the current interest rate is 7% compounded continuously.
    (a) Find the total income over the next 12 years.
    (b) Find the present value over the next 12 years.
    (c) Find the capital value of the stream.

11. Find the area between $y = 2x + 4$ and $y = x^2 - x$.

12. The figure shows typical supply and demand curves. On the figure, sketch and shade the region whose area represents the consumer's surplus.

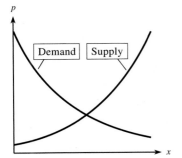

13. In an effort to make the distribution of income more nearly equal, the government of a country passes a tax law that changes the Lorenz curve from $y = 0.998x^{2.6}$ for one year to $y = 0.57x^2 + 0.43x$ for the next year. Find the Gini coefficient of income for each year and determine whether the distribution of income is more or less equitable after the tax law is passed. Interpret the result.

14. With data from the U.S. Department of Energy, the number of billions of barrels of U.S. crude oil produced each year from 2010 and projected to 2030 can be modeled by the function

$$f(t) = -0.001t^2 + 0.037t + 1.94$$

where t is the number of years past 2010.

(a) Find the total number of barrels of oil produced from 2010 to 2020.

(b) Find the average number of barrels produced per year from 2010 to 2018.

15. Use the Trapezoidal Rule to approximate

$$\int_1^3 (x \ln x)\, dx$$

with $n = 4$ subintervals.

16. The environmental effects of a chemical spill in the Clarion River can be estimated from the river's flow volume. To measure this flow volume, it is necessary to find the cross-sectional area of the river at a point downriver from the spill. The distance across the river is 240 feet, and the table gives depth measurements, $D(x)$, of the river at various distances x from one bank of the river. Use these measurements to estimate the cross-sectional area with Simpson's Rule.

x	0	40	80	120	160	200	240
$D(x)$	0	22	35	48	32	24	0

I. Retirement Planning

A 52-year-old client asks an accountant how to plan for his future retirement at age 62. He expects income from Social Security in the amount of $21,600 per year and a retirement pension of $40,500 per year from his employer. He wants to make monthly contributions to an investment plan that pays 8%, compounded monthly, for 10 years so that he will have a total income of $83,700 per year for 30 years. What will the size of the monthly contributions have to be to accomplish this goal, if it is assumed that money will be worth 8%, compounded continuously, throughout the period after he is 62?

To help you answer this question, complete the following.

1. How much money must the client withdraw annually from his investment plan during his retirement so that his total income goal is met?
2. How much money S must the client's account contain when he is 62 so that it will generate this annual amount for 30 years? (*Hint: S* can be considered the present value over 30 years of a continuous income stream with the amount you found in Question 1 as its annual rate of flow.)
3. The monthly contribution R that would, after 10 years, amount to the present value S found in Question 2 can be obtained from the formula

$$R = S\left[\frac{i}{(1 + i)^n - 1}\right]$$

where i represents the monthly interest rate and n the number of months. Find the client's monthly contribution, R.

II. Purchasing Electrical Power (Modeling)

In order to plan its purchases of electrical power from suppliers over the next 5 years, the PAC Electric Company needs to model its load data (demand for power by its customers) and use this model to predict future loads. The company pays for the electrical power each month on the basis of the peak load (demand) at any point during the month. The table gives, for the years 1994–2012, the load in megawatts (that is, in millions of watts) for the month when the maximum load occurred and the load in megawatts for the month when the minimum load occurred. The maximum loads occurred in summer, and the minimum loads occurred in spring or fall.

Year	Maximum Monthly Load	Minimum Monthly Load
1994	40.9367	19.4689
1995	45.7127	22.1504
1996	48.0460	25.3670
1997	56.1712	28.7254
1998	55.5793	31.0460
1999	62.4285	31.3838
2000	76.6536	34.8426
2001	73.8214	38.4544
2002	74.8844	40.6080
2003	83.0590	47.3621
2004	88.3914	45.8393
2005	88.7704	48.7956
2006	94.2620	48.3313
2007	105.1596	52.7710
2008	95.8301	54.4757
2009	97.8854	55.2210
2010	102.8912	55.1360
2011	109.5541	57.2162
2012	111.2516	58.3216

The company wishes to predict the average monthly load over the next 5 years so that it can plan its future monthly purchases. To assist the company, proceed as follows.

1. (a) Using the years and the maximum monthly load given for each year, graph the data, with x representing the number of years past 1994 and y representing the maximum load in megawatts.
   (b) Find the equation that best fits the data, using both a quadratic model and a cubic model.
   (c) Graph the data and both of these models from 1994 to 2014 (that is, from $x = 0$ to $x = 20$).
2. Do the two models appear to fit the data equally well in the interval 1994–2014? Which model appears to be a better predictor for the next decade?
3. Use the quadratic model to predict the maximum monthly load in the year 2017. How can this value be used by the company? Should this number be used to plan monthly power purchases for each month in 2017?
4. To create a "typical" monthly load function:
   (a) Create a table with the year as the independent variable and the average of the maximum and minimum monthly loads as the dependent variable.
   (b) Find the quadratic model that best fits these data points, using $x = 0$ to represent 1994.
5. Use a definite integral with the typical monthly load function to predict the average monthly load over the years 2014–2019.
6. What factors in addition to the average monthly load should be considered when the company plans future purchases of power?

Financial Tables

| TABLE 1 |

Future Value of an Ordinary Annuity of \$1 ($s_{\overline{n}|i}$)

Periods	1%	2%	3%	4%	5%	6%
1	1.000 000	1.000 000	1.000 000	1.000 000	1.000 000	1.000 000
2	2.010 000	2.020 000	2.030 000	2.040 000	2.050 000	2.060 000
3	3.030 100	3.060 400	3.090 900	3.121 600	3.152 500	3.183 600
4	4.060 401	4.121 608	4.183 627	4.246 464	4.310 125	4.374 616
5	5.101 005	5.204 040	5.309 136	5.416 323	5.525 631	5.637 093
6	6.152 015	6.308 121	6.468 410	6.632 975	6.801 913	6.975 319
7	7.213 535	7.434 284	7.662 462	7.898 294	8.142 008	8.393 838
8	8.285 670	8.582 969	8.892 336	9.214 226	9.549 109	9.897 468
9	9.368 527	9.754 629	10.159 106	10.582 795	11.026 564	11.491 316
10	10.462 212	10.949 721	11.463 879	12.006 107	12.577 893	13.180 795
11	11.566 834	12.168 716	12.807 796	13.486 351	14.206 787	14.971 643
12	12.682 503	13.412 090	14.192 030	15.025 805	15.917 126	16.869 941
13	13.809 328	14.680 332	15.617 790	16.626 838	17.712 983	18.882 138
14	14.947 421	15.973 939	17.086 324	18.291 911	19.598 632	21.015 066
15	16.096 895	17.293 418	18.598 914	20.023 588	21.578 564	23.275 970
16	17.257 864	18.639 286	20.156 881	21.824 531	23.657 492	25.672 529
17	18.430 443	20.012 072	21.761 588	23.697 512	25.840 366	28.212 880
18	19.614 747	21.412 313	23.414 435	26.645 413	28.132 385	30.905 653
19	20.810 895	22.840 559	25.116 869	27.671 229	30.539 004	33.759 992
20	22.019 004	24.297 371	26.870 375	29.778 079	33.065 954	36.787 592
21	23.239 194	25.783 318	28.676 486	31.969 202	35.719 252	39.992 727
22	24.471 586	27.298 985	30.536 780	34.247 970	38.505 214	43.392 291
23	25.716 301	28.844 964	32.452 884	36.617 889	41.430 475	46.995 829
24	26.973 464	30.421 864	34.426 470	39.082 604	44.501 999	50.815 578
25	28.243 199	32.030 301	36.459 264	41.645 908	47.727 099	54.864 513
26	29.525 631	33.670 907	38.553 042	44.311 745	51.113 454	59.156 384
27	30.820 887	35.344 325	40.709 634	47.084 214	54.669 126	63.705 767
28	32.129 096	37.051 212	42.930 923	49.967 583	58.402 583	68.528 113
29	33.450 387	38.792 236	45.218 850	52.966 286	62.322 712	73.639 800
30	34.784 891	40.568 081	47.575 416	56.084 938	66.438 847	79.058 188
31	36.132 740	42.379 443	50.002 678	59.328 335	70.760 790	84.801 679
32	37.494 067	44.227 031	52.502 759	62.701 469	75.298 829	90.889 780
33	38.869 008	46.111 572	55.077 842	66.209 528	80.063 771	97.343 167
34	40.257 698	48.033 804	57.730 177	69.857 909	85.066 959	104.183 757
35	41.660 275	49.994 480	60.462 082	73.652 225	90.320 307	111.434 783
36	43.076 878	51.994 369	63.275 945	77.598 314	95.836 323	119.120 870
37	44.507 646	54.034 257	66.174 223	81.702 247	101.628 139	127.268 122
38	45.952 723	56.114 942	69.159 450	85.970 336	107.709 546	135.904 209
39	47.412 250	58.237 241	72.234 233	90.409 150	114.095 023	145.058 462
40	48.886 373	60.401 986	75.401 260	95.025 516	120.799 774	154.761 970

(continued)

| TABLE 1 |

Future Value of an Ordinary Annuity of $1 ($s_{\overline{n}|i}$) (*Continued*)

Periods	7%	8%	9%	10%	11%	12%
1	1.000 000	1.000 000	1.000 000	1.000 000	1.000 000	1.000 000
2	2.070 000	2.080 000	2.090 000	2.100 000	2.110 000	2.120 000
3	3.214 900	3.246 400	3.278 100	3.310 000	3.342 100	3.374 400
4	4.439 943	4.506 112	4.573 129	4.641 000	4.709 731	4.779 328
5	5.750 739	5.866 601	5.984 711	6.105 100	6.227 801	6.352 847
6	7.153 291	7.335 929	7.523 335	7.715 610	7.912 860	8.115 189
7	8.654 021	8.922 803	9.200 435	9.487 171	9.783 274	10.089 012
8	10.259 803	10.636 628	11.028 474	11.435 888	11.859 434	12.299 693
9	11.977 989	12.487 558	13.021 036	13.579 477	14.136 972	14.775 656
10	13.816 448	14.486 563	15.192 930	15.937 425	16.722 009	17.548 735
11	15.783 599	16.645 488	17.560 293	18.531 167	19.561 430	20.654 583
12	17.888 451	18.977 127	20.140 720	21.384 284	22.713 187	24.133 133
13	20.140 643	21.495 297	22.953 385	24.522 712	26.211 638	28.029 109
14	22.550 488	24.214 920	26.019 189	27.974 984	30.094 918	32.392 602
15	25.129 022	27.152 114	29.360 916	31.772 482	34.405 359	37.279 715
16	27.888 054	30.324 283	33.003 399	35.949 730	39.189 949	42.753 281
17	30.840 218	33.750 226	36.973 705	40.544 703	44.500 843	48.883 674
18	33.999 033	37.450 244	41.301 338	45.599 174	50.395 936	55.749 715
19	37.378 965	41.446 263	46.018 458	51.159 091	56.939 489	63.439 681
20	40.995 493	45.761 965	51.160 120	57.275 000	64.202 833	72.052 443
21	44.865 177	50.422 922	56.764 530	64.002 501	72.265 145	81.698 736
22	49.005 740	55.456 756	62.873 338	71.402 750	81.214 310	92.502 584
23	53.436 142	60.893 296	69.531 939	79.543 025	91.147 885	104.602 894
24	58.176 672	66.764 760	76.789 813	88.497 328	102.174 152	118.155 242
25	63.249 039	73.105 940	84.700 896	98.347 061	114.413 309	133.333 871
26	68.676 471	79.954 416	93.323 977	109.181 767	127.998 773	150.333 935
27	74.483 824	87.350 769	102.723 135	121.099 944	143.078 638	169.374 007
28	80.697 692	95.338 831	112.968 217	134.209 938	159.817 288	190.698 888
29	87.346 531	103.965 937	124.135 357	148.630 932	178.397 190	214.582 755
30	94.460 788	113.283 212	136.307 539	164.494 026	199.020 881	241.322 686
31	102.073 043	123.345 869	149.575 217	181.943 428	221.913 178	271.292 608
32	110.218 156	134.213 539	164.036 987	201.137 771	247.323 628	304.847 721
33	118.933 427	145.950 622	179.800 316	222.251 548	275.529 227	342.429 447
34	128.258 767	158.626 671	196.982 344	245.476 703	306.837 442	384.520 981
35	138.236 881	172.316 805	215.710 755	271.024 374	341.589 561	431.663 499
36	148.913 462	187.102 150	236.124 723	299.126 811	380.164 413	484.463 119
37	160.337 405	203.070 322	258.375 948	330.039 493	422.982 498	543.598 693
38	172.561 023	220.315 948	282.629 783	364.043 442	470.510 573	609.830 536
39	185.640 295	238.941 223	309.066 464	401.447 787	523.266 737	686.010 201
40	199.635 116	259.056 521	337.882 446	442.592 566	581.826 078	767.091 425

■ | **TABLE 2** | ■■■■■■■■■■■■■■■■■■■■■■■■

Present Value of an Ordinary Annuity of $1 ($a_{\overline{n}|i}$)

Periods	1%	2%	3%	4%	5%	6%
1	0.990 099	0.980 392	0.970 874	0.961 538	0.952 381	0.943 396
2	1.970 395	1.941 561	1.913 470	1.886 095	1.859 410	1.833 393
3	2.940 985	2.883 883	2.828 611	2.775 091	2.723 248	2.673 012
4	3.901 965	3.807 729	3.717 098	3.629 895	3.545 951	3.465 106
5	4.853 431	4.713 460	4.579 707	4.451 822	4.329 477	4.212 364
6	5.795 476	5.601 431	5.417 191	5.242 137	5.075 692	4.917 324
7	6.728 194	6.471 991	6.230 283	6.002 055	5.786 373	5.582 381
8	7.651 678	7.325 482	7.019 692	6.732 745	6.463 213	6.209 794
9	8.566 017	8.162 237	7.786 109	7.435 332	7.107 822	6.801 692
10	9.471 304	8.982 585	8.530 203	8.110 896	7.721 735	7.360 087
11	10.367 628	9.786 848	9.252 624	8.760 477	8.306 414	7.886 875
12	11.255 077	10.575 342	9.954 004	9.385 074	8.863 252	8.383 844
13	12.133 740	11.348 374	10.634 955	9.985 648	9.393 573	8.852 683
14	13.003 703	12.106 249	11.296 073	10.563 123	9.898 641	9.294 984
15	13.865 052	12.849 264	11.937 935	11.118 387	10.379 658	9.712 249
16	14.717 874	13.577 710	12.561 102	11.652 296	10.837 770	10.105 895
17	15.562 251	14.291 872	13.166 118	12.165 669	11.274 066	10.477 260
18	16.398 268	14.992 032	13.753 513	12.659 297	11.689 587	10.827 604
19	17.226 008	15.678 462	14.323 799	13.133 939	12.085 321	11.158 117
20	18.045 553	16.351 434	14.877 475	13.590 326	12.462 210	11.469 921
21	18.856 983	17.011 210	15.415 024	14.029 160	12.821 153	11.764 077
22	18.660 379	17.658 049	15.936 917	14.451 115	13.163 003	12.041 582
23	20.455 821	18.292 205	16.443 608	14.856 842	13.488 574	12.303 379
24	21.243 387	18.913 926	16.935 542	15.246 963	13.798 642	12.550 358
25	22.023 155	19.523 457	17.413 148	15.622 080	14.093 945	12.783 356
26	22.795 203	20.121 036	17.876 842	15.982 769	14.375 185	13.003 166
27	23.559 607	20.706 898	18.327 032	16.329 586	14.643 034	13.210 534
28	24.316 443	21.281 273	18.764 108	16.663 063	14.898 127	13.406 164
29	25.065 785	21.844 385	19.188 455	16.983 715	15.141 074	13.590 721
30	25.807 708	22.396 456	19.600 441	17.292 033	15.372 451	13.764 831
31	26.542 285	22.937 702	20.000 429	17.588 494	15.592 810	13.929 086
32	27.269 589	23.468 335	20.388 766	17.873 552	15.802 677	14.084 043
33	27.989 692	23.988 564	20.765 792	18.147 646	16.002 549	14.230 230
34	28.702 666	24.498 592	21.131 837	18.411 198	16.192 904	14.368 141
35	28.408 580	24.998 620	21.487 220	18.664 613	16.374 194	14.498 246
36	30.107 505	25.488 843	21.832 253	18.908 282	16.546 852	14.620 987
37	30.799 510	25.969 454	22.167 235	19.142 579	16.711 287	14.736 780
38	31.484 663	26.440 641	22.492 462	19.367 864	16.867 893	14.846 019
39	32.163 033	26.902 589	22.808 215	19.584 485	17.017 041	14.949 075
40	32.834 686	27.355 480	23.114 772	19.792 774	17.159 086	15.046 297

(continued)

| TABLE 2 |

Present Value of an Ordinary Annuity of $1 ($a_{\overline{n}|i}$) (*Continued*)

Periods	7%	8%	9%	10%	11%	12%
1	0.934 579	0.925 926	0.917 431	0.909 091	0.900 901	0.892 857
2	1.808 018	1.783 265	1.759 111	1.735 537	1.712 523	1.690 051
3	2.624 316	2.577 097	2.531 295	2.486 852	2.443 715	2.401 831
4	3.387 211	3.312 127	3.239 720	3.169 865	3.102 446	3.037 349
5	4.100 197	3.992 710	3.889 651	3.790 787	3.695 897	3.604 776
6	4.766 540	4.622 880	4.485 919	4.355 261	4.230 538	4.111 407
7	5.389 289	5.206 370	5.032 953	4.868 419	4.712 196	4.563 757
8	5.971 299	5.746 639	5.534 819	5.334 926	5.146 123	4.967 640
9	6.515 232	6.246 888	5.995 247	5.759 024	5.537 048	5.328 250
10	7.023 582	6.710 081	6.417 658	6.144 567	5.889 232	5.650 223
11	7.498 674	7.138 964	6.805 191	6.495 061	6.206 515	5.937 699
12	7.942 686	7.536 078	7.160 725	6.813 692	6.492 356	6.194 374
13	8.357 651	7.903 776	7.486 904	7.103 356	6.749 870	6.423 548
14	8.745 468	8.244 237	7.786 150	7.366 687	6.981 865	6.628 168
15	9.107 914	8.559 479	8.060 688	7.606 080	7.190 870	6.810 864
16	9.446 649	8.851 369	8.312 558	7.823 709	7.379 162	6.973 986
17	9.763 223	9.121 638	8.543 631	8.021 553	7.548 794	7.119 630
18	10.059 087	9.371 887	8.755 625	8.201 412	7.701 617	7.249 670
19	10.335 595	9.603 599	8.950 115	8.364 920	7.839 294	7.365 777
20	10.594 014	9.818 147	9.128 546	8.513 564	7.963 328	7.469 444
21	10.835 527	10.016 803	9.292 244	8.648 694	8.075 070	7.562 003
22	11.061 241	10.200 744	9.442 425	8.771 540	8.175 739	7.644 646
23	11.272 187	10.371 059	9.580 207	8.883 218	8.266 432	7.718 434
24	11.469 334	10.528 758	9.706 612	8.984 744	8.348 137	7.784 316
25	11.653 583	10.674 776	9.822 580	9.077 040	8.421 745	7.843 139
26	11.825 779	10.809 978	9.928 972	9.160 945	8.488 058	7.895 660
27	11.986 709	10.935 165	10.026 580	9.237 223	8.547 800	7.942 554
28	12.137 111	11.051 079	10.116 128	9.306 567	8.601 622	7.984 423
29	12.277 674	11.158 406	10.198 283	9.369 606	8.650 110	8.021 806
30	12.409 041	11.257 783	10.273 654	9.429 914	8.693 793	8.055 184
31	12.531 814	11.349 799	10.342 802	9.479 013	8.733 146	8.084 986
32	12.646 555	11.434 999	10.406 240	9.526 376	8.768 600	8.111 594
33	12.753 790	11.513 888	10.464 441	9.569 432	8.800 541	8.135 352
34	12.854 009	11.586 934	10.517 835	9.608 575	8.829 316	8.156 564
35	12.947 672	11.654 568	10.566 821	9.644 159	8.855 240	8.175 504
36	13.035 208	11.717 193	10.611 763	9.676 508	8.878 594	8.192 414
37	13.117 017	11.775 179	10.652 993	9.705 917	8.899 635	8.207 513
38	13.193 473	11.828 869	10.690 820	9.732 651	8.918 590	8.220 993
39	13.264 928	11.878 582	10.725 523	9.756 956	8.935 666	8.233 030
40	13.331 709	11.924 613	10.757 360	9.779 051	8.951 051	8.243 777

Areas Under the Standard Normal Curve

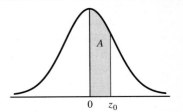

The value of A is the area under the standard normal curve between $z = 0$ and $z = z_0$, for $z_0 \geq 0$. Areas for negative values of z_0 are obtained by symmetry.

z_0	A	z_0	A	z_0	A	z_0	A
0.00	0.0000	0.43	0.1664	0.86	0.3051	1.29	0.4015
0.01	0.0040	0.44	0.1700	0.87	0.3079	1.30	0.4032
0.02	0.0080	0.45	0.1736	0.88	0.3106	1.31	0.4049
0.03	0.0120	0.46	0.1772	0.89	0.3133	1.32	0.4066
0.04	0.0160	0.47	0.1808	0.90	0.3159	1.33	0.4082
0.05	0.0199	0.48	0.1844	0.91	0.3186	1.34	0.4099
0.06	0.0239	0.49	0.1879	0.92	0.3212	1.35	0.4115
0.07	0.0279	0.50	0.1915	0.93	0.3238	1.36	0.4131
0.08	0.0319	0.51	0.1950	0.94	0.3264	1.37	0.4147
0.09	0.0359	0.52	0.1985	0.95	0.3289	1.38	0.4162
0.10	0.0398	0.53	0.2019	0.96	0.3315	1.39	0.4177
0.11	0.0438	0.54	0.2054	0.97	0.3340	1.40	0.4192
0.12	0.0478	0.55	0.2088	0.98	0.3365	1.41	0.4207
0.13	0.0517	0.56	0.2123	0.99	0.3389	1.42	0.4222
0.14	0.0557	0.57	0.2157	1.00	0.3413	1.43	0.4236
0.15	0.0596	0.58	0.2190	1.01	0.3438	1.44	0.4251
0.16	0.0636	0.59	0.2224	1.02	0.3461	1.45	0.4265
0.17	0.0675	0.60	0.2258	1.03	0.3485	1.46	0.4279
0.18	0.0714	0.61	0.2291	1.04	0.3508	1.47	0.4292
0.19	0.0754	0.62	0.2324	1.05	0.3531	1.48	0.4306
0.20	0.0793	0.63	0.2357	1.06	0.3554	1.49	0.4319
0.21	0.0832	0.64	0.2389	1.07	0.3577	1.50	0.4332
0.22	0.0871	0.65	0.2422	1.08	0.3599	1.51	0.4345
0.23	0.0910	0.66	0.2454	1.09	0.3621	1.52	0.4357
0.24	0.0948	0.67	0.2486	1.10	0.3643	1.53	0.4370
0.25	0.0987	0.68	0.2518	1.11	0.3665	1.54	0.4382
0.26	0.1026	0.69	0.2549	1.12	0.3686	1.55	0.4394
0.27	0.1064	0.70	0.2580	1.13	0.3708	1.56	0.4406
0.28	0.1103	0.71	0.2612	1.14	0.3729	1.57	0.4418
0.29	0.1141	0.72	0.2642	1.15	0.3749	1.58	0.4430
0.30	0.1179	0.73	0.2673	1.16	0.3770	1.59	0.4441
0.31	0.1217	0.74	0.2704	1.17	0.3790	1.60	0.4452
0.32	0.1255	0.75	0.2734	1.18	0.3810	1.61	0.4463
0.33	0.1293	0.76	0.2764	1.19	0.3830	1.62	0.4474
0.34	0.1331	0.77	0.2794	1.20	0.3849	1.63	0.4485
0.35	0.1368	0.78	0.2823	1.21	0.3869	1.64	0.4495
0.36	0.1406	0.79	0.2852	1.22	0.3888	1.65	0.4505
0.37	0.1443	0.80	0.2881	1.23	0.3907	1.66	0.4515
0.38	0.1480	0.81	0.2910	1.24	0.3925	1.67	0.4525
0.39	0.1517	0.82	0.2939	1.25	0.3944	1.68	0.4535
0.40	0.1554	0.83	0.2967	1.26	0.3962	1.69	0.4545
0.41	0.1591	0.84	0.2996	1.27	0.3980	1.70	0.4554
0.42	0.1628	0.85	0.3023	1.28	0.3997	1.71	0.4564

(continued)

z_0	A	z_0	A	z_0	A	z_0	A
1.72	0.4573	2.26	0.4881	2.80	0.4974	3.34	0.4996
1.73	0.4582	2.27	0.4884	2.81	0.4975	3.35	0.4996
1.74	0.4591	2.28	0.4887	2.82	0.4976	3.36	0.4996
1.75	0.4599	2.29	0.4890	2.83	0.4977	3.37	0.4996
1.76	0.4608	2.30	0.4893	2.84	0.4977	3.38	0.4996
1.77	0.4616	2.31	0.4896	2.85	0.4978	3.39	0.4997
1.78	0.4625	2.32	0.4898	2.86	0.4979	3.40	0.4997
1.79	0.4633	2.33	0.4901	2.87	0.4980	3.41	0.4997
1.80	0.4641	2.34	0.4904	2.88	0.4980	3.42	0.4997
1.81	0.4649	2.35	0.4906	2.89	0.4981	3.43	0.4997
1.82	0.4656	2.36	0.4909	2.90	0.4981	3.44	0.4997
1.83	0.4664	2.37	0.4911	2.91	0.4982	3.45	0.4997
1.84	0.4671	2.38	0.4913	2.92	0.4983	3.46	0.4997
1.85	0.4678	2.39	0.4916	2.93	0.4983	3.47	0.4997
1.86	0.4686	2.40	0.4918	2.94	0.4984	3.48	0.4998
1.87	0.4693	2.41	0.4920	2.95	0.4984	3.49	0.4998
1.88	0.4700	2.42	0.4922	2.96	0.4985	3.50	0.4998
1.89	0.4706	2.43	0.4925	2.97	0.4985	3.51	0.4998
1.90	0.4713	2.44	0.4927	2.98	0.4986	3.52	0.4998
1.91	0.4719	2.45	0.4929	2.99	0.4986	3.53	0.4998
1.92	0.4726	2.46	0.4931	3.00	0.4987	3.54	0.4998
1.93	0.4732	2.47	0.4932	3.01	0.4987	3.55	0.4998
1.94	0.4738	2.48	0.4934	3.02	0.4987	3.56	0.4998
1.95	0.4744	2.49	0.4936	3.03	0.4988	3.57	0.4998
1.96	0.4750	2.50	0.4938	3.04	0.4988	3.58	0.4998
1.97	0.4756	2.51	0.4940	3.05	0.4989	3.59	0.4998
1.98	0.4762	2.52	0.4941	3.06	0.4989	3.60	0.4998
1.99	0.4767	2.53	0.4943	3.07	0.4989	3.61	0.4999
2.00	0.4773	2.54	0.4945	3.08	0.4990	3.62	0.4999
2.01	0.4778	2.55	0.4946	3.09	0.4990	3.63	0.4999
2.02	0.4783	2.56	0.4948	3.10	0.4990	3.64	0.4999
2.03	0.4788	2.57	0.4949	3.11	0.4991	3.65	0.4999
2.04	0.4793	2.58	0.4951	3.12	0.4991	3.66	0.4999
2.05	0.4798	2.59	0.4952	3.13	0.4991	3.67	0.4999
2.06	0.4803	2.60	0.4953	3.14	0.4992	3.68	0.4999
2.07	0.4808	2.61	0.4955	3.15	0.4992	3.69	0.4999
2.08	0.4812	2.62	0.4956	3.16	0.4992	3.70	0.4999
2.09	0.4817	2.63	0.4957	3.17	0.4992	3.71	0.4999
2.10	0.4821	2.64	0.4959	3.18	0.4993	3.72	0.4999
2.11	0.4826	2.65	0.4960	3.19	0.4993	3.73	0.4999
2.12	0.4830	2.66	0.4961	3.20	0.4993	3.74	0.4999
2.13	0.4834	2.67	0.4962	3.21	0.4993	3.75	0.4999
2.14	0.4838	2.68	0.4963	3.22	0.4994	3.76	0.4999
2.15	0.4842	2.69	0.4964	3.23	0.4994	3.77	0.4999
2.16	0.4846	2.70	0.4965	3.24	0.4994	3.78	0.4999
2.17	0.4850	2.71	0.4966	3.25	0.4994	3.79	0.4999
2.18	0.4854	2.72	0.4967	3.26	0.4994	3.80	0.4999
2.19	0.4857	2.73	0.4968	3.27	0.4995	3.81	0.4999
2.20	0.4861	2.74	0.4969	3.28	0.4995	3.82	0.4999
2.21	0.4865	2.75	0.4970	3.29	0.4995	3.83	0.4999
2.22	0.4868	2.76	0.4971	3.30	0.4995	3.84	0.4999
2.23	0.4871	2.77	0.4972	3.31	0.4995	3.85	0.4999
2.24	0.4875	2.78	0.4973	3.32	0.4996	3.86	0.4999
2.25	0.4878	2.79	0.4974	3.33	0.4996		

Graphing Calculator Guide

Operating the TI-83 and TI-84 Plus Calculators

Turning the Calculator On and Off

| ON | Turns the calculator on. |

| 2nd | ON | Turns the calculator off. |

Adjusting the Display Contrast

| 2nd | ▲ | Increases the display (darkens the screen). |

| 2nd | ▼ | Decreases the contrast (lightens the screen). |

Note: If the display begins to dim (especially during calculations), and you must adjust the contrast to 8 or 9 in order to see the screen, then batteries are low and you should replace them soon.

The TI-83 and TI-84 Plus keyboard are divided into four zones: graphing keys, editing keys, advanced function keys, and scientific calculator keys (Figure 1).

Courtesy of Texas Instruments

Home screen

Graphing keys

Editing keys (Allow you to edit expressions and variables)

Advanced function keys (Display menus that access advanced functions)

Scientific calculator keys

Figure 1

Chapter 1
Section 1.4 Graphing Equations

Entering Equations for Graphing

To graph an equation in the variables x and y, first solve the equation for y in terms of x. If the equation has variables other than x and y, solve for the dependent variable and replace the independent variable with x. Press the Y= key to access the function entry screen and enter the equation. To erase an equation, press CLEAR. To return to the home-screen, press 2nd MODE (QUIT).

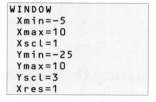

Setting Windows

The window defines the highest and lowest values of x and y on the graph of the function that will be shown on the screen. The values that define the viewing window can be set by using ZOOM keys. The standard window (ZOOM 6) is often appropriate. The standard window gives x- and y-values between -10 and 10.

To set the window manually, press the WINDOW key and enter the values that you want.

Graphing Equations

Determine an appropriate viewing window. The window should be set so that the important parts of the graph are shown and the unseen parts are suggested. Such a graph is called **complete**. Using the displayed coordinates from TRACE helps to determine an appropriate window. Pressing GRAPH or a ZOOM key will activate the graph.

With standard window   Using $[-5, 10]$ by $[-25, 10]$

Section 1.4 Finding Function Values

Using TRACE on the Graph

Enter the function to be evaluated in Y_1. Choose a window so that it contains the x-value whose y-value you seek. Press TRACE and then enter the selected x-value followed by ENTER. The cursor will move to the selected value and give the resulting y-value if the selected x-value is in the window. If the selected x-value is not in the window, Err: INVALID occurs. If the x-value is in the window, the y-value will occur even if it is not visible in the window.

To evaluate $y = -x^2 + 8x + 9$ when $x = -5$ and when $x = 3$, graph the function using the window $[-10, 10]$ by $[-10, 30]$.

Using the TABLE ASK Feature

Enter the function with the Y= key. {Note: The = sign must be highlighted.) Press 2nd WINDOW (TBLSET), move the cursor to Ask opposite Indpnt:, and press ENTER. This allows you to input specific values for x. Pressing DEL will clear entries in the table. Then press 2nd TABLE and enter the specific values. The table on the right evaluates $y = -x^2 + 8x + 9$ at -5 and at 3.

Making a Table of Values

If the Indpnt variable is on Auto, enter an initial x-value for the table in TblStart, and enter the desired change in the x-value as ΔTbl.

Enter 2nd TABLE to get a list of x-values and the corresponding y-values. The value of the function at the given value of x can be read from the table. Use the up or down arrows to find the x-values where the function is to be evaluated. The table on the right evaluates $y = -x^2 + 8x + 9$ for integer x-values from -3 to 3.

Section 1.4 Solving Linear Equations
by the *X*-Intercept Method

To find the solution to $f(x) = 0$ (the x-value where the graph crosses the x-axis):

1. Set one side of the equation to 0 and enter the other side as Y_1 in the Y= menu.
2. Set the window so that the x-intercept to be located can be seen.
3. Press 2nd TRACE to access the CALC menu and select 2:zero.
4. Answer the question "*Left Bound?*" with ENTER after moving the cursor close to and to the left of an x-intercept.
5. Answer the question "*Right Bound?*" with ENTER after moving the cursor close to and to the right of this x-intercept.
6. To the question "*Guess?*" press ENTER. The coordinates of the x-intercept are displayed. The x-value is a solution.

The solution to $5x - 9 = 0$ is found to be $x = 1.8$.

Section 1.5 Solving Systems of Equations
in Two Variables

To solve a system of linear equations in two variables graphically:

1. Solve both equations for y.
2. Graph the first equation as Y_1 and the second as Y_2.
3. To find the point of intersection of the graphs:
   (a) Press 2nd TRACE to access the CALC menu and select 5:intersect.
   (b) Answer the question "*First curve?*" by pressing ENTER and "*Second curve?*" by pressing ENTER.
   (c) To the question "*Guess?*" press ENTER. The solution is shown on the right.

If the two lines intersect in one point, the coordinates give the x- and y-values of the solution.

The solution of the system above is $x = 2$, $y = 1$.

To solve $\begin{cases} 4x + 3y = 11 \\ 2x - 5y = -1 \end{cases}$ graphically, graph $y_1 = -\dfrac{4}{3}x + \dfrac{11}{3}$ and $y_2 = \dfrac{2}{5}x + \dfrac{1}{5}$, then use Intersect.

Chapter 2

Section 2.1 Solving Nonlinear Equations by the X-Intercept Method

To find the solutions to $f(x) = 0$ (the x-values where the graph crosses the x-axis):

1. Set one side of the equation to 0 and enter the other side as Y_1 in the $Y=$ menu.
2. Set the window so that the x-intercepts to be located can be seen.
3. Press 2nd TRACE to access the CALC menu and select 2:zero.
4. Answer the question "*Left Bound?*" with ENTER after moving the cursor close to and to the left of an x-intercept.
5. Answer the question "*Right Bound?*" with ENTER after moving the cursor close to and to the right of this x-intercept.
6. To the question "*Guess?*" press ENTER. The coordinates of the x-intercept are displayed. The x-value is a solution.
7. Repeat to get all x-intercepts. The graph of a linear equation will cross the x-axis at most 1 time; the graph of quadratic equation will cross the x-axis at most 2 times, etc.

The solutions to $0 = -x^2 + 8x + 9$ are found to be 9 and -1.

Section 2.1 Solving Nonlinear Equations by the Intersection Method

To solve nonlinear equations by the intersection method:

1. Graph the left side of the equation as Y_1 and the right side as Y_2.
2. Find a point of intersection of the graphs as shown in Section 1.5.
3. To find another point of intersection, repeat while keeping the cursor near the second point.

The solutions to $7x^2 = 16x - 4$ are found at the right.

Section 2.2 Graphing Quadratic Functions

To graph a quadratic function:

1. Solve for y in terms of x and enter it in the $Y=$ menu.
2. Find the coordinates of its vertex, with $x = -b/a$.
3. Set the window so the x-coordinate of its vertex is near its center and the y-coordinate is visible.
4. Press Graph.

To graph $P(x) = -0.1x^2 + 300x - 1200$, enter $y_1 = -0.1x^2 + 300x - 1200$ on a window with its center near $x = (-300)/[2(-0.1)] = 1500$ and with $y = P(1500) = 223{,}800$ visible, and graph.

Section 2.4 Graphing Polynomial Functions

To graph a polynomial function:

1. See Table 2.1 in the text to determine possible shapes for the graph.
   (The graph of the function $y = x^3 - 16x$ has one of four shapes in the table.)
2. Graph the function in a window large enough to see the shape of the complete graph. This graph is like the graph of Degree 3(b) in the table in Section 2.4.
3. If necessary, adjust the window for a better view of the graph.

$[-40, 40]$ by $[-100, 100]$ $[-6, 6]$ by $[-30, 30]$

$y = x^3 - 16x$ $y = x^3 - 16x$

(Better view)

Section 2.4 Graphing Rational Functions

To graph a rational function:

1. Determine the vertical and horizontal asymptotes.
2. Set the window so that the x range is centered near the x-value of the vertical asymptote.
3. Set the window so that the horizontal asymptote is near the center of the y range.
4. Graph the function in a window large enough to see the shape of the complete graph.
5. If necessary, adjust the window for a better view of the graph.

To graph $y = \dfrac{12x + 8}{3x - 9}$, set the center of the window near the vertical asymptote $x = 3$ and near the horizontal asymptote $y = 4$.

Section 2.4 Graphing Piecewise Defined Functions

A piecewise defined function is defined differently over two or more intervals.

To graph a piecewise defined function $y = \begin{cases} f(x) & \text{if } x \le a \\ g(x) & \text{if } x > a \end{cases}$

1. Go to the Y= key and enter

   $Y_1 = f(x)/(x \le a)$ and $Y_2 = g(x)/(x > a)$

   (The inequality symbols are found under the TEST menu.)
2. Graph the function using an appropriate window.
3. Evaluating a piecewise defined function at a given value of x requires that the correct equation ("piece") be selected.

To graph $y = \begin{cases} x + 7 & \text{if } x \le -5 \\ -x + 2 & \text{if } x > -5 \end{cases}$

Section 2.5 Modeling

A. To Create a Scatter Plot

1. Press STAT and under EDIT press 1:Edit. This brings you to the screen where you enter data into lists.
2. Enter the *x*-values (input) in the column headed L1 and the corresponding *y*-values (output) in the column headed L2.
3. Go to the Y= menu and turn off or clear any functions entered there. To turn off a function, move the cursor over the = sign and press ENTER.
4. Press 2nd STAT PLOT, 1:Plot 1. Highlight ON, and then highlight the first graph type (Scatter Plot), Enter Xlist:L1, Ylist:L2, and pick the point plot mark you want.
5. Choose an appropriate WINDOW for the graph and press GRAPH, or press ZOOM, 9:ZoomStat to plot the data points.

B. To Find an Equation That Models a Set of Data Points

1. Observe the scatter plot to determine what type function would best model the data. Press STAT, move to CALC, and select the function type to be used to model the data.
2. Press the VARS key, move to Y-VARS, and select 1:Function and 1:Y$_1$. Press ENTER.
   The coefficients of the equation will appear on the screen and the regression equation will appear as Y$_1$ on the Y= screen.

Pressing ZOOM 9 shows how well the model fits the data.

The model is $y = -0.00376x^2 + 0.690x + 42.007$.

Chapter 3

Section 3.1 Entering Data into Matrices

To enter data into matrices, press the MATRIX key. Move the cursor to EDIT. Enter the number of the matrix into which the data is to be entered. Enter the dimensions of the matrix, and enter the value for each entry of the matrix. Press ENTER after each entry.

For example, we enter the matrix below as [A].

$$\begin{bmatrix} 1 & 2 & 3 \\ 2 & -2 & 1 \\ 3 & 1 & -2 \end{bmatrix}$$

1. Enter 3's to set the dimension, and enter the numbers.
2. To perform operations with the matrix or leave the editor, first press 2nd QUIT.
3. To view the matrix, press MATRIX, the number of the matrix, and ENTER.

Section 3.1 Operations with Matrices

To find the sum of two matrices, [A] and [D], enter [A] + [D], and press ENTER. For example, the sum

$$\begin{bmatrix} 1 & 2 & 3 \\ 2 & -2 & 1 \\ 3 & 1 & -2 \end{bmatrix} + \begin{bmatrix} 7 & -3 & 2 \\ 4 & -5 & 3 \\ 0 & 2 & 1 \end{bmatrix}$$ is shown at right.

To find the difference, enter [A] − [D] and press ENTER. We can multiply a matrix [D] by a real number (scalar) k by entering k [D].

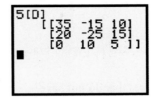

Section 3.2 Multiplying Two Matrices

To find the product of two matrices, [C] times [A], enter [C][A] and press ENTER. For example, we compute the product

$$\begin{bmatrix} 1 & 2 & 4 \\ -3 & 2 & -1 \end{bmatrix} \begin{bmatrix} 1 & 2 & 3 \\ 2 & -2 & 1 \\ 3 & 1 & -2 \end{bmatrix}$$ at right.

Note that entering [A][C] gives an error message. [A][C] cannot be computed because the dimensions do not match in this order.

Section 3.3 Solution of Systems— Reduced Echelon Form

To solve a 3 × 3 system:
1. Enter the coefficients and the constants in an augmented matrix.
2. Under the MATRIX menu, choose MATH and B:rref, then enter the matrix to be reduced followed by ")", and press ENTER.
3.

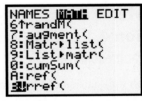

(a) If each row in the coefficient matrix (first 3 columns) contains a 1 with the other elements 0's, the solution is unique and the number in column 4 of a row is the value of the variable corresponding to a 1 in that row.

For example, the system $\begin{cases} 2x - y + z = 6 \\ x + 2y - 3z = 9 \\ 3x \qquad - 3z = 15 \end{cases}$ is solved at right.

The solution to the system above is unique: $x = 4$, $y = 1$, and $z = -1$.

(b) If the reduced matrix has all zeros in the third row, the solution is nonunique.

(c) If the reduced matrix has 3 zeros in a row and a non-zero element in the fourth column in that row, there is no solution.

Section 3.4 Finding the Inverse of a Matrix

To find the inverse of a matrix:
1. Enter the elements of the matrix using MATRIX and EDIT. Press 2nd QUIT.
2. Press MATRIX, the number of the matrix, and ENTER, then press the x^{-1} key and ENTER.

For example, the inverse of $E = \begin{bmatrix} 2 & 0 & 2 \\ -1 & 0 & 1 \\ 4 & 2 & 0 \end{bmatrix}$

is shown at right.
3. To see the entries as fractions, press MATH, press 1:Frac, and press ENTER.

Not all matrices have inverses. Matrices that do not have inverses are called singular matrices.

Section 3.4 Solving Systems of Linear Equations with Matrix Inverses

The matrix equation $AX = B$ can be solved by computing $X = A^{-1}B$ if a unique solution exists.

The solution to $\begin{cases} 25x + 20y + 50z = 15{,}000 \\ 25x + 50y + 100z = 27{,}500 \\ 250x + 50y + 500z = 92{,}250 \end{cases}$

is found at the right to be $x = 254$, $y = 385$, $z = 19$.

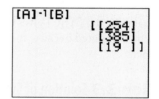

Chapter 4

Section 4.1 Graphing Solution Regions of Linear Inequalities

To graph the solution of a linear inequality in two variables, first solve the inequality for the independent variable and enter the other side of the inequality in Y_1, so that $Y_1 = f(x)$. If the inequality has the form $y \le f(x)$, shade the region below the graphed line and if the inequality has the form $y \ge f(x)$, shade the region above the line.

In this example, we shade the region above the line with SHADE under the DRAW menu and enter Shade $(Y_1, 10)$ on the home screen.

To solve $4x - 2y \le 6$, convert it to $y \ge 2x - 3$ and graph $Y_1 = 2x - 3$.

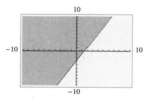

Section 4.1 Graphing Solutions of Systems of Linear Inequalities

To graph the solution region for a system of linear inequalities in two variables, write the inequalities as equations solved for y, and graph the equations.

For example, to find the region defined by the inequalities

$$\begin{cases} 5x + 2y \leq 54 \\ 2x + 4y \leq 60 \\ x \geq 0, y \geq 0 \end{cases}$$

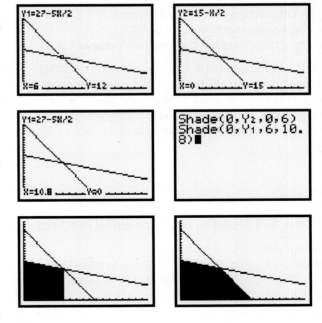

1. Choose a window with $x\min = 0$ and $y\min = 0$ because the inequalities $x \geq 0, y \geq 0$ limit the graph to Quadrant I.
2. Write $y = 27 - 5x/2$ and $y = 15 - x/2$ and graph.
3. Testing points determines the region that satisfies the inequalities.
4. Using TRACE or INTERSECT with the pair of equations and finding the intercepts give the corners of the solution region, where the borders intersect. These corners of the region are $(0, 0)$ $(0, 15)$, $(6, 12)$, and $(10.8, 0)$.
5. Use SHADE to shade the region determined by the inequalities. Shade under the border from $x = 0$ to a corner and shade under the second border from the corner to the x-intercept.

Section 4.2 Linear Programming

To solve a linear programming problem involving constraints in two variables:
1. Graph the constraint inequalities as equations, solved for y.
2. Test points to determine the region and use TRACE or INTERSECT to find each of the corners of the region, where the borders intersect.
3. Then evaluate the objective function at each of the corners.

For example, to maximize $f = 5x + 11y$ subject to the constraints

$$\begin{cases} 5x + 2y \leq 54 \\ 2x + 4y \leq 60 \\ x \geq 0, y \geq 0 \end{cases}$$

we graphically find the constraint region (as shown above), and evaluate the objective function at the coordinates of each of the corners of the region.

Evaluating $f = 5x + 11y$ at each of the corners determines where this objective function is maximized or minimized.

The corners of the region determined by the inequalities are $(0, 0)$ $(0, 15)$, $(6, 12)$, and $(10.8, 0)$.

At $(0, 0)$, $f = 0$ At $(0, 15)$, $f = 165$
At $(6,12)$, $f = 162$ At $(10.8, 0)$, $f = 54$

The maximum value of f is 165 at $x = 0$, $y = 15$.

Chapter 5
Section 5.1 Graphing Exponential Functions

1. Enter the function as Y_1 in the Y= menu.
2. Set the x-range centered at $x = 0$.
3. Set the y-range to reflect the function's range of $y > 0$.

Note that some graphs (such as the graph of $y = 4^x$ shown here) appear to eventually merge with the negative x-axis. Adjusting the window can show that these graphs never touch the x-axis. For more complicated exponential functions, it may be helpful to use TABLE to find a useful window.

Section 5.1 Modeling with Exponential Functions

1. Create a scatter plot for the data.
2. Choose STAT, then CALC. Scroll down to 0:ExpReg and press ENTER, then VARS, Y-VARS, FUNCTION, Y_1, and ENTER.

   (Recall that this both calculates the requested exponential model and enters its equation as Y_1 in the Y= menu.)

The last screen shows how well the model fits the data.

Find the exponential model for the following data.

x	1	2	3	4	5	6	7	8	9	10
y	43	38	33	29	25	22	19	15	14	12

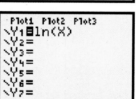

Section 5.2 Graphing Base e and Base 10 Logarithmic Functions

Enter the function as Y_1 in the Y= menu.

1. For $y = \ln(x)$ use the LN key.
2. For $y = \log(x)$ use the LOG key.
3. Set the window x-range to reflect that the function's domain is $x > 0$.
4. Center the window y-range at $y = 0$.

Section 5.2 Modeling with Logarithmic Functions

1. Create a scatter plot for the data.
2. Choose STAT, then CALC. Scroll down to 9:LnReg and press ENTER, then VARS, Y-VARS, FUNCTION, Y_1, and ENTER.

The last figure on the right shows how well the model fits the data.

Find the logarithmic model for the following data.

x	10	20	30	38
y	2.21	3.79	4.92	5.77

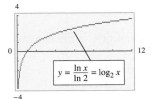

Section 5.2 Graphing Logarithmic Functions with Other Bases

1. Use a change of base formula to rewrite the logarithmic function with base 10 or base e.

$$\log_b x = \frac{\log x}{\log b} \quad \text{or} \quad \log_b x = \frac{\ln x}{\ln b}$$

2. Proceed as described above for graphing base e and base 10 logarithms.

Chapter 6
Section 6.2 Future Value of a Lump Sum

To find the future value of a lump-sum investment:

1. Press the APPS key and select Finance, press ENTER.
2. Select TVM Solver, press ENTER.
3. Set N = the total number of periods, set I% = the annual percentage rate.
4. Set the PV = the lump sum preceded by a "−" to indicate the lump sum is leaving your possession.
5. Set PMT = 0 and set both P/Y and C/Y = the number of compounding periods per year.
6. Put the cursor on FV and press ALPHA ENTER to get the future value.

The future value of \$10,000 invested at 9.8% compounded quarterly for 17 years is shown at the right.

Section 6.3 Future Value of an Annuity

To find the future value of an ordinary annuity:

1. Press the APPS key and select Finance, press ENTER.
2. Select TVM Solver, press ENTER.
3. Set N = the total number of periods, set I% = the annual percentage rate.
4. Set the PV = 0 and set both P/Y and C/Y = the number of compounding periods per year. END should be highlighted.
5. Set PMT = the periodic payment preceded by a "−" to indicate the lump sum is leaving your possession.
6. Put the cursor on FV and press ALPHA ENTER to get the future value.

   The future value of an ordinary annuity of $200 deposited at the end of each quarter for $2\frac{1}{4}$ years, with interest at 4% compounded quarterly, is shown.

For annuities due, all steps are the same except that BEGIN is highlighted.

Ordinary annuity

Annuity due

Section 6.4 Present Value of an Annuity

To find the present value of an ordinary annuity:

1. Press the APPS key and select Finance, press ENTER.
2. Select TVM Solver, press ENTER.
3. Set N= the total number of periods, set I% = the annual percentage rate.
4. Set the FV = 0 and set both P/Y and C/Y = the number of compounding periods per year. END should be highlighted.
5. Set PMT = the periodic payment.
6. Put the cursor on PV and press ALPHA ENTER to get the present value.

The lump sum that needs to be deposited to receive $1000 at the end of each month for 16 years if the annuity pays 9%, compounded monthly is shown at the right.
For annuities due, BEGIN is highlighted.

Ordinary annuity

Annuity due

Section 6.5 Finding Payments to Amortize a Loan

To find the size of periodic payments to amortize a loan:

1. Press the APPS key and select Finance, press ENTER.
2. Select TVM Solver, press ENTER.
3. Set N = the total number of periods, set I% = the APR.
4. Set the PV = loan value and set both P/Y and C/Y = the number of periods per year.
5. Set FV = 0.
6. Put the cursor on PMT and press ALPHA ENTER to get the payment.

To repay a loan of $10,000 in 5 annual payments with annual interest at 10%, each payment must be $2637.97.

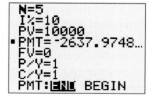

Section 6.5 Finding the Number of Payments to Amortize a Loan

To find the number of payments needed to amortize a loan:

1. Press the APPS key and select Finance, press ENTER.
2. Select TVM Solver, press ENTER.
3. Set the PV = loan value, set both P/Y and C/Y = the number of periods per year, set I% = the APR.
4. Set PMT = required payment and set FV = 0.
5. Put the cursor on N and press ALPHA ENTER to get the payment.

The number of monthly payments to pay a $2500 credit card loan with $55 payments and 18% interest is 76.9 months, or 6 years, 5 months.

Chapter 7
Section 7.5 Evaluating Factorials

To evaluate factorials:

1. Enter the number whose factorial is to be calculated.
2. Choose MATH, then PRB. Scroll to 4: ! and press ENTER.

Press ENTER again to find the factorial.
7! is shown on the right.

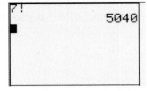

Section 7.5 Evaluating Permutations

To evaluate permutations:

1. For a "permutation of n objects taken r at a time" (such as $_{20}P_4$), first enter the value of n (such as $n = 20$).
2. Choose MATH, then PRB. Scroll to 2: nPr and press ENTER.
3. Enter the value of r (such as $r = 4$), and press ENTER to find the value of nPr.
   $_{20}P_4$ is shown on the right.

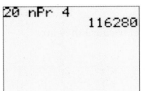

Section 7.5 Evaluating Combinations

To evaluate combinations:

1. For a "combination of n objects taken r at a time" (such as $_{20}C_4$), first enter the value of n (such as $n = 20$).
2. Choose MATH, then PRB. Scroll to 3:nCr and press ENTER.
3. Enter the value of r (such as $r = 4$), and press ENTER to find the value of nCr.

Note that nCr = nC(n − r), as the figure on the right shows for $_{20}C_4$ and $_{20}C_{16}$.

Section 7.6 Finding Probabilities Using Permutations and Combinations

To solve a probability problem that involves permutations or combinations:

1. Determine if permutations or combinations should be used.
2. Enter the ratios of permutations or combinations to find the probability.
3. If desired, use MATH, then 1:Frac to get the probability as a fraction.

If there are 5 defective computer chips in a box of 10, the probability that 2 chips drawn together from the box will both be defective is

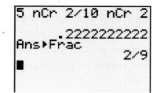

Section 7.7 Evaluating Markov Chains

To evaluate a Markov chain:

1. Enter the initial probability vector as matrix A and the transition matrix as matrix B.
2. To find the probabilities for the nth state, calculate $[A][B]^n$. The 3rd state, $[A][B]^3$, is shown on the right.

```
[A]
       [[.4 .4 .2]]
[B]
       [[.5 .4 .1]
        [.4 .5 .1]
        [.3 .3 .4]]
■
```

```
[A][B]^3
[[.4278 .4278 ...
```

Section 7.7 Finding Steady-State Vectors for Markov Chains

If the transition matrix contains only positive entries, the probabilities will approach a steady-state vector, which is found as follows.

1. Calculate and store $[C] = [B] - [I]$, where $[B]$ is the regular transition matrix and $[I]$ is the appropriately sized identity matrix.
2. Solve $[C]^T = [0]$ as follows:
   (a) Find $[C]^T$ with MATRIX, then MATH, 2:^{T}.
   (b) Find rref$[C]^T$.
3. Choose the solutions that add to 1, because they are probabilities.

```
identity(3)→[I]
       [[1 0 0]
        [0 1 0]
        [0 0 1]]
■
```

```
[B]-[I]
  [[-.5 .4   .1 ]
   [.4  -.5 .1 ]
   [.3  .3  -.6]]
Ans→[C]■
```

```
rref([C]T)
       [[1 0 -3]
        [0 1 -3]
        [0 0 0 ]]
```

Thus $x = 3z$ and $y = 3z$, and $3z + 3z + z = 1$ gives $z = 1/7$, so the probabilities are given in the steady-state vector

$$\begin{bmatrix} \dfrac{3}{7} & \dfrac{3}{7} & \dfrac{1}{7} \end{bmatrix}.$$

Chapter 8
Section 8.1 Binomial Probabilities

To find binomial probabilities:

1. 2nd DISTR A:binompdf(n,p,x) computes the probability of x success in n trials of a binomial experiment with probability of success p. Using MATH 1:Frac gives the probabilities as fractions.
   The probability of 3 heads in 6 tosses of a fair coin is found using 2nd DISTR, binompdf(6,.5,3).
2. The probabilities can be computed for more than one number in one command, using 2nd DISTR, binompdf($n,p,\{x_1,x_2,...\}$).
   The probabilities of 4, 5, or 6 heads in 6 tosses of a fair coin are found using 2nd DISTR, binompdf(6,.5,{4,5,6}).
3. 2nd DISTR, binomcdf(n,p,x) computes the probability that the number of successes is less than or equal to x for the binomial distribution with n trials and probability of success p.

   The probability of 4 or fewer heads in 6 tosses of a fair coin is found using 2nd DISTR, binomcdf(6,.5,4).

Section 8.2 Histograms

To find a frequency histogram for a set of data:

1. Press STAT, EDIT, 1:edit to enter each number in a column headed by L1 and the corresponding frequency of each number in L2.
2. Press 2nd STAT PLOT, 1:Plot 1. Highlight ON, and then press ENTER on the histogram icon. Enter L1 in xlist and L2 in Feq.
3. Press ZOOM, 9:ZoomStat or press Graph with an appropriate window.
4. If the data is given in interval form, a histogram can be created using the steps above with the class marks used to represent the intervals.

The frequency histogram for the scores 38, 37, 36, 40, 35, 40, 38, 37, 36, 37, 39, 38 is shown.

Section 8.2 Finding the Mean and Standard Deviation of Raw Data

To find descriptive statistics for a set of data:

1. Enter the data in list L1.
2. To find the mean and standard deviation of the data in L1, press STAT, move to CALC, and press 1:1-Var Stats, and ENTER.

The mean and sample standard deviation of the data 1, 2, 3, 3, 4, 4, 4, 4, 5, 5, 6, 7 are $\bar{x} = 4$ and $s \approx 1.65$.

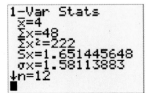

Section 8.2 Finding the Mean and Standard Deviation of Grouped Data

To find descriptive statistics for a set of data:

1. Enter the data in list L1 and the frequencies in L2.
2. To find the mean and standard deviation of the data in L1, press STAT, move to CALC, and press 1:1-Var Stats L1, L2, and ENTER.

The mean and standard deviation for the data in the table are shown on the right.

Salary	Number	Salary	Number
$59,000	1	$31,000	1
30,000	2	75,000	1
26,000	7	35,000	1
34,000	2		

The mean is $34,000 and the sample standard deviation is $14,132.84.

Section 8.4 Calculating Normal Probabilites

To calculate normal probabilities:

The command 2nd DISTR, 2:normalcdf(lowerbound, upperbound, μ, σ) gives the probability that x lies between the lower bound and the upper bound when the mean is μ and the standard deviation is σ.

The probability that a score lies between 33 and 37 when the mean is 35 and the standard deviation is 2 is found below.

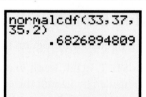

Section 8.4 Graphing Normal Distributions

To graph the normal distribution, press Y= and enter 2nd DIST 1:normalpdf(x, μ, σ) into Y_1.

Then set the window values xmin and xmax so the mean μ falls between them and press ZOOM, 0:Zoomfit.

Chapter 9
Section 9.1 Evaluating Limits

To evaluate $\lim\limits_{x \to c} f(x)$

1. Enter the function as Y_1 in the $Y=$ menu.
2. Set the x-range so it contains $x = c$.
3. Evaluate $f(x)$ for several x-values near $x = c$ and on each side by c by using one of the following methods.
   (a) Graphical Evaluation
   TRACE and ZOOM near $x = c$. If the values of y approach the same number L as x approaches c from the left and the right, there is evidence that the limit is L.
   (b) Numerical Evaluation
   Use TBLSET with Indpnt set to *Ask*. Enter values very close to and on both sides of c. The y-values will approach the same limit as above.

Evaluate $\lim\limits_{x \to 3} \dfrac{x^2 - 9}{x - 3}$.

The y-values seem to approach 6.

The limit as x approaches 3 of $f(x)$ appears to be 6.

Section 9.1 Limits of Piecewise Functions

Enter the function, then use one of the methods for evaluating limits discussed above.

Find $\lim\limits_{x \to -5} f(x)$ where $f(x) = \begin{cases} x + 7 & \text{if } x \le -5 \\ -x + 2 & \text{if } x > -5 \end{cases}$

First enter $Y_1 = (x + 7)/(x \le -5)$ and $Y_2 = (-x + 2)/(x > -5)$.

Both methods indicate that the limit does not exist (DNE).

Section 9.2 Limits as $x \to \infty$

Enter the function as Y_1, then use large values of x with one of the methods for evaluating limits discussed above. Note: Limits as $x \to -\infty$ are done similarly.

Evaluate $\displaystyle\lim_{x \to \infty} \frac{3x - 2}{1 - 5x}$.

Both methods suggest that the limit is -0.6.

Sections 9.3–9.7 Approximating

Derivatives

To find the numerical derivative (approximate derivative) of $f(x)$ at $x = c$, use Method 1 or Method 2.

Find the numerical derivative of $f(x) = x^3 - 2x^2$ at $x = 2$.

Method 1
1. Choose MATH, then 8:nDeriv(and press ENTER.
2. Enter the function, x, and the value of c, so the display shows nDeriv($f(x)$, x, c) then press ENTER. The approximate derivative at the specified value will be displayed.

 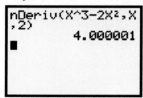

The numerical derivative is approximately 4.

Method 2
1. Enter the function as Y_1 in the Y=menu, and graph in a window that contains both c and $f(c)$.
2. Choose CALC by using 2nd TRACE, then 6:dy/dx, enter the x-value, c, and press ENTER. Then approximate derivative at the specified value will be displayed.

Warning: Both approximation methods above require that the derivative exists at $x = c$ and will give incorrect information when $f'(c)$ does not exist.

The value of the derivative is approximately 4.

Sections 9.3–9.7 Checking Derivatives

To check the correctness of the derivative function $f(x)$:

1. In the Y= menu, enter as Y_1 the derivative $f'(x)$ that you found, and graph it in a convenient window.
2. Enter the following as Y_2:nDeriv(f(x), x, x).
3. If the second graph lies on top of the first, the derivative is correct.

Verify the derivative of $f(x) = x^3 - 2x^2$ is $f'(x) = 3x^2 - 4x$.

Section 9.8 Approximating the Second Derivative

To approximate $f''(c)$:

1. Enter $f(x)$ as Y_1 in the Y= menu.
2. Enter nDeriv(Y_1,x,x) as Y_2.
3. Estimate $f''(c)$ by using nDeriv(Y_2,x,c).

Find the second derivative of $f(x) = x^3 - 2x^2$ at $x = 2$.

Thus $f''(2) = 8$.

Chapter 10
Section 10.1 Finding Critical Values

To find or approximate critical values of $f(x)$, that is x-values that make the derivative equal to 0 or undefined:

I. Find the derivative of $f(x)$.

II. Use Method 1 or Method 2 to find the critical values.

Method 1

1. Enter the derivative in the Y= menu as Y_1 and graph it in a convenient window.
2. Find where $Y_1 = 0$ by one of the following:
   (a) Using TRACE to find the x-intercepts of Y_1.
   (b) Using 2nd CALC then 2:zero.
   (c) Using TBLSET then TABLE to find the values of x that give $Y_1 = 0$.
3. Use the graph of Y_1 (and TRACE or TABLE) to find the values of x that make the derivative undefined.

Method 2

1. Enter the derivative in the Y= menu as Y_1.
2. Press MATH and select Solver. Press the up arrow revealing EQUATION SOLVER equ:0=, and enter Y_1 (the derivative).
3. Press the down arrow or ENTER and the variable x appears with a value (not the soltion). Move the cursor to the line containing the variable whose value is sought.
4. Press ALPHA SOLVE (ENTER). The value of the variable changes to the solution that is closest to that value originally shown.
5. To find additional solutions (if they exist), change the value of the variable and press ALPHA SOLVE (ENTER). The value of the variable that gives the solution of $Y_1 = 0$ that is closest to that value.
6. If appropriate, use 0:Solver to solve (Denominator of Y_1) = 0 to find the critical values for which the derivative is undefined.

Methods 1 and 2 show how to find the critical values of $f(x) = \frac{1}{3}x^3 - 4x$. Note that the derivative is $f'(x) = x^2 - 4$.

The only critical values are $x = 2$ and $x = -2$.

The only critical values are $x = 2$ and $x = -2$.

Section 10.1 Relative Maxima and Minima

To find relative maxima and minima:

1. In the Y=menu enter the function as Y_1 and the derivative is Y_2.
2. Use TBLSET and TABLE to evaluate the derivative to the left and to the right of each critical value.
3. Use the signs of the values of the derivative to determine whether f is increasing or decreasing around the critical values, and thus to classify the critical values as relative maxima, relative minima, or horizontal points of inflection.
4. Graph the function to confirm your conclusions.

Find the relative maxima and minima of $f(x) = \dfrac{1}{3}x^3 - 4x$. Note that the derivative is $f'(x) = x^2 - 4$.

 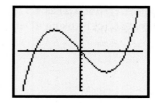

The relative max is at $(-2, 16/3)$ and the relative min is at $(2, -16/3)$.

Section 10.1 Critical Values and Viewing Windows

To use critical values to set a viewing window that shows a complete graph:

1. Once the critical values for a function have been found,
   (a) Enter the function as Y_1 and the derivative as Y_2. Use TABLE to determine where the function is increasing and where it is decreasing.
   (b) In WINDOW menu set x-min so that it is smaller than the smallest critical value and set x-max so that it is larger than the largest critical value.
2. Use TABLE or VALUE to determine the y-coordinates of the critical values. Set y-min and y-max to contain the y-coordinates of the critical points.
3. Graph the function.

Let $f(x) = 0.0001x^3 + 0.003x^2 - 3.6x + 5$. Given that the critical values for $f(x)$ are $x = -120$ and $x = 100$, set a window that shows a complete graph and graph the function.

X	Y₁	Y₂
-150	275	2.25
-120	307.4	0
0	5	-3.6
100	-225	0
150	-130	4.05
X=0		

Section 10.2 Exploring f, f', and f'' Relationships

To explore relationships among the graphs of a function and its derivatives:

1. Find the functions for f' and f''.
2. Graph all three functions in the same window.
   • Notice that f increases when f' is above the x-axis $(+)$ and decreases when f' is below the x-axis $(-)$.
   • Notice that f is concave up when f'' is above the x-axis $(+)$ and is concave down when f'' is below the x-axis $(-)$.

Let $f(x) = x^3 - 9x^2 + 24x$. Graph f', f'', and f'' on the interval $[0, 5]$ to explore the relationships among these functions.

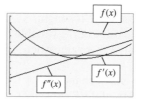

Sections 10.3–10.4 Finding Optimal Values

To find the optimal values of a function when the goal is not to produce a graph:

1. Enter the function as Y_1 in the Y= menu.
2. Select a window that includes the x-values of interest and graph the function.
3. While looking at the graph of the function, choose the CALC menu, scroll to 3:minimum or 4:maximum depending on which one is to be found, and press ENTER. This will result in a "*Left Bound?*" prompt.
    (a) Move the cursor to a point to the left of the point of interest. Press ENTER to select the left bound.
    (b) Move the cursor to the right of the point of interest. Press ENTER to select the right bound.
    (c) Press ENTER at the "*Guess?*" prompt. The resulting point is an approximation of the desired optimum value.

Let $f(x) = 100\sqrt{2304 + x^2} + 50(100 - x)$. Find the minimum value of $f(x)$ on the interval $[0, 100]$ for x. Note: the following screens use the window x: $[-10, 110]$ and y: $[-2500, 12500]$

The minimum value is $y \approx 9157$ and occurs when $x \approx 27.7$.

Note: Finding a maximum value works similarly.

Section 10.5 Asymptotes and Window Setting

To use asymptotes and critical values to set a viewing window that shows a complete graph:

1. Once the asymptotes and critical values for a function have been found,
    (a) Determine where the function is increasing and where it is decreasing (by using TABLE and with Y_1 as the function and Y_2 as the derivative).
    (b) In WINDOW menu set x-min so that it is smaller than the smallest x-value that is either a vertical asymptote or a critical value and set x-max so that it is larger than the largest of these important x-values.
2. Use TABLE or VALUE to determine the y-coordinates of the critical values. Set y-min and y-max so they contain the y-coordinates of any horizontal asymptotes and critical points.
3. Graph the function.

Let $f(x) = \dfrac{x^2}{x - 2}$. Given that $f(x)$ has the line $x = 2$ as a vertical asymptote, has no horizontal asymptote, and has critical values $x = 0$ and $x = 4$. Set the window and graph $y = f(x)$.

The critical points for $f(x)$ are $(0, 0)$ and $(4, 8)$. The window needs an x-range that contains 0, 2, and 4, and a y-range that contains 0 and 8.

Chapter 11
Section 11.1 Derivatives of Logarithmic Functions

To check that the derivative of $y = \ln(2x^6 - 3x + 2)$

is $Y_1 = \dfrac{12x^5 - 3}{2x^6 - 3x + 2}$, we show that the graph of

$Y_2 = \text{nDeriv}(\ln(2x^6 - 3x + 2), x, x)$ lies on the graph of

$y_1 = \dfrac{12x^5 - 3}{2x^6 - 3x + 2}$.

Section 11.1 Finding Critical Values

To find the critical values of a function $y = f(x)$:

1. Enter the function as Y_1 in the Y= menu, and the derivative as Y_2.
2. Press MATH and select Solver. Press the up arrow revealing EQUATION SOLVER equ:0=, and enter Y_2 (the derivative).
3. Press the down arrow or ENTER and the variable x appears with a value (not the solution). Place the cursor on the line containing the variable whose value is sought.
4. Press ALPHA SOLVE (ENTER). The value of the variable changes to the solution of the equation that is closest to that value.
5. To find additional solutions (if they exist), change the value of the variable and press ALPHA SOLVE (ENTER). The value of the variable gives the solution of $Y_2 = 0$ that is closest to that value.

To find the critical values of $y = x^2 - 8 \ln x$, we solve
$$0 = 2x - \frac{8}{x}.$$

The two critical values are $x = 2$ and $x = -2$.

Section 11.1 Finding Optimal Values

To find the optimal values of a function $y = f(x)$:

1. Find the critical values of a function $y = f(x)$. (Use the steps for finding critical values discussed above.)
2. Graph $y = f(x)$ on a window containing the critical values.
3. The y-values at the critical values (if they exist) are the optimal values of the function.

To find the optimal values of $y = x^2 - 8 \ln x$, we solve
$$0 = 2x - \frac{8}{x}$$ and evaluate $y = x^2 - 8 \ln x$ at the solutions.

The two critical values are $x = 2$ and $x = -2$.

The minimum of $y = x^2 - 8 \ln x$ is -1.545 at $x = 2$.
The function $y = x^2 - 8 \ln x$ is undefined for all negative values because $\ln x$ is undefined for all negative values. Thus there is no optimum value of the function at $x = -2$.

Section 11.2 Derivatives of Exponential Functions

To check that the derivative of $y = 5^{x^2 + x}$ is
$y' = 5^{x^2 + x}(2x + 1) \ln 5$, we show that the graph of
$Y_2 = \text{nDeriv}(5^{x^2 + x}, x, x)$ lies on the graph of
$Y_1 = 5^{x^2 + x}(2x + 1) \ln 5$.

Section 11.2 Finding Critical Values

To find the critical values of a function $y = f(x)$:

1. Enter the function as Y_1 in the Y= menu, and the derivative as Y_2.
2. Press MATH and select Solver. Press the up arrow revealing EQUATION SOLVER equ:0=, and enter Y_2 (the derivative).
3. Press the down arrow or ENTER and the variable appears with a value (not the solution). Place the cursor on the variable whose value is sought.
4. Press ALPHA SOLVE (ENTER). The value of the variable changes to the solution of the equation that is closest to that value.
5. To find additional solutions (if they exist), change the value of the variable and press ALPHA SOLVE (ENTER). The value of the variable gives the solution of $Y_2 = 0$ that is closest to that value.

To find the critical values of $y = e^x - 3x^2$, we solve $0 = e^x - 6x$.

A relative maximum of $y = e^x - 3x^2$ occurs at $x \approx 0.204$ and a relative minimum occurs at $x \approx 2.833$.

Chapter 12

Sections 12.1–12.2 Checking Indefinite Integrals

To check a computed indefinite integral with the command fnInt:

1. Enter the integral of $f(x)$ (without the $+ C$) as Y_1 in Y= menu.
2. Move the cursor in Y_2, press MATH, 9:fnInt(and enter $f(x)$, x, 0, x) so the equation is $Y_2 = $ fnInt $(f(x), x, 0, x)$.
3. Pressing ENTER with the cursor to the left of Y_2 changes the thickness of the second graph, making it more evident that the second lies on top of the first.
4. Press GRAPH with an appropriate window. If the second graph lies on top of the first, the graphs agree and the computed integral checks.

Checking that the integral of $f(x) = x^2$ is $\int x^2 \, dx = \dfrac{x^3}{3} + C$:

Sections 12.1–12.2 Families of Functions

To graph some functions in the family of indefinite integrals of $f(x)$:

1. Integrate $f(x)$.

2. Enter equations of the form $\int f(x) \, dx + C$ for different values of C.

3. Press GRAPH with an appropriate window. The graphs will be shifted up or down, depending on C.

The graphs of members of the family $y = \displaystyle\int (2x - 4) \, dx + C$ with $C = 0, 1, -2,$ and 3.

Section 12.5 Differential Equations

To solve initial value problems in differential equations:

1. Integrate $f(x)$, getting $y = F(x) + C$. If a value of x and a corresponding value of y in the integral $y = F(x) + C$ is known, this initial value can be used to find one function that satisfies the given conditions.
2. Press MATH and select Solver. Press the up arrow to see EQUATION SOLVER.
3. Set 0 equal the integral minus y, getting $0 = F(x) + C - y$, and press the down arrow.
4. Enter the given values of x and y, place the cursor on C, and press ALPHA, SOLVE. Replace C with this value to find the function satisfying the conditions.

To solve $\dfrac{dy}{dx} = 2x - 4$, we note that the integral of both sides is $y = x^2 - 4x + C$. If $y = 8$ when $x = -1$ in this integral, we can find C, and thus a unique solution, shown below.

The unique solution is $y = x^2 - 4x + 3$.

Chapter 13

Section 13.1 Approximating Definite Integrals—
Areas Under Curves

To approximate the area under the graph of $y = f(x)$ and above the x-axis:

1. Enter $f(x)$ under the Y= menu and graph the function with an appropriate window.

2. Press 2nd CALC and $7:\int f(x)\,dx$.
3. Press ENTER. Move the cursor to, or enter, the lower limit (the left x-value).
4. Press ENTER. Move the cursor to, or enter, the upper limit (the right x-value).

5. Press ENTER. The area will be displayed.

The approximate area under the graph of $f(x) = x^2$ from $x = 0$ to $x = 3$ is found below.

Section 13.1 Approximating Definite Integrals— Alternative Method

To approximate the definite integral of $f(x)$ from $x = a$ to $x = b$:

1. Press MATH, 9: fnInt(. Enter $f(x)$, x, a, b) so the display shows fnInt($f(x)$, x, a, b).
2. Press ENTER to find the approximation of the integral.
3. The approximation may be made closer than that in Step 2 by adding a fifth argument with a number (tolerance) smaller than 0.00001.

The approximation of $\int_{-1}^{3} (4x^2 - 2x)\,dx$ is found as follows.

Section 13.2 Approximating the Area Between Two Curves

To approximate the area between the graphs of two functions:

1. Enter one function as Y_1 and the second as Y_2. Press GRAPH using a window that shows all points of intersection of the graphs.
2. Find the x-coordinates of the points of intersection of the graphs, using 2nd CALC: intersect.
3. Determine visually which graph is above the other over the interval between the points of intersection.
4. Press MATH, 9: fnInt(. Enter $f(x)$, x, a, b) so the display shows fnInt($f(x)$, x, a, b) where $f(x)$ is $Y_2 - Y_1$ if the graph of Y_2 is above the graph of Y_1 between a and b, or $Y_1 - Y_2$ if Y_1 is above Y_2.

The area enclosed by the graphs of $y = 4x^2$ and $y = 8x$ is found as follows.

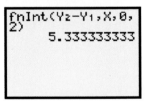

The area between the curves is 16/3.

Section 13.2 Approximating the Area Between Two Curves—Alternate Method

The area between the graphs can also be found by using

2nd CALC, $\int f(x)\, dx$.

1. Enter $Y_3 = Y_2 - Y_1$ where Y_2 is above Y_1.
2. Turn off the graphs of Y_1 and Y_2 and graph Y_3 with a window showing where $Y_3 > 0$.

3. Press 2nd CALC and $\int f(x)\, dx$.

4. Press ENTER. Move the cursor to, or enter, the lower limit (the left x-value).
5. Press ENTER. Move the cursor to, or enter, the upper limit (the right x-value).
6. Press ENTER. The area will be displayed.

Answers

Below are the answers to odd-numbered Section Exercises and all the Chapter Review and Chapter Test problems.

0.1 EXERCISES

1. $\in$ 3. $\notin$ 5. $\{1, 2, 3, 4, 5, 6, 7\}$

7. $\{x : x$ is a natural number greater than 2 and less than 8$\}$

9. $\varnothing, A, B$ 11. no   13. $D \subseteq C$

15. $A \subseteq B$ or $B \subseteq A$ 17. yes   19. no

21. A and B, B and D, C and D

23. $A \cap B = \{4, 6\}$ 25. $A \cap B = \varnothing$

27. $A \cup B = \{1, 2, 3, 4, 5\}$

29. $A \cup B = \{1, 2, 3, 4\} = B$

31. $A' = \{4, 6, 9, 10\}$

33. $A \cap B' = \{1, 2, 5, 7\}$ 35. $(A \cup B)' = \{6, 9\}$

37. $A' \cup B' = \{1, 2, 4, 5, 6, 7, 9, 10\}$

39. $\{1, 2, 3, 5, 7, 9\}$ 41. $\{4, 6, 8, 10\}$

43. $A - B = \{1, 7\}$

45. $A - B = \varnothing$ or $\{\,\}$

47. (a) $L = \{00, 01, 04, 05, 06, 07\}$

     $H = \{00, 01, 06, 07, 08\}$

     $C = \{01, 02, 03, 08, 09\}$

  (b) no

  (c) C' is the set of years when the percent change from low to high was 35% or less.

  (d) $\{00, 02, 03, 04, 05, 06, 07, 09\}$ = the set of years when the high was 11,000 or less or the percent change was 35% or less.

  (e) $\{02, 03, 08, 09\}$ = the set of years when the low was 8000 or less and the percent change exceeded 35%.

49. (a) 130   (b) 840   (c) 520

51.

    (a) 40
    (b) 85
    (c) 25

53.

    (a) 25
    (b) 43
    (c) 53

55. (a) and (b)

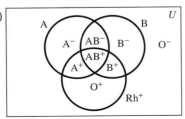

0.2 EXERCISES

(c) A^+: 34%; B^+: 9%; O^+: 38%; AB^+: 3%; O^-: 7%; A^-: 6%; B^-: 2%; AB^-: 1%

1. (a) irrational   (b) rational, integer

  (c) rational, integer, natural   (d) meaningless

3. (a) Commutative   (b) Distributive

5. (a) Multiplicative identity   (b) Additive inverse

7. $<$ 9. $<$ 11. $<$ 13. $>$

15. 11   17. 4   19. 2   21. $\frac{-4}{3}$ 23. 3   25. $\frac{17}{11}$

27. entire line   29. $(1, 3]$; half open   31. $(2, 10)$; open

33. $-3 \le x < 5$ 35. $x > 4$

37. $(-3, 4)$

39. $(4, +\infty)$

41. $[-1, +\infty)$

43. $(-\infty, 0) \cup (7, +\infty)$

45. -0.000038585

47. 9122.387471 49. 3240.184509

51. (a) $\$1088.91$ (b) $\$258.62$ (c) $\$627.20$

53. (a) Formula (2) is slightly more accurate, giving 15.762%.

  (b) (1): 17.665%; (2): 28.983%

55. (a) $82{,}401 \le I \le 171{,}850$; $171{,}851 \le I \le 373{,}650$; $I > 373{,}650$

  (b) $T = \$4681.25$ for $I = \$34{,}000$

     $T = \$16{,}781.25$ for $I = \$82{,}400$

  (c) $[4681.25, 16{,}781.25]$

0.3 EXERCISES

1. 256   3. -64 5. $\frac{1}{9}$ 7. $-\frac{9}{4}$

9. 6^8 11. $\frac{1}{10}$ 13. $9^0 = 1$ 15. 3^9

17. $\left(\frac{3}{2}\right)^2 = \frac{9}{4}$ 19. $1/x^6$ 21. x/y^2 23. x^7

25. $x^{-2} = 1/x^2$ 27. x^4 29. y^{12} 31. x^{12}

33. $x^2 y^2$ 35. $16/x^{20}$ 37. $x^8/(16y^4)$

39. $-16a^2/b^2$ 41. $2/(xy^2)$ 43. $1/(x^9 y^6)$

45. $(a^{18}c^{12})/b^6$

47. (a) $1/(2x^4)$ (b) $1/(16x^4)$ (c) $1/x^4$ (d) 8

49. x^{-1} 51. $8x^3$ 53. $\frac{1}{4}x^{-2}$

55. $-\frac{1}{8}x^3$ 57. 2.0736 59. 0.1316872428

61. $S = \$2114.81$; $I = \$914.81$

63. $S = \$9607.70$; $I = \$4607.70$

65. $\$7806.24$

67. (a) 5, 15, 22

  (b) $\$3421.6$, $\$6070.0$, $\$9066.9$ billion

  (c) $\$16{,}085$ billion

  (d) yes

69. (a) 456, 971, 1143

  (b) 439

(c) Two possibilities might be more environmental protections and the fact that there are only a limited number of species.

(d) There are only a limited number of species. Also, below some threshold level the ecological balance might be lost, perhaps resulting in an environmental catastrophe (which the equation could not predict). Upper limit = 1883

71. (a) 10   (b) $1385.5 billion
(c) $2600.8 billion   (d) $4304.3 billion

0.4 EXERCISES

1. (a) $\frac{16}{3} \approx 5.33$ (b) 1.2
3. (a) 8   (b) not real   5. $\frac{9}{4}$
7. (a) 4   (b) $\frac{1}{4}$ 9. $(6.12)^{4/9} \approx 2.237$
11. $m^{3/2}$ 13. $(m^2n^5)^{1/4}$ 15. $2\sqrt{x}$
17. $\sqrt[6]{x^7}$ 19. $-1/(4\sqrt[4]{x^5})$ 21. $y^{3/4}$
23. $z^{19/4}$ 25. $1/y^{5/2}$ 27. x
29. $1/y^{21/10}$ 31. $x^{1/2}$ 33. $1/x$
35. $8x^2$ 37. $8x^2y^2\sqrt{2y}$ 39. $2x^2y\sqrt[3]{5x^2y^2}$
41. $6x^2y\sqrt{x}$ 43. $42x^3y^2\sqrt{x}$ 45. $2xy^5/3$
47. $2b\sqrt[4]{b}/(3a^2)$ 49. $1/9$ 51. 7
53. $\sqrt{6}/3$ 55. $\sqrt{mx}/x$ 57. $\sqrt[3]{mx^2}/x^2$
59. $-\frac{2}{3}x^{-2/3}$ 61. $3x^{3/2}$ 63. $(3\sqrt{x})/2$
65. $1/(2\sqrt{x})$
67. (a) $10^{8.5} = 10^{17/2} = \sqrt{10^{17}}$
(b) $10^{9.0} = 1{,}000{,}000{,}000$ (c) $10^{2.1} \approx 125.9$
69. (a) $S = 1000\sqrt{\left(1 + \dfrac{r}{100}\right)^5}$
(b) $1173.26 (nearest cent)
71. (a) $P = 0.924\sqrt[100]{t^{13}}$
(b) 2005 to 2010; 0.1074 billion vs. 0.0209 billion. By 2045 and 2050 the population will be much larger than earlier in the 21st century, and there is a limited number of people that any land can support—in terms of both space and food.
73. 74 kg   75. 39,491
77. (a) 10   (b) 259

0.5 EXERCISES

1. (a) 2   (b) -1 (c) 10   (d) one
3. (a) 5   (b) -14 (c) 0   (d) several
5. (a) 5   (b) 0   (c) 2   (d) -5
7. -12 9. -296 11. $\frac{-7}{31}$
13. 87.4654   15. $21pq - 2p^2$
17. $m^2 - 7n^2 - 3$ 19. $3q + 12$
21. $x^2 - 1$ 23. $35x^5$ 25. $3rs$
27. $2ax^4 + a^2x^3 + a^2bx^2$ 29. $6y^2 - y - 12$
31. $12 - 30x^2 + 12x^4$ 33. $16x^2 + 24x + 9$
35. $0.01 - 16x^2$ 37. $36x^2 - 9$
39. $x^4 - x^2 + \frac{1}{4}$ 41. $0.1x^2 - 1.995x - 0.1$

43. $x^3 - 8$ 45. $x^8 + 3x^6 - 10x^4 + 5x^3 + 25x$
47. (a) $9x^2 - 21x + 13$ (b) 5
49. $3 + m + 2m^2n$ 51. $8x^3y^2/3 + 5/(3y) - 2x^2/(3y)$
53. $x^3 + 3x^2 + 3x + 1$ 55. $8x^3 - 36x^2 + 54x - 27$
57. $x^2 - 2x + 5 - 11/(x + 2)$
59. $x^2 + 3x - 1 + (-4x + 2)/(x^2 + 1)$
61. $x + 2x^2$ 63. $x - x^{1/2} - 2$ 65. $x - 9$
67. $4x^2 + 4x$ 69. $55x$
71. (a) $49.95 + 0.49x$ (b) $114.63
73. (a) $4000 - x$ (b) $0.10x$
(c) $0.08(4000 - x)$ (d) $0.10x + 0.08(4000 - x)$
75. $(15 - 2x)(10 - 2x)x$

0.6 EXERCISES

1. $3b(3a - 4a^2 + 6b)$ 3. $2x(2x + 4y^2 + y^3)$
5. $(7x^2 + 2)(x - 2)$ 7. $(6 + y)(x - m)$
9. $(x + 2)(x + 6)$ 11. $(x - 16)(x + 1)$
13. $(7x + 4)(x - 2)$ 15. $(x - 5)^2$
17. $(7a + 12b)(7a - 12b)$
19. (a) $(3x - 1)(3x + 8)$ (b) $(9x + 4)(x + 2)$
21. $x(4x - 1)$ 23. $(x^2 - 5)(x + 4)$
25. $(x - 3)(x + 2)$ 27. $2(x - 7)(x + 3)$
29. $2x(x - 2)^2$ 31. $(2x - 3)(x + 2)$
33. $3(x + 4)(x - 3)$ 35. $2x(x + 2)(x - 2)$
37. $(5x + 2)(2x + 3)$ 39. $(5x - 1)(2x - 9)$
41. $(y^2 + 4x^2)(y + 2x)(y - 2x)$
43. $(x + 2)^2(x - 2)^2$
45. $(2x + 1)(2x - 1)(x + 1)(x - 1)$
47. $x + 1$ 49. $1 + x$ 51. $(x + 1)^3$
53. $(x - 4)^3$ 55. $(x - 4)(x^2 + 4x + 16)$
57. $(3 + 2x)(9 - 6x + 4x^2)$ 59. $P(1 + rt)$
61. $m(c - m)$
63. (a) $p(10{,}000 - 100p)$; $x = 10{,}000 - 100p$ (b) 6200
65. (a) $R = x(300 - x)$ (b) $300 - x$

0.7 EXERCISES

1. $2y^3/z$ 3. $\frac{1}{3}$ 5. $(x - 1)/(x - 3)$
7. $20x/y$ 9. $\frac{32}{3}$ 11. $3x + 9$
13. $\dfrac{-(x + 1)(x + 3)}{(x - 1)(x - 3)}$ 15. $15bc^2/2$
17. $5y/(y - 3)$ 19. $\dfrac{-x(x - 3)(x + 2)}{x + 3}$
21. $\dfrac{1}{x + 1}$ 23. $\dfrac{4a - 4}{a(a - 2)}$
25. $\dfrac{-x^2 + x + 1}{x + 1}$ 27. $\dfrac{16a + 15a^2}{12(x + 2)}$
29. $\dfrac{79x + 9}{30(x - 2)}$ 31. $\dfrac{9x + 4}{(x - 2)(x + 2)(x + 1)}$
33. $(7x - 3x^3)/\sqrt{3 - x^2}$ 35. $\frac{1}{6}$
37. xy 39. $\dfrac{x + 1}{x^2}$
41. $\dfrac{1}{\sqrt{a}} = \dfrac{\sqrt{a}}{a}$ 43. $\dfrac{x - 2}{(x - 3)\sqrt{x^2 + 9}}$

45. (a) -12 (b) $\frac{25}{36}$

47. $2b^2 - a$

49. $(1 - 2\sqrt{x} + x)/(1 - x)$

51. $1/(\sqrt{x + h} + \sqrt{x})$

53. $(bc + ac + ab)/abc$

55. (a) $\dfrac{0.1x^2 + 55x + 4000}{x}$

    (b) $0.1x^2 + 55x + 4000$

57. $\dfrac{t^2 + 9t}{(t + 3)^2}$

CHAPTER 0 REVIEW EXERCISES

1. yes   2. no   3. no

4. $\{1, 2, 3, 4, 9\}$ 5. $\{5, 6, 7, 8, 10\}$

6. $\{1, 2, 3, 4, 9\}$

7. yes, $(A' \cup B')' = \{1, 3\} = A \cap B$

8. (a) Commutative Property of Addition
    (b) Associative Property of Multiplication
    (c) Distributive Law

9. (a) irrational   (b) rational, integer
    (c) meaningless

10. (a) $>$ (b) $<$ (c) $>$

11. 6   12. 142   13. 10

14. $5/4$ 15. 9   16. -29

17. $13/4$ 18. -10.62857888

19. (a) $[0, 5]$, closed

    (b) $[-3, 7)$, half-open

    (c) $(-4, 0)$, open

    $\begin{array}{l}\end{array}$
    $-6\ -5\ -4\ -3\ -2\ -1\ \ 0\ \ 1\ \ 2$

20. (a) $-1 < x < 16$ (b) $-12 \le x \le 8$
    (c) $x < -1$

21. (a) 1   (b) $2^{-2} = 1/4$ (c) 4^6 (d) 7

22. (a) $1/x^2$ (b) x^{10} (c) x^9 (d) $1/y^8$
    (e) y^6

23. $-x^2y^2/36$ 24. $9y^8/(4x^4)$ 25. $y^2/(4x^4)$

26. $-x^8z^4/y^4$ 27. $3x/(y^7z)$ 28. $x^5/(2y^3)$

29. (a) 4   (b) $2/7$ (c) 1.1

30. (a) $x^{1/2}$ (b) $x^{2/3}$ (c) $x^{-1/4}$

31. (a) $\sqrt[3]{x^2}$ (b) $1/\sqrt{x} = \sqrt{x}/x$ (c) $-x\sqrt{x}$

32. (a) $5y\sqrt{2x}/2$ (b) $\sqrt[3]{x^2y}/x^2$

33. $x^{5/6}$ 34. y

35. $x^{17/4}$ 36. $x^{11/3}$

37. $x^{2/5}$ 38. x^2y^8

39. $2xy^2\sqrt{3xy}$ 40. $25x^3y^4\sqrt{2y}$

41. $6x^2y^4\sqrt[3]{5x^2y^2}$ 42. $8a^2b^4\sqrt{2a}$

43. $2xy$ 44. $4x\sqrt{3xy}/(3y^4)$

45. $-x - 2$ 46. $-x^2 - x$

47. $4x^3 + xy + 4y - 4$ 48. $24x^5y^5$

49. $3x^2 - 7x + 4$ 50. $3x^2 + 5x - 2$

51. $4x^2 - 7x - 2$ 52. $6x^2 - 11x - 7$

53. $4x^2 - 12x + 9$ 54. $16x^2 - 9$

55. $2x^4 + 2x^3 - 5x^2 + x - 3$

56. $8x^3 - 12x^2 + 6x - 1$

57. $x^3 - y^3$

58. $(2/y) - (3xy/2) - 3x^2$

59. $3x^2 + 2x - 3 + (-3x + 7)/(x^2 + 1)$

60. $x^3 - x^2 + 2x + 7 + 21/(x - 3)$ 61. $x^2 - x$

62. $2x - a$ 63. $x^3(2x - 1)$

64. $2(x^2 + 1)^2(1 + x)(1 - x)$ 65. $(2x - 1)^2$

66. $(4 + 3x)(4 - 3x)$ 67. $2x^2(x + 2)(x - 2)$

68. $(x - 7)(x + 3)$ 69. $(3x + 2)(x - 1)$

70. $(x - 3)(x - 2)$ 71. $(x - 12)(x + 2)$

72. $(4x + 3)(3x - 8)$ 73. $(2x + 3)^2(2x - 3)^2$

74. $x^{2/3} + 1$

75. (a) $\dfrac{x}{(x + 2)}$ (b) $\dfrac{2xy(2 - 3xy)}{2x - 3y}$

76. $\dfrac{x^2 - 4}{x(x + 4)}$ 77. $\dfrac{(x + 3)}{(x - 3)}$

78. $\dfrac{x^2(3x - 2)}{(x - 1)(x + 2)}$ 79. $(6x^2 + 9x - 1)/(6x^2)$

80. $\dfrac{4x - x^2}{4(x - 2)}$ 81. $-\dfrac{x^2 + 2x + 2}{x(x - 1)^2}$

82. $\dfrac{x(x - 4)}{(x - 2)(x + 1)(x - 3)}$

83. $\dfrac{(x - 1)^3}{x^2}$ 84. $\dfrac{1 - x}{1 + x}$

85. $3(\sqrt{x} + 1)$ 86. $2/(\sqrt{x} + \sqrt{x - 4})$

87. (a)

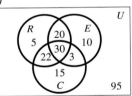

    R: recognized
    E: exercise
    C: community involvement

    (b) 10   (c) 100

88. 52.55%

89. 16

90. (a) \$4115.27   (b) \$66,788.69

91. (a) 939,577   (b) 753,969

92. (a) 1.1 inch, about quarter-sized
    (b) 104 mph

93. (a) $10,000\left[\dfrac{(0.0065)(1.0065)^n}{(1.0056)^n - 1}\right]$ (b) \$243.19 (for both)

94. (a) $S = k\sqrt[3]{A}$ (b) $\sqrt[3]{2.25} \approx 1.31$

95. $26x - 300 - 0.001x^2$

96. $1,450,000 - 3625x$

97. $(50 + x)(12 - 0.5x)$

98. (a) $\dfrac{12,000p}{100 - p}$

    (b) \$0. It costs nothing if no effort is made to remove pollution.

(c) $588,000

(d) Undefined. Removing 100% would be impossible, and the cost of getting close would be enormous.

99. $\dfrac{56x^2 + 1200x + 8000}{x}$

CHAPTER 0 TEST

1. (a) $\{3, 4, 6, 8\}$ (b) $\{3, 4\}; \{3, 6\};$ or $\{4, 6\}$
   (c) $\{6\}$ or $\{8\}$

2. 21

3. (a) 8   (b) 1   (c) $\frac{1}{2}$ (d) -10
   (e) 30   (f) $\frac{5}{6}$ (g) $\frac{2}{3}$ (h) -3

4. (a) $\sqrt[5]{x}$ (b) $\dfrac{1}{\sqrt[4]{x^3}}$

5. (a) $\dfrac{1}{x^5}$ (b) $\dfrac{x^{21}}{y^6}$

6. (a) $\dfrac{\sqrt{5x}}{5}$ (b) $2a^2b^2\sqrt{6ab}$ (c) $\dfrac{1 - 2\sqrt{x} + x}{1 - x}$

7. (a) 5   (b) -8 (c) -5

8. $(-2, 3]$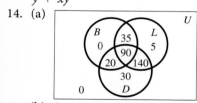

9. (a) $2x^2(4x - 1)$ (b) $(x - 4)(x - 6)$
   (c) $(3x - 2)(2x - 3)$ (d) $2x^3(1 + 4x)(1 - 4x)$

10. (c); -2

11. $2x + 1 + \dfrac{2x - 6}{x^2 - 1}$

12. (a) $19y - 45$ (b) $-6t^6 + 9t^9$
    (c) $4x^3 - 21x^2 + 13x - 2$ (d) $-18x^2 + 15x - 2$
    (e) $4m^2 - 28m + 49$ (f) $\dfrac{x^4}{3x + 9}$ (g) $\dfrac{x^7}{81}$
    (h) $\dfrac{6 - x}{x - 8}$ (i) $\dfrac{x^2 - 4x - 3}{x(x - 3)(x + 1)}$

13. $\dfrac{y - x}{y + xy^2}$

14. (a)

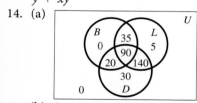

   (b) 0
   (c) 175

15. $4875.44 (nearest cent)

1.1 EXERCISES

1. $x = -9/4$ 3. $x = 0$ 5. $x = -32$
7. $x = -29/2$ 9. $x = -5$ 11. $x = 17/13$
13. $x = -1/3$ 15. $x = 3$ 17. $x = 5/4$
19. no solution   21. $x \approx -0.279$
23. $x \approx -1147.362$ 25. $y = \frac{3}{4}x - \frac{15}{4}$
27. $y = -6x + \frac{22}{3}$ 29. $t = \dfrac{S - P}{Pr}$

31. $x < 2$ 33. $x < -4$ 35. $x \le -1$

37. $x < -3$

39. $x < -6$

41. $x < 2$

43. 145 months

45. $3356.50   47. 440 packs, or 220,000 CDs

49. $29,600

51. (a) 77.7% (b) $t \approx 14.5$, during 2015

53. 96

55. $90,000 at 9%; $30,000 at 13%

57. $2160/month; 8% increase

59. $x > 80$ x

61. $695 + 5.75x \le 900$; 35 or fewer

63. (a) $t = 15$ (b) $t > 21.7$ (c) in 2017

65. (a) $0.479 \le h \le 1$; $h = 1$ means 100% humidity
    (b) $0 \le h \le 0.237$

1.2 EXERCISES

1. (a) To each x-value there corresponds exactly one y-value.
   (b) domain: $\{-7, -1, 0, 3, 4.2, 9, 11, 14, 18, 22\}$
        range: $\{0, 1, 5, 9, 11, 22, 35, 60\}$
   (c) $f(0) = 1, f(11) = 35$

3. yes; to each x-value there corresponds exactly one y-value; domain $= \{1, 2, 3, 8, 9\}$, range $= \{-4, 5, 16\}$

5. The vertical-line test shows that graph (a) represents a function of x, but graph (b) does not.

7. yes   9. no

11. (a) -10 (b) 6   (c) -34 (d) 2.8

13. (a) -3 (b) 1   (c) 13   (d) 6

15. (a) -251 (b) -128 (c) 22   (d) -4.25

17. (a) $63/8$ (b) 6   (c) -6

19. (a) no, $f(2 + 1) = f(3) = 13$ but $f(2) + f(1) = 10$
    (b) $1 + x + h + x^2 + 2xh + h^2$
    (c) no, $f(x) + f(h) = 2 + x + h + x^2 + h^2$
    (d) no, $f(x) + h = 1 + x + x^2 + h$
    (e) $1 + 2x + h$

21. (a) $-2x^2 - 4xh - 2h^2 + x + h$
    (b) $-4x - 2h + 1$

23. (a) 10   (b) 6

25. (a) $(1, -3)$, yes   (b) $(3, -3)$, yes
    (c) $b = a^2 - 4a$ (d) $x = 0, x = 4$, yes

27. domain: all reals; range: reals $y \ge 4$

29. domain: reals $x \ge -4$; range: reals $y \ge 0$

31. $x \ge 1, x \ne 2$ 33. $-7 \le x \le 7$

35. (a) $3x + x^3$ (b) $3x - x^3$ (c) $3x^4$ (d) $\dfrac{3}{x^2}$

37. (a) $\sqrt{2x} + x^2$ (b) $\sqrt{2x} - x^2$
    (c) $x^2\sqrt{2x}$ (d) $\dfrac{\sqrt{2x}}{x^2}$

39. (a) $-8x^3$ (b) $1 - 2(x - 1)^3$
    (c) $[(x - 1)^3 - 1]^3$ (d) $(x - 1)^6$

41. (a) $2\sqrt{x^4 + 5}$ (b) $16x^2 + 5$
(c) $2\sqrt{2\sqrt{x}}$ (d) $4x$

43. (a) $f(20) = 103{,}000$ means that if \$103,000 is borrowed, it can be repaid in 20 years (of \$800-per-month payments).
(b) no; $f(5 + 5) = f(10) = 69{,}000$, but $f(5) + f(5) = 40{,}000 + 40{,}000 = 80{,}000$
(c) 15 years; $f(15) = 89{,}000$

45. (a) $f(1950) = 16.5$ means that in 1950 there were 16.5 workers supporting each Social Security beneficiary.
(b) 3.4
(c) Through 2050, the graph must be the same. After 2050, the graph might be the same.
(d) domain: $1950 \le t \le 2050$
range: $1.9 \le n \le 16.5$

47. (a) $f(105) \approx 1.45; g(105) \approx 0.78$
(b) $f(107) \approx 1.51$ means that at the end of 2007 there were 1.51 million persons in state prisons.
(c) $g(92) = 0.66$ means that at the end of 1992 there were 0.66 million persons on parole.
(d) $(f - g)(107) = f(107) - g(107) = 1.51 - 0.82 = 0.69$ means that at the end of 2007 there were 0.69 million more persons in state prisons than there were on parole.
(e) $(f - g)(105)$ is greater because for 2005 there is a greater distance between the graphs.

49. (a) $s \ge 0$
(b) $f(10) \approx -29.33$ means that if the air temperature is $-5°F$ and there is a 10 mph wind, then the temperature feels like $-29.33°F$.
(c) $f(0) = 45.694$ from the formula, but $f(0)$ should equal the air temperature, $-5°F$.

51. (a) $C(10) = \$4210$
(b) $C(100) = \$32{,}200$
(c) $C(100)$ The total cost of producing 100 items is \$32,200.

53. (a) $0 \le p < 100$
(b) \$5972.73; to remove 45% of the particulate pollution would cost \$5972.73.
(c) \$65,700; to remove 90% of the particulate pollution would cost \$65,700.
(d) \$722,700; to remove 99% of the particulate pollution would cost \$722,700.
(e) \$1,817,700; to remove 99.6% of the particulate pollution would cost \$1,817,700.

55. (a) yes   (b) $A(2) = 96; A(30) = 600$
(c) $0 < x < 50$

57. (a) $(P \circ q)(t) = 180(1000 + 10t)$
$$- \frac{(1000 + 10t)^2}{100} - 200$$
(b) $x = 1150, P = \$193{,}575$

59. (a) yes; the output of g (customers) is the input for f.

(b) no; the output of f is revenue, and this is not the input for g.
(c) $f \circ g$: input (independent variable) is advertising dollars.
output (dependent variable) is revenue dollars.
$f \circ g$ shows how advertising dollars result in revenue dollars.

61. $L = 2x + 3200/x$

63. $R = (30 + x)(100 - 2x)$

1.3 EXERCISES

1. x-intercept 4   **3.** x-intercept 12
y-intercept 3 y-intercept -7.5

5. $m = 4$ **7.** $m = -1/2$ **9.** $m = 0$ **11.** 0
13. 0   **15.** (a) negative   (b) undefined
17. $m = 7/3, b = -1/4$ **19.** $m = 0, b = 3$

   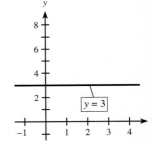

21. undefined slope,   **23.** $m = -2/3, b = 2$
no y-intercept

25.   **27.**

29.

31.

33.

35. $y = 2x - 4$ **37.** $-x + 13y = 32$

39. perpendicular   **41.** neither; same line

43. $y = -\frac{3}{5}x - \frac{41}{5}$ **45.** $y = -\frac{6}{5}x + \frac{23}{5}$

47. (a)

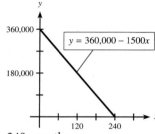

(b) 240 months

(c) After 60 months, the value of the building is $270,000.

49. (a) $m = 4.97; b = -6.49$

(b) The percent of the U.S. population with Internet service is changing at the rate of 4.97 percentage points per year.

(c)

51. (a) $m = -0.065; b = 31.39$

(b) The F-intercept represents the percent of the world's land that was forest in 1990.

(c) -0.065 percentage points per year. This means that after 1990, the world forest area as a percent of land area changes by -0.065 percentage points per year.

53. (a) $m = 0.78$

(b) This means that the average annual earnings of females increases $0.78 for each $1 increase in the average annual earnings of males.

(c) $45,484

55. $y = 0.0838x + 16.37$

57. (a) $B = 1.05W - 182.80$ (b) $709.70

59. (a) $y = 10.585x - 20,898.025$

(b) The CPI-U is changing at the rate of $10.59/year.

61. $p = 85,000 - 1700x$ **63.** $R = 3.2t - 0.2$

65. $y = 0.48x - 71$

1.4 EXERCISES

1.

3.

5.

7.

9.

11. $y = (3x + 7)/(x^2 + 4)$

13. (a) $y = 0.01x^3 + 0.3x^2 - 72x + 150$

(b) standard window

15. (a) $y = \dfrac{x + 15}{x^2 + 400}$

(b) standard window

17. (a) x-intercept 30, y-intercept -0.03

(b)

19.

21.

23.

25.

27.

29. $f(-2) = -18; f(\frac{3}{4}) = 0.734375$

31.

33.

35. $x = 3.5$ **37.** either $x = 5$ or $x = -2$

39. (a) -1.1098, 8.1098 (b) -1.1098, 8.1098

41. (a)

(b) When average annual earnings for males is
     $50,000, average annual earnings for females is
     $37,684.   (c) $47,434

43. (a)

(b) $E \geq 0$ when $0 \leq p \leq 100$

45. (a)

(b) decreasing; as more people become aware of the
     product, there are fewer to learn about it, so the rate
     will decrease.

47. (a) x-min $= 0$, x-max $= 120$

(b) y-min $= 15$, y-max $= 80$

(c)

(d)

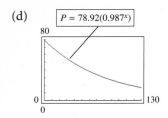

$$P = 78.92(0.987^x)$$

(e) The percent decreases from 78.9% in 1890 to 16.4% in 2010.

49. (a)

$$C = \frac{285{,}000}{p} - 2850$$

(b) Near $p = 0$, cost grows without bound.

(c) The coordinates of the point mean that obtaining stream water with 1% of the current pollution levels would cost $282,150.

(d) The p-intercept means that stream water with 100% of the current pollution levels would cost $0.

51. (a)

$$T = 1.19x^2 + 34.61x + 104.7$$

(b) increasing; the per capita federal tax burden is increasing.

1.5 EXERCISES

1. one solution; $(-1, -2)$

3. infinitely many solutions (each point on the line)

5. $x = 2, y = 2$ **7.** no solution

9. $x = 10/3, y = 2$ **11.** $x = 14/11, y = 6/11$

13. $x = 4, y = -1$

15. $x = 3, y = -2$ **17.** $x = 2, y = 1$

19. $x = -52/7, y = -128/7$ **21.** $x = 1, y = 1$

23. dependent

25. $x = 4, y = 2$ **27.** $x = -1, y = 1$

29. $x = -17, y = 7, z = 5$

31. $x = 4, y = 12, z = -1$

33. $x = 44, y = -9, z = -1/2$

35. $x \approx 2.455$; during 1998; amount $\approx \$842.67$ billion

37. (a) $x + y = 1800$ (b) $20x$ (c) $30y$

(d) $20x + 30y = 42{,}000$

(e) 1200 tickets at $20; 600 tickets at $30

39. $68,000 at 18%; $77,600 at 10%

41. 10%: $27,000; 12%: $24,000

43. 4 oz of A, $6\frac{2}{3}$ oz of B

45. 4550 of species A, 1500 of species B

47. 7 cc of 20%; 3 cc of 5%

49. 10,000 at $40; 6000 at $60

51. 80 cc   **53.** 5 oz of A, 1 oz of B, 5 oz of C

55. 200 type A, 100 type B, 200 type C

1.6 EXERCISES

1. (a) $P(x) = 34x - 6800$ (b) $95,200

3. (a) $P(x) = 37x - 1850$

(b) $-\$740$, loss of $740   (c) 50

5. (a) $m = 5, b = 250$

(b) $\overline{MC} = 5$ means each additional unit produced costs $5.

(c) slope = marginal cost; C-intercept = fixed costs

(d) 5, 5

7. (a) 27

(b) $\overline{MR} = 27$ means each additional unit sold brings in $27.

(c) 27, 27

9. (a) $P(x) = 22x - 250$ (b) 22   (c) $\overline{MP} = 22$

(d) Each unit sold adds $22 to profits at all levels of production, so produce and sell as much as possible.

11. $P = 58x - 8500, \overline{MP} = 58$

13. (a) $C(x) = 35x + 6600$ (b) $R(x) = 60x$

(c) $P(x) = 25x - 6600$

(d) $C(200) = 13{,}600$ dollars is the cost of producing 200 helmets.

$R(200) = 12{,}000$ dollars is the revenue from sale of 200 helmets.

$P(200) = -1600$ dollars; will lose $1600 from production and sale of 200 helmets.

(e) $C(300) = 17{,}100$ dollars is the cost of producing 300 helmets.

$R(300) = 18{,}000$ dollars is the revenue from sale of 300 helmets.

$P(300) = 900$ dollars; will profit $900 from production and sale of 300 helmets.

(f) $\overline{MP} = 25$ dollars per unit; each additional unit produced and sold increases profit by $25.

15. (a) Revenue passes through the origin.

(b) $2000   (c) 400 units

(d) $\overline{MC} = 2.5; \overline{MR} = 7.5$

17. 33

19. (a) $R(x) = 12x; C(x) = 8x + 1600$

(b) 400 units

21. (a) $P(x) = 4x - 1600$

(b) $x = 400$ units to break even

23. (a) $C(x) = 4.5x + 1045$

(b) $R(x) = 10x$

(c) $P(x) = 5.5x - 1045$

(d) 190 surge protectors

25. (a) $R(x) = 54.90x$ (b) $C(x) = 14.90x + 20{,}200$

(c) 505

27. (a) *R* starts at origin and is the steeper line.
   FC is a horizontal line.
   VC starts at origin and is not as steep as *R*.
   (See figure.)

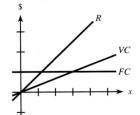

(b) *C* starts where *FC* meets the $-axis and is parallel to
   VC. Where *C* meets *R* is the break-even point (*BE*).
   P starts on the $-axis at the negative of *FC* and
   crosses the *x*-axis at *BE*. (See figure.)

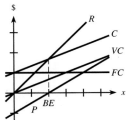

29. Demand decreases.
31. (a) 600   (b) 300   (c) shortage
33. 16 demanded, 25 supplied; surplus
35. $p = -2q/3 + 1060$
37. $p = 0.0001q + 0.5$
39. (a) demand falls; supply rises   (b) (30, $25)
41. (a) $q = 20$ (b) $q = 40$
   (c) shortage, 20 units short
43. shortage   **45.** $q = 20, p = \$18$
47. $q = 10, p = \$180$ **49.** $q = 100, p = \$325$
51. (a) $15   (b) $q = 100, p = \$100$
   (c) $q = 50, p = \$110$ (d) yes
53. $q = 8; p = \$188$ **55.** $q = 500; p = \$40$
57. $q = 1200; p = \$15$

CHAPTER 1 REVIEW EXERCISES

1. $x = \frac{31}{3}$ **2.** $x = -13$ **3.** $x = -\frac{29}{8}$
4. $x = -\frac{1}{9}$ **5.** $x = 8$
6. no solution   **7.** $y = -\frac{2}{3}x - \frac{4}{3}$
8. $x \leq 3$

9. $x \geq -20/3$

10. $x \geq -15/13$

11. yes   **12.** no   **13.** yes
14. domain: reals $x \leq 9$; range: reals $y \geq 0$
15. (a) 2   (b) 37   (c) 29/4
16. (a) 0   (b) 9/4   (c) 10.01
17. $9 - 2x - h$ **18.** yes   **19.** no   **20.** 4

21. $x = 0, x = 4$
22. (a) domain: $\{-2, -1, 0, 1, 3, 4\}$
   range: $\{-3, 2, 4, 7, 8\}$
(b) 7   (c) $x = -1, x = 3$
(d)

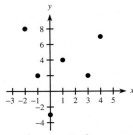

(e) no; for $y = 2$, there are two different *x*-values,
   -1 and 3.
23. (a) $x^2 + 3x + 5$ (b) $(3x + 5)/x^2$
   (c) $3x^2 + 5$ (d) $9x + 20$
24. $x: 2, y: 5$ **25.** $x: 3/2, y: 9/5$

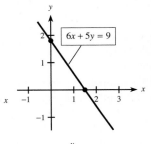

26. $x: -2, y:$ none

27. $m = 1$ **28.** undefined   **29.** $m = -\frac{2}{5}, b = 2$
30. $m = -\frac{4}{3}, b = 2$ **31.** $y = 4x + 2$
32. $y = -\frac{1}{2}x + 3$ **33.** $y = \frac{2}{5}x + \frac{9}{5}$
34. $y = -\frac{11}{8}x + \frac{17}{14}$ **35.** $x = -1$ **36.** $y = 4x + 2$
37. $y = \frac{4}{3}x + \frac{10}{3}$
38.

39.

40. (a)

(b)

(c) The graph in (a) shows a complete graph. The graph in (b) shows a piece that rises toward the high point and a piece between the high and low points.

41. (a) (b)

(c) The graph in (a) shows a complete graph. The one in (b) shows pieces that fall toward the minimum point and rise from it.

42. reals $x \geq -3$ with $x \neq 0$

43. $0.2857 \approx 2/7$ **44.** $x = 2, y = 1$

45. $x = 10, y = -1$ **46.** $x = 3, y = -2$

47. no solution   **48.** $x = 10, y = -71$

49. $x = 1, y = -1, z = 2$

50. $x = 11, y = 10, z = 9$

51. (a) 1997   (b) 27   (c) $x = 30.0$; in 2010

52. 95%

53. 40,000 miles. He would normally drive more than 40,000 miles in 5 years, so he should buy diesel.

54. (a) yes   (b) no   (c) 4

55. (a) $565.44

(b) The monthly payment on a $70,000 loan is $494.75.

56. (a) $(P \circ q)(t) = 330(100 + 10t)$
$\qquad - 0.05(100 + 10t)^2 - 5000$

(b) $x = 250, P = \$74{,}375$

57. $(W \circ L)(t) = 0.03\left[65 - 0.1(t - 25)^2\right]^3$

58. (a)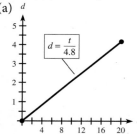

(b) When the time between seeing lightning and hearing thunder is 9.6 seconds, the storm is 2 miles away.

59.

60. (a) $P = 58x - 8500$

(b) The profit increases by $58 for each unit sold.

61. (a) yes

(b) $m = 427, b = 4541$

(c) In 2000, average annual health care costs were $4541 per consumer.

(d) Average annual health care costs are changing at the rate of $427 per year.

62. $F = \frac{9}{5}C + 32$ or $C = \frac{5}{9}(F - 32)$

63. (a)   (b) $0 \leq x \leq 6$

64. (a) $v^2 = 1960(h + 10)$

$\dfrac{v^2}{1960} = h + 10$

$h = \dfrac{1}{1960}v^2 - 10$

(b) 12.5 cm

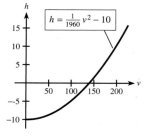

65. $100,000 at 9.5%; $50,000 at 11%

66. 2.8 liters of 20%; 1.2 liters of 70%

67. (a) 12 supplied; 14 demanded   (b) shortfall

(c) increase

68.

69. (a) 38.80   (b) 61.30   (c) 22.50   (d) 200

70. (a) $C(x) = 22x + 1500$ (b) $R(x) = 52x$

(c) $P(x) = 30x - 1500$ (d) $\overline{MC} = 22$

(e) $\overline{MR} = 52$ (f) $\overline{MP} = 30$ (g) $x = 50$

71. $q = 300, p = \$150$ **72.** $q = 700, p = \$80$

CHAPTER 1 TEST

1. $x = -6$

2. $x = 18/7$ **3.** $x = -3/7$ **4.** $x = -38$

5. $5 - 4x - 2h$

6. $t \geq -9$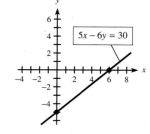

7. x: 6; y: -5 **8.** x: 3; y: $21/5$

9. (a) domain: $x \geq -4$
    range: $f(x) \geq 0$
 (b) $2\sqrt{7}$ (c) 6
10. $y = -\frac{3}{2}x + \frac{1}{2}$ **11.** $m = -\frac{5}{4}; b = \frac{15}{4}$
12. (a) $x = -3$ (b) $y = -4x - 13$
13. (a) no; a vertical line intersects the curve twice.
 (b) yes; there is exactly one y-value for each x-value.
 (c) no; one value of x gives two y-values.
14. (a)

 (b)

15. $x = -2, y = 2$
16. (a) $5x^3 + 2x^2 - 3x$ (b) $x + 2$
 (c) $5x^2 + 7x + 2$
17. (a) 30   (b) $P = 8x - 1200$ (c) 150
 (d) $\overline{MP} = 8$; the sale of each additional unit gives $8
    more profit.
18. (a) $R = 50x$
 (b) 19,000; it costs $19,000 to produce 100 units.
 (c) 450
19. $q = 200, p = \$2500$
20. (a) 720,000; original value of the building
 (b) -2000; building depreciates $2000 per month.
21. 400
22. 12,000 at 9%, 8000 at 6%

2.1 EXERCISES

 1. $x^2 + 2x - 1 = 0$ **3.** $y^2 + 3y - 2 = 0$
 5. $-2, 6$ **7.** $\frac{3}{2}, -\frac{3}{2}$ **9.** $0, 1$ **11.** $\frac{1}{2}$
13. (a) $2 + 2\sqrt{2}, 2 - 2\sqrt{2}$ (b) $4.83, -0.83$
15. no real solutions   **17.** $\sqrt{7}, -\sqrt{7}$ **19.** $4, -4$
21. $1, -9$ **23.** $-7, 3$ **25.** $8, -4$ **27.** $-\frac{7}{4}, \frac{3}{4}$
29. $-6, 2$ **31.** $(1 + \sqrt{31})/5, (1 - \sqrt{31})/5$
33. $-2, 5$ **35.** $-300, 100$ **37.** $0.69, -0.06$
39. $8, 1$ **41.** $1/2$ **43.** $-9, -10$
45. $x = 20$ or $x = 70$
47. (a) $x = 10$ or $x = 345\frac{5}{9}$
 (b) yes; for any $x > 10$ and $x < 345\frac{5}{9}$
49. 6 seconds
51. (a) ± 50
 (b) $s = 50$; there is no particulate pollution in the air
    above the plant.

53. 97.0 mph
55. 2012   **57.** $80   **59.** $x \approx 27.0$, during 2017
61. (a) 18   (b) ≈ 31
 (c) Speed triples, but K changes only by a factor
    of 1.72.

2.2 EXERCISES

 1. (a) $\left(-1, -\frac{1}{2}\right)$ (b) minimum
 (c) -1 (d) $-\frac{1}{2}$
 3. (a) $(1, 9)$ (b) maximum   (c) 1   (d) 9
 5. (a) $(3, 9)$ (b) maximum   (c) 3   (d) 9
 7. maximum, $(2, 1)$; zeros $(0, 0)$, $(4, 0)$

 9. minimum, $(-2, 0)$; zero $(-2, 0)$

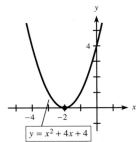

11. minimum, $\left(-1, -3\frac{1}{2}\right)$; zeros $\left(-1 + \sqrt{7}, 0\right)$,
 $\left(-1 - \sqrt{7}, 0\right)$

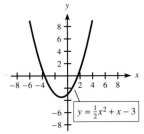

13. (a) 3 units to the right and 1 unit up
 (b)

15. $y = (x + 2)^2 - 2$
 (a) 2 units to the left and 2 units down

(b)

17. vertex $(1, -8)$; zeros $(-3, 0)$, $(5, 0)$

$$y = \tfrac{1}{2}x^2 - x - \tfrac{15}{2}$$

19. vertex $(-6, 3)$; no real zeros

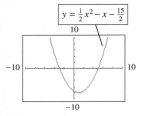

$$y = \tfrac{1}{4}x^2 + 3x + 12$$

21. -5

23. vertex $(10, 64)$; zeros $(90, 0)$, $(-70, 0)$

$$y = 63 + 0.2x - 0.01x^2$$

25. vertex $(0, -0.01)$; zeros $(10, 0)$, $(-10, 0)$

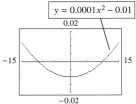

$$y = 0.0001x^2 - 0.01$$

27. (a) $(1, -24)$ (b) $x \approx -0.732, 2.732$

29. (a) $x = 2$ (b) $x - 2$
(c) $(x - 2)(3x - 2)$ (d) $x = 2, \tfrac{2}{3}$

31. (a) 80 units   (b) $540   **33.** 400 trees

35. dosage = 500 mg   **37.** intensity = 1.5 lumens

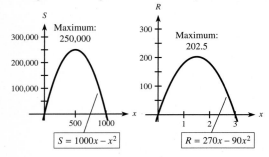

39. equation (a) $(384.62, 202.31)$ (b) $(54, 46)$
Projectile (a) goes higher.

41. (a) From b to c. The average rate is the same as the slope of the segment. Segment b to c is steeper.
(b) $d > b$ to make segment a to d be steeper (have greater slope).

43. (a)

Rent	Number Rented	Revenue
600	50	$30,000
620	49	$30,380
640	48	$30,720

(b) increase
(c) $R = (50 - x)(600 + 20x)$
(d) $800

45. (a) quadratic
(b) $a < 0$ because the graph opens downward.
(c) The vertex occurs after 2004 (when $x > 0$). Hence $-b/2a > 0$ and $a < 0$ means $b > 0$. The value $c = f(0)$, or the y-value in 2004. Hence $c > 0$.

47. Yes; rises at an average rate of $176 billion per year from 2005 to 2010, at $226 billion per year from 2010 to 2015.

49.

$$u = -0.013x^2 + 1.56x - 18.87$$

51. (a) $x \approx 106.4$; 2007
(b) 2007 and after, when $u(x) < 0$

2.3 EXERCISES

1. $x = 40$ units, $x = 50$ units

3. $x = 50$ units, $x = 300$ units

5. $x = 15$ units; reject $x = 100$ **7.** $41,173.61

9. $87.50   **11.** $x = 55$, $P(55) = $2025

13. (a)

$$P(x) = 80x - 0.1x^2 - 7000$$

(b) $(400, 9000)$; maximum point   (c) positive
(d) negative   (e) closer to 0 as a gets closer to 400

15. (a) $P(x) = -x^2 + 350x - 15,000$; maximum profit is $15,625
(b) no   (c) x-values agree

17. (a) $x = 28$ units, $x = 1000$ units
(b) $651,041.67

(c) $P(x) = -x^2 + 1028x - 28,000$; maximum profit is $236,196

(d) $941.60

19. (a) $t \approx 5.1$, in 2009; $R \approx \$60.79$ billion

(b) The data show a smaller revenue, $R = \$60.27$ billion, in 2008.

(c)

(d) The model fits the data quite well.

21. (a) $P(t) = -0.019t^2 + 0.284t - 0.546$

(b) 2008

(c)

(d) The model projects decreasing profits, and except for 2012, the data support this.

(e) Management would be interested in increasing revenues or reducing costs (or both) to improve profits.

23. (a)

(b) See E on graph.   (c) $q = 4, p = \$14$

25. $q = 10, p = \$196$ **27.** $q = 216\frac{2}{3}, p = \$27.08$

29. $p = \$40, q = 30$ **31.** $q = 90, p = \$50$

33. $q = 70, p = \$62$

2.4 EXERCISES

1. l   **3.** d   **5.** h   **7.** i   **9.** k

11. a   **13.** (a) cubic   (b) quartic   **15.** d

17. a   **19.** c   **21.** f

23.

25.

27.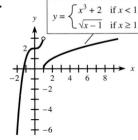

29. (a) 8/3   (b) 9.9   (c) −999.999   (d) no

31. (a) 64   (b) 1   (c) 1000   (d) 0.027

33. (a) 2   (b) 4   (c) 0   (d) 2

35. (a)

(b) polynomial   (c) no asymptotes

(d) turning points at $x = 0$ and approximately $x = -2.8$ and $x = 2.8$

37. (a)

(b) rational

(c) vertical: $x = -1$, horizontal: $y = 2$

(d) no turning points

39. (a) $f(x) = \begin{cases} -x & \text{if } x < 0 \\ 5x & \text{if } x \geq 0 \end{cases}$

(b) piecewise defined

(c) no asymptotes

(d) turning point at $x = 0$

41. (a) 6800; 11,200   (b) $0 < x < 27$

43. (a) downward   (b)

$y = 252.576x^{0.296}$

(c) 2010

45. (a) yes; $p = 100$
(b) $p \neq 100$
(c) $0 \leq p < 100$
(d) It increases without bound.

47. (a) $A(2) = 96$; $A(30) = 600$
(b) $0 < x < 50$

49. (a)
$$y = \begin{cases} 90.742x + 210.291 & \text{if } 10 \leq x \leq 60 \\ 66.786x^2 - 7820.9x + 238{,}565.429 & \text{if } 60 \leq x \end{cases}$$

(b) \$3840 billion (\$3.840 trillion)
(c) \$27,669 billion (\$27.669 trillion)

51. (a) $p = \begin{cases} 44 & \text{if } 0 < x \leq 1 \\ 64 & \text{if } 1 < x \leq 2 \\ 84 & \text{if } 2 < x \leq 3 \\ 104 & \text{if } 3 < x \leq 4 \end{cases}$

(b) 64; it costs 64 cents to mail a 1.2 oz letter.
(c) Domain $0 < x \leq 4$; Range $\{44, 64, 84, 104\}$
(d) 64 cents and 84 cents

53. (a) $p = \dfrac{200}{2 + 0.1x}$

(b) yes, when $p = \$100$

55. $C(x) = 30(x - 1) + \dfrac{3000}{x + 10}$

(a)

(b) Any turning point would indicate the minimum or the maximum cost. In this case, $x = 0$ gives a minimum.
(c) The y-intercept is the fixed cost of production.

2.5 EXERCISES

1. linear   **3.** quadratic   **5.** quartic
7. quadratic or power
9. $y = 2x - 3$ **11.** $y = 2x^2 - 1.5x - 4$

13. $y = x^3 - x^2 - 3x - 4$ **15.** $y = 2x^{0.5}$

17. (a)

(b) linear
(c) $y = 5x - 3$

19. (a)

(b) quadratic
(c) $y = 0.09595x^2 + 0.4656x + 1.4758$

21. (a)

(b) quadratic
(c) $y = 2x^2 - 5x + 1$

23. (a)

(b) cubic
(c) $y = x^3 - 5x + 1$

25. (a)

(b) $y = 0.807x - 2.395$
(c) 0.807; Women's annual earnings increase by \$807 for each \$1000 increase in men's earnings.

27. (a) $y = -0.039x^3 + 1.69x^2 - 18.2x + 71.1$
(b) 2002; no, data maximum is in 2000.

29. (a)

(b) $y = 168.319x - 1061.592$

(c) $y = 0.1195x^3 - 7.9690x^2 + 193.370x + 575.369$

(d)

Cubic model is the better fit.

31. (a) $y = 0.0052x^2 - 0.62x + 15.0$

(b) $x \approx 59.6$

(c) No, it is unreasonable for the temperature to feel warmer for winds greater than 60 mph.

33. (a) quadratic and power

(b) $y = 2.025x^2 - 86.722x + 853.890$,
$y = 0.0324x^{2.737}$

(c) Quadratic is better.

(d) $4708 billion ($4.708 trillion)

35. (a) power: $y = 0.5125x^{4.038}$
cubic: $y = -4.62x^3 + 900x^2 - 13,480x + 51,120$

(b) power: 880,320 thousand
cubic: 483,738 thousand

(c) Both exceed the estimate of the total U.S. population in 2015.

CHAPTER 2 REVIEW EXERCISES

1. $x = 0, x = -\frac{5}{3}$ **2.** $x = 0, x = \frac{4}{3}$

3. $x = -2, x = -3$

4. $x = (-5 + \sqrt{47})/2, x = (-5 - \sqrt{47})/2$

5. no real solutions   **6.** $x = \frac{\sqrt{3}}{2}, x = -\frac{\sqrt{3}}{2}$

7. $\frac{5}{7}, -\frac{4}{5}$ **8.** $(-1 + \sqrt{2})/4, (-1 - \sqrt{2})/4$

9. $7/2, 100$ **10.** $13/5, 90$

11. no real solutions   **12.** $z = -9, z = 3$

13. $x = 8, x = -2$ **14.** $x = 3, x = -1$

15. $x = (-a \pm \sqrt{a^2 - 4b})/2$

16. $r = (2a \pm \sqrt{4a^2 + x^3c})/x$

17. $1.64, -7051.64$ **18.** $0.41, -2.38$

19. vertex $(-2, -2)$;   **20.** vertex $(0, 4)$;
zeros $(0, 0), (-4, 0)$ zeros $(4, 0), (-4, 0)$

    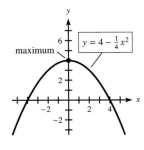

21. vertex $\left(\frac{1}{2}, \frac{25}{4}\right)$;
zeros $(-2, 0), (3, 0)$

22. vertex $(2, 1)$;
no real zeros

23. vertex $(-3, 0)$;
zero $(-3, 0)$

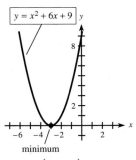

24. vertex $\left(\frac{3}{2}, 0\right)$;
zero $\left(\frac{3}{2}, 0\right)$

25. vertex $(0, -3)$;
zeros $(-3, 0), (3, 0)$

26. vertex $(0, 2)$;
no real zeros

27. vertex $(-1, 4)$;
no real zeros

28. vertex $\left(\frac{7}{2}, \frac{9}{4}\right)$;
zeros $(2, 0), (5, 0)$

29. vertex $(100, 1000)$;
zeros $(0, 0), (200, 0)$

30. vertex $(75, -6.25)$;
zeros $(50, 0), (100, 0)$

31. 20   **32.** 30

33. (a) $\left(1, -4\frac{1}{2}\right)$ (b) $x = -2, x = 4$ (c) B

34. (a) $(0, 49)$ (b) $x = -7, x = 7$ (c) D

35. (a) $(7, 25)$ approximately, actual is $(7, 24\frac{1}{2})$
(b) $x = 0, x = 14$ (c) A

36. (a) $(-1, 9)$ (b) $x = -4, x = 2$ (c) C

37. (a)

(b)

(c)

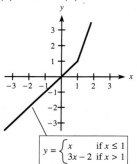

38. (a) 0   (b) 10,000   (c) -25 (d) 0.1

39. (a) -2 (b) 0   (c) 1   (d) 4

40.

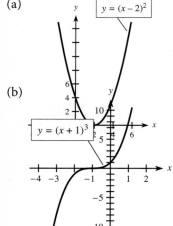

$y = \begin{cases} x & \text{if } x \le 1 \\ 3x - 2 & \text{if } x > 1 \end{cases}$

41. (a)

$y = (x - 2)^2$

(b)

$y = (x + 1)^3$

42. Turns: $(1, -5), (-3, 27)$

$y = x^3 + 3x^2 - 9x$

43. Turns: $(1.7, -10.4)$, $(-1.7, 10.4)$

$y = x^3 - 9x$

44. VA: $x = 2$;
HA: $y = 0$

$y = \dfrac{1}{x - 2}$

45. VA: $x = -3$;
HA: $y = 2$

$y = \dfrac{2x - 1}{x + 3}$

46. (a)

(b) $y = -2.1786x + 159.8571$
(c) $y = -0.0818x^2 - 0.2143x + 153.3095$

47. (a)

(b) $y = 2.1413x + 34.3913$
(c) $y = 22.2766x^{0.4259}$

48. (a) $t = -1.65, t = 3.65$ (b) Just $t = 3.65$
(c) at 3.65 seconds

49. $x = 20, x = 800$

50. (a) 2000 and 2008   (b) 2004; 8.59

51. (a) $x = 200$ (b) $A = 30,000$ square feet

52.

$p = 2q^2 + 4q + 6$

53.

$p = 18 - 3q - q^2$

54. (a)

$p = 85 - 0.2q - 0.1q^2$

Market Equilibrium

$p = 0.1q^2 + 1$

(b) $p = 41, q = 20$

55. $p = 400, q = 10$ **56.** $p = 10, q = 20$

57. $x = 46 + 2\sqrt{89} \approx 64.9, x = 46 - 2\sqrt{89} \approx 27.1$

58. $x = 15, x = 60$

59. max revenue $= \$2500$; max profit $= \$506.25$

60. max profit $= 12.25$; break-even at $x = 100, x = 30$

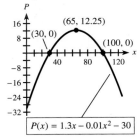

61. $x = 50, P(50) = 640$

62. (a) $C = 15{,}000 + 140x + 0.04x^2$;
    $R = 300x - 0.06x^2$
  (b) $100, 1500$ (c) 2500
  (d) $P = 160x - 15{,}000 - 0.1x^2$; max at 800
  (e) at 2500: $P = -240{,}000$; at 800: $P = 49{,}000$

63. (a) power   (b) 36.7 million
  (c) 40.8; the number of HIV infections will be 40.8
    million in 2015.

64. (a)   (b) $0 \le x \le 6$

65. (a) rational   (b) $0 \le p < 100$
  (c) 0; it costs $\$0$ to remove no pollution.
  (d) $\$475{,}200$

66. (a) $x = 12$; $C(12) = \$30.68$
  (b) $x = 825$; $C(825) = \$1734.70$

67. (a) and (b)
  (c) 55 mph   (d) 9.9 seconds

68. (a) $y = 2.94x^2 + 32.7x + 640$
  (b) $x \approx 23.3$, in 2024
  (c) Very little; projections were made before the Health
    Care Bill of 2010.

69. (a) $y = 5.66x^{1.70}$
  (b) $y = 2.46x^2 - 34.7x + 399$
  (c) Both are quite good.

CHAPTER 2 TEST

1. (a)   (b)

  (c) (d)

2. b; a   **3.**

4. (a)

  (b)

5. b; the function is cubic, $f(1) < 0$

6. (a) -10 (b) $-16\frac{1}{2}$ (c) -7

7.

8. vertex $(-2, 25)$;
zeros $-7, 3$

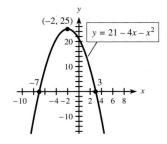

9. $x = 2, x = 1/3$

10. $x = \dfrac{-3 + 3\sqrt{3}}{2}, x = \dfrac{-3 - 3\sqrt{3}}{2}$

11. $x = 2/3$

12. c; $g(x)$ has a vertical asymptote at $x = -2$, as does graph c.

13. HA: $y = 0$; VA: $x = 5$

14. 42

15. (a) quartic   (b) cubic

16. (a)

model: $y = -0.3577x$
$\qquad + 19.9227$
(b) $f(x) = 5.6$
(c) at $x = 55.7$

17. $q = 300, p = \$80$

18. (a) $P(x) = -x^2 + 250x - 15,000$
(b) 125 units, $625   (c) 100 units, 150 units

19. (a) $f(15) = -19.5$ means that when the air temperature is 0°F and the wind speed is 15 mph, the air temperature feels like -19.5°F.
(b) -31.4°F

20. (a)

model (b) linear:
$\qquad y = 30.65x + 667.43$
cubic: $y = 0.118x^3 - 2.51x^2$
$\qquad + 40.28x + 676$

(c) linear: $1280.43; cubic: $1420.70   (d) no

3.1 EXERCISES

1. 3   **3.** A, F, Z   **5.** $\begin{bmatrix} -1 & -2 & -3 \\ 1 & 0 & -1 \\ -2 & 3 & 4 \end{bmatrix}$

7. A, C, D, F, G, Z

9. 1   **11.** $\begin{bmatrix} 1 & 3 & 4 \\ 0 & 2 & 0 \\ -2 & 1 & 3 \end{bmatrix}$ **13.** $\begin{bmatrix} 0 & 0 & 0 \\ 0 & 0 & 0 \\ 0 & 0 & 0 \end{bmatrix}$

15. $\begin{bmatrix} 9 & 5 \\ 4 & 7 \end{bmatrix}$ **17.** $\begin{bmatrix} 0 & -2 & -5 \\ 4 & 2 & 0 \\ 2 & 3 & 7 \end{bmatrix}$ **19.** $\begin{bmatrix} 2 & 3 & 2 \\ 3 & 4 & 1 \\ 2 & 1 & 6 \end{bmatrix}$

21. impossible   **23.** $\begin{bmatrix} 3 & 3 & 9 & 0 \\ 12 & 6 & 3 & 3 \\ 9 & 6 & 0 & 3 \end{bmatrix}$

25. $\begin{bmatrix} 28 & 16 \\ 10 & 18 \end{bmatrix}$ **27.** impossible

29. $x = 3, y = 2, z = 3, w = 4$

31. $x = 4, y = 1, z = 3, w = 3$

33. $x = 2, y = 2, z = -3$

35. (a) $A = \begin{bmatrix} 69 & 75 & 13 & 13 & 74 \\ 12 & 14 & 24 & 10 & 65 \end{bmatrix}$
$B = \begin{bmatrix} 256 & 176 & 65 & 8 & 11 \\ 20 & 6 & 16 & 1 & 1 \end{bmatrix}$
(b) $A + B = \begin{bmatrix} 325 & 251 & 78 & 21 & 85 \\ 32 & 20 & 40 & 11 & 66 \end{bmatrix}$
(c) $\begin{bmatrix} 187 & 101 & 52 & -5 & -63 \\ 8 & -8 & -8 & -9 & -64 \end{bmatrix}$
more species in the United States

37. (a) $\begin{bmatrix} 11{,}041.7 & 8978.4 & 6461 \\ 8739.8 & 9159.6 & 6877.3 \\ 9798.1 & 9086.7 & 6448.4 \\ 9696.6 & 8926.7 & 6109.5 \end{bmatrix}$
(b) air pollution

39. (a) $\begin{bmatrix} 825 & 580 & 1560 \\ 810 & 650 & 350 \end{bmatrix}$ (b) $\begin{bmatrix} -75 & 20 & -140 \\ 10 & -50 & 50 \end{bmatrix}$

41. $A = \begin{matrix} & \text{M} & \text{F} \\ & \begin{bmatrix} 54.4 & 55.6 \\ 62.1 & 66.6 \\ 67.4 & 74.1 \\ 70.7 & 78.1 \\ 74.9 & 80.1 \\ 75.7 & 80.6 \end{bmatrix} \end{matrix}$ $B = \begin{matrix} & \text{M} & \text{F} \\ & \begin{bmatrix} 45.5 & 45.2 \\ 51.5 & 54.9 \\ 61.1 & 67.4 \\ 63.8 & 72.5 \\ 68.3 & 75.2 \\ 69.7 & 76.5 \end{bmatrix} \end{matrix}$

$A - B = C = \begin{bmatrix} 8.9 & 10.4 \\ 10.6 & 11.7 \\ 6.3 & 6.7 \\ 6.9 & 5.6 \\ 6.6 & 4.9 \\ 6.0 & 4.1 \end{bmatrix}$

43. (a) $\begin{bmatrix} -823.2 & 121.1 \\ -834.6 & 135.8 \\ -506.9 & 132.0 \end{bmatrix}$ billions of dollars of U.S. trade balance in goods and services for 2007–2009
(b) $\begin{bmatrix} 3144.0 & 855.5 \\ 3444.4 & 932.4 \\ 2643.9 & 872.6 \end{bmatrix}$ total value (in billions of dollars) of U.S. trade for goods and services, 2007–2009
(c) $\begin{bmatrix} 96.70 & 40.69 \\ 108.74 & 44.51 \\ 89.04 & 41.86 \end{bmatrix}$ average monthly value (in billions of dollars) for U.S. exports of goods and services, 2007–2009

45. (a) $\begin{bmatrix} 46.20 & 84.00 & 210.00 & 10.50 \\ 42.00 & 84.00 & 42.00 & 0.00 \\ 58.80 & 147.00 & 94.50 & 0.00 \\ 31.50 & 147.00 & 42.00 & 21.00 \\ 42.00 & 0.00 & 210.00 & 10.50 \end{bmatrix}$

(b) $\begin{bmatrix} 48.40 & 88.00 & 220.00 & 11.00 \\ 44.00 & 88.00 & 44.00 & 0.00 \\ 61.60 & 154.00 & 99.00 & 0.00 \\ 33.00 & 154.00 & 44.00 & 22.00 \\ 44.00 & 0.00 & 220.00 & 11.00 \end{bmatrix}$

47. (a) $A = \begin{bmatrix} 0 & 1 & 1 & 0 \\ 1 & 0 & 1 & 1 \\ 0 & 0 & 0 & 1 \\ 0 & 1 & 1 & 0 \end{bmatrix}$

(b) $B = \begin{bmatrix} 0 & 1 & 1 & 1 \\ 1 & 0 & 1 & 1 \\ 0 & 1 & 0 & 1 \\ 1 & 1 & 1 & 0 \end{bmatrix}$ (c) person 2

49. (a) $\begin{bmatrix} 80 & 75 \\ 58 & 106 \end{bmatrix}$ (b) $\begin{bmatrix} 176 & 127 \\ 139 & 143 \end{bmatrix}$

(c) $\begin{bmatrix} 10 & 4 \\ 7 & 2 \end{bmatrix}$ (d) $\begin{bmatrix} -10 & 19 \\ -7 & 20 \end{bmatrix}$ shortage, taken from inventory.

51. (a) 3, 4, 5, 6   (b) 1

Worker 1:   0.9625   Worker 2:   0.9375

Worker 3:   0.9125   Worker 4:   0.8875

53. Worker 5:   0.85   Worker 6:   0.875

Worker 7:   0.90   Worker 8:   0.925

Worker 9:   0.95

Worker 5 is least efficient; performs best at center 5

3.2 EXERCISES

1. (a) $\begin{bmatrix} 32 \end{bmatrix}$ (b) $\begin{bmatrix} 11 & 17 \end{bmatrix}$ 3. $\begin{bmatrix} 29 & 25 \\ 10 & 12 \end{bmatrix}$

5. $\begin{bmatrix} 14 & 2 & 16 \\ 28 & 5 & 12 \end{bmatrix}$

7. $\begin{bmatrix} 7 & 5 & 3 & 2 \\ 14 & 9 & 11 & 3 \\ 13 & 10 & 12 & 3 \end{bmatrix}$ 9. impossible

11. $\begin{bmatrix} 13 & 9 & 3 & 4 \\ 9 & 7 & 16 & 1 \end{bmatrix}$ 13. $\begin{bmatrix} 9 & 7 & 16 \\ 5 & 17 & 20 \end{bmatrix}$

15. $\begin{bmatrix} 9 & 0 & 8 \\ 13 & 4 & 11 \\ 16 & 0 & 17 \end{bmatrix}$ 17. $\begin{bmatrix} 161 & 126 \\ 42 & 35 \end{bmatrix}$ 19. no

21. no   23. $\begin{bmatrix} -55 & 88 & 0 \\ -42 & 67 & 0 \\ 28 & -44 & 1 \end{bmatrix}$ 25. $\begin{bmatrix} 0 & 0 & 0 \\ 0 & 0 & 0 \\ 0 & 0 & 0 \end{bmatrix}$

27. $\begin{bmatrix} 0 & 0 & 0 \\ 0 & 0 & 0 \\ 0 & 0 & 0 \end{bmatrix}$ 29. A 31. Z

33. no (see Problem 25)

35. (a) $AB = \begin{bmatrix} 1 & 0 \\ 0 & 1 \end{bmatrix}$, $BA = \begin{bmatrix} 1 & 0 \\ 0 & 1 \end{bmatrix}$

(b) $ad - bc \neq 0$

37. $\begin{bmatrix} 2 - 2 + 2 \\ 6 - 4 - 4 \\ 4 + 0 - 2 \end{bmatrix} = \begin{bmatrix} 2 \\ -2 \\ 2 \end{bmatrix}$; solution

39. $\begin{bmatrix} 1 + 2 + 2 \\ 4 + 0 + 1 \\ 2 + 2 + 1 \end{bmatrix} = \begin{bmatrix} 5 \\ 5 \\ 5 \end{bmatrix}$; solution

41. $\begin{bmatrix} 1 & 0 & 0 & 0 & 0 \\ 0 & 1 & 0 & 0 & 0 \\ 0 & 0 & 1 & 0 & 0 \\ 0 & 0 & 0 & 1 & 0 \\ 0 & 0 & 0 & 0 & 1 \end{bmatrix}$ (Some entries may appear as decimal approximations of 0.)

43. $\begin{bmatrix} 31{,}680 & 36{,}960 \\ 42{,}500 & 47{,}600 \end{bmatrix}$

The entries represent the dealer's cost for each car.

45. (a) $A = \begin{bmatrix} 2378 & 2071 \\ 2723 & 2980 \\ 5114 & 4850 \\ 1581 & 1627 \\ 2490 & 2573 \\ 1245 & 1289 \\ 824 & 823 \end{bmatrix}$ $B = \begin{bmatrix} 131.0 & 113.0 \\ 47.8 & 40.6 \\ 86.8 & 84.3 \\ 118.0 & 125.0 \\ 107.0 & 116.0 \\ 64.2 & 57.8 \\ 96.3 & 98.3 \end{bmatrix}$

(b) 7×7 (c) the diagonal entries

47. (a) $\begin{bmatrix} 0.55 & 0.45 \end{bmatrix}$ After 5 years, M has 55% and S has 45% of the population.

(b) 10 years: $(PD)D = PD^2$; 15 years: PD^3

(c) 60% in M and 40% in S. Population proportions are stable.

49. 172, 208, 268, 327, 101, 123, 268, 327, 216, 263, 162, 195, 176, 215, 343, 417

51. (a)

$B = \begin{bmatrix} \frac{3}{4} & \frac{2}{5} & \frac{1}{4} \\ \frac{1}{4} & \frac{3}{5} & \frac{3}{4} \end{bmatrix}$; $D = \begin{bmatrix} 22 & 30 \\ 12 & 20 \\ 8 & 11 \end{bmatrix}$; $BD = \begin{bmatrix} 23.3 & 33.25 \\ 18.7 & 27.75 \end{bmatrix}$

Houston's need for black crude is 23,300 gal and for gold crude is 18,700 gal. Gulfport needs 33,250 gal of black and 27,750 gal of gold.

(b) $PBD = \begin{bmatrix} 135.945 & 197.3255 \end{bmatrix}$; Houston's cost = \$135,945; Gulfport's cost = \$197,532.50

53. (a) $B = \begin{bmatrix} 0.7 & 8.5 & 10.2 & 1.1 & 5.6 & 3.6 \\ 0.5 & 0.2 & 6.1 & 1.3 & 0.2 & 1.0 \\ 2.2 & 0.4 & 8.8 & 1.2 & 1.2 & 4.8 \\ 251.8 & 63.4 & 81.6 & 35.2 & 54.3 & 144.2 \\ 30.0 & 1.0 & 1.0 & 1.0 & 1.0 & 1.0 \\ 788.9 & 0 & 0 & 0 & 0 & 0 \end{bmatrix}$

(b) $A = \begin{bmatrix} 1.11 & 0 & 0 & 0 & 0 & 0 \\ 0 & 0.95 & 0 & 0 & 0 & 0 \\ 0 & 0 & 1.11 & 0 & 0 & 0 \\ 0 & 0 & 0 & 1.11 & 0 & 0 \\ 0 & 0 & 0 & 0 & 0.95 & 0 \\ 0 & 0 & 0 & 0 & 0 & 0.95 \end{bmatrix}$

3.3 EXERCISES

1. $\begin{bmatrix} 1 & -2 & -1 & | & -7 \\ 0 & 7 & 5 & | & 21 \\ 4 & 2 & 2 & | & 1 \end{bmatrix}$

3. $\begin{bmatrix} 1 & -3 & 4 & | & 2 \\ 2 & 0 & 2 & | & 1 \\ 1 & 2 & 1 & | & 1 \end{bmatrix}$ 5. $x = 2, y = 1/2, z = -5$

7. $x = -5, y = 2, z = 1$

9. $x = 4, y = 1, z = -2$ 11. $x = 15, y = -13, z = 2$

13. $x = 15, y = 0, z = 2$

15. $x = 1, y = 3, z = 1, w = 0$

17. no solution

19. (a) $x = (11 + 2z)/3, y = (-1 - z)/3$,
    z = any real number
    (b) many possibilities, including $x = 11/3, y = -\frac{1}{3}$,
    $z = 0$ and $x = 13/3, y = -2/3, z = 1$

21. If a row of the matrix has all 0's in the coefficient matrix
    and a nonzero number in the augment, there is no
    solution.

23. $x = 0, y = -z, z$ = any real number

25. no solution

27. $x = 1 - z, y = \frac{1}{2}z, z$ = any real number

29. $x = 1, y = -1, z = 1$

31. $x = 2z - 2, y = 1 + z, z$ = any real number

33. $x = \frac{7}{2} - z, y = -\frac{1}{2}, z$ = any real number

35. $x = \frac{26}{5} - \frac{7}{5}z, y = \frac{4}{5} + \frac{2}{5}z, z$ = any real number

37. $x_1 = 20, x_2 = 60, x_3 = 40$

39. $x_1 = 1, x_2 = 0, x_3 = 1, x_4 = 0$

41. $x = 7/5, y = -3/5, z = w, w$ = any real number

43. no solution

45. $x_1 = 1 - 2x_4 - 3x_5, x_2 = 4 + 5x_4 + 7x_5$,
    $x_3 = -3 - 3x_4 - 5x_5, x_4$ = any real number,
    x_5 = any real number

47. $x = (b_2c_1 - b_1c_2)/(a_1b_2 - a_2b_1)$

49. beef: 2 cups; sirloin: 8 cups

51. (a) $50,000 at 12%, $85,000 at 10%, $100,000 at 8%
    (b) $6000 at 12%, $8500 at 10%, $8000 at 8%

53. AP = 1100, DT = 440, CA = 660

55. AF: 2 oz, FP: 2 oz, NMG: 1 oz

57. 2 of portfolio I, 2 of portfolio II

59. $\frac{3}{8}$ pound of red meat, 6 slices of bread, 4 glasses of milk

61. type I = 3(type IV), type II = 1000 − 2(type IV),
    type III = 500 − type IV, type IV = any integer satisfy-
    ing $0 \le$ type IV ≤ 500

63. bacteria III = any amount satisfying
    $1800 \le$ bacteria III ≤ 2300
    bacteria I = 6900 − 3 (bacteria III)
    bacteria II = $\frac{1}{2}$(bacteria III) − 900

65. (a) $C = 2800 + 0.6R$
    $U = 7000 - R$
    R = any integer satisfying $0 \le R \le 7000$

(b) $R = 1000: C = 3400$
        $U = 6000$
    $R = 2000: C = 4000$
        $U = 5000$

(c) Min $C = 2800$ when $R = 0$ and $U = 7000$

(d) Max $C = 7000$ when $R = 7000$ and $U = 0$

67. There are three possibilities:
    (1) 4 of I and 2 of II
    (2) 5 of I, 1 of II, and 1 of III
    (3) 6 of I and 2 of III

3.4 EXERCISES

1. $\begin{bmatrix} 1 & 0 & 0 \\ 0 & 1 & 0 \\ 0 & 0 & 1 \end{bmatrix}$ 3. yes   5. $\begin{bmatrix} 2 & -7 \\ -1 & 4 \end{bmatrix}$

7. no inverse   9. $\begin{bmatrix} -\frac{1}{10} & \frac{7}{10} \\ \frac{1}{5} & -\frac{2}{5} \end{bmatrix}$

11. $\begin{bmatrix} \frac{1}{3} & 0 & 0 \\ 0 & \frac{1}{3} & 0 \\ 0 & 0 & \frac{1}{3} \end{bmatrix}$ 13. $\begin{bmatrix} -1 & 1 & 0 \\ 1 & 0 & 0 \\ -1 & 0 & 1 \end{bmatrix}$

15. $\begin{bmatrix} \frac{1}{3} & -\frac{1}{3} & \frac{1}{3} \\ -\frac{2}{3} & -\frac{1}{3} & \frac{7}{3} \\ \frac{1}{3} & \frac{2}{3} & -\frac{5}{3} \end{bmatrix}$

17. no inverse   19. no inverse

21. $\begin{bmatrix} 2 & 2 & 0 & 2 & 2 \\ 1 & 0 & 2 & 2 & 1 \\ 0 & 1 & 0 & 2 & 1 \\ 2 & 0 & 2 & 2 & 1 \\ 1 & 0 & 0 & 0 & 2 \end{bmatrix}$ 23. $\begin{bmatrix} 13 \\ 5 \end{bmatrix}$ 25. $\begin{bmatrix} 9 \\ 6 \\ 3 \end{bmatrix}$

27. $\begin{bmatrix} x \\ y \\ z \end{bmatrix} = \begin{bmatrix} 1 \\ 1 \\ 2 \end{bmatrix}$ 29. $x = 2, y = 1$

31. $x = 1, y = 2$ 33. $x = 1, y = 1, z = 1$

35. $x = 1, y = 3, z = 2$

37. $x_1 = 5.6, x_2 = 5.4, x_3 = 3.25, x_4 = 6.1, x_5 = 0.4$

39. (a) -2 (b) inverse exists

41. (a) 0   (b) no inverse

43. (a) -5 (b) inverse exists

45. (a) -19 (b) inverse exists

47. Hang on   49. Answers in back

51. $x_0 = 2400, y_0 = 1200$

53. (a) A = 5.5 mg and B = 8.8 mg for patient I
    (b) A = 10 mg and B = 16 mg for patient II

55. $68,000 at 18%, $77,600 at 10%

57. (a) 2 Deluxe, 8 Premium, 32 Ultimate
    (b) 22 Deluxe, 8 Premium, 22 Ultimate
    $[\text{New}] = [\text{Old}] + 8[\text{Col. 1 of } A^{-1}]$

59. $200,000 at 6%, $300,000 at 8%, $500,000 at 10%

61. (a) $\begin{bmatrix} 0 & 1 & 0 \\ 0 & 0 & 1 \\ 1 & 1 & 1 \end{bmatrix}$ (b) 108

63. (a) $M = \begin{bmatrix} 0 & 1 & 0 \\ 0 & 0 & 1 \\ 1 & 1 & 1 \end{bmatrix}$ (b) 30

3.5 EXERCISES

1. (a) 15 (b) 4   **3.** 8   **5.** 40
7. most: raw materials; least: fuels
9. raw materials, manufacturing, service
11. farm products = 200; machinery = 40
13. utilities = 200; manufacturing = 400
15. (a) agricultural products = 244; oil products = 732
      (b) agricultural products = 0.4; oil products = 1.2
17. (a) mining = 106; manufacturing = 488
      (b) mining = 1.4; manufacturing = 1.2
19. (a)

$\begin{array}{cc} & EC \quad\ C \end{array}$
$A = \begin{bmatrix} 0.3 & 0.6 \\ 0.2 & 0.2 \end{bmatrix} \begin{array}{l} \text{Electronic components} \\ \text{Computers} \end{array}$
      (b) electronic components = 1200; computers = 320
21. (a)

$\begin{array}{cc} & F \qquad O \end{array}$
$A = \begin{bmatrix} 0.30 & 0.04 \\ 0.35 & 0.10 \end{bmatrix} \begin{array}{l} \text{Fishing} \\ \text{Oil} \end{array}$
      (b) fishing = 100; oil = 1250
23. development = \$21,000; promotional = \$12,000
25. engineering = \$15,000; computer = \$13,000
27. fishing = 400; agriculture = 500; mining = 400
29. electronics = 1240; steel = 1260; autos = 720
31. service = 90; manufacturing = 200; agriculture = 100
33. products $= \frac{7}{17}$ households;
      machinery $= \frac{1}{17}$ households
35. government $= \frac{10}{19}$ households;
      industry $= \frac{11}{19}$ households
37. (a)

$\begin{array}{ccc} M & U & H \end{array}$
$A = \begin{bmatrix} 0.5 & 0.4 & 0.3 \\ 0.4 & 0.5 & 0.3 \\ 0.1 & 0.1 & 0.4 \end{bmatrix} \begin{array}{l} \text{Manufacturing} \\ \text{Utilities} \\ \text{Households} \end{array}$
      (b) manufacturing = 3 households;
         utilities = 3 households
39. $\begin{bmatrix} 24 \\ 96 \\ 24 \\ 120 \\ 492 \\ 3456 \end{bmatrix}$ 3456 bolts, 492 braces, 120 panels

41. $\begin{bmatrix} 10 \\ 10 \\ 20 \\ 56 \\ 20 \\ 26 \\ 300 \end{bmatrix}$ 56 2 × 4s, 20 braces, 26 clamps, 300 nails

CHAPTER 3 REVIEW EXERCISES

1. 4   **2.** 0   **3.** A, B **4.** none   **5.** D, F, G, I
6. $\begin{bmatrix} -2 & 5 & 11 & -8 \\ -4 & 0 & 0 & -4 \\ 2 & 2 & -1 & -9 \end{bmatrix}$
7. zero matrix   **8.** order
9. $\begin{bmatrix} 6 & -1 & -9 & 3 \\ 10 & 3 & -1 & 4 \\ -2 & -2 & -2 & 14 \end{bmatrix}$ **10.** $\begin{bmatrix} 3 & -3 \\ 4 & -1 \\ 2 & -6 \\ 1 & -2 \end{bmatrix}$
11. $\begin{bmatrix} 2 & 1 \\ 5 & 1 \end{bmatrix}$ **12.** $\begin{bmatrix} 12 & -6 \\ 15 & 0 \\ 18 & 0 \\ 3 & 9 \end{bmatrix}$ **13.** $\begin{bmatrix} 4 & 0 \\ 0 & 4 \end{bmatrix}$
14. $\begin{bmatrix} 2 & -12 \\ -8 & -22 \end{bmatrix}$ **15.** $\begin{bmatrix} 9 & 20 \\ 4 & 5 \end{bmatrix}$ **16.** $\begin{bmatrix} 5 & 16 \\ 6 & 15 \end{bmatrix}$
17. $\begin{bmatrix} 2 & 37 & 61 & -55 \\ -2 & 9 & -3 & -20 \\ 10 & 10 & -14 & -30 \end{bmatrix}$ **18.** $\begin{bmatrix} 43 & -23 \\ 33 & -12 \\ -13 & 15 \end{bmatrix}$
19. $\begin{bmatrix} 10 & 16 \\ 15 & 25 \\ 18 & 30 \\ 6 & 11 \end{bmatrix}$ **20.** $\begin{bmatrix} 17 & 73 \\ 7 & 28 \end{bmatrix}$ **21.** $\begin{bmatrix} 3 & 7 \\ 23 & 42 \end{bmatrix}$
22. F **23.** F **24.** $\begin{bmatrix} -19 & 12 \\ -8 & 5 \end{bmatrix}$ **25.** F
26. (a) infinitely many solutions (bottom row of 0's)
      (b) $x = 6 + 2z$
         $y = 7 - 3z$
         z = any real number
         Two specific solutions:
         If $z = 0$, then $x = 6$, $y = 7$.
         If $z = 1$, then $x = 8$, $y = 4$.
27. (a) no solution (last row says $0 = 1$)
      (b) no solution
28. (a) Unique coefficient matrix is I_3.
      (b) $x = 0, y = -10, z = 14$
29. $(1, 2, 1)$ **30.** $x = 22, y = 9$
31. $x = -3, y = 3, z = 4$
32. $x = -\frac{3}{2}, y = 7, z = -\frac{11}{2}$ **33.** no solution
34. $x = 2 - 2z, y = -1 - 2z, z$ = any real number

35. $x = -2 + 8z$
$y = -2 + 3z$
$z =$ any real number

36. $x_1 = 1, x_2 = 11, x_3 = -4, x_4 = -5$ **37.** yes

38. $\begin{bmatrix} \frac{1}{2} & \frac{1}{4} \\ \frac{5}{2} & \frac{7}{4} \end{bmatrix}$ **39.** $\begin{bmatrix} -1 & -2 & 8 \\ 1 & 2 & -7 \\ 1 & 1 & -4 \end{bmatrix}$

40. $\begin{bmatrix} 2 & 1 & -2 \\ 7 & 5 & -8 \\ -13 & -9 & 15 \end{bmatrix}$

41. $x = -33, y = 30, z = 19$

42. $x = 4, y = 5, z = -13$

43. $A^{-1} = \begin{bmatrix} -41 & 32 & 5 \\ 17 & -13 & -2 \\ -9 & 7 & 1 \end{bmatrix}; x = 4, y = -2, z = 2$

44. no   **45.** (a) 16   (b) yes, det $\neq 0$

46. (a) 0   (b) no, det $= 0$

47. $\begin{bmatrix} 250 & 140 \\ 480 & 700 \end{bmatrix}$ **48.** $\begin{bmatrix} 1030 & 800 \\ 700 & 1200 \end{bmatrix}$

49. (a) higher in June   (b) higher in July

50. $\begin{matrix} \text{Men} & \text{Women} \\ \begin{bmatrix} 865 & 885 \\ 210 & 270 \end{bmatrix} & \begin{matrix} \text{Robes} \\ \text{Hoods} \end{matrix} \end{matrix}$ **51.** $\begin{bmatrix} 1750 \\ 480 \end{bmatrix} \begin{matrix} \text{Robes} \\ \text{Hoods} \end{matrix}$

52. (a) $\begin{bmatrix} 13{,}500 & 12{,}400 \\ 10{,}500 & 10{,}600 \end{bmatrix}$

(b) Department A should buy from Kink; Department B should buy from Ace.

53. (a) $\begin{bmatrix} 0.20 & 0.30 & 0.50 \end{bmatrix}$

(b) $\begin{bmatrix} 0.013469 \\ 0.013543 \\ 0.006504 \end{bmatrix}$

(c) $\begin{bmatrix} 0.20 & 0.30 & 0.50 \end{bmatrix} \begin{bmatrix} 0.013469 \\ 0.013543 \\ 0.006504 \end{bmatrix} = 0.20(0.013469) +$
$0.30(0.013543) + 0.50(0.006504) = 0.0100087$

(d) The historical return of the portfolio, 0.0100087, is the estimated expected monthly return of the portfolio. This is roughly 1% per month.

54. 400 fast food, 700 software, 200 pharmaceutical

55. (a) $A = 2C, B = 2000 - 4C, C =$ any integer satisfying $0 \leq C \leq 500$
(b) yes; $A = 500, B = 1000, C = 250$
(c) max $A = 1000$ when $B = 0, C = 500$

56. (a) 3 passenger, 4 transport, 4 jumbo
(b) 1 passenger, 3 transport, 7 jumbo
(c) column 2

57. (a) shipping $= 5680$; agriculture $= 1960$
(b) shipping $= 0.4$; agriculture $= 1.8$

58. (a) $\begin{matrix} & \text{S} & \text{C} \\ A = & \begin{bmatrix} 0.1 & 0.1 \\ 0.2 & 0.05 \end{bmatrix} & \begin{matrix} \text{Shoes} \\ \text{Cattle} \end{matrix} \end{matrix}$

(b) shoes $= 1000$; cattle $= 500$

59. mining $= 360$; manufacturing $= 320$; fuels $= 400$

60. government $= \frac{64}{93}$ households; agriculture $= \frac{59}{93}$ households; manufacturing $= \frac{40}{93}$ households

CHAPTER 3 TEST

1. $\begin{bmatrix} 3 & 1 & 5 \\ 1 & 3 & 6 \end{bmatrix}$ **2.** $\begin{bmatrix} -1 & 2 & 2 \\ 1 & -1 & 6 \end{bmatrix}$

3. $\begin{bmatrix} -12 & -16 & -155 \\ 5 & 12 & 87 \end{bmatrix}$ **4.** $\begin{bmatrix} 23 & 6 \\ 182 & 45 \\ 21 & 1 \end{bmatrix}$

5. $\begin{bmatrix} 0 & -7 \\ 26 & 1 \end{bmatrix}$ **6.** $\begin{bmatrix} -43 & -46 & -207 \\ 39 & 30 & -77 \\ 17 & 5 & -216 \end{bmatrix}$

7. $\begin{bmatrix} -2 & 3/2 \\ 1 & -1/2 \end{bmatrix}$ **8.** $\begin{bmatrix} -3 & 2 & 2 \\ 1 & 0 & -1 \\ 1/2 & -1/2 & 0 \end{bmatrix}$

9. $\begin{bmatrix} 5 \\ 14 \\ 15 \end{bmatrix}$ **10.** $x = -0.5, y = 0.5, z = 2.5$

11. $x = 4 - 1.8z, y = 0.2z, z =$ any real number

12. no solution   **13.** $x = 2, y = 2, z = 0, w = -2$

14. $x = 6w - 0.5, y = 0.5 - w, z = 2.5 - 3w, w =$ any real number

15. (a) $B = \$45{,}000, E = \$40{,}000$
(b) $\$0 \leq H \leq \$25{,}000$ (so $B \geq 0$)
(c) min $E = \$20{,}000$ when $H = \$0$ and $B = \$75{,}000$

16. (a) $\begin{bmatrix} 0.08 & 0.22 & 0.12 \\ 0.10 & 0.08 & 0.19 \\ 0.05 & 0.07 & 0.09 \\ 0.10 & 0.26 & 0.15 \\ 0.12 & 0.04 & 0.24 \end{bmatrix}$

(b) 0.08, 0.22, 0.12 consumed by carnivores 1, 2, 3
(c) plant 5 by 1, plant 4 by 2, plant 5 by 3

17. (a) $\begin{bmatrix} 1000 & 4000 & 2000 & 1000 \end{bmatrix}$
(b) $\begin{bmatrix} 45{,}000 & 55{,}000 & 90{,}000 & 70{,}000 \end{bmatrix}$

(c) $\begin{bmatrix} 5 \\ 3 \\ 4 \\ 4 \end{bmatrix}$ (d) $[\$1{,}030{,}000]$ (e) $\begin{matrix} & \$ \\ A & \begin{bmatrix} 65 \\ 145 \\ 125 \\ 135 \end{bmatrix} \\ B & \\ C & \\ D & \end{matrix}$

18. (a) 121, 46, 247, 95, 261, 99, 287, 111, 179, 69, 169, 64
(b) Frodo lives

19. growth, 2000; blue-chip, 400; utility, 400

20. (a) agriculture $= 245$; minerals $= 235$
(b) agriculture $= 7$; minerals $= 1$
(c) agriculture $= 0.5$; minerals $= 1.5$

21. profit $=$ households
nonprofit $= \frac{2}{3}$ households

22.

$$\begin{array}{cccc} \text{Ag} & \text{M} & \text{F} & \text{S} \\ \begin{bmatrix} 0.2 & 0.1 & 0.1 & 0.1 \\ 0.3 & 0.2 & 0.2 & 0.2 \\ 0.2 & 0.2 & 0.3 & 0.3 \\ 0.1 & 0.4 & 0.2 & 0.2 \end{bmatrix} & & & \begin{array}{l} \text{Agriculture} \\ \text{Machinery} \\ \text{Fuel} \\ \text{Steel} \end{array} \end{array}$$

23. agriculture: 5000; machinery: 8000; fuel: 8000; steel: 7000

24. agriculture: $\frac{520}{699}$ households; steel: $\frac{236}{233}$ households; fuel: $\frac{159}{233}$ households

4.1 EXERCISES

1.

3.

5.

7. $(0, 0), (20, 10), (0, 15), (25, 0)$

9. $(5, 0), (15, 0), (6, 9), (2, 6)$

11. $(0, 5), (1, 2), (3, 1), (6, 0)$

13.

15.

17.

19.

21.

23.

25.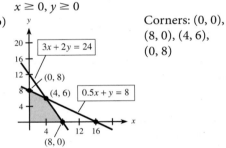

27. (a) Let $x =$ the number of deluxe models and $y =$ the number of economy models.
$3x + 2y \le 24$
$\frac{1}{2}x + y \le 8$
$x \ge 0, y \ge 0$

(b) Corners: $(0, 0),$ $(8, 0), (4, 6),$ $(0, 8)$

29. (a) Let $x =$ the number of cord-type trimmers and $y =$ the number of cordless trimmers. Constraints are
$x + y \le 300$
$2x + 4y \le 800$
$x \ge 0, y \ge 0$

(b)

31. (a) Let $x =$ the number of minutes on finance programs and $y =$ the number of minutes on sports programs.
$$7x + 2y \geq 30$$
$$4x + 12y \geq 28$$
$$x \geq 0, y \geq 0$$

(b)

33. (a) Let $x =$ the number of minutes of radio and $y =$ the number of minutes of television. Constraints are
$$x + \quad y \geq 80$$
$$0.006x + 0.09y \geq 2.16$$
$$x \geq 0, y \geq 0$$

(b)

35. (a) Let $x =$ the number of pounds of regular hot dogs and $y =$ the number of pounds of all-beef hot dogs.
$$0.18x + 0.75y \leq 1020$$
$$0.2x \ + 0.2y \ \geq 500$$
$$0.3x \qquad \leq 600$$

(b)

$A = (2000, 500)$
$B = (2000, 880)$
$C = (1500, 1000)$

4.2 EXERCISES

1. max $= 76$ at $(4, 4)$; min $= 0$ at $(0, 0)$
3. no max; min $= 11$ at $(1, 3)$
5. $(0, 0), (0, 20), (10, 18), (15, 10), (20, 0)$;
max $= 66$ at $(10, 18)$; min $= 0$ at $(0, 0)$
7. $(0, 60), (10, 30), (20, 20), (70, 0)$; min $= 100$ at $(20, 20)$; no max
9. max $= 1260$ at $x = 12, y = 18$

11. min $= 66$ at $x = 0, y = 3$ **13.** max $= 22$ at $(2, 4)$
15. max $= 30$ on line between $(0, 5)$ and $(3, 4)$
17. min $= 32$ at $(2, 3)$ **19.** min $= 9$ at $(2, 3)$
21. max $= 10$ at $(2, 4)$ **23.** min $= 3100$ at $(40, 60)$
25. If $x =$ the number of deluxe models and $y =$ the number of economy models, then max $= \$132$ at $(4, 6)$.
27. If $x =$ the number of cord-type trimmers and $y =$ the number of cordless trimmers, then max $= \$9000$ at any point with integer coordinates on the segment joining $(0, 200)$ and $(200, 100)$, such as $(20, 190)$.
29. radio $= 60$, TV $= 20$, min $C = \$16,000$
31. inkjet $= 45$, laser $= 25$, max $P= \$3300$
33. 250 fish: 150 bass and 100 trout
35. (a) Max $P = \$315,030$ when corn $= 3749.5$ acres and soybeans $= 2251.5$ acres
(b) Max $P = \$315,240$ when corn $= 3746$ acres and soybeans $= 2262$ acres
(c) $\$30$/acre
37. 30 days for factory 1 and 20 days for factory 2; minimum cost $= \$700,000$
39. 60 days for location I and 70 days for location II; minimum cost $= \$86,000$
41. reg $= 2000$ lb; all-beef $= 880$ lb; maximum profit $= \$1328$
43. From Pittsburgh: 20 to Blairsville, 40 to Youngstown; From Erie: 15 to Blairsville, 0 to Youngstown; minimum cost $= \$1540$
45. (a) $R = \$366,000$ with 6 satellite and 17 full-service branches
(b) Branches: used 23 of 25 possible; 2 not used (slack)
New employees: hired 120 of 120 possible; 0 not hired (slack)
Budget: used all $\$2.98$ million; $\$0$ not used (slack)
(c) Additional new employees and additional budget. These items are completely used in the current optimal solution; more could change and improve the optimal solution.
(d) Additional branches. The current optimal solution does not use all those allotted; more would just add to the extras.

4.3 EXERCISES

1. $3x + 5y + s_1 = 15, 3x + 6y + s_2 = 20$
3. $\begin{bmatrix} 2 & 5 & 1 & 0 & 0 & | & 400 \\ 1 & 2 & 0 & 1 & 0 & | & 175 \\ -3 & -7 & 0 & 0 & 1 & | & 0 \end{bmatrix}$

5. $\begin{bmatrix} 2 & 7 & 9 & 1 & 0 & 0 & 0 & | & 100 \\ 6 & 5 & 1 & 0 & 1 & 0 & 0 & | & 145 \\ 1 & 2 & 7 & 0 & 0 & 1 & 0 & | & 90 \\ -2 & -5 & -2 & 0 & 0 & 0 & 1 & | & 0 \end{bmatrix}$

7. one slack variable for each constraint row (above the last row)

9. (a) $x_1 = 0, x_2 = 0, s_1 = 200, s_2 = 400, s_3 = 350, f = 0$

(b) not complete

(c) $\begin{bmatrix} \boxed{10} & 27 & 1 & 0 & 0 & 0 & 200 \\ 4 & 51 & 0 & 1 & 0 & 0 & 400 \\ 15 & 27 & 0 & 0 & 1 & 0 & 350 \\ -8 & -7 & 0 & 0 & 0 & 1 & 0 \end{bmatrix}$

$\frac{1}{10}R_1 \to R_1$, then $-4R_1 + R_2 \to R_2$,

$-15R_1 + R_3 \to R_3, 8R_1 + R_4 \to R_4$

11. (a) $x_1 = 0, x_2 = 45, s_1 = 14, s_2 = 0, f = 75$

(b) not complete

(c) $\begin{bmatrix} \boxed{2} & 0 & 1 & -\frac{3}{4} & 0 & 14 \\ 3 & 1 & 0 & \frac{1}{3} & 0 & 45 \\ -6 & 0 & 0 & 3 & 1 & 75 \end{bmatrix}$

$\frac{1}{2}R_1 \to R_1$, then $-3R_1 + R_2 \to R_2, 6R_1 + R_3 \to R_3$

13. (a) $x_1 = 24, x_2 = 0, x_3 = 21,$

$s_1 = 16, s_2 = 0, s_3 = 0, f = 780$

(b) complete (no part (c))

15. (a) $x_1 = 0, x_2 = 0, x_3 = 12,$

$s_1 = 4, s_2 = 6, s_3 = 0, f = 150$

(b) not complete

(c) $\begin{bmatrix} 4 & 4 & 1 & 0 & 0 & 2 & 0 & 12 \\ \boxed{2} & \boxed{4} & 0 & 1 & 0 & 1 & 0 & 4 \\ -3 & -11 & 0 & 0 & 1 & -1 & 0 & 6 \\ -3 & -3 & 0 & 0 & 0 & 4 & 1 & 150 \end{bmatrix}$

Either circled number may act as the next pivot entry, but only one of them. If 4 is used,

$\frac{1}{4}R_2 \to R_2$, then $-4R_2 + R_1 \to R_1,$

$11R_2 + R_3 \to R_3, 3R_2 + R_4 \to R_4$. If 2 is used,

$\frac{1}{2}R_2 \to R_2$, then $-4R_2 + R_1 \to R_1,$

$3R_2 + R_3 \to R_3, 3R_2 + R_4 \to R_4.$

17. (a) $x_1 = 0, x_2 = 0, x_3 = 12,$

$s_1 = 5, s_2 = 0, s_3 = 6, f = 120$

(b) no solution (no part (c))

19. $x = 11, y = 9; f = 20$

21. $x = 0, y = 14, z = 11; f = 525$

23. $x = 50, y = 10; f = 100$. Multiple solutions are possible.

Next pivot is circled.

$\begin{bmatrix} 1 & 0 & 3 & 0 & 6 & 0 & 50 \\ 0 & 0 & 4 & 1 & -4 & 0 & 6 \\ 0 & 1 & -2 & 0 & \boxed{2} & 0 & 10 \\ 0 & 0 & 9 & 0 & 0 & 1 & 100 \end{bmatrix}$

25. $x = 0, y = 5; f = 50$

27. $x = 4, y = 3; f = 17$

29. $x = 4, y = 3; f = 11$

31. $x = 0, y = 2, z = 5; f = 40$

33. $x = 15, y = 15, z = 25; f = 780$

35. $x = 6, y = 2, z = 26; f = 206$

37. $x_1 = 36, x_2 = 24; x_3 = 0, x_4 = 8; f = 1728$

39. $x = 8, y = 16; f = 32$

41. no solution

43. $x = 0, y = 50$ or $x = 40, y = 40; f = 600$

45. (a) $\begin{bmatrix} 1 & 1 & 1 & 0 & 0 & 60 \\ 1 & 3 & 0 & 1 & 0 & 120 \\ -40 & 60 & 0 & 0 & 1 & 0 \end{bmatrix}$

(b) Maximum profit is \$3000 with 30 inkjet and 30 laser printers.

47. 300 style-891, 450 style-917, maximum $P = \$5175$

49. Maximum profit is \$3900 with 11 axles and 2 wheels

51. premium and light = 175 each; maximum $P = \$35{,}000$

53. 21 newspapers, 13 radio; 230,000 exposures

55. medium 1 = 10, medium 2 = 10, medium 3 = 12

57. \$1650 profit with 46 A, 20 B, 6 C

59. 8000 Regular, 0 Special, and 1000 Kitchen Magic; maximum profit = \$32,000

61. (a) 26 one-bedroom; 40 two-bedroom; 48 three-bedroom

(b) \$100,200 per month

63. 20-in. LCDs = 40, 42-in. LCDs =115, 42-in. plasma = 0, 50-in. plasma = 38; max $P = \$12{,}540$

4.4 EXERCISES

1. (a) $\begin{bmatrix} 5 & 2 & 16 \\ 1 & 2 & 8 \\ 4 & 5 & g \end{bmatrix}$ transpose $= \begin{bmatrix} 5 & 1 & 4 \\ 2 & 2 & 5 \\ 16 & 8 & g \end{bmatrix}$

(b) maximize $f = 16x_1 + 8x_2$ subject to $5x_1 + x_2 \leq 4, 2x_1 + 2x_2 \leq 5, x_1 \geq 0, x_2 \geq 0.$

3. (a) $\begin{bmatrix} 1 & 2 & 30 \\ 1 & 4 & 50 \\ 7 & 3 & g \end{bmatrix}$ transpose $= \begin{bmatrix} 1 & 1 & 7 \\ 2 & 4 & 3 \\ 30 & 50 & g \end{bmatrix}$

(b) maximize $f = 30x_1 + 50x_2$ subject to $x_1 + x_2 \leq 7, 2x_1 + 4x_2 \leq 3, x_1 \geq 0, x_2 \geq 0$

5. (a) $y_1 = 7, y_2 = 4, y_3 = 0$; min $g = 452$

(b) $x_1 = 15, x_2 = 0, x_3 = 29$; max $f = 452$

7. maximize $f = 11x_1 + 11x_2 + 16x_3$ subject to

$2x_1 + x_2 + x_3 \leq 2$

$x_1 + 3x_2 + 4x_3 \leq 10$

primal: $y_1 = 16, y_2 = 0; g = 32$ (min)

dual: $x_1 = 0, x_2 = 0, x_3 = 2; f = 32$ (max)

9. maximize $f = 11x_1 + 12x_2 + 6x_3$ subject to

$4x_1 + 3x_2 + 3x_3 \leq 3$

$x_1 + 2x_2 + x_3 \leq 1$

primal: $y_1 = 2, y_2 = 3; g = 9$ (min)

dual: $x_1 = 3/5, x_2 = 1/5, x_3 = 0; f = 9$ (max)

11. min = 28 at $x = 2, y = 0, z = 1$

13. $y_1 = 2/5, y_2 = 1/5, y_3 = 1/5; g = 16$ (min)

15. (a) minimize $g = 120y_1 + 50y_2$ subject to

$3y_1 + y_2 \geq 40$

$2y_1 + y_2 \geq 20$

(b) primal: $x_1 = 40, x_2 = 0, f = 1600$ (max)

dual: $y_1 = 40/3, y_2 = 0, g = 1600$ (min)

17. min = 480 at $y_1 = 0, y_2 = 0, y_3 = 16$

19. min = 90 at $y_1 = 0, y_2 = 3, y_3 = 1, y_4 = 0$

21. Atlanta = 150 hr, Fort Worth = 50 hr; min C = \$210,000

23. line 1 for 4 hours, line 2 for 1 hour; \$1200

25. A = 12 weeks, B = 0 weeks, C = 0 weeks;
cost = $12,000

27. factory 1: 50 days, factory 2: 0 days; min cost $500,000

29. 105 minutes on radio, nothing on TV; min cost $10,500

31. (a) Georgia package = 10
Union package = 20
Pacific package = 5
(b) $4630

33. (a) min cost = $16
(b) Many solutions are possible; two are: 16 oz of food I,
0 oz of food II, 0 oz of food III and 11 oz of food I,
1 oz of food II, 0 oz of food III.

35. Mon. = 8, Tues. = 0, Wed. = 5, Thurs. = 4,
Fri. = 5, Sat. = 0, Sun. = 3; min = 25

4.5 EXERCISES

1. $-3x + y \le -5$ **3.** $-6x - y \le -40$

5. (a) maximize $f = 2x + 3y$ subject to
$7x + 4y \le 28$
$3x - y \le -2$
$x \ge 0, y \ge 0$
(b) $\begin{bmatrix} 7 & 4 & 1 & 0 & 0 & | & 28 \\ 3 & -1 & 0 & 1 & 0 & | & -2 \\ -2 & -3 & 0 & 0 & 1 & | & 0 \end{bmatrix}$

7. (a) Maximize $-g = -3x - 8y$ subject to
$4x - 5y \le 50$
$x + y \le 80$
$x - 2y \le -4$
$x \ge 0, y \ge 0$
(b) $\begin{bmatrix} 4 & -5 & 1 & 0 & 0 & 0 & | & 50 \\ 1 & 1 & 0 & 1 & 0 & 0 & | & 80 \\ 1 & -2 & 0 & 0 & 1 & 0 & | & -4 \\ 3 & 8 & 0 & 0 & 0 & 1 & | & 0 \end{bmatrix}$

9. $x = 6, y = 8, z = 12; f = 120$

11. $x = 10, y = 17; f = 57$

13. $x = 5, y = 7; f = 31$

15. $x = 5, y = 15; f = 45$

17. $x = 10, y = 20; f = 120$

19. $x = 20, y = 10, z = 0; f = 40$

21. $x = 5, y = 0, z = 3; f = 22$

23. $x = 70, y = 0, z = 40; f = 2100$

25. $x_1 = 20, x_2 = 10, x_3 = 20, x_4 = 80,$
$x_5 = 10, x_6 = 10; f = 3250$

27. regular = 2000 lb; beef = 880 lb; profit = $1328

29. 400 filters, 300 housing units; min cost = $5145

31. Produce 200 of each at Monaca; produce 300 commercial components and 550 domestic furnaces at Hamburg;
profit = $355,250

33. Produce 200 of each at Monaca; produce 300 commercial components and 550 domestic furnaces at Hamburg;
cost = $337,750

35. I = 3 million, II = 0, III = 3 million;
cost = $180,000

37. 2000 footballs, 0 soccer balls, 0 volleyballs; $60,000

CHAPTER 4 REVIEW EXERCISES

1. **2.**

3. **4.**
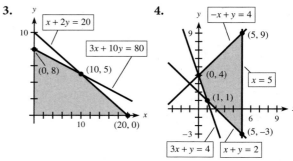

5. max = 25 at (5, 10); min = −12 at (12, 0)

6. max = 194 at (17, 23); min = 104 at (8, 14)

7. max = 140 at (20, 0); min = −52 at (20, 32)

8. min = 115 at (5, 7); no max exists, f can be made
arbitrarily large

9. $f = 66$ at (6, 6)   **10.** $f = 43$ at (7, 9)

11. $g = 24$ at (3, 3)   **12.** $g = 84$ at (64, 4)

13. $f = 76$ at (12, 8)   **14.** $f = 75$ at (15, 15)

15. $f = 168$ at (12, 7)   **16.** $f = 260$ at (60, 20)

17. $f = 360$ at (40, 30)   **18.** $f = 80$ at (20, 10)

19. $f = 640$ on the line between (160, 0) and (90, 70)

20. no solution   **21.** $g = 32$ at $y_1 = 2, y_2 = 3$

22. $g = 20$ at $y_1 = 4, y_2 = 2$

23. $g = 7$ at $y_1 = 1, y_2 = 5$

24. $g = 1180$ at $y_1 = 80, y_2 = 20$

25. $f = 165$ at $x = 20, y = 21$

26. $f = 54$ at $x = 6, y = 5$ **27.** $f = 270$ at (5, 3, 2)

28. $g = 140$ at $y_1 = 0, y_2 = 20, y_3 = 20$

29. $g = 1400$ at $y_1 = 0, y_2 = 100, y_3 = 100$

30. $f = 156$ at $x = 15, y = 2$

31. $f = 31$ at $x = 4, y = 5$ **32.** $f = 4380$ at (40, 10, 0, 0)

33. $f = 1000$ at $x_1 = 25, x_2 = 62.5, x_3 = 0, x_4 = 12.5$

34. $g = 2020$ at $x_1 = 0, x_2 = 100, x_3 = 80, x_4 = 20$

35. $P = \$14{,}750$ when 110 large and 75 small swing sets
are made

36. $C = \$300{,}000$ when factory 1 operates 30 days, factory
2 operates 25 days

37. $P = \$320$; I = 40, II = 20

38. $P = \$420$; Jacob's ladders = 90,
locomotive engines = 30

39. (a) Let x_1 = the number of 27-in LCD sets,
x_2 = the number of 32-in LCD sets,
x_3 = the number of 42-in LCD sets,
x_4 = the number of 42-in plasma sets.

(b) Maximize $P = 80x_1 + 120x_2 + 160x_3 + 200x_4$
subject to
$$8x_1 + 10x_2 + 12x_3 + 15x_4 \le 1870$$
$$2x_1 + 4x_2 + 4x_3 + 4x_4 \le 530$$
$$x_1 + x_2 + x_3 + x_4 \le 200$$
$$x_3 + x_4 \le 100$$
$$x_2 \le 120$$

(c) $x_1 = 15, x_2 = 25, x_3 = 0, x_4 = 100$;
max profit = \$24,200

40. food I = 0 oz; food II = 3 oz; $C =$ \$0.60 (min)
41. cost = \$5.60; A = 40 lb, B = 0 lb
42. cost = \$8500; A = 20 days, B = 15 days, C = 0 days
43. pancake mix = 8000 lb; cake mix = 3000 lb;
profit = \$3550
44. Texas: 55 desks, 65 computer tables; Louisiana:
75 desks, 65 computer tables; cost = \$4245
45. Midland: grade 1 = 486.5 tons, grade 2 = 0 tons;
Donora: grade 1 = 13.5 tons, grade 2 = 450 tons;
Cost = \$90,635

CHAPTER 4 TEST

1. max = 120 at $(0, 24)$
2. (a)
$$-2R_2 + R_1 \to R_1 \quad -3R_2 + R_3 \to R_3$$
(b) A; pivot column is column 3, but new pivot is
undefined.
(c) B; $x_1 = 40, x_2 = 12, x_3 = 0, s_1 = 0,$
$s_2 = 20, s_3 = 0; f = 170$; This solution is not
optimal; the next pivot is the 3-6 entry.

3. (a)

(b)

(c)

4. maximize $f = 100x_1 + 120x_2$ subject to
$$3x_1 + 4x_2 \le 2$$
$$5x_1 + 6x_2 \le 3$$
$$x_1 + 3x_2 \le 5$$
$$x_1 \ge 0, \ x_2 \ge 0$$

5. min = 21 at $(1, 8)$; no max exists, f can be made
arbitrarily large
6. min = 136 at $(28, 52)$
7. maximize $-g = -7x - 3y$ subject to
$$x - 4y \le -4$$
$$x - y \le 5$$
$$2x + 3y \le 30$$
8. max: $x_1 = 17, x_2 = 15, x_3 = 0; f = 658$ (max)
min: $y_1 = 4, y_2 = 18, y_3 = 0; g = 658$ (min)
9. max: = 6300 at $x = 90, y = 0$
10. max = 1200 at $x = 0, y = 16, z = 12$
11. If $x =$ the number of barrels of beer and $y =$ the
number of barrels of ale, then maximize $P = 35x + 30y$
subject to
$$3x + 2y \le 1200$$
$$2x + 2y \le 1000$$
$P =$ \$16,000 (max) at $x = 200, y = 300$
12. If $x =$ the number of day calls and $y =$ the number of
evening calls, then minimize $C = 3x + 4y$ subject to
$$0.3x + 0.3y \ge 150$$
$$0.1x + 0.3y \ge 120$$
$$x \le 0.5(x + y)$$
$C =$ \$1850 (min) at $x = 150, y = 350$
13. max profit = \$5000 when product 1 = 25 tons,
product 2 = 62.5 tons, product 3 = 0 tons,
product 4 = 12.5 tons

5.1 EXERCISES

1. (a) 3.162278   (b) 0.01296525
3. (a) 1.44225   (b) 7.3891
5.   7.

9.

$y = \left(\dfrac{4}{5}\right)^x$

11.

$y = 5^{-x}$

13.

$y = 2e^x$

15.

$y = 3^{-2x}$

17. (a) $y = 3(2.5)^{-x}$

(b) Decay. They have the form $y = C \cdot b^x$ for $0 < b < 1$
or $y = C \cdot a^{-x}$ for $a > 1$.

(c) The graphs are identical.

19. (a) and (b)

$y = 2(1.5)^{-x}$

$y = 2\left(\dfrac{2}{3}\right)^x$

(c) $(1.5)^{-x} = \left(\dfrac{3}{2}\right)^{-x} = \left(\dfrac{2}{3}\right)^x$

21. $y = \left(\dfrac{5}{4}\right)^{-x}$

23. All graphs have the same basic shape. For larger positive values of k, the graphs fall more sharply. For positive values of k nearer 0, the graphs fall more slowly.

$f(x) = e^{-0.5x}$ $f(x) = e^{-x}$ $f(x) = e^{-0.1x}$

$f(x) = e^{-x}$ $f(x) = e^{-5x}$ $f(x) = e^{-2x}$

25. $y = f(x) + C$ is the same graph as $y = f(x)$ but shifted
C units on the y-axis.

$f(x) = 4^x + 6$ $f(x) = 4^x$

$f(x) = 4^x + 3$

$f(x) = 4^x - 5$ $f(x) = 4^x - 2$

27. (a)

$f(x) = 100(1 + e^{-x})$

$f(x) = 50(1 + e^{-x})$

$f(x) = 10(1 + e^{-x})$

(b) As c changes, the
y-intercept and the
asymptote change.

29. \$1884.54

31.

$S = 1000e^{0.1n}$

33. At time 0, the concentration is 0. The concentration rises
rapidly for the first 4 minutes and then tends toward
100% as time nears 10 minutes.

$y = 100(1 - e^{-0.462t})$

35.

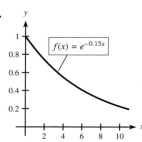

$f(x) = e^{-0.15x}$

As the TV sets age
(x increases), the fraction
of sets still in service
declines.

37.

$N = 4.1(1.02)^t$

39.

$N = 4.1(1.05)^t$

41. (a) Growth; $e > 1$ and the exponent is positive for $t > 0$.

(b)

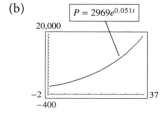

$P = 2969e^{0.051t}$

43. The linear model fails in 2007, giving a negative number of processors.

45. (a) $y = 492.4(1.070^x)$
(b) \$24,608 billion is an overestimate   (c) 2021

47. (a) $y = 2.74(1.042^x)$
(b) 284.1
(c) 2015

49. (a) $y = 98.221(0.870^x)$
(b) decay; base satisfies $0 < b < 1$
(c) 1.5

5.2 EXERCISES

1. $2^4 = 16$ **3.** $4^{1/2} = 2$ **5.** $x = 81$ **7.** $x = \frac{1}{4}$

9. $x = 16$ **11.** $x = 26.75$ **13.** $x \approx 2.013$

15. $\log_2 32 = 5$

17. $\log_4\left(\frac{1}{4}\right) = -1$ **19.** $3x + 5 = \ln(0.55)$; $x \approx -1.866$

21.

23.

25.

27. (a) 3   (b) -1 **29.** x **31.** 3

33. (a) 4.9   (b) 0.4   (c) 12.4   (d) 0.9

35. $\log x - \log(x + 1)$ **37.** $\log_7 x + \frac{1}{3}\log_7(x + 4)$

39. $\ln(x/y)$ **41.** $\log_5\left[x^{1/2}(x + 1)\right]$

43. equivalent; Properties V and III

45. not equivalent; $\log\left(\sqrt[3]{8}/5\right)$

47. (a)

(b) For each c, the domain is $x > c$ and the vertical asymptote is at $x = c$.
(c) Each x-intercept is at $x = c + 1$.
(d) The graph of $y = f(x - c)$ is the graph of $y = f(x)$ shifted c units on the x-axis.

49. (a) 4.0875   (b) -0.1544

51.

53.

55. If $\log_a M = u$ and $\log_a N = v$, then $a^u = M$ and $a^v = N$. Therefore, $\log_a(M/N) = \log_a(a^u/a^v) = \log_a(a^{u-v}) = u - v = \log_a M - \log_a N$.

57. 63.1 times as severe   **59.** 3.2 times as severe

61. 40

63. $L = 10 \log(I/I_0)$

65. 0.1 and 1×10^{-14}

67. $\text{pH} = \log\dfrac{1}{[\text{H}^+]} = \log 1 - \log[\text{H}^+] = -\log[\text{H}^+]$

69. $\log_{1.02} 2 = 4t$; $t \approx 8.75$ years

71. (a)

(b) 83.6 million   (c) 2023

73. $y = -3130.317 + 4056.819 \ln x$; \$11,293

75. (a) $y = 47.725 + 12.785 \ln x$
(b) reasonably good fit   (c) 88.9%

5.3 EXERCISES

1. $\frac{5}{3}$ **3.** 2.943   **5.** 9.390   **7.** 18.971   **9.** 151.413

11. 6.679   **13.** $10^5 = 100,000$ **15.** 7

17. $5e^{10}$ **19.** $\dfrac{10^6}{2} = 5 \cdot 10^5$ **21.** 3

23. (a)

(b) Different c-values change the y-intercept and how the graph approaches the asymptote.

25. (a) 2038   (b) 4.9 months
27. (a) 13.86 years   (b) $105,850.00
29. 24.5 years   **31.** 128,402
33. (a) 2015
  (b) The intent of such plan would be to reduce future increases in health care expenditures. A new model might not be exponential, or, if it were, it would be one that rose more gently.
35. (a) $4.98   (b) 8   **37.** $502   **39.** $420.09
41. $2706.71   **43.** (a) $10,100.31   (b) 6.03 years
45. (a) $5469.03
  (b) 7 years, 9 months (approximately)
47. (a) $142.5 billion   (b) 35.3 years, in 2021
  (c) the Financial Crisis of 2008
49. (a) 109.99, 307.66; It would have taken $109.99 in 1990, and will take $307.66 in 2015, to buy what cost $100 in 1982.
  (b) 2022
51. $x \approx 993.3$; about 993 units
53. (a) 600   (b) 2119   (c) 3000
  (d)

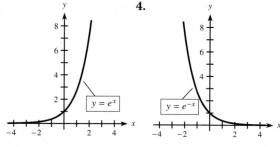

55. (a) 10   (b) 2.5 years
57. (a) 37   (b) 1.5 hours
59. (a) 52   (b) the 10th day
61. (a) 2%   (b) 20 months ($x = 19.6$)
63. (a) 0.23 km^3 (b) 5.9 years
65. (a) 160.48 million
  (b) $t \approx 84.7$; in 2025
67. (a) $y = \dfrac{80.8}{1 + 0.2e^{-0.324x}}$
  (b) 80.69%
  (c) in 2023

CHAPTER 5 REVIEW EXERCISES

1. (a) $\log_2 y = x$ (b) $\log_3 2x = y$
2. (a) $7^{-2} = \frac{1}{49}$ (b) $4^{-1} = x$
3.

4.

5.

6.

7.

8.

9.

10.

11.

12.

13. 0   **14.** 3   **15.** $\frac{1}{2}$ **16.** -1 **17.** 8
18. 1   **19.** 5   **20.** 3.15   **21.** -2.7
22. 0.6   **23.** 5.1   **24.** 15.6   **25.** $\log y + \log z$
26. $\frac{1}{2}\ln(x+1) - \frac{1}{2}\ln x$ **27.** no   **28.** -2
29. 5   **30.** 1   **31.** 0   **32.** 3.4939   **33.** -1.5845
34.

35.

36. $x = 1.5$ **37.** $x \approx 51.224$
38. $x \approx 28.175$ **39.** $x \approx 40.236$
40. $x = 8$ **41.** $x = 14$ **42.** $x = 6$
43. Growth exponential, because the general outline has the same shape as a growth exponential.

44. Decay exponential, because the general shape is similar to the graph of a decay exponential, and the number will diminish toward 0.

45. (a) $32,627.66

(b)

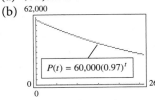

$$P(t) = 60,000(0.97)^t$$

46. (a) $y = 266.4(1.074^x)$ (b) $4598 billion

(c) 2017

47. (a) $11,293   (b)

$$y = -3130.3 + 4056.8 \ln(x)$$

48. (a) $y = -11.4 + 19.0 \ln x$

(b) 68.0%   (c) 2023

49. (a) -3.9 (b) $0.14B_0$ (c) $0.004B_0$ (d) yes

50. (a) 27,441   (b) 12 weeks

51. 1366   **52.** 5.8 years

53. (a) $5532.77   (b) 5.13 years

54. logistic, because the graph begins like an exponential function but then grows at a slower rate

55. (a) 3000   (b) 8603   (c) 10,000

56. (a)

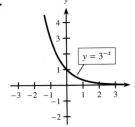

$$y = \frac{5000}{1 + 1000e^{-0.8x}}$$

(b) 5   (c) 4970   (d) 10 days

CHAPTER 5 TEST

1.

$y = 5^x$

2.

$y = 3^{-x}$

3.

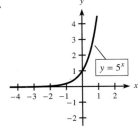

$y = \log_5 x$

4.

$y = \ln x$

5.

$y = 3^{0.5x}$

6.

$y = \ln(0.5x)$

7.

$y = e^{2x}$

8.

$y = \log_7 x$

9. 54.598   **10.** 0.100   **11.** 1.386

12. 1.322   **13.** $x = 7^{3.1}, x \approx 416.681$

14. $\log_3(27) = 2x; x = 1.5$ **15.** $x \approx 0.203$

16. $x = 8$ **17.** 3   **18.** x^4 **19.** 3   **20.** x^2

21. $\ln M + \ln N$ **22.** $\ln(x^3 - 1) - \ln(x + 2)$

23. $\dfrac{\ln(x^3 + 1)}{\ln 4} \approx 0.721 \ln(x^3 + 1)$

24. $x \approx 38.679$

25. a decay exponential

26. With years on the horizontal axis, a growth exponential would probably be the best model.

27. (a) $3363.3 billion

(b) about 11.2 years

28. about 6.2 months

29. (a) about $16,716 billion

(b) $x \approx 39.8$; in 2025

30. (a) exponential; data continue to rise rapidly

(b) $y = 165.550(1.055^x)$

(c) $819.42 billion

6.1 EXERCISES

1. $r = 0.0625, I = 250, P = 1000, t = 4$

3. $P = 8000, S = 9600, I = 1600, r = 0.05, t = 4$

5. (a) $9600   (b) $19,600

7. (a) $30   (b) $1030

9. $864   **11.** $3850   **13.** 13%

15. (a) 5.13%   (b) 4.29%   **17.** $1631.07

19. $12,000   **21.** 10 years   **23.** pay on time

25. (a) $2120   (b) $2068.29 (nearest cent)

27. 3, 6, 9, 12, 15, 18, 21, 24, 27, 30

29. $-\frac{1}{3}, \frac{1}{5}, -\frac{1}{7}, \frac{1}{9}, -\frac{1}{11}, \frac{1}{13}$ **31.** $-1, -\frac{1}{4}, -\frac{1}{15}, 0; a_{10} = \frac{1}{20}$

33. (a) $d = 3, a_1 = 2$ (b) 11, 14, 17

35. (a) $d = \frac{3}{2}, a_1 = 3$ (b) $\frac{15}{2}, 9, \frac{21}{2}$

37. -35 **39.** 203   **41.** 2185   **43.** 1907.5

45. −15,862.5 **47.** 21, 34, 55 **49.** $4800
51. the job starting at $40,000 ($58,000 versus $57,600)
53. (a) $3000 (b) $4500 (c) plan II, by $1500
  (d) $10,000 (e) $13,500 (f) plan II, by $3500
  (g) plan II

6.2 EXERCISES

(Minor differences may occur because of rounding.)
 1. $S = 3216.87$ = future value; principal = 2000;
   rate = 0.02; periods = 24
 3. $P = 6049.97$ = principal; future value = 25,000;
   rate = 0.03; periods = 48
 5. (a) 8% (b) 7 (c) 2% = 0.02 (d) 28
 7. (a) 9% (b) 5 (c) $\left(\frac{9}{12}\right)$% = 0.0075 (d) 60
 9. $24,846.79 **11.** S = $4755.03; I = $1555.03
13. $13,322.92 **15.** $5583.95
17. $7309.98 **19.** $502.47
21. (a) $12,245.64 (b) $11,080.32
  (c) A $\frac{1}{2}$% increase in the interest rate reduces the
   amount required by $1165.32.
23. $50.26 more at 8% **25.** (a) 7.55% (b) 6.18%
27. 8% compounded monthly, 8% compounded quarterly,
  8% compounded annually
29. 8.2% continuously yields 8.55%. 8.4% compounded
  quarterly yields 8.67% and so is better.
31. The higher graph is for continuous compounding
  because its yield (its effective annual rate) is higher.
33. 37.02% **35.** 3 years **37.** 4% **39.** $3996.02
41. (a) $2,124,876.38 (b) $480,087.44 more
43. 5.12 years (approximately) **45.** $13,916.24
47.

	A	B	C
1		Future Value	(Yearly)
2	End of Year	Quarterly	Monthly
3	0	$5000.00	$5000.00
4	1	$5322.52	$5324.26
5	2	$5665.84	$5669.54
6	3	$6031.31	$6037.22
7	4	$6420.36	$6428.74
8	5	$6834.50	$6845.65
9	6	$7275.35	$7289.60
10	7	$7744.64	$7762.34
11	8	$8244.20	$8265.74
12	9	$8775.99	$8801.79
13	10	$9342.07	$9372.59

49. (a) from quarterly and monthly spreadsheets: after
   $6\frac{1}{2}$ years (26 quarters or 78 months)
  (b) See the spreadsheet.
49. (a) 24, 48, 96 (b) 24, 16, $\frac{32}{3}$
51. $10(2^{12})$ **53.** $4 \cdot \left(\frac{3}{2}\right)^{15}$ **55.** $\dfrac{6(1 - 3^{17})}{-2}$
57. $\dfrac{3^{35} - 1}{2}$ **59.** $18\left[1 - \left(\frac{2}{3}\right)^{18}\right]$
61. $350,580 (approx.) **63.** 24.4 million (approx.)
65. 35 years **67.** 40.5 ft **69.** $4096
71. 320,000 **73.** $7,231,366 **75.** 6; 5^6 = 15,625
77. 305,175,780

6.3 EXERCISES

 1. S = $285,129 = future value; R = 2500; i = 0.02;
   n = 60
 3. R = $1426 = payment; S = 80,000; i = 0.04; n = 30
 5. (a) The higher graph is $1120 per year.
  (b) R = $1000: S = $73,105.94;
   R = $1120: S = $81,878.65;
   Difference = $8772.71
 7. $7328.22 **9.** $1072.97 **11.** $1482.94
13. $n \approx 27.1$; 28 quarters
15. A sinking fund is a savings plan, so the 10% rate
  in part (a) is better.
17. $4651.61 **19.** $1180.78 **21.** $4152.32
23. $3787.92
25. (a) ordinary annuity (b) $4774.55
27. (a) annuity due (b) $3974.73
29. (a) ordinary annuity (b) $1083.40
31. (a) ordinary annuity (b) $266.10
33. (a) ordinary annuity (b) $n \approx 108.5$; 109 months
35. (a) annuity due (b) $235.16
37. (a) annuity due (b) $26,517.13
39. (a) ordinary annuity (b) $795.75
41. $53,677.40
43. (a) $n \approx 35$ quarters (b) $1,062,412 (nearest dollar)
45. The spreadsheet shows the amounts at the end of each of
  the first 12 months and at the end of the last 12 months.
  The amount after 10 years is shown.

	A	B	C
1		Future Value	
2	End of Month	Ordinary Ann.	Annuity Due
3	0	0	100
4	1	$100.00	$100.60
5	2	$200.60	$201.80
6	3	$301.80	$303.61
7	4	$403.61	$406.04
8	5	$506.04	$509.07
9	6	$609.07	$612.73
10	7	$712.73	$717.00
11	8	$817.00	$821.91
12	9	$921.91	$927.44
13	10	$1027.44	$1033.60
14	11	$1133.60	$1140.40
15	12	$1240.40	$1247.85
⋮	⋮	⋮	⋮
112	109	$15324.39	$15416.34
113	110	$15516.34	$15609.44
114	111	$15709.44	$15803.70
115	112	$15903.70	$15999.12
116	113	$16099.12	$16195.71
117	114	$16295.71	$16393.49
118	115	$16493.49	$16592.45
119	116	$16692.45	$16792.60
120	117	$16892.60	$16993.96
121	118	$17093.96	$17196.52
122	119	$17296.52	$17400.30
123	120	$17500.30	$17605.30

(a) $12,000

(b) Annuity due. Each payment for an annuity due earns 1 month's interest more than that for an ordinary annuity.

6.4 EXERCISES

1. $A_n = \$22,480 =$ present value; $R = 1300$; $i = 0.04$; $n = 30$

3. $R = \$809 =$ payment; $A_n = 135,000$; $i = 0.005$; $n = 360$

5. $69,913.77   **7.** $2,128,391   **9.** $4595.46

11. $n \approx 73.8$; 74 quarters   **13.** $1141.81; premium

15. (a) The higher graph corresponds to 8%.
    (b) $1500 (approximately)
    (c) With an interest rate of 10%, a present value of about $9000 is needed to purchase an annuity of $1000 for 25 years. If the interest rate is 8%, about $10,500 is needed.

17. Ordinary annuity—payments at the end of each period
    Annuity due—payments at the beginning of each period

19. $69,632.02   **21.** $445,962.23   **23.** $2145.59

25. (a) ordinary annuity (b) $10,882.46

27. (a) annuity due   (b) $316,803.61

29. (a) ordinary annuity
    (b) Taking $500,000 and $140,000 payments for the next 10 years has a slightly higher present value: $1,506,436.24.

31. (a) annuity due   (b) $146,235.06

33. (a) annuity due   (b) $22,663.74

35. (a) ordinary annuity (b) $11,810.24

37. (a) ordinary annuity (b) $27,590.62

39. (a) $8629.16   (b) $9883.48

41. (a) $30,078.99   (b) $16,900   (c) $607.02
    (d) $36,421.20

43. (a) $4504.83   (b) $n \approx 21.9$; 22 withdrawals

45. $7957.86   **47.** $74,993.20   **49.** $59,768.91

51. $1317.98   **53.** $257,412.87

55. (a) The spreadsheet below shows the payments for the first 12 months and the last 12 months. Full payments for $13\frac{1}{2}$ years.

	A	B	C	D
1	End of Month	Acct. Value	Payment	New Balance
2	0	$100000.00	$0.00	$100000.00
3	1	$100650.00	$1000.00	$99650.00
4	2	$100297.73	$1000.00	$99297.73
5	3	$99943.16	$1000.00	$98943.16
6	4	$99586.29	$1000.00	$98586.29
7	5	$99227.10	$1000.00	$98227.10
8	6	$98865.58	$1000.00	$97865.58
9	7	$98501.70	$1000.00	$97501.70
10	8	$98135.47	$1000.00	$97135.47
11	9	$97766.85	$1000.00	$96766.85
12	10	$97395.83	$1000.00	$96395.83
13	11	$97022.40	$1000.00	$96022.40
14	12	$96646.55	$1000.00	$95646.55
⋮	⋮	⋮	⋮	⋮
154	152	$10684.71	$1000.00	$9684.71
155	153	$9747.66	$1000.00	$8747.66
156	154	$8804.52	$1000.00	$7804.52
157	155	$7855.25	$1000.00	$6855.25
158	156	$6899.81	$1000.00	$5899.81
159	157	$5938.16	$1000.00	$4938.16
160	158	$4970.25	$1000.00	$3970.25
161	159	$3996.06	$1000.00	$2996.06
162	160	$3015.53	$1000.00	$2015.53
163	161	$2028.64	$1000.00	$1028.64
164	162	$1035.32	$1000.00	$35.32
165	163	$35.55	$35.55	$0.00

(b) The spreadsheet below shows the payments for the first 12 months and the last 12 months. Full payments for almost 4 years.

	A	B	C	D
1	End of Month	Acct. Value	Payment	New Balance
2	0	$100000.00	$0.00	$100000.00
3	1	$100650.00	$2500.00	$98150.00
4	2	$98787.98	$2500.00	$96287.98
5	3	$96913.85	$2500.00	$94413.85
6	4	$95027.54	$2500.00	$92527.54
7	5	$93128.97	$2500.00	$90628.97
8	6	$91218.05	$2500.00	$88718.05
9	7	$89294.72	$2500.00	$86794.72
10	8	$87358.89	$2500.00	$84858.89
11	9	$85410.47	$2500.00	$82910.47
12	10	$83449.39	$2500.00	$80949.39
13	11	$81475.56	$2500.00	$78975.56
14	12	$79488.90	$2500.00	$76988.90
⋮	⋮	⋮	⋮	⋮
38	36	$27734.95	$2500.00	$25234.95
39	37	$25398.98	$2500.00	$22898.98
40	38	$23047.83	$2500.00	$20547.83
41	39	$20681.39	$2500.00	$18181.39
42	40	$18299.57	$2500.00	$15799.57
43	41	$15902.26	$2500.00	$13402.26
44	42	$13489.38	$2500.00	$10989.38
45	43	$11060.81	$2500.00	$8560.81
46	44	$8616.45	$2500.00	$6116.45
47	45	$6156.21	$2500.00	$3656.21
48	46	$3679.98	$2500.00	$1179.98
49	47	$1187.65	$1187.65	$0.00

6.5 EXERCISES

1. (a) the 10-year loan, because the loan must be paid more quickly

(b) the 25-year loan, because the loan is paid more slowly

3. $1288.29

5. $553.42   **7.** $10,345.11

9.

Period	Payment	Interest
1	$39,505.50	$9000.00
2	39,505.50	6254.51
3	39,505.43	3261.92
	118,516.43	18,516.43

Period	Balance Reduction	Unpaid Balance
		$100,000.00
1	$30,505.50	69,494.50
2	33,250.99	36,243.51
3	36,243.51	0.00
	100,000.00	

11.

Period	Payment	Interest
1	$5380.54	$600.00
2	5380.54	456.58
3	5380.54	308.87
4	5380.54	156.71
	21,522.16	1,522.16

Period	Balance Reduction	Unpaid Balance
		$20,000.00
1	$4780.54	15,219.46
2	4923.96	10,295.50
3	5071.67	5,223.83
4	5223.83	0.00
	20,000.00	

13. $8852.05

15. $5785.83

17. (a) $17,436.92
(b) $348,738.40 + $150,000 = $498,738.40
(c) $148,738.40

19. (a) $1237.78
(b) $9902.24 + $2000 = $11,902.24
(c) $1902.24

21. $8903.25

23. (a) $276,991.32   (b) $263,575.30

25. (a) $89,120.53   (b) $6451.45

27. (a) $368.43; $383.43   (b) $n \approx 57.1$
(c) $211.95

29. (a) The line is the total amount paid ($644.30 per month × the number of months). The curve is the total amount paid toward the principal.
(b)

31.

	Rate	Payment	Total Interest
(a)	8%	$366.19	$2577.12
	8.5%	$369.72	$2746.56
(b)	6.75%	$518.88	$106,796.80
	7.25%	$545.74	$116,466.40

(c) The duration of the loan seems to have the greatest effect. It greatly influences payment size (for a $15,000 loan versus one for $80,000), and it also affects total interest paid.

33.

		Payment	Points	Total Paid
(a)	(i)	$738.99	–	$221,697
	(ii)	$722.81	$1000	$217,843
	(iii)	$706.78	$2000	$214,034

(b) The 7% loan with 2 points.

35. (a) $17,525.20   (b) $508.76
(c) $n \approx 33.2$; 34 quarters   (d) $471.57

37. The spreadsheet shows the amortization schedule for the first 12 and the last 12 payments.

	A	B	C	D	E
1	Period	Payment	Interest	Bal. Reduction	Unpaid Bal.
2	0				$16700.00
3	1	$409.27	$114.12	$295.15	$16404.85
4	2	$409.27	$112.10	$297.17	$16107.68
5	3	$409.27	$110.07	$299.20	$15808.48
6	4	$409.27	$108.02	$301.25	$15507.23
7	5	$409.27	$105.97	$303.30	$15203.93
8	6	$409.27	$103.89	$305.38	$14898.55
9	7	$409.27	$101.81	$307.46	$14591.09
10	8	$409.27	$99.71	$309.56	$14281.52
11	9	$409.27	$97.59	$311.68	$13969.84
12	10	$409.27	$95.46	$313.81	$13656.03
13	11	$409.27	$93.32	$315.95	$13340.08
14	12	$409.27	$91.16	$318.11	$13021.97
	⋮	⋮	⋮	⋮	⋮
39	37	$409.27	$32.11	$377.16	$4322.49
40	38	$409.27	$29.54	$379.73	$3942.75
41	39	$409.27	$26.94	$382.33	$3560.43
42	40	$409.27	$24.33	$384.94	$3175.49
43	41	$409.27	$21.70	$387.57	$2787.91
44	42	$409.27	$19.05	$390.22	$2397.70
45	43	$409.27	$16.38	$392.89	$2004.81
46	44	$409.27	$13.70	$395.57	$1609.24
47	45	$409.27	$11.00	$398.27	$1210.97
48	46	$409.27	$8.27	$401.00	$809.97
49	47	$409.27	$5.53	$403.74	$406.24
50	48	$409.27	$2.78	$406.24	$0.00

CHAPTER 6 REVIEW EXERCISES

1. $1, \frac{1}{4}, \frac{1}{9}, \frac{1}{16}$
2. Arithmetic: (a) and (c) (a) $d = -5$ (c) $d = \frac{1}{6}$
3. 235   **4.** 109   **5.** 315
6. Geometric: (a) and (b) (a) $r = 8$ (b) $r = -\frac{3}{4}$
7. 8   **8.** 2, 391, $484\frac{4}{9}$
9. $S = R\left[\dfrac{(1 + i)^n - 1}{i}\right]$ **10.** $I = Prt$
11. $A_n = R\left[\dfrac{1 - (1 + i)^{-n}}{i}\right]$ **12.** $S = P(1 + i)^n$
13. $A_n = R\left[\dfrac{1 - (1 + i)^{-n}}{i}\right]$, solved for R
14. $S = Pe^{rt}$ **15.** \$10,880   **16.** $6\frac{2}{3}\%$
17. \$2941.18   **18.** \$4650
19. the \$40,000 job (\$490,000 versus \$472,500)
20. (a) 40   (b) $2\% = 0.02$
21. (a) $S = P(1 + i)^n$ (b) $S = Pe^{rt}$
22. (b) monthly   **23.** \$372.79   **24.** \$14,510.26
25. \$1616.07   **26.** \$21,299.21   **27.** 34.3 quarters
28. (a) 13.29%   (b) 14.21%
29. (a) 7.40%   (b) 7.47%
30. 2^{63} **31.** $2^{32} - 1$ **32.** \$29,428.47
33. \$6069.44   **34.** \$31,194.18   **35.** \$10,841.24
36. $n \approx 36$ quarters
37. \$130,079.36 **38.** \$12,007.09
39. (a) \$11.828 million   (b) \$161.5 million
40. \$1726.85   **41.** \$5390.77
42. $n \approx 16$ half-years (8 years)
43. \$88.85   **44.** \$3443.61   **45.** \$163,792.21

46.

Payment Number	Payment Amount	Interest	Balance Reduction	Unpaid Balance
57	\$699.22	\$594.01	\$105.21	\$94,936.99
58	\$699.22	\$593.36	\$105.86	\$94,831.13

47. 16.32%   **48.** \$213.81
49. (a) \$1480   (b) \$1601.03
50. \$9319.64   **51.** 14.5 years   **52.** 79.4%
53. \$4053.54; discount
54. (a) \$4728.19   (b) \$5398.07   (c) \$1749.88
    (d) 10.78%
55. \$21,474.08   **56.** \$12,162.06
57. Quarterly APY = 6.68%. This rate is better for the bank; it pays less interest. Continuous APY = 6.69%. This rate is better for the consumer, who earns more interest.
58. \$32,834.69   **59.** \$3,466.64
60. (a) \$1185.51   (b) \$355,653   (c) \$171,653
    (d) \$156,366.25
61. (a) \$95,164.21   (b) \$1300.14   **62.** \$994.08
63. Future value of IRA = \$172,971.32
    Present value needed = \$2,321,520.10
    Future value needed from deposits = \$2,148,548.78
    Deposits = \$711.60
64. Regular payment = \$64,337.43

Unpaid balance = \$2,365,237.24
Number of \$70,000 payments = $n \approx 46.1$
Savings = \$118,546.36

CHAPTER 6 TEST

1. 25.3 years (approximately)   **2.** \$840.75
3. 6.87%   **4.** \$158,524.90   **5.** 33.53%
6. (a) \$698.00 (b) \$112,400
7. \$2625   **8.** \$7999.41   **9.** 8.73%
10. \$119,912.92 **11.** \$40,552.00
12. \$32,488 (to the nearest dollar) **13.** \$6781.17
14. $n \approx 66.8$; 67 half-years
15. \$1688.02
16. (a) \$279,841.35   (b) \$13,124.75
17. \$116,909.10   **18.** \$29,716.47
19. (a) The difference between successive terms is always -5.5.
    (b) 23.8   (c) 8226.3
20. 1000 mg (approximately)
21. \$12,975.49; premium
22. (a) \$145,585.54 (with the \$2000);
        \$147,585.54 (without the \$2000)
    (b) $n \approx 318.8$ months
        Total interest = \$243,738.13
    (c) $n \approx 317.2$ months
        Total interest = \$245,378.24
    (d) Paying the \$2000 is slightly better; it saves about \$1640 in interest.

7.1 EXERCISES

1. (a) $\frac{2}{5}$ (b) 0   (c) 1   **3.** $\frac{1}{4}$ **5.** 1
7. (a) $\frac{3}{10}$ (b) $\frac{1}{2}$ (c) $\frac{1}{5}$ (d) $\frac{3}{5}$ (e) $\frac{7}{10}$
9. (a) $\frac{1}{13}$ (b) $\frac{1}{2}$ (c) $\frac{1}{4}$
11. {HH, HT, TH, TT};   (a) $\frac{1}{4}$ (b) $\frac{1}{2}$ (c) $\frac{1}{4}$
13. (a) $\frac{1}{12}$ (b) $\frac{1}{12}$ (c) $\frac{1}{36}$ **15.** (a) $\frac{1}{2}$ (b) $\frac{5}{12}$
17. (a) 431/1200
    (b) If fair, $\Pr(6) = \frac{1}{6}$; 431/1200 not close to $\frac{1}{6}$, so not a fair die
19. (a) 2:3 (b) 3:2 **21.** (a) $\frac{1}{21}$ (b) $\frac{20}{21}$
23. 0.46 **25.** (a) 63/425 (b) 32/425
27. (a) R: 0.63   D: 0.41   I: 0.51
    (b) Republican
29. (a) 1/3601 (b) 100/3601 (c) 3500/3601
    (d) 30%
31. (a) 0.402 (b) 0.491 (c) 100%; yes
33. $S = \{A+, A-, B+, B-, AB+, AB-, O+, O-\}$; No. Type O+ is the most frequently occurring blood type.
35. (a) 0.04 (b) 0.96 **37.** (a) 0.13 (b) 0.87
39. 0.03 **41.** 0.75 **43.** $\frac{1}{3}$ **45.** $\frac{1}{3}$
47. 0.22; yes, 0.39 is much higher than 0.22 **49.** $\frac{3}{8}$
51. (a) no (b) {BB, BG, GB, GG} (c) $\frac{1}{2}$
53. $\frac{1}{8}$ **55.** $\frac{3}{125}$
57. $\Pr(A) = 0.000019554$, or about 1.9 accidents per 100,000

$\Pr(B) = 0.000035919$, or about 3.6 accidents per 100,000

$\Pr(C) = 0.000037679$, or about 3.8 accidents per 100,000

Intersection C is the most dangerous.

59. (a) 557/1200 (b) 11/120
61. (a) boy: 1/5; girl: 4/5
(b) boy: 0.4946; girl: 0.5054 (c) part (b)
63. 3/4 **65.** $3/3995 \approx 0.00075$

7.2 EXERCISES

1. $\frac{1}{6}$ **3.** $\frac{2}{3}$ **5.** $\frac{2}{5}$ **7.** (a) $\frac{1}{7}$ (b) $\frac{5}{7}$
9. $\frac{3}{4}$ **11.** $\frac{2}{3}$ **13.** $\frac{10}{17}$ **15.** $\frac{2}{3}$
17. (a) $\frac{1}{2}$ (b) $\frac{1}{3}$ (c) $\frac{8}{9}$ (d) $\frac{1}{9}$
19. 0.54 **21.** (a) 362/425 (b) $\frac{66}{85}$
23. $\frac{17}{50}$ **25.** (a) $\frac{5}{6}$ (b) $\frac{1}{6}$
27. (a) 0.35 (b) 0.08 (c) 0.83
29. (a) 0.508 (b) 0.633 (c) 0.761
31. (a) 0.267 (b) 0.371 (c) 0.931
33. (a) $\frac{11}{12}$ (b) $\frac{5}{6}$ **35.** (a) $\frac{1}{2}$ (b) $\frac{7}{8}$ (c) $\frac{3}{4}$
37. 0.56 **39.** 0.965
41. (a) 0.72 (b) 0.84 (c) 0.61
43. $\frac{31}{40}$ **45.** 0.13

7.3 EXERCISES

1. (a) $\frac{1}{2}$ (b) $\frac{1}{13}$ **3.** (a) $\frac{1}{3}$ (b) $\frac{1}{3}$ **5.** $\frac{4}{7}$
7. (a) $\frac{2}{3}$ (b) $\frac{4}{9}$ (c) $\frac{3}{5}$ **9.** (a) $\frac{1}{4}$ (b) $\frac{1}{2}$
11. $\frac{1}{36}$ **13.** (a) $\frac{1}{8}$ (b) $\frac{7}{8}$
15. (a) $\frac{3}{50}$ (b) $\frac{1}{15}$
(c) The events in part (a) are independent because the result of the first draw does not affect the probability for the second draw.
17. (a) $\frac{4}{25}$ (b) $\frac{9}{25}$ (c) $\frac{6}{25}$ (d) 0 **19.** $\frac{5}{68}$
21. (a) $\frac{1}{5}$ (b) $\frac{3}{5}$ (c) 0 **23.** (a) $\frac{1}{17}$ (b) 13/204
25. (a) $\frac{13}{17}$ (b) $\frac{4}{17}$ (c) $\frac{8}{51}$ **27.** $\frac{31}{52}$ **29.** $\frac{25}{96}$
31. $\frac{43}{50}$ **33.** $\frac{65}{87}$ **35.** $35/435 = \frac{7}{87}$ **37.** $\frac{1}{10}$
39. 1/144,000,000 **41.** 0.004292 **43.** 0.06
45. 0.045 **47.** $(0.95)^5 = 0.774$ **49.** 0.06
51. (a) 0.366 (b) 0.634
53. (a) 0.4565 (b) 0.5435
55. (a) $(\frac{1}{3})^3(\frac{1}{5})^4 = 1/16{,}875$
(b) $(\frac{2}{3})^3(\frac{4}{5})^4 = 2048/16{,}875$ (c) 14,827/16,875
57. 4/11; 4:7 **59.** (a) 364/365 (b) $\frac{1}{365}$
61. (a) 0.59 (b) 0.41

7.4 EXERCISES

1. $\frac{2}{5}$ **3.** (a) $\frac{2}{21}$ (b) $\frac{4}{21}$ (c) $\frac{23}{35}$
5. (a) $\frac{5}{42}$ (b) $\frac{10}{21}$ (c) $\frac{4}{9}$
7. (a) $\frac{1}{30}$ (b) $\frac{1}{2}$ (c) $\frac{5}{6}$ **9.** $\frac{3}{5}$
11. (a) $\frac{6}{25}$ (b) $\frac{9}{25}$ (c) $\frac{12}{25}$ (d) $\frac{19}{25}$
13. $\frac{2}{3}$ **15.** $\frac{2}{3}$ **17.** 0.3095
19. (a) 81/10,000 (b) 1323/5000

21. (a) $\frac{6}{35}$ (b) $\frac{6}{35}$ (c) $\frac{12}{35}$
23. (a) $\frac{4}{7}$ (b) $\frac{5}{14}$ (c) $\frac{7}{10}$ (d) $\frac{16}{25}$ **25.** $\frac{17}{45}$
27. 0.079 **29.** (a) 49/100 (b) $\frac{12}{49}$

7.5 EXERCISES

1. 360 **3.** 151,200 **5.** 1
7. (a) $6 \cdot 5 \cdot 4 \cdot 3 = 360$ (b) $6^4 = 1296$ **9.** $n!$
11. $n + 1$ **13.** 16 **15.** 4950 **17.** 1 **19.** 1
21. 10 **23.** (a) 8 (b) 240 **25.** 604,800
27. 120 **29.** 24 **31.** 64 **33.** 720
35. $2^{10} = 1024$ **37.** $4(_{13}C_5) = 5148$
39. 10,816,000 **41.** 30,045,015 **43.** 792
45. 210 **47.** 2,891,999,880 **49.** 3,700,000

7.6 EXERCISES

1. $\frac{1}{120}$ **3.** (a) 120 (b) $\frac{1}{120}$
5. 0.639 **7.** (a) 1/10,000 (b) 1/5040
9. $1/10^6$ **11.** 0.000048 **13.** $1/10! = 1/3{,}628{,}800$
15. (a) $\frac{1}{22}$ (b) $\frac{6}{11}$ (c) $\frac{9}{22}$
17. 0.098 **19.** $\dfrac{_{90}C_{28} \cdot {_{10}}C_2}{_{100}C_{30}}$
21. (a) 0.119 (b) 0.0476 (c) 0.476
23. 0.0238 **25.** (a) 0.721 (b) 0.262 (c) 0.279
27. (a) $\frac{1}{3}$ (b) $\frac{1}{6}$ **29.** $\dfrac{_{20}C_{10}}{_{80}C_{10}} = 0.00000011$
31. (a) 0.033 (b) 0.633
33. (a) 0.0005 (b) 0.002 **35.** 0.00198

7.7 EXERCISES

1. can **3.** cannot, sum $\neq 1$
5. cannot, not square **7.** can
9. $[0.248 \quad 0.752]$ **11.** $[0.228 \quad 0.236 \quad 0.536]$
13. $[0.25 \ 0.75]$ **15.** $[0.249 \ 0.249 \ 0.502]$
17. $[\frac{1}{4} \quad \frac{3}{4}]$ **19.** $[\frac{1}{4} \quad \frac{1}{4} \quad \frac{1}{2}]$
21. $[0.5 \quad 0.4 \quad 0.1]$; $[0.44 \quad 0.43 \quad 0.13]$;
$[0.431 \quad 0.43 \quad 0.139]$; $[0.4292 \quad 0.4291 \quad 0.1417]$
23.
$$\begin{array}{c} \\ R \\ N \end{array} \begin{array}{cc} R & N \\ \begin{bmatrix} 0.8 & 0.2 \\ 0.3 & 0.7 \end{bmatrix} \end{array}$$
25. 0.45
27.
$$\begin{array}{c} \\ A \\ F \\ V \end{array} \begin{array}{ccc} A & F & V \\ \begin{bmatrix} 0 & 0.7 & 0.3 \\ 0.6 & 0 & 0.4 \\ 0.8 & 0.2 & 0 \end{bmatrix} \end{array}$$
29. $[0.3928 \quad 0.37 \quad 0.2372]$
31. $[46/113 \quad 38/113 \quad 29/113]$
33.
$$\begin{array}{c} \\ r \\ u \end{array} \begin{array}{cc} r & u \\ \begin{bmatrix} 0.7 & 0.3 \\ 0.1 & 0.9 \end{bmatrix} \end{array}; [1/4 \ 3/4]$$
35. $[\frac{1}{14} \quad \frac{3}{14} \quad \frac{5}{7}]$ **37.** $[\frac{4}{7} \quad \frac{2}{7} \quad \frac{1}{7}]$
39. $[49/100 \quad 42/100 \quad 9/100]$

CHAPTER 7 REVIEW EXERCISES

1. (a) $\frac{5}{9}$ (b) $\frac{1}{3}$ (c) $\frac{2}{9}$
2. (a) $\frac{3}{4}$ (b) $\frac{1}{2}$ (c) $\frac{1}{6}$ (d) $\frac{2}{3}$
3. (a) 3:4 (b) 4:3 4. (a) $\frac{1}{4}$ (b) $\frac{1}{2}$ (c) $\frac{1}{4}$
5. (a) $\frac{3}{8}$ (b) $\frac{1}{8}$ (c) $\frac{3}{8}$ 6. $\frac{2}{13}$ 7. 16/169
8. $\frac{3}{4}$ 9. $\frac{2}{13}$ 10. $\frac{7}{13}$ 11. (a) $\frac{2}{9}$ (b) $\frac{2}{3}$ (c) $\frac{7}{9}$
12. $\frac{2}{7}$ 13. $\frac{1}{2}$ 14. 7/320
15. 7/342 16. 3/14 17. $\frac{8}{15}$
18. (a) $\frac{3}{14}$ (b) $\frac{4}{7}$ (c) $\frac{3}{8}$ 19. 49/89
20. 30 21. 35 22. 26^3 23. 56
24. (a) Not square
    (b) The row sums are not 1.
25. [0.76 0.24], [0.496 0.504]
26. [0.2 0.8]
27. $\frac{5}{8}$ 28. $\frac{1}{4}$ 29. $\frac{29}{50}$
30. $\frac{5}{56}$ 31. $\frac{33}{56}$ 32. $\frac{15}{22}$ 33. 0.72
34. (a) 63/2000 (b) $\frac{60}{63}$ 35. 39/116 36. 4! = 24
37. $_8P_4 = 1680$ 38. $_{12}C_4 = 495$ 39. $_8C_4 = 70$
40. (a) $_{12}C_2 = 66$ (b) $_{12}C_3 = 220$ 41. 62,193,780
42. If her assumption about blood groups is accurate, there would be $4 \cdot 2 \cdot 4 \cdot 8 = 256$, not 288, unique groups.
43. $\frac{1}{24}$ 44. $\frac{3}{500}$ 45. $\frac{3}{1250}$
46. (a) 0.3398 (b) 0.1975 47. $\frac{1}{10}$
48. (a) $\left(_{10}C_5\right)\left(_2C_1\right)/_{12}C_6$
    (b) $\dfrac{\left(_{10}C_5\right)\left(_2C_1\right) + \left(_{10}C_4\right)\left(_2C_2\right)}{_{12}C_6}$
49. [0.135 0.51 0.355], [0.09675 0.3305 0.57275], [0.0640875 0.288275 0.6476375]
50. [12/265 68/265 37/53]

CHAPTER 7 TEST

1. (a) $\frac{4}{7}$ (b) $\frac{3}{7}$ 2. (a) $\frac{2}{7}$ (b) $\frac{5}{7}$
3. (a) 0 (b) 1 4. $\frac{1}{7}$ 5. $\frac{1}{7}$
6. (a) $\frac{2}{7}$ (b) $\frac{4}{7}$ 7. $\frac{2}{7}$ 8. $\frac{3}{7}$ 9. $\frac{2}{3}$
10. 1/17,576 11. 0.2389 12. (a) $\frac{1}{5}$ (b) $\frac{1}{20}$
13. (a) $\frac{3}{95}$ (b) $\frac{6}{19}$ (c) $\frac{21}{38}$ (d) 0
14. (a) 5,245,786 (b) 1/5,245,786
15. (a) 2,118,760 (b) 1/2,118,760
16. 0.064 17. (a) 0.633 (b) 0.962 18. 0.229
19. (a) $\frac{1}{5}$ (b) $\frac{1}{14}$ (c) $\frac{13}{14}$ 20. $\frac{3}{14}$
21. (a) 2^{10} (b) $\dfrac{1}{2^{10}}$ (c) $\frac{1}{3}$ (d) Change the code.
22. (a) $A = \begin{bmatrix} 0.80 & 0.20 \\ 0.07 & 0.93 \end{bmatrix}$ (b) $[0.25566 \quad 0.74434]$; about 25.6% (c) $\frac{7}{27}$; 25.9% of market

8.1 EXERCISES

1. 0.0595
3. (a) 1/6 (b) 5/6 (c) 18 (d) 0.045
5. (a) $\frac{1}{64}$ (b) $\frac{5}{16}$ (c) $\frac{15}{64}$ 7. 0.0284
9. (a) 0.2304 (b) 0.0102 (c) 0.3174
11. 0.0585 13. 0.2759

15. (a) 0.375 (b) 0.0625
17. (a) 0.1157 (b) 0.4823
19. (a) $\frac{27}{64}$ (b) $\frac{27}{128}$ (c) $\frac{81}{256}$
21. (a) 0.0729 (b) 0.5905 (c) 0.9914
23. 0.2457 25. 0.0007
27. (a) 0.1323 (b) 0.0308
29. (a) 0.9044 (b) 0.0914 (c) 0.0043
31. (a) 0.8683 (b) 0.2099 33. 0.740

8.2 EXERCISES

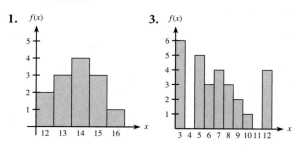

1. 3 11. 13 13. 5 15. 10.5
17. mode = 2, median = 4.5, mean = 6
19. mode = 17, median = 18.5, mean = 23.5
21. mode = 5.3, median = 5.3, mean = 5.32
23. 12.21, 14.5, 14.5 25. 9 27. 14
29. 4, 8.5714, 2.9277 31. 14, 4.6667, 2.1602
33. 2.73, 1.35 35. 6.75, 2.96
37. (a)

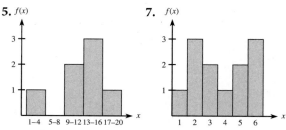

(b) $\bar{x} = 6.13, s = 2.02$
39. (a) (b) $\bar{x} = 8.82$

Expenditures ($ thousands)

41. The mean will give the highest measure.

43. The median will give the most representative average.

45. (a) 70.09%   (b) 8.79%

47.

49. $\bar{x} = 3.32$ kg; $s = 0.677$ kg

51. (a) $60,000   (b) $36,000   (c) $32,000

53. (a) $23.325   (b) $5.139

55. (a) 5.47%   (b) 6.41%   (c) 1.55%

57. (a)

(b) 46.3   (c) 26.0   (d) no

8.3 EXERCISES

1. no; $\Pr(x) \not\geq 0$ **3.** yes; both conditions satisfied

5. yes; both conditions satisfied

7. no; $\sum \Pr(x) > 1$ **9.** $\frac{15}{8}$ **11.** 5

13. $\mu = \frac{13}{8}, \sigma^2 = 1.48, \sigma = 1.22$

15. $\mu = \frac{13}{3}, \sigma^2 = 2.22, \sigma = 1.49$

17. 3   **19.** 2

21. (a)

x	$\Pr(x)$
0	125/216
1	25/72
2	5/72
3	1/216

(b) $3(\frac{1}{6}) = \frac{1}{2}$ (c) $\sqrt{3(\frac{1}{6})(\frac{5}{6})} = (\frac{1}{6})\sqrt{15}$

23. (a) 42   (b) 3.55

25. (a) 30   (b) 3.464

27. 125

29. $a^6 + 6a^5b + 15a^4b^2 + 20a^3b^3 + 15a^2b^4 + 6ab^5 + b^6$

31. $x^4 + 4x^3h + 6x^2h^2 + 4xh^3 + h^4$

33. 1.85

35. TV: 37,500; personal appearances: 35,300

37. $-$67.33   **39.** Expect to lose $2 each time.

41. 100

43. E(cost with policy) = $108,
E(cost without policy) = $80;
save $28 by "taking the chance"

45. no; some pipes may be more than 0.01 in. from 2 in. even if average is 2 in.

47. (a) $100(0.10) = 10$ (b) $\sqrt{100(0.10)(0.90)} = 3$

49. (a) 60,000   (b) $\sqrt{24,000} = 154.919$

51. 59,690   **53.** (a) 4   (b) 1.79

55. 2, 1.41   **57.** 300

8.4 EXERCISES

1. 0.4641   **3.** 0.2258   **5.** 0.9153   **7.** 0.1070

9. 0.0166   **11.** 0.0227   **13.** 0.8849   **15.** 0.1915

17. 0.3944   **19.** 0.3830   **21.** 0.7745   **23.** 0.9773

25. 0.0668   **27.** (a) 0.3413   (b) 0.3944

29. 0.9876

31. (a) 0.4192   (b) 0.0227   (c) 0.0581   (d) 0.8965

33. (a) 0.0668   (b) 0.3085   (c) 0.3830

35. (a) 0.0475   (b) 0.2033   (c) 0.5934

37. (a) 0.0227   (b) 0.1587   (c) 0.8186

8.5 EXERCISES

1. yes   **3.** no   **5.** 0.0668   **7.** 0.0001

9. 0.0521   **11.** 0.0110   **13.** 0.9890

15. 0.7324   **17.** 0.3520   **19.** 0.0443

21. 0.5398   **23.** 0.7852   **25.** 0.0129

27. 0.2514   **29.** 0.0011   **31.** 0.9990

33. 0.1272; 0.4364

35. (a) 0.0038   (b) yes; students were smarter or questions were leaked   **37.** 0.0166

CHAPTER 8 REVIEW EXERCISES

1. 0.0774   **2.** (a) 0.3545   (b) 0.5534

3. 0.407

4. $f(x)$

5. 3

6. $\frac{77}{26} \approx 2.96$

7. 3

8. $f(x)$

9. 14

10. 14

11. 14.3

12. $\bar{x} = 3.86; s^2 = 6.81; s = 2.61$

13. $\bar{x} = 2; s^2 = 2.44; s = 1.56$

14. 2.4   **15.** yes   **16.** no; $\sum \Pr(x) \neq 1$

17. yes   **18.** no; $\Pr(x) \not\geq 0$ **19.** 2

20. (a) 4.125   (b) 2.7344   (c) 1.654

21. (a) $\frac{37}{12}$ (b) 0.9097   (c) 0.9538

22. $\mu = 4, \sigma = (2\sqrt{3})/3$ **23.** 3

24. $x^5 + 5x^4y + 10x^3y^2 + 10x^2y^3 + 5xy^4 + y^5$
25. 0.9165 **26.** 0.1498 **27.** 0.1039 **28.** 0.3413
29. 0.6826 **30.** 0.1360 **31.** not good **32.** good
33. 0.0151 **34.** 0.9625 **35.** 0.8475 **36.** 0.0119
37. 0.297 **38.** 0.16308 **39.** 0.2048
40. (a) $(99,999/100,000)^{99,999} \approx 0.37$
   (b) $1 - (99,999/100,000)^{100,000} \approx 0.63$

41.

Class Marks

42. 30.3%
43. 8.35%
44. 455
45. 3
46. $18.00
47. –$0.50

48. (a) 1 (b) $\left(\frac{4}{5}\right)^4$
49. (a) 0.4773 (b) 0.1360 (c) 0.0227
50. 15% **51.** 0.3821 **52.** 0.4090
53. 0.0262 **54.** 0.1788

CHAPTER 8 TEST

1. (a) $\frac{40}{243}$ (b) $\frac{51}{243} = \frac{17}{81}$
2. (a) 4 (b) $\mu = 4, \sigma^2 = \frac{8}{3}, \sigma = \frac{2}{3}\sqrt{6}$
3. (i) For each $x, 0 \le \Pr(x) \le 1$ (ii) $\Sigma\Pr(x) = 1$
4. 5.1
5. $\mu = 16.7, \sigma^2 = 26.61, \sigma = 5.16$
6. $\bar{x} = 21.57$, median $= 21$, mode $= 21$
7. (a) 0.4706 (b) 0.8413 (c) 0.0669
8. (a) 0.3891 (b) 0.5418 (c) 0.1210
9. 0.9554 **10.** 0.6331

11.

12. $\bar{x} = 48.3, s = 15.6$
13. (a) 38.5 (b) under 30; it would be lower
14. (a) 73.8 (b) It might be higher; cell use is spreading.
15. (a) 0.00003 (b) 30
16. 2 (1.8) **17.** 5 (5.4)
18. 0 (0.054) with correct use
19. (a) 0.0158 (b) 0.0901 (c) 0.5383
20. 0.1814

9.1 EXERCISES

1. (a) -8 (b) -8
3. (a) 10 (b) does not exist
5. (a) 0 (b) -6
7. (a) does not exist $(+\infty)$ (b) does not exist $(+\infty)$
  (c) does not exist $(+\infty)$ (d) does not exist
9. (a) 3 (b) -6 (c) does not exist
  (d) -6

11.

x	$f(x)$
0.9	-2.9
0.99	-2.99
0.999	-2.999
1.001	-3.001
1.01	-3.01
1.1	-3.1

$\lim\limits_{x \to 1} f(x) = -3$

13.

x	$f(x)$
0.9	3.5
0.99	3.95
0.999	3.995
1.001	4.995999
1.01	4.9599
1.1	4.59

$\lim\limits_{x \to 1^-} f(x) = 4$ and $\lim\limits_{x \to 1^-} f(x) = 5$. These limits differ so $\lim\limits_{x \to 1} f(x)$ does not exist

15. -1 **17.** -4 **19.** -2 **21.** 6
23. 3/4 **25.** 3/2 **27.** 0 **29.** does not exist
31. -3 **33.** does not exist **35.** does not exist
37. $3x^2$ **39.** $\frac{1}{30}$ **41.** does not exist
43. -4 **45.** 9

47.

a	$(1 + a)^{1/a}$
0.1	2.5937
0.01	2.7048
0.001	2.7169
0.0001	2.7181
0.00001	2.71827
$\downarrow$	$\downarrow$
0	≈ 2.718

49. (a) 2 (b) 6 (c) -8 (d) $-\frac{1}{2}$
51. (a) -6 (b) -85 (c) $-33/17$
53. $150,000
55. (a) $32 (thousands) (b) $55.04 (thousands)
57. (a) $2800 (b) $700 (c) $560
59. (a) 1.52 units/hr (b) 0.85 units/hr (c) lunch
61. (a) 0; $p \to 100^-$ means the water approaches not being treated (containing 100% or all of its impurities); the associated costs of nontreatment approach zero.
  (b) ∞ (c) no, because $C(0)$ is undefined
63. (a) $4,681.25 (b) $4,681.25 (c) $4,681.25

65. $C(x) = \begin{cases} 12.76 + 15.96x & 0 \le x \le 10 \\ 172.36 + 13.56(x - 10) & 10 < x \le 120 \\ 1675 & x > 120 \end{cases}$

$\lim_{x \to 10} C(x) = 172.36$

67. 11,228.00. This corresponds to the Dow Jones opening average.

69. (a) 11.5

   (b) This predicts the percent of U.S. workers in unions as the year approaches 2015.

   (c) Yes. Union membership seems to be dropping, but slowly since 2000.

9.2 EXERCISES

1. (a) continuous

   (b) discontinuous; $f(1)$ does not exist

   (c) discontinuous; $\lim_{x \to 3} f(x)$ does not exist

   (d) discontinuous; $f(0)$ does not exist and $\lim_{x \to 0} f(x)$ does not exist

3. continuous

5. discontinuous; $f(-3)$ does not exist

7. discontinuous; $\lim_{x \to 2} f(x)$ does not exist

9. continuous

11. discontinuity at $x = -2$; $g(-2)$ and $\lim_{x \to -2} g(x)$ do not exist

13. continuous   **15.** continuous

17. discontinuity at $x = -1$; $f(-1)$ does not exist

19. discontinuity at $x = 3$; $\lim_{x \to 3} f(x)$ does not exist

21. vertical asymptote: $x = -2$;

   $\lim_{x \to +\infty} f(x) = 0$; $\lim_{x \to -\infty} f(x) = 0$; $y = 0$

23. vertical asymptotes: $x = -2, x = 3$;

   $\lim_{x \to +\infty} f(x) = 2$; $\lim_{x \to -\infty} f(x) = 2$; $y = 2$

25. (a) 0   (b) $y = 0$ is a horizontal asymptote.

27. (a) 1   (b) $y = 1$ is a horizontal asymptote.

29. (a) 5/3   (b) $y = 5/3$ is a horizontal asymptote.

31. (a) does not exist $(+\infty)$

   (b) no horizontal asymptotes

33. (a)

$\lim_{x \to +\infty} f(x) = 0.5$

   (b) The table indicates $\lim_{x \to +\infty} f(x) = 0.5$.

35. (a) $x = -1000$ (b) 1000

   (c) These values are so large that experimenting with windows may never locate them.

37. $\lim_{x \to \infty} \dfrac{a_n + \dfrac{a_{n-1}}{x} + \cdots + \dfrac{a_1}{x^{n-1}} + \dfrac{a_0}{x^n}}{b_n + \dfrac{b_{n-1}}{x} + \cdots + \dfrac{b_1}{x^{n-1}} + \dfrac{b_0}{x^n}}$

$= \dfrac{a_n + 0 + \cdots + 0 + 0}{b_n + 0 + \cdots + 0 + 0} = \dfrac{a_n}{b_n}$

39. (a) no, not at $p = -8$ (b) yes   (c) yes

   (d) $p > 0$

41. (a) yes, $q = -1$ (b) yes

43. (a) R/i (b) \$10,000   **45.** yes, $0 \le p \le 100$

47. 100%; No, for p to approach 100% (as a limit) requires spending to increase without bound, which is impossible.

49. $R(x)$ is discontinuous at $x = 16,750$; $x = 68,000$; $x = 137,300$; $x = 209,250$; and $x = 373,650$.

51. (a) \$79.40

   (b) $\lim_{x \to 100} C(x) = 19.40$; $\lim_{x \to 500} C(x) = 49.40$

   (c) yes

53. (a) $m(x) = 0.59x + 43.20$; $w(x) = 0.79x + 20.86$

   (b) $r(x) = \dfrac{0.59x + 43.20}{0.79x + 20.86}$

   (c) $\lim_{x \to 0} r(x) \approx 2.07$ means that in 1950 there were about 2.07 men per woman in the U.S. work force. $\lim_{x \to 100} r(x) \approx 1.02$ means that in 2050 it is projected that there will be 1.02 men per woman in the U.S. work force.

   (d) $\lim_{x \to \infty} r(x) \approx 0.75 = 3/4$ means that the long term projection is for 3 men per 4 women in the U.S. work force.

9.3 EXERCISES

1. (a) 6   (b) 8   **3.** (a) $\frac{10}{3}$ (b) -5

5. (a) $-3.9, -3.99$ (b) $-4.1, -4.01$ (c) -4

7. (a) 32   (b) 32   (c) $(4, 64)$

9. (a) verification   (b) -8 (c) -8

   (d) $(-1, 5)$

11. (a) $P(1, 1), A(3, 0)$ (b) $-\frac{1}{2}$ (c) $-\frac{1}{2}$ (d) $-\frac{1}{2}$

13. (a) $P(1, 3), A(0, 3)$ (b) 0   (c) 0   (d) 0

15. (a) $f'(x) = 10x + 6$ (b) $10x + 6$; -14

   (c) -14

17. (a) $p'(q) = 4q + 1$ (b) $4q + 1$; 41   (c) 41

19. (a) 89.000024   (b) 89.0072   (c) ≈ 89

21. (a) 294.000008   (b) 294.0084   (c) ≈ 294

23. -31

25. (a) At A the slope is positive; at B it is negative.

   (b) $-1/3$

27. $f'(4) = 7/3$; $f(4) = -11$ **29.** $y = 5x - 14$

31. (a) a, b, d (b) c (c) A, C, E

33. (a) A, B, C, D (b) A, D

35. (a) $f'(x) = 2x + 1$ (b) $f'(2) = 5$

   (c) $y = 5x - 4$ (d)

37. (a) $f'(x) = 3x^2$ (b) $f'(1) = 3$

   (c) $y = 3x + 1$

(d)

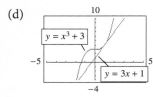

39. (a) 43 dollars per unit (b) 95.50 dollars per unit
(c) The average cost per printer when 100 to 300 are produced (a) is $43 per printer, and the average cost when 300 to 600 are produced (b) is $95.50 per printer.

41. (a) $-100/3$ (b) $-4/3$

43. AB, AC, BC. Average rate is found from the slope of a segment; AB rises most slowly; BC is steepest.

45. (a) $R'(x) = \overline{MR} = 300 - 2x$
(b) 200; the predicted change in revenue from selling the 51st unit is about $200.
(c) -100; the predicted change in revenue from the 201st unit is about -100 dollars.
(d) 0 (e) It changes from increasing to decreasing.

47. 200

49. (a) 100; the expected profit from the sale of the 201st car is $100.
(b) -100; the expected profit from the sale of the 301st car is a loss of $100.

51. (a) 1.039
(b) If humidity changes by 1%, the heat index will change by about 1.039°F.

53. (a) Marginal revenue is given by the slope of the tangent line, which is steeper at 300 cell phones. Hence marginal revenue is greater for 300 cell phones.
(b) Marginal revenue predicts the revenue from the next unit sold. Hence, the 301st item brings in more revenue because the marginal revenue for 300 cell phones is greater than for 700.

9.4 EXERCISES

1. $y' = 0$ **3.** $f'(t) = 1$

5. $y' = -8 + 4x = 4x - 8$ **7.** $f'(x) = 12x^3 - 6x^5$

9. $y' = 50x^4 - 9x^2 + 5$ **11.** $w'(z) = 7z^6 - 18z^5$

13. $g'(x) = 24x^{11} - 30x^5 + 36x^3 + 1$

15. (a) 30 (b) 30 **17.** (a) 6 (b) 6

19. $y' = -5x^{-6} - 8x^{-9} = \frac{-5}{x^6} - \frac{8}{x^9}$

21. $y' = 11x^{8/3} - \frac{7}{2}x^{3/4} - \frac{1}{2}x^{-1/2}$

$= 11\sqrt[3]{x^8} - \frac{7}{2}\sqrt[4]{x^3} - \frac{1}{2\sqrt{x}}$

23. $f'(x) = -4x^{-9/5} - \frac{8}{3}x^{-7/3}$

$= \frac{-4}{\sqrt[5]{x^9}} - \frac{8}{3\sqrt[3]{x^7}}$

25. $g'(x) = \frac{-15}{x^6} - \frac{8}{x^5} + \frac{2}{\sqrt[3]{x^2}}$

27. $y = -7x + 10$ **29.** $y = 3$

31. $(1, -1), (5, 31)$ **33.** $(0, 9), (3, -18)$

35. (a) $-1/2$ (b) -0.5000 (to four decimal places)

37. (a) $f'(x) = 6x^2 + 5$
(b)

Graph of $f'(x)$ and numerical derivative of $f(x)$

39. (a) $h'(x) = -30x^{-4} + 4x^{-7/5} + 2x$

$= \frac{-30}{x^4} + \frac{4}{\sqrt[5]{x^7}} + 2x$

(b)

Graph of $h'(x)$ and numerical derivative of $h(x)$

41. (a) $y = 8x - 3$
(b) (c) $x: 0.7 \to 1.6$; $y: 3.0 \to 7.9$

43. (a) $f'(x) = -2 - 2x$
(b)

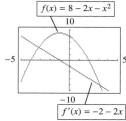

(c) $f'(x) = 0$ at $x = -1$; $f'(x) > 0$ for $x < -1$; $f'(x) < 0$ for $x > -1$
(d) $f(x)$ has a maximum when $x = -1$. $f(x)$ rises for $x < -1$. $f(x)$ falls for $x > -1$.

45. (a) $f'(x) = 3x^2 - 12$
(b)

(c) $f'(x) = 0$ at $x = -2$ and $x = 2$ $f'(x) > 0$ for $x < -2$ and $x > 2$ $f'(x) < 0$ for $-2 < x < 2$

(d) $f(x)$ has a maximum when $x = -2$, a minimum when $x = 2$
   $f(x)$ rises when $x < -2$ and when $x > 2$
   $f(x)$ falls when $-2 < x < 2$

47. (a) 40; the expected change in revenue from the 301st unit is about $40
   (b) -20; the expected change in revenue from the 601st unit is about -20 dollars

49. (a) 920   (b) 926

51. (a) -4; if the price changes to $26, the quantity demanded will change by approximately -4 units
   (b) $-\frac{1}{2}$; if the price changes to $101, the quantity demanded will change by approximately $-\frac{1}{2}$ unit

53. (a) $\overline{C}'(x) = (-4000/x^2) + 0.1$ (b) 200
   (c) $C'(200) = \overline{C}(200) = 95$

55. (a) $-120{,}000$
   (b) If the impurities change from 1% to 2%, then the expected change in cost is $-120{,}000$ (dollars).

57. (a) $WC = 45.0625 - 29.3375s^{0.16}$
   (b) -0.31
   (c) At 15° F, if the wind speed changes by $+1$ mph (to 26 mph), then the wind chill will change by approximately -0.31°F.

59. (a) $S(x) = 0.105x^{2.53}$
   (b) 20.113 million subscriberships per year
   (c) $S'(x) = 0.266x^{1.53}$
      $S'(23) \approx 32.19$ means that for the next year (2009), the number of subscriberships will change by about 32.19 million.

61. (a) $P(t) = -0.0000729t^3 + 0.0138t^2 + 1.98t + 183$
   (b) $P'(t) = -0.0002187t^2 + 0.0276t + 1.98$
   (c) 2000: $P'(40) \approx 2.73$ means that for 2001, the U.S. population will rise by about 2.73 million people.
      2025: $P'(65) \approx 2.85$ means that for 2026, the U.S. population is expected to rise by about 2.85 million people.

9.5 EXERCISES

1. $y' = 15x^2 - 14x - 6$

3. $f'(x) = (x^{12} + 3x^4 + 4)(6x^2) + (2x^3 - 1) \cdot (12x^{11} + 12x^3) = 30x^{14} - 12x^{11} + 42x^6 - 12x^3 + 24x^2$

5. $y' = (7x^6 - 5x^4 + 2x^2 - 1)(36x^8 + 21x^6 - 10x + 3) + (4x^9 + 3x^7 - 5x^2 + 3x)(42x^5 - 20x^3 + 4x)$

7. $y' = (x^2 + x + 1)(\frac{1}{3}x^{-2/3} - x^{-1/2}) + (x^{1/3} - 2x^{1/2} + 5)(2x + 1)$

9. (a) 40   (b) 40

11. $\dfrac{dp}{dq} = \dfrac{2q^2 - 2q - 6}{(2q - 1)^2}$

13. $\dfrac{dy}{dx} = \dfrac{4x^5 - 4x^3 - 16x}{(x^4 - 2x^2 + 5)^2}$

15. $\dfrac{dz}{dx} = 2x + \dfrac{2x - x^2}{(1 - x - 2x^2)^2}$

17. $\dfrac{dp}{dq} = \dfrac{2q + 1}{\sqrt[3]{q^2}(1 - q)^2}$ 19. $y' = \dfrac{2x^3 - 6x^2 - 8}{(x - 2)^2}$

21. (a) $\frac{3}{5}$ (b) $\frac{3}{5}$ 23. $y = 44x - 32$

25. $y = \frac{10}{3}x - \frac{10}{3}$ 27. 104

29. 1.3333 (to four decimal places)

31. (a) $f'(x) = 3x^2 - 6x - 24$

Graph of both $f'(x)$ and numerical derivative of $f(x)$
(b) Horizontal tangents where $f'(x) = 0$; at $x = -2$ and $x = 4$

(c)

33. (a) $y' = \dfrac{x^2 - 4x}{(x - 2)^2}$

Graph of both y' and the numerical derivative of y
(b) Horizontal tangents where $y' = 0$; at $x = 0$ and $x = 4$
(c)

35. (a) $f'(x) = \dfrac{20x}{(x^2 + 1)^2}$ (b)
   (c) $f' = 0$ at $x = 0$
      $f' > 0$ for $x > 0$
      $f' < 0$ for $x < 0$
   (d) f has a minimum at $x = 0$.
      f is increasing for $x > 0$.
      f is decreasing for $x < 0$.

37. $f'(x) = \displaystyle\lim_{h \to 0} \dfrac{\dfrac{u(x + h)}{v(x + h)} - \dfrac{u(x)}{v(x)}}{h}$

$= \displaystyle\lim_{h \to 0} \dfrac{u(x + h)v(x) - u(x)v(x + h)}{h \cdot v(x)v(x + h)}$

$= \displaystyle\lim_{h \to 0} \dfrac{u(x + h)v(x) - u(x)v(x) + u(x)v(x) - u(x)v(x + h)}{h \cdot v(x)v(x + h)}$

$= \displaystyle\lim_{h \to 0} \dfrac{v(x)\left[\dfrac{u(x + h) - u(x)}{h}\right] - u(x)\left[\dfrac{v(x + h) - v(x)}{h}\right]}{v(x)v(x + h)}$

$= \dfrac{v(x)u'(x) - u(x)v'(x)}{[v(x)]^2}$

39. $C'(p) = 810{,}000/(100 - p)^2$

41. $R'(49) \approx 30.00$ The expected revenue from the sale of the next unit (the 50th) is about $30.00.

43. $R'(5) = -50$ As the group changes by 1 person (to 31), the revenue will drop by about $50.

45. $S = 1000x - x^2$

47. $\dfrac{dR}{dn} = \dfrac{r(1 - r)}{[1 + (n - 1)r]^2}$

49. (a) $P'(6) \approx 0.045$ During the next (7th) month of the campaign, the proportion of voters who recognize the candidate will change by about 0.045, or 4.5%.

  (b) $P'(12) \approx -0.010$ During the next (13th) month of the campaign, the proportion of voters who recognize the candidate will drop by about 0.010, or 1%.

  (c) It is better for $P'(t)$ to be positive—that is, to have increasing recognition.

51. (a) $f'(20) \approx -0.79$

  (b) At 0°F, if the wind speed changes by 1 mph (to 21 mph), the wind chill will change by about -0.79°F.

53. (a) $B'(t) = (0.01t + 3)(0.04766t - 9.79)$
   $+ (0.01)(0.02383t^2 - 9.79t + 3097.19)$

  (b) $B'(60) = 1.00634$ means that in 2010 the number of beneficiaries will be changing at the rate of 1.00634 million per year.

  (c) [2000, 2010]: 0.85
   [2010, 2020]: 1.55
   [2000, 2020]: 1.2
   The average rate over [2000, 2010] is best but is still off by almost 0.15 million per year.

55. (a) $p'(t) = \dfrac{2154.06}{(1.38t + 64.1)^2}$

  (b) 2005: $p'(55) \approx 0.110$; 2020: $p'(70) \approx 0.083$

  (c) $p'(55)$ means that in 2005, the percent of women in the work force was changing about 0.110 percentage points per year. $p'(70)$ predicts the rate in 2020 will be 0.083 percentage points per year.

9.6 EXERCISES

1. $\dfrac{dy}{du} = 3u^2, \dfrac{du}{dx} = 2x, \dfrac{dy}{dx} = 3u^2 \cdot 2x = 6x(x^2 + 1)^2$

3. $\dfrac{dy}{du} = 4u^3, \dfrac{du}{dx} = 8x - 1, \dfrac{dy}{dx} = 4u^3(8x - 1)$
   $= 4(8x - 1)(4x^2 - x + 8)^3$

5. $f'(x) = 20(3x^5 - 2)^{19}(15x^4) = 300x^4(3x^5 - 2)^{19}$

7. $h'(x) = 6(x^5 - 2x^3 + 5)^7(5x^4 - 6x^2)$
   $= 6x^2(5x^2 - 6)(x^5 - 2x^3 + 5)^7$

9. $s'(t) = 5 - 9(2t^4 + 7)^2(8t^3) = 5 - 72t^3(2t^4 + 7)^2$

11. $g'(x) = -2(x^4 - 5x)^{-3}(4x^3 - 5) = \dfrac{-2(4x^3 - 5)}{(x^4 - 5x)^3}$

13. $f'(x) = -12(2x^5 + 1)^{-5}(10x^4) = \dfrac{-120x^4}{(2x^5 + 1)^5}$

15. $g'(x) = -\dfrac{3}{4}(2x^3 + 3x + 5)^{-7/4}(6x^2 + 3)$
   $= \dfrac{-3(6x^2 + 3)}{4(2x^3 + 3x + 5)^{7/4}}$

17. $y' = \dfrac{1}{2}(3x^2 + 4x + 9)^{-1/2}(6x + 4)$
   $= \dfrac{3x + 2}{\sqrt{3x^2 + 4x + 9}}$

19. $y' = \dfrac{66}{9}(x^3 - 7)^5(3x^2) = 22x^2(x^3 - 7)^5$

21. $y' = \dfrac{15(3x + 1)^4 - 3}{7}$

23. (a) and (b) 96,768

25. (a) and (b) 2   **27.** $y = 3x - 5$

29. $9x - 5y = 2$

31. (a) $f'(x) = 6x(x^2 - 4)^2$

  (b)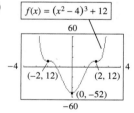

  (c) $x = 0, x = 2,$
   $x = -2$

  (d) $(0, -52),$
   $(2, 12),$
   $(-2, 12)$

  Graph of both $f'(x)$ and numerical derivative of $f(x)$

  (e)

33. (a) $f'(x) = 8x(1 - x^2)^{1/3}$

  (b)

  (c) $f'(x) = 0$ at $x = -1, x = 0, x = 1$
   $f'(x) > 0$ for $x < -1$ and $0 < x < 1$
   $f'(x) < 0$ for $-1 < x < 0$ and $x > 1$

  (d) $f(x)$ has a maximum at $x = -1$ and $x = 1$, a minimum at $x = 0$.
   $f(x)$ is increasing for $x < -1$ and $0 < x < 1$.
   $f(x)$ is decreasing for $-1 < x < 0$ and $x > 1$.

35. (a) $y' = 2x^2$ (b) $y' = -2/x^4$

  (c) $y' = 2(2x)^2$ (d) $y' = \dfrac{-18}{(3x)^4}$

37. 120 in./sec

39. $1499.85 (approximately); if a 101st unit is sold, revenue will change by about $1499.85

41. (a) -0.114 (approximately)

(b) If the price changes by \$1, to \$22, the weekly sales volume will change by approximately -0.114 thousand unit.

43. (a) $-\$3.20$ per unit

(b) If the quantity demanded changes from 49 to 50 units, the change in price will be about $-\$3.20$.

45. $\dfrac{dy}{dx} = \left(\dfrac{8k}{5}\right)(x - x_0)^{3/5}$

47. $\dfrac{dp}{dq} = -100(2q + 1)^{-3/2} = \dfrac{-100}{(2q + 1)^{3/2}}$

49. $\dfrac{dK_c}{dv} = 8(4v + 1)^{-1/2} = \dfrac{8}{\sqrt{4v + 1}}$

51. (a) \$658.75. If the interest changed from 6% to 7%, the amount of the investment would change by about \$658.75.

(b) \$2156.94. If the interest rate changed from 12% to 13%, the amount of the investment would change by about \$2156.94.

53. (a) 2008: $A'(8) \approx 126.3$; 2015: $A'(15) \approx 231.4$ These mean that the total national expenditures for health are predicted to change by about \$126.3 billion from 2008 to 2009 and about \$231.4 billion from 2015 to 2016.

(b) The average rate for 2014 to 2015 is best: \$228 billion/year.

55. (a) 2005: $G'(5) \approx 1370.64$; 2015: $G'(15) \approx 934.56$ These mean that the GDP was changing at the rate of \$1370.64 billion per year in 2005 and \$934.5 billion per year in 2015.

(b) 912.5 (billion per year)

(c) 2010: $G'(10) \approx 1024.86$. The answer from part (b) is not a good approximation to $G'(10)$.

9.7 EXERCISES

1. 0   **3.** $4(-4x^{-5})$; $-16/x^5$

5. $15x^2 + 4(-x^{-2})$; $15x^2 - 4/x^2$

7. $(x^2 - 2)1 + (x + 4)(2x)$; $3x^2 + 8x - 2$

9. $\dfrac{x^2(3x^2) - (x^3 + 1)(2x)}{(x^2)^2}$; $(x^3 - 2)/x^3$

11. $(3x^2 - 4)(x^3 - 4x)^9$

13. $\frac{5}{3}x^3[3(4x^5 - 5)^2(20x^4)] + (4x^5 - 5)^3(5x^2)$; $5x^2(4x^5 - 5)^2(24x^5 - 5)$

15. $(x - 1)^2(2x) + (x^2 + 1)2(x - 1)$; $2(x - 1)(2x^2 - x + 1)$

17. $\dfrac{(x^2 + 1)3(x^2 - 4)^2(2x) - (x^2 - 4)^3(2x)}{(x^2 + 1)^2}$; $\dfrac{2x(x^2 - 4)^2(2x^2 + 7)}{(x^2 + 1)^2}$

19. $3[(q + 1)(q^3 - 3)]^2[(q + 1)3q^2 + (q^3 - 3)1]$; $3(4q^3 + 3q^2 - 3)[(q + 1)(q^3 - 3)]^2$

21. $4[x^2(x^2 + 3x)]^3[x^2(2x + 3) + (x^2 + 3x)(2x)]$; $4x^2(4x + 9)[x^2(x^2 + 3x)]^3 = 4x^{11}(4x + 9)(x + 3)^3$

23. $4\left(\dfrac{2x - 1}{x^2 + x}\right)^3\left[\dfrac{(x^2 + x)2 - (2x - 1)(2x + 1)}{(x^2 + x)^2}\right]$; $\dfrac{4(-2x^2 + 2x + 1)(2x - 1)^3}{(x^2 + x)^5}$

25. $(8x^4 + 3)^2 3(x^3 - 4x)^2(3x^2 - 4) + (x^3 - 4x)^3 2(8x^4 + 3)(32x^3)$; $(8x^4 + 3)(x^3 - 4x)^2(136x^6 - 352x^4 + 27x^2 - 36)$

27. $\dfrac{(4 - x^2)\frac{1}{3}(x^2 + 5)^{-2/3}(2x) - (x^2 + 5)^{1/3}(-2x)}{(4 - x^2)^2}$; $\dfrac{2x(2x^2 + 19)}{3\sqrt[3]{(x^2 + 5)^2}(4 - x^2)^2}$

29. $(x^2)\frac{1}{4}(4x - 3)^{-3/4}(4) + (4x - 3)^{1/4}(2x)$; $(9x^2 - 6x)/\sqrt[4]{(4x - 3)^3}$

31. $(2x)\frac{1}{2}(x^3 + 1)^{-1/2}(3x^2) + (x^3 - 1)^{1/2}(2)$; $(5x^3 + 2)/\sqrt{x^3 + 1}$

33. (a) $F_1'(x) = 12x^3(x^4 + 1)^4$

(b) $F_2'(x) = \dfrac{-12x^3}{(x^4 + 1)^6}$

(c) $F_3'(x) = 12x^3(3x^4 + 1)^4$

(d) $F_4'(x) = \dfrac{-300x^3}{(5x^4 + 1)^6}$

35. $dP/dx = 90(3x + 1)^2$

37. (a) \$59,900

(b) An 11th camper sold would change revenue by about \$59,900.

39. $dC/dy = 1/\sqrt{y + 1} + 0.4$

41. $dV/dx = 144 - 96x + 12x^2$

43. -1.6; This means that from the 9th to the 10th week, sales are expected to change by -1600 dollars (decrease).

45. (a) 2005: \$350/year; 2015: \$549/year

(b) In 2015, the per capita expenditures for health care are predicted to be changing at the rate of \$549 per year.

(c) Average rate $= 380$; This approximates the instantaneous rate in 2005 quite well.

9.8 EXERCISES

1. $180x^8 - 360x^3 - 72x$ **3.** $6x - 2x^{-3}$

5. $6x + \frac{1}{4}x^{-3/2}$ **7.** $60x^2 - 96$ **9.** $1008x^6 - 720x^3$

11. $-6/x^4$ **13.** $20x^3 + \frac{1}{4}x^{-3/2}$ **15.** $\frac{3}{8}(x + 1)^{-5/2}$

17. 0   **19.** $-15/(16x^{7/2})$ **21.** $24(4x - 1)^{-5/2}$

23. $-2(x + 1)^{-3}$ **25.** 26

27. 16.0000 (to four decimal places)

29. 0.0004261

31. (a) $f'(x) = 3x^2 - 6x$ $f''(x) = 6x - 6$

(b)

(c) $f''(x) = 0$ at $x = 1$
$f''(x) > 0$ for $x > 1$
$f''(x) < 0$ for $x < 1$

(d) $f'(x)$ has a minimum at $x = 1$.
     $f'(x)$ is increasing for $x > 1$.
     $f'(x)$ is decreasing for $x < 1$.
(e) $f''(x) < 0$ (f) $f''(x) > 0$.

33. $a = 0.12$ m/sec^2 **35.** -0.02 \$/unit per unit

37. (a) $\dfrac{dR}{dm} = mc - m^2$ (b) $\dfrac{d^2R}{dm^2} = c - 2m$

(c) second

39. (a) 0.0009 (approximately)
(b) When 1 more unit is sold (beyond 25), the marginal revenue will change by about 0.0009 thousand dollars per unit, or \$0.90 per unit.

41. (a) $S' = \dfrac{-3}{(t+3)^2} + \dfrac{36}{(t+3)^3}$ (b) $S''(15) = 0$
(c) After 15 weeks, the rate of change of the rate of sales is zero because the rate of sales reaches a minimum value.

43. (a) $y' = 1.175x^{-0.06}$ (b) $y'' = -0.0705x^{-1.06}$
(c) $y'(18,000) \approx 0.65$; $y''(18,000) \approx 0$
     These mean that when the total Starbucks stores number 18,000, the number of U.S. stores is expected to be changing at the rate of 0.65 U.S. stores per total store (or 65 U.S. per 100 total), and this rate is expected to be constant there.

45. (a) $R(x) = -0.0002x^3 + 0.052x^2 - 4.06x + 192$
(b) $R'(x) = -0.0006x^2 + 0.104x - 4.06$
(c) $R''(x) = -0.0012x + 0.104$
(d) $R'(90) \approx 0.44$; $R''(90) \approx -0.004$
     In 2040, the economic dependency ratio is expected to be changing at the rate of 0.44 per year, but this rate is expected to be changing at the rate of –0.004 per year per year.

9.9 EXERCISES

1. (a) $\overline{MR} = 4$
(b) The sale of each additional item brings in \$4 revenue at all levels of production.

3. (a) \$3500; this is revenue from the sale of 100 units.
(b) $\overline{MR} = 36 - 0.02x$
(c) \$34; Revenue will increase by about \$34 if a 101st item is sold and by about \$102 if 3 additional units past 100 units are sold.
(d) Actual revenue from the sale of the 101st item is \$33.99.

5. (a) $R(x) = 80x - 0.4x^2$ (in hundreds of dollars)
(b) 7500 subscribers $(x = 75)$; $R = \$375,000$
(c) Lower the price per month.
(d) $\overline{MR} = R'(x) = 80 - 0.8x$; when $p = 50, x = 75$
     $\overline{MR}(75) = 20$ means that if the number of customers increased from 75 to 76 (hundred), the revenue would increase by about 20 (hundred dollars), or \$2000. This means the company should try to increase subscribers by lowering its monthly charge.

7. (a)
(b) $x = 1800$
(c) \$32,400

9. $\overline{MC} = 8$ **11.** $\overline{MC} = 13 + 2x$
13. $\overline{MC} = 3x^2 - 12x + 24$ **15.** $\overline{MC} = 27 + 3x^2$
17. (a) \$10; the cost will increase by about \$10.
(b) \$11
19. \$46; the cost will increase by about \$46. For 3 additional units, the cost will increase by about \$138.
21.

23. (a) The 101st item costs more. The tangent line slope is greater at $x = 100$ than at $x = 500$, and the slope of the tangent line gives the marginal cost and predicts the cost of the next item.
(b) More efficient. As x increases, the slopes of the tangents decrease. This means that the costs of additional items decrease as x increases.

25. $\overline{MP} = 5$; This means that for each additional unit sold, profit changes by \$5.

27. (a) \$5600   (b) $\overline{MP} = 20 - 0.02x$
(c) 10; profit will increase by about \$10 if a 501st unit is sold.
(d) 9.99; the sale of the 501st item results in a profit of \$9.99.

29. (a) $P(x) = R(x) - C(x)$, so profit is the distance between $R(x)$ and $C(x)$ (when $R(x)$ is above $C(x)$). $P(100) < P(700) < P(400)$; $P(100) < 0$, so there is a loss when 100 units are sold.
(b) This asks us to rank $\overline{MP}(100)$, $\overline{MP}(400)$, and $\overline{MP}(700)$. Because $\overline{MP} = \overline{MR} - \overline{MC}$, compare the slopes of the tangents to $R(x)$ and $C(x)$ at the three x-values. Thus $\overline{MP}(700) < \overline{MP}(400) < \overline{MP}(100)$. $\overline{MP}(700) < 0$ because $C(x)$ is steeper than $R(x)$ at $x = 700$. At $x = 100$, $R(x)$ is much steeper than $C(x)$.

31. (a) $A < B < C$. Amount of profit is the height of the graph. There is a loss at A.
(b) $C < B < A$. Marginal profit is the slope of the tangent to the graph. Marginals (slopes) are positive at all three points.

33. (a)

(b) 15 hundred units
(c) 15 hundred units
(d) \$25 thousand

35. 700   **37.** \$9000

CHAPTER 9 REVIEW EXERCISES

1. (a) 2   (b) 2   **2.** (a) 0   (b) 0
3. (a) 2   (b) 1   **4.** (a) 2   (b) does not exist
5. (a) does not exist   (b) 2
6. (a) does not exist   (b) does not exist
7. 55   **8.** 0   **9.** -2 **10.** 4/5   **11.** $\frac{1}{2}$
12. $\frac{1}{5}$ **13.** no limit   **14.** 0   **15.** 4
16. no limit   **17.** 3   **18.** no limit   **19.** $6x$
20. $1 - 4x$ **21.** -14 **22.** 5
23. (a) yes   (b) no   **24.** (a) yes   (b) no
25. 2   **26.** no limit   **27.** 1   **28.** no   **29.** yes
30. yes   **31.** discontinuity at $x = 5$
32. discontinuity at $x = 2$ **33.** continuous
34. discontinuity at $x = 1$
35. (a) $x = 0, x = 1$ (b) 0   (c) 0
36. (a) $x = -1, x = 0$ (b) $\frac{1}{2}$ (c) $\frac{1}{2}$
37. $-2; y = -2$ is a horizontal asymptote.
38. 0; $y = 0$ is a horizontal asymptote.
39. 7   **40.** true   **41.** false
42. $f'(x) = 6x + 2$ **43.** $f'(x) = 1 - 2x$
44. $[-1, 0]$; the segment over this interval is steeper.
45. (a) no   (b) no   **46.** (a) yes   (b) no
47. (a) -5.9171 (to four decimal places)   (b) -5.9
48. (a) 4.9/3   (b) 7   **49.** about $-1/4$
50. B, C, A: $B < 0$ and $C < 0$; the tangent line at $x = 6$ falls more steeply than the segment over $[2, 10]$.
51. $20x^4 - 18x^2$ **52.** $90x^8 - 30x^5 + 4$
53. 1   **54.** $1/(2\sqrt{x})$ **55.** 0   **56.** $-4/(3\sqrt[3]{x^4})$
57. $\dfrac{-1}{x^2} + \dfrac{1}{2\sqrt{x^3}}$ **58.** $\dfrac{-3}{x^3} - \dfrac{1}{3\sqrt[3]{x^2}}$
59. $y = 15x - 18$ **60.** $y = 34x - 48$
61. (a) $x = 0, x = 2$ (b) $(0, 1) \, (2, -3)$
(c)

```
        f(x) = x³ − 3x² + 1
              5


            (0, 1)
   −3 ─────────────── 4


            (2, −3)
             −5
```

62. (a) $x = 0, x = 2, x = -2$
(b) $(0, 8) \, (2, -24) \, (-2, -24)$

(c)

```
    f(x) = x⁶ − 6x⁴ + 8
          20
            (0, 8)
   −4 ─────────────── 4

      (−2, −24)  (2, −24)
          −30
```

63. $9x^2 - 26x + 4$ **64.** $21x^6 + 4x^3 + 27x^2$
65. $\dfrac{15q^2}{(2q^3 + 1)^2}$ **66.** $\dfrac{1 - 3t}{[2\sqrt{t}(3t + 1)^2]}$ **67.** $\dfrac{9x + 2}{2\sqrt{x}}$
68. $\dfrac{5x^6 + 2x^4 + 20x^3 - 3x^2 - 4x}{(x^3 + 1)^2}$
69. $(9x^2 - 24x)(x^3 - 4x^2)^2$
70. $6(30x^5 + 24x^3)(5x^6 + 6x^4 + 5)^5$
71. $72x^3(2x^4 - 9)^8$ **72.** $\dfrac{-(3x^2 - 4)}{2\sqrt{(x^3 - 4x)^3}}$
73. $2x(2x^4 + 5)^7(34x^4 + 5)$ **74.** $\dfrac{-2(3x + 1)(x + 12)}{(x^2 - 4)^2}$
75. $36[(3x + 1)(2x^3 - 1)]^{11}(8x^3 + 2x^2 - 1)$
76. $\dfrac{3}{(1 - x)^4}$ **77.** $\dfrac{(2x^2 - 4)}{\sqrt{x^2 - 4}}$ **78.** $\dfrac{2x - 1}{(3x - 1)^{4/3}}$
79. $y'' = \frac{-1}{4}x^{-3/2} - 2$ **80.** $y'' = 12x^2 - 2/x^3$
81. $\dfrac{d^5y}{dx^5} = 0$ **82.** $\dfrac{d^5y}{dx^5} = -30(1 - x)$
83. $\dfrac{d^3y}{dx^3} = -4[(x^2 - 4)^{3/2}]$ **84.** $\dfrac{d^4y}{dx^4} = \dfrac{2x(x^2 - 3)}{(x^2 + 1)^3}$
85. (a) \$400,000   (b) \$310,000   (c) \$90,000
86. (a) \$70,000; this is fixed costs.
(b) \$0; $x = 1000$ is break-even.
87. (a) \$140 per unit
(b) $\overline{C}(x) \to +\infty$; the limit does not exist.
88. (a) $C(x) \to +\infty$; the limit does not exist. As the number of units produced increases without bound, so does the total cost.
(b) \$60 per unit. As more units are produced, the average cost of each unit approaches \$60.
89. The average annual percent change of (a) elderly men in the work force is 0.29 percentage points per year and of (b) elderly women in the work force is 0.26 percentage points per year.
90. (a) Annual average rate of change of percent of elderly men in the work force:
1950–1960: -1.27 percentage points per year
2000–2008: 0.48 percentage points per year
(b) Annual average rate of change of percent of elderly women in the work force
1950–1960: 0.11 percentage points per year
2000–2008: 0.49 percentage points per year
91. (a) $x'(10) = -1$ means that if price changes from \$10 to \$11, the number of units demanded will change by about -1.
(b) $x'(20) = -\frac{1}{4}$ means that if price changes from \$20 to \$21, the number of units demanded will change by about $-\frac{1}{4}$.

92. $h(100) \approx 4.15$; $h'(100) \approx 0.08$ means that when the updraft speed is 100 mph, the hail diameter is about 4.15 inches (softball-sized) and changing at the rate of 0.08 inch per mph of updraft.

93. The slope of the tangent at A gives $\overline{MR}(A)$. The tangent line at A is steeper (so has greater slope) than the tangent line at B. Hence, $\overline{MR}(A) > \overline{MR}(B)$, so the $(A + 1)$st unit will bring more revenue.

94. $R'(10) = 1570$. Raised. An 11th rent increase of $30 (and hence an 11th vacancy) would change revenue by about $1570.

95. (a) $P(20) = 23$ means productivity is 23 units per hour after 20 hours of training and experience.
(b) $P'(20) \approx 1.4$ means that the 21st hour of training or experience will change productivity by about 1.4 units per hour.

96. $\dfrac{dq}{dp} = \dfrac{-p}{\sqrt{0.02p^2 + 500}}$

97. $x'(10) = \frac{1}{6}$ means if price changes from $10 to $11, the number of units supplied will change by about $\frac{1}{6}$.

98. $s''(t) = a = -2t^{-3/2}$; $s''(4) = -0.25$ ft/sec/sec

99. $P'(x) = 70 - 0.2x$; $P''(x) = -0.2$
$P'(300) = 10$ means that the 301st unit brings in about $10 in profit.
$P''(300) = -0.2$ means that marginal profit $(P'(x))$ is changing at the rate of -0.2 dollars per unit, per unit.

100. (a) $\overline{MC} = 6x + 6$ (b) 186
(c) If a 31st unit is produced, costs will change by about $186.

101. $C'(4) = 53$ means that a 5th unit produced would change total costs by about $53.

102. (a) $\overline{MR} = 40 - 0.04x$ (b) $x = 1000$ units

103. $\overline{MP}(10) = 48$ means that if an 11th unit is sold, profit will change by about $48.

104. (a) $\overline{MR} = 80 - 0.08x$ (b) 72
(c) If a 101st unit is sold, revenue will change by about $72.

105. $\dfrac{120x(x + 1)}{(2x + 1)^2}$ **106.** $\overline{MP} = 4500 - 3x^2$

107. $\overline{MP} = 16 - 0.2x$

108. (a) C: Tangent line to $R(x)$ has smallest slope at C, so $\overline{MR}(C)$ is smallest and the next item at C will earn the least revenue.
(b) B: $R(x) > C(x)$ at both B and C. Distance between $R(x)$ and $C(x)$ gives the amount of profit and is greatest at B.
(c) A: $\overline{MR}$ greatest at A and $\overline{MC}$ least at A, as seen from the slopes of the tangents. Hence $\overline{MP}(A)$ is greatest, so the next item at A will give the greatest profit.
(d) C: $\overline{MC}(C) > \overline{MR}(C)$, as seen from the slopes of the tangents. Hence $\overline{MP}(C) < 0$, so the next unit sold reduces profit.

CHAPTER 9 TEST

1. (a) $\frac{3}{4}$ (b) $-8/5$ (c) $9/8$ (d) does not exist

2. (a) $f'(x) = \lim\limits_{h \to 0} \dfrac{f(x + h) - f(x)}{h}$
(b) $f'(x) = 6x - 1$

3. $x = 0, x = 8$

4. (a) $\dfrac{dB}{dW} = 0.523$ (b) $p'(t) = 90t^9 - 42t^6 - 17$
(c) $\dfrac{dy}{dx} = \dfrac{99x^2 - 24x^9}{(2x^7 + 11)^2}$
(d) $f'(x) = (3x^5 - 2x + 3)(40x^9 + 40x^3) + (4x^{10} + 10x^4 - 17)(15x^4 - 2)$
(e) $g'(x) = 9(10x^4 + 21x^2)(2x^5 + 7x^3 - 5)^{11}$
(f) $y' = 2(8x^2 + 5x + 18)(2x + 5)^5$
(g) $f'(x) = \dfrac{6}{\sqrt{x}} + \dfrac{20}{x^3}$

5. $\dfrac{d^3y}{dx^3} = 6 + 60x^{-6}$

6. (a) $y = -15x - 5$ (b) $(4, -90), (-2, 18)$

7. -15 **8.** (a) 2 (b) does not exist (c) -4

9. $g(-2) = 8$; $\lim\limits_{x \to -2^-} g(x) = 8$, $\lim\limits_{x \to -2^+} g(x) = -8$
$\therefore \lim\limits_{x \to -2} g(x)$ does not exist and $g(x)$ is not continuous at $x = -2$.

10. (a) $\overline{MR} = R'(x) = 250 - 0.02x$
(b) $R(72) = 17{,}948.16$ means that when 72 units are sold, revenue is $17,948.16.
$R'(72) = 248.56$ means that the expected revenue from the 73rd unit is about $248.56.

11. (a) $P(x) = 50x - 0.01x^2 - 10{,}000$
(b) $\overline{MP} = 50 - 0.02x$
(c) $\overline{MP}(1000) = 30$ means that the predicted profit from the sale of the 1001st unit is approximately $30.

12. 104

13. (a) -5 (b) -1 (c) 4 (d) does not exist
(e) 2 (f) $3/2$ (g) $-4, 1, 3, 6$
(h) $-4, 3, 6$
(i) $f'(-2) <$ average rate over $[-2, 2] < f'(2)$

14. (a) $2/3$ (b) -4 (c) $2/3$

15. (a) B: $R(x) > C(x)$ at B, so there is profit. Distance between $R(x)$ and $C(x)$ gives the amount of profit.
(b) A: $C(x) > R(x)$
(c) A and B: slope of $R(x)$ is greater than the slope of $C(x)$. Hence $\overline{MR} > \overline{MC}$ and $\overline{MP} > 0$.
(d) C: Slope of $C(x)$ is greater than the slope of $R(x)$. Hence $\overline{MC} > \overline{MR}$ and $\overline{MP} < 0$.

10.1 EXERCISES

1. (a) $(1, 5)$ (b) $(4, 1)$ (c) $(-1, 2)$
3. (a) $(1, 5)$ (b) $(4, 1)$ (c) $(-1, 2)$
5. (a) $3, 7$ (b) $3 < x < 7$ (c) $x < 3, x > 7$
(d) 7 (e) 3

7. (a) $x = 0, x = 4$

(b)

min: $(4, -58)$; max: $(0, 6)$

9. (a) $x = -2, x = 0$

(b) max: $(-2, 5)$; min: $(0, -11)$

11. (a) max: $(-1, 6)$; min: $(1, 2)$

(b) $dy/dx = 3x^2 - 3$; $x = 1, x = -1$

(c) $(1, 2), (-1, 6)$

(d) yes

13. (a) HPI: $(-1, -3)$

(b) $dy/dx = 3x^2 + 6x + 3$; $x = -1$

(c) $(-1, -3)$

(d) yes

15. (a) $\dfrac{dy}{dx} = x - 1$ (e)

(b) $x = 1$

(c) $\left(1, -\tfrac{1}{2}\right)$

(d) decreasing: $x < 1$
increasing: $x > 1$

17. (a) $dy/dx = x^2 + x - 2$

(b) $x = -2, x = 1$ (c) $\left(-2, \tfrac{13}{3}\right), \left(1, -\tfrac{1}{6}\right)$

(d) increasing: $x < -2$ and $x > 1$
decreasing: $-2 < x < 1$

(e)

19. (a) $\dfrac{dy}{dx} = \dfrac{2}{3x^{1/3}}$ (b) $x = 0$ (c) $(0, 0)$

(d) decreasing: $x < 0$
increasing: $x > 0$

(e)

21. (a) $f'(x) = 0$ at $x = -\tfrac{1}{2}$
$f'(x) > 0$ for $x < -\tfrac{1}{2}$
$f'(x) < 0$ for $x > -\tfrac{1}{2}$

(b) $f'(x) = -1 - 2x$ verifies these conclusions.

23. (a) $f'(x) = 0$ at $x = 0, x = -3, x = 3$
$f'(x) > 0$ for $-3 < x < 3, x \neq 0$
$f'(x) < 0$ for $x < -3$ and $x > 3$

(b) $f'(x) = \tfrac{1}{3}x^2(9 - x^2)$ verifies these conclusions.

25. HPI $\left(1, \tfrac{4}{3}\right)$
no max or min

27. $(-6, 128)$ rel max;
$\left(4, -38\tfrac{2}{3}\right)$ rel min

29. $(-1, 3)$ rel max;
$(1, -1)$ rel min;
HPI $(0, 1)$

31. $(1, 1)$ rel max;
$(0, 0), (2, 0)$ rel min

33. $(3, 4)$ rel max;
$(5, 0)$ rel min; HPI $(0, 0)$

35. $(0, 0)$ rel max;
$(2, -4.8)$ rel min

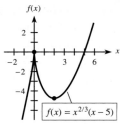

$f(x) = x^{2/3}(x - 5)$

37. $(50, 300{,}500)$, $(100, 238{,}000)$
$0 \le x \le 150, 0 \le y \le 301{,}000$

39. $(0, -40{,}000)$, $(60, 4{,}280{,}000)$
$-20 \le x \le 90, \ -500{,}000 \le y \le 5{,}000{,}000$

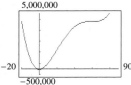

41. $(0, 2)$
$(0.1, 1.99975)$
$-0.1 \le x \le 0.2$
$1.9997 \le y \le 2.0007$

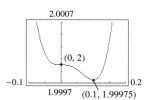

43. critical values: $x = -1, x = 2$
$f(x)$ increasing for $x < -1$ and $x > 2$
$f(x)$ decreasing for $-1 < x < 2$
rel max at $x = -1$; rel min at $x = 2$

possible graph of $f(x)$

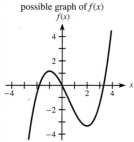

45. critical values: $x = 0, x = 3$
$f(x)$ increasing for $x > 3$
$f(x)$ decreasing for $x < 3, x \ne 0$
rel min at $x = 3$; HPI at $x = 0$

possible graph of $f(x)$

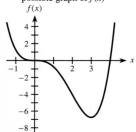

47. Graph on left is $f(x)$; on right is $f'(x)$ because $f(x)$ is increasing when $f'(x) > 0$ (i.e., above the x-axis) and $f(x)$ is decreasing when $f'(x) < 0$ (i.e., below the x-axis).

49. decreasing for $t \ge 0$

51. (a) $2 \pm \sqrt{13}$
(b) $2 + \sqrt{13} \approx 5.6$
(c) $0 \le t < 2 + \sqrt{13}$

(d)

$(5.6, 164)$ Rel max

$P(t) = 27t + 6t^2 - t^3$

53. (a) $x = 5$ (b) $0 < x < 5$
(c) increasing for $x > 5$

55. (a) at $x = 150$, increasing; at $x = 250$, changing from increasing to decreasing; at $x = 350$, decreasing
(b) increasing for $x < 250$ (c) 250 units

57. (a) $t = 6$ (b) 6 weeks

59. (a) 10   (b) January 1

61. (a) $x \approx 86.2$ (in 1937). Model achieves its maximum later than the data.
(b) No. For 2010, $R'(160) \approx -3.4$ thousand per year; not approaching 0.

63. (a) $y = 0.000123x^3 - 0.0205x^2 + 0.910x - 2.91$
(b) $x \approx 30.7$; in 1981

65. (a) $y = 0.094t^3 - 25.94t^2 + 2273t - 45{,}828$
(b) $t \approx 72.5$ gives a maximum and $t \approx 110.7$ gives a minimum.
(c) Model's prediction for the year (1973) is fairly close to the data, but its prediction for the thousands of workers is too low.
(d) No, membership is more likely to remain fairly stable.

10.2 EXERCISES

1. (a) concave down   (b) concave up

3. (a, c) and (d, e)   **5.** (c, d) and (e, f)   **7.** c, d, e

9. concave up when $x > 2$; concave down when $x < 2$; POI at $x = 2$

11. concave up when $x < -2$ and $x > 1$
concave down when $-2 < x < 1$
points of inflection at $x = -2$ and $x = 1$

13. no points of inflection;
$(2, -2)$ min

$y = x^2 - 4x + 2$

15. $\left(1, \frac{10}{3}\right)$ max; $(3, 2)$ min;
$\left(2, \frac{8}{3}\right)$ point of inflection

17. $(0, 0)$ rel max; $\left(2\sqrt{2}, -64\right), \left(-2\sqrt{2}, -64\right)$ min;
points of inflection: $\left(2\sqrt{6}/3, -320/9\right)$ and
$\left(-2\sqrt{6}/3, -320/9\right)$

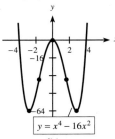

19. $(-2, 64)$ rel max; $(2, -64)$
rel min; points of inflection:
$\left(-\sqrt{2}, 39.6\right), (0, 0)$, and
$\left(\sqrt{2}, -39.6\right)$

21. $(1, -3)$ min; points of
inflection: $(-2, 7.6)$
and $(0, 0)$

23. (a) $f''(x) = 0$ when $x = 1$
$f''(x) > 0$ when $x < 1$
$f''(x) < 0$ when $x > 1$
(b) rel max for $f'(x)$ at $x = 1$; no rel min
(c)

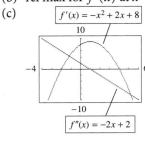

25. (a) concave up when $x < 2$; concave down when $x > 2$
(b) point of inflection at $x = 2$
(c)

(d) possible graph of $f(x)$

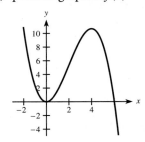

27. (a) G (b) C (c) F (d) H (e) I
29. (a) concave up when $x < 0$
concave down when $x > 0$
point of inflection at $x = 0$
(b) concave up when $-1 < x < 1$
concave down when $x < -1$ and $x > 1$
POI at $x = -1$ and $x = 1$
(c) concave up when $x > 0$
concave down when $x < 0$
point of inflection at $x = 0$
31. (a) $P'(t)$ (b) B (c) C
33. (a) C (b) right   (c) yes
35. (a) in an 8-hour shift, max when $t = 8$ (b) 4 hr
37. (a) 9 days   (b) 15 days
39. when $x \approx 29.3$, during 1980
41. (a) $y = 0.0000477x^3 - 0.00526x^2 + 0.00509x + 14.4$
(b) $(73.0, 5.30)$
(c) According to the model, in 1973 the percent
foreign-born reached a minimum of 5.3%.
43. (a) $y = -0.405x^3 + 6.02x^2 - 18.0x + 52.0$
(b) $x = 1.83$, during 1914
(c) $x = 8.07$, during 1921

10.3 EXERCISES

1. min -6 at $x = 2$, max $3.\overline{481}$ at $x = -2/3$
3. min -1 at $x = -2$, max 2 at $x = -1$
5. (a) $x = 1800$ units, $R = \$32,400$
(b) $x = 1500$ units, $R = \$31,500$
7. $x = 20$ units, $R = \$24,000$ **9.** 85 people
11. $p = \$47.50$, $R = \$225,625$
13. (a) max $= \$2100$ at $x = 10$
(b) $\overline{R}(x) = \overline{MR}$ at $x = 10$
15. $x = 50$ units, $\overline{C} = \$43$
17. $x = 90$ units, $\overline{C} = \$18$

19. 10,000 units ($x = 100$), $\overline{C} = \$216$ per 100 units
21. $\overline{C}(x)$ has its minimum and $\overline{C}(x) = \overline{MC}$ at $x = 5$.
23. (a) A line from $(0, 0)$ to $(x, C(x))$ has slope
$C(x)/x = \overline{C}(x)$; this is minimized when the line has the least rise—that is, when the line is tangent to $C(x)$.
(b) $x = 600$ units
25. $x = 80$ units, $P = \$280,000$
27. $x = 10\sqrt{15} \approx 39$ units, $P \approx \$71,181$ (using $x = 39$)
29. $x = 1000$ units, $P = \$39,700$
31. (a) B (b) B (c) B (d) $\overline{MR} = \overline{MC}$
33. $\$860$ **35.** $x = 600$ units, $P = \$495,000$
37. (a) 60   (b) $\$570$ (c) $\$9000$
39. (a) 1000 units   (b) $\$8066.67$ (approximately)
41. 2000 units priced at $\$90$/unit; max profit is $\$90,000$/wk
43. (a) $R(x) = 2x - 0.0004x^2$
$P(x) = 1.8x - 0.0005x^2 - 800$
(b) $p = \$1.28$, $x = 1800$, $P(1800) = \$820$
(c) $p = \$1.25$, $x = 1875$, $P(1875) = \$817.19$
Coastal would still provide sodas; profits almost the same.
45. (a) $y = 0.000252x^3 - 0.0279x^2 + 1.63x + 2.16$
(b) $(36.9, 37.0)$
(c)

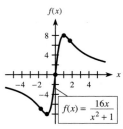

The *rate* of change of the number of beneficiaries was decreasing until 1987, after which the rate has been increasing. Hence, since 1987 the number of beneficiaries has been increasing at an increasing rate.
47. (a) about mid-May
(b) just after September 11, when the terrorists' planes crashed into the World Trade Center and the Pentagon
49. (a) 16.5
(b) 1.9
(c) Rise. As the number of workers per beneficiary drops, either the amount contributed by each worker must rise or support must diminish.

10.4 EXERCISES

1. (a) $x_1 = \$25$ million, $x_2 = \$13.846$ million
(b) $\$38.846$ million
3. 100 trees   **5.** (a) 5   (b) 237.5   **7.** $\$50$
9. $m = c$ **11.** 1 week   **13.** $t = 8$, $p = 45\%$
15. 240 ft   **17.** 300 ft $\times$ 150 ft
19. 20 ft long, $6\frac{2}{3}$ ft across (dividers run across)
21. 4 in. $\times$ 8 in. $\times$ 8 in. high   **23.** 30,000
25. 12,000   **27.** $x = 2$ **29.** 3 weeks from now
31. 25 plates
33. (a) $t \approx 22.8$; in 2018

(b) No. Unless some new technology replaces cell phones, the number will probably level off but not decrease.

10.5 EXERCISES

1. (a) $x = 2$ (b) 1   (c) 1   (d) $y = 1$
3. (a) $x = 2, x = -2$ (b) 3   (c) 3   (d) $y = 3$
5. HA: $y = 2$; VA: $x = 3$
7. HA: $y = 0$; VA: $x = -2, x = 2$
9. HA: none; VA: none
11. HA: $y = 2$; VA: $x = 3$
no max, min, or points of inflection

13. VA: $x = 0$;
$(-2, -4)$ rel max;
$(2, 4)$ rel min

15. VA: $x = -1$; HA: $y = 0$;
$(0, 0)$ rel min; $(2, 4)$ rel max;

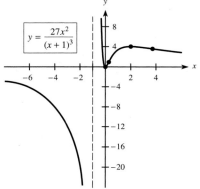

17. HA: $y = 0$; $(1, 8)$ rel max;
$(-1, -8)$ rel min

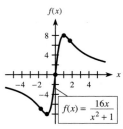

19. HA: $y = 0$; VA: $x = 1$;
$\left(-1, -\frac{1}{4}\right)$ rel min;
point of inflection: $(-2, -2/9)$

21. VA: $x = 3$;
$(2, -1)$ rel max;
$(4, 7)$ rel min

23. HA: $y = 0$;
VA: $x = 0$;
$(2, 0)$ rel min;
$(3, 1)$ rel max;
points of inflection:
$(1.87, 0.66)$,
$(4.13, 0.87)$

25. (a) HA: approx. $y = -2$; VA: approx. $x = 4$
(b) HA: $y = -\frac{9}{4}$, VA: $x = \frac{17}{4}$

27. (a) HA: approx. $y = 2$;
VA: approx. $x = 2.5$, $x = -2.5$
(b) HA: $y = \frac{20}{9}$, VA: $x = \frac{7}{3}$, $x = -\frac{7}{3}$

29. $f(x) = \dfrac{x + 25}{x^2 + 1400}$

(a)

(b) HA: $y = 0$; rel min $(-70, -0.0071)$;
rel max $(20, 0.025)$
(c) x: -500 to 400
y: -0.01 to 0.03

31. $f(x) = \dfrac{100(9 - x^2)}{x^2 + 100}$

(a)

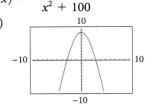

(b) HA: $y = -100$;
rel max $(0, 9)$
(c) x: -75 to 75
y: -120 to 20

33. $f(x) = \dfrac{1000x - 4000}{x^2 - 10x - 2000}$

(a)

(b) HA: $y = 0$; VA: $x = -40$,
$x = 50$; no max or min

(c) x: -200 to 200
y: -200 to 200

35. (a) none   (b) $C \geq 0$ (c) $p = 100$ (d) no

37. (a)

(b) 6 weeks
(c) 22 weeks after its release

39. (a) yes, $x = -1$
(b) no; domain is $x \geq 5$
(c) yes, $y = -58.5731$
(d) At 0°F, as the wind speed increases, there is a limiting wind chill of about -58.6°F. This is meaningful because at high wind speeds, additional wind probably has little noticeable effect.

41. (a) $P = C$ (b) C (c) $P' = 0$ (d) 0

43. (a) 57.0
(b) The model predicts that in the long run, 57% of workers will be female.
(c) No. Vertical asymptote is only at $t \approx -46.4$.
(d) $p(t) > 0$ for $t > 0$ and $p(t)$ never exceeds 100, so the model is never inappropriate.

45. (a) No. Barometric pressure can drop off the scale (as shown), but it cannot decrease without bound. In fact, it must always be positive.
(b) See your library with regard to the "storm of the century" in March 1993.

CHAPTER 10 REVIEW EXERCISES

1. $(0, 0)$ max   **2.** $(2, -9)$ min   **3.** HPI $(1, 0)$
4. $\left(1, \frac{3}{2}\right)$ max, $\left(-1, -\frac{3}{2}\right)$ min
5. (a) $\frac{1}{3}, -1$
  (b) $(-1, 0)$ rel max, $\left(\frac{1}{3}, -\frac{32}{27}\right)$ rel min
  (c) none   (d)

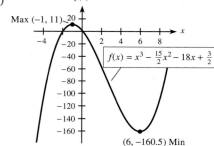

6. (a) $3, 0$ (b) $(3, 27)$ max   (c) $(0, 0)$
  (d)

7. (a) $-1, 6$
  (b) $(-1, 11)$ rel max, $(6, -160.5)$ rel min
  (c) none   (d)

8. (a) $0, \pm 1$ (b) $(-1, 1)$ rel max, $(1, -3)$ rel min
  (c) $(0, -1)$ (d)

9. (a) 0 (b) $(0, -1)$ min   (c) none
  (d)

10. (a) $0, 1, 4$
  (b) $(0, 0)$ rel min, $(1, 9)$ rel max, $(4, 0)$ rel min
  (c) none   (d)

11. concave up
12. concave up when $x < -1$ and $x > 2$; concave down when $-1 < x < 2$; points of inflection at $(-1, -3)$ and $(2, -42)$
13. $(-1, 15)$ rel max; $(3, -17)$ rel min; point of inflection $(1, -1)$
14. $(-2, 16)$ rel max; $(2, -16)$ rel min; point of inflection $(0, 0)$

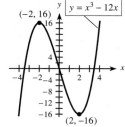

15. $(1, 4)$ rel max; $(-1, 0)$ rel min; points of inflection: $\left(\dfrac{1}{\sqrt{2}}, 2 + \dfrac{7}{4\sqrt{2}}\right)$, $(0, 2)$, and $\left(-\dfrac{1}{\sqrt{2}}, 2 - \dfrac{7}{4\sqrt{2}}\right)$

16. (a) $(0, 0)$ absolute min; $(140, 19{,}600)$ absolute max
  (b) $(0, 0)$ absolute min; $(100, 18{,}000)$ absolute max
17. (a) $(50, 233{,}333)$ absolute max; $(0, 0)$ absolute min
  (b) $(64, 248{,}491)$ absolute max; $(0, 0)$ absolute min
18. (a) $x = 1$ (b) $y = 0$ (c) 0 (d) 0
19. (a) $x = -1$ (b) $y = \frac{1}{2}$ (c) $\frac{1}{2}$ (d) $\frac{1}{2}$
20. HA: $y = \frac{3}{2}$, VA: $x = 2$
21. HA: $y = -1$; VA: $x = 1, x = -1$
22. (a) HA: $y = 3$; VA: $x = -2$
  (b) no max or min   (c)

23. (a) HA: $y = 0$; VA: $x = 0$
(b) $(4, 1)$ max   (c)

24. (a) HA: none; VA: $x = 1$
(b) $(0, 0)$ rel max; $(2, 4)$ rel min
(c)

25. (a) $f'(x) > 0$ for $x < \frac{2}{3}$ (approximately) and $x > 2$
$f'(x) < 0$ for about $\frac{2}{3} < x < 2$
$f'(x) = 0$ at about $x = \frac{2}{3}$ and $x = 2$
(b) $f''(x) > 0$ for $x > \frac{4}{3}$
$f''(x) < 0$ for $x < \frac{4}{3}$
$f''(x) = 0$ at $x = \frac{4}{3}$
(c)

(d)

26. (a) $f'(x) > 0$ for about $-13 < x < 0$ and $x > 7$
$f'(x) < 0$ for about $x < -13$ and $0 < x < 7$
$f'(x) = 0$ at about $x = 0$, $x = -13$, $x = 7$
(b) $f''(x) > 0$ for about $x < -8$ and $x > 4$
$f''(x) < 0$ for about $-8 < x < 4$
$f''(x) = 0$ at about $x = -8$ and $x = 4$
(c)

(d)

27. (a) $f(x)$ increasing for $x < -5$ and $x > 1$
$f(x)$ decreasing for $-5 < x < 1$
$f(x)$ has rel max at $x = -5$, rel min at $x = 1$
(b) $f''(x) > 0$ for $x > -2$ (where $f'(x)$ increases)
$f''(x) < 0$ for $x < -2$ (where $f'(x)$ decreases)
$f''(x) = 0$ for $x = -2$
(c)

(d)

$f''(x) = 2x + 4$

28. (a) $f(x)$ increasing for $x < 6$, $x \neq 0$
$f(x)$ decreasing for $x > 6$
$f(x)$ has rel max at $x = 6$, point of inflection at $x = 0$
(b) $f''(x) > 0$ for $0 < x < 4$
$f''(x) < 0$ for $x < 0$ and $x > 4$
$f''(x) = 0$ at $x = 0$ and $x = 4$
(c)

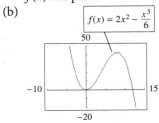

(d)

$f''(x) = 12x - 3x^2$

29. (a) $f(x)$ is concave up for $x < 4$.
$f(x)$ is concave down for $x > 4$.
$f(x)$ has point of inflection at $x = 4$.
(b)

$f(x) = 2x^2 - \dfrac{x^3}{6}$

30. (a) $f(x)$ is concave up for $-3 < x < 2$.

$f(x)$ is concave down for $x < -3$ and $x > 2$.

$f(x)$ has points of inflection at $x = -3$ and $x = 2$.

(b)

31. $x = 5$ units, $\overline{C} = \$45$ per unit

32. (a) $x = 1600$ units, $R = \$25,600$

(b) $x = 1500$ units, $R = \$25,500$

33. $P = \$54,000$ at $x = 100$ units   **34.** $x = 300$ units

35. $x = 150$ units   **36.** $x = 7$ units

37. $x = 500$ units, when $\overline{MP} = 0$ and changes from positive to negative.

38. 30 hours

39. (a) $I = 60$. The point of diminishing returns is located at the point of inflection (where bending changes).

(b) $m = f(I)/I =$ the average output

(c) The segment from $(0, 0)$ to $y = f(I)$ has maximum slope when it is tangent to $y = f(I)$, close to $I = 70$.

40. $\$260$ per bike   **41.** $\$360$ per bike

42. $\$93,625$ at 325 units

43. (a) 150   (b) $\$650$

44. $\$208,490.67$ at 64 units

45. $x = 1000$ mg   **46.** 10:00 A.M.

47. 325 in 2015   **48.** 20 mi from A, 10 mi from B

49. 4 ft $\times$ 4 ft   **50.** $8\frac{3}{4}$ in. $\times$ 10. in.

51. 500 mg

52. (a) $x \approx 7.09$; during 2008

(b) point of inflection

53. 24,000

54. (a) vertical asymptote at $x = 0$

(d)

55. (a) 3%

(b) $y = 38$. The long-term market share approaches 38%.

CHAPTER 10 TEST

1. max $(-3, 3)$; min $(-1, -1)$;

POI $(-2, 1)$

2. max $(3, 17)$; HPI $(0, -10)$; POI $(2, 6)$

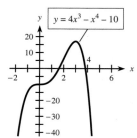

3. max $(0, -3)$;

min $(4, 5)$;

vertical asymptote $x = 2$

4. $\left(-\dfrac{1}{\sqrt{2}}, 0\right)$ and $\left(\dfrac{1}{\sqrt{2}}, \infty\right)$

5. $(0, 2)$, HPI; $\left(-\dfrac{1}{\sqrt{2}}, 3.237\right)$, $\left(\dfrac{1}{\sqrt{2}}, 0.763\right)$

6. max $(-1, 4)$; min $(1, 0)$

7. max 67 at $x = 8$; min -122 at $x = 5$

8. horizontal asymptote $y = 200$; vertical asymptote $x = -300$

9.

Point	f	f'	f''
A	−	+	−
B	+	−	0
C	+	0	+

10. (a) 2   (b) $x = -3$
   (c) $y = 2$
11. local max at $(6, 10)$
12. (a) maximum: $x \approx 153.3$ (in 2024)
      minimum: $x \approx 27.3$ (in 1898)
   (b) The rise of agri-business and the disappearance of the "family farm."
13. (a) $x = 7200$ (b) $518,100   **14.** 100 units
15. $250   **16.** $\frac{10}{3}$ centimeter   **17.** 28,000 units
18. (a) $y = -0.0000700x^3 + 0.00567x^2 + 0.863x + 16.0$
   (b) $x \approx 27.0$; during 1977
   (c) x-coordinate of the point of inflection

11.1 EXERCISES

1. $f'(x) = 4/x$ **3.** $y' = 1/x$

5. $y' = 4/x$ **7.** $f'(x) = \dfrac{4}{4x + 9}$

9. $y' = \dfrac{4x - 1}{2x^2 - x} + 3$ **11.** $dp/dq = 2q/(q^2 + 1)$

13. (a) $y' = \dfrac{1}{x} - \dfrac{1}{x - 1} = \dfrac{-1}{x(x - 1)}$

   (b) $y' = \dfrac{-1}{x(x - 1)}$; $\ln\left(\dfrac{x}{x - 1}\right) = \ln(x) - \ln(x - 1)$

15. (a) $y' = \dfrac{2x}{3(x^2 - 1)}$

   (b) $y' = \dfrac{2x}{3(x^2 - 1)}$; $\ln(x^2 - 1)^{1/3} = \frac{1}{3}\ln(x^2 - 1)$

17. (a) $y' = \dfrac{4}{4x - 1} - \dfrac{3}{x} = \dfrac{-8x + 3}{x(4x - 1)}$

   (b) $y' = \dfrac{-8x + 3}{x(4x - 1)}$;

      $\ln\left(\dfrac{4x - 1}{x^3}\right) = \ln(4x - 1) - 3\ln(x)$

19. $\dfrac{dp}{dq} = \dfrac{2q}{q^2 - 1} - \dfrac{1}{q} = \dfrac{q^2 + 1}{q(q^2 - 1)}$

21. $\dfrac{dy}{dt} = \dfrac{2t}{t^2 + 3} - \dfrac{1}{2}\left(\dfrac{-1}{1 - t}\right) = \dfrac{3 + 4t - 3t^2}{2(1 - t)(t^2 + 3)}$

23. $\dfrac{dy}{dx} = \dfrac{3}{x} + \dfrac{1}{2(x + 1)} = \dfrac{7x + 6}{2x(x + 1)}$

25. $y' = 1 - \dfrac{1}{x}$ **27.** $y' = (1 - \ln x)/x^2$

29. $y' = 8x^3/(x^4 + 3)$ **31.** $y' = \dfrac{4(\ln x)^3}{x}$

33. $y' = \dfrac{8x^3\ln(x^4 + 3)}{x^4 + 3}$ **35.** $y' = \dfrac{1}{x\ln 4}$

37. $y' = \dfrac{4x^3 - 12x^2}{(x^4 - 4x^3 + 1)\ln 6}$

39. rel min $(e^{-1}, -e^{-1})$

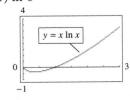

41. rel min $(2, 4 - 8\ln 2)$

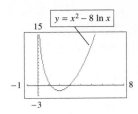

43. (a) $\overline{MC} = \dfrac{400}{2x + 1}$

   (b) $\overline{MC} = \dfrac{400}{401} \approx 1.0$; the approximate cost of the 201st unit is $1.00

   (c) $\overline{MC} > 0$. Yes

45. (a) $\overline{MR} = \dfrac{2500[(x + 1)\ln(10x + 10) - x]}{(x + 1)\ln^2(10x + 10)}$

   (b) 309.67; at 100 units, selling 1 additional unit yields about $309.67.

47. (a) -5.23 (b) -1.89 (c) increasing
49. A/B **51.** $dR/dI = 1/(I\ln 10)$
53. (a) $y = -2923 + 4013\ln(x)$
   (b) $114.66 per year

11.2 EXERCISES

1. $y' = 5e^x - 1$ **3.** $f'(x) = e^x - ex^{e-1}$
5. $g'(x) = 50e^{-0.1x}$ **7.** $y' = 3x^2e^{x^3}$
9. $y' = 36xe^{3x^2}$
11. $y' = 12x(x^2 + 1)^2e^{(x^2 + 1)^3}$ **13.** $y' = 3x^2$
15. $y' = e^{-1/x}/x^2$ **17.** $y' = \dfrac{2}{x^3}e^{-1/x^2} - 2xe^{-x^2}$
19. $ds/dt = te^t(t + 2)$ **21.** $y' = 4x^3e^{x^4} - 4e^{4x}$
23. $y' = \dfrac{4e^{4x}}{e^{4x} + 2}$ **25.** $y' = e^{-3x}/x - 3e^{-3x}\ln(2x)$
27. $y' = (2e^{5x} - 3)/e^{3x} = 2e^{2x} - 3e^{-3x}$
29. $y' = 30e^{3x}(e^{3x} + 4)^9$ **31.** $y' = 6^x\ln 6$
33. $y' = 4^{x^2}(2x\ln 4)$
35. (a) $y'(1) = 0$ (b) $y = e^{-1}$
37. (a) $z = 0$ (b)

39. rel min at $x = 1$, $y = e$
41. rel max at $x = 0$, $y = -1$
43. (a) $(0.1)\,Pe^{0.1n}$ (b) $(0.1)\,Pe^{0.1}$
   (c) Yes, because $e^{0.1n} > 1$ for any $n \geq 1$.
45. (a) $\dfrac{dS}{dt} = -50,000e^{-0.5t}$

   (b) The function is a decay exponential. The derivative is always negative.
47. $40e \approx 108.73$ dollars per unit

49. (a) $\dfrac{dy}{dt} = 46.2e^{-0.462t}$

  (b) 29.107 percent per hour

51. $\dfrac{dx}{dt} = -0.0684e^{-0.38t}$

53. 177.1 ($billion/year) **55.** $\dfrac{dI}{dR} = 10^R \ln 10$

57. (a) $d'(t) = 0.138e^{0.0825t}$

  (b) 1950: $d'(50) \approx \$8.54$ billion per year
    2015: $d'(115) \approx \$1820.7$ billion per year

59. $y' = \dfrac{98{,}990{,}100e^{-0.99t}}{(1 + 9999e^{-0.99t})^2}$

61. (a) $P'(t) = \dfrac{1.2595e^{-0.029t}}{(1 + 3.97e^{-0.029t})^2}$

  (b) $P'(100) \approx 0.0467$ means that in 2045 the population is expected to change at the rate of 0.0467 billion people per year.

  (c) $P''(95) < 0$ means the rate is decreasing.

63. (a) $P'(48) \approx -0.018$

  (b) This means that in 2008, the purchasing power of $1 was changing at the rate of -0.018 dollars per year.

  (c) For 2007–2008, average rate $= -0.018$ dollars per year.

65. (a) $y' = 8.864(1.055^x)$

  (b) $33.8 billion

67. (a) $y' = 2.74(1.042^x)$

  (b) 14.5

  (c) logistic; $y = \dfrac{334}{1 + 390e^{-0.06x}}$

  (d) 3.73

11.3 EXERCISES

1. $\frac{1}{2}$ **3.** $-\frac{1}{2}$ **5.** $-\frac{5}{3}$ **7.** $-x/(2y)$

9. $-(2x + 4)/(2y - 3)$ **11.** $y' = -x/y$

13. $y' = \dfrac{-y}{2x - 3y}$ **15.** $\dfrac{dp}{dq} = \dfrac{p^2}{4 - 2pq}$

17. $\dfrac{dy}{dx} = \dfrac{x(3x^3 - 2)}{3y^2(1 + y^2)}$ **19.** $\dfrac{dy}{dx} = \dfrac{4x^3 + 6x^2y^2 - 1}{-4x^3y - 3y^2}$

21. $\dfrac{dy}{dx} = \dfrac{(4x^3 + 9x^2y^2 - 8x - 12y)}{(18y + 12x - 6x^3y + 10y^4)}$ **23.** undefined

25. 1   **27.** $y = \frac{1}{2}x + 1$ **29.** $y = 4x + 5$

31. $\dfrac{dy}{dx} = \dfrac{1}{2xy}$ **33.** $\dfrac{dy}{dx} = \dfrac{-y}{2x \ln x}$ **35.** -15

37. $-1/x$ **39.** $\dfrac{-xy - 1}{x^2}$

41. $ye^x/(1 - e^x)$ **43.** $\frac{1}{3}$ **45.** $y = 3 - x$

47. (a) $(2, \sqrt{2}), (2, -\sqrt{2})$

  (b) $(2 + 2\sqrt{2}, 0), (2 - 2\sqrt{2}, 0)$

49. (a) and (b) are verifications

  (c) yes, because $x^2 + y^2 = 4$

51. $1/(2x\sqrt{x})$

53. max at $(0, 3)$; min at $(0, -3)$

55. $\frac{1}{2}$, so an additional 1 (thousand dollars) of advertising yields about $\frac{1}{2}$ (thousand) additional units

57. $-\frac{243}{128}$ hours of skilled labor per hour of unskilled labor

59. At $p = \$80$, $q = 49$ and $dq/dp = -\frac{5}{16}$, which means that if the price is increased to $81, quantity demanded will decrease by approximately $\frac{5}{16}$ unit.

61. $-0.000436y$ **63.** $\dfrac{dh}{dt} = -\dfrac{3}{44} - \dfrac{h}{12}$

11.4 EXERCISES

1. 36   **3.** $\frac{1}{8}$ **5.** $-\frac{24}{5}$ **7.** $\frac{7}{6}$

9. -5 if $z = 5$, -10 if $z = -5$

11. -80 units/sec   **13.** 12π ft^2/min

15. $\frac{16}{27}$ in/sec   **17.** $1798/day

19. $0.42/day

21. 430 units/month   **23.** 36π mm^3/month

25. $\dfrac{\frac{dW}{dt}}{W} = 3\left(\dfrac{\frac{dL}{dt}}{L}\right)$ **27.** $\dfrac{\frac{dC}{dt}}{C} = 1.54\left(\dfrac{\frac{dW}{dt}}{W}\right)$

29. $\dfrac{1}{4\pi}$ micrometer/day   **31.** $1/(20\pi)$ in/min

33. 0.75 ft/sec   **35.** $-120\sqrt{6}$ mph ≈ -294 mph

37. approaching at 61.18 mph   **39.** $\frac{1}{25}$ ft/hr

11.5 EXERCISES

1. (a) 1   (b) no change

3. (a) 84   (b) Revenue will decrease.

5. (a) $\frac{100}{99}$ (b) elastic   (c) decrease

7. (a) 0.81   (b) inelastic   (c) increase

9. (a) $\eta = 11.1$ (approximately)   (b) elastic

11. (a) $\eta = \dfrac{375 - 3q}{q}$

  (b) unitary: $q = 93.75$; inelastic: $q > 93.75$; elastic: $q < 93.75$

  (c) As q increases over $0 < q < 93.75$, p decreases, so elastic demand means R increases. Similarly, R decreases for $q > 93.75$.

  (d) maximum for R when $q = 93.75$; yes.

13. (a) $p = 250 - 0.125q$

  (b) $\eta = \dfrac{2000}{q} - 1$

  (c) $\eta \approx 2.33$; elastic. no

  (d) $q = 1000$; $p = \$125$; max $R = \$125{,}000$

15. $12/item   **17.** $t = 350 **19.** $115/item
21. $483 per item; $40,100   **23.** $1100/item

CHAPTER 11 REVIEW EXERCISES

1. $dy/dx = (6x - 1)e^{3x^2 - x}$ **2.** $y' = 2x$

3. $\dfrac{dp}{dq} = \dfrac{1}{q} - \dfrac{2q}{q^2 - 1}$

4. $dy/dx = e^{x^2}(2x^2 + 1)$

5. $f'(x) = 10e^{2x} + 4e^{-0.1x}$

6. $g'(x) = 18e^{3x+1}(2e^{3x+1} - 5)^2$

7. $\dfrac{dy}{dx} = \dfrac{12x^3 + 14x}{3x^4 + 7x^2 - 12}$

8. $\dfrac{ds}{dx} = \dfrac{9x^{11} - 6x^3}{x^{12} - 2x^4 + 5}$ **9.** $dy/dx = 3^{3x-3} \ln 3$

10. $dy/dx = \dfrac{1}{\ln 8}\left(\dfrac{10}{x}\right)$ **11.** $\dfrac{dy}{dx} = \dfrac{1 - \ln x}{x^2}$

12. $dy/dx = -2e^{-x}/(1 - e^{-x})^2$

13. $y = 12ex - 8e$, or $y \approx 32.62x - 21.75$

14. $y = x - 1$ **15.** $\dfrac{dy}{dx} = \dfrac{y}{x(10y - \ln x)}$

16. $dy/dx = ye^{xy}/(1 - xe^{xy})$ **17.** $dy/dx = 2/y$

18. $\dfrac{dy}{dx} = \dfrac{2(x + 1)}{3(1 - 2y)}$ **19.** $\dfrac{dy}{dx} = \dfrac{6x(1 + xy^2)}{y(5y^3 - 4x^3)}$

20. $d^2y/dx^2 = -(x^2 + y^2)/y^3 = -1/y^3$ **21.** $5/9$

22. $(-2, \pm\sqrt{\tfrac{2}{3}})$ **23.** $3/4$ **24.** 11 square units/min

25. (a) $y'(t) = \dfrac{2.62196}{t}$

  (b) $y(50) \approx 6.343$ is the predicted number of hectares of deforestation in 2000.
  $y'(50) \approx 0.05244$ hectares per year is the predicted rate of deforestation in 2000.

26. (a) 0.328 percentage points per year
  (b) increasing, $y'(x) > 0$ for all $x > 0$

27. 135.3 dollars/year

28. (a) 152.5 dollars/year   **(b)** 1.13 times as fast

29. (a) $-0.00001438A_0$ units/year
  (b) $-0.00002876A_0$ units/year   **(c)** less

30. $1200e \approx 3261.94 per unit

31. $-$603.48$ per year   **32.** $-1/(25\pi)$ mm/min

33. $\tfrac{48}{25}$ ft/min   **34.** $\dfrac{dS/dt}{S} = \dfrac{1}{3}\left(\dfrac{dA/dt}{A}\right)$ **35.** yes

36. $t = 1466.67, $T \approx $58,667$

37. $t = 880, $T = 3520

38. (a) 1   **(b)** no change

39. (a) $\tfrac{25}{12}$, elastic   **(b)** revenue decreases

40. (a) 1   **(b)** no change

41. (a)

  (b) $q = 100$

(c) max revenue at $q = 100$

(d) Revenue is maximized where elasticity is unitary.

CHAPTER 11 TEST

1. $y' = 15x^2 e^{x^3} + 2x$ **2.** $y' = \dfrac{12x^2}{x^3 + 1}$

3. $y' = \dfrac{12x^3}{x^4 + 1}$ **4.** $f'(x) = 20(3^{2x}) \ln 3$

5. $\dfrac{dS}{dt} = e^{t^4}(4t^4 + 1)$ **6.** $y' = \dfrac{e^{x^3+1}(3x^3 - 1)}{x^2}$

7. $y' = \dfrac{1 - \ln x}{x^2}$ **8.** $g'(x) = \dfrac{8}{(4x + 7) \ln 5}$

9. $y' = \dfrac{-3x^3}{y}$ **10.** $-\tfrac{3}{2}$ **11.** $y' = \dfrac{-e^y}{xe^y - 10}$

12. $1349.50 per week   **13.** $\eta = 3.71$; decreases

14. -0.05 unit per dollar   **15.** 586 units per day

16. (a) $y' = 81.778e^{0.062t}$
  (b) 2005: $y'(5) \approx 111.5$ (billion dollars per year)
  2020: $y'(20) \approx 282.6$ (billion dollars per year)

17. $540

18. (a) $y = -12.97 + 11.85 \ln x$
  (b) $y' = \dfrac{11.85}{x}$
  (c) $y(25) \approx 25.2$ means the model estimates that 25.2% of the U.S. population will have diabetes in 2025.
  $y'(25) \approx 0.474$ predicts that in 2025 the percent of the U.S. population with diabetes will be changing by 0.474 percentage points per year.

19. $P'(t) = -0.1548(1.046)^{-t}$; $P'(55) \approx -0.013$ means that in 2015 the purchasing power of a dollar is changing at the rate of $-$0.013$ per year.

12.1 EXERCISES

1. $x^4 + C$ **3.** $\tfrac{1}{7}x + C$ **5.** $\tfrac{1}{8}x^8 + C$

7. $2x^4 + C$ **9.** $27x + \tfrac{1}{14}x^{14} + C$

11. $3x - \tfrac{2}{5}x^{5/2} + C$ **13.** $\tfrac{1}{5}x^5 - 3x^3 + 3x + C$

15. $13x - 3x^2 + 3x^7 + C$

17. $2x + \tfrac{4}{3}x\sqrt{x} + C$ **19.** $\tfrac{24}{5}x\sqrt[4]{x} + C$

21. $-5/(3x^3) + C$ **23.** $\tfrac{3}{2}\sqrt[3]{x} + C$

25. $\dfrac{1}{4}x^4 - 4x - \dfrac{1}{x^5} + C$

27. $\dfrac{1}{10}x^{10} + \dfrac{1}{2x^2} + 3x^{2/3} + C$

29. $2x^8 - \frac{4}{3}x^6 + \frac{1}{4}x^4 + C$ **31.** $-1/x - 1/(2x^2) + C$

33.

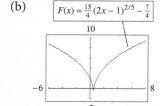

$f(x) = x^2 + 3x + C$
$(C = -8, -4, 0, 4, \text{ and } 8)$

35. $f(x) = 18x^8 - 35x^4$ **37.** $\int(5 - \frac{1}{2}x)dx$

39. $\int(3x^2 - 6x)\,dx$ **41.** $R(x) = 30x - 0.2x^2$

43. $R(50) = \$22{,}125$ **45.** $P(t) = \frac{1}{4}t^4 + \frac{4}{3}t^3 + 6t$

47. (a) $x = t^{7/4}/1050$ (b) 0.96 ton

49. (a) $\overline{C}(x) = x/4 + 100/x + 30$ (b) \$56 per unit

51. (a) $H(t) = 5.033t^2 + 100.5t + 1376.8$

(b) \$4016.7 billion

53. (a) The wind chill temperature decreases because

$$\frac{dt}{dw} < 0 \quad \text{for} \quad w > 0.$$

The rate increases because $\dfrac{d^2t}{dw^2} > 0$ for $w > 0$.

(b) $t = 48.12 - 27.2w^{0.16}$

55. (a) $t \approx 63.1$; in 2024

(b) $P(t) = -0.0000729t^3 + 0.0138t^2 + 1.98t + 181$

(c) 348 million

12.2 EXERCISES

1. $du = 10x^4\,dx$ **3.** $\frac{1}{4}(x^2 + 3)^4 + C$

5. $\frac{1}{5}(5x^3 + 11)^5 + C$ **7.** $\frac{1}{3}(3x - x^3)^3 + C$

9. $\frac{1}{28}(7x^4 + 12)^4 + C$ **11.** $\frac{1}{4}(4x - 1)^7 + C$

13. $-\frac{1}{6}(4x^6 + 15)^{-2} + C$ **15.** $\frac{1}{10}(x^2 - 2x + 5)^5 + C$

17. $-\frac{1}{8}(x^4 - 4x + 3)^{-4} + C$ **19.** $\frac{7}{6}(x^4 + 6)^{3/2} + C$

21. $\frac{3}{8}x^8 + \frac{6}{5}x^5 + \frac{3}{2}x^2 + C$ **23.** $10.8x^{10} - 12x^6 + 6x^2 + C$

25. $\frac{2}{9}(x^3 - 3x)^{3/2} + C$ **27.** $\dfrac{-1}{[10(2x^5 - 5)^3]} + C$

29. $\dfrac{-1}{[8(x^4 - 4x)^2]} + C$ **31.** $\frac{2}{3}\sqrt{x^3 - 6x^2 + 2} + C$

33. $f(x) = 70(7x - 13)^9$

35. (a) $f(x) = \frac{1}{8}(x^2 - 1)^4 + C$

(b)

$f(x) = \frac{1}{8}(x^2 - 1)^4 + C$
$(C = -5, 0, 5)$

37. (a) $F(x) = \frac{15}{4}(2x - 1)^{2/5} + C$

(b)

$F(x) = \frac{15}{4}(2x - 1)^{2/5} - \frac{7}{4}$

(c) $x = \frac{1}{2}$

(d) vertical

39. $\displaystyle\int \frac{8x(x^2 - 1)^{1/3}}{3}\,dx$

41. (b) $\dfrac{-7}{3(x^3 + 4)} + C$

(d) $\int (x^2 + 5)^{-4}\,dx$ (Many answers are possible.)

43. $R(x) = \dfrac{15}{2x + 1} + 30x - 15$

45. 3720 bricks   **47.** (a) $s = 10\sqrt{x + 1}$ (b) 50

49. (a) $A(t) = 100/(t + 10) - 1000/(t + 10)^2$

(b) 2.5 million

51. 7400

53. (a) $p(t) = -0.0000716(2t + 3)^4 + 0.00742(2t + 3)^3$
$\qquad\qquad -0.2436(2t + 3)^2 + 5.572t + 35.515$

(b)

(c) The equation fits quite well overall.

55. (a) $p(t) = 56.19 - \dfrac{1561}{1.38t + 64.1}$

(b)

(c) The model is a good fit to the data.

12.3 EXERCISES

1. $e^{3x} + C$ **3.** $-e^{-x} + C$ **5.** $10{,}000e^{0.1x} + C$

7. $-1200e^{-0.7x} + C$ **9.** $\frac{1}{12}e^{3x^4} + C$

11. $-\frac{3}{2}e^{-2x} + C$ **13.** $\frac{1}{18}e^{3x^6 - 2} + C$

15. $\frac{1}{4}e^{4x} + 6/e^{x/2} + C$

17. $\ln|x^3 + 4| + C$ **19.** $\frac{1}{4}\ln|4z + 1| + C$

21. $\frac{3}{4}\ln|2x^4 + 1| + C$ **23.** $\frac{2}{5}\ln|5x^2 - 4| + C$

25. $\ln|x^3 - 2x| + C$ **27.** $\frac{1}{3}\ln|z^3 + 3z + 17| + C$

29. $\frac{1}{3}x^3 + \ln|x - 1| + C$ **31.** $x + \frac{1}{2}\ln|x^2 + 3| + C$

33. $f(x) = h(x), \int f(x)\,dx = g(x)$

35. $F(x) = -\ln|3 - x| + C$

$F(x) = \ln 3 - \ln|3 - x|$

37. $f(x) = 1 + \dfrac{1}{x}; \displaystyle\int\left(1 + \frac{1}{x}\right)dx$

39. $f(x) = 5e^{-x} - 5xe^{-x}; \int (5e^{-x} - 5xe^{-x})\,dx$

41. (c) $\frac{1}{3}\ln|x^3 + 3x^2 + 7| + C$;   (d) $\frac{5}{8}e^{2x^4} + C$

43. $1030.97   **45.** $n = n_0 e^{-Kt}$ **47.** 55
49. (a) $S = Pe^{0.1n}$ (b) ≈ 7 years
51. (a) $p = 95e^{-0.491t}$ (b) ≈ 90.45
53. (a) $l(t) = 11.028 + 14.304 \ln(t + 20)$
(b)

(c) The model is a very good fit to the data.
55. (a) Yes. The rate is an exponential that is always positive. Hence the function is always increasing.
(b) $C(t) = 80.39e^{0.0384t} + 0.6635$
(c) $C(35) \approx 308.91; C'(35) \approx 11.84$
For 2025, the model predicts that the CPI will be $308.91 and will be changing at the rate of $11.84 per year.

12.4 EXERCISES

1. $C(x) = x^2 + 100x + 200$
3. $C(x) = 2x^2 + 2x + 80$ **5.** $3750
7. (a) $x = 3$ units is optimal level
(b) $P(x) = -4x^2 + 24x - 200$ (c) loss of $164
9. (a) profit of $3120   (b) 896 units
11. (a) $\overline{C}(x) = \frac{6}{x} + \frac{x}{6} + 8$ (b) $10.50
13. (a) and   (b)

(c) Maximum profit is $114.743 thousand at $x = 200$ thousand units.
15. $C(y) = 0.80y + 7$
17. $C(y) = 0.3y + 0.4\sqrt{y} + 8$
19. $C(y) = 2\sqrt{y + 1} + 0.4y + 4$
21. $C(y) = 0.7y + 0.5e^{-2y} + 5.15$
23. $C(y) = 0.85y + 5.15$
25. $C(y) = 0.8y + \dfrac{2\sqrt{3y + 7}}{3} + 4.24$

12.5 EXERCISES

1. $4y - 2xy' = 4x^2 - 2x(2x) = 0$ ✔
3. $2y\,dx - x\,dy = 2(3x^2 + 1)\,dx - x(6x\,dx) = 2\,dx$ ✔
5. $y = \frac{1}{2}e^{x^2 + 1} + C$ **7.** $y^2 = 2x^2 + C$
9. $y^3 = x^2 - x + C$ **11.** $y = e^{x-3} - e^{-3} + 2$
13. $y = \ln|x| - \dfrac{x^2}{2} + \dfrac{1}{2}$ **15.** $\dfrac{y^2}{2} = \dfrac{x^3}{3} + C$

17. $\dfrac{1}{2x^2} + \dfrac{y^2}{2} = C$ **19.** $\dfrac{1}{x} + y + \dfrac{y^3}{3} = C$
21. $\dfrac{1}{y} + \ln|x| = C$ **23.** $x^2 - y^2 = C$
25. $y = C(x + 1)$ **27.** $x^2 + 4\ln|x| + e^{-y^2} = C$
29. $3y^4 = 4x^3 - 1$
31. $2y = 3x + 4xy$ or $y = \dfrac{3x}{2 - 4x}$
33. $e^{2y} = x^2 - \dfrac{2}{x} + 2$ **35.** $y^2 + 1 = 5x$
37. $y = Cx^k$
39. (a) $x = 10{,}000e^{0.06t}$ (b) $10,618.37; $13,498.59
(c) 11.55 years
41. $P = 100{,}000e^{0.05t}$; 5%   **43.** ≈ 8.4 hours
45. $y = \dfrac{32}{(p + 8)^{2/5}}$ **47.** $\approx 23{,}100$ years
49. $x = 6(1 - e^{-0.05t})$ **51.** $x = 20 - 10e^{-0.025t}$
53. $V = 1.86e^{2 - 2e^{-0.01t}}$ **55.** $V = \dfrac{k^3 t^3}{27}$
57. $t \approx 4.5$ hours
59. (a) $E(t) = 85.53e^{0.0309t}$
(b)

The graph is a similar, but smooth, representation of the data.
61. (a) $P(t) = 80{,}000e^{-0.05t}$ (b) $37,789.32

CHAPTER 12 REVIEW EXERCISES

1. $\frac{1}{7}x^7 + C$ **2.** $\frac{2}{3}x^{3/2} + C$
3. $3x^4 - x^3 + 2x^2 + 5x + C$
4. $\frac{7}{5}x^5 - \frac{14}{3}x^3 + 7x + C$
5. $\frac{7}{6}(x^2 - 1)^3 + C$ **6.** $\frac{1}{18}(x^3 - 3x^2)^6 + C$
7. $\frac{3}{8}x^8 + \frac{24}{5}x^5 + 24x^2 + C$ **8.** $\frac{5}{63}(3x^3 + 7)^7 + C$
9. $\frac{1}{3}\ln|x^3 + 1| + C$ **10.** $\dfrac{-1}{3(x^3 + 1)} + C$
11. $\frac{1}{2}(x^3 - 4)^{2/3} + C$ **12.** $\frac{1}{3}\ln|x^3 - 4| + C$
13. $\dfrac{1}{2}x^2 - \dfrac{1}{x} + C$
14. $\frac{1}{3}x^3 + \frac{1}{2}x^2 - 2x - \ln|x - 1| + C$
15. $\frac{1}{3}e^{y^3} + C$ **16.** $\frac{1}{39}(3x - 1)^{13} + C$
17. $\frac{1}{2}\ln|2x^3 - 7| + C$ **18.** $\dfrac{-5}{4e^{4x}} + C$
19. $x^4/4 - e^{3x}/3 + C$ **20.** $\frac{1}{2}e^{x^2 + 1} + C$
21. $\dfrac{-3}{40(5x^8 + 7)^2} + C$ **22.** $-\frac{7}{2}\sqrt{1 - x^4} + C$
23. $\frac{1}{4}e^{2x} - e^{-2x} + C$ **24.** $x^2/2 + 1/(x + 1) + C$
25. (a) $\frac{1}{10}(x^2 - 1)^5 + C$ (b) $\frac{1}{22}(x^2 - 1)^{11} + C$
(c) $\frac{3}{16}(x^2 - 1)^8 + C$ (d) $\frac{3}{2}\ln(x^2 - 1)^{1/3} + C$

26. (a) $\ln|x^2 - 1| + C$ (b) $\dfrac{-1}{x^2 - 1} + C$

(c) $3\sqrt{x^2 - 1} + C$ (d) $\frac{3}{2}\ln|x^2 - 1| + C$

27. $y = C - 92e^{-0.05t}$

28. $y = 64x + 38x^2 - 12x^3 + C$

29. $(y - 3)^2 = 4x^2 + C$ **30.** $(y + 1)^2 = 2\ln|t| + C$

31. $e^y = \dfrac{x^2}{2} + C$ **32.** $y = Ct^4$

33. $3(y + 1)^2 = 2x^3 + 75$

34. $x^2 = y + y^2 + 4$ **35.** \$28,800   **36.** 472

37. $P(t) = 400[1 - 5/(t + 5) + 25/(t + 5)^2]$

38. $p = 1990.099 - 100,000/(t + 100)$

39. (a) $y = -60e^{-0.04t} + 60$ (b) 23%

40. $R(x) = 800\ln(x + 2) - 554.52$

41. (a) \$1000   (b) $C(x) = 3x^2 + 4x + 1000$

42. 80 units, \$440

43. $C(y) = \sqrt{2y + 16} + 0.6y + 4.5$

44. $C(y) = 0.8y - 0.05e^{-2y} + 7.85$ **45.** $W = CL^3$

46. (a) $\ln|P| = kt + C_1$ (b) $P = Ce^{kt}$

(c) $P = 50,000\,e^{0.1t}$ (d) The interest rate is
$k = 0.10 = 10\%$.

47. ≈ 10.7 million years   **48.** $x = 360(1 - e^{-t/30})$

49. $x = 600 - 500e^{-0.01t}$; ≈ 161 min

CHAPTER 12 TEST

1. $2x^3 + 4x^2 - 7x + C$ **2.** $4x + \frac{2}{3}x\sqrt{x} + \frac{1}{x} + C$

3. $\dfrac{(4x^3 - 7)^{10}}{24} + C$ **4.** $-\frac{1}{6}(3x^2 - 6x + 1)^{-2} + C$

5. $\dfrac{\ln|2s^4 - 5|}{8} + C$ **6.** $-10,000e^{-0.01x} + C$

7. $\frac{5}{8}e^{2y^4 - 1} + C$ **8.** $e^x + 5\ln|x| - x + C$

9. $\dfrac{x^2}{2} - x + \ln|x + 1| + C$ **10.** $6x^2 - 1 + 5e^x$

11. $y = x^4 + x^3 + 4$ **12.** $y = \frac{1}{4}e^{4x} + \frac{7}{4}$

13. $y = \dfrac{4}{C - x^4}$ **14.** 157,498

15. $P(x) = 450x - 2x^2 - 300$

16. $C(y) = 0.78y + \sqrt{0.5y + 1} + 5.6$

17. 332.3 days   **18.** $x = 16 - 16e^{-t/40}$

13.1 EXERCISES

1. 7 square units   **3.** 7.25 square units

5. 3 square units   **7.** 11.25 square units

9. $S_L(10) = 4.08$; $S_R(10) = 5.28$

11. Both equal 14/3.

13. It would lie between $S_L(10)$ and $S_R(10)$. It would equal 14/3.

15. 3   **17.** 42   **19.** -5 **21.** 180   **23.** 11,315

25. $3 - \dfrac{3(n + 1)}{n} + \dfrac{(n + 1)(2n + 1)}{2n^2} = \dfrac{2n^2 - 3n + 1}{2n^2}$

27. (a) $S = (n - 1)/n$ (b) 9/10 (c) 99/100
(d) 999/1000 (e) 1

29. (a) $S = \dfrac{(n + 1)(2n + 1)}{6n^2}$

(b) $77/200 = 0.385$ (c) $6767/20,000 \approx 0.3384$

(d) $667,667/2,000,000 \approx 0.3338$ (e) $\frac{1}{3}$

31. $\frac{20}{3}$

33. (a) 7405.7 square units

(b) This represents the total per capita out-of-pocket expenses for health care between 2006 and 2014.

35. There are approximately 90 squares under the curve, each representing 1 second by 10 mph, or

$$1 \text{ sec} \times \frac{10 \text{ mi}}{1 \text{ hr}} \times \frac{1 \text{ hr}}{3600 \text{ sec}} = \frac{1}{360} \text{ mile.}$$

The area under the curve is approximately
$90\left(\frac{1}{360} \text{ mile}\right) = \frac{1}{4} \text{ mile.}$

37. 1550 square feet

39. 107.734 square units. This represents the total sulphur dioxide emissions (in millions of short tons) from electricity generation from 2010 to 2015.

13.2 EXERCISES

1. 18   **3.** 2   **5.** 60   **7.** $12\sqrt[3]{25}$ **9.** 0   **11.** 98

13. $-\frac{1}{10}$ **15.** 12,960 **17.** 0   **19.** 0   **21.** $\frac{49}{3}$

23. 2   **25.** $e^3/3 - 1/3$ **27.** 4   **29.** $\frac{8}{3}(1 - e^{-8})$

31. (a) $\frac{1}{6}\ln(112/31) \approx 0.2140853$ (b) 0.2140853

33. (a) $\frac{3}{2} + 3\ln 2 \approx 3.5794415$ (b) 3.5794415

35. (a) A, C (b) B

37. $\int_0^4 (2x - \frac{1}{2}x^2)dx$ (b) 16/3

39. (a) $\int_{-1}^0 (x^3 + 1)\,dx$ (b) 3/4

41. $\frac{1}{6}$ **43.** $\frac{1}{2}(e^9 - e)$

45. $\int_0^a g(x)\,dx > \int_0^a f(x)\,dx$; more area under $g(x)$

47. same absolute values, opposite signs

49. 6   **51.** 0   **53.** (a) \$450,000   (b) \$450,000

55. (a) \$5390   (b) \$2450

57. \$20,405.39

59. 4146 represents the total million metric tons of CO_2 emissions from 2010 to 2020.

61. 0.04 cm^3 **63.** 1222 (approximately)

65. 0.1808

67. (a) 0.5934   (b) 0.1733

69. (a) $P(t) = -0.0041t^3 + 0.038t^2 + 0.052t + 4.14$

(b) 24.12; the total amount of oil and petroleum products imported during this time period is 24.12 billion barrels.

13.3 EXERCISES

1. (a) $\int_0^2 (4 - x^2)\,dx$ (b) $\frac{16}{3}$

3. (a) $\int_1^8 [\sqrt[3]{x} - (2 - x)]\,dx$ (b) 28.75

5. (a) $\int_1^2 [(4 - x^2) - (\frac{1}{4}x^3 - 2)]\,dx$ (b) 131/48

7. (a) $(-1, 1), (2, 4)$ (b) $\int_{-1}^2 [(x + 2) - x^2]\,dx$
(c) 9/2

9. (a) $(0, 0), \left(\frac{5}{2}, -\frac{15}{4}\right)$

(b) $\int_0^{5/2} \left[(x - x^2) - (x^2 - 4x) \right] dx$ (c) $\frac{125}{24}$

11. (a) $(-2, -4), (0, 0), (2, 4)$

   (b) $\int_{-2}^0 \left[(x^3 - 2x) - 2x \right] dx + \int_0^2 \left[2x - (x^3 - 2x) \right] dx$
   (c) 8

13. $\frac{28}{3}$ **15.** $\frac{1}{4}$ **17.** $\frac{16}{3}$ **19.** $\frac{1}{3}$ **21.** $\frac{37}{12}$

23. $4 - 3 \ln 3$ **25.** $\frac{8}{3}$ **27.** 6   **29.** 0   **31.** $-\frac{4}{9}$

33. $11.8\overline{3}$

35. average profit $= \dfrac{1}{x_1 - x_0} \displaystyle\int_{x_0}^{x_1} \left[R(x) - C(x) \right] dx$

37. (a) $1402 per unit   (b) $535,333.33

39. (a) 102.5 units   (b) 100 units

41. (a) 40.05 million/year   (b) 69.93 million/year

43. 147 mg

45. 1988: 0.4034; 2000: 0.4264
   More equally distributed after Reagan. This is contrary to conventional wisdom.

47. Blacks: 0.4435; Asians: 0.4297
   Income was more nearly equally distributed among Asians, although both distributions were similar and not particularly equal.

49. $G = \dfrac{p - 1}{p + 1}$

13.4 EXERCISES

1. $126,205.10   **3.** $346,664 (nearest dollar)

5. $506,000 (nearest thousand)

7. $18,660 (nearest dollar)

9. $82,155 (nearest dollar)

11. $PV = \$2,657,807$ (nearest dollar), $FV = \$3,771,608$ (nearest dollar)

13. $PV = \$190,519$ (nearest dollar), $FV = \$347,148$ (nearest dollar)

15. Gift Shoppe, $151,024; Wine Boutique, $141,093. The gift shop is a better buy.

17. $83.33   **19.** $161.89   **21.** $(5, 56); \$83.33$

23. $11.50   **25.** $204.17   **27.** $2766.67

29. $17,839.58   **31.** $133.33   **33.** $2.50

35. $103.35

13.5 EXERCISES

1. formula 5: $\frac{1}{8} \ln |(4 + x)/(4 - x)| + C$

3. formula 11: $\frac{1}{3} \ln \left[(3 + \sqrt{10})/2 \right]$

5. formula 14: $w(\ln w - 1) + C$

7. formula 12: $\frac{1}{3} + \frac{1}{4} \ln \left(\frac{3}{7} \right)$

9. formula 13: $\frac{1}{8} \ln \left| \dfrac{v}{3v + 8} \right| + C$

11. formula 7: $\frac{1}{2} \left[7\sqrt{24} - 25 \ln (7 + \sqrt{24}) + 25 \ln 5 \right]$

13. formula 16: $\dfrac{(6w - 5)(4w + 5)^{3/2}}{60} + C$

15. formula 3: $\frac{1}{2}(5^{x^2}) \log_5 e + C$

17. formula 1: $\frac{1}{3}(13^{3/2} - 8)$

19. formula 9: $-\frac{5}{2} \ln \left| \dfrac{2 + \sqrt{4 - 9x^2}}{3x} \right| + C$

21. formula 10: $\frac{1}{3} \ln |3x + \sqrt{9x^2 - 4}| + C$

23. formula 15: $\frac{3}{4} \left[\ln |2x - 5| - \dfrac{5}{2x - 5} \right] + C$

25. formula 8: $\frac{1}{3} \ln |3x + 1 + \sqrt{(3x + 1)^2 + 1}| + C$

27. formula 6: $\frac{1}{4} \left[10\sqrt{109} - \sqrt{10} + 9 \ln (10 + \sqrt{109}) - 9 \ln (1 + \sqrt{10}) \right]$

29. formula 2: $-\frac{1}{6} \ln |7 - 3x^2| + C$

31. formula 8: $\frac{1}{2} \ln |2x + \sqrt{4x^2 + 7}| + C$

33. $2(e^{\sqrt{2}} - e) \approx 2.7899$

35. $\frac{1}{32}[\ln (9/5) - 4/9] \approx 0.004479$ **37.** $3391.10

39. (a) $C = \frac{1}{2}x\sqrt{x^2 + 9} + \frac{9}{2} \ln |x + \sqrt{x^2 + 9}| + 300 - \frac{9}{2} \ln 3$

   (b) $314.94

41. $3882.9 thousand

13.6 EXERCISES

1. $\frac{1}{2}xe^{2x} - \frac{1}{4}e^{2x} + C$ **3.** $\frac{1}{3}x^3 \ln x - \frac{1}{9}x^3 + C$

5. $\dfrac{104\sqrt{2}}{15}$ **7.** $-(1 + \ln x)/x + C$ **9.** 1

11. $\dfrac{x^2}{2} \ln (2x - 3) - \frac{1}{4}x^2 - \frac{3}{4}x - \frac{9}{8} \ln (2x - 3) + C$

13. $\frac{1}{5}(q^2 - 3)^{3/2}(q^2 + 2) + C$ **15.** 282.4

17. $-e^{-x}(x^2 + 2x + 2) + C$ **19.** $(9e^4 + 3)/2$

21. $\frac{1}{4}x^4 \ln^2 x - \frac{1}{8}x^4 \ln x + \frac{1}{32}x^4 + C$

23. $\frac{2}{15}(e^x + 1)^{3/2}(3e^x - 2) + C$ **25.** II; $\frac{1}{2}e^{x^2} + C$

27. IV; $\frac{2}{3}(e^x + 1)^{3/2} + C$ **29.** I; $-5e^{-4} + 1$

31. $2794.46   **33.** $34,836.73   **35.** 0.264

37. $5641.3 billion

13.7 EXERCISES

1. 1/5   **3.** 2   **5.** 1/e   **7.** diverges   **9.** diverges

11. 10   **13.** diverges   **15.** diverges   **17.** 0

19. 0   **21.** 0.5   **23.** 1/(2e)   **25.** $\frac{3}{2}$

27. $\int_{-\infty}^{\infty} f(x)\, dx = 1$ **29.** $c = 1$ **31.** $c = \frac{1}{4}$

33. 20   **35.** area $= \frac{8}{3}$ **37.** $\int_0^{\infty} Ae^{-rt}\, dt = A/r$

39. $2,400,000   **41.** $700,000

43. (a) 0.368   (b) 0.018

45. 0.147

47. (a) $500 \left[\dfrac{e^{-0.03b} + 0.03b - 1}{0.0009} \right]$

   (b) The amount approaches ∞.

13.8 EXERCISES

1. $h = \frac{1}{2}; x_0 = 0, x_1 = \frac{1}{2}, x_2 = 1, x_3 = \frac{3}{2}, x_4 = 2$

3. $h = \frac{1}{2}; x_0 = 1, x_1 = \frac{3}{2}, x_2 = 2, x_3 = \frac{5}{2}, x_4 = 3, x_5 = \frac{7}{2}, x_6 = 4$

5. $h = 1; x_0 = -1, x_1 = 0, x_2 = 1, x_3 = 2, x_4 = 3, x_5 = 4$

7. (a) 9.13   (b) 9.00   (c) 9   (d) Simpson's

9. (a) 0.51   (b) 0.50   (c) $\frac{1}{2}$ (d) Simpson's

11. (a) 5.27   (b) 5.30   (c) 5.33   (d) Simpson's

13. (a) 3.283   (b) 3.240

15. (a) 0.743   (b) 0.747

17. (a) 7.132   (b) 7.197   **19.** 7.8   **21.** 10.3

23. 119.58 ($119,580)   **25.** $32,389.76

27. $14,133.33   **29.** 1222.35 (1222 units)

31. (a)

x	0	0.2	0.4	0.6	0.8	1
$L_a - L_b$	0	0.001	−0.005	−0.002	0.012	0

(b) 0.0024

(c) positive; 1990

33. (a) Yes   (b) Simpson's   (c) 1586.67 ft²

CHAPTER 13 REVIEW EXERCISES

1. 212   **2.** $\dfrac{3(n+1)}{2n^2}$ **3.** $\frac{91}{72}$ **4.** 1   **5.** 1

6. 14   **7.** $\frac{248}{5}$ **8.** $-\frac{205}{4}$ **9.** $\frac{825}{4}$ **10.** $\frac{4}{13}$

11. −2   **12.** $\frac{1}{6}\ln 47 - \frac{1}{6}\ln 9$ **13.** $\frac{9}{2}$

14. $\ln 4 + \frac{14}{3}$ **15.** 190/3   **16.** $\frac{1}{2}\ln 2$

17. $(1 - e^{-2})/2$ **18.** $(e - 1)/2$ **19.** 95/2

20. 36   **21.** $\frac{1}{4}$ **22.** $\frac{1}{2}$

23. $\frac{1}{2}x\sqrt{x^2 - 4} - 2\ln|x + \sqrt{x^2 - 4}| + C$

24. $2\log_3 e$ **25.** $\frac{1}{2}x^2(\ln x^2 - 1) + C$

26. $\frac{1}{2}\ln|x| - \frac{1}{2}\ln|3x + 2| + C$

27. $\frac{1}{6}x^6\ln x - \frac{1}{36}x^6 + C$

28. $-e^{-2x}(x^2/2 + x/2 + 1/4) + C$

29. $2x\sqrt{x + 5} - \frac{4}{3}(x + 5)^{3/2} + C$

30. 1   **31.** diverges   **32.** −100

33. $\frac{5}{3}$ **34.** $-\frac{1}{2}$

35. (a) $\frac{8}{9} \approx 0.889$ (b) 1.004   (c) 0.909

36. 3.135   **37.** 3.9

38. (a) $n = 5$ (b) $n = 6$ **39.** $28,000

40. $e^{-2.8} \approx 0.061$ **41.** $1297.44   **42.** $76.60

43. 1969: 0.3737; 2000: 0.4264; more equally distributed in 1969

44. (a) (7, 6)   (b) $7.33   **45.** $24.50

46. $1,621,803   **47.** (a) $403,609   (b) $602,114

48. $217.42   **49.** $10,066 (nearest dollar)

50. $86,557.41

51. $C(x) = 3x + 30(x + 1)^2\ln(x + 1)$
$\qquad - 15(x + 1)^2 + 2015$

52. $e^{-1.4} \approx 0.247$

53. $4000 thousand, or $4 million

54. $197,365   **55.** $480,000

CHAPTER 13 TEST

1. 3.496 (approximately)

2. (a) $5 - \dfrac{n+1}{n}$ (b) 4

3. $\int_0^6 (12 + 4x - x^2)\,dx; 72$

4. (a) 4   (b) 3/4   (c) $\frac{5}{4}\ln 5$ (d) 7

(e) 0; limits of integration are the same

(f) $\frac{5}{6}(e^2 - 1)$

5. (a) $3xe^x - 3e^x + C$ (b) $\dfrac{x^2}{2}\ln(2x) - \dfrac{x^2}{4} + C$

6. −8

7. (a) $x[\ln(2x) - 1] + C$

(b) $\dfrac{2(9x + 14)(3x - 7)^{3/2}}{135} + C$

8. 16.089   **9.** (a) $4000   (b) $16,000/3

10. (a) $961.18 thousand   (b) $655.68 thousand

(c) $1062.5 thousand

11. 125/6   **12.**

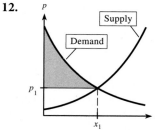

13. Before, 0.446; After, 0.19. The change decreases the difference in income.

14. (a) 20.92 billion barrels

(b) 2.067 billion barrels per year

15. 2.96655   **16.** 6800 ft²

14.1 EXERCISES

1. $\{(x, y): x \text{ and } y \text{ are real numbers}\}$

3. $\{(x, y): x \text{ and } y \text{ are real numbers and } y \neq 0\}$

5. $\{(x, y): x \text{ and } y \text{ are real numbers and } 2x - y \neq 0\}$

7. $\{(p_1, p_2): p_1 \text{ and } p_2 \text{ are real numbers and } p_1 \geq 0\}$

9. −2   **11.** $\frac{5}{3}$ **13.** 2500   **15.** 36   **17.** 3

19. $\frac{1}{25}\ln(12)$ **21.** $\frac{13}{3}$

23. $6640.23; the amount that results when $2000 is invested for 20 years

25. 500; if the cost of placing an order is $200, the number of items sold per week is 625, and the weekly holding cost per item is $1, then the most economical order size is 500.

27. Max: $S \approx 112.5°F; A \approx 106.3°F$
Min: $S \approx 87.4°F; A \approx 77.6°F$

29. (a) $752.80; when $90,000 is borrowed for 20 years at 8%, the monthly payment is $752.80.

(b) $1622.82; when $160,000 is borrowed for 15 years at 9%, the monthly payment is $1622.82.

31. (a) $x = 4$ (b) $y = 2$

(c)

33. (a) 37,500 units

(b) $30(2K)^{1/4}(2L)^{3/4} = 30(2^{1/4})(2^{3/4})K^{1/4}L^{3/4} = 2[30K^{1/4}L^{3/4}]$

(c)

35. (a) 7200 units   (b) 5000 units   37. \$284,000

14.2 EXERCISES

1. $\dfrac{\partial z}{\partial x} = 4x^3 - 10x + 6$ $\dfrac{\partial z}{\partial y} = 9y^2 - 5$

3. $z_x = 3x^2 + 8xy$ $z_y = 4x^2 + 12y$

5. $\dfrac{\partial f}{\partial x} = 9x^2(x^3 + 2y^2)^2$ $\dfrac{\partial f}{\partial y} = 12y(x^3 + 2y^2)^2$

7. $f_x = 2x(2x^2 - 5y^2)^{-1/2}$ $f_y = -5y(2x^2 - 5y^2)^{-1/2}$

9. $\dfrac{\partial C}{\partial x} = -4y + 20xy$ $\dfrac{\partial C}{\partial y} = -4x + 10x^2$

11. $\dfrac{\partial Q}{\partial s} = \dfrac{2(t^2 + 3st - s^2)}{(s^2 + t^2)^2}$ $\dfrac{\partial Q}{\partial t} = \dfrac{3t^2 - 4st - 3s^2}{(s^2 + t^2)^2}$

13. $z_x = 2e^{2x} + \dfrac{y}{x}$ $z_y = \ln x$

15. $\dfrac{\partial f}{\partial x} = \dfrac{y}{xy + 1}$ $\dfrac{\partial f}{\partial y} = \dfrac{x}{xy + 1}$ 17. 2

19. 7   21. -19

23. (a) 0   (b) $-2xz + 4$ (c) $2y$ (d) $-x^2$

25. (a) $8x_1 + 5x_2$ (b) $5x_1 + 12x_2$ (c) 1

27. (a) 2   (b) 0   (c) 0   (d) $-30y$

29. (a) $2y$ (b) $2x - 8y$ (c) $2x - 8y$ (d) $-8x$

31. (a) $2 + y^2e^{xy}$ (b) $xye^{xy} + e^{xy}$

(c) $xye^{xy} + e^{xy}$ (d) x^2e^{xy}

33. (a) $1/x^2$ (b) 0   (c) 0   (d) $2 + 1/y^2$

35. -6 37. (a) $\dfrac{188}{4913}$ (b) $\dfrac{-188}{4913}$ 39. $2 + 2e$

41. 0   43. (a) $24x$ (b) $24x$ (c) 0

45. (a) For a mortgage of \$100,000 and an 8% interest rate, the monthly payment is \$1289.

(b) The rate of change of the payment with respect to the interest rate is \$62.51. That is, if the rate goes from 8% to 9% on a \$100,000 mortgage, the approximate increase in the monthly payment is \$62.51.

47. (a) If the number of items sold per week changes by 1, the most economical order quantity should also increase. $\dfrac{\partial Q}{\partial M} = \sqrt{\dfrac{K}{2Mh}} > 0$

(b) If the weekly storage costs change by 1, the most economical order quantity should decrease.

$$\frac{\partial Q}{\partial h} = -\sqrt{\frac{KM}{2h^3}} < 0$$

49. (a) 23.912; If brand 2 is held constant and brand 1 is increased from 100 to 101 liters, approximately 24,000 additional insects will be killed.

51. (a) $2xy^2$ (b) $2x^2y$

53. $\dfrac{\partial Q}{\partial K} = 100$; If labor hours are held constant at 5832 and K changes by \$1 (thousand) to \$730,000, Q will change by about 100 units. $\dfrac{\partial Q}{\partial L} = 25$; If capital expenditures are held constant at \$729,000 and L changes by 1 hour (to 5833), Q will change by about 25 units.

55. (a) $\dfrac{\partial WC}{\partial s} = 0.16s^{-0.84}(0.4275t - 35.75)$

(b) At $t = 10$, $s = 25$, $\dfrac{\partial WC}{\partial s} \approx -0.34$

This means that if wind speed changes by 1 mph (from 25 mph) while the temperature remains at 10°F, the wind chill temperature will change by about -0.34°F.

14.3 EXERCISES

1. (a) \$105 (b) $C_x = 3$ means total costs would change by \$3 if labor costs changed by \$1 and raw material costs stayed the same.

3. (a) $2 + y/50$ (b) $4 + x/50$

5. (a) \$25.78   (b) \$74.80

7. (a) If y remains at 10, the expected change in cost for a 9th unit of X is \$36.

(b) If x remains at 8, the expected change in cost for an 11th unit of Y is \$19.

9. (a) $\sqrt{y^2 + 1}$ dollars per unit

(b) $xy/\sqrt{y^2 + 1}$ dollars per unit

11. (a) $1200y/(xy + 1)$ dollars per unit

(b) $1200x/(xy + 1)$ dollars per unit

13. (a) $\sqrt{y/x}$ (b) $\sqrt{x/y}$

15. (a) $\ln{(y + 1)}/(2\sqrt{x})$ (b) $\sqrt{x}/(y + 1)$

17. $z = 1092$ crates (approximately)

19. $z_x = 3.6$; If 500 acres are planted, the expected change in productivity from a 301st hour of labor is 3.6 crates.

21. (a) $z_x = \dfrac{240y^{2/5}}{x^{2/5}}$ (b)

(c) $z_y = \dfrac{160x^{3/5}}{y^{3/5}}$ (d)

(e) Both z_x and z_y are positive, so increases in both capital investment and work-hours result in increases in productivity. However, both are decreasing, so such increases have a diminishing effect on productivity. Also, z_y decreases more slowly than z_x, so that increases in work-hours have a more significant impact on productivity than increases in capital investment.

23. $q_1 = 188$ units; $q_2 = 270$ units
25. any values for p_1 and p_2 that satisfy $6p_2 - 3p_1 = 100$ and that make q_1 and q_2 nonnegative, such as $p_1 = \$10$, $p_2 = \$21\frac{2}{3}$
27. (a) -3 units per dollar   (b) -2 units per dollar
    (c) -6 units per dollar   (d) -5 units per dollar
    (e) complementary
29. (a) -50 units per dollar
    (b) $600/(p_B + 1)^2$ units per dollar
    (c) $-400/(p_B + 4)^2$ units per dollar
    (d) $400/(p_A + 4)^2$ units per dollar
    (e) competitive
31. (a) Competitive; as the price of one type of car declines, demand for the other declines
    (b) (i) $q_{NEW} = 2600 - p_{NEW}/30 + p_{USED}/15$
           $q_{USED} = 750 - 0.25\,p_{USED} + 0.0125\,p_{NEW}$
        (ii) Since the mixed partials are both positive ($1/15$ and 0.0125), the products are competitive.

14.4 EXERCISES

1. max$(0, 0, 9)$ 3. min$(0, 0, 4)$
5. saddle$(-2, -3, 16)$ 7. min$(1, -2, 0)$
9. saddle$(1, -3, 8)$ 11. max$(12, 24, 456)$
13. min$(-8, 6, -52)$
15. saddle$(0, 0, 0)$; min$(2, 2, -8)$
17. $\hat{y} = 5.7x - 1.4$
19. $x = 5000, y = 128; P = \$25{,}409.60$
21. $x = \frac{20}{3}, y = \frac{10}{3}; W \approx 1926$ lb
23. $x = 28, y = 100; P = 5987.84$ tons
25. $x = 20$ thousand, $y = 30$ thousand; $P = \$1900$ thousand
27. length $= 100$ in., width $= 100$ in., height $= 50$ in.
29. $x = 15$ thousand, $y = 24$ thousand; $P = \$295$ thousand
31. (a) eat-in $= 2400$; take-out $= 3800$
    (b) eat-in @ \$3.60; take-out @ \$3.10; max profit $=$ \$12,480
    (c) Change pricing; more profitable
33. (a) $\hat{y} = 0.81x - 2400$
    (b) $m = 0.81$; means that for every \$1 that males earn, females earn \$0.81.
    (c) The slope would probably be smaller. Equal pay for women for equal work is not yet a reality, but much progress has been made since 1965.
35. (a) $\hat{y} = 0.06254x + 6.191$, x in years past 2000, $\hat{y}$ in billions
    (b) 6.942 billion
    (c) World population is changing at the rate of 0.06254 billion persons per year past 2000.

14.5 EXERCISES

1. 18 at $(3, 3)$ 3. 35 at $(3, 2)$ 5. 32 at $(4, 2)$
7. -28 at $\left(3, \frac{5}{2}\right)$ 9. 15 at $(5, 3)$
11. 3 at $(1, 1, 1)$ 13. 1 at $(0, 1, 0)$
15. $x = 2, y = 2$
17. $x = 40, y = \frac{40}{3}$

19. (a) $x = 400, y = 400$
    (b) $-\lambda = 1.6$; means that each additional dollar spent on production results in approximately 1.6 additional units produced.
    (c)

21. $x = 900, y = 300$; 900 units at plant X, 300 units at plant Y
23. $x = \$10{,}003.33, y = \$19{,}996.67$
25. length $= 100$ cm, width $= 100$ cm, height $= 50$ cm

CHAPTER 14 REVIEW EXERCISES

1. $\{(x, y): x$ and y are real numbers and $y \neq 2x\}$
2. $\{(x, y): x$ and y are real numbers with $y \geq 0$ and $(x, y) \neq (0, 0)\}$
3. -5 4. 896,000
5. $15x^2 + 6y$ 6. $24y^3 - 42x^3y^2$
7. $z_x = 8xy^3 + 1/y$; $z_y = 12x^2y^2 - x/y^2$
8. $z_x = x/\sqrt{x^2 + 2y^2}$; $z_y = 2y/\sqrt{x^2 + 2y^2}$
9. $z_x = -2y/(xy + 1)^3$; $z_y = -2x/(xy + 1)^3$
10. $z_x = 2xy^3e^{x^2y^3}$; $z_y = 3x^2y^2e^{x^2y^3}$
11. $z_x = ye^{xy} + y/x$; $z_y = xe^{xy} + \ln x$
12. $z_x = y$; $z_y = x$ 13. -8 14. 8
15. (a) $2y$ (b) 0   (c) $2x - 3$ (d) $2x - 3$
16. (a) $18xy^4 - 2/y^2$ (b) $36x^3y^2 - 6x^2/y^4$
    (c) $36x^2y^3 + 4x/y^3$ (d) $36x^2y^3 + 4x/y^3$
17. (a) $2e^{y^2}$ (b) $4x^2y^2e^{y^2} + 2x^2e^{y^2}$
    (c) $4xye^{y^2}$ (d) $4xye^{y^2}$
18. (a) $-y^2/(xy + 1)^2$ (b) $-x^2/(xy + 1)^2$
    (c) $1/(xy + 1)^2$ (d) $1/(xy + 1)^2$
19. max$(-8, 16, 208)$
20. saddles at $(2, -3, 38)$ and $(-2, 3, -38)$; min at $(2, 3, -70)$; max at $(-2, -3, 70)$
21. 80 at $(2, 8)$ 22. 11,664 at $(6, 3)$
23. (a) $x^2y = 540$ (b) 3 units

24. (a) $46,204

(b) When the monthly contribution is $250 and the interest rate is 7.8%, the accumulated value is about $143,648.

(c) When the contribution is $250, if the interest rate changed from 7.8% to 8.8%, the approximate change in the account would be $17,770.

(d) $A_R \approx 574.59$ means that with an interest rate of 7.8%, if the monthly contribution changed from $250 to $251, the approximate change in the accumulated value would be $574.59.

25. (a) 8.996 thousand, or $8996

(b) 0.009; means that when the benefits are paid for 20 years, if the account value changes from 1000 to 1001 (thousand dollars), the monthly benefit increases by about 0.009 (thousand), or $9.

(c) -0.161; means that when the account value is $1,000,000, if the duration of benefits changes from 20 to 21 years, the monthly benefit decreases by about $161.

26. (a) If selling price is fixed, more dollars spent for advertising will increase sales.

(b) If advertising dollars are fixed, an increase in the selling price will decrease sales.

27. (a) 280 dollars per unit of x

(b) 2400/7 dollars per unit of y

28. $\partial Q/\partial K = 81.92$ means that when capital expenditures increase by $1000 (to $626,000) and work-hours remain at 4096, output will change by about 8192 units; $\partial Q/\partial L = 37.5$ means that when labor hours change by 1 (to 4097) and capital expenditures remain at $625,000, output will change by about 3750 units.

29. (a) -2 (b) -6 (c) complementary

30. competitive   **31.** $x = 20, y = 40; P = 2000$

32. 200 units at plant I; 100 units at plant II

33. $x = 10, y = 4$

34. (a) $x = 1000, y = 500$

(b) $-\lambda \approx 3.17$; means that each additional dollar spent on production results in approximately 3 additional units.

(c)

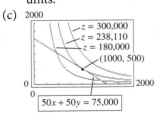

35. (a) $\hat{y} = 0.1274x + 8.926$ (b) $901 billion

36. $\hat{y} = 28.10x + 1175$

CHAPTER 14 TEST

1. (a) all pairs (x, y) with $y < x^2$ (b) 14

2. $z_x = 5 + 10y(xy + 1)^4$ $z_y = -18y + 10x(xy + 1)^4$
$z_{xx} = 40y^2(xy + 1)^3$ $z_{yy} = -18 + 40x^2(xy + 1)^3$
$z_{xy} = z_{yx} = 10(5xy + 1)(xy + 1)^3$

3. $(0, 2)$, a relative minimum; $(4, -6)$ and $(-4, -6)$, saddle points

4. (a) $1625 thousand

(b) 73.11; means that if capital investment increases from $10,000 to $11,000, the expected change in monthly production value will be $73.11 thousand, if labor hours remain at 1590.

(c) 0.56; means that if labor hours increase by 1 to 1591, the expected change in monthly production value will be $0.56 thousand, if capital investment remains at $10,000.

5. (a) When $94,500 is borrowed for 25 years at 7%, the monthly payment is $667.91.

(b) If the percent goes from 7% to 8%, the expected change in the monthly payment is $49.76, if the loan amount remains at $94,500 for 25 years.

(c) Negative. If the loan amount remains at $94,500 and the percent remains at 7%, increasing the time to pay off the loan will decrease the monthly payment, and vice versa.

6. $8xy\, e^{x^2y^2}(x^2y^2 + 1)$

7. Find $\dfrac{\partial q_1}{\partial p_2}$ and $\dfrac{\partial q_2}{\partial p_1}$ and compare their signs. Both positive means competitive. Both negative means complementary. These products are complementary.

8. $x = 7, y = 11; P = 5065$

9. $x = 200, y = 100$

10. (a) $\hat{y} = 0.24x + 5.78$

(b) The fit is excellent.

(c) 16.58%

Index